53rd Annual Conference of the Environmental Design Research Association 2022 (EDRA53)

Health in All Design: Promoting Health, Equity, Sustainability and Resilience Through Environmental Design

Greenville, South Carolina, USA
1-4 June 2022

ISBN: 978-1-7138-6844-6

Printed from e-media with permission by:

Curran Associates, Inc.
57 Morehouse Lane
Red Hook, NY 12571

Some format issues inherent in the e-media version may also appear in this print version.

Printed with permission by Curran Associates, Inc. (2023)

The Environmental Design Research Association (EDRA)

2010 Pear St.
#1060 Pinole, CA
94564-9998

www.edra.org

Additional copies of this publication are available from:

Curran Associates, Inc.
57 Morehouse Lane
Red Hook, NY 12571 USA
Phone: 845-758-0400
Fax: 845-758-2633
Email: curran@proceedings.com
Web: www.proceedings.com

HEALTH IN ALL DESIGN

PO Box 43023 Washington, D.C., 20010, USA

Web: www.edra.org

Email: proceedings@edra.org

EDRA 53 Program Committee

Lindsay McCunn, Ph.D. -- *Chair*
Alexandre H. Champagne
David de la Peña, Ph.D.
Deni Ruggeri, Ph.D.
Hui Cai, Ph.D.
Rich Wener, Ph.D.
Sharmin Kader, Ph.D.

EDRA53 Local Committee

Anjali Joseph, Ph.D. -- *Co-Chair*
Dina Battisto, Ph.D. -- *Co-Chair*
B.D. Wortham-Galvin, Ph.D. -- *Co-Chair*
James Lyndon McCracken -- *Support*

EDRA Board of Directors

Sharmin Kader, Ph.D. -- *Chair*
Lindsay McCunn, Ph.D. -- *Chair-Elect*
Shauna Mallory-Hill, Ph.D. -- *Past-Chair*
David de la Peña, Ph.D. -- *Treasurer*
Robert Gifford, Ph.D. -- *Secretary*
Hui Cai, Ph.D. -- *Diversity, Equity, & Inclusiveness Officer*
Mallika Bose, Ph.D. -- *Board Member*
Lesa Lorusso, Ph.D. -- *Board Member*
Elif Tural, Ph.D. -- *Board Member*
Alexandre H. Champagne, MLA -- *Board Member & Student Representative*
Rich Wener, Ph.D. -- *Emeritus Board Member, Ex-Officio*
Deni Ruggeri, Ph.D. -- *Executive Director*

EDRA Committee Chairs

Shauna Mallory-Hill, Ph.D. -- *Governance Committee*
Lindsay McCunn, Ph.D. -- *Program Committee*
David de la Peña, Ph.D. -- *Fundraising & Finance Committee*
Hui Cai, Ph.D. -- *Recognition & Awards Committee*
Lesa Lorusso, Ph.D. -- *Members & Partners Committee*
Elif Tural, Ph.D. -- *Communications Committee*
Alexandre H. Champagne, MLA -- *Student Affairs Committee*
Sharmin Kader, Ph.D. -- *Executive Committee*

EDRA Organizational Members

Arizona State University
Auburn University
Boston Architectural College
Kuwait University
Michigan State University
Rutgers Center for Green Building
Texas Tech University - College of Architecture
The Pennsylvania State University
University at Buffalo - School of Architecture & Planning
University of Colorado Boulder - Program in Environmental Design
University of Detroit, Mercy - School of Architecture
University of Idaho - College of Art & Architecture
University of Manitoba
University of Maryland, College Park
University of Utah - College of Architecture & Planning
University of Virginia - School of Architecture

EDRA Sponsors

Michael Brill Research Grant in Urban Communication and Community Design Sponsor
Urban Communication Foundation
Nana Kirk Student Travel Scholarship Sponsor
Jay Farbstein & Associates, Inc.

EDRA Corporate Members

Cannon Design
DLR Group
EYP
Gresham-Smith
HGA Architects & Engineers
HKS, Inc.
Smith Group

EDRA Partner Organizations

International Association of People-Environment Studies
Project for Public Spaces

EDRA Placemakers

Gowri Betrabet Gulwadi
Keith Diaz Moore
Peter Hourihan
Lynn Paxson

EDRA Wayfinders

Cherif Amor
Dan Meade
Julia Robinson
(B) Bonnie Sanborn
Dan Stokols
Richard Wener
Craig Zimring

EDRA Lifetime Members

Clinton J. Andrews
Mohamad Araji
Meredith Banasiak
John Barbour
Mallika Bose
Susan Drucker
Kelleann Foster
Peter Haratonik
Esperanza Harper
Vibhavari Jani
Lisa Lim
Maria Papiez
David Seamon
Nicholas Wise
Julie Zook

EDRA 53 Sponsors

Herman Miller
HKS, Inc.
Leo A Daly
McMillan | Pazdan | Smith Architecture

EDRA 53 Exhibitors

Clemson University - College of Architecture, Arts & Humanities
Kwalu, LLC
Texas Tech University - Department of Design

Table of Contents

Welcome to EDRA53

Greetings! It is our great pleasure to share with you the Proceedings of EDRA53—Health in All Design. This collection of work serves as a formal record of insights from the international and interdisciplinary community of researchers and practitioners from academia, not-for-profit organizations, public, and private sectors working in diverse areas of environmental design and research who took part in EDRA53. Although we remain in a pandemic era, the conference's organizing committee made EDRA's 53rd annual conference in June 2022 a success. More than 500 attendees came to the event held in Greenville, South Carolina. However, restrictions and risks related to the COVID 19 pandemic hindered travel and attendance for many individuals. The decision to live stream keynote and plenary speakers' talks, along with selected group sessions, was important to ensure that more people could engage with the conference's content this summer—and for years to come.

Overall, EDRA53 was a celebratory and hopeful event. After two years of seeing and speaking with each other online, EDRA's motivated and committed community met in-person to share, reflect, debate, and experience the joy of being together in the same space. All conference attendees contributed actively to a range of individual and group sessions with a strong and renewed sense of dedication to EDRA's mission and vision.

The COVID-19 pandemic has emphasized for many of us the importance of the built environment when promoting safe and healthy lifestyles. These settings can and should provide access to the outdoors and green, natural spaces for physical activity, exposure to nature, and good air quality. Building layouts that promote hygienic practices, and ergonomic designs that afford wellness and safety in workplaces are at the forefront of many conversations among today's administrators, designers, and researchers alike. The conference's theme, "Health in All Design—Promoting Health, Equity, Sustainability, and Resilience through Environmental Design," set a framework for the EDRA community to share their research and design projects related to healthy environments, and to engage in discovery and discourse on how health can be integrated into teaching practices, research, and design efforts as a key goal. Indeed, the location of EDRA53, in Greenville, South Carolina, is a strong example of the conference's theme. The city was largely derelict 40 years ago, but is now thriving with many urban attributes that support physical activity and social engagement. Faculty and students from Clemson University's School of Architecture leveraged their

expertise at the intersection of architecture and public health to collaborate with the EDRA Program Committee to plan and implement a truly impactful conference.

Keynote and plenary sessions, the graduate student workshop, group sessions (i.e., workshops, intensives, researcher-practitioner collaborations), and individual paper and poster sessions each highlighted work fitting into one or more of six dedicated tracks: 1) Health, equity, resilience, and sustainability, 2) Designing for diverse populations, 3) Designing for health and well-being, 4) Activism and advocacy, 5) Transdisciplinary collaborations, and 6) Pedagogies and methods. These topics were chosen so that the conference could cogently bring together diverse clusters of interest (e.g., children's environments) and focus dialogues on health in the built environment in novel and helpful ways.

One of the most distinctive aspects of EDRA is its commitment to supporting and mentoring students. Many EDRA'ites fondly remember becoming involved with EDRA as students. To promote student attendance and further inclusiveness, EDRA has awarded the Nana Kirk Travel Scholarship to 22 student members. EDRA53 showcased a range of opportunities for student learning and engagement. The conference started with an intensive all-day graduate student workshop and, in addition to traditional opportunities for students to receive feedback on their research projects from long-time EDRA members, EDRA53 included panels aimed at supporting doctoral students in their careers. The topics for the three panels were: 1) Discussing opportunities for practice-based research in firms, 2) Preparing for the academic job interview, and 3) Grant writing. Each panel was facilitated by leading researchers and academics with experience in honing student engagement and participation. Students also had numerous opportunities to network and learn from others during the conference's many social events, especially the sponsored student networking social hour.

We were honored to host two wonderful keynote speakers, Michael Murphy, and Andrew Ibrahim. Both individuals are recognized and lauded thought leaders in the field and were able to thoughtfully speak about the theme of EDRA53 from different perspectives. In fact, Andrew Ibrahim coined the term 'health in all design' to highlight the importance of focusing on humane design strategies to improve physical and psychosocial outcomes for everyone, in all types of settings. Michael Murphy shared with attendees his journey towards an architecture of dignity and health through his many award-winning projects.

The opening plenary featured Robin Guenther, Mike Lydon, and long-time EDRA member Craig Zimring who discussed emerging environment-behavior realities in a post-pandemic society, along with some of the implications for designers wishing to account for planetary, community, and individual-level health on various spatial scales. The pandemic has highlighted stark inequalities, with black, indigenous, and people of color (BIPOC) communities being disproportionately impacted in terms of mortality, illness, and unemployment. Our closing plenary speakers, Rupa Valdez, Lynn Paxson, and Debarati (Mimi) Majumdar Narayan discussed how health disparities have manifested at different scales during the COVID-19 pandemic—and how EDRA can play a role in addressing these challenges as we move forward as a compassionate and driven community.

As we write this introduction, many people are beginning to re-engage with families and friends, their communities, and at the workplace to forge a 'new normal' in a post-pandemic world. However, a number of occupations have adopted a hybrid model for employees, and the memory of public health restrictions, as well as the social, emotional, and behavioral outcomes that accompanied them, are still quite recent for healthcare workers, educators, emergency responders, and others who work in important and unique ways during times of humanitarian crises. It seems clear that most, if not all, new buildings and urban design projects will now involve conversations about how to appropriately respond to future pandemic circumstances. EDRA members have an opportunity and a responsibility to actively contribute to these discussions and help create environments that are healthy, safe, and fulfilling. This is, in part, why we are so appreciative of all the conference organizers, EDRA board members, reviewers, and student volunteers who worked tirelessly to make this conference a success. If this conference inspired participants to make a difference, we have done what we set out to do at EDRA53. We hope that these Proceedings communicate the immense talent and passion that EDRA members and attendees brought to the conference in 2022. We look forward to seeing you at EDRA54 in Mexico City, Mexico.

Sincerely,

Anjali Joseph, PhD, EDAC
EDRA53 Local Program Committee Co-chair

Lindsay McCunn, PhD
EDRA53 Program Committee Chair, EDRA Board Member

Sharmin Kader, PhD
Chair of Board of Directors, EDRA

Special thanks to:

EDRA53 Student Volunteers:
Monica Gripko
Sara Kennedy
Hadley Taylor
Taylor Wahler
Isabel Korn
Swati Goel
Mina Ardekani
Devi Soman

EDRA53 Logo Designers:
Faequa Uniza Rahman
Rutali Joshi

CONFERENCE TRACKS

EDRA53 invited abstracts and papers focusing on research methods, theories, practices, histories, and design solutions related to promoting health, sustainability, resilience, and equity through the design of the natural and built environment under six conference tracks:

Health Equity, Resilience and Sustainability

How are we generating knowledge to address the significant challenges of our time that influence intersections across human, community, and planetary health?

Designing for Diverse Populations

How do we design environments that recognize the needs of diverse populations shaped by people's unique life experiences, cultural influences, socio-demographics, perspectives, identities, geography, and more?

Designing for Health and Well-Being

How do we define health, and how does the concept of health affect design, methods, approaches, and tools used to design for health and well-being?

Activism & Advocacy

How do we improve advocacy for better-designed environments that promote health and well-being for all people, communities, animals, ecosystems, and living systems? In particular, how do we create equitable design practices, improve diversity within the design community, and move toward higher-quality environments?

Transdisciplinary Collaborations

Armed with new perspectives gained from the pandemic, how are professionals and academics crossing boundaries to address emerging issues that compromise health, sustainability, resilience, and equity in a post-pandemic world?

Pedagogies & Methods

How does teaching promote design and research excellence, innovation, and activism related to health, equity, resiliency, and sustainability, and what methodologies are environmental design faculty embracing to innovate and stimulate teaching and research?

Keynote Speakers

Michael Murphy, Int FRIBA, is a Founding Principal and Executive Director of MASS Design Group, a collective of architecture and design advocates dedicated to the construction of dignity. Michael's portfolio includes work in over a dozen countries since MASS's beginnings and spans the areas of healthcare, education, housing, urban development, food systems, Indigenous sovereignty, and the public monument. His 2016 TED talk has reached over a million views, and he received the Al Filipov Medal for Peace and Justice in 2017. Under Michael's guidance, MASS has been awarded globally and featured in over 900 publications. MASS recently received recognition as the AIA's 2021 Collaborative Achievement Award winner and the Wall Street Journal's 2020 Architecture Innovator. MASS's design of the National Memorial for Peace and Justice was named the "single greatest work of American architecture in the 21st century" by Mark Lamster from the Dallas Morning News.

Andrew M. Ibrahim MD, MSc, is an Assistant Professor of Surgery, Architecture, and Urban Planning at the University of Michigan and Chief Medical Officer at HOK, a global design and architecture firm. At the interface of healthcare, policy evaluation, and architecture, Dr. Ibrahim's research has resulted in numerous publications, book chapters, international presentations, and his appointment to the editorial board at the JAMA Network. He directs the Health and Design Fellowship at the University of Michigan and co-directs the Center for Healthcare Outcomes and Policy. More information about his work is at www.SurgeryRedesign.com.

Video recordings of EDRA53 keynote and plenary presentations are available at:
https://www.youtube.com/channel/UCpDJ3E_7FUvzuaTQ30h5AXw

Opening Plenary

Health in All Design in a Post-Pandemic World

The pandemic has highlighted the importance of health – a state of physical, mental, and social well-being – for individuals, communities, and nations. This plenary focused on the key role played by the physical environment (parks, homes, healthcare settings) in promoting health and safety during this pandemic and the emerging issues related to the built environment that will need to be addressed in the design of all future environmental design projects (workspaces, outdoor environments, schools, homes, healthcare). Given what we have learned during this pandemic – how should we design spaces in the future to support individual health, community health, and global health?

Robin Guenther, FAIA, LEED AP, is a leading expert and textbook co-author of Sustainable Healthcare Architecture. As Principal at the firm Perkins + Will, Robin has designed many innovative healthcare buildings, many of which have seen national and international publication. In addition to her practice, Robin works at the intersection of healthcare architecture and sustainability policy, participating in an array of advocacy initiatives. She is Senior Advisor to Health Care Without Harm, co-coordinated the Green Guide for Health Care, and served on the LEED for Healthcare committee. Healthcare Design Magazine named her the "#1 Most Influential Designer in Healthcare."

Mike Lydon is Founder and Principal at Street Plans and an internationally recognized planner, writer, speaker, and advocate for livable cities. Having delivered more than 250 keynotes, workshops, training, and lectures since 2009, Mike has globally influenced how people think about city transformation. In 2018, Planetizen named him one of the top 100 most influential urbanists of all time. He is the creator of The Open Streets Project and the globally-acclaimed Tactical Urbanism Short-Term Action, Long-Term Change Vol. 1-5. He remains active in local and national planning, design, and smart-growth advocacy issues as a founding member of the New England chapter of the Congress for New Urbanism, a Board Member for CNU New York, and a steering committee member of the Next Generation of New Urbanists.

Craig Zimring, Ph.D., is an environmental psychologist and professor of architecture. Craig is dedicated to using design research and education to create better healthcare safety, quality, and experience. He has conducted research and innovative design projects with the Huntsman Mental Health Institute, Emory Healthcare, Military Health System, Mayo Clinic, and many others. He has served on the board of EDRA, The Center for Health Design, and many others and has hundreds of publications in the academic and professional press.

Closing Plenary

The Physical environment & Health Equity

This closing plenary addressed how design impacts health disparities at different scales, how COVID-19 has affected these disparities, and how can we move forward and address these challenges through design of the physical envrionment.

Rupa Valdez, Ph.D., is an associate professor at the University of Virginia with joint appointments in the School of Medicine and the School of Engineering and Applied Sciences and is affiliated with Global Studies and the Disability Studies initiative. Dr. Valdez merges the disciplines of human factors engineering, health informatics, and cultural anthropology to understand and support the ways in which people manage health at home and in the community. Her work is deeply community-engaged and relies on co-design and participatory design principles. Her research and teaching focus on underserved populations, including racial/ethnic minorities, people living in under-resourced settings, and individuals living with physical, sensory, and/or cognitive disabilities. Her work has been supported by NIH, AHRQ, NSF, USDA, and the Kellogg Foundation. She also serves on PCORI's Patient Engagement Advisory Panel and is on the American Association of People with Disabilities Board of Directors. She lives with multiple chronic health conditions and disabilities, which have (and continue to) influence her research and advocacy.

Lynn Paxson, Ph.D., is a professor at Iowa State University with experience in teaching social and cultural design classes, history of Native American architecture classes, and studios. Her primary focus is on students understanding architecture and design as a cultural phenomenon. Dr. Paxson's professional design work experience ranges from master planning to interiors and has included working on the design of computer software and traditional architectural projects. She is currently collaborating with colleagues to develop a database and a national exhibition of Contemporary Indigenous Architecture and is co-editing a book on the topic.

Debarati (Mimi) Majumdar Narayan, Ph.D., is an Officer with the Health Impact Project, a collaboration of the Robert Wood Johnson Foundation and the Pew Charitable Trusts that encourages state, local, and national organizations to consider health in decisions across sectors. Dr. Narayan leads research efforts and provides strategic guidance to community-based initiatives to improve health outcomes equitably. Currently, she is leading partnerships with national organizations that can support the scale and spread f evidence-informed policies and practices that promote health equity. She is also an Adjunct at the University of Maryland's School of Architecture, Planning, and Preservation, where she teaches environmental psychology. The relevant nature of her work and its potential impact on communities has attracted national and international interest and recognition.

Video recordings of EDRA53 keynote and plenary, presentations are available at:
https://www.youtube.com/channel/UCpDJ3E_7FUvzuaTQ30h5AXw

Mobile Sessions

Bicycling the Swamp Rabbit Trail
Session Host: Reedy Rides

The two-hour tour included destinations like the Liberty Bridge and Reedy Falls, Swamp Rabbit Café & Grocery, and the Old Rail Car. Along the way, the guide provided a general description of the trail, its economic impact, improved quality of life, and the planning and history of the trail and old rail bed.

The four-hour tour option added stops at Furman University - a small private college with a beautiful campus that showcases a bell tower on a lake with views of Paris Mountain - and Tandem Coffee in Travelers Rest for coffee, rest, and the history of Travelers Rest - a quaint town that has grown with the addition of the Swamp Rabbit Trail.

Downtown Greenville Redevelopment Walking Tour
Session Host: Barry Nocks, PhD, FAICP

This walking tour explored the elements of Downtown Greenville's success. The tour highligthed "anchor" developments that served as growth poles between which development filled in and discussed ongoing and creative partnerships between government and private businesses that enabled projects to succeed in downtown Greenville. On the tour, guests also learned about the Reedy River Master Plan and redevelopment process, the importance of planning and community engagement in setting specific direction and design standards for development, how Greenville's government leveraged its resources using private philanthropy, and the city's very successful deployment of adaptive reuse that has helped transform many derelict former textile mills and warehouses into restaurants, bars, art galleries, and more.

Textile Mills & Villages Bus Tour
Session Host: John Nolan

The textile industry is the most significant aspect of Greenville's history. It employed one out of every three people here for many years and had worldwide reach and importance. This driving tour first took guests to eight of the mills from the "early years" - built up between 1874-1902. The tour then continued to explore major mills from the "second wave" of mill building (between 1910-30) for a full tour of Greenville's famous "Textile Crescent." Guests learned in-depth about the mill leaders, workers, buildings, village life, what the mills produced, why they closed, and what is going on there now.

Tour guests saw hundreds of historical photos that dramatically illustrated the themes discussed as they drove through the villages. They also had a chance to actually touch and hold vintage artifacts from this era - like an antique flying shuttle, mill money, and century-old mill company letters.

Creative Placemaking Through Public Art
Session Host: Tracy Ramseur

Greenville has enjoyed quite a bit of recognition for its growing public art scene, including recent mentions in Condé Nast Traveler and Architectural Digest, to name a few. This mobile session explored Greenville's public art program as a key placemaking and neighborhood revitalization strategy. Participants learned about the impact public art can have on a community, and the tour detailed the planning and implementation of public art in Greenville.

This session also discussed the Arts in Public Places Commission, which plays a large role in the placement of public art in Greenville, funding, and notable projects. Following a walking tour of public art along Main Street (from the Hyatt to City Hall), guests traveled by bus to the Village of West Greenville, an area known locally as the "arts district," where they saw first-hand how public art has served as an effective tool for neighborhood revitalization.

Awards & Recognitions

GREAT PLACES AWARDS

EDRA's Great Places Awards seek to recognize work that combines expertise in design, research, and practice and contributes to the creation of dynamic, humane places that engage our attention and imagination. Award-winning projects reflect an interdisciplinary approach that is enduring, human-centered, sustainable, and concerned with the experiential relationship between people and their environments (built and natural) over time.

Applications represented a range of design and research disciplines whose significance extends beyond any one profession or field and demonstrated how the understanding of the experience of place may be used to generate insightful design.

A jury comprised of individuals with diverse backgrounds in design, research, and practice evaluated how each project addressed the human experience of well-designed places and paid special attention to the transferability of research on this topic into design and planning practice. The jury selected exceptional submissions from five categories - place design, place planning, place research, place book, and place art - and presented awards at the EDRA53 conference in Greenville. Winning entries were displayed throughout the conference and publicized throughout the year in various print and electronic publications.

EDRA is proud to partner with Project for Public spaces (PPS) for the Great Places Awards. PPS is a nonprofit planning, design, and educational organization dedicated to helping people create and sustain public spaces that build stronger communities. Their pioneering placemaking approach helps citizens transform their public spaces into vital places that highlight local assets, spur rejuvenation, and serve common needs.

Committee Members:

Lisa Lim | GPA Committee Co-Chair
Assistant Professor, Korea Advanced Institute of Science and Technology

Dagmar Rittenbacher | GPA Committee Co-Chair
Design Researcher, Gresham Smith

Claudia Wigger | GPA Committee Member
Lecturer, University of Michigan

Elisa Worden | GPA Committee Member
Design Researcher, Gresham Smith

Mallika Bose | GPA Committee Adviser
Professor & Associate Dean for Research, Creative Activity and Graduate Studies, Pennsylvania State University

Yeinn Oh | GPA Committee Volunteer
Ph.D. Student, Georgia Institute of Technology

EDRA Recognition Committee Chair

Hui Cai, Ph.D.
Chair, Department of Architecture, University of Kansas; Associate Director, Institute of Health & Wellness Design, KU

Great Places Awards: Jurors

Place Art

Kevin Hamilton

Professor of New Media and Dean of the College of Fine and Applied Arts, University of Illinois, Urbana-Champaign

Kevin Hamilton is Dean of the College of Fine and Applied Arts at the University of Illinois, Urbana-Champaign, where he supports programs in Architecture, Landscape Architecture, and Urban and Regional Planning. His primary research in recent years has been on the role of photography in nuclear weapons testing, culminating in his 2019 book with Ned O'Gorman, Lookout America! The Secret Hollywood Studio at the Heart of the Cold War (Dartmouth). Kevin's other work has included the co-founding of Ground Works, a peer-reviewed publishing platform for interdisciplinary arts research, and contribution to early influential work on racial bias in algorithmic systems.

Place Art

Todd Palmer

Director, Diversity in Design

Todd Palmer is a strategist, leader and curator of purpose-driven design, learning and equity platforms. As the founding Director, Diversity in Design (DID) he steers a Collaborative of design-focused organizations aligned to dismantle design sector barriers facing Black talent. As an Executive Director, Palmer orchestrated the 2017 and 2019 Chicago Architecture Biennial editions - defining the emergent global platform's catalytic linking of spatial experimentation and civic urgencies. As Curator and Associate Director, Todd facilitated the rehabilitation of the National Public Housing Museum's grassroots community site as a pilot cultural generator for "the public good." Palmer has exhibited at the Studio Museum in Harlem, published in The Avery Review, and taught as a Critic in RISD's MArch program.

Place Book

Jeff Hou

Professor of Landscape Architecture, Director of the Urban Commons Lab, University of Washington

Jeffrey Hou, PhD, is Professor of Landscape Architecture and director of the Urban Commons Lab (https://commons.be.uw.edu/) at the University of Washington, Seattle. His work focuses on public space, democracy, community design, and civic engagement. In a career that spans the Pacific, Hou has worked with indigenous tribes, farmers, fishers, and villagers in Asia and inner-city immigrant youths and elders in North American cities, on projects ranging from conservation of wildlife habitats to bottom-up placemaking. Hou is the author and editor of numerous publications including Insurgent Public Space: Guerrilla Urbanism and the Remaking of Contemporary Cities.

Ann Sussman

Place Book

Architect, Author, President of the Human Architecture + Planning Institute Inc.

Ann Sussman, RA, an architect, author and researcher is passionate about understanding how buildings influence people emotionally. Her book, Cognitive Architecture, Designing for How We respond to the Built Environment (Routledge, 2015) co-authored with Justin B. Hollander, won the 2016 Place Research Award from the Environmental Design Research Association (EDRA). A 2nd edition, featuring eye-tracked architecture, came out in 2021. Ann teaches a course on the human experience of buildings at the Boston Architectural College (BAC), blogs at geneticsofdesign.com, and serves as President of the educational non-profit, the Human Architecture and Planning Institute, Inc. (theHapi.org). More info: annsussman.com.

David Hays

Place Design

Professor of Landscape Architecture, University of Illinois, Urbana-Champaign

David L. Hays is Professor and Brenton H. and Jean B. Wadsworth Head of the Department of Landscape Architecture at the University of Illinois at Urbana-Champaign, co-editor of Forty-Five: A Journal of Outside Research, co-curator of the Chicago-based gallery Space p11, and founding principal of Analog Media Lab. Trained in architecture (M.Arch., Princeton) and history of art (A.B., Harvard; Ph.D., Yale), his research explores contemporary landscape theory and practice, the history of garden and landscape design in early modern Europe, interfaces between architecture and landscape, landscape in popular media, and pedagogies of history and design.

Alessandra Galletti

Place Design

Architect and Landscape Architect, Project for Public Spaces

Alessandra is the Director of Design Practice at Project for Public Spaces, and she joined the team in 2007. Her expertise is in placemaking, and in designing inclusive and welcoming spaces for the community, using strategies that allow people to bring lasting changes. Prior to joining PPS, she had a career in Landscape Architecture, based in the New York area, with projects in the United States and abroad. Alessandra's recent projects included low-impact designs for parks, urban sites, waterfronts, and greenways. Alessandra is very passionate about design and placemaking, and she led professional training and workshops. She is currently a visiting professor at the NY Institute of Technology in NYC.

GREAT PLACES AWARDS: JURORS

Place Planning

Joy Knoblauch
Associate Professor, Director, PhD Program in Architecture, University of Michigan

Joy Knoblauch is an Associate Professor of Architecture at the University of Michigan, teaching history and theory of architecture as an exploration of architecture's engagement with politics and science. She is the Director of the Architecture PhD Program and a member of the Design Health faculty research group. Her first book on The Architecture of Good Behavior: Psychology and Modern Institutional Design in Postwar America connects psyche and form to examine a growing tendency to govern behavior through the environment. Her current research is critical history of ergonomics. The upcoming issue of the Journal of Architectural Education (JAE), will address the theme of Health shaped by theme editors Knoblauch and Sara Stevens.

Place Planning

Elena Madison
Director of Projects, Project for Public Spaces

Elena Madison is an urban planner with rich experience in the planning and design of parks, plazas, campuses, and the public spaces of civic and cultural institutions. A veteran of Placemaking, Elena has a passion for working with people in communities to create the places they love. She is a dedicated practitioner of collaborative work in all aspects of placemaking from visioning, concept development and design, to programming, place management and implementation. Elena has directed many of Project for Public Spaces' most impactful and exciting projects. She is forging relationships with corporate and philanthropic partners through Corporate Social Responsibility initiatives to support placemaking.

Place Research

Keith Diaz Moore

Professor and College of Architecture + Planning Dean, University of Utah

Keith Diaz Moore is Dean of the College of Architecture and Planning at the University of Utah and has served as both interim Chief Sustainability Officer and interim Senior Vice President for Academic Affairs (iSVPAA). Dr. Diaz Moore is an international expert in the connection between culture, health and place, particularly regarding design for people experiencing dementia with several books, over 40 refereed publications and more than 100 presentations on the topic. Whether in his academic, professional or community roles, he is an ardent proponent for the power of good design to promote health and social wellbeing.

Place Research

Kathryn Anthony

ACSA Distinguished Professor, School of Architecture, University of Illinois at Urbana-Champaign

Kathryn H. Anthony is ACSA Distinguished Professor at the School of Architecture, University of Illinois at Urbana-Champaign, recipient of national awards from the American Institute of Architects, the Association of Collegiate Schools of Architecture, EDRA, the 2020 Lifetime Achievement Award - Chicago Women in Architecture, and the 2021 AIA/ACSA Topaz Medallion for Excellence in Architectural Education. She has authored five books including "Defined by Design: The Surprising Power of Hidden Gender, Age and Body Bias in Everyday Products and Places", "Designing for Diversity: Gender, Race, and Ethnicity in the Architectural Profession" and "Design Juries on Trial: The Renaissance of the Design Studio"

Great Places Awards

2022 Winner | Place Art

Black Bottom Street View

Emily Kutil, *Assistant Professor, Department of Architecture, Lawrence Technological University*

Black Bottom Street View is a commendable and timely experiment that discovers innovative means of eliciting community voice and makes the systemic forces operating behind seemingly void and evidently neglected sites in Detroit more tangible to diverse publics. The project also aptly demonstrates the potential of place-based interventions that are temporal, iterative and flexible.

The Black Bottom Street View team has conceived of a means for place sensitive redeployment and reconfiguration of its design elements across disparate sites, thus expanding its potential to connect to distinct publics and diverse communities.

The project conceptually manifests as a design intervention which at once responds to discrete site situations while also revealing the physical evidence of systems operating across space and time. The project also grapples with the absences that haunt places in ways that galvanize memories and otherwise amplifies community perspectives. Taken together Black Bottom Street View unpacks histories and legacies of urban renewal and eminent domain, exposing racism and discriminatory practices intertwined across discourses of design, urbanism and public policy.

Black Bottom Street View begins with an all-too-common project - that of reconstructing a part of Black history erased through anti-Black spatial and archival violence. Former residents and descendants of a Black neighborhood in Detroit razed by white planners in the 1950s are reconstructing the place using photographic, spatial, and oral information. The project's innovation, however, is in how it makes this project itself a portable spatial one, creating opportunities for gathering at multiple scales. Walkable maps and reconstructed stoops spur memory and catalyze social interactions. An effort to remember the past becomes a platform for making a new present.

Project Team: Emily Kutil, Lama Chamseddine, Bilqees Salie, Jalen Smith, Tyler Schaafsma, Sina Almassi

Exhibit Owner and Manager: Black Bottom Archives

Project Advisors: Marsha Battle Philpot, Jamon Jordan, Bert Dearing, Jiam Desjardins, We the People of Detroit

Pedal to Porch Project Team: Pedal to Porch, Mogo Detroit, Black Bottom Archives, Black Bottom Street View, Marsha Music / Salon De'troit, Bert's Warehouse Theater, Pirahnahead

With Support From: The John S. and James L. Knight Foundation, Metabolic Studio, Detroit Public Library Foundation, University of Detroit Mercy

2022 Winner | Place Book

Cities for Life: How Communities Can Recover from Trauma and Rebuild for Health

Jason Corburn, *Professor, School of Public Health, University of California Berkeley*

Focusing on racism, health, and urban trauma, this book presents a timely and inspiring account of innovative programs in three cities that speak to the structural violence against marginalized communities, both historically and today. Through three case studies, in Richmond California, Medellin, Columbia, and Nairobi, Kenya, the book makes a compelling case for the ecological model of health, the engagement of citizens, and the healing power of placemaking. For to design successfully for people, we need to acknowledge, and no longer ignore, that we are a relational species and as such create places that promote social cohesion and connection, worldwide.

2022 Honorable Mention | Place Book

Restorative Cities: Urban Design for Mental Health and Wellbeing

Jenny Roe, *Professor, School of Architecture, University of Virginia;* ***Layla McCay,*** *Director, Centre for Urban Design and Mental Health*

Written by a psychiatrist and a public health specialist, this impeccably well-organized book delivers a timely and important guidebook to redesigning our cities for human and ecological health. Conceptual yet practical, the book is unusual in the way it places mental health at the fore, connecting scientific, sensory, and social dimensions of health in built environments, to do so. It provides a template for all urban design and planning professionals to follow to make cities more livable and inclusive places that better fit our human psychology and essential biology.

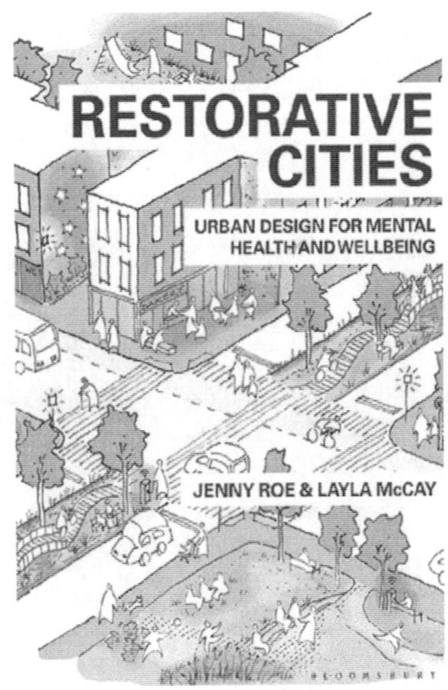

GREAT PLACES AWARDS

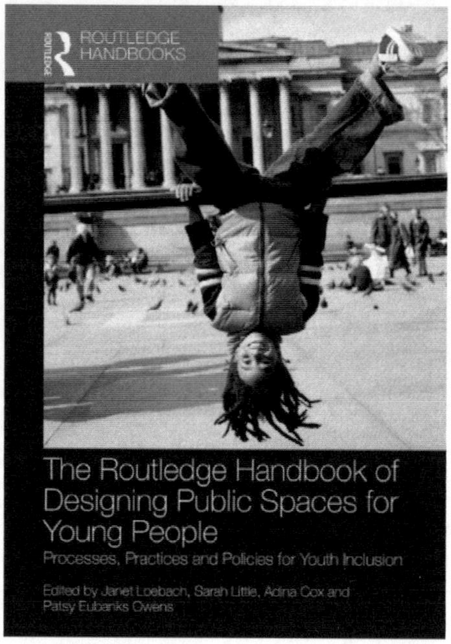

2022 Honorable Mention | Place Book

The Routledge Handbook of Designing Public Spaces for Young People: Process, Practices and Policies for Youth Inclusion

Patsy Owens, *Professor, Landscape Architecture and Environmental Design, University of California, Davis;* ***Sarah Little,*** *Assistant Professor, Landscape Architecture, University of Oklahoma;* ***Janet Loebach,*** *Assistant Professor, College of Human Ecology, Cornell University;* ***Adina Cox,*** *Postdoctoral Scholar, College of Architecture, Food and the Environment, University of Kentucky*

Through an impressive collection of work from leading and emerging scholars, this book assembles a phenomenal body of knowledge on the making of public spaces for and with young people. Through a framework of why, how, and what (cases), the book is packed with lessons, and investigations that offer tools for engaging young people in the making and activation of public space. It leaves the reader thinking about place-making in new ways, highlighting how not having appropriate outdoor spaces impedes young people's social and intellectual development, and defining our adult responsibility as building environments where we are not needed.

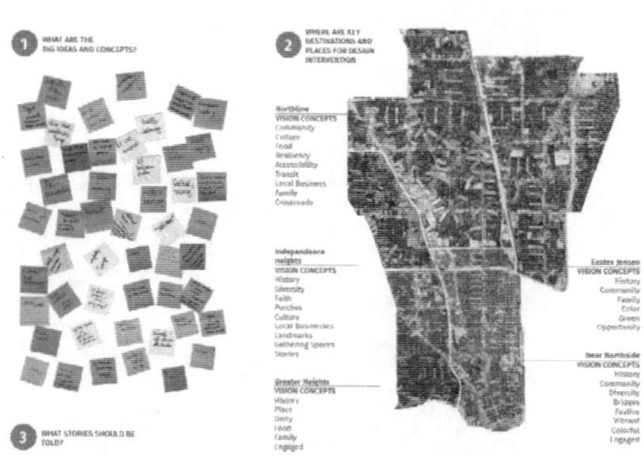

2022 Winner | Place Planning

Greater Northside Urban Design Toolkit

Susan Rogers

The Urban Design Toolkit was developed through community meetings focused on identifying concepts and strategies to promote the identity of each neighborhood and key locations for intervention. Two shared values guided the toolkit's development: all planning efforts should begin and end in conversation with community leaders and stakeholders, and the everyday streets, buildings, and infrastructure of our neighborhoods can become a basis for developing innovative design interventions. The toolkit's core commitment was to honor and amplify the community-centered stories of place, culture, history, and tradition while also weaving these stories into a broader textile. The resounding impact is a set of grounded design interventions that are specific to the context, affordable, practical, strategic, and celebrate the existing qualities of place.

2022 Honorable Mention | Place Planning

Longfellow Middle School: Sharing Space for Equitable Design

Patricia Algara, *Principal in Charge, BASE Landscape Architecture;* ***Jessica Rozul,*** *Landscape/Irrigation Designer, BASE Landscape Architecture*

Sharing Space for Equitable Design The team explains the context as one of disinvested and disenchanted neighborhood in Berkeley CA. African American and Latinx residents in particular did not initially wish to trust the planning group due to past experiences of being ignored or worse. The process includes Spanish-only workshops and inviting African American students and their families to lead the workshop on the African Descent Family Village. The listening sessions yielded a particular focus on health. The impact seems to be the creation of a conversation, with the project itself pending.

2022 Winner | Place Research

The Campus Landscape As Laboratory: Experiential Learning, Research, Outreach, and Stewardship

A. Kiers, *Assistant Professor, Landscape Architecture and Environmental Design, University of California, Davis;* ***Patsy Owens,*** *Professor, Landscape Architecture and Environmental Design, University of California, Davis*

This project documents the transformation of an outdoor courtyard at Hunt Hall on the University of California, Davis campus through the systematic, repeated involvement of landscape architecture students and faculty, along with staff at UC Davis' Campus Planning and Grounds, as well as local contractors, irrigation specialists, and horticulturalists. Photographs documenting phased landscape improvements, starting in 2013 to the present, clearly convey the scope of the project and its detailed progress each year. While constructing a project of their own design, students use the campus itself as an educational tool, gaining hands-on experience in assembly, installation, project management, and, perhaps more important, in sustainability, community engagement, research processes, and stewardship.

Findings reaffirmed previously explored pedagogical benefits and introduced novel ones, including experiencing design as an iterative process, understanding real-world applicability, developing an understanding and respect for construction and maintenance factors, and building a sense of pride and ownership. The project is extremely well presented and serves as a model showing how collaborative research, design, and implementation bridge strong connections between academia and the "real-world."

GREAT PLACES AWARDS

2022 Honorable Mention | Place Research

A Workplace for Employee Wellness & Community Connection

Jeri Brittin, *Director of Research, HDR*

This research documents the effects of workplace setting design on sedentary behavior and physical activity, a public health issue that has gained increased prominence in recent years, as excessive "sitting has become the new smoking", causing a variety of serious costly negative health impacts. Participants in this experimental study at a large corporate setting wore accelerometers for 3 to 5 days at two points in time before and after the move of their corporate headquarters and completed a daily online log of self-reported activity. Results from pre- and post-move were compared across the intervention and control groups and by other respondent and workspace characteristics. The net effect of the design intervention alone was equivalent to an average 3.3 additional hours of physical activity per month, or ~50 minutes per week. The programmatic intervention—called Step Challenge which prompted ending sedentary behavior--nearly doubled these effects.

As one of the first studies of its kind to document the pre- and post-move impacts of wellness-inspired design, it serves as a model for future research. It is extremely well conceived, well researched, well documented and well presented.

2022 Winner | Place Design

Cities for Life: How Communities Can Recover from Trauma and Rebuild for Health

Elizabeth Golden, *Associate Professor, Department of Architecture, University of Washington;* ***Brice Maryman,*** *Founding Principal, MxM Landscape Architecture;* ***Richard Mohler,*** *Associate Professor, Department of Architecture, University of Washington*

People without housing live entirely within public space. It's wonderful to see how this project acknowledges, engages, and supports those residents. It's also wonderful that Real Change, sink hosts, and end users collaborated in the development, assessment, and revision of prototypes.

While not claiming to resolve larger social issues, the constellation of sinks creates a positive presence in the streets of Seattle. Each provides access to water, creates a destination, and fosters interactions among users, making handwashing accessible for all.

2022 Honorable Mention | Place Design

Yanaguana Garden

Daniel S. Iacofano*, CEO, CFO, Moore Iacofano Goltsman (MIG) Inc;* ***ML Rhee****, Moore Iacofano Goltsman (MIG) Inc.*

Yanaguana Garden is set in a context that celebrates San Antonio's legacy as a multicultural community, setting a new standard of community-building through play. Extensive outreach and input from the community made this garden a major destination for residents of San Antonio and visitors alike. The community contributed to the environmental and sustainability themes, as well as the educational and health component, adding an emotional bond to the place. The impact of Yanaguana Garden on the area and region is impressive, as is its catalytic function for economic development and the future of the Hemisfair Park Area, in which the project is located.

It's heartening to see the many ways the community was engaged in the park's development, how cultural heritage was respected and celebrated, and how the resulting project is welcoming to all.

Paper & Poster Awards

2022 Best Paper Award

Sadiqa Al Awadh | *Presenting Author, University of Oregon*

Space Syntax Applications for Window Access and Daylight Design

2022 Best Student Paper Award

Hossein Saedi | *Presenting Author, North Carolina State University*

The Positive Impact on Individuals' Sustained-Attention Level of Micro Interactions with Natural Green Elements in Low-Income Communities

2022 Best Poster Award -- First Place

Carolina Kolodziej | *Technische Universität Dresden*

Typologies of Therapy Cluster in Radiotherapy Departments Developed From Comparative Floorplan Analysis

2022 Best Poster Award -- Second Place

Dagmar Rittenbacher | *Gresham Smith*

ICU Design & Nurse Stress: Developing a Nurses' Physical Environment Stress Scale (NPESS)

Michael Brill Grant for Communication, Design & Human Behavior

urbancommunication foundation

Established in 2015, the Michael Brill Research Grant in Urban Communication and Community Design supports innovative research that seeks to enhance the quality of community life by examining human communicative behavior in the context of the technologies and the physical environments in which those interactions occur. This research should address and connect theoretical perspectives from the fields of communication, design and the social sciences. Research supported by the Brill Grant may focus on how physical community places influence the mode, nature, and content of human communicative behavior or use a communication lens for examining community places and human activity. The award honors Mike Brill, whose life's work encompassed these fields. The grant is funded by The Urban Communication Foundation and EDRA.

EDRA members are eligible to apply for this annual award of $3,000. Research results based on the grant must be presented at an EDRA conference within 3 years of Grant's award. The awardee must acknowledge the Grant when presenting or publishing work resulting from research supported by the Grant.

Chair

Gary Gumpert, Ph.D.

Jury Coordinator, 2022

Peter Hecht, Ph.D.

EDRA Recognition Committee Chair

Hui Cai, Ph.D.

Grant Committee

Gary Gumpert, Ph.D.
Susan Drucker, J.D.
E. Sue Weidemann, Ph.D.
Sheila Gobes-Ryan, Ph.D.
Richard Wener, Ph.D.
Peter Hecht, Ph.D.

2022 Winner
Anya Domlesky | *Director of Research, SWA Group*
Project Title: *Life in the Urban Night*

This practice-based research project looks at user behavior and occupation in 10 small public spaces in a temperate American downtown in the evening and night. The goal is to understand how mediated communication technologies and processes impact the use of designed places by individuals and groups.

This work adds to that of W.H. Whyte regarding small, urban public spaces

2022 EDRA Service Award

Nisha A. Fernando, Ph.D.
Director of Interior Architecture, School of Architecture and Design, University of Kansas

The EDRA service award is awarded annually in recognition of contributions of services that advance the field of environmental design research. This year's winner, Nisha A. Fernando, is an associate professor and the director of Interior Architecture at the University of Kansas's School of Architecture. Dr. Fernando earned a Bachelor of Science and Master of Science degree in architecture from the University of Moratuwa in Sri Lanka before earning a Ph.D. in environment-behavior studies with a minor in historic preservation. She was previously a tenured professor of interior architecture at the University of Wisconsin – Stevens Point. She was the associate dean and division head during six of her more than 18 years there.

Dr. Fernando's research involves cultural aspects of design and spatial experiences, sensory values of architecture and design, and environment-behavior interactions of spaces. Her work is regularly published in peer-reviewed journals and presented at conferences. She has been a member of the editorial board of the Journal of Interior Design and regularly reviews submissions for research grants, book proposals, and journal papers.

A long-time EDRA member, Dr. Fernando has made several significant contributions that have promoted the mission of EDRA. She has co-chaired the Cultural Aspects of Design Knowledge Network since 2009, served on the membership subcommittee from 2011-2013, was a member and secretary of EDRA's board of directors from 2015-2018, served as editor of EDRA Connections and coordinated the annual Environment by Design newsletter from 2016-2018, and co-chaired the EDRA46 Conference in Los Angeles in 2015.

2022 EDRA Career Award

Kent Spreckelmeyer, D.Arch, FAIA Emeritus

Professor of Architecture, School of Architecture and Design, University of Kansas

The EDRA career award is annually awarded to recognize a career of sustained and significant contributions to environment design research, practice, or teaching. The 2022 award winner, Dr. Kent Spreckelmeyer, is a Professor of Architecture at the University of Kansas School of Architecture and Design and an active consultant in architectural research and programming. He has taught design, architectural programming, building evaluation, and research methods courses since 1981, with a primary focus on studying the relationship between human well-being and the built environment. Since 2009 he has directed the Health & Wellness internship program at the University of Kansas. He has served in leadership positions in the School of Architecture and Design, creating the professional Master of Architecture program in the late 1990s and the Doctor of Philosophy program in 2007. In addition to his teaching in architecture, he has been active in the Department of Humanities and Western Civilization. He has also taught the history of architecture and urban design course for the school's study-abroad component in Florence and Paris and was awarded a 2009 W.T. Kemper Fellowship for Excellence in Teaching for recognition of his work in the classroom, studio, and graduate seminars.

Professor Spreckelmeyer has consulted on more than fifty architectural projects in workplace and healthcare facilities in partnership with Frank Zilm & Associates. He is a Fellow of the American Institute of Architects, a long-time EDRA member, a member of the AIA Architecture for Health Committee, and has served on the editorial boards of the AIA/AHA Journal, Environment & Behavior, the Journal of Architectural Education, Health Environments Research & Design Journal, and the Journal of Architectural and Planning Research. He has co-authored five books that advance architectural knowledge by integrating new theories and research methods into the design process. He is the author of numerous peer-reviewed journal articles, research reports, conference presentations, and guest lectures. He has been a visiting professor at the Edinburgh College of Art in Scotland and Moratuwa College of Architecture in Sri Lanka.

Students working under his direction have incorporated the principles of his research into their practices, and he maintains connections with these practicing professionals through studio juries, sponsored design and research programs, advisory boards, and funded-research projects. He is active in national organizations that promote design research and is a Fellow of the American Institute of Architects. Dr. Spreckelmeyer is a graduate of the University of Kansas and holds a postgraduate diploma from University College London, Bartlett School of Architecture, and a doctorate in architecture from the University of Michigan. He apprenticed in St. Joseph, Missouri, at the firm of Brunner and Brunner and served as a captain in the 35th Civil Engineering Squadron of the U.S. Air Force.

2022 EDRA Career Award

Habib Chaudhury, Ph.D.
Professor and Chair, Department of Gerontology, Simon Fraser University; Associate Director of the Gerontology Research Centre

The EDRA career award annually recognizes a career of sustained and significant contributions to environment design research, practice, or teaching. The 2022 award winner, Dr. Habib Chaudhury, is Chair and Professor in the Department of Gerontology at Simon Fraser University, where he has worked for over twenty years and has extensive research experience in the field of environmental gerontology. He holds a B.Arch degree from Bangladesh University of Engineering and Technology, an M.A. in architecture from Texas A&M University, and a Ph.D. in Architecture and Environmental Gerontology from the University of Wisconsin-Milwaukee. His research and consulting work focuses on physical environments for people with dementia in long-term care facilities, memories of home and personhood in dementia, community planning and urban design for active aging, and dementia-friendly communities.

Dr. Chaudhury has published several books – including Environments in an Aging Society: Autobiographical Perspectives in Environmental Gerontology, Remembering Home: Rediscovering the Self in Dementia, and Home and Identity in Later Life: International Perspectives – book chapters and peer-reviewed articles. Dr. Chaudhury conducts research consulting with various national and international organizations in the planning and design of senior housing and long-term care facilities. He has received funding from the Canadian Institute of Health Research (CIHR), Social Science and Humanities Research Council (SSHRC), Canada Mortgage and Housing Corporation (CMHC), CapitalCare Foundation, and the Centre for Health Design. Dr. Chaudhury is also affiliated with the Centre for Research on Personhood in Dementia at the University of British Columbia, Vancouver, Alzheimer Catalonia, Barcelona, Spain, and serves as the Editor-in-Chief of the Journal of Aging and Environment.

A dedicated teacher, Dr. Chaudhury has supervised over forty graduate (M.A. and Ph.D.) students in gerontology and social science and received the Excellence in Teaching Award at Simon Fraser University in 2013. His students have received external support and recognitions, including the SSHRC Graduate Scholarship, Michael Smith Foundation Graduate Trainee Award, Best Research Poster Award from the Canadian Association on Gerontology, and Best Research Poster Award from the CIHR.

CORE AWARDS

edra core

improving environments through research excellence

EDRA CORE recognizes and celebrates exceptional, rigorous, and impactful practice-based research. Applications undergo a double-blind review based on research rigor and research value.

CORE Chair:

Amin Mojtahedi, Ph.D., Assoc AIA
Design Innovation Manager, HGA Architects & Engineers

CORE Fellows:

Megan Cackett
Human Factors / UX Resarcher, Google

Danya Hakky, Ph.D., NCIDQ
Interior Designer and Design Researcher, Perkins Eastman.

EDRA Recognition Committee Chair

Hui Cai, Ph.D.
Chair, Department of Architecture, University of Kansas; Associate Director, Institute of Health & Wellness Design, KU

Panel of Reviewers

Alison McDougal-Weil
UX Research Design Application Lead, Google

Brian Schermer, Ph.D., AIA
Professor, School of Architecture & Urban Planning, University of Wisconsin-Milwaukee; Principal, Design Research, Workshop Architects Inc.

Danya Hakky, Ph.D., NCIDQ
Interior Designer and Design Researcher, Perkins Eastman

Hui Cai, Ph.D.
Chair, Department of Architecture, University of Kansas; Associate Director, Institute of Health & Wellness Design, KU

Kara Freihoefer, Ph.D., NCIDQ, LEED ID+C, EDAC
Director of Research, HGA Architects & Engineers

Lesa Lorusso, Ph.D., NCIDQ
Healthcare Director of Research & Insights, Gresham Smith

Megan Cackett
Human Factors / UX Researcher, Google

Sharmin Kader, Ph.D., Assoc AIA
Chair, EDRA Board of Directors
Research Scholar, Kent State University

Terri Zborowsky, Ph.D.
Design Researcher, HGA Architects & Engineers
Adjunct Faculty, University of Minnesota

Zhe Wang, Ph.D., EDAC, LEED AP BD+C
Professor, Henan University
Founder, International Green

The Outpatient Experience Index - 2021: A National Study of American Outpatient Consumers' Experiences of Outpatient Care Facilities

EDRA CORE Merit Certification

Submitted by: *Gensler & Hanken School of Economics*

Study Team: *Nicholas Watkins, James Crispino, April Spivack, Kyle Sellers*

Study Description: What brick-and-mortar and digital solutions can positively impact and influence outpatient consumers' decision making? The Outpatient Experience Index – 2021 survey, a nationwide study of outpatients conducting during the pandemic, reveals that experiences with outpatient design accounted for upwards of 70 percent of outpatient loyalty.

Project Budget: More than $100,000

Funding: Design firm, 100%

Research Question: A first-of-its kind self-report market survey of American outpatient consumers, the Outpatient Experience Index – 2021 (O-EXI 2021) consisted of 3,578 respondents. The survey had the following objectives: • Explore with a nation-wide survey with stratified random sampling the impact of outpatient facility design on outpatient consumers' experiences • Understand broader consumer and decision-making trends among outpatients before, during, and following the pandemic • Statistically identify factors that define the outpatient consumer experience • Create an instrument that can be readministered over time • Measure the statistical impact of design and digital solutions on outpatient consumer experience • Find indirect statistical links between outpatient care facility design and the outpatient consumer experience that illustrate the downstream effects of a design intervention or digital solutions • Identify optimal outpatient facility design and digital solutions • Develop a dashboard of the data so designers, planners, consultants, and strategists can work directly with the O-EXI 2021 data and apply the findings directly to their project work *Separate subsections of the survey were only for outpatient consumers who experienced a remote virtual health session. They are not included in the sample size given above and their data was not included in the analyses reported in this EDRA CORE submission. This submission will focus on results from consumers who experienced an outpatient visit in-person and in a clinical setting.

Existing Knowledge: The O-EXI 2021 focused on outpatient experiences because of a major shift to outpatient care. Ambulatory care revenues are growing at rate of 6% and are projected to reach $36 billion by 2023 (McKinsey, 2020). The O-EXI 2021 advanced understanding of outpatient consumer experiences with facility design and digital solutions, thereby revealing and filling gaps not covered by current standardized surveys of patient experience. According to Moore, Quelch, and Boudreau (2018), the shift in volumes and revenues toward outpatient care has been accompanied by a surge in consumerism among patients who are taking direct responsibility for their healthcare decisions and costs. However, traditional metrics of healthcare design's value measure efficiencies—square footage, labor, and material costs. The O-EXI 2021 offers snapshots of outpatient consumers' experiences, loyalty behaviors, and outcomes. For a healthcare industry attuned to reimbursements influenced by Centers for Medicare and Medicaid Services surveys, the O-EXI 2021 rounds out the picture with design's impact on consumer experience. The O-EXI 2021 builds upon previous research of outpatient facility design. There is a growing body of reputable research of outpatient facility design's impact on patients', visitors', and care providers' experiences (Becker et al., 2008; Brittin et al., 2020; Campos et al., 2013; Freihoefer et al., 2017; Freihoefer et al., 2021; Jafarifiroozabadi et al., 2020). Among other findings, these investigations have provided evidence that on/off stage clinic configurations are associated with improved workflow efficiencies, privacy, and wayfinding. However, these investigations are limited to convenience samples from one facility or a set of facilities belonging to a system. Given the variability of outpatient organizations, services, settings, ethnicities, and income levels, and growth of digital technologies and recent historical events (i.e., the pandemic, healthcare reform, etc.), consumers' expectations and experiences of their care is in flux and may substantially differ among localities. Second, studies would benefit from a greater focus on the entire user journey. This could reveal gaps, continuities, resonations, and complex relationships among experiences with spaces (Zook, 2017).

Study Team: The O-EXI 2021 was one of a series of internal grants awarded and administered over the span of 2019 and 2020. Similar to the cadence and structure of a dissertation or master's thesis, each annual research grant cycle consists of three rounds of internal review and one review consisting of external reviewers. Reviews are scheduled for each quarter of the business calendar. The first year of the Outpatient EXI's development was dedicated to the following steps: • Workplan and budget development • Secondary research of existing theory and instruments • Instrument/ survey development • Face and content validation with internal experts (i.e., designers, planners, consultants, and strategists) and external experts (i.e., patients, nurses, physicians, healthcare administrators, and expert environmental psychologists who specialize in healthcare design research and not affiliated with the grant administrator). This validation established appropriate clarity and length. • Identification of a nation-wide survey panel provider who regularly nurtures and maintains a representative sample of American outpatients • A pilot/"soft launch" of the survey consisting of 1,000 respondents across the nation. • A re-calibration of the survey's stratified random sampling strategy and quotas • An extensive revision to the piloted survey based on results from univariate and multivariate analyses, factor analyses, and the application of item-response theory The second year of the investigation consisted of the full study including the 3,459 respondents who experienced an in-person clinic visit. The survey took most respondents 30 to 40 minutes to complete. The team partnered with an outside statistician and researcher who has expertise in the fields of organizational and environmental psychology. She/he was able to objectively replicate analyses and to validate inferences from the analyses. The team followed the same cadence and structure of the research grant cycle from the prior year (i.e., 2019).

Research Design: Please refer to the appendices, page 11, for details on the study's methodology, tools, and timeline. It should be noted that the survey was open 5 months to meet quotas. Respondents were screened by whether their last outpatient visit was with a physician. Interestingly, respondents were disqualified from taking the survey because they did not make a distinction between a physician and a dentist or physical therapist. Going forward, similar studies by other organizations and teams should also proactively take such measures to prevent a real threat of bias in their findings.

Research Analysis: Please refer to the appendices, pages 3 through 10, for samples of O-EXI 2021 findings. To a reviewer of this submission, the absence of some findings may be just as telling as the reported findings. For example, there is a notable absence of the waiting area's influence on outpatient consumer experiences and outcomes. This was contrary to the team's expectations and seemingly contrary to a sizable amount of prior research that has focused specifically on the importance of the waiting area experience. In this study, controlling for all other factors, it became apparent that waiting areas may be evolving to be more disjointed and amorphous in outpatient consumers' minds. Specific activities in and experiences with waiting area features are emerging as having a greater impact than the "area" itself. Perhaps this shift is partly influenced by digital technologies consumers can use to book and manage their outpatient visit outside of the clinical setting. Also, please refer to page 11 of the appendices to learn more about the specific statistical analyses used for the data.

Application to Practice: This third year (i.e., 2021) was committed to synthesis of the research findings into reports, presentations, and a tableau-based interactive dashboard the designers, planners, consultants, and strategists co-created and use to inform their project work. A feedback loop from these practitioners provides documentation that validates the utility of the O-EXI 2021 when applied to projects and is guiding the development of future O-EXI investigations that will examine trends over time. At least 9 outpatient healthcare design projects have been directly informed by the information the O-EXI offers the practitioners during design delivery.

Dissemination Approach: Practitioners such as the designers, planners, consultants, and strategists have been discussed in a prior response. Other audiences include outpatient consumers, consumer advocates, policy makers, care providers, healthcare administrators, students, and healthcare researchers in practice and academia. The organization who awarded the internal grant has a research communications division that guided the development of a self-published report. This report is included in the appendices to this submission. This research communications division was also responsible for a boilerplate presentation and talking points for use by the practitioners. A dashboard of the data that is used by the practitioners was co-created with the practitioners and internal survey developers. Currently, the findings are being disseminated at conferences (i.e., EDRA, European Healthcare Design, the Center for Health Design, the American Telehealth Association, and others) and are publicly available on a website and through blogs. There are ongoing publications with industry periodicals and the team has been encouraged to take necessary steps toward submission to refereed journals.

Study Impact: The impacts have been wide and extensive. For design delivery, the implications have been: • Identification of frictionless experiences with design and digital solutions throughout a consumers' journey and any drop-offs or pitfalls • Application of these findings to experience mappings and Lean work sessions • Enhancements to spaces, technology, and services along the outpatient consumer journey including apps for seeking out a care provider and pre-registration, transportation services, multi-purpose entry and waiting areas, welcoming and team-friendly exam rooms that accommodate telehealth and a consumers' digital and health technology, and optimal protocols for follow-up care. Results have also informed allocation and placement of outpatient services within communities and healthcare campuses.

Study Reach: A commitment to a study of this type, size, and rigor is without precedent. We hope this study and its dissemination encourages a greater commitment among architectural and engineering practices, professional organizations, governing bodies, and healthcare organizations to be bold with their healthcare design research. The gains to the industry and society are far greater than concerns with risk and cost.

Research Innovation: The study successfully enlisted a large online survey panel using a stratified random sampling strategy based on recent census data. Traditional frequentist statistics and classification analyses can overlook smaller groups of people who can be greatly impacted by changes to design, policy, and technology or may be marginalized. The fuzzy set Qualitative Comparative Analyses allowed for a detailed and deeper understanding of specific demographics, their resources, and decision-making influencers when it comes to outpatient care. The dashboard of O-EXI 2021 data is accessible to the practitioners and is directly applied by them to design delivery on current projects.

IRB Process: This study involved human subjects, but IRB review was not sought and/or obtained for this study. The O-EXI 2021 qualified as market research. The nation-wide survey panel provider partnered with on the O-EXI 2021 has a dedicated division for healthcare research. This division has been in practice for 13 years and employs reviewers who evaluate a survey and its methods for legal and ethical standards for market research with patients and care providers. These standards were in practice. Case in point, there were instances when team members wanted to ask specific questions of outpatient consumers but were not aware these questions would be problematic. However, the survey panel provider reviewed the draft questions and alerted the team that the questions could not be asked due to ethical and legal standards. In addition, the survey panel provider only provided anonymized de-identified data to the team. The recent encouragement to publish O-EXI 2021 findings in refereed journals has prompted the team to compile a list of third-party IRB reviewers of which one will be selected.

On the Restorative Break: Understanding the Role of Break Room Design on Nurse Engagement and Satisfaction

EDRA CORE Merit Certification

Submitted by: *Gresham Smith, Steelcase Health & University of Florida Health North*

Study Team: *Lesa Lorusso, Steelcase Health, Linda Lawson, Carolyn Blake, Penny Houchens, and Robin Maddalena*

Study Description: Attracting and retaining nursing staff is mission-critical to healthcare organizations and break room design may influence nurses' engagement in breaks, improving job satisfaction. This study seeks to understand nurses' perception of and engagement with breaks and the impact of culture and design on frequency, duration and location of breaks.

Project Budget: $25,001-$50,000

Funding: Design Firm, 80%; Manufacturer, 20%

Research Question: The overall goal of this study is understand nurses' perception of and engagement with breaks and the impact of culture and design on frequency, duration and location of breaks. Research Question: Do nurses take breaks, where do they take them and what design features impact nurse engagement and satisfaction with breaks?

Existing Knowledge: The need to attract and retain nursing staff is mission-critical to healthcare organizations (Khan, Jackson, Stayt, Walthall, 2018; Boston-Fleischhauer, C. 2022). Nursing is demanding, with chronically high turnover rates (Lu et al., 2012). Registered Nurses (RNs) constitute most of the healthcare workforce and loss of RNs directly impacts the quality of patient care as well as organizational operating costs and efficiencies (Duffield et al., 2014). Overall, retention is preferable over hiring new nursing staff due to the high cost of recruiting, training and onboarding (Eckman, 2014) and the physical environment of the rest break area has been shown as a viable factor in influencing nurses engagement in breaks and their overall satisfaction (Happell et al., 2013; Nejati et al., 2016). While the hypothesized and apparently positive effect of breaks is such that over 90 papers have been published since 1990, the moderating factors remain poorly understood (Wendsche, Ghadiri, Bengsch, & Wegge, 2017). Nejati et al (2016) found that 22.4% of the variance in reported total break minutes per shift (M 35 min, SD 16.07 min) was related to environmental qualities of break spaces, such as proximity to non-meal break space, outdoor break space, and satisfaction with break areas (10.3%), ($p \leq 0.05$). The authors reported that 25.9% of the variance in nurse satisfaction with indoor break areas was related to amenities such as equipment, appliances, and furniture (15.5%), environmental features such as plants, artworks, windows, and access to outdoor spaces (7%), and views to specific outdoor elements such as buildings or landscapes (3.4%), ($p \leq 0.05$). While this is the first study of its kind it remains unknown if this correlation persists in situ. This research is the logical next step to bridging the gap in understanding the elements within the built environment that impact nursing engagement with and satisfaction of nurse breaks.

Study Team: Study Team: PI: AVP Nursing, Academic Medical Health System Co-PI: Dir Research AEC Firm Co-Investigator: Dir Research Healthcare Furniture Manufacturer Co-Investigator: Sr. Interior Designer AEC Firm Co-Investigator: Interior Designer AEC Firm Co-Investigator: Sales Manager Healthcare Furniture Manufacturer Participants: 374 Registered Nurses

Research Design: The study team followed a mixed methods approach in this two year, two-part study from 2019-2021. Part one, described in this report, sought to understand if, how and where nurses took breaks. The team received Institutional board approval before beginning the study. The study site was conducted within a medical tower on two identical medical surgical inpatient units on floors A and B (fig 1, 2 & 3). This academic medical center had been designed using evidence-based design principles, with specific input from nursing staff regarding break areas (fig 1). Spaces studied in this research included meal-break and non-meal break areas on the medical surgical floors identically located in relation to the nurse station, one with a lounge-like layout and one with a collaborative work layout (fig 2). On both floors, the meal-break room was directly adjacent to the nurse station with a refrigerator, TV and seating with no windows. The non-meal break areas were each about twenty feet away from the nurse station, without TVs or refrigerators and with views to outdoor landscaping. Usage of additional break areas within the tower including lounges, cafes, gardens and a fitness area was also studied. A mixed methods approach was selected in order to gain a more complete understanding of nursing behavior, from multiple perspectives. Methods included: (1) an anonymous online survey completed by nursing staff regarding their perspectives on restorative break environments, (2) nursing behavior during breaks was mapped over a 24 hour, five day period using a GPS-enabled, web-based tool that integrated the floor plans and a consistent observational route, (3) break room usage rates from de-identified card reader access, and (4) design thinking focus groups to gather staff perceptions regarding engagement and satisfaction with breaks and break areas.

Research Analysis: Survey: Nurses rated the floor A & B non-meal break rooms using a 10-point Likert scale in terms of how well the room was perceived to relieve stress (table 1). A Wilcoxon signed rank text and mixed effects regression analysis was used to understand the within-subjects effect of each room. The Floor B room was rated significantly higher than the Floor A room, with a mean (M) and standard deviation (SD) of $M = 4.81$ ($SD = 2.66$) and $M = 3.86$ ($SD = 2.30$), respectively. A mixed effects regression (allowing room ratings to vary between participants) also revealed a significant effect of the lounge break room in Floor B versus Floor A rating, $b = 1.02$, $p = .007$. Behavior Mapping: The team used a prescribed observational route that began on the first floor and ended on the top floor of the medical tower. Results showed that both non-meal break rooms on floors A & B were underutilized while the meal-break rooms were highly utilized (fig 3). Break room usage rates: Total number of visits per staff member, the average number of minutes each staff member spent in the lounge room, maximum number of minutes spent in the room and the total duration of time spent in the room was analyzed. A series of negative binomial regression models tested for differences between floors. There were no significant differences between floors in any duration outcomes but floor B had more monthly visits per staff member with mean and standard deviation of 31.8 and 32.7 relative to floor A with a mean of 19.7 and standard deviation of 36. Focus groups: 15 nurses participated in a two hour session asked to define nurse breaks, perception of break importance and insights into a typical day-in-the-life of nursing working on the two medical-surgical floors. While restorative breaks were more desired, most only tool quick bio-breaks. Six major design themes were desired for a restorative break environment including technology, nutrition, relaxing décor, access to nature and ergonomic furniture.

Application to Practice: Despite the health system's efforts to encourage restorative breaks, the lack of nurses' engagement with restorative breaks was surprising to the study team. Nejati and colleagues' survey-based work identified key environmental attributes that set up the basis of this study, but these did not hold when isolated from basic human needs: hydration, nutrition, and toileting. These needs should inform the basic requirements of future break rooms. Once bodily sustenance was satisfied, however, nurses demonstrated a preference for the 'work-oriented' lounge setting in terms of number of visits. Upon greater inspection, these nurses were seeking the work-like setting for team meetings, a finding that may be particular to this case study. The culture of 'no breaks' cannot be underestimated. Within this study, even accounting for half-hour breaks or longer, staff members spent small amounts of time in the break rooms. It is a mindset that threatens nurse sustainability and patient safety. Future studies should investigate leadership activities impacting nurses' perception of shifts and break-taking behavior. Once these core issues are resolved, the restorative nature of break rooms becomes paramount given their potential influence on break behavior. Focus groups revealed the need for staff's sense of ownership, attention to sensorial elements, ability to connect with others or 'get away' via technological means, and physical rest and comfort. Staff also reported concerns for physical safety—as evidenced by cleaning protocols and clean air exchanges—as part of a restorative break, an unsurprising result of their pandemic experience.

Dissemination Approach

The AEC design research team has partnered with the academic medical center's administration on the dissemination plan of these findings. The goal of the collective group is to share the findings with both healthcare administrative, specifically nursing staff, as well as design professionals. Within the AEC firm that initiated the study, results have been shared with cross-functional design teams. Findings have also been shared directly with the academic medical center's staff to be applied to ongoing facility design projects. The team has also presented the material at healthcare design settings that incorporate both healthcare system administration and design team members. The healthcare furniture manufacturer has also integrated the findings into its publications and documents informing its wide client base.

Study Impact: The restorative break has never been more important. The COVID-19 pandemic stretched nurse mental health to its limit, challenging the entire generational cohort of practicing nurses. Perhaps most concerning are the novice nurses handling patient mortality and in turn profound family sorrow and mourning at the rate one would expect across an entire nursing career. Nurse tendency to place patient needs above their own will need to be tempered by that other core ethic: you cannot care for others if you do not care for yourself. Nursing leadership is uniquely positioned to make this principle manifest in tangible ways. A safe, biologically and psychologically restorative space as part of the design element of a nursing unit allows for the nursing staff to quickly reset, if only for a few minutes. Design teams and healthcare administration should mindfully integrate the six major design themes desired for a restorative break environment including technology, nutrition, relaxing décor, access to nature and ergonomic furniture. It will be critical for nurse leaders to offer permission and even assign breaks when they see signs of a nurse in or headed towards crisis. Future research should investigate the importance and effect of administrative and environmental design interventions on the restorative break beyond the fundamentals as described. Since this study was conducted the academic medical center has engaged in designing an additional medical-surgical tower adjacent to the one in this study. The design team, researchers and healthcare administration are collaborating to learn from the finding of this study and implement design lessons learned to the new space for optimal restorative nurse break engagement. Human health and safety are dependent upon the mental and physical state of nurses globally. Attention to the restorative break is part of an ongoing effort to maintain and support this valuable resource—nursing care.

Study Reach: This study pushes the boundaries of practice because it highlights the critical importance of integration of both organizational culture and the design of the healthcare environment. Both elements must work in tandem to achieve maximum impact. Just because a healthcare organization encourages its employees to take breaks doesn't mean they will or that they understand the difference between a short bio-break and a truly restorative break. Conversely, just because you integrate staff input into the design of a facility with opportunities for breaks doesn't mean that employees will engage in truly restorative breaks. So much of the findings from this part one of two part study includes the impact of both organizational culture and the built environment. The medical-surgical tower studied in this research was a relatively new facility and the administration was dedicated to communicating the importance of nurse breaks and the facility was designed to also encourage nurse engagement with breaks. Despite all these efforts, the over-arching, global nurse culture of "nurses don't have time to take breaks" prevailed. The healthcare administration has learned that they must play a more active role in encouraging staff to take breaks and defining the difference between bio-breaks and restorative breaks and the critical importance of the latter. The design team learned the specific elements that will make the most impact within the break rooms, namely an opportunity to eat, and the weighted importance of nutrition and water in any break environment. Because of this, the team seeks to share the outcomes and lessons learned with both design and care teams to bridge the gap in understanding and enable effective restorative break engagement.

Research Innovation: This study utilized a mixed methods approach that included innovative ways to engage with study participants and investigate the impact of the built environment on behavior. Two of the most impactful innovations were the behavior mapping tool and the design thinking methods within the focus groups. The web-based, GPS enabled behavior mapping tool was created by one of the interior designers employed at the AEC firm. Building from the lack of an easy to use, GPS enabled tool that utilized floor plans for on-site behavior mapping, the interior designer collaborated with an "Internet of Things" (IoT) engineer to create the software. Floorplans were uploaded to the web-based application and the design research team worked with the app developers to create parameters for targeted or anticipated behaviors. The nurses were easily identified visually by the color of their scrubs and the design team was able to access the behavior mapping tool on their smart phones which enabled the research team to inconspicuously conduct staff observations, dropping a pin on the map whenever a staff member was seen taking a break, and their behavior was added to the attributes of the pin. This provided time and location focused heat maps of break space usage, which was a major asset to the research team. Design thinking was another innovative way data was collected during this study. This human-centered, empathetic method allowed the design team to engage with nursing staff in a genuine and heartfelt way, while being effective within time constraints. The nursing staff readily engaged with the research team during the workshop which used design thinking to put the staff at the center of the research question and enable them to tell their own stories which provided great depth of insight and understanding to the study team.

IRB Process: This study involved human subjects and was granted approval by the University of Florida IRB (approval date: 2019-01-18).

IRB Approval Date:

Realized Enrollment Decisions in Redesigned Active Learning Spaces

EDRA CORE Merit Certification

Submitted by: *Gould Evans & University of Kansas*
Study Team: *Michael Ralph, Blair Schneider, David Benson, Douglas Ward, and Anthony Vartia*

Study Description: We examined student enrollment choices when faced with limited access to newly renovated active learning spaces. A comparison with the same course, instructor, and teaching showed more women enroll in the active learning space, they rely more on peer influences to make the decision, and student success is much higher in the active learning space.

Project Budget: $0-$5,000

Funding: Academic Institution, 100%

Research Question: Colleges and universities are seeking to enroll and retain more students, and a key element in many institutions' strategy is the promotion of active learning. Stains et al. (2018) examined the teaching practices of STEM faculty at universities across the North America and found teaching are varied considerably between locations and over time, with encouraging numbers of instructors using active learning methods. As higher education further adopts active learning, demand will continue to rise for classroom spaces that eschew conventional lecture halls in favor of spaces that support active student participation and collaboration. Incremental efforts to expand the capacity and quality of active learning spaces have been popular among institutions of higher education. While new and redesigned spaces explicitly designed to support and encourage faculty to use active learning techniques in their classes are a critical step in the evolution of higher education, very little is known about the impact of these spaces while they are in early adoption. At the study institution, active learning classrooms had been created and scheduled with classes. However, demand for the classrooms outpaced the capacity in an undergraduate chemistry course. This situation offered an opportunity to study the impact of campus planning decisions for students with a choice between learning environments and peer competition for limited access to the redesigned environment. Specifically, we sought to understand how students were sorting between new active learning classrooms and existing lecture theaters that remained in use for delivery of the same instruction (see Figure 1 in the Additional Content). Our study measured section demographics (with particular focus on gender – see Figure 2 in Additional Content), student attitudes, student course success, and student decision-making priorities. We compared students who enrolled in a section of an undergraduate chemistry course held in an active learning space and a section of the same undergraduate chemistry course (taught by the same instructor using the same teaching materials) held in a lecture theater space. Our research question was: What are the differences in student outcomes between those who enrolled in a collaborative teaching and learning space and the lecture theater space?

Existing Knowledge: Babad and Tayeb (2003) demonstrated that course selection is an opportunity to study decision-making processes. Students often must make compromises in their attempt to construct an ideal schedule, and the amount of potentially relevant information far outpaces what humans can simultaneously consider when making judgements. In response, students develop heuristics to simplify the enrollment task (Coleman & McKeachie, 1981; Zocco, 2009). Past work has measured the impact of intuitive factors affecting student enrollment decisions – like instructor charisma, course scheduling, and perceived ease of material – far less is currently known about how students respond to the unique decision-making task presented by limited active learning space. In these cases, factors commonly assumed to dominate the decision-making process (such as time and course ease) are rendered moot by otherwise identical options. The element of competition between students for limited space also complicates the choice. While this study simplified learning spaces as a dichotomy, "active learning space" versus "passive learning space," we recognize learning spaces are more nuanced. We used the Pedagogy, Space and Technology (PST) framework to describe the degree to which each learning space supports active learning (Radcliffe, 2008). Multiple studies have already shown collaborative physical spaces interact with active learning instructional methods to produce positive results (Baepler et al., 2014; Beichner et al., 2006; Park & Choi, 2014). However, the degree to which students are aware of these benefits, expect the benefits to apply to themselves directly, or are prioritized relative to other considerations is not currently understood. A recent study from Clinton and Wilson (2019) found students report active learning classrooms are more enjoyable and more effective at supporting collaborative learning. Our study sought to fill the gap in understanding how students consider the benefits of active learning relative to other enrollment factors in the face of limited access to active learning space. We further sought to understand how those decision-making priorities differ between students or associated with differences in attitudes toward learning.

Study Team: The study team convened as a result of a teaching scholarship collaborative meeting where we hosted the eventual study course instructor for an informal conversation about active learning techniques. Professionals in the room included a STEM scholar with extensive work in advocacy for gender inclusion, a leader of the campus center for teaching improvement, a teaching staff member with expertise in active learning practices for STEM, and a junior faculty member with discipline-specific pedagogy expertise in the course. During the conversation, we identified a focused research question relevant to all of us. We also saw an opportunity to collect comparable data given the feasibility of a quasi-experimental design. The interdisciplinary nature of our team afforded expertise across research methodologies (both quantitative and qualitative) and within the disciplinary setting of the course context. The study participants (students enrolled in the course) offered a broad cross-section of students at the study institution. The course is required by a wide variety of majors, which means the demographics of the target population closely matched the overall demographics of the institution. Response rates were very good, with the lowest sampling rate on any instrument in any section being 67% of the course's enrollment.

Research Design: The study team convened in the middle of the spring 2018 semester in response to the opportunity to collect data with the quasi-experimental design. We conducted some informal, non-research information such as visiting the learning spaces and talking with institutional offices to obtain general descriptive data on course enrollment and student demographics. Our opportunity to conduct research was time-limited as course scheduling shifted. As a result, we resolved to collect data at the end of the spring semester to seize the opportunity rather than risk losing access to comparable data due to teaching or scheduling changes. The research team vetted research instruments for the relevant learner constructs and identified the Colorado Learning Attitudes toward Science Survey for Chemistry (CLASS-C) as a useful tool to measure student attitudes with existing evidence for validity and reliability. We also identified the COPUS observational protocol as a method to confirm each course included closely comparable instructional techniques. We crafted decision-making questions to collect data on student enrollment processes to target our area of research interest. Finally, we collected student grade data in an aggregate format, to examine overall trends in student success without the measurement flaws of using individual grades as research outcomes. We conducted the study through April and May of 2018, which included researcher class visits and the online delivery of our survey instrument using the existing learning management system (LMS). Following the conclusion of the semester, we obtained de-identified grade summary data in the summer of 2018 and concluded our data collection. Data analysis and research communication continued through the 2018-2019 academic year, informing subsequent research, classroom design, and scheduling efforts through a partnership with the design firm responsible for creating the learning spaces. The COVID-19 pandemic disrupted the late stages of analysis and communication efforts, which resulted in the conclusion of the study being delayed until 2021. Study publications included general articles written for a lay audience and a peer reviewed publication written for a scholarly audience.

Research Analysis: We analyzed 5 data sources: enrollment demographics, systematic course observations, synchronous polling, asynchronous surveys, and course performance. Student enrollment reveals a higher proportion of honors students and women enrolling in the active learning space compared to the lecture hall (see Figure 2 in Additional Content). The teaching observations showed instructional behaviors between classrooms were a very close match, with no significant differences between either instructor or student behaviors. Polling data on student enrollment decisions was generated by delivering 5-option Likert items via an individual classroom response system ("clickers"). We analyzed results with both Mann-Whitney U hypothesis testing and confidence interval comparisons. Results showed peer influence and classroom type had a greater importance for those in the active learning space (see Figures 3 & 4). We analyzed CLASS-C survey data by first using structural equation modeling to examine instrument validity and reliability. A theory-driven scale revision included direct construct articulation and item pruning, producing a new model with acceptable fit (tested by Chi square and fit indices RMSEA, SRMR and CFI). Model regressions revealed associations for gender and learning space with learning attitudes. Aggregated course performance revealed the active learning section outperformed the lecture hall section in both class GPA and frequency of failure/withdraw (see Figure 5).

Application to Practice: Study findings have design applications to both campus planning and classroom design. The study institution is one of many planning to expand facilities that anticipate and support active learning strategies for their instructors (Association of American Universities, 2017). Those efforts to expand access to active learning facilities, due to the relatively slow implementation process outlined by the AAU, result in limited access for students attending those institutions right now. Simultaneously, many institutions are devoting increased attention and resources toward diversity, equity, inclusion, and justice (DEIJ) goals. These study findings illuminated a link between the limited access to courses held in active learning spaces and a sorting mechanism with differential impacts along various axes of human identity (ex: gender and race). Immediately following the conclusion of this investigation, this institution was commissioning additional new facilities to serve this student population in this study. Our findings contributed to both teaching and research faculty understanding of the impact of scheduling decisions within the new facility, particularly the impact learning space planning and scheduling can have on DEIJ outcomes. Our study also described in detail the difference in student attitude and success between the conventional passive learning setting and the newer active learning space. Our application of the PST theoretical framework to describe the differences between the learning spaces equipped the study institution to understand opportunities to create new spaces that better balanced financial considerations like capacity with the affordances of active learning environments. In the new instructional facility described above, the course studied here was moved into a more active learning-focused lecture hall. The new space was a departure from the conventional lecture theater studied here and instead moved toward what the PST describes as a "next generation lecture theatre," with swivel seating to facilitate grouping and distributed markerboard walls for collaboration. These elements are key drivers of the benefits of active learning spaces, and the new facilities that followed this study included more of these elements for all students.

Dissemination Approach: We engaged essential stakeholders in the author team, published in the scholarly literature, and shared via popular outlets. Assembling an author team that included departmental faculty and the design firm that created the active learning space connected our research to those who could act upon the results immediately. Our internal dissemination included a firmwide presentation across 5 design studios, providing an overview of the study for designers and architects able to advocate for and create more active learning spaces at universities across the United States. Our team also published our findings in a peer-reviewed journal published by a major scholarly publisher. The journal carries a CiteScore of 4.2 for 2021, and our paper's attention since publication was ranked in the 81st percentile out of more than 336,419 articles compared across all journals by Altmetric at the time of this writing. This publication makes the full depth of our analysis, including revised measurement tools, available for future research. We also shared our results in a variety of more accessible outlets for designers, policy makers, and other non-academic readers. These pieces were written for less technical audiences, made available without a paywall, and kept shorter for quick consumption. Publications included the design firm blog (earned 4x the industry standard organic social engagement rate), university news blog (≈900 views), and Phys.org (a popular science outlet with a wide readership).

Study Impact: A Campus Climate Assessment Project was completed immediately prior to this study, through a collaboration between a campus committee and an external consulting firm. Major findings included differences between men and women in their experiences of academic success and comfort with the campus climate. An outcome from this study was direction for campus units to develop action items in response to the findings. This study illuminated the impact of active learning classrooms to dismantle barriers to a sense of comfort and success for women in STEM. The occupants had the opportunity to act on our findings given the forthcoming opening of a new building to serve the studied population. Recommendations for scheduling and space utilization, delivered directly through author team members representing both the academic department and the university teaching and learning center, could be applied to the space use in the new building. This facility would operate in addition to the newly renovated spaces, which afforded the opportunity to expand the use of the spaces rather than simply replacing what we studied. Our research also had the unexpected opportunity for applications as the institution dealt with the COVID-19 pandemic. As departments struggled with ways to offer effective instruction while implementing public health, safety, and disease mitigation protocols, they were able to use our study findings to advocate for the benefits of active learning in online and hybrid delivery models. The academic benefits and alignment with diversity, equity, and inclusion goals the university had adopted were urgently needed during the pandemic as much as prior to it. Application included outfitting several previously passive lecture spaces with technology to support active learning methods amid pandemic restrictions. Through our publication and dissemination plan, we also built relationships with other design researchers in the community. Through these connections and the shared insights of our research and the work of others, we were able to craft and submit a proposal for funding a space design research conference. Authors from this study collaborated with other Principal Investigators from multiple academic institutions and private design firms to elevate findings like ours in addition to synthesizing and charting the direction of future research in collaboration with the broader environment research community.

Study Reach: This study represents a model for integrated, interdisciplinary approaches to post-occupancy evaluations (POEs). Too many POEs, and survey-based research designs in general, neglect the importance of social science practice and disciplinary expertise in their methods. Our study demonstrates the impact in the quality of data generation a collaborative team can have when it includes faculty members with expertise in the disciplines being taught in the spaces. We were only able to obtain our findings, which connect to developing STEM attitudes and potential opportunities to address disparities in STEM participation, because our team included social scientists, disciplinary experts, and representatives from a professional design practice. Our results show the connection between course offerings in redesigned active learning spaces and increased participation from both highly recruited honors students and women. They also reveal connections between learning spaces and developing student attitudes and enrollment decision-making. The complex interactions between learning spaces, academic outcomes, and social connections on campus represent a more comprehensive evaluation of the impact of redesigned learning spaces on higher education campuses. Analyses of energy usage and general comfort metrics are valuable POE measures, but they are only a small fraction of the information that could inform future design and space evaluation when an interdisciplinary team designs more robust survey measures. This study's findings can inform efforts from national organizations, like the Association of American Universities, to continue supporting effective teaching approaches like active learning while also managing the impact of changing facility availability on students and faculty. The design industry must consider the implications of limited access throughout campus planning projects and when preparing methods of phasing large campus construction and renovation projects. Coming investments in infrastructure and the growing adoption of active learning present an opportunity for studies like ours to impact thousands of students in the coming decade as colleges and universities consider how to address ways to provide active learning facilities on U.S. campuses.

Research Innovation: This study connected design research with robust methodology from social science and psychometrics. We leveraged previously validated instrumentation with robust reliability evidence (the Colorado Learning Attitudes toward Science Survey for Chemistry – CLASS-C), alongside real-time polling and a similarly validated observation protocol (Classroom Observation Protocol for Undergraduate STEM – COPUS). Our method also represents the use of a robust comparison design using a quasi-experimental grouping that is rarely used in typical POE studies. Our comparison controlled for well-studied factors influencing the learning experience, such as course instructor and instructional methods. Our analysis of those measures also used best-in-field measures that offered improved credibility for our findings compared to more common conventional tools. For example, we used structural equation modeling to identify a need to further refine the CLASS-C based on more robust construct definitions and reliability metric thresholds. For individual scale reliability measures, we calculated coefficient omega as an alternative to the commonly used coefficient alpha. This update in practice addressed the common problem of scale items violating the assumption of tau equivalence (which we empirically confirmed was present in our data). Coefficient omega let to more accurate – and generally higher – measures of reliability for our research scales. Our analysis also represents improved methodology in its intentional omission of several problematic design choices common in education research. Our treatment of subgroups included the National Science Foundation-recognized designation of "Underrepresented Group" (URG), but we recognized the tension in treating such a broad designation as a monolith. Our treatment of the group included presenting multiple interpretations of the categorization, as well as avoiding interpretations that suggest all learners who could be categorized as a member of a URG experience the same forces of marginalization. Similarly, we also limited our analysis of student grades as a research tool. We examined aggregate student performance as a relevant consideration for course performance, but we intentionally did not collect or interpret student-level grade data. We avoided this approach in recognition of the tension this would place between grades as a learning feedback tool and their use as an outcome variable.

IRB Process: This study involved human subjects and was granted approval by the University of Kansas IRB (2018-11-05).

Innovate and Validate: Scenario Modeling to Test Centralized Registration Feasibility in a Multi- Specialty Clinic

EDRA CORE Certified

Submitted by: *EwingCole*

Study Team: *Alice Gittler, Maryam Hosseini, and Michael Hoak*

Study Description: A new healthcare facility represents an opportunity to enhance quality through innovation. Uncertainty however, can often thwart the adoption of new ideas, such as a fully centralized registration model. As integrated members of the design team, our goal was to demonstrate the feasibility of central registration using hybrid scenario modeling.

Project Budget: $25,001-$50,000

Funding: Client/Provider, 100%

Research Question: In the early planning of an urban multi-specialty clinic, the team was challenged to rethink the building design and operational model to maximize clinical space, reduce duplication, and streamline patient flow. A key strategy was the consolidation of multiple specialty practices currently operating in distinct locations across the campus into one facility. The team was committed to a transparent design process bringing together business strategy, operations, practice administrators, clinical leaders, and the design team members on the client and consultant side to develop, vet, and test new ideas and concepts. Creating a single point of entry for multiple practices that included cardiology, neurology, and maternal and fetal medicine to name a few, was proposed. The team developed the concept of a wellness level that would centralize check-in and registration with an integrated digital and in-person strategy as well as offering patient and visitor amenities. As the first location in the health system initiating this centralized strategy, the team had neither previous experience nor "hard data" to assess the feasibility of the strategy within the given space available. Among the questions posed to the design team from the operation and strategy team were related to whether there was adequate space to accommodate the expected future state volume of patients and their companions. The health system was rolling out a more robust electronic pre-registration strategy. Assuming that the pre-registration adoption would increase over time, a second question of interest was how the level of pre-registration adoption would impact both the number of registration staff assigned to the centralized site as well as required space for patients and visitors expected to be on the wellness floor during a busy day. The team proposed a scenario modeling study that would use lean-led process and simulation-optimization to determine demand for seats and registration stations/staffing under multiple pre-registration adoption scenarios. An overarching objective of the research was to provide insights into the feasibility of the operational innovations proposed within the constraints of the available space and functional needs of the health system practitioners.

Existing Knowledge: Discrete event simulation (DES) modeling is recognized as a valuable approach to test options (Alvarado et al., 2018), support decision making, and demonstrate performance (Cai & Jia, 2019; Halawa et al., 2020; Kaba & Barnes, 2019) in healthcare facility planning. It is one of a full complement of operations research (OR) methods pioneered in manufacturing and now applied to design. A recent literature review noted that, despite their relevancy, OR is yet to be fully embraced in architectural practice (Halawa et al., 2020). Hybrid approaches such as simulation-optimization (SO) are increasing being applied in health care settings for forecasting, planning, and operational planning (Ordu et al., 2021). Simulation and optimization can be applied independently or with mixed integer programming models (Vahdat et al., 2019), data from electronic medical records, real-time location systems, and space syntax analysis (Cai & Jia, 2019). In the clinic setting specifically, scenario modeling using DES alone or in combination with other methods is increasingly being adopted. Researchers have used DES to determine the optimal daily volume of patients (J. Morrice et al., 2020), compare layout options based on walking distances and wait times (Gosavi et al., 2016) and explore how room utilization is impacted by growth rate scenarios (Cai & Jia, 2019). These authors note that DES is able to incorporate stochastic variables and uncertainty, capture relationships between spaces and processes, while meeting expectations for decision support that quantifies performance. DES studies in clinic settings have typically focused on locations where all processes occur in a dedicated specialty unit. Fewer consider centralized registration like the concept proposed in this project. A 2020 study applied DES to compare centralized versus decentralized admission processes for multiple clinics, exploring the benefits of a centralized location and investigating factors such as patient mix, arrival rates, appointment types, and number of clinics to demonstrate the feasibility of the approach (Smyth, 2020). The approach here incorporates Lean methods, and a hybrid SO approach and represents research embedded in practice, demonstrating how Lean and DES can be fully integrated into early conceptual design and decision making.

Study Team: The multidisciplinary design team included representatives from both the client-side as well as the consultant team with roles in strategic planning, business development, finance, regional operations, facilities services and engineering, healthcare planning, healthcare interior design, ambulatory operations, hospital operations, ancillary services, and design research. Two design researchers undertook the data collection, analysis, and modeling. One researcher has been active in design research in practice for more than 7 years, with training in healthcare interior design, systems science, industrial engineering; including simulation modeling, lean and six-sigma and design thinking. The other researcher is an industrial engineer with advanced training in machine learning, simulation modeling, and statistics and has been working for one year as a researcher in practice. The larger design team brought expertise and skill sets related to healthcare architecture and planning, interior design, healthcare administration, and healthcare clinical operations. Members of the team from both the client and consultant side were actively involved in discussing future state process flows, operational performance targets, facilitating data gathering, and defining research questions. Clinical leaders were also engaged throughout the process to validate and build consensus on operational flows. Stakeholder meetings, test-fits and space planning was undertaken by the architectural and design team leading the design efforts.

Research Design: The study was tailored to questions during conceptual design of the clinic and combined lean-led design methods together with discrete event simulation modeling (DES). Over 4 months, a simulation model of future state registration processes was developed in an iterative approach. Interviews and workshops with staff and managers were conducted to map current processes, identify bottlenecks, and imagine future state. Annual forecasted volumes were converted into expected daily volumes on a busy clinic day. Inputs were based on 10 months of deidentified practice data. Datasets were processed in Python to remove non-completed encounters, estimate weekly peaks, distribution fitting for arrival off-set, and calculate arrivals per schedule slot. The future state flow begins with arrival and proceeds through check-in (see Fig 1). Processing times were determined in consultation with practice managers. Arrival patterns showed considerable variability (Fig 2). Patient arrival rate per visit slot was based on the median number of visits per slot. The number of patient companions was reached by consensus of the group. 140 seats and 8 check-in stations were set as the upper cap on capacity. The team collaboratively set the baseline level (30%) for pre-registration and a higher 50% for future state. The primary hypothesis was that a higher level of digital pre-registration would be required to accommodate volumes. Performance measures for the optimization included a maximum wait time for check-in of less than 2 minutes, and a utilization cap of 85% for check-in staff. The simulation model was created using FlexSim Healthcare® Software with the Optimizer engine. The results of the simulation model were validated based on review of all assumptions and workflows during regular meetings, statistical comparison between model outputs and historical data, observation of 3D animation of the model, and review of preliminary results with those experienced within the actual clinic. All scenarios were run for one week with 32 replications. Seating demand and utilization were partitioned by hour of the day including 95% CI for average and maximum values. Frequency of maximum wait times and census values were also calculated. Dashboards were used to visualize results.

Research Analysis: We report the findings for Scenario 1A: 70% in-person registration with 4 check-in stations; Scenario 1B: 70% with 5 stations; Scenario 2A: 50% in-person registration with 4 stations; and Scenario 2B: 50% with 5 stations. The number of check-in stations was found to have an impact on total floor census and waiting times for check-in. For Scenario 1A, check-in station utilization ranged between 51% to 68% during peak hours with a maximum of 80%. The maximum floor census reached 100 to 110 people during peak times. For Scenario 1B, the utilization of stations ranged from 41% to 54% with a maximum of 64% and the maximum floor census ranged between 82 to 98. Both were well within seating capacity of 140 chairs. For Scenario 2A, the maximum floor census reached 69 to 83 during peak hours. In Scenario 2B, the floor census reached a maximum of 63 to 74. For Scenario 2A, check-in station utilization ranged between 51% to 68% during peak hours with a maximum of 80%. For Scenario 2B, station utilization ranged from 41% to 54% with a maximum of 64%. With a higher pre-registration rate (50%) of Scenario 2, the optimal number of check-in stations was 4 and ensured that 99% of patients wait less than 2 minutes. The centralized floor could accommodate peak patient and companion census as well as throughout of 2,000 people per day even with lower pre-registration and still reduced demand for seating by up to 20%.

Application to Practice: Using a lean-led approach focused the team on streamlining process and understanding the visit from the patient perspective. Mapping the current and future state provided a valuable consensus-building exercise for the team, while also building the needed information for the model. Simulation modeling was chosen specifically because of the ability to capture variability inherent in the clinic process and because multiple scenarios could be experimented with simultaneously. The process of developing, discussing, and reaching consensus on future operations and assumptions is integral to scenario modeling and provided the team the ability to understand the interactions between the layout/designed environment and operational concepts. The combination of simulation-optimization in the modeling environment allowed multiple scenarios to be run and to find the optimal combination that would meet the performance targets. The team commitment to integrating the voice of the multidisciplinary team members into the process was reflected in the highly iterative and transparent process. The scenario modeling provided the decision support to quantify seating and check-in station needs and gain insight into the variables that would impact the feasibility of centralized registration. The process provided impetus to explore and gain input on operational changes required as the health system plans the new facility, including cross-training of registration staff and adoption of pre-registration rates. This study distinguishes itself from other similar work in that is adopted a simulation-optimization approach. Specific variables/ performance measures were defined by the team and used in the Optimizer tool to simulate different scenarios and search for the best combination of values of the variables when we changed one variable at a time. Results showed trade-offs between waiting time and utilization metrics that could be explored by the group.

Dissemination Approach: The findings of the scenario modeling were shared with the design team at multiple points in the study's development and progression. This included preliminary findings during validation and review as well as final results. These were presented and discussed during virtual sessions with practice administrators, regional ambulatory leaders, and facilities team members. The findings were visualized and shared in a report format. In 2021, the study was shared with an audience of students, academics, and practitioners as part of a visiting lecture series webinar series focused on multidisciplinary approaches to facility design presented by a prominent university with a strong program in healthcare design. Members of the team including the project architect, health system facilities team member, and researchers presented the early concepts and planning innovations for the clinic, along with the processes and findings of the simulation modeling. Our study was recently accepted for a presentation at an upcoming international design research conference where the team will be sharing the innovative concepts of the clinic, along with the multidisciplinary process including the methodology and findings of the iterative scenario modeling research. It is the study team's intent to submit the study for publication in a peer-reviewed journal in the coming months and to produce a case study document for public distribution via a web-based platform.

Study Impact: The impacts of the study can be described as fourfold: demonstration of feasibility, supporting consensus-building, informing future state operational planning, and building familiarity and utility of scenario modeling during conceptual design. First, the study provided evidence of the feasibility of the centralized registration concept within expected volumes and space available, and specifically quantify the demand for seating and check-in stations. By providing a worst case or conservative approach, the scenario modeling results provided the decision support to allow the team to gain insights into the variables that would impact the feasibility of the centralized registration process. The detailed and iterative team discussions of operational flows and systems represented an important step towards better preparing the future state team to operate successfully in the new building. The data analysis of historical data provided insight to management team about the operations such as: peak load, peak times, as well as utilization of registration areas during peak and non-peak hours. The meetings with the multidisciplinary team provided an impetus to explore and gain input on operational changes required as the health system plans the new facility, including cross-training of registration staff, the upstream effects of visitor management systems and screening, as well as support for increasing adoption of pre-registration rates. Through this exercise, the health system identified the necessary technology requirements that would need to be designed, built, and implemented to supplement the central registration process. Likewise, the team realized a consensus among the many ambulatory practices would need to be reached so that the operational functioning of the building could be sustainable. Scheduling and cancellation policies, areas designated for special needs, and privacy were a few of the considerations that this exercise brought to light. The collaborative nature of scenario modeling provided direct decision inputs for the design team to identify the most efficient space design and validate estimates on the seat capacity in the wellness lounge, while also considering the constraints and concerns expressed by the larger project team.

Study Reach: Simulation modeling is increasing being adopted by design firms to test performance or determine capacity requirements for facilities in a data-driven manner. Fewer published studies represent research which is fully integrated into conceptual design process. If the experience of this team can be generalized, architecture and design firms are still working towards how research, data analytics, and predictive or prescriptive methods can be successfully woven into the design process. This study was developed and refreshed throughout the period of conceptual design with wide participation of stakeholders representing multiple disciplines on both the client and firm side. This study distinguishes itself from other similar work in that it adopted a hybrid simulation-optimization approach and was fully integrated within a lean-led design process. Specific performance measures were defined by the team and used in the optimizer function to provide results whereby trade-offs between waiting time and utilization metrics could be explored by the group. Once optimal seating and check-in stations were determined, experimentation could proceed under the different pre-registration levels. Because the model was collectively developed, it was available to the team as a resource that could be used for further experimentation. This study created a groundwork for future studies that examine the impact of technology integrated centralized registration versus decentralized one on occupancy, waiting times, and staff utilization.

Research Innovation: Simulation modelling is still a relatively new methodology in design process, and teams are still understanding how to successfully integrate the process in such a way as to enhance, rather than complicate or slow down, planning. The use of simulation-optimization was novel in the context of testing centralized registration concepts that incorporated in-person and technology-enhanced self-service concepts. In this case, the modeling provided an important link between innovative ideas and working out the details of those ideas. The ability to simultaneously and dynamically represent both design and operations continues to build the bridge between ideas and implementation and promote innovation adoption within what is typically a risk-adverse environment. Researchers have noted the fact that few models are reused, resulting in duplication in efforts (Roberts, 2011). In this endeavor, the model was built in a flexible manner to be reused as assumptions or layouts change over future design phases. Due to the pandemic, much of the interaction and model building was conducted virtually. The team made use of electronic shared whiteboards and other virtual means to share the model, model findings, map flows, and review data. This ongoing documentation and sharing opens research process and findings review to the non-researcher members of the team and has created greater opportunities for data-driven design process. Our collaborative working relationships on both the client and consultant side has led to opportunities for co-presenting and co-publishing this work in the future.

IRB Process: This study did not involve human subjects so did not submit to an IRB.

A Pre-Post Outcomes Evaluation Study of an Inpatient Unit: An Inevitable Step Toward Continuous Process Improvement

EDRA CORE Certified

Submitted by: *HKS, Inc., ProMedica & Toledo Hospital*
Study Team: *Rutali Joshi, Upali Nanda, Camilla Moretti, Paula Grieb, Martyna Falloni, Parsa Aghaei, and Deborah Wingler*

Study Description: This rigorous, multi-method, pre-post outcomes evaluation study was conducted in an inpatient tower to link design intent and desired outcomes. Diagnostics prior to design, and robust evaluations after occupancy, build the foundation for research integrated design that can elevate how we practice in the AEC industry and healthcare facilities.

Project Budget: $10,001-$25,000

Funding: Design Firm, 100%

Research Question: A leading Midwest healthcare organization wanted to utilize an evidence-based design approach when embarking on the design of a new inpatient tower. To support this vision, a Design Diagnostic was conducted by the research team in the Surgical Intensive Care unit (SICU) and Med-surg unit of the existing facility in 2015. Findings from the research revealed long walking distances for staff, excessive noise levels, and limited point-of-use access to medications and supplies, underutilized spaces, and unaccommodated workstations-on-wheel (WOWs). The data from field research resulted in development of simulation models which allowed the team to optimize the design throughout the process to support the goals of increased efficiency, improved team communication, increased patient safety and enhanced patient and family experiences. The final plan configuration (see Figure 1. design intent in the uploaded pdf) resulted in simulated walking distances to reduce in half, even though the overall floor plate was larger. Other innovative design solutions implemented in the new facility to improve outcomes included blended acuity staffing model, setting up units as two 12- bed pods, dual access nurse servers in each patient room for point-of-care supplies, decentralized nursing stations, provision of collaboration hubs, and distributed support spaces like medication, supplies and nourishment in multiple locations within the central core. Following construction and phased move-in, occupancy evaluation was performed in 2021 in the SICU, acute care unit and the overall inpatient tower to address the key question, "Does the facility effectively meet user needs and support organizational goals as envisioned?". The specific objectives of this evaluation study were to: -Assess strategies that were most effective in achieving improved outcomes -Validate the simulation results and compare outcomes to the baseline measured in 2015 -Identify opportunities for further improvement that will inform existing processes -Generate guidelines for new capital projects

Existing Knowledge: Walking distances were a major concern in the current state identified through the Design Diagnostic. Nurse walking is a key component of the staff experience that has been discussed at length in the healthcare literature. Studies show that nurses can walk as much as 6 miles during a shift (Pati, Harvey, & Thurston, 2012), prompting researchers to examine how much this walking is relevant and of value and how much time is being wasted in nonessential walking that can be directed toward patient care and nurse well-being. There in an ongoing debate around centralized versus decentralized nurse station. Pati, Harvey, and Thurston (2012) examined nursing support spaces and the impact the different unit configurations had on the nurse's walking distances. The study compared centralized, decentralized, and room/ bedside models. In a decentralized model, support spaces were distributed in more than one places in the central core and reduced walking distance by 26.8% in comparison to the centralized model. The team relied on this and several such studies to design the new SICU and acute care unit which provided decentralized stations for tasks like documentation and patient monitoring and distributed support spaces. In keeping with the existing literature, we found drastic reduction in nurse walking distances by implementing these strategies. Interestingly, our study uncovered aspects not reported in existing literature around the differences in utilization of decentralized care team stations in the SICU and acute care unit owing to room allocations of patients on the unit and their acuity.

Study Team: Our study involved staff members and the organizations leadership team as participants. All staff working in the tower as well as specifically within the SICU and Acute care unit were eligible to participate. Separate surveys for developed for staff on the two units and those working on other units in the facility. The survey was developed using an online platform and distributed via a link that was sent to participants through a distribution email. A total of 155 responses were obtained from staff across the entire facility (n=138, 89%) and the observed SICU (n=12, 8%) and acute care unit (n=5; 3%). A total of 9 semi-structured interviews were conducted with SICU staff and 7 with acute care staff. The participants included RN, charge nurses, unit managers, educators, EVS personnel, respiratory therapists, physicians, concierge staff and general supply staff. The focus group was conducted with 12 participants including the lead nursing director, lead director, director, unit manager, critical care nurse, AVP clinical, chief nursing officer. The protocol development and field data collection logistics were led by two trained health researchers in coordination with the Chief Nursing Officer of the facility and the unit managers.

Research Design: A multi-method data collection approach was used to gather observational, reported, and operational data. OBSERVATIONAL DATA: Field data was collected within the guides of an approach developed during the design diagnostic in 2015. It entailed 2.5 days of shadowing, behavioral mapping, noise measurements and photo documentation (July 2021). Behavior mapping-To understand who is in the unit, with whom are they interacting and where the interaction occurred. Maps (total 12) were captured as a snapshot in time across day and night shifts using an observation sheet. Color coding was used to map staff roles, patients, and visitors. Registered Nurse (RN) shadowing-To gather deeper insights into nurse activities, duration, and walking distance. It entailed shadowing 2 RNs in each unit over 17 hours between day and night shift and recording data using a shadowing sheet. Decibel Readings-To record decibel levels using a smart phone app and the sources of noise levels. Data was captured at 30 pre-identified locations in both the units Photo Essay- Using imagery of significant spaces in the units to highlight successes and pinch points. REPORTED DATA: Interviews and focus groups were conducted on-site. In addition, a staff survey was developed with feedback from the facility leadership and deployed in September 2021. Semi-structured interviews and focus groups-To garner staff feedback regarding their experience with the department and identify potential environmental and operational facilitators and barriers within key spaces of the department. A total of 16 interview participants and 12 focus group participants were recruited. Surveys-To measure staff experience and perceived effectiveness of the overall department and specific units. Closed questions in the survey were rated on a 5-point Likert scale across the five constructs of safety, efficiency, experience, access, and flexibility. The Likert scales rated items in terms of agreement, satisfaction, ease, and safety. Participants were also asked 6 open-ended questions to provide further insight into the above constructs and basic demographic information. OPERATIONAL DATA: Data from Hospital Consumer Assessment of Healthcare Providers & Systems (HCAHPS) was obtained to assess changes in the outcomes impacting patient experience.

Research Analysis: Overlaying all behavior maps provided insight regarding utilization of space by clinical and non-clinical members of both units. Shadowing data were imported to a spreadsheet format for location, activity and walking distance analysis. Survey data was analyzed in Microsoft Excel and reported as a composite score for each construct. Top-box HCAHPS scores were calculated and compared from 2016 to 2021. Thematic content analysis was used to analyze qualitative data. KEY FINDINGS -Uniform 1:4 ratio and standardization of the unit layouts supported the blended acuity model in terms of floating staff easily and improving efficiencies -Proximity between SICU and acute care unit streamlined patient transfers from critical to acute care and staff workflows -The sunroom was well utilized by patients, staff, and family/visitors -Staff expressed satisfaction with universal patient room design, headwall design, sufficient space around the patient bed to perform care activities and space for family -Dual access nurse servers provided access to point of care supplies, a greater level of flexibility, and safety, which has been a vital advantage during COVID -The unit layout and integration of nurse servers reduced staff walking distance by about 43%. -A significant reduction in noise levels was recorded in both units. There was 7% improvement in quietness scores in the HCAHPS survey -Designated alcoves for WOWs and sufficient storage were effective in minimizing hallway clutter

Application to Practice: Certain unexpected results came to the forefront during this study that turned into opportunities for improvement for this and several other projects. 1. Patients were allotted rooms based on acuity and availability, rather than nurse assignment making it challenging to operationalize the Pod model as envisioned. This can be attributed to lack of appropriately conveying design intent to the staff on the floor and due to leadership changes during transition. 2. Inconsistent and untimely stocking of nurse servers resulted in unnecessary walking to find supplies, and increased staff frustration 3. While decentralized team stations were well-utilized for patient monitoring as well as documentation and debriefing in the acute care unit, they were underutilized in the SICU. High acuity patients in the SICU required constant monitoring of vitals displayed on large electronic monitors in the collaboration hub, owing to which nurses are found in the collaboration hub more than the nurse stations. While visibility into patient room remains important for patient safety, proximity to the patient room at all times may not be required in the SICU as in the acute care unit. 4. Some level of nesting happened in the collaboration hub as staff claimed spots because they did not have an office, or it was to too far. Moreover, the facility was not designed as an academic medical center. Academic teams claim spaces in the collaboration hub, making availability of space challenging. These shortcomings impacted the ability to link some intended design strategies to desired outcomes (refer to figure 2 for details). To overcome these, we were also able to provide a set of "do now" recommendations and recommendations for the future including operational, technological, and design recommendations. Another important lesson learnt from this study was that design and operational intent often can get lost in the transition process. It is important that an operational handbook ,and functional narrative accompany the design intent documents so that units are operated the way they are planned, irrespective of leadership changes, while remaining agile and nimble to new challenges. A 3-month, 6-month and 12-month check-in between design team and operational team is suggested for health projects in our firm to help with a smooth transition.

Dissemination Approach: The audience for this study was external to support the AEC industry's knowledge of design of inpatient units, as well as internal to support our practitioners in having a deeper understanding of the need to consider various aspects of the healthcare system, including operations, technology, and user behaviors, to ensure that the design can support seamless functioning of healthcare spaces and help achieve organizational goals. Key innovation from this project will continue to influence future projects moving forward. These findings have been shared at a variety of conferences and will be extensively shared at conferences in the coming year, including EDRA, to support the integration of these findings into healthcare design practice. While findings from the design diagnostic conducted in 2015 have been published in a peer-reviewed journal, we hope to publish comparative findings from this pre-post occupancy study as well.

Study Impact

Leadership and staff impact: Through this study, design and research teams were able to work in concert with the owner to develop specific guiding principles for the project that informed design and operational innovations like the blended acuity staffing model and acuity blocking, standardized units and universal patient rooms, access to point of care supplies through nurses' servers, provision of sunrooms. These solutions were then evaluated based on data gathered from various perspectives - leadership, staff, patients as well as healthcare researchers. Collating evidence gathered from various data sources highlighted that the facility design supported development of strong staff-patient relationships, allowed staff to deliver clinical excellence that the health system is known for and is a safe and rewarding environment that 'cares for the caregivers'. Survey data also revealed that the majority of staff were satisfied or very satisfied with the overall facility. The insights from this study were shared with leadership and facility staff on several occasions and will be used for continuous quality improvement in existing processes. Firmwide healthcare designers and industry at large: This study makes it evident that there's a degree of variability between different delivery models and sites, hence design decisions should be backed by a strong body of research and context-specific evaluation. Firmwide presentations were made as well as a detailed internal report was published to emphasize and disseminate findings and lessons learnt from the study. Moreover, since this study was conducted in the COVID era, it brings to forefront considerations that can support healthcare facilities in their quest for agility and resiliency while continuing to strive for improved health outcomes moving forward.

Study Reach: This project is a case study that successfully bridges that gap between research and its application to design. Through a robust evidence-based process all the way from establishing a vision for the project, articulating project goals, understanding baseline conditions via diagnostics, to designing using Evidence-based Design principles, and finally measuring the results, this project is a prototype project for research integration. It also makes a strong case for the use of nested room layouts, flexible and nature-infused staff spaces, and blended acuity inpatient units. Despite the integration of research throughout, the post-move evaluation revealed that the lack of continued engagement of the team through transition and occupancy can cause small, but critical oversights. Careful documentation of design intent, and the development of a transition plan, to bridge the gap between design intent and operations were found to be key contributors to achieving intended outcomes. It is vital that the AEC and healthcare industry at large ensure frequent check-ins between the design and operational teams to allow for a smooth transition and translation of design intent to operational practices.

Research Innovation: This project was innovative in that the guiding principles and intent of the design was established based on research right at the beginning of the design and documented in the form of a design intent document. The layering of human, spatial and environmental data in the mixed-methods approach is a key innovation of the research method. The mixed methods "design diagnostic" approach to data gathering, deployed in an agile way to sync to project needs, has been published in HERD journal. The design diagnostic tool developed also won the AIA Technology award in Detroit for a novel use of parametric modeling for spatial analysis. Use of a design to outcomes framework is another key innovation. Findings from the occupancy outcomes evaluation in the new facility were linked back to the original design intent to understand the effectiveness of the implemented design strategies, and reasons for challenges as represented in the matrix in figure 2. While not reported in this submission, the on-site data collection was also used to validate the firm's internal digital tools for data collection. While the on-site data collection process was led by a health researcher, this was used as an opportunity to train two emerging design professionals and equip them with the tools necessary for field research in a conscious step toward integrating design and research efforts within the firm.

IRB Process: This study involved human subjects, but IRB review was not sought and/or obtained for this study. Staff evaluations were considered Quality Improvement projects and thus exempt from IRB review.

Re-Imagining the Employee Experience in a Manufacturing Plant

EDRA CORE Certified

Submitted by: *HGA Architects and Engineers & Marvin®*

Study Team: *Adaheid Mestad, Ashley Macaulay, Mashid Jalalian, Oshana Reich, Anoosha Baladi, and Marvin®*

Study Description: The goal of this study is to reimagine a 400,000 SF manufacturing plant as a place of wellbeing which also strengthens a sense of community and pride for the employees. Through a design thinking process that included mixed-method research and participatory design approaches, 12 experience insights were identified to drive a five-year masterplan.

Project Budget: $50,001-$100,000

Funding: Client/Provider, 100%

Research Question: The study's objective was to make data-driven design recommendations to improve the employee's experience who work in a 400,000 SF manufacturing plant and amplify employees' advocacy and agency through the study and design process. For this study, experience is framed as the physical environment, workplace culture and process, and technology that support employees to do their best work. To support these objectives, research questions included: 1. What is leadership's perception of the employee experience? 2. What is the employee's perception of their overall experience? 3. What problems are significantly impacting employees' experiences? 4. How and where do employees feel motivation and pride in the plant? 5. How do employees seek respite and recharge throughout their day? 6. How do employees move about the plant? 7. How can the design process engage and facilitate employee advocacy? 8. What is the best way to foster collaboration specifically among R&D and Engineering? Although, there is ample literature on employee experience and workplace culture within a corporate workplace, there are very limited studies that have focused on a manufacturing setting. This study, therefore, had an additional aim to understand and fill the knowledge gap on manufacturing workplace, explicitly highlighting employee well-being, and sense of community and pride.

Existing Knowledge: There is a general lack of existing literature which focuses on the collective employee wellbeing in a manufacturing setting. This study, therefore, serves to fill that gap by providing a case study of manufacturing employee wellbeing needs and priorities. There are a handful of studies which corroborate and validate aspects of wellbeing defined in our research: • McHugh et al. (2020) found that manufacturing plant workers perceive shift work as detrimental to their well-being in four domains: physical environment and safety; health; work experience; and home, community, and society. This indicates shift work negatively influences manufacturing worker well-being in a holistic way. • Kralikova et al. (2021) Evaluated the impact of workplace lighting on employee health and wellbeing and found that night shift workers were more prone to feelings of visual discomfort, headache, and Seasonal Affective Disorder (SAD) symptoms. • Pubuduni & Prabodanie (2018), in a study of a manufacturing site, found both high temperature levels and high noise levels can lead to lower productivity. Higher temperature levels in factories have a negative impact on both workers' productivity and day-to-day health, impacting the percentage of workers getting headaches and other illnesses such as allergic reactions. Excessive noise can also create an irritating work environment which lowers productivity levels. Through the review of the existing literature, the research team found some other studies which provide insights into addressing the wellbeing concerns that is also raised in the existing research: • Rueff & Logomarsino (2016) found positive results for the effectiveness of worksite health-promotion interventions to increase fruit and vegetable consumption among manufacturing workers. Multiple levels of intervention, an emphasis on employee participation in planning, higher self-efficacy, and social support were found to be effective. • Two studies which were not manufacturing-setting specific, but considered a range of workplace settings, provide guidance on effective workplace sponsored weight management programs (Staniford et al., 2020), and workplace mental health programs (Davenport et al., 2016).

Study Team: The research team comprised of five

researchers. The role of the design anthropologist was central to this project considering her skills in ethnography, equitable design thinking, and participatory planning. She was a key person in understanding the culture and experiences and translating those into insights. The design researchers' background in architectural research and familiarity with both qualitative and quantitative approaches to research was crucial to the development of tools to collect and analyze data. The data visualization specialist had a significant role by taking quantitative data and translating them into graphics. The designer in the team was also instrumental in translating the research findings into design applications. The study's participants included 50 employees (changemakers) who were selected to represent the larger plant employees and were recruited through diverse demographics including department, role, tenure, gender, age, and ethnicity. The changemakers participated in five design thinking workshops and presented final design recommendations to the Steering Committee. 109 Plant leaders also contributed their perspectives through a questionnaire. This was an important data set to compare leadership and employee perspectives. A group of eight individuals consisting of the firm's and Plant's leadership were identified as the Steering Committee, who oversaw the process and was responsible for prioritizing a phased masterplan through capital budgets.

Research Design: The study took place in May through October 2021. The research followed an equitable design thinking process to engage changemakers and drive innovative design (Figure 1). A mixed method approach was developed to facilitate triangulation of findings. Leadership Questionnaire: An online survey was distributed to supervisors, directors, and managers at the Plant in June of 2021. The questionnaire was designed to understand leadership's perspective on current employee experience. It was important to compare the leadership perspectives with that o employees to identify commonalities and discrepancies to inform cultural analysis and point-of-view. The survey was open from June 25-July 9, 2021, with a response rate of 80% (96 respondents out of 120 leaders) Changemaker Workshop: Five, 90-minute Changemaker workshops were organized with 50 plant employees to support their advocacy through participatory planning. The workshops aligned with design thinking process to first identify employee's perspective and needs, define and prioritize problems and assets, ideate solutions, test concept designs, and advocate recommendations at report-out. The workshops took place in July – October 2021. The employees were selected to be a diverse representative of the plant employees within departments, roles, shifts, age, gender, and ethnicity. Remote Ethnography: Eight diverse Plant employees, from the Changemaker group, were self-selected to participate in remote ethnography to bring their daily experiences into context. The participants received an Android phone with an Indeemo® remote ethnography application on each phone. The ethnography was open for 8 workdays where employees were asked to take images, record videos, and journal on three themes: what hinders or supports their work throughout the day, how they recharge and take respite, and what motivates them during the day or provides a sense of pride. The remote ethnography took place from July 26, 2021, through August 4, 2021. Badge Check-in Data: Door usage data from April 20, 2021, until May 20, 2021, was collected from all available doors on the plant and analyzed. Door usage was a valuable method to understand the highest door used at arrival times by employees, as well as the number of people leaving during shift for breaks, length of break, and which doors were used.

Research Analysis: The research team conducted parallel analysis to define common themes of problems and assets. The leadership questionnaire data was exported into Power BI to allow segmentation of the data based on department and leadership role. The qualitative data from Changemaker workshops was entered into excel to code and quantity themes. Door data was exported into Power BI platform to understand utilization of doors and percentage of employees that leave during breaks and the average break duration. The team synthesized the findings to define the current experience state of the Plant including: • Culture: Employees are dedicated, hard-working, and take pride in their craft. Micro-communities based on tenure, department, and shifts exist. • Process: Work is organized by cells, and cell facilitators play a significant role in team dynamics. Outside of cells, there is a gap between how people see the complete process of the Plant and how their work has a purpose to the end user. • Place: Employees' demanding work and dedication is not reflected in the environment they are in. The Plant is extremely loud with little daylight and extreme temperatures. Entrances lack a welcoming greeting and circulation is confusing and unsafe. • Technology: Employees do not feel supported to do their best work due to unreliable equipment and lack of technology that supports their craft and development of new products. Twelve Experience Insights emerged, the full list of which is included in Figure 2.

Application to Practice: Building upon the research findings, practical solutions were collaboratively ideated by the research team and Changemakers. The practical solutions were then translated into scalable design responses to address each of the twelve Experience Insights (Figure 2). Ranging from light, to medium, to heavy touch, solutions offered flexibility in their implementation based on available resources and time. Practicality of solutions was maintained by focusing on four key areas of implementation: culture, process, place, and technology. Collaboration and co-creation were key in translating findings into practical solutions. The research team ensured that the employees' ideas for solutions were heard, incorporated, and built upon. Practical solutions were developed through a process of combining changemaker expertise in the Plant conditions and employee priorities, with research and design team expertise in design and best practices. Beyond addressing individual Experience Insights, the research team worked with the designers to develop a comprehensive Employee Experience Master Plan, which outlines a strategy for when, where, and how to incorporate solutions across the Plant campus. The Master Plan provides a framework for coordinating spatial improvements to maximize positive and equitable impact on employee experience.

Dissemination Approach: Considering the recent completion of this study in November 2021, external dissemination of findings has not been undertaken, though the research team does intend to share findings with wider audiences moving forward. To date, internal dissemination of findings has included: Plant Leadership • The final report of research findings, design solutions, and Master Plan strategy were presented to the Plant Steering Committee by the Changemakers and supported by the research and design team. It was important for the Changemakers to 'own' the final findings and recommendations and have a platform to speak to leadership directly, as this was a culmination of the effort to amplify and support their advocacy and agency. Internal to the Architectural Firm • The research process, findings, and design solutions from this project were presented at a firm-wide conference, an internal platform for highlighting resources and expertise in the firm. The research team highlighted the application of remote ethnography tools used in conjunction with more familiar engagement tools such as workshops and surveys. Overall, the presentation emphasized how to integrate values of engagement and collaboration in the design process. • The same presentation was delivered to the Public Corporate Market Sector to share knowledge with design teams for future manufacturing plant projects.

Study Impact: The study's impact was significant by greatly expanding the initial scope of the project and highlighting how employee experience has interconnections within the entire Plant campus. Initially, the Plant leadership had anticipated simple renovations to update lunchrooms, breakrooms, bathrooms, and patio spaces. However, with data-supported Experience Insights that the Changemakers advocated, the final scope led to a complete five-year phased masterplan which included: - HVAC installment - Circulation and wayfinding study - Complete plant daylight study and window and skylight renovation - Significant landscaping and outdoor spaces to support outdoor respite - Phased removal of older, underutilized buildings with new constructions to centralize R&D and Engineering and create a Plant community hub - Decentralized respite areas to provide privacy to plant employees who work on the Plant floor and do not have an office. In addition, the Steering Committee and the firm's Culture and Innovation Team continue to meet with Changemakers to identify policy and cultural prototypes. The prototypes include mental wellbeing support, PTO sharing, leadership and management training, and shift assessment to support families with multiple family members working at the Plant.

Study Reach: This study supports the growing literature of a much-needed paradigm shift in the manufacturing industry to rethink the employee experience past productivity and incorporate employee well-being best practices. The data-supported Experience Insights developed through the study were significant to drive a complete masterplan. It is also noteworthy that Participatory Planning through the Changemaker workshops exemplifies leadership and a research-design team relinquishing power to the employees. During a reflection meeting with the Changemakers, they noted that they felt a sense of pride in their contribution to the Plant. They also reflected a more positive attitude within their teams, departments, and the Company's leadership. The Changemakers acknowledged that changes in the built environment take time, and the short-term prototypes were essential to maintain their trust in change. In parallel, leadership felt the process was transparent and identified that the engagement goals were respected to create an authentic engagement process to strengthen the company's relationship with its employees.

Research Innovation: Two innovative approaches were conducted and applied in this study. The first is integrating remote ethnography, which is a form of applied anthropology methodology. Ethnography seeks to understand humans in their natural settings and is traditionally done through qualitative, researcher-participant observations and interactions, which support an emic approach. In this study, the employees observed and understood what is important to them through an emic approach. The value of integrating remote ethnography provided a deeper contextual inquiry of the daily life of a manufacturing employee, which is not gleaned from a survey or reflective journey mapping workshop activity. The ethnographic data was essential to understanding the "why" around the identified Experience Insights. Secondly, the d.School's Equitable Design Thinking process and the Changemaker engagement process supported best practices of co-design in participatory planning. The development of this framework and the engagement process required the research and design team to change their practice from usually being the leaders and voice of design to be acting as facilitators. The Changemakers were the voice of design based on their lived experience and needs.

IRB Process: This study involved human subjects, but IRB review was not sought and/or obtained for this study. Due to the time sensitivity of the project, there was not enough time for the study to go through an Institutional review board, however, the Principal Investigator and most other researchers on the team had received human subject training through CITI program and ensured to adhere to ethical standards of the research and protect participants privacy.

The Learning Futures Project: Imagining Higher Education in 2025

EDRA CORE Certified

Submitted by: *Perkins Eastman*

Study Team: *Danya Hakky, Joshua Jackson, and David Levo*

Study Description: This study used the COVID-19 crisis as a tool to reveal underlying opportunities and challenges faced by institutions of higher learning. A multidisciplinary panel of experts engaged in virtual focus group interviews to imagine the campus of 2025 and generate questions for colleges and universities to address in the immediate and near future.

Project Budget: $10,001-$25,000

Funding: Design Firm, 100%

Research Question: This study explored questions facing higher learning while the COVID-19 pandemic, economic turbulence, social justice movement, and American political turmoil impacted institutions across the country. With the future of higher education brought into question, this study aimed to provide paths forward in a sea of change. The study was designed to be shared publicly so many could learn from the experience of the educators, administrators, and technologists that participated in focus group interviews. The study focused on how we could positively get from today (at the time, 2020) to the year 2025—when institutes of higher learning would likely have gained some distance and perspective from the COVID-19 pandemic and disruption it triggered. This study centered on three main research questions: (1) What are the anticipated challenges to equity and access in current higher education environments? (2) How can pedagogy and technology evolve to support an equitable educational experience by 2025? (3) What space types/facilities will institutes of higher learning need to support equitable pedagogies by 2025? By delving into these questions, the researchers sought to create a report that could be used by designers, decision-makers, and stakeholders of institutes of higher learning to help set a course of action. The study offers an understanding of the impact of existing challenges coupled with the harsh realities revealed during the COVID-19 pandemic. By discussing these issues head-on, the research team and panel of experts were able to explore the future of learning and what institutions need to prepare. This information was then packaged and disseminated such that many others associated with the higher education industry could benefit and learn from these conversations. The study and its resulting report were targeted to a wide audience, including all those within the higher education community (e.g., administrators, faculty, etc.) and those serving it (including design professionals). As such, the study's published findings focused on the complex academic behaviors and programmatic shifts institutions would need to consider as well as a discussion of the places that would support such changes. Together, this information is incredibly relevant and useful to the higher education industry now and in coming years.

Existing Knowledge: Prior to this study, another research-based effort had been undertaken by the same design firm to explore the shift to virtual learning during the COVID-19 pandemic. For that study, relevant literature was reviewed about higher education, hybrid learning, and current and historical pandemic responses. In addition to building upon that foundational work, the research team of this study also leaned into the expertise and knowledge of the study's highly regarded participants. The participants' wisdom, experience, and perspectives on existing literature and previous research in the area was tapped. Further, guided by the study's exploratory and qualitative design, the research team purposefully allowed for supplemental literature to emerge during interactions with the participating experts. Any such recommendations were added to the data collected by this study's research team and were consider during analysis and reporting. Additionally, in developing the study's research questions, the researchers conducted a targeted review of relevant literature, including reviewing methods for futures thinking and foresight tools. This exploration, along with research team members' long-standing experiences in campus planning, resulted in the identification of the four core themes explored through the research questions, namely: pedagogy, technology, equity, and place. So, though this study's research team did not dig deeply into the existing knowledge base as a primary methodology for this study, they did purposefully build off prior research and literature, tap experts' knowledge, and dive into literature at key points in the study, with the aim to synthesize that knowledge to determine how it could be applied to practice through architectural solutions (either adaptations to current facilities or new capital improvements).

Study Team: For this exploratory qualitative study, the researchers convened an expert panel from different disciplines, roles, institutional scales, and regions. This multidisciplinary group offered diverse viewpoints in focus group discussions about post-pandemic learning. Participants included: • An Assistant Professor and Architect whose current research focuses on academic environments and neurodiversity • An Assistant Professor who specializes in learning analytics and the use of "big data" in education • A University Librarian and Assistant Vice Chancellor who focuses on academic technology • An Assistant Professor who researches educational technologies and active learning formats • An Assistant Professor whose area of focus is public health and psychosocial aspects for promoting healthy behavior • An Environmental Psychologist and Visiting Instructor at a design college expertise in psychosocial impacts of higher education environments • An Associate Professor and Associate Dean of a university who is also an architect and fabricator • The Chief of Staff for Academic Planning at a major university, who specializes in campus space planning • A Principal at a technology consulting group, who advises on the design of learning environments • The Director of a center for universal design focused on social learning processes and the use of online and blended learning

Research Design: This study's design was based in qualitative social science research methods and used a revised Delphi method to capture data from experts through successive rounds of discussion. The choice of the Delphi method, originally developed for the purpose of forecasting (see: www.rand.org/topics/delphi-method), was suitable to this study's objective. Instead of collecting individual responses from an expert panel and then sharing results as is with Delphi (Robinson, 2011), the methodology for this study included focus groups. Focus groups, popular in applied social science research, enabled collection of a range of data and provided inspiration as participants heard different ideas and reacted to them (Robinson, 2011). Focus groups can create power imbalances, however, and to address this, the researchers shared findings from each of the workshops via a virtual whiteboard providing an opportunity for everyone to respond—especially those who were perhaps less comfortable in expressing themselves during group discussions. As a result of this modified methodological process, this study's design consisted of concurrent sub-group discussions (called dialogues) followed by full panel meetings (called roundtables), during which an aggregate of findings from the previous set of dialogues were shared with the full panel for deliberation, and discussion. For each of the 3 research questions, the expert panel participated in a dialogue and a follow-up roundtable. A final roundtable was also held to discuss the overall study findings, as synthesized from the previous workshop sessions. Thus, in total, there were 3 dialogue workshops and 4 roundtables. This data collection process took about 8 weeks during the summer of 2020. As the majority of the expert panel consisted of academicians and university administrators, the summer months were perceived as most suitable due to a somewhat reduced workload for the participants during that time. The full study (including initial planning/coordination, data collection, analysis, and reporting/dissemination) took a total of 8 months (May to December 2020).

Research Analysis: The panelists, each with their own unique perspective, collaborated over numerous months debating and discussing this investigation. They were charged with the goal of positing possible futures and imagining the opportunities and potential threats for higher education. The focus was on a not-so-distant 2025. Each of the three dialogues were recorded and followed by full or partial transcriptions to enable a thematic analysis of the information shared. Themes from each concurrent set of dialogues were then aggregated and shared back with the team through a roundtable discussion. At the end of the (3) sets of dialogues, the researchers analyzed results from each of the dialogues separately and collectively, synthesizing them into themes/topic areas. Overall, analysis of participant input showed that rather than creating new issues, the COVID-19 pandemic revealed or accelerated pre-existing trends. Themes that emerged from the panelist discussions were further contemplated and explored by the research team and summarized into 5 key topic areas. 1. Expand Reach to Expand Equity 2. Teach Professional Skills Holistically 3. Elevate Life Skills 4. Building Lifelong Networks 5. Treat the Campus as the Essential Ecosystem

Application to Practice: Findings were distilled into a white paper that communicated the study's process, findings, and value. The white paper also includes helpful high-level summary snapshots alongside a narrative to promote readability and distribution. The research team synthesized the findings thusly: 1. Expand Reach to Expand Equity There are populations for whom higher education is financially and/or culturally inaccessible. To address this, institutions can revise admissions methods, connect to marginalized populations, or open new markets by delivering corporate continuing education. Incorporating a diverse mix of students into higher education creates better outcomes for all, but will require institutions to navigate financial and social challenges. 2. Teach Professional Skills Holistically Many students seek guaranteed job prospects upon graduation. In response, American colleges and universities have offered ever-more vocationally and professionally-focused programs. Yet content mastery must be synthesized with other types of learning with long-term value, such as the liberal arts, interdisciplinary collaboration, and civics. 3. Elevate Life Skills Life skills — such as collaboration, communication, and self-care — are needed by effective citizens in society. An exciting expression of this topic by our panelists was the convergence of Academic Affairs and Student Affairs into a single holistic platform for supporting all aspects of the student experience. 4. Building Lifelong Networks The social and professional bonds forged in a traditional four-year college can be the most durable connections a person forms, but this is not always articulated as an institutional imperative. Creating intentional cohorts can lead to better student persistence and educational outcomes, while creating a secondary opportunity for alumni to continually re-engage with their alma mater. 5. Treat the Campus as the Essential Ecosystem Throughout 2020, the desire to return to campus and the college community, was profound. In-person campus experience remains invaluable as it provides faculty with a full-range of pedagogies that allow students to grapple with content together. They also provide equitable access to the resources necessary for learning and research.

Dissemination Approach: The goal was to reach a broad audience in the higher education industry: designers, decision-makers, administrators, and stakeholders. A marketing and communications strategy was established to widely share the study's findings with a variety of audiences. The study resulted in a white paper that is publicly available through the sponsoring design firm's website. To inform people of the report's availability and direct them to where they can download it for free, e-blasts advertising the report were sent to the firm's higher education clients and contacts list (consisting of approximately 1,850 people). Further, the paper was highlighted and hyperlinked on the firm's LinkedIn, Facebook, and Twitter accounts, which have a combined following of over 82,000 people. Independent industry press also picked up the story of the study. To date, the study has been featured by multiple independent publications and podcasts. For example, one affiliated with a university highlighted the report's relevance to the future of libraries, and another publication focused on design discourse and future visioning. This knowledge-sharing is meant to better support higher education institutes, advocate for designers to create meaningful and equitable campuses, and allow key decision-makers to make more informed decisions on future projects.

Study Impact

The value of this study is that it did not just consider how one university would address the currently evolving issues of pedagogy, technology, equity, and place – instead, this study was focused on the higher education sector as a whole. By exploring the future of learning and disseminating the findings broadly, the research team was able to share a report that could be used by designers, decision-makers, and stakeholders of institutes of higher learning to set a course of action in a time of great uncertainty. With this information, people can take steps to prepare themselves for the future, making well-informed decisions and investing in more strategic solutions—whether they be programmatic updates, operational changes, technological enhancements, and/or adaptations to current facilities or new capital improvements. Thus, the information shared through this study is incredibly relevant and useful to the higher education industry now and in coming years. However, in addition to educating the intended audience (i.e., the sponsoring design firm's higher education practice, designers at-large, and higher education institutions), this study also directly benefited the participants. By attending and contributing to the study's workshop sessions and virtual whiteboard documentation, the expert panelists were able to not only consider for themselves the issues posed by the research questions, but they also had the opportunity to expand and challenge their thinking by listening to what other panelists said and ruminating on how others reacted to the conversations. Combined, this mutual exchange of knowledge and iterative mindset approach benefited not only the study and its report but also strengthened the participants' expertise that much further.

Study Reach: This study is built on previous research that looked at hybrid learning in light of the COVID-19 pandemic, and broadened the investigation to consider further disruptors facing higher education in 2020, including the pandemic, economic turbulence, social justice movement, and American political turmoil. This study did not aim to help one university or any particular group of decision-makers; it instead targeted a broad audience in order to provide an educated path forward during a time of great uncertainty. Through an iterative process of focus groups and feedback loops, this exploratory study resulted in a report that can be used by designers, decision-makers, and stakeholders of institutes of higher learning. By curating a panel of diverse and knowledgeable experts, the researchers were able to cultivate and share insights about fundamental questions facing higher education today and in the near future. The findings from this study enable all those within the higher education community (e.g., administrators, faculty, etc.) and those serving it (including design professionals) to prepare for the future by making well-informed decisions and investing in strategic solutions, including program updates, operational changes, enhanced technology, and/or architectural adaptations to current facilities or new capital improvements. The researchers believe that this study offers valuable information that can lead to positive impacts and more informed decision-making. In fact, as one reader of the report told the authors, "I appreciate the thought and effort that went into the publication. [It is] required readings for my deans because you use a framework that forces us to think more globally—beyond the self-limiting constraints of our own policies." By facing head-on the challenges and harsh realities of today, this study is helping institutes of higher learning prepare themselves for the near future.

Research Innovation: This study was innovative in several ways; the first pertaining to its methodological design and the second to the reporting of the study's findings. In terms of the study design, the researchers adapted the Delphi method by merging it with the focus group method to create a future-casting, iterative knowledge-sharing approach. Some of the unique advantages to using Delphi and focus groups include: • Collecting data from a diverse panel of experts simultaneously, rather than individually • Exploring a series of inter-related questions with a degree of depth that would otherwise have been difficult with a different method(s) • Panelist sub-group interactions were carefully planned to ensure all participants had a chance to interact with one another in smaller, more intimate groups (unlike other methods that are more focused on the individual, by providing the participants exposure to one another and their respective views, going through the research study process was intended to be both a challenging and enriching experience for the participants) • Interactions between the research team and the panel of experts over a period of time helped develop a level of comfort and familiarity, which could've contributed to a richer data-sharing experience and, therefore, more robust findings In terms of the study's reporting: • Findings were clearly broken into five main themes, enabling easy comprehension and targeted applicability • Each theme was discussed in its own chapter, so readers could dive into a topic as desired • Each chapter begins with a snapshot, which summarizes: what we know, what's held true, what we need to do, and opportunities vs. risks. These snapshots arguably distill the knowledge into bite-size, actionable findings for readers to ponder and explore.

IRB Process: This study involved human subjects, but IRB review was not sought and/or obtained for this study. This study did not seek IRB approval because it was designed as a quality improvement project, intended to assess and improve internal project work. The researchers decided to share the findings publicly so others could learn from their work, but did not set out for their conclusions to be applied universally. Further, the research had very little associated risk to the participants. (Though the researchers fully understand that this determination is for an IRB to decide, they felt that this further supported their decision not to seek IRB approval).

Integrating Prediction and Performance Models into Scenario-Based Resilient Community Design

EDRA CORE Certified

Submitted by: *Texas A&M University*

Study Team: *Galen Newman, Karishma Joshi, and Jiali Liu*

Study Description: This research uses the Land Transformation model to predict three different urban growth scenarios for Tampa, FL then integrates the Long Term Hydrologic Impact Assessment model to determine how effective the current comprehensive plan is in adapting urban growth to decreasing flood risk and pollutant load.

Project Budget: More than $100,000

Funding: Grant, 100%

Research Question: Sea level rise due to climate change makes coastal populations more susceptible to flood risks. The use of land change prediction modelling to inform scenario-based planning has been shown to help increase capabilities when dealing with uncertainties in urbanization. This research asks, how effective is the current comprehensive plan in adapting urban growth to decreasing flood risk and pollutant load? The research uses the Land Transformation model to predict three different urban growth scenarios for Tampa and develops master plans according to each scenario then assesses their probable impact using the Long-Term Hydrologic Impact Analysis Low Impact Development Spreadsheet as a performance model. The site under investigation is one of the most socially and physically vulnerable coastal neighborhoods in Tampa, FL. It is both heavily effected by flooding and characterized by industrial land uses, brown fields, and sites listed by the US Environmental Protection Agency's Toxic Release Inventory. A series of tools are used on multi-scalar spatial datasets with a purpose of increasing resiliency in a flood prone neighborhood. The Land Transformation Model (LTM), a GIS-based neural network for Land Change Modelling (LCM), is used to predict potential future urban growth of Tampa according to three different scenarios: 1) Business as usual – predicted urban growth based on current growth patterns; 2) Growth as planned – predicted urban growth based on the current land use plan; and 3)

Resilient growth – predicted urban growth based on all future development occurring outside of the floodplain. Findings show that the current future land use plan for Tampa, while it appears to be better than current patterns of development, has higher flood exposure, stormwater runoff, and pollutant discharge that current conditions but more than a purely resilient approach to future growth.

Existing Knowledge: Floods are the costliest natural hazard globally. Given the far-reaching impacts of recent major US storms, such as Hurricanes Katrina (2008), Ike (2005), Sandy (2012), and Harvey (2017), it is clear that the increased frequency and damage costs of flooding is not an issue solved through only engineering. Conversion of natural landscapes to urban or suburban developments can reduce the functionality of hydrological systems leading to reduced soil infiltration and increased surface runoff and peak discharge in nearby streams (BHADURI et al. 2000). In an observational study of 37 coastal counties in Texas, BRODY et al. (2008) found that each square meter of impervious surface added to the landscape translated into approximately $3,602 of added property damage caused by floods per year from 1997–2001. Land Change Modeling is a planning support system which applies future land predictions to land use planning processes (BERKE & KAISER 2006). The Land Transformation Model (LTM)is a GIS-based tool used to predict land use to examine relationships between spatial driving factors and land use changes (PIJANOWSKI et al. 1997). Compared to other prediction models (e. g. logistic regression, SLEUTH, CLUE, etc.), the LTM has reported relatively higher prediction accuracies (LIN et al. 2011, PONTIUS et al. 2008). The LTM is an Artificial Neural Network (ANN) prediction model. ANNs recognize and classify complex behaviours and patterns (PIJANOWSKI et al. 2002) and have been popularly utilized for complicated and practical tasks in many fields including medicine, business, climatology, ecology, and geography. PIJANOWSKI et al. (1997) first introduced the LTM to simulate land cover change. The model has been applied in different locations and scales for forecasting urbanization, vacancy, deforestation (MAS et al. 2004, MÜLLER & MBURU 2009), and loss of agriculture (LI et al. 2012).

Study Team: Climate change, increased coastal populations, and shifts in domestic economic activity markedly increase the risks of catastrophic chemical contamination events resulting from weather-related or human-caused emergencies, all of which increase the risk of potential adverse health impacts. As such a Research team comprising a university Superfund Research Center (Superfund Center) which comprehensively evaluates the complexities of hazardous chemical exposures, potential adverse health impacts, and potential hazards of exposures to complex mixtures through a series of multi-disciplinary projects worked together to achieve the research. The Superfund Center project teams work to measure as many "known-unknown" or "unknown-unknown" contaminants in the sediment and then expand the current understanding of additional exposures, going beyond the "one-chemical-at-a-time" approach by focusing on "whole mixtures," which will allow the work to be applied to other, human-caused environmental crises in other locations. Community engagement with stakeholders, residents, and local organizations occurs through each research project through the team's Community Engagement Core. Through this approach, we team develops a comprehensive set of tools that can be used as models for cities, counties, states, the federal government, and other entities that respond to disasters in an effort to mitigate the health consequences of exposure to hazardous mixtures during emergency-related contamination events.

Research Design: The LTM synthesizes input drivers (factors contributing urban growth mapped as raster data) and input patterns (historic land cover raster images also mapped as raster data) by analysing the change between input patterns and linking the drivers of urbanization to this change. Using 15 proven input drivers (nine proximity variables including distance to waterfront, rivers, open space, highway, residence, commercial, central business district, existing urban areas, and public schools, and six density variables including slope, population density, population increase, employee numbers, poverty, and land value) contributing to urban growth, the LTM was used to predict urban growth by 2040 for the three growth scenarios. The U.S. Geological Survey provided historic land cover data in raster images (30 × 30 m pixels). Hillsborough County provides the Tampa Comprehensive Plan 2040 with future land use data. To delineate future flood risk zones, the 100-year floodplain map from the Flood Insurance Rate Map (FEMA 2018) and future sea-level rise projection data from NOAA (USACE 2017) were used. Masterplans based on each scenario's predicted urban growth were then developed and different land use schemes were utilized to achieve each growth projection. The Long-Term Hydrologic Impact Analysis (L-THIA) Low Impact Development Spreadsheet was used as a performance tool to measure impacts across each predicted/design scenario. The L-THIA is an urban growth analysis tool that is applied to estimate long-term runoff and nonpoint source pollution impacts of different land use development scenarios. It generates estimates of 14 types of non-point sources pollution loadings to waterbodies based on land use changes. The model has been used to track land-use change in watersheds for historical land-use scenarios (TANG et al. 2005), identify non-point source pollution areas and evaluate land use development for pollution management (BHADURI et al. 2000).

Research Analysis: LTM Output Flood exposure calculations compare existing urban area with predicted future urban area through urban growth scenarios at city and neighborhood levels. Urban flood exposure is calculated by overlapping existing urban and projected future urban scenarios with the delineated future flood risk zones. The current 100-year floodplain covers 90.9 km2, or 30 % of Tampa's area. Following the previous land change ratio, there was a change of 8,917 pixels between 2001 and 2011 indicating a change of 32,600 people. The future urban growth scenarios project a change of 48,395 pixels corresponding to a 176,928 population change between 2001 and 2040. The forecasted pixel numbers are the same for all scenarios, but the locations of the pixels are different based on different exclusionary layers in each scenario. Business as usual excludes existing urban areas, rivers and lakes, highways, airports, and parks from future development areas; growth as planned also excludes environmentally sensitive areas from the future land use (according to the comprehensive plan's policy); and resilient growth also excludes development within future flood risk zones (2040 SLR High and 100-year floodplain). A large amount of current urban area (more than 20 %) is under the current 100-year floodplain. Future predicted urban development projects 30 % development of in the business and usual and 22 % in the growth as planned scenario within the current flood zone. NOAA's projection shows that the sea level rise by 2040 in the study site varies from 0.18 m (low) to 0.62 m (extreme). Considering an intermediate-high sea level rise, 35 % of the predicted urban growth in the business as usual, 28 % in growth as planned, and 0 % in the resilient growth scenario would be within the 100-year flood plain. At the neighborhood scale, within the design site, nearly 90% of the new growth would be in the floodplain, 83 % with the currently planned growth and only 5% in the resilient growth scenario.

Application to Practice: The performance model outputs for the current conditions suggest that the business as usual scenario increases impervious surfaces, decreases green infrastructure area, increases area within high flood risk, and increases public exposure to contaminants/pollutants in surface runoff, compared to the other two scenarios. The L-THIA model outputs show an average of around 70 acre-feet of stromwater runoff decrease per scenario, with business as usual having the most runoff and resident growth having the least. A similar trend is found when examining average runoff depth, with resilient growth decreasing the amount nearly by half when compared to business as usual. Compared to the current situation only resilient growth reduces runoff depth and volume, with all other scenarios increasing the rate. All 14 pollutants decrease significantly in the resilient growth scenario, compared to other scenarios. This reduction is nearly 30 % lower than the current situation. While growth as planned reduced pollutants compared to business as usual, both scenarios increase pollutant load in runoff compared to the current land use arrangement. While the resilient growth scenario appears to be a more optimal approach, construction/maintenance costs for low impact facilities and the increased densities to achieve the desired land use regulations can increase upfront costs. These costs are, however, lessened over time due to indirect benefits such as increased groundwater, increased carbon sequestration, decreased runoff, and decreased energy costs.

Dissemination Approach: A collection of scholars, professionals, and community members collaborated to solve local issues through evidence-based design/planning. The Center for Housing and Urban Development, the Institute for Sustainable Communities, the Hazard Reduction and Recovery Center, Texas Target Communities, all within the purview of the Superfund Center worked with faculty and students within the Departments of Landscape Architecture and Urban Planning and School of Public Health to conduct engaged service-learning projects for communities. These organizations work with community members, stakeholders, and local organizations. The process utilized interdisciplinary affiliates from these centers and institutes in conjunction with local stakeholders, residents and organizations to conduct in-depth site analyses using multisystem input and layering approach, quantitative comparisons of spatial and temporal phenomena, participatory design feedback, and design alternative development. Upon initiation of the project, the design team held community meetings to introduce the project and identify problems, as well as to acquire local knowledge of issues. Journal articles, research presentations, presentations to the community to disease information and allow for feedback, a series of research synthesis pamphlets and a full project process PDF were created to share information across residents and the broader public at large.

Study Impact: The research examined future urbanization using prediction modelling coupled with scenario planning to advance conditions for uncertain future climate change. The research used the city of Tampa, FL as an example to demonstrate a scenario matrix using urban growth and flood risk with SLR scenarios and impact analysis with scenario evaluation. Our findings show that the current future land use plan for Tampa may not be the best approach for dealing with climate change, in terms of urban flood exposure, stormwater runoff increase, and pollutant discharge. In the city scaled comparison of urban flood exposure, the future urban area according to the current plan would have fewer impacted urban areas by all future risk scenarios than the growth without development regulations, but much more urban flood exposure than the scenario with strong floodplain regulations. Moreover, at the neighborhood level, the amount of runoff and pollutant load in the design site exposed to flood risk in planned growth is larger than in resident growth and higher than the current status. Thus, the current land use plan may be not well-prepared enough to achieve resilient communities, when compared to other urban growth simulations.

Study Reach: Never before have repercussions from storm events driven by both surge and rainfall been so damaging to local communities. Urban pollution due to excessive industrial development along the coast is also a global crisis in many cities and neighborhoods. Both flood mitigation and contamination crises can only be understood and eventually reduced through integrated investigations across multiple disciplines, cultures, and boundaries. Coastal flooding and hazardous substance transferal are both worldwide problems and there is still a lack of comprehensive research on the strategies, methods, and design program for increasing community resiliency to both phenomena. This research is broad-ranging by combining transdisciplinary inquiries which a focus on case sites within a marginalized communities but evaluating 3 different approaches to growth .Through this approach, experts from multiple disciplines worked together to understand and solve common flood problems leading to transformative findings on 1) flood risk reduction through built environmental and infrastructural alteration, 2) methods in which to use technologies to measure and quantify potential design impacts, and 3) innovative strategies for mitigating flood and contamination impacts.

Research Innovation: The presence and density of green infrastructure as part of the urban built environment can influence the resilience of communities and individuals to flooding and the mobilization of hazardous substances such as industrial chemicals. Evidence-based urban planning and designs are increasingly integrating technological and GI elements into master plans for cities and communities to address various urban problems (e.g., urban heat islands, stormwater management, vacancy/abandonment, etc...). Landscape performance – the ability to measure the effectiveness with which designed/planned solutions fulfill their intended purpose – is increasingly being utilized to evaluate the effectiveness of GI. The uniqueness of this study lies in its ability to link LPT outputs with urban prediction modeling to test design effectiveness in solving urban issues. The LAF's LPTs measure economic, ecological, and social performance of urban GI, but fail to apply these tools to mater plans as they are utilized primarily as post occupancy evaluation tools for built designs. Currently available LPTs are also not fully applicable to the evaluation of GI impacts at a community scale and are rarely applied in underserved neighborhoods. This interdisciplinary team deployed instruments and tools cross three design scenarios to directly measure the hydrologic and pollutant load impacts of differing growth schemes. The knowledge gained will allow cities to be (re)built in ways that enhance public health, mitigate flooding, reduce urban heat islands, support land use change, and more sustainably prepare cities for population in-migrations. It also sets the stage for new performance models to be developed which link together multiple models in a streamlined framework.

IRB Process: This study involved human subjects and was deemed exempt by the Texas A&M IRB (IRB2021-1051M, 2021-10-14).

Reimagining the Workplace Environment for a Flexible Work Model

EDRA CORE Certified

Submitted by: *HGA Architects and Engineers*

Study Team: *Kara Freihoefer, Sarah Berseth, Paula Storsteen, Renae Rich, and Mashid Jalalian*

Study Description: A national architecture and engineering firm studied the pandemic's impact on workplace strategy and design to understand their own employees' perceptions and experiences and develop design criteria to inform an office renovation. The iterative research-based process will be used assist other organizations in reimagining their office environments.

Project Budget: $10,001-$25,000

Funding: Design Firm, 100%

Research Question: Employees of most corporate companies have spent nearly two years in virtual and remote work environments due to the COVID-19 pandemic. Most of these employees previously worked in an open office setting with dedicated workstations that were highly exposed to distractions and lacked environmental control. Remote work has completely flipped these experiences as many employees have minimal disruptions and more choice over preferred conditions at home. As corporations plan for a return to offices post-pandemic, employees are expecting a different type of work environment that offers accommodations similar to those they experienced while working remotely and focuses on purposeful in-person work activities. As part of the effort to study the impact of the pandemic on workplace strategy and design with their clients, a national architecture and engineering firm looked to their own offices. This study details results of a multi-method research approach to inform the renovation of the firm's largest office, located in the mid-west. The findings helped shape the firm's flexible work policy and informed the office redesign. Research questions developed for this project were exploratory and open-ended. 1. What are the lasting effects of the COVID-19 pandemic and remote work on workplace strategy (people, place, process and technology)? 2. What will motive employees to return to the office? 3. How will the design of office environments support flexible work preferences, policies and procedures? These research questions were explored by gathering insights from employees, followed by the development of design criteria that outlined four return to office themes. Another objective of this study was to create an iterative design process of gathering insights, applying findings to initial designs, prototyping, testing, updating, and finalizing design solutions for reimagining office designs of the future. Because of the success of this study, this process is now being utilized to help other corporations study and redesign their office environments to align with their organizational goals, cultures, and employees' expectations.

Existing Knowledge: The COVID-19 pandemic has brought the topics of remote and distributed work front and center. Many workplace experts, employers, and workers themselves, believe the world of work will never be the same. In the existing literature, the concept of remote work is not new—several companies had experimented with it prior to start of the pandemic in 2020. Significant differences and nuances also exist among the terms being used and discussed. For example, the following definitions were created by Range, a team management software company: • Remote worker: An individual who works from a different location than other members of their team, often from home or a co-working space. • Remote team: A team of individuals who work in the same space, but in a different location to the company HQ or other teams they collaborate with. • Distributed team: A team where members regularly work from multiple different locations. • Fully distributed team: A team where every individual is in a unique location. There are only a few shared spaces, if any, and no HQ. The literature also demonstrates that not all work can be done remotely. Research from McKinsey and Co. revealed that highly skilled and highly educated workers in finance, management, professional services, and information sectors have the highest potential for remote work. The study estimated more than 20 percent of the entire workforce could work remotely three to five days per week as effectively as from an office. The researchers found numerous studies on relevant topics including: • What makes for successful remote work • Where remote and distributed work is thriving • Where (and why) remote work has been less than successful • Strategic post-pandemic approaches • Balancing remote and on-site work to create the best of both worlds Through literature findings, the team concluded that unprecedented effects of the pandemic will significantly shift workplace strategies that could allow companies to reduce office space needed per employee in coming years (fulltime employee equivalent per leasable square feet), thereby decreasing real estate expenses. Sustained growth in remote work could also have significant consequences for urban economies in the form of falling real estate and rental prices, increased residential and commercial vacancies, and fewer retail and restaurant customers.

Study Team: The study team consisted of a senior design researcher, an associate design researcher, a senior interior designer and workplace strategist, and the office director who is a senior mechanical engineer. The role of the senior design researcher was central to this project, considering her experience in spearheading firm-wide research initiatives and development of a process of gathering insights to inform workplaces of the future. Her background and expertise in evidence-based research guided the design of this study as well as the methods of data collection and analysis. The research associate's background in design research and interest in the impact of the built environment on user experience facilitated completion of the literature review, development of research objectives, and assistance with data collection and analysis. The senior workplace strategist and office director were instrumental in translating the research findings into design applications. Their review and critical feedback on the process, tools, and data analyses were valuable in guiding the study. They assisted with administering the questionnaire, coordinating focus groups, interpreting general findings, relating relevant information back to the users and the design team, and ensuring that results were applied to final design solutions. Office employees participated in the questionnaire and focus groups. Their experiences and insights were key in developing workplace solutions that fit their needs.

Research Design: This study was part of a greater

effort to develop a research-based process to assist corporations in reimagining their office environments as the risk of the pandemic weans and employees return to offices. This process of surveying, ideating, prototyping, applying/ revising, and investigating was applied to the firm's mid-west office as part of a pilot test, in addition to informing their own back to office strategy. During the surveying phase of this project, in the summer of 2021, a company-wide employee questionnaire was issued and included four sections: demographics, prior to the pandemic, remote work, and post-pandemic. Questions centered around employees' overall satisfaction with work environmental qualities, perceived productivity, desired workplace attributes, and motivating factors for visiting the office. The questionnaire received a 68% response rate (n= 222). Following the survey, 10 semi-structured focus groups were conducted, each with about 10 employees from various departments of the mid-west office. Questionnaire findings informed focus groups questions around collaborative spaces, individual work areas, technology needs, and workplace amenities. Other important topics were discussed, including how to best foster mentorship and encourage spontaneity within a flexible work model. The data was synthesized into design criteria that outlined four return to office themes, each detailing conceptual design solutions, technology responses, and process/protocol considerations. The criteria, along with quantitative and qualitative results, were shared with the design team to begin the ideation phase in the fall of 2021. The design team reviewed solutions derived from the data and criteria throughout the ideation phase to ensure insights were translated and applied. Once solutions were solidified, physical prototypes were created in the winter of 2021 for employees to test workstation configurations and small-group breakout set-ups. Slight modifications were made, and final design solutions are being constructed in January of 2022. Once the office renovation is completed and employees have occupied the space for approximately six months, the research team plans to conduct a post-occupancy evaluation (POE) to investigate the performance of key metrics outlined in the criteria.

Research Analysis: Questionnaire data was analyzed by office and department and reported in aggregated form, detailed with descriptive statistics. Inferential statistical analyses, such as t-tests and ANOVA, were performed to understand if significant differences were present between office locations, departments, and roles. No significant differences were found, demonstrating that regardless of these factors, responses among participants were similar. The questionnaire distribution and analyses were conducted in Qualtrics.com, an advanced online surveying and analytical tool. Questionnaire data specific to the mid-west office of this study was further analyzed and shared with the research team and employees. Key themes emerged that helped to developed questions for the focus groups. Ten, semi-structured, 60-minute focus groups were recorded and then transcribed by the research associate. Transcriptions were coded in Excel to uncover and sort key themes, which translated conceptual design concepts, procedure and policy recommendations, and technology needs into design criteria. The design criteria are data-derived insights that align prioritized themes with potential design solutions. The criteria were shared with and leveraged by the design team throughout the project as a cross-check tool for informed decision-making.

Application to Practice: According to questionnaire participants, 91% indicated the pandemic made them think differently about how they can work, while 80% were satisfied with their remote work experience during the pandemic. The top benefit of remote work selected among participants was not having a commute which, in turn, enables a more flexible work schedule. Ergonomic discomfort was the top negative impact of remote work. Overwhelmingly, participants selected that collaboration, face-to-face meetings, and socialization are the top three reasons they will come into the office post-pandemic, followed by a change of workspace scenery. While roughly 80% strictly worked in the office or on a job site prior to the pandemic, only 2% prefer to work like this upon returning to the office. Likewise, roughly 88% had a dedicated workspace prior to the pandemic, while 48% preferred a dedicated workspace upon returning to the office. Focus group findings suggested that spaces of particular importance for those who return to the office are collaboration areas that provide an inclusive and engaging experience for all attendees (virtual + in-person), are equipped with the right technology, and promote creativity, nimbleness and spontaneity. A variety of individual work space types were also desired to support focus, private, small group, and virtual work. Overall, the data was synthesized into design criteria that outlined four return to office themes: support for a collaborative, studio-like work environment; space organized to showcase work and to encourage spontaneity, mentorship, and socialization; flexibility and variety provided for individual work; and an aesthetic and appealing environment reflective of the company's core values. Each theme details several attributes to consider for design, procedure/policy, and technology responses. For example, to support a collaborative environment, the design team must provide solutions that promote an equitable experience for all meeting attendees whether they are in-person or virtual. Designers must ideate to create flexible collaborative spaces with multi-technology solutions, such as dual displays to simultaneously show documentation or boards and the speaker. Specific conference procedures are being developed to foster a respectful and equalized experience for all employees.

Dissemination Approach: Overall questionnaire results of the entire firm were presented at a firm-wide leadership meeting of 60+ individuals. After this presentation, the data were analyzed by the nine different office locations, a script was produced, and respective office directors presented findings to all employees at monthly office meetings in June or July 2021. The insights and feedback gathered from these events helped to formulate the 'flex work' policy that was issued in the fall of 2021 by executive leadership. Office leadership and employees of the mid-west office of this study received ongoing updates and information at monthly office meetings include topics on project vision, research-based plan, project goals and justification, design criteria, workplace strategy, proposed floor plans and their benefits, and floor plan adjustments based on feedback from pilot testing. In addition, the study team distributed one list entitled "Why we need to change," geared toward organizational leadership, and another entitled "What does it mean for you, the employee?" intended for employees at all levels. These documents explained the reasons for exploring new office environment options and justified the necessity and impact at a personal level to create leadership and employee buy-in. The firm is developing a knowledge sharing campaign to highlight various components of this project. The first step of external dissemination will be a presentation of the research at EDRA53 in June 2022.

Study Impact: The study directly informed the creation of design criteria for the new office environments, which will impact all occupants and stakeholders as employees and leaders of the organization. Specific design solutions fell under four categories: collaboration focused, highly integrated, variety and choice, and design appeal. The category of collaboration focused called for the addition of design labs, a new post-pandemic space type reflecting a shift to the use of the in-person workplace for collaboration and interaction rather than individual tasks and focus work. The individual workstation ratio will be reduced to allow more space for collaboration, and updated technology will also be incorporated to improve hybrid meeting functionality. The design concept of being highly integrated focused on breaking down silos and creating opportunities for ambient learning and spontaneous sharing of knowledge through less segregation and definition between departments. Concepts for creating integrated design teams also follow the principles of the AIA framework. Variety and choice will be achieved through a shift from floor plans focused on individual assigned workstations to plans that offer flexibility through various seating options and space types, including booths, design labs, and phone rooms. The new hybrid workplace will allow individuals to choose spaces and locations to work that fit their needs and tasks each day. The new design will create appeal through an amazing new color pallet and spaces for visual display, including work in progress, original art created by office colleagues, and collateral for office visits by project teams and clients. As these solutions were a result of feedback and recommendations from those who will work in the offices, their implementation will directly impact and improve the options for employees to work in the ways that fit their desires and needs and contribute to an energetic and enthusiastic place to collaborate, meet, learn, and be inspired.

Study Reach: The traditional corporate workplace has evolved many times over the decades, a design pendulum swinging from an open concept to enclosed workstations and back again. More recently, the concepts of flexible work and new communal space types had been introduced and were gaining popularity, but the pandemic suddenly disrupted the expectation of 100% office-based work, brought remote and hybrid work capabilities to the mainstream employee, and accelerated the need to explore how best to utilize physical office settings. As organizations are considering how and when to welcome employees back to an in-person office and discerning the policies and procedures that should be in place, there is an urgent need to understand how the office will be used in the future and how these spaces should be designed and applied. The addition of high employee turnover across industries creates impetus to explore ways to make work engaging and productive, and offer solutions, including for physical spaces and amenities, that employees desire. As with any innovative workplace design approach, it's vitally important to study the needs and expectations of users to develop a plan that will not only better support the way people want to work today but will allow and even motivate people to work differently. This research occurred at a time when people were not largely in the office, mostly working from home with the intent to do so temporarily or permanently, full-time or following some kind of hybrid model, in the time to come. There is no longer any standard for work, any expectation that the future of work will look like the past, and people are dealing with more uncertainty in their personal lives than ever before. It was imperative that this study took all of that into consideration and approached the gathering and analysis of information and the development of solutions in a thoughtful and considerate way, while taking the opportunity to make radical and impactful changes. The results of this study will influence not only how this organization approaches their physical workplace, but through the sharing of findings, design solutions, and the success or failure of trialed approaches, will potentially impact additional workplaces to come. As a design firm that plans workplaces of all types, this internal research will provide not only knowledge but first-hand experience that will inform recommendations for other organizations.

Research Innovation: Through this study, an innovative and iterative design process was developed, along with validated tools for data collection. The process is now being utilized on various projects to help corporations reimagine their future office designs and workplace strategies. The process was also designed to promote change management through engagement, communication, and application of users' insights. The use of design criteria is an effective tool that translates quantitative and qualitative data into meaningful and research-based concepts that are easy for the design team to understand and apply to their solutions. The criteria also align measures of success for POE creation. The research and design teams remain well connected and plan to conduct a longitudinal POE once construction is complete and the office has been occupied for six months. The criteria also provided insights for technology needs and policy development. These are now separate initiatives occurring concurrently with the project. For example, technologists are working on a customized application for reserving spaces and alerting others when (and where) employees are in the office. Another group of individuals is designing procedure recommendations for conducting an inclusive meeting experience. This project is utilizing the AIA Framework to set measurable goals to reduce carbon emissions and environmental impact while bolstering occupant and societal wellbeing. The project achieves all 10 AIA Framework principles by incorporating design strategies related to biophilic design, embodied carbon, material and furniture waste reduction, employee wellness, energy usage, water efficiency, and more.

IRB Process: This study did not involve human subjects so did not submit to an IRB.

Student Well-Being on a Live-Learn Campus: A COVID-Era Study

EDRA CORE Certified

Submitted by: HKS, Inc.

Study Team: Upali Nanda and Renae Mantooth

Study Description: The New Sixth College is a living lab that uses architecture to augment positive behaviors and outcomes and integrates that understanding into current academics and future capital planning. This study investigates the relationship between built environment design strategies and student well-being, social connection, and environmental health.

Project Budget: $25,001-$50,000

Funding: Client/Provider, 100%

Research Question: The research aim of this longitudinal study was to understand (and advance) the impact of the built environment on the student experience by fulfilling the following objectives: 1. Assess student behaviors and habits related to social connection, learning, health and well-being, and environmental stewardship in the new NTPLLN as compared to the previous residence hall (Camp Snoopy), focusing on the differences between '19 freshman and '20 freshman cohorts 2. Compare students' space utilization and behavior patterns to assess the efficacy of the new living and learning neighborhood (NTPLLN) 3. Compare overall student well-being and academic achievement in NTPLLN and in Camp Snoopy 4. Lay the foundation for an ongoing program where the living and learning neighborhood can function as a live-learn lab where students can engage with and enhance their environments via a curricular infrastructure. North Torrey Pines Living and Learning Neighborhood (NTPLLN) was designed with health and wellness in mind to positively affect student experience and outcomes. In an effort to hold design decisions accountable, we link design strategies to metrics that matter. The New Sixth College is a living lab that uses architecture to augment positive behaviors and outcomes and integrates that understanding into current academics and future capital planning. Each building in the neighborhood offers scenic coastal views and connections to the tropical climate to facilitate mental and physical wellness. Communal areas such as a rooftop vegetable garden provide opportunities for healthy habit development and physical activities including gardening and fitness classes, and community kitchens on each residence hall floor encourage cooking and socializing.

Existing Knowledge: Before the COVID-19 pandemic, 23.6% of undergraduates reported anxiety and 19.2% of undergraduates reported depression is an impediment to academic performance. In addition, 50.3% of college students reported they experience loneliness (NCHA, 2021). Furthermore, obesity and depression had longitudinal bi-directional correlations, indicating the incidence of either was linked to higher odds of the other (Luppino et al., 2010). The odds of poor mental health were lower for college students who met vigorous activity recommendations than those did not, and socialization partially mediated this association (VanKim & Nelson, 2013). External stress is a significant negative predictor of student persistence (Mason, 1998; Wood & Williams, 2014). Stressors include concerns with food, housing, transportation, and dependents that are external factors which limit a student's ability to concentrate on the academic environment (Astin, 1999; Lundberg, 2014; Wood & Harris III, 2013; Wood & Williams, 2013). In addition to physical and mental well-being, social connection is a primary concern when designing student housing. Belonging to a group is among basic human needs, and a sense of belonging to a college community is an indicator of students' adjustment on campus (e.g., Pittman & Richmond, 2008). Frequent casual encounters can help to build social networks on college campuses (Lieberman, 2013); and the degree of social integration and the amount of available social support have been linked to both physical and mental health (Cohen, 2004). Given that incoming freshman students tend to move away from their existing social ties and experience many other changes at the same time, their social integration into the college community is important for their health and wellbeing (Park, 2018). At NTPLLN, strategies were implemented at multiple scales of the physical environment to enhance physical and mental well-being as well as afford social connection to all end users. In the longitudinal study, physical health, mental well-being, and social connection were measured in multiple ways to investigate the influence of the design strategies on student outcomes.

Study Team: To conduct this research, a unique coalition was formed by a non-profit research center, between the academic institution where the project resides and the global architectural firm that delivered the project. The purpose of the coalition was to set the campus as a Live-Learn Lab that could use the capital project as a vehicle for research and education on campus. Additionally, the coalition aimed to give opportunities to students on the academic campus to act as research scholars and fellows, to promote a larger sense of ownership and authorship over the project by the end users it was designed for. University administrators, architectural researchers, and the design team were all engaged in this project in an integrated fashion to leverage research to inform design decision making as well as measure the impact of the those design decisions on the students that live and learn in the neighborhood.

Research Design: This study employed a mixed methods research design and utilized focus groups, surveys, and behavior mapping. Data were collected one year apart, before and after students moved to NTPLLN to assess health and wellbeing, social connection, and environmental health. In addition, three participant observation first impression studies were conducted at the beginning of each school year (Fall 2019, Fall 2020, Fall 2021). Focus Groups: Originally planned in person, the focus groups shifted to an online virtual meeting platform at the beginning of the pandemic. Students were recruited by the university and were provided a $15 gift card for their participation. 2-4 students were engaged in each focus group and a total of 14 focus groups were conducted in the spring of 2020 and 2021. Informed consent was received prior to the engagement. Content and thematic analyses (Vaismoradi, Turunen, & Bondas, 2013) were performed to analyze the focus group data. Surveys Online surveys were sent to students who opted into the study from the recruitment emails. 5-dollar gift cards were offered as an incentive. A total of 125 students participated in the survey in the summer of 2020 and 160 in the summer of 2021. The following validated scales, Satisfaction with Life Scale (SWLS; Diener et al., 1985), Depression (CES-D; Andresen et al., 1994), International Physical Activity Questionnaire (Craig et al., 2003), fruit and vegetable consumption time usage (Dibsdall et al., 2007), Sense of Belonging (Goodenow, 1993), and Environmental Stewardship (Markle, 2013) were used. Environmental satisfaction was measured with an internal tool that assesses overall and environmental attribute specific items for social, classroom, and private residential spaces. Pre and post survey data were compared across the variables of interest through two-sample t-tests. Behavior Mapping: Using a tablet-based mapping tool, an observer collected data on how students were using the public spaces on the NTPLLN campus. This included recording where students were, what activity they were engaged in, in regular intervals over a period of 14 weeks. Coordinate data were resampled on a grid system and aggregated criteria were visualized on a map for inferences on place based analytics. Field observations were analyzed using descriptive analysis.

Research Analysis: To test the difference between the pre-condition (n=125) and the new condition of North Torrey Pines Living and Learning Neighborhood (n=160), we conducted independent sample t-tests to compare groups. Mental Well-being: The results revealed an 8.2% reduction (pre M = 2.25, post M = 2.06) in depression scores which was statistically significant. There was no significant change in Life Satisfaction (Diener et al., 1985). Overall satisfaction with healthy food amenities significantly increased by 11% from pre (M = 5.46) to post (M = 5.67). Physical Well-being: There was no significant change in Life Satisfaction (Diener et al., 1985). Overall satisfaction with healthy food amenities significantly increased by 11% from pre (M = 5.46) to post (M = 5.67). Walking behaviors (n= 1,695) were observed more than any other mobility activity (biking/scooting/skating n = 305). The vast majority of walking behaviors were observed on the east side of the main street, directly adjacent to the market and dining hall. Exercising behaviors (n = 60) in the exterior of the neighborhood were infrequent. However, the neighborhood was more active than not, with active behaviors (n = 2,060) observed more than double stationary behaviors (n = 960). Social Connection: Overall, students spent more time socializing (n = 1,380) than being alone (n = 1,072). Socializing behaviors were closer to the activated public areas (e.g., dining hall and market), whereas alone behaviors were more frequent in spaces that were slightly removed from the bustle, yet positioned so their peers were still visible. Fridays and Sundays were prime social days while Wednesdays and Mondays were more solitary days. Results from the focus groups emphasize the variety of social spaces provided and that Sixth College has the most energy of the neighborhoods at UC San Diego. However, we did not observe a significant change in student sense of belonging. Environmental Health: There was a 12.85% increase in overall satisfaction with campus social spaces and 27.96% increase in overall satisfaction of residential spaces. Detailed improvements for changes in satisfaction of physical attributes (light, aesthetic quality, cleanliness, etc) can be found in the attached detailed report. There were no significant changes in environmental stewardship.

Application to Practice: Linking design to outcomes was one of the foundations of this project. By mapping evidence informed design strategies to the metrics that matter, we are able to provide rationale for future design decisions within similar contexts. This longitudinal studiy at NTPLLN has led to design enhancements for UC San Diego's next campus project, the Theatre District Living and Learning Neighborhood. Through this research, we found that the Open Quad and Central Green Spaces, Visible Stairs, Communal Kitchens, Dining Hall, Market, Exterior Rooftop Terraces, Central Gathering Spaces/ Living Rooms, Double-Height Connectivity of Suites, and Dorm Study Rooms were popular design elements. However, opportunities for improvement were also identified. Transparency of Blinds, Lack of Color in Interior Spaces, More Personalization Opportunities, Availability and Location of Hydration Stations, and Hard Surfaces and Noise Transfer were identified through focus group and participant observation data that were taken into consideration for the next neighborhood project at UC San Diego. Four big ideas emerged from the findings and takeaways from this study that can serve as a guiding principles for future integrated student housing projects on university campuses. Integrating Life in the Micro emphasizes the design of students' immediate surroundings (physical and virtual) that connect them to their larger community. Creating Diverse Affordances provide spaces that are versatile and capable of flexing to diverse user needs - social, physical, cognitive, and sensory. Enabling Phy-gital Community leverages design by converging digital and physical environments to ensure a seamless social experience. Lastly, Fostering Agency + Activation ensures that spaces are activated to entice engagement that gives students choice and agency.

Dissemination Approach: This longitudinal study has just been completed and the first step for dissemination is with the published report that is shared widely by the nonprofit, the global architecture firm, and the university involved in the this study. The university, in partnership with the architecture firm, plans to develop a playbook that displays the designer's intent behind strategies that were implemented within the neighborhood as well as the student outcome metrics that are associate with each strategy. Throughout different phases of this work, the project has been presented at several student housing industry conferences (SCUP, FEFPA) and will be presented at EDRA53. A manuscript is current under development that will be published in a peer-reviewed journal that serves both the student housing and architecture industries.

Study Impact: Existing research informed the design project in terms of point of decision design principles, and concepts for fostering social connection. To do the research undergraduate and graduate students were engaged, and faculty members were included prototyping a unique collaboration between the university and the architecture firm. The data will be shared with other university collaborators as well to keep the coalition alive. The impact of the design on occupants and surrounding environment has already been illustrated in the findings around reduced depression, increased satisfaction, and overall positive responses. Insights from this research have already informed the design and construction of the next UCSD project. Most recently, this study was used to argue for the importance of views and access to nature as a key argument against the recent, highly controversial, windowless student housing project in California.

Study Reach: A rare component of this project was an extremely Detailed Project Program (DPP) that was highly qualitative in nature and relied on extensive stakeholder engagement with students. The idea of creating a "neighborhood" and "connection" to college, university and community were all embedded in the DPP. Most unusual was a research requirement that was added to the DPP, asking design teams to study their designs and measure outcomes after occupancy. To our knowledge, this live-learn lab concept and the coalition are the first of its kind that truly integrates research, design, and operations. The study's findings around mental and physical health are significant in their own regard, but it is the partnership, and the concept of using capital projects as a vehicle of learning and discovering on college campuses, which is the most meaningful impact. In other words the study's success is in the fact that it will be the foundation of not only new projects built on campus, but new research studies by students and faculty for years to come.

Research Innovation: Tools Innovation: 1. Design Intent documents. Annotated drawings that link design to outcomes on design deliverables, making implicit design intent, explicit 2. Onion. A place-based analytics tool to capture student behaviors on campus and correlate them to spatial affordances using space syntax principles 3. Coalition based research. Engaging on campus students to live, learn, and observe on campus behaviors, while working with faculty and industry based researchers Dissemination Innovation 1.The work done by the coalition is shared via non-profit's open source website 2.Student research scholars post blogs on the website 3.Information is shared informally by small groups via data-exchanges between firm and college faculty

IRB Process:

This study involved human subjects and was granted approval by the University of California, San Diego IRB (approval date: 2020-01-07).

Findings from a Multi-Method Evaluation of Inpatient and Outpatient Settings at Utah Valley Hospital

EDRA CORE Certified

Submitted by: *HDR, Inc.*

Study Team: *Abigail Heithoff, Francesqca Jimenez, Annette Himelick, Tina Nolan, Katie Fricke, Susan McDevitt, Neil Cristal, Todd Tierney, and Jeri Brittin*

Study Description: Utah Valley Hospital undertook a major project, replacing more than half of campus buildings. The design team incorporated system values into design, relying on best evidence to enhance their patient and familycentered model. In summer 2021, a mixed method evaluation was completed to assess the effects of design on staff and patient experience.

Project Budget: $25,001-$50,000

Funding: Client/Provider, 100%

Research Question: This research evaluated design strategies incorporated into inpatient and outpatient facilities at the hospital, including "onstage/offstage" layout models. Current literature on inpatient and outpatient design lacks substantial strong empirical evidence to suggest an objective effect of design strategies on staff outcomes. For example, findings from studies of decentralized nursing models have been mixed, with a range of design definitions. There have been even fewer studies addressing onstage/offstage definitions and effects in inpatient and outpatient environments. This study focused on staff effects of the newly designed inpatient and outpatient settings in facilities at the hospital, and used staff as proxies to assess patient experience. The research aims, and relationship to design goals, follow: Specific Aim 1: Evaluate the role of the new design related to teamwork and collaboration. A goal was to support and improve collaboration and teamwork of the interdisciplinary teams who care for patients. Specific Aim 2: Associate the design in new facilities with change in satisfaction with the care environment among nurses. To promote a healthy working environment, nurses need to be satisfied with their ability to provide care to patients. Specific Aim 3: Explore the role of the design in relation to staff satisfaction, work-related quality of life and fatigue. The new facilities provide amenities to decrease fatigue overall and improve work-related quality of life. This study will explore linkages between design and domains of work-related quality of life. Specific Aim 4: Assess the role of the design with regard to aspects of patient experience. The new design intended to contribute to improved patient satisfaction and experience outcomes, as perceived by nurses and other staff, including wait times, throughput and auditory and visual privacy.

Existing Knowledge: In the body of literature pertaining to the design of healthcare environments, there is little strong evidence for common design strategies. Single-patient room design is effectively required in the U.S. for new and renovation hospital construction based on current FGI guidelines, and access to views and nature is broadly supported. The concept of "onstage/offstage" design has been used successfully in industries that create superb customer experiences by limiting their exposure to behind-the-scenes operations and activities. Segregation of healthcare populations through an onstage/offstage model, with distinct areas accessible only to staff, intends to ensure privacy for both patients and staff, improve staff collaboration, promote operational efficiencies, and improve patient experience. Proposed benefits of onstage/offstage design include noise reduction, a hospitality-like ambiance, improved patient privacy, and more effective staff collaboration. There is no substantive empirical research to support onstage/offstage design as a best practice in healthcare environments or its trending popularity, especially in inpatient settings. A review of current literature found work that explored the relationship between staff and patient outcomes and an onstage/offstage approach in outpatient facilities. In a study of an onstage/offstage design (central staff area, separate patient corridor) vs. a traditional clinic without a central staff area, Freihoefer et al. (2017) found that with the onstage/offstage design, staff workflow, travel distance and communication were better, and patient wait times were lower. However, there was no comparison to a similar clinic design without the private patient corridor. Another team found staff preferred communicating in private areas (Lim et al., 2020), but that staff and patient's perceptions of teamwork were diminished when collaboration was less visible (Lim et al., 2021). This study is the first we know of to address onstage/offstage design in both inpatient and outpatient settings within the same healthcare campus. This study provides new insights for both inpatient and outpatient healthcare design.

Study Team: The study protocol and instrumentation for surveys and focus groups were developed by researchers from the architecture firm, with inputs and information about the design and intent provided by architects and planners who had worked on the project. To avoid potential bias, only the research team collected and analyzed data. The online survey included validated, published, and well-tested measures, and data were analyzed using descriptive and comparative statistics. Qualitative data collection was conducted in-person at the hospital during summer, 2021. Two CITI-certified individuals with research degrees facilitated staff focus groups and several interviews with leadership. The staff survey was open to all employees and providers involved in clinical care or environmental services who work on the hospital campus. Participants were included in the survey part of the evaluation by self-selection and choosing to access the survey. Participants from a broad cross section of roles within the hospital were invited to participate. Surveying from a variety of roles within the hospital allowed researchers to assess the effect of the design at different levels across the organization. The focus groups and interviews were conducted with a purposive sample of physicians, clinical and administrative staff, and leadership from inpatient units and outpatient clinics on the campus. Staff were invited to participate via an email invitation targeted to staff who met the study criteria.

Research Design: This was a multi-method cross-sectional study to assess staff and patient (by proxy) experience in a new hospital. Researchers worked with a senior hospital administrator to gain permission and access for the work. The study assessed environmental affordance for care activities and addressed definitions and effects of "onstage-offstage" designs in both inpatient and outpatient areas. An online staff survey included validated and well-tested quantitative measures and several open-ended questions. The staff survey was open to all employees and providers involved in clinical care or environmental services who work on the new hospital campus. Participants were included in the study by self-selection and choosing to access the survey. The survey remained open for approximately 2½ weeks, and reminder emails were sent on a weekly basis to boost response. Questions included assessments of change from the previous environment. Qualitative data collection included semi-structured interviews with leaders and physicians and semi-structured focus group facilitation with nurses and other staff from the areas of interest as follows: • Semi-structured 45-minute interviews with selected inpatient and outpatient physicians (4 participants) • Semi-structured 45-minute interviews with selected administrators (2 participants) • Focus groups (75 minutes each) with inpatient and outpatient clinical staff and managers (separate group) (4 groups, 6-10 participants each) Thematic saturation was assessed to confirm adequacy of the samples. Data collection occurred during the summer of 2021. Data for the staff survey were collected from July 14 – August 2, 2021. Qualitative data were collected from July 5 – 8, 2021. Analysis, interpretation and reporting took place over the following months. A manuscript is currently being developed for publication based on further analysis. All members of the research team are educated in research fields, have first-hand experience in conducting human subjects research, are CITI certified, and understand the utmost importance of confidentiality in research. To protect the privacy of participants, all data were stored on secured servers and were de-identified as appropriate for analysis. The protocol and all study materials, including informed consent forms, were approved by WCG IRB.

Research Analysis: uantitative data analysis was conducted using R statistical software and included descriptive and comparative procedures. Interviews and focus groups were audio recorded and transcribed to text. Qualitative textual data were coded using Atlas.Ti qualitative data management software and were analyzed thematically. There were a total of 565 respondents, a plurality of whom were in nursing roles. (See Figure 1 in the Additional Content.) A majority of respondents from inpatient units indicated that patients can see views to the outdoors from their beds. Windows, natural light and views were frequently mentioned in the qualitative data. (Figure 2.) The onstage/offstage approach generally offered a positive experience for patients and families, improved ease of navigation, and provided caregivers with private space for collaboration and communication that is in close proximity to patient care areas. A majority of respondents from outpatient clinics and a substantial proportion from inpatient units felt that onstage areas support a patient centered experience and quality patient care. (Figure 5.) Overall, affordance of the care environment for caregiving activities was higher in outpatient clinics than in inpatient units. (Figure 3.) Based on comments, this may largely be due to the much larger size of inpatient units. In both inpatient and outpatient environments, collaboration effectiveness among staff providing direct patient care was very high. (Figure 4.)

Application to Practice: Overall, outpatient clinic environments were rated more positively than inpatient environments for affordance of ease for caregiving activities, and the onstage/offstage approach for clinics, with a central staff core area surrounded by patient exam rooms, was appreciated for consistency. Two key issues emerged regarding the outpatient clinics, however: Those with core work areas with access to natural light were far more preferred than those without natural light, suggesting that designers should work toward solutions that provide this important feature. Also, acoustic privacy for confidential conversations was rated lower in outpatient environments compared to inpatient units. Staff comments indicated that sound travels between the staff area and clinic rooms, putting privacy at risk. Additional acoustical insulation may be installed, and designers should consider this sound barrier need for privacy in high-density clinic designs including those with a central core staff work area. Findings about the inpatient unit design convey benefits for both staff and patient privacy with the onstage/offstage model. Regarding decentralized nursing, mixed findings echo those seen in other studies. At the hospital, caregiver participants reported most of their charting activities occur at a decentralized station in the hallway or at the patient bedside. Respondents appreciated the ability to remain near the patient to complete charting activities. However, they also indicated that the lack of a centralized caregiver workstation where staff can connect and discuss their work can leave them feeling isolated and disconnected from their colleagues. With colleagues spread out along the hallway, it can be difficult to find help when needed. Such feedback indicates that there is still work to do to innovate inpatient unit designs that support both quality patient care and caregiver social wellbeing and learning.

Dissemination Approach: To date, findings from the study have been shared with the client and project team, and have contributed to a major submission for project recognition. The EDRA CORE report will likely be the first public sharing of key findings. A full detailed report is being finalized and will soon be shared across the Health sector in a virtual meeting within the architecture firm. Conference abstracts have been submitted, and we anticipate presentation at industry events this fall. Additionally, we plan to publish a manuscript with particular focus on "onstage/offstage" design in inpatient and outpatient settings in a scientific journal.

Study Impact: As this was a post-occupancy study, its findings did not impact the campus and facilities design. However, hospital leadership was keenly interesting in findings of an objective evaluation to influence future decision-making. Some issues identified, such an inadequate sound isolation in clinics, may be addressed in the near-term with minor facility improvements. Some other issues, such as differences in key organizational outcomes across units with the same physical layouts, may be further studied and addressed operationally. The study also confirmed that aspects of the overall campus design are much viewed, appreciated and used by staff, patients and families, such as the very large landscaped pond and gardens between the two towers; notably, this amenity is also open to and well-used by the community at large. Beyond this campus, the architecture firm is engaged with other projects within this health system, and architects and designers will build on the learning gleaned from this study. Additionally, study findings will be disseminated to others as noted in the previous response.

Study Reach: Even today, for multiple reasons including a lack of resources and funding, post-occupancy evaluations including data collection from users are often not conducted on healthcare projects. When firms do post-occupancy evaluations, they often do not use best scientific practice such as validated measures and appropriate management and analysis of data. Even if this is done, findings are often not shared beyond firms, to the detriment of knowledge sharing and real progress in design. This research uses a high quality, systematic approach to evaluation engaging human subjects, and uses validated research measures and appropriate statistical analysis techniques to assess the functional performance of facilities within a health system from the user perspective. This study also incorporates novel measures relevant to facility performance during the COVID-19 pandemic. There is currently little strong evidence associating ambulatory design to human outcomes, and this study will be a contribution to the literature. In addition, the study is the first, to our knowledge, to address "onstage/offstage" design in both inpatient and outpatient settings within the same healthcare campus.

Research Innovation: While survey-based and qualitative approaches to data collection are common in design research, validated measurement and appropriate rigorous statistical analysis and systematic qualitative content analysis are not yet the norm in the architecture industry. In that sense, the methodology of this study is distinctive. When replication of validated measures—which perform reliably and robustly with repeated iteration—across systems and projects allows for comparison, i.e., through meta-analysis of studies, true progress will be achieved. In addition to well-tested measures of relatively standard IEQ constructs commonly implemented for post-occupancy evaluation, this research also included several measures designed to understand how the facilities responded to operational changes necessitated by the COVID-19 pandemic, also a contribution to be further tested in other research. The study also provides further contribution on the topic of decentralized nursing, and explores the current trend of "onstage/offstage" design in inpatient and outpatient settings.

IRB Process: This study involved human subjects and was granted approval by the WCG IRB (approval date: 2021-06-24).

Making a Champion: Re-Envisioning the Elite Student-Athlete Experience

EDRA CORE Certified

Submitted by: *Perkins Eastman*

Study Team: *Emily Chmielewski, Joshua Jackson, and Scott Schiamberg*

Study Description: This post-occupancy evaluation study was conducted at an athletic performance center located at a major State University. Using interviews and surveys to gather feedback, researchers found that the center enhanced student-athlete performance, campus connections, recruiting, fundraising, resiliency, and flexibility—even through the COVID19 pandemic.

Project Budget: $10,001-$25,000

Funding: Design Firm, 100%

Research Question: The study objective was to evaluate an athletic performance center at a major University, which incorporated innovative programming and an integrated health clinic in the building. A post-occupancy evaluation was conducted in 2020 to understand the facility use and the impact of the design on the institution, athletics programs, and building occupants (i.e., staff, student-athletes). The center evaluated by this study is a 307,000 SF 4-story structure that houses the University's basketball, gymnastics, and wrestling programs. Along with state-of-the-art practice facilities for each of these sports, the building also incorporates sports medicine, hydrotherapy, strength/conditioning, a nutrition center, and dedicated health clinic. The center's design was intended to support student-athletes of the highest caliber and create a one-stop-shop that transforms the student-athlete experience. Research questions included: (1) What impact does co-locating healthcare and community spaces have on student-athletes and staff of collegiate athletic practice facilities? (2) For the University and its athletic programs, what are the costs/benefits of augmenting practice facilities with healthcare and community elements? (3) What outcomes may be observed from this facility's unconventional programming? (4) What lessons may be learned from operating the center during the pandemic? The researchers analyzed the impact of nontraditional design elements in the center that were intended to provide a high-quality experience for student-athletes and more positive outcomes for the institution. The researchers found that the center creates a place that is more than the sum of its parts. When synthesized into a unified whole, the contribution of each component to the community of student-athletes, coaches and staff, athletics program, and university campus exceeds the impact on any one aspect of the design. The findings from this study are extremely valuable to sport-facility designers and institutes of higher learning because the knowledge gained can help reshape the way collegiate athletic practice facilities are designed moving forward. By understanding the innovations and impacts of this particular center, others across the globe can be better positioned to fulfill the vision of making champions.

Existing Knowledge: The study team's efforts were built upon existing knowledge and research in two key ways. The first was in terms of understanding how to modify conventional post-occupancy evaluation methodologies, as a necessary response to pandemic-related restrictions regarding on-site and in-person data collection. Secondly, the researchers based this work on previous studies of sports and educational facilities. Regarding the understanding and application of previous research in the realm of post-occupancy evaluations, this study was built on the work and findings of previous post-occupancy evaluations conducted by the research team. These previous studies had explored facility performance, occupant perceptions, and innovation impacts. The methodological processes and surveying tools from those previous studies—as well as the researchers' extensive review of post-occupancy literature and example studies from the knowledge base—were embedded into the overall design of this study. Further, due to the fact that this study occurred during the COVID19 pandemic, the research team referred to the knowledge base when adapting their methodology and when designing the virtual data collection engagements for this study. In terms of existing knowledge and research related to sports and educational facilities, the study's research team heavily relied on the expertise of the study's participants. The participants' wisdom, experience, and perspectives on existing literature and previous research in the area was tapped. The research team also allowed for supplemental literature to emerge during interactions with the participating experts. Any recommendations were added to the data collected by this study's research team and were consider during analysis and reporting.

Study Team: The research team was a combination of researchers + designers. The study was led by a design researcher, who helped design the study, collected/analyzed data, and translated findings for industry use. The co-researcher is an architect/planner with a background in sports & higher education design, who provided industry insights and helped with data collection, analysis, and reporting. A Principal architect, who leads the sponsoring firm's sports practice, was also involved, offering insights into the design's intent and helping translate study findings into applicable feedback that could be used by the industry. This multidisciplinary team met weekly to advance the study, and worked closely to craft a final report that would be meaningful to stakeholders. In addition, a number of participants were engaged for the study. Student-athletes who train in the facility were given the opportunity to complete an online questionnaire, with participants from all 4 sports: men's basketball (N=11), women's basketball (N=5), men's wrestling (N=22), and women's gymnastics (N=11). Facility staff were also surveyed, with 18 responses to an online questionnaire. Extensive interviews were also conducted with 11 University staff. The interviews were with a broad range of coaches and staff at different professional levels, from administrators to specialists to coaches. The breadth of participation among both student-athletes and staff ensured that multiple perspectives were included in the study.

Research Design: A post-occupancy evaluation approach was used, in which the facility was assessed against original design goals and to understand impacts of its innovative program. Given the study transpired during the pandemic, all interactions and data collection occurred virtually. The study was designed in Spring 2020, but had to adjust as the seriousness of the pandemic became apparent. In Summer 2020, participants were identified and survey questions were crafted. In Fall 2020, data was collected. This timing was chosen as it was a year after the building's initial occupancy and since participants were less busy than usual (slowdown in academic activities + delayed sports season as a result of the pandemic). From Winter 2020 to Spring 2021, data was analyzed and findings summarized into a report, with subsequent industry dissemination. Due to the pandemic, the researchers used digital tools and meeting platforms in lieu of in-person communications and interactions. New lines of investigation were also added to the study's scope to evaluate pandemic-related impacts and performance. The study used both quantitative + qualitative methods of inquiry, as follows. These methods were chosen as they provided robust post-occupancy information from multiple perspectives and differing data sets. • Student-Athlete Questionnaire: to understand the student-athlete perspective on the use and impact of the facility, an anonymous online questionnaire was distributed to student-athletes who regularly use the building. This questionnaire received 49 responses, with participants from all 4 sports: men's basketball (N=11), women's basketball (N=5), men's wrestling (N=22), and women's gymnastics (N=11). • Staff Questionnaire: an online questionnaire was used to collect feedback from facility staff about their satisfaction with and perspectives from working in the facility (N=18). • Staff Interviews: one-on-one virtual interviews were held with select staff to further understand their perspectives on the use and impact of the facility. There were 11 participants, including coaches, specialists, and administrators. • Archival Data: publicly available data was collected, with particular attention to before vs. after the facility opened. Data included: team wins, tournaments, attendance, fundraising, and recruiting metrics.

Research Analysis: The study's goal was to understand facility use and its impact on the institution, athletics programs, and building occupants. Accordingly, analysis focused on: (1) how the facility performed against the original design intent; (2) the research questions centered on the impact of the innovative program; (3) the facility's performance during the COVID19 pandemic. The quantitative data (questionnaires and archival data) underwent a process of descriptive statistics. The qualitative data (interviews) were coded and analyzed for repeating themes and to provide context for comparison against the quantitative data. Study findings include: • Positive outcomes related to the student-athlete experience: The building supports a sense of community, connection to the University, and improved athletic performance. • Recruiting and fundraising have improved; and the University's reputation has been enhanced. • The center demonstrates the University's commitment to supporting student-athletes; and creates a one-stop-shop that transforms the student-athlete experience. • The center enabled the athletics program to adapt and continue practice, training, and recovery throughout the pandemic. The designed-in flexibility, indoor/outdoor venues, and innovative inclusion of a health clinic enabled the center to be an asset.

Application to Practice: Several themes were identified in analysis, centering on student-athlete experience, recruiting and fundraising, and the building's structure and flexibility. To communicate findings clearly to a wide audience, each of these categories became a key element in the framework of the final report. This report was crafted as a white paper with strong graphic design to communicate successfully with a broad audience. The report's introduction describes the facility, its design intent and innovative approach, and the research approach. Next, outcomes associated with the student-athlete experience are described, including report sub-sections on how the center impacted sense of community, campus connections, alumni relations, and improved performance. Next, findings related to recruiting and fundraising are reported, followed by findings about the building's structure and flexibility. A section of the report is also devoted to the building's pandemic response and how the facility became an asset to the University throughout the pandemic. The main body of the report is then followed by 3 appendices, which provide details on the study's methodology and participants, a full array of data from the questionnaire, and a visual summary of the archival data findings. In addition to the well-thought-out organizing framework and strong graphic layout of the report, the white paper also includes direct pull-outs from the data collected by the study. Charts of pertinent information from the questionnaires as well as pull-quotes from the interviews are liberally included throughout the report to provide information to back up the summarizing statements regarding the facility's impacts on the institution, athletics program, and building occupants. All findings are presented in a way that the paper not only relays the results from this particular case study but also shares with the reader how this information is relevant to other similar projects. Overall, the aim was to make the report and its findings applicable to practice. From the organizing framework to its use of infographics, from the journalistic tone-of-voice to the appealing graphic layout, this approach to reporting was intentionally used by the researchers as a means to increase the findings' understandability, accessibility, and adaptability to future projects.

Dissemination Approach: To reach a broad audience across sports, higher education, and healthcare sectors, a communications strategy was established to widely share the study's findings. In particular, there are 3 audiences for this study, with the approach for dissemination matched to each. The 1st audience consists of the decision-makers, building users, and other stakeholders at the University where the study took place. This study explored what is working well/not well in the facility and if/how the project met the original design goals. By sharing these findings with the building owner/users, they could fine-tune for better performance or continue what is successful. To reach this audience, the white paper was shared directly with the University and building users, followed by strategic conversations to explain the results, answer questions, and discuss future implications. The 2nd audience is designers/decision-makers associated with sports, healthcare, and higher education around the world, who may have an interest in learning from the evaluated building. The 3rd audience is the design research community, who can apply the lessons learned from executing this study amidst the COVID19 pandemic. To reach these last two audiences, the white paper was published on the sponsoring firm's website, with advertising communications distributed broadly to the firm's clients/contacts lists and social media. There are also plans to share the study at several conferences, in multiple industry sectors.

Study Impact: The researchers assessed the center's impact through lenses of performance, wellness, and experience, with a goal to understand the effect of the building's innovative program, where healthcare and community spaces are co-located with athletic practice facilities. The researchers uncovered that the center's design creates a place that is more than the sum of its parts. When synthesized into a unified whole, the contribution to student-athletes, staff, athletics programs, and campus exceeds the impact on any one aspect of athletic performance or experience. The findings reveal practical solutions regarding the convergence of design approaches from athletics, higher education, and healthcare. By synthesizing athletic spaces with healthcare and community elements, the facility has ensured that student-athletes have easy access to resources well beyond those typically found in collegiate athletic practice facilities. There were also impressive impacts on staff, alumni relations, recruiting, fundraising, and campus connections. By learning these valuable insights, University stakeholders (from administrative decision-makers to day-to-day building users) can understand the return on investment. This allows them to continue the successes they've been experiencing, as well as leverage this info for further benefits. For instance, the building's success has enabled the University to improve their recruiting, with the center and its lifestyle-efficiency (as a result of creating a one-stop-shop for student-athletes) becoming a major selling point for recruits. Further, recruits' parents feel confident their child will be taken care of. Fundraising also improved; the study showed that the University can effectively and responsibly transform donations into real results. Rather than a leap of faith, donors now have evidence their investment will be spent wisely. The researchers were also able to show the University that the center offers momentum for fundraising, as other potential sponsors may see the quality of the center and decide they want their name on the next building. The data uncovered by this study has provided the necessary evidence to the University that this building has been a success. It also provides a shining example for other institutes to learn from and apply the findings to future projects.

Study Reach: What sets the evaluated center apart from its peers is the incorporation of community spaces, its one-stop-shop approach, and the presence of an in-house health clinic staffed by a hospital system partner and the University's medical school/hospital system. On-site medical care promotes a culture of wellness, and student-athletes no longer have to travel to remote locations across town for care. They can visit a doctor or specialist and rejoin practice, rehab, or their locker room suite in mere minutes. Further, COVID19 testing and seasonal flu vaccination programs were conducted swiftly and efficiently on-site by the University, with minimal hassle and good compliance. The center also helped improve sports performance and academic achievement of student-athletes by increasing access to resources, technology, wellness services, and the rest of campus. 93% of student-athletes who participated in the study reported their overall wellness is better. 98% said the center makes practicing their sport better. 100% said the center is influential in improving their ability to compete for the University. Staff also spoke of the building's benefits, from more collaborative work opportunities to time gained by having technology at their fingertips. For instance, the basketball team can now run a drill, replay it in real time using courtside smart boards, and then run the drill again. The study provides specific program and design examples with corresponding evidence for how the design positively impacts student-athlete performance, wellness, and experience; coaching and support staff; alumni relations; recruiting; fundraising; and campus connections. As such, the study pushes the boundaries of practice by showing sports, higher education, and healthcare sectors how nontraditional design elements integrated into a collegiate athletic practice facility can provide a higher-quality experience for building users and more positive outcomes for the athletics program and institution. These findings are valuable to designers and decision-makers across multiple industry sectors, since they can use the study to design better and invest more strategically in the future. By understanding the innovations and impacts of this center, others across the globe can be better positioned to fulfill the vision of making champions.

Research Innovation: This study's primary innovation pertains to its methodology. The post-occupancy evaluation of this building required adaptations in order to complete the study in the context of a global pandemic. Accordingly, all research team interactions and data collection processes were conducted virtually. These adaptations actually resulted in the refinement and development of methods that may have applicability in broader contexts in the future. Online surveys, while not a new development, nonetheless demonstrated new value. Likewise, the use of online meeting platforms to conduct interviews is also not new, but the breadth of interviews and efficiency with which they were conducted present a new model for collecting data that may enable future post-occupancy evaluations to be conducted in a more efficient and cost-effective manner. Thus, the methodology used was a big step forward for the design research industry.

IRB Process: This study involved human subjects, but IRB review was not sought and/or obtained for this study. This study did not seek IRB approval because it began as an internal program evaluation/quality improvement project, which was intended to assess and improve internal project work. During this process, the researchers offered participant anonymity to those who desired it, and ensured all study data were secure. Further, the research had very little associated risk to the participants. (Though the researchers fully understand that this determination is for an IRB to decide, they felt that this further supported their decision not to seek IRB approval.) The researchers ultimately decided to share the findings publicly so others could learn from their work, but did not set out for their conclusions to be applied universally or be highly generalizable.

Learning and Re-LearningL Researching the Impact of the Pandemic on People, Work, and the Future Workplace

EDRA CORE Certified

Submitted by: *Gensler*

Study Team: *Janet McLaurin, Christine Barber, Tim Pittman, Kyle Sellers, Anita Grabowska, Michelle DeCurtis, Stella Donovan, Kerri Henderson, Julia Simet, Phillippe Pare, Dhiraj Kumar, Tom Owens, Cathy Jameson, Neil Christopher, Claire Stephens, Xiaomei Lee, Smita Gupta, and Shravan Bendapudi*

Study Description: The pandemic has fundamentally shifted how, where, & when people work. As COVID-19 continues, work patterns and worker expectations continue to evolve. This repeated cross-sectional research study measured impacts throughout the pandemic. This research has informed and driven significant new thinking focused on the future of the office.

Project Budget: More than $100,000

Funding: Design Firm, 100%

Research Question: The pandemic has fundamentally shifted how, where, and when people work. As COVID-19 and its variants continue, work patterns and worker expectations continue to evolve. This repeated cross-sectional research study consists of multiple surveys to capture changes and nuances in behavior throughout the pandemic, building upon each other as the pandemic unfolded. The following are key research questions explored: • What are the impacts and benefits of the work from home (WFH) experience? Does this vary by role, generation or living situation? • How is work changing? What are the new work activities and where are the preferred work locations for individual and team performance? What is the impact of hybrid work? • Where are people currently working? What are future ideal preferences? What would make employees comfortable returning to the office? What are the lessons learned from China which had already returned to the office in full force? • What are leaders planning in terms of returning to the office? What are employees expecting? • What matters most to office workers? How do we rethink buildings and the physical workplace for a post-pandemic future?

Existing Knowledge: The workplace surveys conducted throughout the pandemic draw on previous workplace research efforts as an iterative research process in which learnings from past work, insights from other peer research, and insights gained through direct client work inform evolving research questions and topics of study. A 2008 workplace study represented foundational work drawing on numerous external sources to define language and approach to "work modes," which have now become industry standard terminology and continue to evolve as work shifts; numerous studies on social capital and employee engagement, including work by the Conference Board and Gallup; and studies defining "top performing companies," referencing the work of the Hay Group, Boston Consulting, Business Week, and others. The series of studies conducted during the pandemic in particular, which are the focus of this submission, built on this existing knowledge, and drew heavily on both experience with clients and the team's own experience transitioning to remote work in early Spring 2020. Numerous surveys by peers and other consulting/design agencies were conducted concurrently, and this work was referenced in an ongoing manner. Given the unprecedented nature of the transition, the work was highly exploratory and iterative, with primary question development and design being based on the analysis of prior studies and the evolution of the pandemic and companies' approach to remote work.

Study Team: The core research team was highly multi-disciplinary, including a senior expert in workplace strategy and design, a research director with decades of experience specifically focused on workplace research, research analysts with expertise in survey development and statistical analytics and modeling, research strategists focused on interpreting and communicating findings, and graphic designers who led the expression and visualization of data and created the reports. The team also interfaced frequently with advisors throughout the company, including numerous workplace design experts working directly with clients around issues related to COVID-19 and the workplace, and executive leadership. Study participants were recruited via third-party panel providers; all responses were collected via anonymous, online surveys that required respondents to work at least part time, and had experience working in an office environment prior to COVID-19. Additional detail on participants is outlined in the methodology under question #4.

Research Design: Nine surveys were conducted over the course of the pandemic per timeline below. We measured how work, experiences and expectations were changing as the pandemic progressed: • Spring 2020: Surveyed 2,349 U.S. office workers to explore the work-from-home experience, ideal preferences, and key workplace changes for employees to feel comfortable to return to the office. Data collected Apr 16-May 4; completed June 2020. • Fall 2020: Surveyed 9,607 workers in U.S., UK, France & Australia (4 surveys with same question set for global comparison). Data collected July 9-Aug 24; completed Dec 2020. • Spring 2021: Surveyed 3,130 workers in China to understand post-pandemic workplaces, as most workers had already returned to the office. Data collected Jan 13-31; completed Apr 2021. • Summer 2021: Surveyed 2,506 workers in India to expand global comparisons. Data collected Apr 12-May 17; completed July 2021. • Summer 2021: Surveyed 2,005 U.S. workers to explore how the ongoing pandemic is shifting employee & employer expectations. Data collected Apr 20-May 17; completed Sept 2021. • Winter 2021: Surveyed 2,031 U.S. workers to understand employee expectations and leadership plans to return to the office. Data collected Oct 6-21 and Nov 12-14; completed Dec 2021. Data gathered consistently via separate online survey panels of office workers to represent a statistically significant sampling for each country. Responses were gathered anonymously via an independent third-party and are not connected to firm's clients or projects. Respondents were required to work full-time for a company of 100+ people and to have spent at least part of their work week in an office environment pre-pandemic. Each sampling had a strong distribution of industries, roles, generations, and living conditions. Multiple checks were put in place to manage response validity, including time and attention filters embedded in each survey.

Research Analysis: Key findings: • Working from home supports focus, flexibility & autonomy, but the office is still the preferred place to connect, collaborate, and socialize. Workers universally want the best of both worlds, but a preference to work full-time from home has steadily risen from 12% to 29%. • The pandemic has changed expectations about work – leaders and employees have a new awareness of how they work best and many have re-prioritized work in their lives. • Hybrid work is not new. In Jan 2021, Chinese office workers had returned but only spend 59% of their time at the office - similar to what we measured in 2016. • Employees view the office as a place to work in-person with others, but also as a place for focus. They expect more privacy in the workplace post-pandemic. • Top-performers expect to use the office differently – for ideation & creative tasks. They also report the office as the best place for many individual activities. • Gen Z has a different conception of the office's value. They prioritize individual productivity and expect to also work in third places throughout the day - activating neighborhoods & city as workplaces. • Most companies will be asking employees to return to the office more than employees consider ideal. Younger generations are most likely to prefer hybrid work and least likely to prefer to full-time remote work. • There are clear differences by industry in how people work & ideal preferences. Consumer Goods, Sciences and Gov't have highest need to access specific spaces, materials & resources and a higher preference for full-time at the office in the future. Technology, Financial, and Mgmt Advisory adjusted quickly to remote work & prefer to work remotely in the future. Statistical analysis was conducted in-house via firm's internal research team with expertise in data analytics, survey design, and data visualization as well as periodic peer reviews by an external PhD research consultant for question sets as well as analytic methodology and emerging insights.

Application to Practice: The return to the office is just beginning. We are entering a time of experimentation + learning as we test new workplace strategies and concepts. This research has informed and driven significant new thinking across a global suite of projects focused on the future of the office. In particular, it has helped to shift narratives toward leveraging the workplace as a destination, and a focus on testing new ideas as we look to the future. Some specific examples of how the research has been applied and driven practical solutions: • A global virtual "Workplace 360" pop-up event, coordinated across five time zones, to gather and share 32 different project examples that are exploring and piloting new ideas inspired by the research. • Conceptual design explorations of the future of office buildings, developed specifically in response to new behaviors/expectations for the office as identified in the research. • The development of an updated diagnostic tool to measure employee sentiment in relation to the office, and the performance of workplace environments in light of new needs/ behaviors that were identified in this research.

Dissemination Approach: Since this research was a series of timely surveys, the research was sought after by media, clients, and design/real estate industry who were trying to make sense of the pandemic as it was unfolding, as well as the short and long-term impacts on the built environment. Mainstream publications like WSJ, The Atlantic, Financial Times, Fast Company, The Washington Post were publishing key findings as they were becoming available to reimagine the workplace. Internally to the firm, a series of learning and engagement events, each with hundreds of global attendees, were leveraged to share the findings with designers, strategists, and consultants who then applied the work directly to project work and thinking. Applied research and lessons learned were later shared internal and externally creating a continuous research/design learning cycle. Externally, a series of research briefings, blogs, webinars and "salons" with clients took the research directly to the marketplace, driving one-on-one discussions about the future of the workplace and how specific companies and industries are planning and thinking. Client questions drove subsequent survey questions and additional areas of exploration. Research has been shared at numerous industry conferences for CoreNet Global, AIA, ULI, World FM Day, and Financial Times Future of Work, to name a few.

Study Impact: This research study is not related to a single occupant, project or site. The value of this research is understanding how work has changed and how the work experience needs to evolve as well. This impacts the physical workplaces, office buildings, corporate campuses, and business districts that we are planning, designing, or repositioning. The pandemic has created a once-in-a-lifetime opportunity not to go back to what was but imagine what could be. As strategists, planners, and designers, this research is foundational in rethinking how we work and what matters most to those that use our spaces as we reimagine the future. It provides people-centric data and insights to create better work experiences across an ecosystem of spaces – office, home, third places – impacting commercial design, residential design, retail & hospitality design, and urban planning as a fully integrated experience for people.

Study Reach: This research has changed the dialogue with our clients. It is no longer just about space utilization and efficiency. It's not just about how employees do their work best, but how do we also engage their hearts as well as their minds? What is needed for people to excel? What HR policies need to be put into place? This research has provided a framework and data for many of these questions including policy, technology, equity, and inclusion. This research has changed our firm's design engagements from space-focused to people-centric projects. We are seeing our clients shifting from corporate real estate and facility managers to HR, chief innovation officers, and CEOs who want to explore how design can impact talent recruitment & retention, employee wellbeing & engagement, culture, belonging & community. These were not traditional design metrics. In addition, clients are seeking expanded services like change management and organizational design for a wholistic approach to space, policy, technology and work process. As a design industry, our role is being elevated to leverage a data and research-driven design process to uncover how individuals, team/groups, and organizations can not only work better, but provide better work experiences for their people to drive business performance.

Research Innovation: Data was collected via online

surveys on the Qualtrics platform. Significant effort was made to optimize the user/respondent experience, including the development of custom graphics and question types to enhance the clarity of questions and improve response quality. Statistical methods included both descriptive and inferential analytics—for clarity of storytelling, findings often focus on descriptive statistics and comparative insights between interesting demographic groups. Inferential analytics were leveraged to validate findings, and search for improvements to the quality of the survey instrument over time. The research was published and disseminated in multiple ways, which are addressed more deeply in question #7.

IRB Process: This study did not involve human subjects so did not submit to an IRB.

Graduate Student Mentoring Workshop

Each year, EDRA offers graduate students a variety of opportunities explicitly tailored for them. In addition to the traditional paper and poster sessions, graduate students can share their research and receive feedback from accomplished environmental design academics and professionals during the Graduate Student Mentoring Workshop sessions.

The Mentoring Workshop is designed to provide a forum for graduate students to present and discuss their ongoing research with senior mentors in environmental design research and affiliated fields. The purpose of the workshop is to strengthen and further thesis/dissertation work, as well to support the development of networks for young researchers, both with senior researchers and with other graduate students.

The EDRA53 Mentoring Workshop included a full day of sessions at Clemson University. The morning included a welcome presentation and three break-out sessions with approximately eight students and two to three faculty mentros in each group. The afternoon session brought all students and mentors together for an interactive panel discussion that offered students practical advice on job searching, grant writing, and insights into research in practice.

Panel Sessions

Session 1: Academic Job Search

Herminia Machry, Ph.D.
Kate Schwennsen, FAIA
James Stevens, AIA, Ph.D.

Panel Session 2: Grant Writing

Anjali Joseph, Ph.D.
Deborah Wingler, Ph.D.

Panel Session 3: Research in Practice

Michelle Ossmann, Ph.D.
Kara Freihofer, Ph.D.
Lorissa MacAllister, BSW, AIA

GROUP A: Health Equity, Resilience & Sustainability

Mentors:

Lesa Lorusso, Ph.D.
Rich Wener, Ph.D.
Elisa Worden, B.S.

Students:

Benjamin Okenwa
Devi Soman
Fullah Hazazi
Gisou Salkhi
Holly Nelson
Jiaying Dong
Sophia Philip

GROUP B: Designing for Diverse Populations

Mentors:

Sharmin Kader, Ph.D.
Dagmar Rittenbacher, MID, CKBD
B.D. Wortham-Galvin, Ph.D.

Students:

Alicia Valencia
Anne Cramer
Manju Aishwarya Adikesavan
Michael Lekan-Kehinde
Seyedmohammad Ahmadshahi
Stacy Scott
Widya Ramadhani
Xiaoyu (Alice) Chen

GROUP C: Designing for Health & Well-Being

Mentors:

David Allison, FAIA, FACHA
Sue Weidemann, Ph.D.
Emily Roberts, Ph.D., M.A., M.Arch

Students:

Carolina Kolodziej
Hannah Myers
Julia Jaffe
Kulsum Fatima
Marzia Akhter Chowdhury
Mina Shokrollahi Ardekani
Udday Datta

See Appendix B for abstracts from the EDRA53 Graduate Student Mentoring Workshop.

Refereed Full Papers

Architecture Student and Faculty Understanding of Evidence-Based Design and Environmental Psychology in Korea

Jina Lee (WSP Korea); *Mardelle McCuskey Shepley* (Cornell University)

ABSTRACT

This study examined student and faculty perceptions in architecture schools in Korea regarding the evidence-based design concept, emphasizing design research and environmental psychology principles focusing on the relationship between the human and physical environment. Students and faculty perceptions were measured by their understanding of design research in architectural programs accredited by the Korea Architectural Accrediting Board, human-environment relations principles, and design guidelines. Architecture undergraduates and faculty at seven different universities in Seoul, Korea, participated in the survey (n = 61). Twenty-five individuals participated in the follow-up interviews. Survey data collected was analyzed inferentially to interpret the quantitative results and compare students and faculty responses across various themes. Interviews were transcribed and analyzed using qualitative analysis methods regarding the overarching theme of each question. The results help understand the status quo and limitations of Korean architectural education regarding human-environment relations and provide useful recommendations to incorporate design research.

KEYWORDS

design research; architectural education; evidence-based design; environmental psychology; mixed methods

1. INTRODUCTION

Discourse on architecture has evolved as an independent discipline incorporating perspectives on design methodology, history, criticism, technology, and engineering. Interdisciplinary perspectives in the architecture field enabled designers, engineers, and critics to discover the substantial meaning of architectural design beyond just a physical mass. Despite all these movements, contributions of researchers in understanding the relationship between humans and the physical environment may have been overlooked, whereas design and design theory have been more dominant in the architecture field (Hicks, 2014; Zhang, 2016). Lack of human-environment relations (HER) studies in the architecture discipline does not mean that designers or researchers have intentionally excluded the relevant issues from their projects. Rather, it is evident to them that architecture stands on a foundation of human existence. Although design practitioners may recognize the significance of HER to achieve ideal design outcomes, they may disregard the essential principles during the actual design process due to practical constraints. For example, designers follow traditional design methods, which seem more reliable and efficient than adopting a new challenge with time and budget constraints (Lee, Geon, & Yoo, 2012). Moreover, since there are innumerable environmental and individual variables to consider, practitioners, untrained in HER, may face difficulties in addressing those variables properly, especially in the context of a hectic schedule (Hicks, 2014; Kim & Kim, 2004; Shepley, 2011; Shepley, 2014).

The other reason for inadvertent omission of human-focused research in the design process may come from the learning environment in architecture schools. Pedagogy offered to professional degree students in architecture (i.e., Bachelor or Master of Architecture) is almost homogeneous across schools internationally, using design studios and lectures as the vehicles for teaching. Generally, design studio projects are the primary task for students each semester, and the activity in which they dedicate most of their time and effort (Kim, 2011; Ochshorn, 2014). Research-oriented lectures may be implicitly regarded as a lower priority by students. Those students represent the majority of future design practitioners because a professional degree in architecture is usually the primary requirement for becoming a licensed architect in many countries, including the US, Korea, Canada, and UK (ARB, n.d.; CACB, n.d.; KAAB, n.d.; NCARB, n.d.). This linear pathway to becoming design practitioners may explain how their limited exposure to design research in an educational environment could have resulted in less familiarity with research in practice.

1.1 Significance of Research

The concept of evidence-based design (EBD) indicates an iterative process incorporated into the design process instead of referring to a certain design outcome (Hamilton, 2009). Although the term "evidence" generally signifies research findings gathered using a systematic process on broad areas of investigation, the current study is mainly focusing on the research pertinent to HER. EBD is typically associated with healthcare facilities to explore HER issues from design to construction to post-occupancy. For instance, such facilities' architectural compositions often reflect research results showing that the built environmental factors affect the occupants' (i.e., patients, visitors, and staff) feelings and behaviors (Cama, 2009; Leibrock & Harris, 2011). However, the research-based design process is not limited to a certain architectural typology. This process enables integration of different design methodologies within an interdisciplinary team, as long as EBD processes are maintained (Cama, 2009; Shepley, 2011). Theoretically and practically, the EBD concept complements the traditional design process to benefit a larger community, regardless of building type.

The EBD process is useful because both the procedure and outcomes are intended to be reproducible. The procedure for conducting the EBD process includes more than finding an answer for a single research question. Indeed, the journey consists of building the hypotheses, using proper measurements for data collection, obtaining results, and distributing the outcomes. Once a project has been completed with such a procedure, it becomes an exemplar that other researchers and designers may replicate or revise based on the previous model's success and drawbacks. Due to this accumulative feature, the growth of the EBD process supports not only the quantitative richness of research but also the qualitative development of design provisions. Accumulating the well-organized precedents means that design practitioners may avoid repeating the same failure, thereby saving cost and time and concentrating on creative design approaches.

It is a noteworthy fact that many designers are not familiar with research methods in social science within which the EBD process is conducted. The designers often pay more attention to the abstract physical environment, which is different from the delicate investigations regarding humans. Thus, learning and getting used to the research methodology for HER is a separate matter from conceptually acknowledging the necessity for design research. Even though designers are not required to obtain high social science expertise, they should learn basic research methods to conduct valid design research. Given that design practitioners' highest education level is typically a professional undergraduate program (i.e., B.Arch.) (Seo, Yu, & Bak, 2017), universities should be encouraged to include design research methodology in their architectural pedagogy. Moreover, even if students do not apply the EBD process to their design projects, providing a research-based design methodology distinct from the conventional one is worthwhile.

This study could provide insights into the extent to which students and faculty in Korean architecture schools understand the EBD process and its relevance to HER. Given that few studies have been conducted in Korea related to EBD or environmental psychology, this study would become more significant by identifying the educational needs and limitations within the specific populations in architecture schools. For those participants who had never heard about EBD or environmental psychology before, this study may well have served as a brief introduction that may encourage their interest in design research.

1.2 Design Pedagogy in Korean Architecture Schools

Since 2002, Korean architecture schools have made sweeping changes in their curriculum from traditional 4-year education to a 5-year design-centered education. The first architecture programs accredited by the Korea Architectural Accrediting Board (KAAB) were introduced to the students in 2007 (KAAB, n.d.). By January 2020, there were 64 programs, including 61 B.Arch. and three M.Arch. programs with valid accreditation. KAAB presents 26 Student Performance Criteria (SPCs) as the primary standards for accrediting, comprising four categories of education required for a professional architect: critical thinking in architecture, design, engineering/ technology, and professional practice (KAAB, 2018). Korean SPCs are mostly comparable to the SPCs from the National Architectural Accrediting Board (NAAB) of the U.S. (Kim, 2011) since KAAB attempted to benchmark several precedents abroad (Jeon, 2014).

However, since the inauguration of KAAB, many researchers and educators have asserted urgent need for a supplement to the current accrediting system. A survey conducted by KAAB site visit team members pointed out that many evaluators were not fully aware of the SPC objectives, and ambiguous standards did not address the practical demands in schools (Lee, 2015).

Among the 26 SPCs from KAAB, there are eight items pertinent to either HER or design research: (1) architecture and society; (2) human behavior and spaces; (3) sustainable architecture and urbanism; (4) research and analysis; (5) accessible design; (6) design of adaptive reuse; (7) ethics of architects and professional responsibility; and (8) the architect's role in project execution. Specifically, "human behavior and spaces" directly mentions human factors and describes the educational requirement as "understanding of applying principles and methodologies of relationship between physical environment and human behavior to the spatial design (KAAB, 2018)."

2. RESEARCH OBJECTIVES

This study investigates how faculty and students in Korean architecture schools perceive the principles of environmental psychology and EBD. Using quantitative and qualitative methods (i.e., survey and structured interview), faculty and student perceptions have been measured by assessing their familiarity with conceptual terminologies and research methods, relevance of their school curricula, and their reflections on HER principles. Given that most architecture curricula in Korean schools have been created under the consolidated criteria from the Korea Architectural Accrediting Board (KAAB) accreditation, this study seeks to understand the status quo and limitations of HER education in the field. Results from this study will contribute to recognizing the possible impediments to integrating HER education in architectural curricula. Furthermore, the results can be used to propose efficient plans to further include design research in pedagogy applicable to design practice. Eventually, this educational transformation is anticipated to foster the association between the two disciplines, environmental psychology and architecture, in order to enhance the human-focused design process and outcomes.

2.1 Research Questions and Hypotheses

The current study aimed to investigate design research and EBD in Korean architectural education based on student and faculty points of view. Data collection and analysis specifically addressed the following research questions:

1. Do architecture students and faculty in Korea consider design research to be significant to architectural design?
2. Regardless of whether they consider design research important, are architecture students

and faculty in Korea familiar with various academic fields and concepts incorporated with design research?
3. Regardless of whether they consider design research important, do architecture students and faculty in Korea have less experience with design research application in practice?
4. Do architecture students and faculty in Korea consider HER to be an overarching theme in architectural design?
5. Do Korean architecture school curricula commonly include HER themes in various courses?
6. Do architecture students and faculty in Korea assess the current education about design research and HER as insufficient?

3. METHODOLOGY

This study used mixed methods, including online surveys and follow-up interviews, to investigate how students and faculty in Korean architecture schools perceive EBD and environmental psychology principles and their relevance to architectural education. A quantitative survey was administered to all participants based on four sections: (1) the importance of design research in architectural education, (2) design research principles, (3) design research and practices, and (4) demographic information. Those interested in the follow-up conversation participated in qualitative interviews to discuss the rationale behind their perceptions of design research, which was unexplored through the survey. For both methods, students and faculty were asked to respond to the same survey and interview questions regarding their schools' design pedagogy and personal background.

3.1 Participants

Faculty in the architecture schools with KAAB accreditation were contacted using email addresses disclosed on each school's website from June to August 2020. As of May 2020, 61 universities (19 universities in Seoul) offered B.Arch. program in Korea. For this study, 84 professors from seven universities in Seoul, Korea, received the official invitation with a digital flyer. Faculty working in their respective universities as full-time professors were recruited, and adjunct professors were excluded. Participants had a specialty either in architectural design, history, theory, or environment.

Undergraduates from the same seven universities were indirectly recruited through emails and an online messenger with the assistance of each school's student association from July to September 2020. In some cases, faculty and students who already participated in this study supported the student recruitment by forwarding the research invitation and flyer. Undergraduates who completed at least six credits of design studios in their architectural schools were eligible to participate in this study.

As a result, 30 professors and 31 students participated in the online survey, and 10 professors and 15 students participated in the follow-up interviews. As compensation, all survey participants received a 5,000 KRW Starbucks gift card (about 4.4 USD) after the data collection. The faculty and student interviewees received a 20,000 KRW (about 17.5 USD) and a 10,000 KRW (about 8.7 USD) Starbucks gift card, respectively, after the interviews

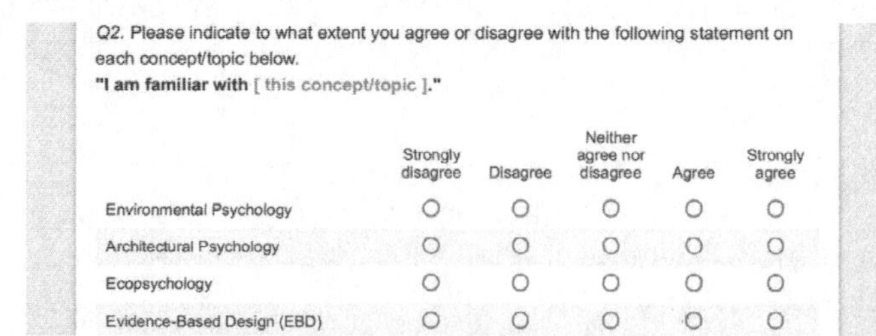
Q2. Please indicate to what extent you agree or disagree with the following statement on each concept/topic below.
"I am familiar with [this concept/topic]."

	Strongly disagree	Disagree	Neither agree nor disagree	Agree	Strongly agree
Environmental Psychology	O	O	O	O	O
Architectural Psychology	O	O	O	O	O
Ecopsychology	O	O	O	O	O
Evidence-Based Design (EBD)	O	O	O	O	O

Figure 1: *Excerpt of survey questionnaire published at Cornell Qualtrics*

3.2 Study Measures

This study used a questionnaire based on a questionnaire by Boarin et al. (2020) focusing on sustainability and architecture education. The original questionnaire included four sections: general information, the importance of sustainability in architectural education, sustainable design, and sustainable thinking. The questions were revised regarding this study's main subjects, including design research, environmental psychology, EBD, and HER, while maintaining the original format targeting architectural education (see Figure 1). The questionnaire was published at Cornell Qualtrics online after being reviewed by several DEA (Design and Environmental Analysis) faculty members at Cornell. A pilot study was also conducted with four Koreans who had recently graduated from architecture schools.

The survey respondents were asked to choose either an English or Korean questionnaire based on their preference. All questions were on the Likert scale, except for demographic questions and one open-ended question asking for additional comments. Additionally, one question asked whether the participants wanted to participate in the interview after completing the survey.

The structured interviews were conducted with faculty and students who voluntarily agreed to participate. Seven interview questions asked which factors in their schools and individual experiences had affected their understanding of EBD and environmental psychology. The questions were grouped into three sections. The first section included three questions about the definition of design research and EBD, relevant education that has been provided to students, and the respondents' evaluation of their current education and its limitations. The second section had the same format as the first section, but only the subject was changed to HER. A question in the last section asked the participants where they usually found new architectural issues and with whom they discuss such issues.

3.3 Procedure

Each survey participant received a unique study code and a survey link through an email. The informed consent form was presented on the first page of the survey. The survey took approximately 5 to 10 minutes to finish. Survey results were statistically analyzed by R (version 4.0.1) based on the raw data exported from Cornell Qualtrics. In addition to reporting descriptive statistics, a series of linear regression models were used for inferential statistics. Correlation tests both between questions and within questions were conducted.

Those who showed their interest in participating in the follow-up interviews via survey were contacted individually to arrange the interview schedule. They were asked to choose either in-person or Zoom interviews based on their preference, and they received the informed consent form and questions via email before the interviews. Each interview lasted approximately 45 minutes and was recorded prior to transcription. Interviews were transcribed in two-steps: roughly by AI transcription services, including Otter.ai for English and Daglo for Korean, and comprehensively by the researcher. Transcriptions (24 Korean and 1 English) were first coded by Atlas.ti software to group them into several themes, and then they were coded in detail based on the 44 codes using Excel. Summarized Korean quotations under each code were translated into English by the researcher. Additionally, some word clouds were created based on the original Korean words that the respondents used.

4 RESULTS: SURVEY

4.1 Demographic Information

61 participants (28 females, 32 males, 1 N/A) completed the survey. The majority of respondents were Korean (91.8%), and the rest were American (n = 2), Spanish (n = 2), and German (n = 1). The student respondents ranged in age from 20 to 30, with a mean age of 23.84, and the faculty respondents ranged in age from 28 to 65, with a mean age of 49.47.

Other than one first-year and one second-year student, most of the student participants were either third-year students (n = 11), fourth-year students (n = 12), or fifth-year students (n = 6). At the time of the survey, 87.1% of students had taken at least one architectural design studio in their schools, and the mean number of architectural design studios that students took was 4.68. The faculty respondents ranged in their years of teaching experience in the current school from 2 to 25, with a mean of 12.17 years. The number of classes that the faculty currently teach ranged from 1 to 7, with a mean of 2.87 classes.

In order to identify significant correlations between demographic variables and the main variables linked to the research question, a set of exploratory analyses was conducted. There was no significant association between the main variables and other demographic variables except the type of respondents (i.e., faculty or student).

4.2 Research Question 1: Significance of Design Research

None of the respondents disagreed with the statement that design research is important in architectural design (M = 4.54, SD = 0.62) and design research is important in architectural education (M = 4.59, SD = 0.59). 93.3% of faculty and 93.5% of students agreed with the importance of design research in architectural design. Likewise, 93.3% of faculty and 96.8% of students agreed with the importance of design research in architectural education. For both questions, there was no significant difference between the faculty and students.

Overall, there was a positive correlation between the two responses that design research is important in architectural design and architectural education (r = 0.62, $p < 0.001$). Within the faculty, the two responses were positively correlated (r = 0.69, $p < 0.001$). However, there was no correlation between the two responses among the students.

4.3 Research Question 2: Familiarity with Design Research Concepts

Among the eight different concepts or fields of design research, overall the respondents showed the highest familiarity with "Ergonomics / Human Factors" (M = 3.85, SD = 0.95) and the lowest familiarity with "Neuroarchitecture" (M = 2.56, SD = 1.31). Within the faculty group, familiarity with "Environment & Behavior" (M = 4.10) and "Ergonomics / Human Factors" (M = 4.07) was relatively high while "Ecopsychology" (M = 2.93) and "Neuroarchitecture" (M = 3.00) was relatively low. Similarly, the students responded that they were familiar with "Ergonomics / Human Factors" (M = 3.65) the most and less familiar with "Neuroarchitecture" (M = 2.13) and "Ecopsychology" (M = 2.39).

However, most of the pairwise comparisons between faculty and students revealed significant differences according to the mean differences and p-values, except for "Behavioral Science" (MD = 0.25, p = 0.3365). The responses were significantly different in familiarity with "Environmental Psychology" (MD = 0.93, $p < 0.01$), "Environment & Behavior" (MD = 0.65, $p < 0.01$), "Neuroarchitecture" (MD = 0.87, $p < 0.01$), "EBD" (MD = 0.88, $p < 0.01$), and "Architectural Psychology" (MD = 0.54, $p < 0.05$). There were moderate differences between the two groups in the responses to "Ecopsychology" (MD = 0.55, p = 0.0604) and "Ergonomics / Human Factors" (MD = 0.42, p = 0.0818).

4.4 Research Question 3: Experience with Design Research

"LEED" (M = 3.74, SD = 1.34) turned out to be the most familiar system to both faculty (M = 4.27) and students (M = 3.23). However, there was a significant difference between the two groups (MD = 1.04, $p < 0.01$) in that 86.7% of faculty were familiar with "LEED," while only 51.6% of students were familiar with it. 60% of faculty (M = 2.23) and 83.9% of students (M = 1.61) responded that they were not familiar with "WELL Building Standard" (M = 1.92, SD = 1.22). For "EDAC" (M = 1.48, SD = 0.85), 83.3% of faculty (M = 1.63) and 93.5% of students (M = 1.32) were not familiar with it. Likewise, 86.7% of faculty (M = 1.63) and 96.8% of students (M = 1.26) were not familiar with "Fitwel" (M = 1.44, SD = 0.81). Lastly, 86.7% of faculty (M = 1.60) and 93.5% of students (M = 1.32) responded as not being familiar with "ULI Building Healthy Places Toolkit" (M = 1.46, SD = 0.83).

A majority of the respondents, including 93.3% of faculty (M = 4.47) and 71.0% of students (M = 3.84), showed high familiarity with "Architectural Programming/Briefing" (M = 4.15, SD = 0.93). However, "Health Impact Assessment (HIA)" (M = 2.33, SD = 1.17) was the least familiar concept to both groups. The two groups showed significantly different responses to "Architectural Programming / Briefing" (MD = 0.63,

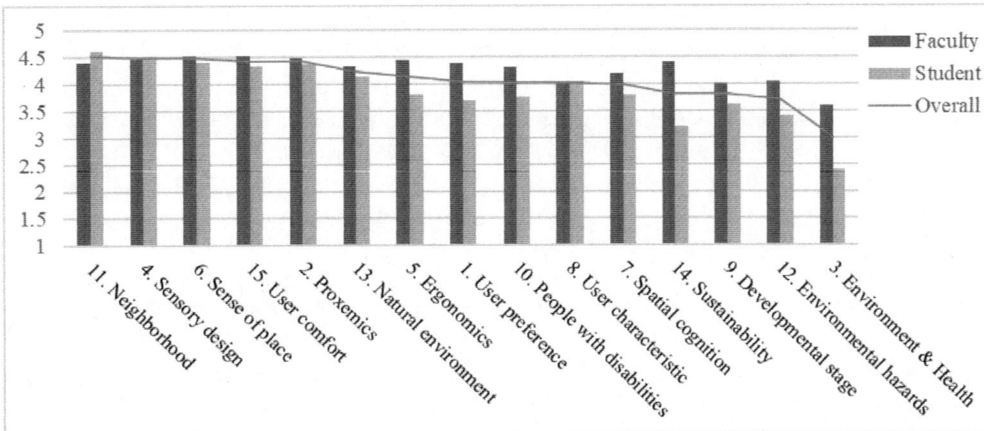

Figure 2: *Mean responses to survey question 5 (descending order of the overall mean)*

$p < 0.01$) and "HIA" (*MD* = 0.80, $p < 0.01$). Familiarity with "EBD" was not high, with the overall mean of 2.77 (*SD* = 1.37). 40% of faculty (*M* = 3.10) and 25.8% of students (*M* = 2.45) were familiar with "EBD." The overall respondents were more familiar with "Post-Occupancy Evaluation (POE)" (*M* = 3.43, *SD* = 1.35) than "Pre-Occupancy Evaluation (PrOE)" (*M* = 2.75, *SD* = 1.25). However, faculty and students showed significant differences in their responses to both "POE" (*MD* = 1.26, $p < 0.001$) and "PrOE" (*MD* = 1.21, $p < 0.001$) concepts.

4.5 Research Question 4: Consideration of HER in Architectural Design

Most respondents agreed with the statements that architectural design affects its users' behaviors (*M* = 4.64, *SD* = 0.58) and its users' health (*M* = 4.62, *SD* = 0.55).

The respondents were asked to indicate to what extent they consider the given 15 HER themes when designing or examining a building (see Figure 2). Overall, "Community and neighborhood: accessibility, public engagement, and cultural identity" ranked first (*M* = 4.52, *SD* = 0.68), "Sensory design: aesthetics, symbols, and colors" (*M* = 4.48, *SD* = 0.68) was second, and "Sense of place: place attachment and place identity" (*M* = 4.47, *SD* = 0.88) was third. In contrast, "Environment and health: physical activity, obesity, illness, psychological health, and wellness" (*M* = 3.00, *SD* = 1.06) turned out to be the least considered, and "Environmental hazards" (*M* = 3.70, *SD* = 1.02) was the second-least. All the faculty's mean responses were greater than or equal to 4, except for "Environment and health" (*M* = 3.60). Student's mean for "Environment and health" (*M* = 2.40) was also the lowest within the group, and it was the only average below 3. "Sense of place" (*M* = 4.52) and "User comfort and satisfaction" (*M* = 4.52) ranked the highest within the faculty, and "Community and neighborhood" (*M* = 4.61) ranked the highest within the students.

4.6 Research Question 5: HER Themes in Korean Architecture Schools

The respondents were asked to respond as to whether they have experienced a certain method to teach or learn HER in their schools and rate how useful it was. Within the faculty, the most used method was "Elective seminars on HER" (*n* = 22, 73.4%), and the rest of the methods were evenly used by 16 to 17 faculty members (53.3% to 56.7%). The students responded that the most used method was "Lecture-based core courses on HER" (*n* = 26, 83.9%). However, 64.5% and 58.1% of students responded that they had no experience with "Hands-on project on HER" (*n* = 20) and "Field trips to building sites/constructions related to HER" (*n* = 18), respectively.

Among the responses to each method's usefulness in teaching or learning HER, "Design studios on HER topics" (*M* = 3.86, *SD* = 1.16) was rated the highest overall, even though all the mean values were almost the same, ranging from 3.40 to 3.86. However, there were significant differences between faculty and student responses to all methods. The most significant difference was regarding "Field trips" (*MD* = 1.25, $p < 0.001$), for which the faculty's rating was 3.94, but the students' evaluation (*M* = 2.69) was lower than 3. Similarly, "Hands-on project" (*MD* = 1.46, $p < 0.01$) and "Elective seminars" (*MD* = 0.89, $p < 0.01$) were rated greater than 4 on average by faculty, but the students' evaluations were 2.73 and 3.20, respectively. The responses to "Design studios" (*MD* = 1.01, $p < 0.01$) and "Lecture-based core courses" (*MD* = 0.65, $p < 0.05$) were also significantly different between faculty and students.

Both the overall and group means suggested that "University course" (*M* = 3.74, *SD* = 0.89) has been the most supportive in understanding HER and "High school course" (*M* = 1.80, *SD* = 0.93) to be the least. However, there were significant differences between the groups when responding to "Conference/ Symposium/ Seminar" (*MD* = 0.87, $p < 0.001$) and "Online resources/SNS (social networking service)" (*MD* = 0.73, $p < 0.01$). Each group's responses to "Extra-curricular course" (*MD* = 0.53, $p = 0.0639$) was also moderately different. The faculty rated those three methods more positively than the students.

4.7 Research Question 6: Education of Design Research and HER

The overall response (*M* = 2.49, *SD* = 0.92) indicated that many respondents rated their current architectural curricula as not offering enough HER education (see Figure 3). The students (*M* = 2.10) responded even more negatively than the faculty (*M* = 2.90), and thus there was a significant difference between them (*MD* = 0.80, $p < 0.001$). When they were asked to indicate how much they wanted to offer or learn further HER education, the overall mean response (*M* = 3.95, *SD* = 0.76) was positive, and 66.7% of faculty (*M* = 3.73) and 83.9% of students (*M* = 4.16) responded positively. On average, since the students wanted further HER education more than the faculty wanted it, there was a significant difference between them (*MD* = −0.43, $p < 0.05$).

Regarding their current understanding, 60% of faculty (*M* = 2.60) and 93.5% of students (*M* = 1.58) disagreed that they have expertise in EBD or environmental psychology. Even though the overall mean response (*M* = 2.08, *SD* = 1.07) was relatively low, the students' responses were even more negative, and there was a significant difference between faculty and students (*MD* = 1.02, $p < 0.001$). However, when the respondents were asked whether they wanted to specialize in EBD or environmental psychology in the future, they responded negatively overall (*M* = 2.82, *SD* = 1.20). In this case, there was no significant difference between faculty (*M* = 2.73) and students (*M* = 2.90). The faculty's current expertise in EBD or environmental psychology was significantly correlated with their willingness to specialize in EBD or environmental psy-

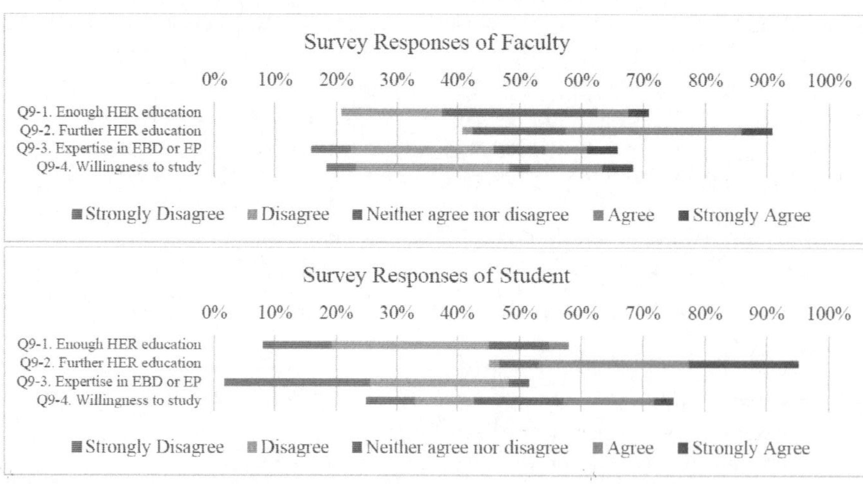

***Figure 3:** Diverging stacked bar chart of faculty and student responses to Research Question 6*

chology in the future ($r = 0.75$, $p < 0.001$). For the students, their willingness to have further HER education in their current architectural studies was significantly correlated with their willingness to specialize in EBD or environmental psychology in the future ($r = 0.63$, $p < 0.001$).

5. RESULTS: INTERVIEW

5.1 Demographic Information

41% of the survey respondents ($n = 25$, 12 females, 13 males) participated in the follow-up interviews. All students ($n = 15$) were either third-, fourth-, or fifth-year students. The faculty interviewees ($n = 10$) ranged in their years of teaching experience in the current school from 2 to 23, with a mean of 11.10. At the time of the interview, seven people were teaching design studios, while the other three were not.

5.2 Understanding of Design Research and EBD

Eight emerging themes were found from the overall interviewees when describing their understanding of design research. The respondents frequently said that design research ought to be scientific or quantifiable. Some people responded that design research has a goal or aim, to study humans and the environment, or be based on existing design outcomes. Many respondents also explained design research as a design development process itself or anything related to design. In order to explain why design research seems necessary, many respondents said that design has no right answer, and there is nothing completely new in design since we always refer to precedents. In terms of the objectives for conducting design research, several recurring themes were identified: creating a better design outcome, enhancing a design process, being guided by research when designing, and understanding the previous cases. The descriptions of design research were different between faculty and students. The faculty used the word human, scientific, analyze, architecture, methodology, people, and response the most, and the students used the word study, process, people, good, and building the most.

Likewise, some recurring words and ideas were found when the respondents explained their thoughts about EBD, and they were categorized into 11 emerging themes. Especially, regardless of their prior understanding of EBD, many interviewees identified the primary features of EBD as quantitative, scientific, numerical/mathematical, objective/convincing, and logical. Some people, including those who searched EBD online before the interviews, responded that EBD is used for hospital design. Other activities mentioned as key features of EBD were: the need to follow manual/guidelines, focus on users/humans, find the best alternative, apply the previous design feedback, and study feasibility.

5.3 Experience with Design Research and EBD Education

For both design research and EBD, more respondents were not familiar with the two concepts than those who were, especially among the students. Each respondent's familiarity with design research and EBD was influenced by their understanding of the terminologies and relevant experiences.
Regarding their current education, half of the faculty respondents thought their schools currently provide design research and EBD education, while the other half thought the opposite. The former respondents frequently mentioned some courses related to human behavior. However, the latter respondents were skeptical about their schools' provision of design research and EBD education to undergraduates, but some responded that their graduate programs might include such components. Likewise, the students revealed two different opinions, although some students were not confident about their opinions because they lacked understanding of design research or EBD. The students who responded that they had such education in their schools pointed out the relevant courses in a broader scope of architecture, ranging from architectural design to building systems to urban planning. A student even said that any design-related education could be design research.

The respondents' experience with design research in school courses was grouped into three categories: hands-on projects, digital design tools, and theoretical study. Many students thought that using or investigating digital tools was also design research, including building environment simulation and 3D modeling/printing. Moreover, many respondents explained that their significant experience with design research occurred within design studios as commonly a studio is where the students put their efforts the most. Some respondents specified the study methods, such as site analysis, case study, and mass study. However, some students understood the entire design development process as something that could be interpreted as design research. Other students said they learned about design research through one-on-one design critiques with professors, perceived as primary and unique pedagogy in design studios.

The respondents' experience with EBD in non-studio courses was grouped into three categories: behavior-focused approach, engineering-focused approach, and studying references. The courses focused on human behavior were about architectural programming, urban planning theory, or sustainability. While five emerging themes were found among the respondents who experienced EBD in design studios, a student who conducted field research during the pre-design phase said that:

> *Since we did not experience such things before, we did not understand how the study results would be used in a design, so many students failed to apply the quantitative results into the design and suffered from this process.*

There were also a few respondents who answered they had no experience with EBD in design studios. Although the reasons they pointed out were varying, there was a consensus among them that they never heard of EBD being emphasized in design studios.

5.4 Limitations of the Current Design Research and EBD Education

One faculty member out of ten responded that their current education on design research and EBD is enough. In contrast, five people responded the opposite, and four people responded neither enough nor not enough. In comparison, most students (n = 12) said that the current education is not enough, while three students said it is enough. Hence, overall, 68% of the interviewees responded that it is currently not enough.

When the respondents explained why their schools currently provide limited education on design research and EBD to students, nine emerging themes were found: KAAB accreditation, a dichotomy between studio and non-studio course, studio-centered education, no person to teach, learning attitudes of students, less understanding of how to do it, difficulties of doing it in a studio, limitations of lectures, and understanding of architecture in Korea. KAAB accreditation was often mentioned when explaining the required courses in a 5-year program that possibly leads to a lack of flexibility in managing curricula. Many respondents also pointed out the dichotomy and imbalance between design studios and non-studio courses regarding the uniqueness of architectural education. Some practical reasons, such as no person to teach and less understanding of research methods, were raised regarding faculty and student general understanding of design research and EBD.

Many students said that design studios had some limitations, including professors' teaching style, lack of time, grading requirements, apprenticeship learning, and a short period for each project, which restricted the respondents from trying new or further design education. In comparison, some respondents revealed limitations in lecture-based courses, which could have dealt with design research more in-depth.

5.5 Understanding of HER

When the respondents were asked to define HER, especially in architecture, many people explained it as an interaction between humans and the environment. Some focused on humans as controlling the environment, while others focused on humans as being influenced by the environment. Various environments were mentioned, including the built and natural environment, and some students specifically indicated HER as informing an eco-friendly architecture.

The respondents used some recurring words to explain or give an example of an environment. The ten most frequently used words by the overall respondents were: natural environment, surroundings, built environment, space, architecture, acoustic, physical environment, urban context, everything except humans, and light.

5.6 Experience with HER Education

Overall, most people responded that their schools were providing HER education. Even though there were some differences across the schools, many respondents thought environmental issues were widely covered in various courses, including both design studios and non-studio courses. A faculty respondent explained that:

> *If HER is about understanding an environment as architecture, or the role of architects is to generate, manipulate, and control the environments for human interaction, then all design studios teach you how to design those environments, and theoretical classes teach the implications of why your design produces this effect, and technical classes teach how you put together them in this environment.*

However, some counterparts identified the meaning of HER more specifically and thus were skeptical about their current HER education. A faculty respondent said that:

> *Design studio may deal with some HER issues in a broader concept, but so many instructors teach studios that their quality control is limited, and the instructors are fully responsible for their studios, and thus it is questionable whether they teach consistently such theories in studios.*

The non-studio courses related to HER identified by the respondents were grouped into several themes, such as space and behavior, sustainability, urbanism, history, and building environmental systems. When explaining their experiences with HER education throughout the courses, the respondents mostly addressed three themes: natural environment, built environment, and society.

Four recurring themes were found in teaching HER in design studios. First, some studios offered students small design exercises that possibly supported their understanding of HER before designing the main project. The second method was co-teaching in which two professors teach one studio together based on their expertise. The third was a design critique from which some students studied the HER principles needed for their design. Fourth, some studios set their semester-long thematic goal as one related to HER.

5.7 Limitations of the Current HER Education

Eighty-four percent of the overall respondents (9 professors, 12 students) said that their current HER education was not enough. Many of those pointed out that even though their schools provided environmental education, it did not completely fulfill the requirements.

The reasons why their current HER education was not enough were categorized into 11 emerging themes: a dichotomy between studios and non-studio courses, studio-centered education, a lack of opportunity to practice, learning attitudes of students, KAAB accreditation, difficulties to change the established settings, a lack of overarching goal in school, no person to teach, no request from students, limitations of studios, and limitations of lecture-based courses.

The respondents also suggested various possible improvements in the current HER education that were grouped into ten emerging themes: application of theory to design, an opportunity to practice, systematic approach, interdisciplinary approach, specialized course, elective courses, studying references, learning it earlier, improving a broader structure, and changing the traditional education format. In addition to some pragmatic suggestions, such as offering a chance to practice, increasing relevant courses, and having a good textbook or a database, many respondents also suggested a much broader approach to improving current architecture education.

5.8 Source of Learning New Architecture Issues

Overall, an online search was the main source of learning about new architectural issues, followed by books and communicating with people. While the faculty frequently used websites and academic conferences, the students used SNS the most as a common source of learning issues. There was also a difference between the two groups regarding those with whom these issues were discussed.

6. DISCUSSION

6.1 Research Question 1: Significance of Design Research

The significance of design research in architectural design was supported unanimously by the survey respondents. As anticipated, faculty and students agreed that design research is important for both architectural design and architectural education.

In the follow-up interviews, when asked about the objectives of design research, most interviewees indicated that research enhances the design process, leads to better design outcomes, and guides a designer. This result is consistent with previous research emphasizing that architectural research enables design professionals to improve their expertise, and that it is important to strengthen the holistic architecture community and enhance the quality of buildings (Kim & Lee, 2007). Interviewees provided many examples of potential design research questions that were related to schematic design and design methodology, including how we design, what design indicates, and the best building mass for a given site. The unanimous support for design research expressed by the survey respondents in this study was also consistent with Hicks's (2014) advocacy for the importance of academic design research that supports academics, students, and professionals found in the Architects' Handbook of Professional Practice. Furthermore, the way in which the respondents defined design also aligned with Owen's (1998) statements about the goal of design research, which is to build a knowledge base. Some interviewees believed that design is inextricable from research, since a design never comes from a zero knowledge-base and always requires studying existing references and new trends. Hence, they ultimately concluded that a designer should not be blinded or working in isolation or making arbitrary decisions; they encouraged collaborative research.

Although all respondents agreed that design research played an important role in architectural design, some of their interview responses indicated that their definition of design research differed from that which was used for this study. Academic design research consists of the three main conditions proposed by Hicks (2014): systematic research methods, well-organized processes, and dissemination platforms for results. Although many interviewees, especially faculty members, explained that design research requires a scientific approach, a considerable number of interviewees identified design research as either schematic design or any study related to design. Their unclear demarcation between design research and designing was also revealed in the methods that interviewees used for design research. Most examples of design research methods included case studies, mass studies, image references, and site research. This result was associated with the previous research finding that architects' primary sources to study user-experience issues were site visits and their personal interpretations (van der Linden, Dong, & Heylighen, 2019). Another previous study about Korean design professionals found that the professionals tended to define substantive architectural research as site visits or collecting visual references to support their schematic design rather than as organization of a theoretical rationale (Kim & Lee, 2007).

6.2 Research Question 2: Familiarity with Design Research Concepts

Regarding various academic fields related to HER, this study asked the participants to rate their familiarity with eight different academic disciplines in the survey. Although many fields were not exclusive to each other and overlapped in terms of their academic goals and methods (e.g., behavioral science vs.

environment and behavior), it was necessary to include all terms indicating the relevant fields. Historically, labels for HER studies have been changed according to the primary perspectives of scholars (Giuliani & Scopelliti, 2009).

As a result, faculty and student familiarity with various HER studies varied depending on different academic field titles. Regarding the overall means, the participants were relatively familiar with ergonomics / human factors, behavioral science, environment and behavior, environmental psychology, and architectural psychology, but they were much less familiar with ecopsychology, EBD, and neuroarchitecture. However, faculty familiarity with environmental psychology was highly correlated with their understanding of other fields, including architectural psychology, ecopsychology, EBD, neuroarchitecture, behavioral science, and environment and behavior. Those significant correlations can be explained by Gifford's (2009) definition of the term environmental psychology as an umbrella potentially encompassing any studies related to interactions between humans and environments.

As expected, familiarity with seven academic fields, except behavioral science, was significantly different between faculty and students. Especially for environmental psychology and EBD, on average, faculty were familiar with the concepts, while students indicated the opposite. The interview results also corroborated this difference. Twelve student interviewees (80%) were not familiar with the term EBD and did not know what it meant.

Many interviewees defined EBD as a process that should be scientific, objective, convincing, and logical. This is consistent with the formal definition of EBD as a process requiring evidence from research and practice to make critical decisions (Hamilton, 2009), and its description as a systematic research process (Hicks, 2014; Cama, 2009). Others, who responded that EBD uses quantitative, numerical, or mathematical data, were correct in the sense that it is crucial in the EBD process to collect both qualitative and quantitative data throughout pre-design and post-design phases (Cama, 2009). A few interviewees pointed out that EBD was started in the medical field and some believed that it was restricted to healthcare facilities. Although EBD has been vigorously used in healthcare facilities (Ulrich et al., 2008), it can be applied to all building typologies. Some interviewees described EBD as a process involving following a manual or a guideline so that their responses were aligned with criticizing the approach as "codebook" architecture (Hamilton, 2009).

Regarding EBD as "the applied outcome of design research" (Shepley, 2011), many interviewees described EBD as finding the best design alternative and applying previous design feedback to a new project. However, those responses were divided into two different perspectives. For example, two professors identified EBD differently, one emphasizing the process and the other emphasizing the data aspects, although both opinions were consistent with the idea that EBD is a process of using the current best evidence from research and practice (Hamilton, 2009). In the former case a professor explained:

> *EBD seems like evidence, data, and methodology themselves drive the architect's decision-making so that EBD has a structure that you could only get a certain outcome based on the research.*

This quote is relevant to what Hamilton (2009) discovered as the reason many designers criticize EBD, which is that it leads them to be less creative. In comparison, other professor noted that EBD research can serve to justify design decisions (Becker et al., 2011) and the EBD process can broaden designer perspectives (Cama, 2009) by saying that:

> *EBD is to accumulate quantitative or qualitative data on how each design alternative derives a certain response and, based on that research, find a clue that can derive desirable alternatives.*

Though the overall interviewees pointed out a variety of important EBD principles, their understanding of EBD was limited. Previous authors have noted that while EBD is not a new concept, it is relatively unfamiliar to some designers (Cama, 2009; Hamilton, 2009; Shepley, 2011).

6.3 Research Question 3: Experience with Design Research

Two survey questions were asked to understand participant familiarity with building certification/ guidelines and the application of design research in practice. Based on the results about building certifications and guidelines, LEED was the most familiar building rating system, with a significantly higher mean than other systems, including WELL, EDAC, Fitwel, and Building Healthy Places Toolkit. On average, faculty and students responded that they were familiar with LEED but either less familiar or not familiar with other certifications and guidelines. This might have resulted from the fact that LEED launched in 1998, at least 10 years prior to the other guidelines, and became one of the most popular green building rating systems internationally (USGBC, n.d.). When asked about school courses relevant to design research or EBD, many interviewees pointed out several courses that addressed green buildings or sustainability, such as Sustainable Architecture, Thermal Environment of Buildings, Ecological Architecture, and Environmental Control Systems.

Regarding EDAC, specifically designed for EBD and launched in 2009 (CHD, n.d.), respondents' familiarity with EBD and EDAC was expected to be similar and correlated. However, familiarity with EDAC was significantly lower than EBD, and both faculty and student responses to EDAC and EBD were not correlated.

Another survey question addressed participants' familiarity with the application methods of design research in practice. Architectural programming, a problem-seeking process in a pre-design phase (Duerk, 1993; Peña & Parshall, 2001) and often associated with EBD, was the most familiar design research process for faculty and students, as predicted. However, there was a striking difference between faculty and students regarding their understanding of POE and PrOE. The faculty were familiar with both concepts, whereas students were not familiar with POE or PrOE. Within each group, familiarity with POE was also significantly correlated with familiarity with PrOE. A difference in understanding of programming versus POE and PrOE, especially in the students, might be attributed to the fact that few studies address PrOEs; they are less popular than POEs since designers are less motivated to examine buildings pre-occupancy (Shepley, 2011). The purpose in evaluating an existing building would be to compare it to a newly completed building and this might be perceived as an extra, expensive task. Additionally, since POE is a process of evaluating a facility's performance after a building has been constructed (Atkins, 2014), students might engage in fewer relevant activities in their design studios or courses, as they are focused on designing new buildings, rather than making comparisons.

HIA was the least known design research application to both faculty and students. This result might pertain to the fact that HIAs are used more often to survey project stakeholders, including residents, planners, and policymakers, in urban-scale projects rather than architectural projects (Bhatia, 2011).

Interview results supported further understanding of why architecture faculty and students had limited experience with design research practices with regard to their research aims and research methods. According to Luck (2019), architectural design research has exploited various research methods that originated from other disciplines, including history, geography, physics, philosophy, and psychology. However, interviewees' experiences with design research or EBD were limited to a handful of study methods, such as site visits and experiential rules, as many previous studies discovered (Kim & Lee, 2007; Lee et al., 2012; van der Linden et al., 2019). The interviewees in this study often mentioned field study and site research as their research experience. Specifically, many students regarded site studies as design research because they collected data to better understand the site context before designing. However, their studies were rarely based on a systematic process as required for design research, including questionnaires, collecting data, designing research procedures, analyzing data, and sharing results (Hicks, 2014).

Interestingly, many students responded that they used several digital design tools in their design research and EBD experience. They mentioned two ways of using those digital tools as part of the design research process: 1) studying computational design based on 3D-modeling programs and 2) building simulation models based on sustainable HVAC systems and lighting. Compared to analog design methods (e.g., sketching, drawing, physical models), many students regarded digital processes to be scientific, objective, and logical, thereby perceiving them as design research. This transition from analogue to digital training has been confirmed in the literature (e.g., Ceylan, 2020), but neither tool necessarily reflects a research process as defined by EBD theorists (Cama, 2009; Halawa et al., 2020; Hicks, 2014).

As predicted, many students responded that a design research process could contribute to creating better design outcomes. Although schematic design and design research are not mutually exclusive concepts, the two processes should be distinguished because design research requires specific components, including research methods, a well-organized procedure, and dissemination of research findings (Hicks, 2014). However, many students indicated that they considered studies typically conducted at the beginning of a design project, such as case studies, building mass studies, or design critique, to be design research. Usually, those studies tend to be visually-oriented learning processes, often preferred by design professionals compared to narrative-intensive documents (Huber, 2016).

6.4 Research Question 4: Consideration of HER in Architectural Design

Faculty and students concurred that architectural design significantly influences the users' behavior and physical and mental health. Gifford (2014) identified environmental psychology as a study of transactions between humans and their physical surroundings. Users' behavior and health are two of the most important and popular research subjects regarding HER.

In order to survey the extent of participant consideration of HER in architectural design, this study asked participants to rate 15 themes frequently studied in environmental psychology (Gifford, 2014; Hall, 1990; Sommer, 1969; Steg, van den Berg, & de Groot, 2019). On average, faculty and students either agreed or strongly agreed that they consider HER themes when designing or examining a building. However, for the subject of environment and health (e.g., physical activity, obesity, illness, psychological health, and wellness), most students responded that they did not usually consider this subject as an aspect of HER when designing a new building or evaluating an existing one. Although there was a significant difference between faculty and students regarding their consideration of this theme, faculty also indicated that the theme of environment and health was the least considered theme. This result was surprising because, ironically, participants advocated the impact of architectural design on user health in the previous question. The respondents' weak consideration of the relationship between environment and health when designing may be related to their lack of familiarity with the design of healthcare facilities in general.

In fact, several previous research findings on healthcare facility design and designers in Korea support this assumption. According to Kim et al.'s (2014) study, which asked medical and design experts in Korea about their perceptions of elder-friendly hospital design, medical groups and design professionals showed significantly different understandings of design elements. The medical groups in Kim et al.'s study consisted of doctors, nurses, administrators, social workers, researchers, and psychotherapists, while the design groups consisted of architects, interior designers, researchers, and facility managers. Specifically, while medical experts focused on patient physical health, designers emphasized patients' psychological and social health. Lee and Noh (2019) also observed that very few studies addressed EBD in relation to healthcare facilities since it was introduced in 2008 in Korea. According to a professor interviewed for this study, Korean architecture schools rarely included designing a healthcare facility in their design studio curriculums because it is considered a specialized facility and young designers should learn its complex design process when working in a design firm, but not in school.

Even though the SPCs from the KAAB include "sustainable architecture and urbanism" to be addressed in architectural education (KAAB, n.d.), sustainability turned out to be the second least considered HER theme among students. A significant difference between faculty and students was also found regarding their consideration of sustainability when designing and examining buildings. This result was consistent with the previous study on sustainability education in Korean schools that suggested that

KAAB accreditation should support theory-to-practice integrated design studios since the current sustainability education is biased toward the technological aspect (Rieh et al., 2017).

Significant differences between faculty and students were revealed in several other HER themes: user preference for built environment; human factors and ergonomics; visual/hearing/mobility issues related to people with disabilities; and environmental hazards. Students considered them less frequently than faculty did. Although the four themes are popular in environmental design research, neither these relevant themes nor the terms are included in the SPCs of KAAB, except for one related to people with disabilities, expressed as "Accessible Design" (KAAB, 2018), so they might have been less familiar to architecture students.

According to the follow-up interviews, most interviewees understood that HER indicates an interaction between humans and the environment, which means that humans influence the environment and vice versa. Gifford (2014) identified five goals and principles of environmental psychology, and the results of this study indicated that interviewees considered three of them to be important aspects of HER: to improve stewardship of the natural and built environment, to consider the human and the setting as a holistic entity, and to recognize that humans actively cope with and shape environments. The respondents recognized that HER is an overarching framework in architecture that should be addressed in architectural and urban design.

6.5 Research Question 5. HER Themes in Korean Architecture Schools

Most interviewees indicated that schools were providing HER education for their students. There were several emerging reasons why they thought their school curricula commonly included HER themes: they had many lectures on HER based on relevant SPC requirements (e.g., Human Behavior and Spaces, Sustainable Architecture and Urbanism, and Environment Control Systems) and the design studios incorporated HER content. Their responses supported one of the KAAB's core competency requirements for students: "Understanding of the relationship between people and buildings, and between buildings and their environment, and of the need to relate buildings and the spaces between them to human needs and scale." (KAAB, 2018). For the handful of faculty and student interviewees who could specify their experience with HER education either related to lectures or design studios, they mentioned hands-on projects (e.g., field study on wayfinding issues, using space syntax), consideration of personal space versus common space, and theoretical understanding of environments (e.g., the role of nature, building energy consumption, people movement in urban scale). On the other hand, many other interviewees struggled with specifying their experiences with HER education. Students and faculty provided different reasons for why they found it difficult. One common explanation among students for the difficulty of remembering their experience was related to exam-based lecture systems. Most students indicated that they considered HER themes in design studios in a holistic way instead of deeply focusing on each theme. Design critique was described as a common way of considering HER.

As per previous studies (e.g., El-Latif et al., 2020), the individual design critique (or desk critique) is described as an indispensable and efficient pedagogy in design studios. However, students' learning experiences may vary depending on different tutors' pedagogical approaches (Yorgancıoğlu & Tunalı, 2020). When students and instructors are in a master-apprentice relationship, students tend to follow their instructors' feedback without thorough consideration (Oh et al., 2013). Therefore, if students study HER themes primarily based on design critiques, it may not be sufficient to understand the contents critically.

Most faculty responded that HER themes were spread out in their curriculum as a theoretical foundation rather than specified as an independent educational subject. This contributed to the fact that faculty could not provide specific examples of HER education in their schools. However, one professor used a co-teaching method in a design studio to support student understanding of the need for a theoretical background before designing:

> *I co-teach the studios for the 4th-year students with professors who have expertise in either urban planning or building structure and let students see both macro and micro environments, but they struggled to do it even though it was good training.*

This co-teaching methodology is consistent with Jeon (2014) who mentions another Korean university that aimed to provide integrated design studios operated collaboratively with design and non-design faculty to support students' development of their interdisciplinary perspectives.

Through the survey, respondents were asked to confirm two issues: whether they had experienced given educational methods to teach or learn HER in their schools and, if they had, whether a particular method had been useful. Five educational methods were given, including design studios, elective seminars, lecture-based core courses, field trips to building sites/constructions, and hands-on projects. More than half of the faculty responded that they used all the given methods, while elective seminars were used the most. However, student responses were different from faculty. Lecture-based core courses were experienced by students the most, and design studios and elective seminars were the second most experienced by students. However, more than half of students never experienced field trips and hands-on projects on HER. This survey result is consistent with the students who said they studied HER themes through lectures compared to hands-on projects or practice.

There were significant differences between faculty and students who evaluated each method's usefulness. Faculty evaluations were higher than student evaluations of usefulness. On average, students rated design studios, elective seminars, and lecture-based core courses as useful, but field trips and hands-on projects were not. Regardless of different pedagogical methods, all responses between faculty and students were significantly different in the degree to which they found these methods useful. This may be due to different understandings of pedagogical methodology. Previous studies confirmed that faculty and students often evaluate their experience with the same educational methods differently, such as active learning (Patrick et al., 2016) and academic reading (Howard et al., 2018).

Overall, design studios were the most useful method to study HER for both faculty and students. Furthermore, faculty ratings of design studios on HER topics were significantly correlated with their understanding of design research's importance in architectural design and education. This result means that faculty who thought design research is important in architectural design and education also found that design studios were useful to teach HER topics to students. Faculty responses implied that design studios may be potentially powerful as a platform to study HER themes, as design studios can exploit student presentations and various critique sessions, including individual critique, peer critique, panel discussion, and public critique (El-Latif et al., 2020), in order to expand the discussion of HER.

Interestingly, on average, faculty responses indicated that they believed all methods were useful except high school courses, but students felt that only university courses were useful. Other significant differences between the two groups involved their ratings on conferences, symposia, and seminars. Faculty responded that these sources were as useful as university courses, but students indicated they were not. Likewise, they rated the online resources/SNS differently, with students rating them as helpful for understanding HER, but faculty rating them as not helpful. This result aligns with the finding that, when asked about their sources for new information, students mostly relied on SNS, books, online searches, and courses in school, whereas faculty mostly used websites, academic conferences, papers, journal articles, communicating with people, and seminars.

6.6 Research Question 6. Education of Design Research and HER

The interviewer asked the participants to evaluate their current design research and EBD education based on personal standards, regardless of the number of relevant courses provided by their schools. Although nearly half of the faculty assessed their current education on design research as "neither enough nor not enough," the overall assessments of faculty and students indicated that the education was not sufficient. Specifically, a few students wanted to have at least one or two additional courses related to design research or EBD that were currently not provided. KAAB requires architecture schools to provide the relevant education based on their SPC requirements, including the item called "Research and Analysis" (KAAB, 2018). However, interview results indicated that faculty offer design research in various courses as a supportive process before designing rather than as an independent course. Students did not seem to recognize this support as meeting KAAB requirements.

Regarding the barriers to promoting design research and EBD education in their schools, many faculty and students pointed out KAAB accreditation as a contributing factor. A common response explained that KAAB led the schools to provide excessive required courses according to SPCs. Therefore, it was difficult to provide advanced design education that focused on design research or EBD to students who were already overwhelmed with requirements. This result is in line with Lee's (2016) review of the after-effect of KAAB that stated that most architectural schools in Korea have changed their program from a 4-year non-accredited B.S. program to a 5-year B.Arch. program since the launch of accredited programs in 2007; thus, it had been almost impossible to find an architecture program that offers flexible and unique curricula not based on the standardized educational program. Furthermore, a few interviewees criticized their architecture curriculum by suggesting that it was too focused on design studios, and the connection between studios and non-studio courses was too weak. The imbalance between studios and theoretical courses, which may hamper an understanding of design research, can be exacerbated when students do not follow recommended course plans for each grade because 5-year architecture programs provide a fixed plan for each student year with a set of design studios and relevant theoretical courses (Ryu & Lee, 2009).

Another important contributing factor identified by interviewees was that there was no expert to teach design research or EBD. This issue was also pertinent to another emerging theme that students were not used to conducting research in general. According to Ku (2017), design instructors often teach their students based on their previous education and personal experiences, without updated formal guidance of education (e.g., teacher education or textbooks). More specifically, current faculty members in architecture schools are less likely to have studied EBD concepts or methods during their college education as EDAC was not launched until 2009 (CHD, n.d.). Architect Kirk Hamilton did not publish Evidence-Based Design for Multiple Building Types, one of the most popular books about EBD, until 2009. The survey found that most faculty had little or no expertise in EBD or environmental psychology.

Unlike the previous barriers focusing on educational systems, a few faculty interviewees pointed out that the learning processes students used could have affected the consequent stagnation of their understanding of research and EBD. For example, even when students could individually consult with professors about their research, students rarely used the opportunities. According to faculty responses, students also relied on online to find references without an in-depth understanding of the study materials.

Besides, the majority of interviewees felt that their current education about HER was not sufficient. Likewise, the survey confirmed that the average respondent believed that current architectural curricula did not offer sufficient HER education to students. Consequently, faculty and students responded that they wanted to offer more course content in HER or expand their own HER knowledge in architecture studies. Regarding the broad range of HER themes, the results support the notion that Korean architecture education should more practically address the priorities of architecture education proposed by Boyer and Mitgang (1996) that include providing inclusive institutional context based on the principle of diversity and a curriculum integrated with interdisciplinary knowledge (Lee, 2016). In terms of providing the institutional context based on diversity, architectural education needs to support not only students pursuing design professions but also students eager to be design researchers, engineers, policy makers, educators, and project managers, while maintaining their architectural perspectives.

Furthermore, there were significant differences in ratings between faculty and students. Students assessed their school's HER education more negatively and were more eager to receive further HER education than faculty. Faculty and student expertise in EBD or environmental psychology was significantly different, although the average response of both groups indicated that they had almost no expertise in this field. When asked about their willingness to specialize in EBD or environmental psychology in the future, less than half the faculty and almost half of the students revealed their interest in such academic fields.

Through the interviews, participants explained potential contributing factors to the limitations of current HER education. Like the interviews about design research and EBD, KAAB accreditation was regarded as a barrier to improving HER education. A professor explained the reason:

> *KAAB should focus on checking the minimum, but it became standardizing our architecture education, and now it functions as if it is the maximum requirements, so there is a lack of elective courses and subject diversity in courses even compared to a decade ago.*

The response is consistent with what Ryu and Lee (2009) suggested to improve accredited architecture programs. The authors emphasized that each school should reflect on their educational objectives and philosophy regarding SPCs as minimum criteria.

Some students supported the argument above by expressing their willingness to have more opportunities to practice or experiment with HER theories. The fact that there are few faculty trained to teach HER themes, design research, or EBD and few requests from students to add this course content may limit its integration. A student explained that they did not ask for the relevant education since they did not know about its significance.

Students' attitudes toward learning also contributed to the limited education, according to a few faculty. They explained that students tended not to voluntarily participate in the relevant lecture series and deeply think about rationales behind their design concepts. However, those faculty respondents blamed the current educational culture instead of students in that it forced students to be obsessed with their grades and employment preparation. According to Hong's (2019) research on the social background of general education in Korea, many Korean universities focus excessively on student majors at the expense of a more general education based on the argument that it supports the students' employment opportunities after graduation.

6.7 Recommendations for Education of Design Research and HER

Based on the literature and the results from survey and interviews, several recommendations can be suggested to promote better understanding of design research and HER themes in architecture schools.

First, architecture schools can enhance the theory-practice associations throughout their curricula to reduce the gap in student understanding between theoretical knowledge and architectural design. This can be achieved by providing theory-based active learning opportunities to students in design studios. According to McLaughlan and Lodge (2019), a studio is an adequate pedagogical model that provides relevant and adaptable strategies to develop epistemic fluency. Informal interaction among students in a design studio, an open environment that enables students to monitor and comment on each other's progress, can facilitate their learning of theories (Oh et al., 2013). Theory-based small exercises in lecture courses encourage students to increase their engagement and retention of course content. Effective in-class exercises may include design charrettes (e.g., Walker & Seymour, 2007).

Second, architecture students can benefit from recognizing a variety of research methodologies from other fields, including social science, natural sciences, and applied sciences, in addition to the traditional design methodology associated with the architecture discipline. For example, a systematic understanding of social science research methods, such as structured interviews, behavioral observations, or focus groups, may help students integrate such methods in their pre-design phases and broaden their academic perspectives.

Third, regarding education in support of design research, EBD, and environmental psychology as advanced architecture design, relevant content can be introduced through elective courses. Those elective courses can fulfill student expectations for further HER education, and given the choice of letter grading versus mastery-based grading (e.g., pass or fail), students would feel less burdened to take the courses simultaneously with other requirements. Furthermore, schools can provide a design studio specialized in HER themes while maintaining the basic guideline of SPCs.

Fourth, continuing education for professionals focusing on EBD and HER can benefit both instructors and students in architecture schools. It can be especially helpful to improve the quality of design studios, many of which are taught by design professionals as adjunct professors. A previous study discovered that successful continuing professional education could result in professionals expanding their content perspectives, developing interpersonal skills, and establishing an interdisciplinary mindset (Johnson et al., 2019), which addresses a recommended skill set for design instructors.

7. CONCLUSION

This study suggests that architecture students and faculty in Korea consider design research significant to architectural design and architectural education, although there were limitations in their understanding of definition and methods of conducting design research. Student and faculty understanding of various academic fields associated with design research (e.g., ergonomics, environmental psychology, EBD) was significantly different. While most interviewees identified EBD as a scientific and logical process, their understanding of it was less comprehensive regarding its versatile applicability in architectural design. Most interviewees' experience with design research and EBD was also limited to site visits and field studies rather than interdisciplinary research methods.

Students and faculty in architecture schools considered HER to be an important and overarching theme in architectural design. Their school curricula addressed various HER themes in both studios and theoretical courses. However, faculty and students provided different assessments of the educational methods of learning HER themes (e.g., design studios, elective seminars, field trips) regarding their usefulness. Consequently, most students and faculty felt their current education about design research and HER was insufficient. Students were more willing than faculty to further integrate HER education in their architectural studies.

7.1 Limitations and Future Research

The current study has some limitations. First, participants in this study might have been biased toward having stronger interests in design research and HER themes than the others in architecture schools due to the voluntary-based participation. Moreover, if the recruitment targeted a greater number of architecture schools in Korea, the results might have differed from the current research findings. Lastly, given the small sample size of a survey group, the research findings may not be transferable to the general population in architecture schools in Korea.

Future studies may focus on cross-cultural comparisons of architecture students and faculty perceptions of EBD and environmental psychology. It will help clarify the limitations in what is perceived to be relevant education and provide useful recommendations that were not uncovered in the current study. Future work may also expand its target audience to master's students in architecture schools who actively engage in advanced design studies based on fundamental architectural knowledge. More broadly, the current research methodology can be used to survey design professionals in architecture firms. Such research will provide more insights to improve continuing education content for professionals.

8. REFERENCES

Architects Registration Board (ARB). (n.d.). Retrieved from https://arb.org.uk/information-for-schools-of-architecture/arb-criteria/

Atkins, J. B. (2014). Project Completion and Post-Construction. In: American Institute of Architects. (15th ed.). *The architect's handbook of professional practice* (pp. 729-739). Hoboken, New Jersey: Wiley.

Becker, F., Bonaiuto, M., Bilotta, E., & Bonnes, M. (2011). Integrated Healthscape Strategies: An Ecological Approach to Evidence-Based Design. *HERD, 4*, 114-129.

Bhatia, R. (2011). *Health Impact Assessment: A Guide for Practice.* Oakland, CA: Human Impact Partners.

Boarin, P., Martinez-Molina, A., & Juan-Ferruses, I. (2020). Understanding students' perception of sustainability in architecture education: A comparison among universities in three different continents. *Journal of Cleaner Production, 248.* doi:10.1016/j.jclepro.2019.119237

Boyer, E., & Mitgang, L. D. (1996). *Building Community: A New Future for Architecture Education and Practice: A Special Report.*

Cama, R. (2009). *Evidence-based healthcare design.* Hoboken, N.J.: John Wiley & Sons.

Canadian Architectural Certification Board (CACB). (n.d.). Retrieved from https://cacb.ca/accreditation/

Center for Health Design (CHD). (n.d.). Retrieved from https://www.healthdesign.org/certification-outreach/edac

Ceylan, S. (2019). A Case Study on the Change of Students' Perception of Architectural Design Based on their Knowledge of Digital Tools. *The International Journal of Design Education, 14*(2), 1-16. doi:10.18848/2325-128X/CGP/v14i02/1-16

Choi, J. (2014). Architectural Education and Its Accreditation. *Review of Architecture and Building Science, 58*(4), 19-22.

Duerk, D. P. (1993). *Architectural programming: information management for design.* New York: Van Nostrand Reinhold.

El-Latif, M. A., Al-Hagla, K. S., & Hasan, A. (2020). Overview on the criticism process in architecture pedagogy. *Alexandria Engineering Journal, 59*(2), 753-762. doi:10.1016/j.aej.2020.01.019

Gifford, R. (2009). Environmental psychology: Manifold visions, unity of purpose. *Journal of Environmental Psychology, 29*(3), 387-389. doi:10.1016/j.jenvp.2009.09.002

Gifford, R. (2014). *Environmental psychology: principles and practice* (Fifth ed.): Optimal Books.

Giuliani, M. V., & Scopelliti, M. (2009). Empirical research in environmental psychology: Past, present, and future. *Journal of Environmental Psychology, 29*(3), 375-386. doi:10.1016/j.jenvp.2008.11.008

Halawa, F., Madathil, S. C., Gittler, A., & Khasawneh, M. T. (2020). Advancing evidence-based healthcare facility design: a systematic literature review. *Health Care Manag Sci, 23*(3), 453-480.

Hall, E. T. (1990). *The hidden dimension* (Anchor Books ed.). New York: Anchor Books.

Hamilton, D. K. (2009). *Evidence-based design for multiple building types.* Hoboken, N.J.: Wiley.

Hicks, T. L. (2014). Evidence-Based Design. In: American Institute of Architects. (15th ed.). *The architect's handbook of professional practice* (pp. 937-949). Hoboken, New Jersey: Wiley.

Hong, S. K. (2019). The Social Background of Strengthening General Education. *The Journal of General Education, 9*, 61-90. doi:10.24173/jge.2019.06.9.3

Howard, P. J., Gorzycki, M., Desa, G., & Allen, D. D. (2018). Academic Reading: Comparing Students' and Faculty Perceptions of Its Value, Practice, and Pedagogy. *Journal of College Reading and Learning, 48*(3), 189-209. doi:10.1080/10790195.2018.1472942

Huber, A. (2016). Is Seeing Intriguing? Practitioner Perceptions of Research Documents. *Journal of Interior Design, 41*(1), 13-32. doi:10.1111/joid.12067

Jeon, B.-H. (2014). A Model of Integrated Academic Curriculum of Architecture and Architectural Engineering : A Case of SNU. *Review of Architecture and Building Science, 58*(4), 71-76.

Johnson, C., Tilt, J. H., Ries, P. D., & Shindler, B. (2019). Continuing professional education for green infrastructure: Fostering collaboration through interdisciplinary trainings. *Urban Forestry & Urban Green-*

ing, 41, 283-291. doi:10.1016/j.ufug.2019.04.021
Kim, J.-W. (2011). A Comparison Study on Accredited Architectural Education Contents between US and Korea. *Architectural Research, 13*(2), 13-21. doi:10.5659/aikar.2011.13.2.13
Kim, K.-C., & Kim, B.-J. (2004). A study on design process for public space by users behavioral characteristics. *Journal of Korean Society of Design Science, 17*(1), 89-98.
Kim, D.-S., & Lee, G.-H. (2007). The Professional Architects' Perception to the Comparative Significance of Architectural Subjects. *Journal of the Architectural Institute of Korea Planning & Design, 23*(2), 71-80.
Kim, D., Lee, J. H., & Ha, M. (2014). Exploring Perceptions of Designers and Medical Staff in South Korea about Design Elements for the Elder-Friendly Hospital. *Journal of Interior Design, 39*(4), 15-32.
Korea Architectural Accrediting Board (KAAB). (n.d.). Retrieved from http://eng.kaab.or.kr/Standards/standards_01
Korea Architectural Accrediting Board (KAAB). (2018). *KAAB Conditions & Procedures for Professional Degree Programs in Architecture*. Seoul: KAAB.
Ku, B.-D. (2017). An Analysis of Characteristics and Pedagogic Models of Architectural Design Studio Tutors in Korea. *Journal of the Architectural Institute of Korea Planning & Design, 33*(3), 77-86.
Lee, J.-S. (2015). A Study on Survey Result by the Site Visit Team Members for the Student Performance Criteria of the Conditions and Procedures of the Korea Architectural Accrediting Board. *Journal of the Architectural Institute of Korea Planning & Design, 31*(6), 55-63.
Lee, J. (2016). The Future of Architectural Education and Accreditation in Korea. *Review of Architecture and Building Science, 60*(7), 39-43.
Lee, K.-S., Geon, K.-R., & Yoo, D. (2012). A Study on Integrating Sustainability into Architectural education Curriculum in Korea. *Journal of the Architectural Institute of Korea Planning & Design, 28*(4), 127-138.
Lee, S. J., & Noh, T. R. (2019). Activation of Evidence-based Design (EBD) and Introduction of Certification (EDAC). *Journal of The Korea Institute of Healthcare Architecture, 25*(1).
Luck, R. (2019). Design research, architectural research, architectural design research: An argument on disciplinarity and identity. *Design Studies, 65*, 152-166. doi:10.1016/j.destud.2019.11.001
McLaughlan, R., & Lodge, J. M. (2018). Facilitating epistemic fluency through design thinking: a strategy for the broader application of studio pedagogy within higher education. *Teaching in Higher Education, 24*(1), 81-97. doi:10.1080/13562517.2018.1461621
National Council of Architectural Registration Boards (NCARB). (n.d.). Retrieved from https://www.ncarb.org/become-architect/basics
Ochshorn, J. (2014). Architecture's Dysfunctional Couple: Design and Technology at the Crossroads. *The International Journal of Design Education, 7*(4), 35-46. doi:10.18848/2325-128X/CGP/v07i04/57910.
Oh, Y., Ishizaki, S., Gross, M. D., & Yi-Luen Do, E. (2013). A theoretical framework of design critiquing in architecture studios. *Design Studies, 34*(3), 302-325. doi:10.1016/j.destud.2012.08.004
Owen, C. L. (1998). Design research: building the knowledge base. *Design Studies, 19*, 9-20.
Patrick, L. E., Howell, L. A., & Wischusen, W. (2016). Perceptions of Active Learning between Faculty and Undergraduates: Differing Views among Departments. *Journal of STEM Education, 17*(3).
Peña, W. M., & Parshall, S. A. (2001). *Problem seeking: an architectural programming primer.* NY: John Wiley & Sons.
Rieh, S.-Y., Lee, B.-Y., Oh, J.-G., Schuetze, T., Porras Álvarez, S., Lee, K., & Park, J. (2017). Integration of Sustainability into Architectural Education at Accredited Korean Universities. *Sustainability, 9*(7).
Ryu, J.-H., & Lee, J.-H. (2009). A Research on the Assessment Process of Academic Curriculum and its Management System in Accreditation Procedures of Architectural Programs in Korea. *Journal of the Architectural Institute of Korea Planning & Design, 25*(2), 175-184.
Seo, S., Yu, J., & Bak, J. (2017). *Research on the trends and the actual condition of architectural service industry.* Sejong: Architecture & Urban Research Institute.
Shepley, M. M. (2011). *Health facility evaluation for design professionals.* Myersville, MD: Asclepion.
Shepley, M. M. (2014). Research and Practice. In: American Institute of Architects. (15th ed.). *The architect's*

handbook of professional practice (pp. 920-936). Hoboken, New Jersey: Wiley.

Sommer, R. (1969). *Personal Space: the Behavioral Basis of Design*. Prentice-Hall.

Steg, L., van den Berg, A. E., & de Groot, J. I. M. (2019). Environmental Psychology: History, Scope, and Methods. In: Steg, L., & de Groot, J. I. M. (Second ed.). *Environmental Psychology: An Introduction* (pp. 1-11). Wiley-Blackwell.

Ulrich, R. S., Zimring, C., Zhu, X., DuBose, J., Seo, H.-B., Choi, Y.-S., . . . Joseph, A. (2008). A Review of the Research Literature on Evidence-Based Healthcare Design. H*ealth Environments Research & Design Journal, 1*(3), 61-125.

US Green Building Council (USGBC). (n.d.). Retrieved from https://www.usgbc.org/leed

van der Linden, V., Dong, H., & Heylighen, A. (2019). Tracing architects' fragile knowing about users in the socio-material environment of design practice. *Design Studies, 63*, 65-91.

Walker, J. B., & Seymour, M. W. (2008). Utilizing the design charrette for teaching sustainability. *International Journal of Sustainability in Higher Education, 9*(2), 157-169.

Yorgancıoglu, D., & Tunalı, S. (2020). Changing pedagogic identities of tutors and students in the design studio: Case study of desk and peer critiques. *Art, Design & Communication in Higher Education, 19*(1), 19-32. doi:10.1386/adch_00011_1

Zhang, X. (2016). *Introduction to Environmental Psychology and Applications for Modern Interior Design*. Paper presented at the International Conference on Education, Sports, Arts and Management Engineering (ICESAME 2016).

Developing Post-Occupancy Evaluation Method Using Social Media to Reveal Usage Pattern of High-Speed Railway Stations

Yi He *(Beijing Jiaotong University);* ***Chunfang Li*** *(Office@Csadi.Cn);* ***Li Wang*** *(Central-South Architectural Design Institute co;Ltd);* ***Yi Yang*** *(Beijing Jiaotong University);* ***Bo Zhang*** *(Oklahoma State University)*

ABSTRACT

After nearly 20 years of development, China's railway technology has reached a relatively mature stage. As of December 2020, there are currently more than 5,000 railway stations in China, including more than 500 high-speed railway stations. According to the statistics of the National Railway Group, the volume of railroad passengers in China reached 357.86 million. Yet the usage of these high-speed railway stations has not been attracted much scholarly attention, as not many empirical studies on this topic are available, partly because the difficulty of long-term on-site observation and survey. Hence, this study developed a post-occupancy evaluation method using social media to reveal the usage patterns at high-speed railway stations in China. By using big data technology and social media, employing the Hangzhoudong Railway Station under transit-oriented-development (TOD)mode as the research object, this study examined break-throughs of limitations in quantity, time,and regional scope. The research also explored passenger behavior activities, internal space and flow of people, so as to analyze passenger flow, functional space,and satisfaction with China's existing large-scale high-speed railway stations. The results provide a new way for designers to study the current situation in the large-scale railway comprehensive transportation hub. The results show that Hangzhoudong Railway Station gave rise to positive passenger experiences. Various behaviors that were codified from the data indicated the order and efficiency of the building complex. The pair analysis also helped to suggests the issues with flow, management, sign design, and other factors.

KEYWORDS

Big data, Hangzhoudong Railway Station, Social media, Gephi analysis.

1. INTRODUCTION

With the rapid development of social media, more and more people have been publishing original comments on the Internet during travel. These comments contain time, specific objects, people's experience, emotion and evaluation data. The forms of data include text, audio,video and geographic location information, etc. (Ross, B., Neuberger, C., Mirbabaie, M., & Stieglitz, S.,2018). Compared with traditional data, these data are time-consuming, massive and wide-ranging (Chen, M., Zhang, Y., & Li, X. F.,2013). Researchers can analyze the data to mine the most important information needed, to better understand the perception of human experiences and the environment. At present, in many fields, social media data has brought new methods and directions to research, such as exploring the characteristics of crowd behavior in the urban dimension (Ryong, L., Kazutoshi S., & Shoko W., 2013), exploring the user needs(Patrick, M., & Jisoo, S., 2019)and tourist preferences of urban parks(Zoé, A. H., Spencer, A. W., Marie, L. D., Bonnie, L.K., Timon, M., & David, M. F., 2018), and analyzing urban infrastructure (Klaus, C. A. & Aksel, E., 2019). These studies not only demonstrate the application methods of social media in different research directions,but also prove the advantages of social media data.

1.1 The Development of Big Data Technology in the Field of Architecture in China

Big data technology in China has made some progress in the field of architecture, such as multi-dimensional evaluations of urban park green spaces based on public comment networks (Zhao, J. N., Yue, W.J., Peng, Y. Y., & Wang, Z. F., 2019), using big data to analyze the satisfaction of tourists with scenic spots used to promote the development of the landscape architecture industry(Li, H. X., & Wu, W. W., 2020), analyzing the tourists' experience of urban scenic spots based on sina (Wang, D. Y., Hu, G., Wang, L. X.,& Hu, S. Q., 2021), exploring the vulnerability of the city to flood disaster (Wang, H. L., Shen, Y. X., & Wu, Z. N.,2019) and the integration of Building Information Modeling (BIM) to improve the integration and distribution of engineering resources (Zhang, Q. Q.,& Liu, X. X., 2019). Big data technology has been used mainly for the application of architectural design, but compared with medicine In the fields of computer, economy and so on, the utilization of big data technology in the construction industry is not high at present. The data and information used in the early stages of the traditional construction industry still come from the existing practical experience(Xiao, W., 2019). Therefore, this article hopes to provide enlightenment and thinking for architecture-related researchers.

1.2 Research Background of Large-Scale Railway Comprehensive Transportation Hub in China

During the past ten years, China's large-scale railway comprehensive transportation hub has developed rapidly, and the total mileage of this high-speed rail ranks first in the world. The TOD mode, guided by public transport, has become an important choice for the development of China's large-scale railway comprehensive transportation hub. TOD mode provides an effective way for the development of China's Station City integration, the optimization of urban layout and the improvements in the people's community living environment (Li,J. X., & Guo, S. W., 2019). At present, research on railway comprehensive transportation hubs mainly focuses on the analysis of existing stations (Liu, C., Mo, F., Xi, Y., & Zhang, Y. N., 2012), forward-looking research on TOD mode (Liu, J.S., 2015), and the current situation in which TOD mode is combined with residents' activities utilizing big data (Luo, J. Zhao, P.J., & Liu, Y.S., 2019). Most of the articles still use traditional research methods, which are time-consuming and energy-consuming to a certain extent. In addition, the research data are relatively small, and there are limitations in time and space distribution. For a large-scale space design such as a high-speed railway station, it is difficult for urban planners and architects to control the human scale of the design. How to balance the scale relationship between human and large spaces is something that designers need to consider (Zhang, B.,& Song, Y., 2020). Social media Big data methods can provide great technical support for studying the preferences of people in buildings. Therefore, it is necessary to use social media to study and reflect the passenger experience in transportation hubs.

2. HANGZHOUDONG RAILWAY STATION

Hangzhoudong Railway Station is a large-scale comprehensive railway transportation hub located in Shangcheng District, Hangzhou City, Zhejiang Province, China. It was reconstructed and put into operation on July 1, 2013. As of January 2014, the scale of the station included 15 sets and 30 lines, and the annual passenger flow reached 71.9 million people. The station covers an area of about 400,000 square meters, the construction area of the station building is 344,000 square meters (Li, C.,& Wang, L., 2015), the supporting area of the square is 813,000 square meters, and the square area is 325,000 square meters. The area of the west square is about 200,000 square meters, while the area of the East Square is about 123,000 square meters.

Hangzhoudong Railway Station was designed by Central-south Architectural Design Institute (CSADI). The main building of the station building adopted the design inspiration of "Qian Jiangchao" to reflect the atmospheric and open city image of Hangzhou (Li, C. Qi, G.,& Yuan, P.,2009). The indoor space and canopy are transparent, open and bright (Figure 1), and the evenly arranged skylights bring mild and uniform natural light to the internal space (Li, C. Qi, G.,& Yuan, P., 2010). Hangzhoudong Railway Station is a five-story structure, including two floors above the ground and three floors underground. The whole system adopts the up in and down out mode. The east and west parts of the exit floor are equipped with traffic transfer halls, where passengers can easily transfer to different means of transportation, such as bus, taxi and metro lines 1, 4 and 6.

We chose Hangzhoudong Railway Station as the research object for several reasons. Firstly, Hangzhoudong Railway Station is a typical case of the TOD development model in China. Secondly, Hangzhoudong Railway Station is the 7th largest high-speed railway station in China, with very large passenger flow and a large amount of available data in all aspects (Li, C., 2018). Third, Hangzhoudong Railway Station has been in operation for more than 7 years since its official launch. During this period, passengers' comment data has accumulated on various social media, which is suitable for analysis using big data technology. This study mainly covered the following issues:

1. What aspects do people pay attention to in the Hangzhoudong Railway Station and is the attention on different aspects affected by the particular month?
2. What are the main behaviors of passengers inside the station building?

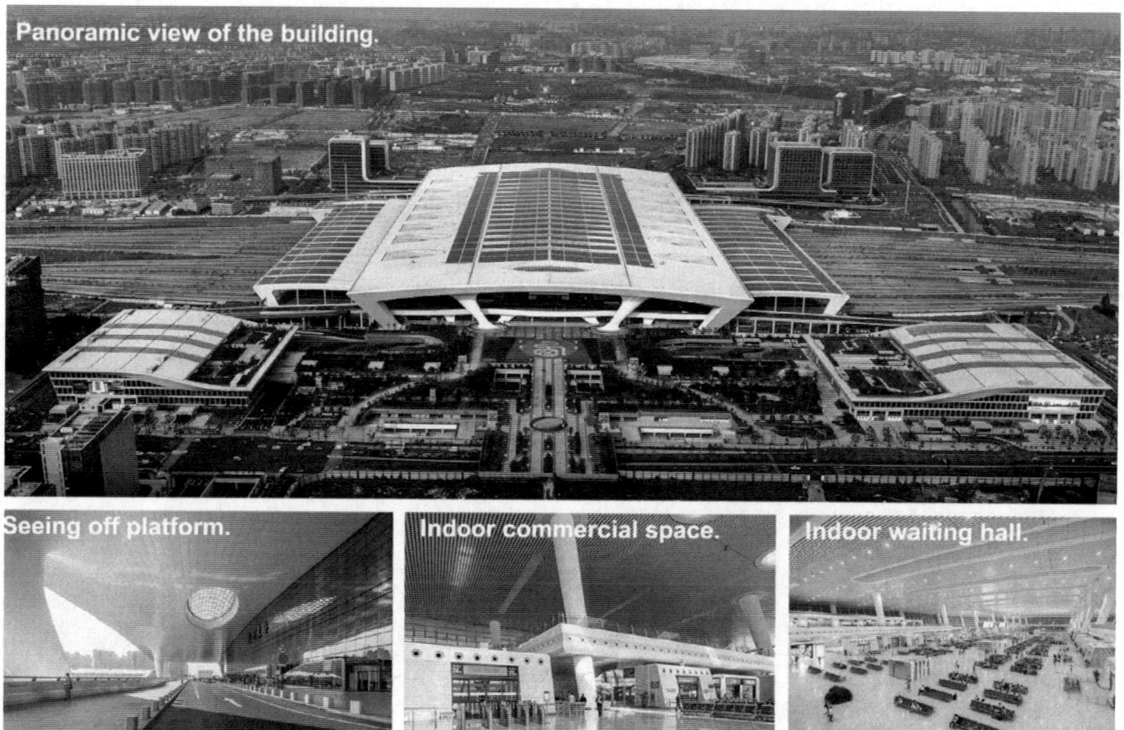

Figure 1: *Photos of the Hangzhoudong Railway Station. Photos by CSADI.*

3. How does the flow of people occur and what is their level of satisfaction with the interior space of Hangzhoudong Railway Station?
4. What factors affect the mood and experience of passengers in Hangzhoudong Railway Station?

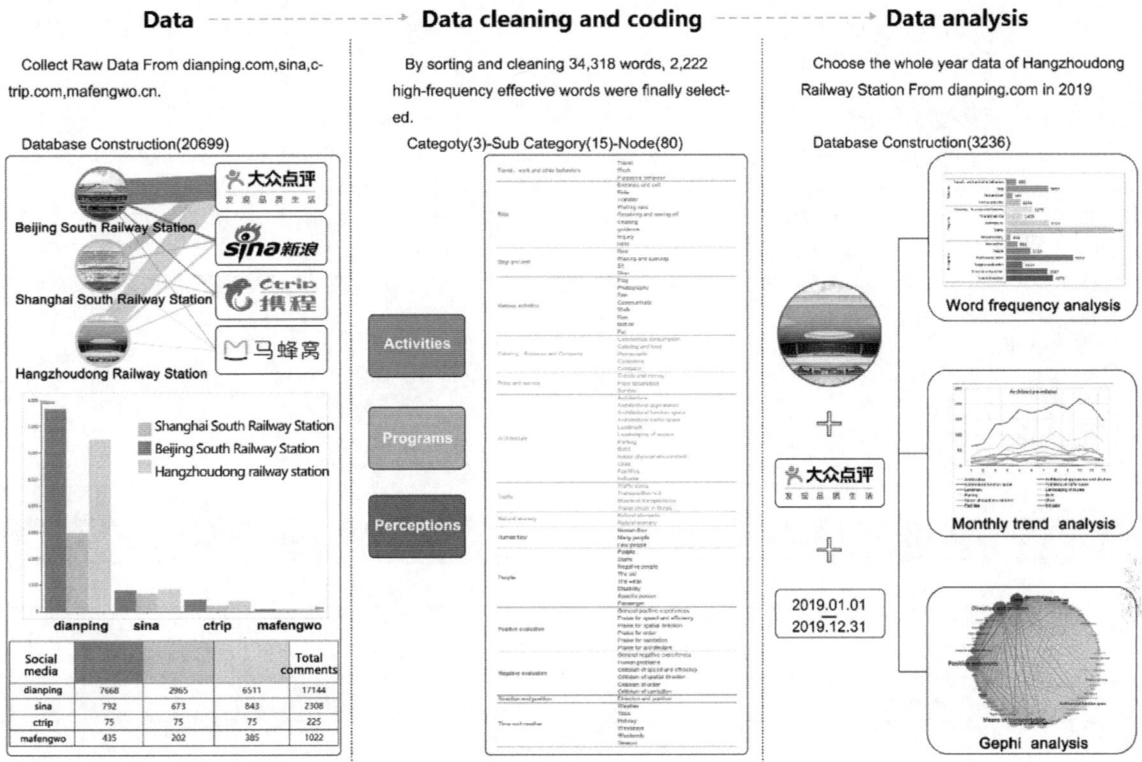

Figure 2: Research Flow Chart (2021). Diagram by the authors.

3. METHODS

This research is based on the data of passenger comments in social media, and after certain logical processing, the effective words in the comments are extracted into three categories to build a vocabulary, and the behaviors, objects and passengers in the Hangzhoudong Railway Station are studied separately. Then we select a section of the data to review, analyze word frequency in that section (Figure 2), change trend and relevance during the year [not at all clear what this means], and put forward a research outlook.

3.1 Data Acquisition

This paper used Python technology to explore the use and feelings people have about the Hangzhoudong Railway Station by utilizing four social media sources: Dianping, Ctrip, Sina, Mafengwo. As of November 7, 2020, we have also combined information about the Beijing South Railway Station and the Shanghai South Railway Station. From the social media data of Dianping, Ctrip, Sina, Mafengwo, we retrieved a total of 20,699 comments, with a total of 2,173,167 characters. The amount of data was huge. Among them, Dianping social media accounted for 83% of the total comment. However, there was still a large amount of data.

As an independent third-party consumer review website, Dianping has a huge amount of data, including original user content reviews with a scoring system. Through the Internet, combined with geographical location and users' personalized needs, it provides users with an interactive platform for business consultation and user evaluation in multiple life fields such as shopping, catering and tourism. Since its launch in 2003, Dianping has become one of the most popular apps for people to use while traveling. We were able to get the passenger evaluation content of Hangzhoudong Railway Station and the information change trend in the time dimension.

3.2 Data Sorting and Cleaning

The collected comment data was organized by textual content, and used word frequency analysis software designed-for word segmentation and word frequency analysis. A total of 34,318 words with word frequency greater than or equal to one were obtained, including a large amount of useless and irrelevant information, which had a great impact on the subsequent analysis. In order to increase the accuracy of the research, some data was filtered and the words were cleaned using word frequency statistics. The following words were filtered out of the data set:

1. Words with a word frequency of less than 15, such as "prison," "archery," etc.
2. Conjunctions, auxiliary words and other meaningless words, such as "because," "not only," and so on.
3. Basic information words, such as "Hangzhou,"."sina," etc.

Table 1: *Data Level Classification (2021). Table by authors*

Activities	Travel, work and other behaviors	Travel; Work; Purposive behavior;
	Ride-related	Entrance and exit; Ride-related; Transfer; Waiting cars; Receiving and seeing off; Cleaning; Guidance; Inquiry; Help;
	Stop and rest	Rest; Waiting and queuing; Sit; Stop;
	Various activities	Play; Photography; See; Communicate; Walk; Run; Motion; Eat; Commercial consumption;
Programs	Catering, Business and Company	Catering and food; Restaurants; Commerce; Company;
	Price and service	Tickets and money; Price description; Service;
	Architecture-related	Architecture; Architectural appearance and structure; Architectural function space; Architectural traffic space; Landmark; Landscaping of square; Parking; Build; Indoor physical environment; Chair; Facilities; Indicator;
	Traffic-related	Traffic terms; Transposition hub; Means of transportation; Travel check-in things;
	Natural scenery	Natural elements; Natural scenery;
Perceptions	Human flow	Human flow; Many people; Few people;
	People	People; Staffs; Negative people; The old; The weak; The sick and disabled; Specific person; Passenger;
	Positive evaluation	General positive experiences; Praise for speed and efficiency; Praise for spatial direction; Praise for order; Praise for sanitation; Praise for architecture;
	Negative evaluation	General negative experiences; Human problems; Criticism of speed and efficiency; Criticism of spatial direction; Criticism of order; Criticism of sanitation;
	Direction and position	
	Time and weather	Weather; Time; Holiday; Weekdays; Weekends; Season;

4. Digital quantifiers, such as "one," "two," etc. By sorting and cleaning 34,318 words, 2,222 high-frequency effective words were finally selected.

3.3 Classification and Data Coding

A total of 2222 high-frequency effective words were classified. The words were distributed into specific categories. Similar words such as "car," "bus," and "taxi" could be classified as "Means of transportation;" "Hamburger," "beef noodles," and "dumplings" could be classified as "Catering and food;" "taking a taxi," "taking the subway," and "taking the train" could be classified as "Ride," with a total of 80 labels. The 80 tags were divided into 15 sub-categories, and then the 15 sub-categories were divided into three more specific categories: activities, programs, perceptions (Table 1, Table 2):

1. Activities: this category includes the main behavior activities of people in Hangzhoudong Railway Station, such as "Enter and leave (enter, security inspection)," "Rest (sleep, rest)," Play (play, play, amuse)," "Eat (eat, drink, taste)," etc.
2. Programs: this category covers the main organizations in the station, such as "Restaurants (KFC, McDonald's, steamed stuffed bun shop)," "Architectural appearance and structure (roof,ceiling, arch)," "Means of transportation (train, high-speed railway, automobile)," etc.
3. Perceptions: this category describe the passengers' emotions and feelings after activities in the station, such as "Positive emotions (beautiful, handsome, like)," "negative emotions (extremely poor, unhappy, depression)," "Weather (typhoon, rain, snow)," etc.

***Table 2:** Examples of Label Coding and Data Inclusion (2021). Table by authors*

Category	Node	Comments Content Words (Original Language)
Activities	Ride-Related	上车；打车；坐地铁；坐车；乘坐；乘车；坐火车；登车；乘火车；坐飞机；搭乘；赶车；下车；发车；上下车；倒车；行驶；坐车到；租车；乘飞机；拼车；开车；改签；约车；搭车；
	Receiving and Seeing Off	送客；拉客；接客；送别；接送；接站；接人；接待；迎接；相聚；告别；团聚；分离；离别；送到；
Programs	Architectural Function Space	大厅；检票口；候车厅；窗口；厕所；卫生间；售票处；洗手间；服务台；二楼；一层；二层；一楼；楼上；三层；两层；休息室；夹层；售票厅；室内；休息区；咨询台；售票口；下层；五层；楼层；柜台；月台；站厅；楼上楼下；贵宾厅；寄存处；服务站；贵宾室；地库；服务区；顶层；每层；女厕所；售票点；吸烟区；女厕；第二层；集散中心；大堂；隔间；办公室；大楼公共场所；候机厅；服务中心；
	Architectural Traffic Space	出口；通道；快速通道；出入口；门口；出站口；地下通道；进出口；进口；过道；入口处；地道；出口处；绿色通道；基建走道；西门；南口；电梯；扶梯；楼梯；自动扶梯；直梯；入口；
Perceptions	Many People	拥挤；人满为患；熙熙攘攘；密集；人来人往；来来往往；爆满；人头攒动；很挤；乌泱；川流不息；人潮；人山人海；涌动；黑压压；长龙；挤满；水泄不通；泱泱；来来去去；人挺多；车水马龙；满满当当；进进出出；络绎不绝；拥挤不堪；挤死；人多；人声鼎沸；闹哄哄；排长龙；座无虚席；人真多；
	Praise for Speed and Efficiency	很快；速度；快速；效率；匆匆；挺快；最快；迅速；特快；高效；方便快捷；快捷；顺利；便捷；准点；四通八达；畅通；提速；加快；节省时间；没多久；急匆匆；真快；越来越快；快快；效率高；有效；便于；省时省力；省事；便民；飞速发展；通达；便利；准时；顺畅；

3.4 Scope and Methods of Data Analysis

From the 20,699 comments collected, the comment data for Hangzhoudong Railway Station from Dianping dated 2019 (from January 1, 2019 to December 31, 2019) were selected, and a total of 3,236 comments were obtained. According to the above three categories, 15 subcategories and 80 tags, word frequency analysis, monthly trend line chart analysis and Gephi visual analysis were carried out respectively (Figure 2).

Word frequency analysis was used to analyze the overall word frequency to obtain the attention of passengers on different aspects in the Hangzhoudong Railway Station. The monthly trend of word frequency reflects the change of different factors with the change of months in a year. By analyzing the monthly trend, we can see the change in passengers' attention to factors during a different season. Gephi analysis was used to analyze the network comment data of Hangzhoudong Railway Station, mine the association relationship and visually display it, find the association relationship between a factor and other information, and to analyze the data results clearly and effectively.

4. RESULTS

4.1 Word Frequency Analysis

The following conclusions can be drawn from the overall word frequency(Figure 3):

In the behavior category, "Ride-related" and "Various activities" were the main behaviors of

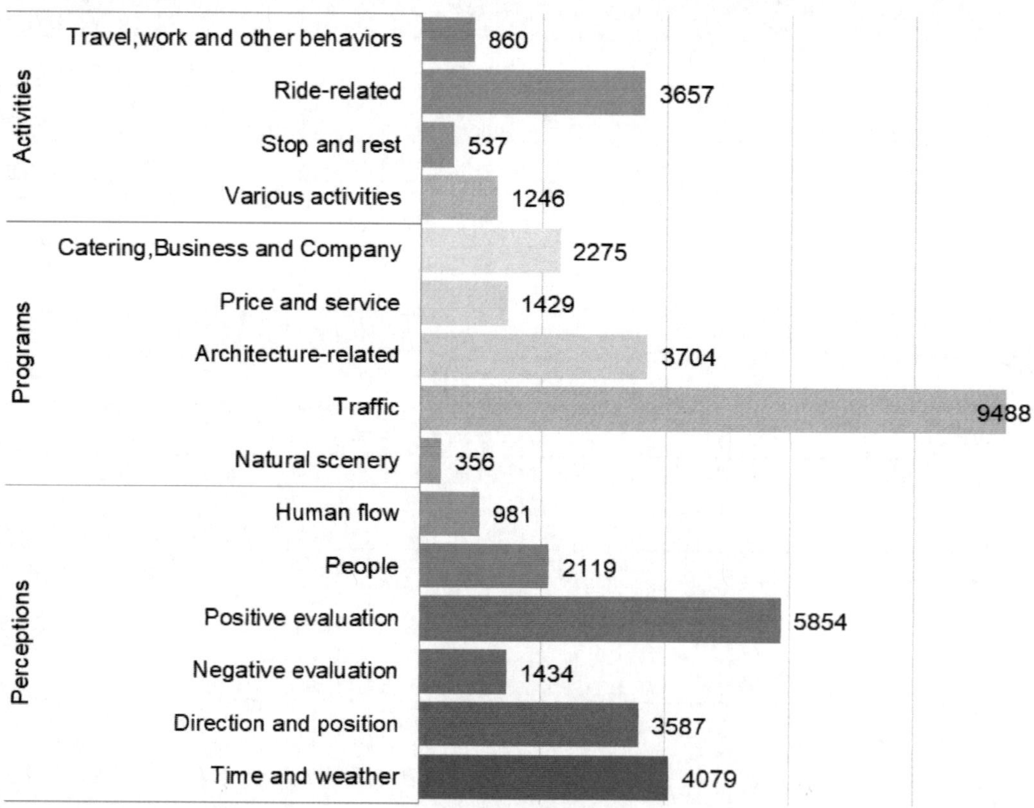

Figure 3: The Overall Word Frequency Analysis of Activities, Programs and Perceptions (2021). Diagram by the authors.

passengers in Hangzhoudong Railway Station. The total frequency of the word "Ride-related" was three times that of "Various activities." The total word frequency of "Stop and rest" was the least used in the behavior category, but there was also a certain amount of data which reflected that passengers participated in "Stop and rest" related behavior activities in the station. However, it was not the key concern of passengers.

When discussing programs, passengers talk a lot about "Catering, business and company," "Architecture" and "Traffic." Among these sub-categories, the proportion of the total word frequency of the three was 2:3:9. Passengers mainly cared about the traffic situation and paid attention to the inside and outside of the station building. The total frequency of the sub-categories"Natural scenery" was the lowest, indicating that passengers rarely talked about the natural environment around Hangzhoudong Railway Station. Passengers did participate in a certain degree of discussion about "Price and service," but this topic subject was not greatly discussed.

For the result and emotion category, "Positive evaluation," "Direction and position," "Time and weather" were the main aspects discussed by passengers, and the proportion of data volume was 6:3.5:4. The word frequency data of "Positive evaluation" was four times that of "Negative evaluation," which indicates that the overall evaluation given by passengers reflected higher praise for the Hangzhoudong Railway Station,rather than the poor evaluation. It can also be seen that the time, weather and the direction of the station were still the factors that people paid more attention to.

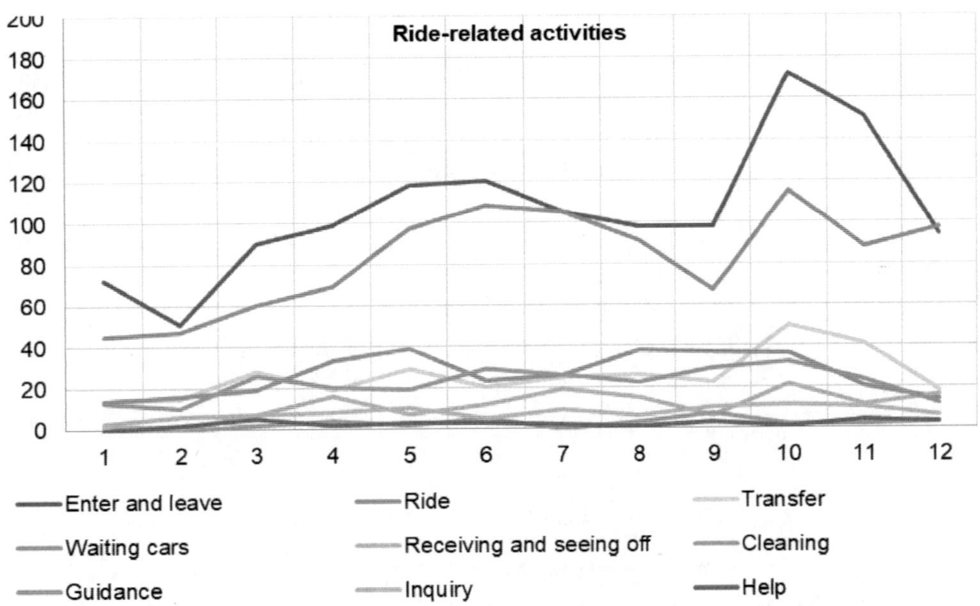

Figure 4: *Monthly Trend Analysis of Ride-related Behavior (2021). Diagram by the authors.*

4.2 Monthly Trend Analysis

By analyzing the monthly trend chart of passengers' specific riding behavior activities (Figure 4), it was found that for passengers,"Enter and leave" and "Ride"were the main subjects of concern. The peaks in these subjects occurred in May, June and October, with an obvious upward trend from February to May and September to October, and a gradual downward trend from June to August and October to December. The reflects that early summer and October are the main travel times for people across cities and provinces. It is speculated that May Day, National Day and the school season in September are

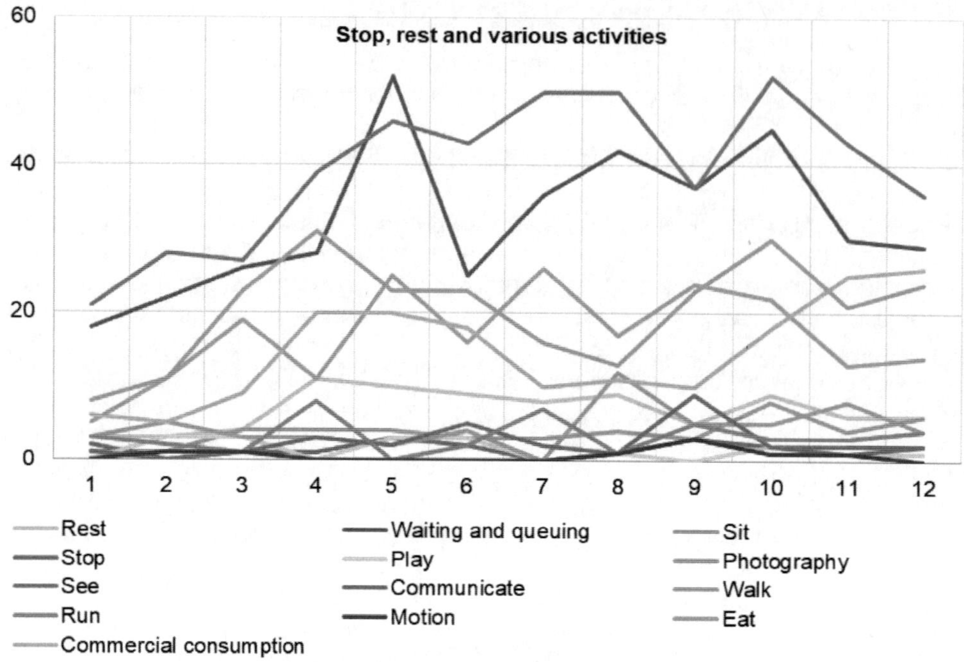

Figure 5: Monthly Trend Analysis of Stop, Rest and Various Activities (2021). Diagram by the authors.

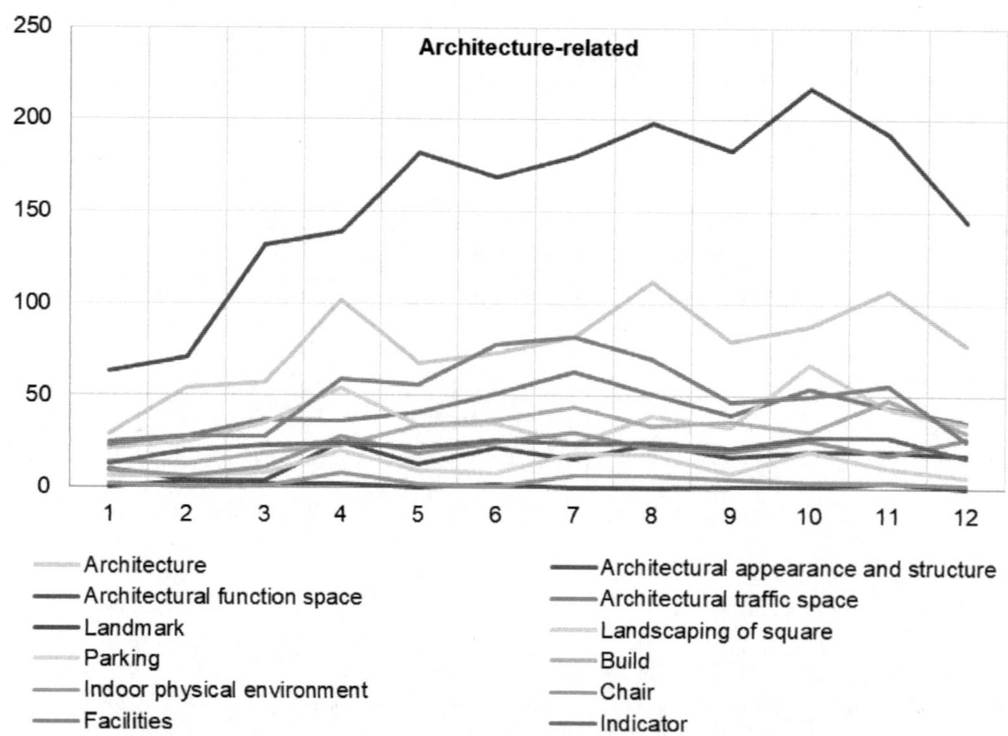

Figure 6: Monthly Trend Analysis of Architecture-related (2021). Diagram by the authors.

important reasons that stimulate an increase in tourists. The monthly trends of "Receiving and seeing off," "Waiting cars," "Transfer," "Guidance," and "Inquiry" were relatively flat and low, and mainly peaked in summer and October.

By analyzing the monthly trend chart of various activities of passengers (Figure 5), it was found that the peak of various activities mainly occurred in May, July, August and October. "Look," "Waiting and queuing," "Commercial consumption," "Walk," and "Eat" were the main activities and behaviors of passengers, which are also greatly affected by months. The overall fluctuation range of other activities was small and there was less available data. The results reflect that the commercial activities in Hangzhoudong Railway Station are more active on May Day, summer and National Day.

"Architectural function space" was the most concerning issue among passengers and shows an upward" Architectural function space" was the most concerning issue among passengers and shows an upward trend as a whole (Figure 6). This subject reached its peak in October and was at the lowest in

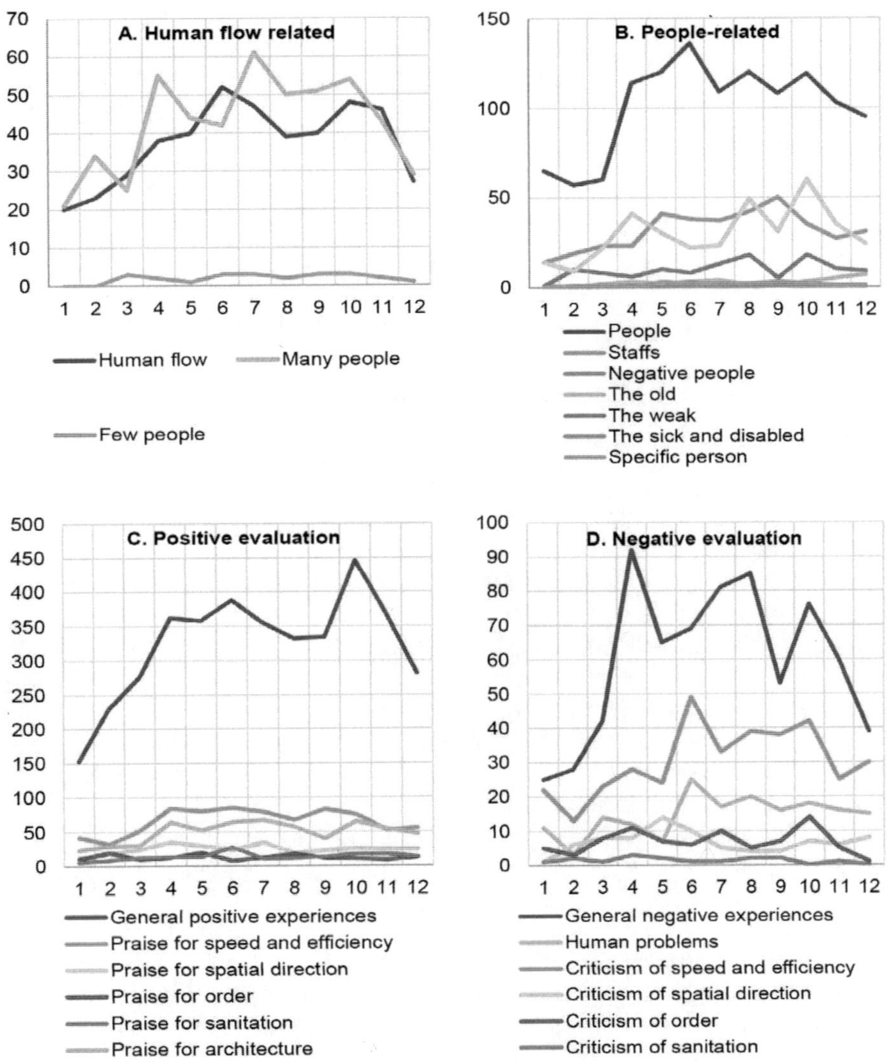

Figure 7: *Monthly Trend Analysis of Human Flow Related (A), People-related (B), Positive Evaluation (C) and Negative Evaluation (2021). Diagram by the authors.*

January. The peak of passengers' attention to "Facilities," "Architectural traffic space" and "Indicator" in the station was in July and October. The peak value of "Landscaping of square " was in April and October, and reached at rough in July. Due to the high outdoor temperature in Hangzhou in summer, people spend less time on the square in summer, mainly in the station. The amount of data related to"Indoor physical environment" and "Landmark" was small, and the monthly trend change during the whole year was low.

As seen from the figure, the peak value occurred mainly in summer and October. The passenger flow was the lowest in January. The monthly trend of "Human flow" was similar to that of "Many people," but it is quite different from that of "Few people," indicating that the overall passenger flow of the Hangzhoudong Railway Station was large, especially in summer and October. The passenger flow in winter was less than that in other seasons, but there were still many people in the Hangzhoudong Railway Station (Figure 7).

From the monthly trend chart of positive and negative evaluation of passengers, the change in the overall curve was not different. The peak occurs in summer and October, and the overall data of positive emotion was higher than that with negative emotion, indicating that people have a better experience of speed efficiency, spatial orientation, order and health in the Hangzhoudong Railway Station. The data for"Praise for speed and efficiency" and "Criticism of speed and efficiency" were higher than other aspects, and they peaked in summer, reflecting the fact that "Speed and efficiency" is still the most concerning factors for transportation hubs, and that attention in summer is higher than that of other seasons. Passengers are less interested in "Sanitation,""Order"and "Spatial direction" (Figure 7).

4.3 Gephi Network Relationship Analysis

In a Gephi graph, the size of each node represents the average weighted degree of these nodes. The larger the node, the higher the average weighting degree, indicating that these nodes are more critical. The edge between nodes indicates the correlation degree of the two nodes. The wider the edge, the higher the surface correlation degree (Figure 8).

1. On the whole, it can be seen that the nodes of "Enter and leave," "Ride," "Tickets and money," "Architectural function space," "Traffic terms," "Transportation hub," "Means of transport," "Travel check-in things," "People," "General positive experiences," "Praise for speed and efficiency," "Direction and position," and "Time" are large, indicating that for the Hangzhoudong Railway Station, people mainly focus on the topics related to riding, the interior of buildings, people and time.
2. The subjects of "Catering and food," "Commerce," "Tickets and price," and "General negative experiences " were not the main factors of concern, but they also showed a certain degree of concern.
3. "Time," "means of transportation," "location" and "positive emotion" were closely related, indicating that time, means of transportation and location are the main factors affecting passengers' positive emotion.
4. "Architectural functional space " had a high degree of connection with "General positive experiences," "Direction and position " and "Time," which reflected the idea that when people use each functional space inside the station building, they mainly pay attention to the location relationship between each space and the time spent in use.
5. The connection degree of "General positive experiences"was greater than that of "General negative experiences,"indicating that passengers had a better spatial experience in the station building.
6. The connection between "Humanflow" and "General positive experiences"was greater than that of"General negative experiences", which reflects that although the passenger flow at the Hangzhoudong Railway Station is large,the overall evaluation is good.
7. The connectivity among"Humanflow," "Many people," "Enter and leave" and "Ride" was strong. It is speculated that the gathering of pedestrian flow mainly occurs in the entering and leaving the station and taking the bus in the station building.
8. The connections between "Humanflow," "Many people," "Time," and "Direction and position" are

high, which reflects that time, architectural space and people's sense of orientation have a great impact on humanflow.

4.4 Gephi Analysis of Ride-Related Behavior Satisfaction

A total of 21 tags related to the three sub-categories of "Ride-related," "Positive evaluation," and "Negative evaluation" were selected for Gephi analysis used to explore the travel-related behavior of passengers in the Hangzhoudong Railway Station. Also included in the evaluation were factors affecting passengers' mood and the correlation between various factors. It can be seen from the figure that (Figure 8):

1. On the whole, the connection between various factors of passengers "Ride-related" and "General positive experiences" was higher than the "General negative experiences," and the passengers' activities in Hangzhoudong Railway Station are in a better mood.
2. The connections between "Enter and leave," "Ride," and "General positive experiences" and "General negative experiences" were the highest. On the surface, the behavior and activities of passengers when entering and leaving the station and taking the bus were the main influencing factors of passengers' emotion.
3. "Waiting cars" and "guidance" were more connected with "General positive experiences" than "Cleaning," "Inquiry" and "Help," which reflects that the passengers in the Hangzhoudong Railway Station are generally in a good mood when waiting for the train. In addition,the staff or identification system in the station gave passengers some help, causing greater positive emotion.
4. The "Cleaning,""Inquiry"and "Help" nodes were small, which indicates that these categories had little impact on passengers' mood.

4.5 Gephi Analysis of Architectural Satisfaction

A total of 24 nodes related to the three sub-categories of "Architecture-related," "Positive evaluation" and "Negative evaluation" were selected for Gephi analysis to explore the satisfaction of passengers inside and outside the building of the Hangzhoudong Railway Station, the factors affecting passengers' mood and the correlation of various factors. As can be seen from the figure (Figure 8):

1. On the whole, the connection between various factors inside the building and "General positive experiences" was higher than "General negative experiences," and the satisfaction of passengers was higher.
2. "Architectural function space" had the highest connection with "General positive experiences" and "General negative experiences."The use of functional space indicates passengers in the building was the main influencing factor on passenger emotion.
3. Compared with "Landmark," "Indoor physical environment," "Chair," and "General positive experiences," the "Facilities" had a higher connection with "General positive experiences,"reflecting that people have a better sense of use of the facilities than other aspects. The facilities in Hangzhou are relatively complete, and can meet most of the needs of passengers.
4. The "Parking" node was small, which reflected that the attention to the parking problem was not high and had little impact on the mood of passengers.
5. The node of "Landscaping of square" was not very large, but passengers paid a certain amount of attention to it.

4.6 Gephi Analysis of Human Flow Related Satisfaction

A total of 23 nodes related to the four sub-categories of "Humanflow," "People," "Positive evaluation" and "Negative evaluation" were selected for Gephi analysis to explore the passenger flow, satisfaction of passenger flow and the correlation of various factors in the Hangzhoudong Railway Station. As can be seen from the figure(Figure 8):

1. On the whole, the nodes of "Human flow,""Many people,""staff," and "Passenger" are large, which

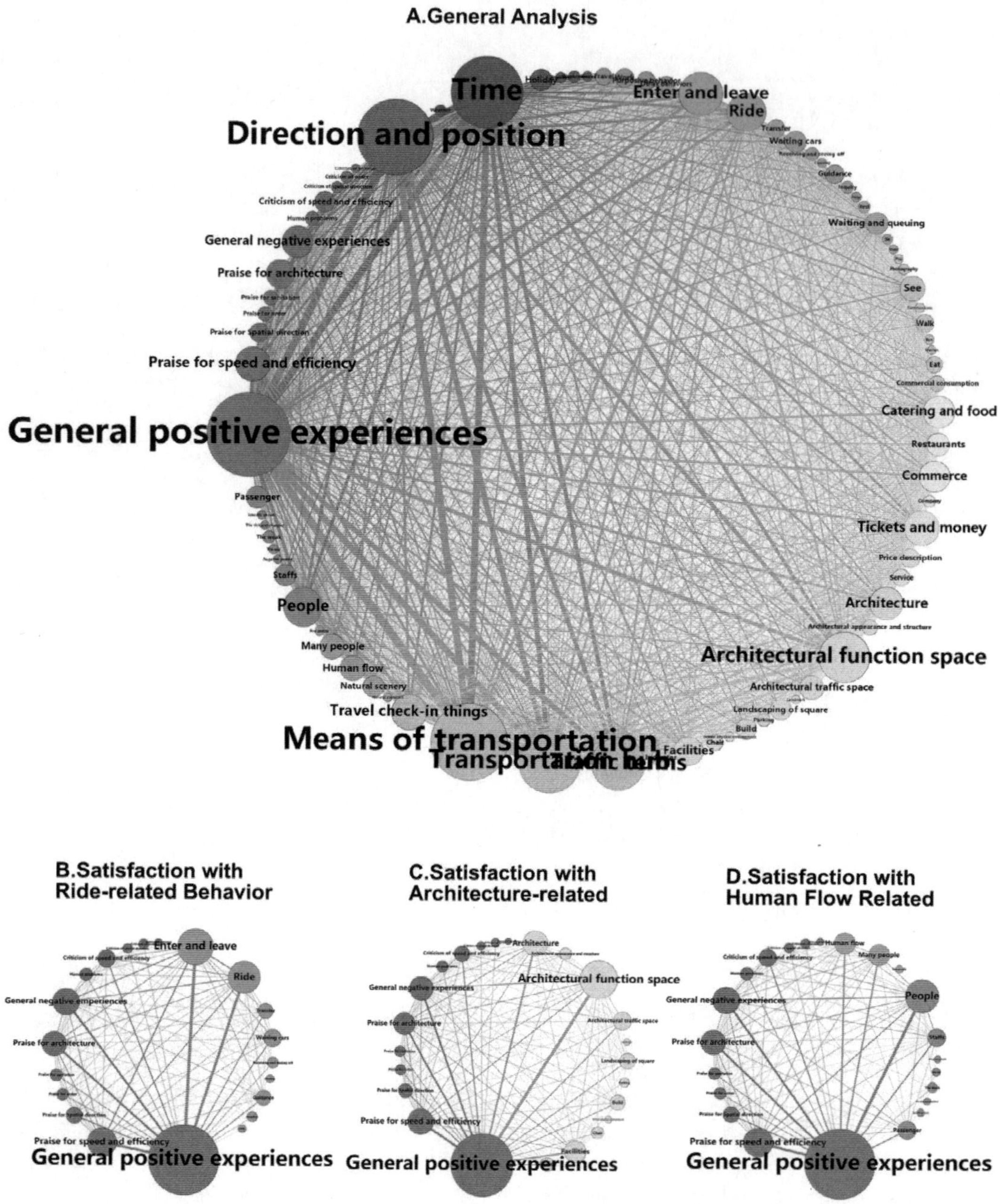

Figure 8: Gephi Visual Analysis of General Analysis (A), Satisfaction with Ride-related Behavior (B), Satisfaction with Architecture-related (C) and Satisfaction with Human Flow Related (2021). Diagram by the authors.

reflects that the passenger flow of Hangzhoudong Railway Station is large, and the main crowd consist of passengers and staff.

2. "The weak" is larger than "The old," "Disability," "Negative people" and other nodes, which reflects that the number of small and medium-sized children of passengers in Hangzhoudong Railway Station is higher than the elderly and disabled. The public security level in the Hangzhoudong Railway Station is good, with few negative people such as thieves.
3. The degree of connection between "Humanflow" and "General positive experiences" at Hang-

zhoudong Railway Station is higher than that of "General negative experiences." Although the surface passenger flow is large, passengers are more satisfied with people flow.

4. "Many people," "Passenger," and "Staffs" have the highest connection with the phrase "Praise for speed and efficiency" and "Criticism of speed and efficiency," The surface passenger flow has a high correlation with the speed and efficiency of passengers' activities in the station.

5. CONCLUSIONS

Passengers are more satisfied with the overall experience of the Hangzhoudong Station. From the results of the above analysis, it seems that passengers' positive emotions are rated higher than negative ones overall, reflecting their general satisfaction with the Hangzhoudong Station. The research shows that the design of the Hangzhoudong Station meets passengers' needs in many aspects to a great extent and brings them a better experience.

The influence of holidays on passenger flow is great, and the overall satisfaction of passengers is higher during holidays. From the results of monthly analysis of different factors, it seems that certain months and holidays have a great influence on each factor, and the positive sentiment of passengers is higher during holiday periods than other periods. Holidays such as May Day, September school season, and National Day stimulate people to travel across provinces and cities.

Passengers are more inclined to perform various activities in the station rather than resting."See," "Walk," "Eat," "Commercial consumption."The categories of "See," "Walk," "Eating" and "Commercial consumption" were mentioned more than "Sit," "Rest," and "Stop." This indicates that people are more willing to walk around, visit, eat and shop than to do static activities. This results show that the design of public activity space needs more attention from designers than just a large waiting space in the station.

Passengers are still concerned about waiting for trains: the nodes of "Waiting cars"are large, reflecting that the passenger flow pattern of Hangzhoudong Station still consists mainly of "Waiting(Chen J. H., Liu J. N., & Xie, Y. H., 2019)." This issue demonstrates the high necessity for waiting space and station building scale. This is in line with the current situation that Hangzhoudong Station has a large waiting area, and the setting of the station's commercial sections provides entertainment for the people waiting for trains. This is in line with the fact that Hangzhoudong Station has a large waiting area, and the commercial facilities in the station provide entertainment for people waiting for trains.

The functional space of the station is the main space for human perception, and passengers are more satisfied with it. For example, the functional space of the lobby, waiting hall, and rest area was the main object of passengers' attention compared with the building exterior decoration, traffic space, indoor facilities, physical environment and station square. The functional space had the highest emotional influence on passengers compared with others, reflecting the relationship between the functional space and people's sense of experience more closely. From the analysis results, it seems that people have a better sense of using the internal space of Hangzhoudong Station, and the good functional space design of the station building increases the satisfaction of users.

"Speed and efficiency" is an important factor influencing passengers' emotion, which brings positive emotion to passengers. Overall, "Speed and efficiency" was more important than "Order," "Spatial direction." The "Speed and efficiency" of Hangzhoudong Railway Station gave passengers a better experience than "Order," "Spatial direction," "Sanitation," etc. For high-speed railway stations, the flow organization inside the station building can directly affect passengers' experience of smoothness in the space, such as how efficient passengers feel in the transfer space,and how fast they can leave the station.

Gatherings of people are easy to happen when entering and leaving the station and taking the train. Entering and leaving the station and taking the train are the main behaviors of passengers and the main activities that produce the feeling of congestion. This indicates that the design optimization for the space where people enter and leave the station can improve the congestion of people to a certain extent.

6. DISCUSSION

This research is based on the research and discussion of TOD in China based on the big data technology in social media, and has certain theoretical reference value for designers in related fields. This research method examines breakthroughs of limitations of quantity, time and space, demonstrates the passenger experience in high-speed rail stations in a more efficient and systematic way, reflects the evaluation of the use of personnel in high-speed railway stations, and provides designers with design thinking and strategy.

6.1 Advantages and Limitations of Research

Based on passenger comments under social media, this study creates a research system of passenger experiences, which provides a new way to study large-scale railway comprehensive transportation hubs. This research method has the following advantages:

1. By obtaining user comments on social media, as opposed to the limitations of data volume, time and space for traditional data acquisition methods, researcher scan obtain massive, rich types of data with complex structures across large time spans. The effective information in the data provides great value for the research in the field of TOD.
2. The big data analysis method makes the fuzzy and generalized passenger behavior in the high-speed railway station quantitative and analyzable. The evaluation system for a large-scale railway comprehensive transportation hub based on this data is more objective and reasonable.
3. This research system can influence and change the way researchers think about architecture. Through it, we can obtain the category relationship, time period relationship and causality between different factors.

However, this study has some limitations. Because the users of social media are mainly middle-aged and young people, children and the elderly don't provide comments, and the age distribution of the data is uneven. In the process of establishing conclusions, there are some problems, such as some words contain multiple meanings and the specific related objects of adjectives are unknown, which requires researchers to add subjective judgment in the process of classification, and then affect the follow-up research. With the combination and development of big data technology and Tod, future research will further make up for the above shortcomings and form a more perfect research system.

7. REFERENCES

Chen J. H., Liu J. N., & Xie,Y. H.(2019).The Basic Pedestrian Mode of High-speed Railway Station in China. *Huazhong Architecture,37*(04),5-8.

Chen, M.,Zhang, Y.,&Li, X. F.(2013).Current status and prospects of big data applications. *Journal of Computer Research and Development,50*(S2),216-233.

Klaus, C. A.,& Aksel,E.(2019).Understanding urban infrastructure via big data: the case of Belo Horizonte. Regional Studies, *Regional Science,6*(1),374-379. https://doi.org/10.1080/21681376.2019.1623068

Li, C. (2018). Creative Design Practice of Modern Railway Transportation Hub. *Architecture Technique*, (09), 20-35.

Li, C.,&Wang,L.(2015). Hangzhou East Railway Station, China. *Urbanism and Architecture, 13*, 56-63.

Li, C.Qi, G.,& Yuan, P. (2009). Hangzhou East Railway Station Architectural Creation. *Railway Economics Research*, (06), 15-21.

Li, C. Qi, G.,& Yuan, P. (2010).Hangzhou East Railway Station, China. *Urbanism and Architecture*, (04), 66-69.

Li, H. X.,& Wu, W. W.(2020). The Application of Big Data in the Evaluation of Tourism Resources of Landscape Architecture. *Journal of Anyang Normal University*,(05),72-75.

Li,J.X.,& Guo,S. W. (2019). *The integrated development of high-speed rail stations and surrounding areas from the perspective of TOD: taking Chengdu East Railway Station, Chengdu South Railway Station, and Chengdu Railway Station as examples.*(eds.)Planning the Southwest • New Image-Proceedings of

the Forum of the Southwest Regional Planning Institute in 2019, (pp.171-176).
Liu,C.,Mo,F.,Xi,Y.,& Zhang,Y.N.(2012). Integration of Station and City to Promote Development: Design Practice of Yizhuang Rail Micro Center. *Beijing Planning Review*,(04),65-70.
Liu,J.S. (2015).Preliminary Exploration of Design for High Speed Rail Station Area in TOD Model. *Huazhong Architecture,33*(06),121-125.
Luo,J. Zhao,P.J., & Liu,Y.S.(2019). Evaluation of Tod Planning Based On Residents' Activities—Taking Beijing As An Example. *Architectural Practice*,(09),158-169.
Patrick, M., & Jisoo,S.(2019). Understanding an Urban Park through Big Data. *Environmental Research and Public Health,16*(20), 3-16. https://doi.org/10.3390/ijerph16203816
Ross, B., Neuberger, C.,Mirbabaie, M., &Stieglitz, S.(2018). Social media analytics-challenges in topic discovery, data collection, and data preparation. *International Journal of Information Management,39*, 156-168. https://doi.org/10.1016/j.ijinfomgt.2017.12.002
Ryong,L., Kazutoshi S.,& Shoko W. (2013). Urban area characterization based on crowd behavioral life logs over Twitter.*Personal and Ubiquitous Computing, 17*, 605–620.https://doi.org/10.1007/s00779-012-0510-9
Wang, D. Y., Hu,G.,Wang,L. X.,& Hu, S. Q. (2021)Tourist Experience of Hangzhou Osmanthus fragrans Landscape Based on Social Media Big Data Analysis. *Landscape Architecture,38*(09), 84-92.
Wang, H.L.,Shen, Y. X.,& Wu,Z.N.(2019). Assessing Urban Areas' Vulnerability to Flood Disaster Based on Text Data: A Case Study in Zhengzhou City. *Sustainability, 11*(17), 45-48. https://doi.org/10.3390/su11174548
Xiao, W. (2019). Changes in architectural design under the background of big data. *Electronic Technology & Software Engineering*, (04), 154.
Zhang, B.,& Song, Y. (2020). Using social media data in understanding site-scale landscape architecture design: taking Seattle Freeway Park as an example. *Landscape Research, 45*(2), 627-648. https://doi.org/10.1080/01426397.2020.1736994
Zhang,Q. Q.,& Liu,X. X. (2019).Research on BIM Development Trend Based on Architectural Design under the Background of Big Data. *Architecture & Culture*,(11),196-197.
Zhao, J. N., YueW. J., Peng, Y. Y., & Wang,Z. F. (2019). Comparative Evaluation of Guangzhou City Parks: Text Analysis Based on Social Media Data. *Landscape Architecture,26*(8), 89-94.
Zoé, A. H., Spencer, A. W., Marie, L.D., Bonnie, L.K., Timon, M.,& David, M. F.(2018). Using social media to understand drivers of urban park visitation in the Twin Cities, MN. *Landscape and Urban Planning,175*, 1-10. https://doi.org/10.1016/j.landurbplan.2018.02.006

8. FIGURES

Figure 1. Photos of the Hangzhoudong Railway Station. Photos by CSADI.
Figure 2. Research Flow Chart (2021). Diagram by the authors. Table 1. Data Level Classification (2021). Diagram by the authors. Table 2. Examples of Label Coding and Data Inclusion (2021). Diagram by the authors.
Figure 3. The Overall Word Frequency Analysis of Activities, Programs and Perceptions (2021). Diagram by the authors.
Figure 4. Monthly Trend Analysis of Ride-related Behavior (2021). Diagram by the authors.
Figure 5. Monthly Trend Analysis of Stop, Rest and Various Activities (2021). Diagram by the authors.
Figure 6. Monthly Trend Analysis of Architecture-related (2021). Diagram by the authors.
Figure 7. Monthly Trend Analysis of Human Flow Related (A), People-related (B), Positive Evaluation (C) and Negative Evaluation (2021). Diagram by the authors.
Figure 8. Gephi Visual Analysis of General Analysis (A),Satisfaction with Ride-related Behavior (B), Satisfaction with Architecture-related (C) and Satisfaction with Human Flow Related (2021). Diagram by the authors.

Modular Deployable Bamboo Structures: Enabling User Participation to Self-Design and Build in Developing Countries

Anastasia Maurina (Clemson University); *Vincent Blouin* (ASHREA)

ABSTRACT

Post-disaster reconstruction requires rapid building on a large scale. The prefabrication approach is often used to fulfill these requirements while maintaining quality. Most of the time, this approach is used to generate uniform designs that lack flexibility to adapt to various users' desires and needs. In developing countries, resources, i.e., modern construction materials, advanced fabrication tools, and skilled labor, are usually limited and even sometimes inexistent. Local materials and adapted technologies are generally preferred so laypeople can participate or even lead the reconstruction process. This paper focuses on the study of modular deployable structures using bamboo as a local material. A typical deployable bamboo structure consists of multiple modules made of bamboo poles connected to each other to form scissor-like elements (S.L.E.s) and referred to as S.L.E. units. Multiple structural modules are arranged to form the entire building structure and create numerous forms varying in size and shape. Several types of S.L.E. units are considered in this research to investigate their impact on various measures such as structural performance, design flexibility, and constructability. This paper describes the result of user participatory experiments in designing and constructing a pavilion using modular deployable bamboo structures. Two groups, i.e., one group of experts and one group of laypeople, were involved in the experiments to evaluate the ability of laypeople to design, fabricate, and install modular deployable bamboo structures and identify which type of S.L.E. unit induces the highest chance of success. The results show that modified modular deployable bamboo structures provide better design flexibility than the typical ones and perform in constructability. Through this study, the laypeople can perform their design-and-build ability with additional aids from researchers/experts. However, using the MDB structures is very potential to enable laypeople to self-design and build.

KEYWORDS

Bamboo; Deployable Structures, user participation, self-design and build

1. INTRODUCTION

Post-disaster reconstruction requires rapid building on a large scale. The prefabrication approach is often used to fulfill these requirements while maintaining quality. This approach mostly generates uniform designs that lack design flexibility to adapt to various users' desires and needs. A modular approach is one of strategies that can provide a means for the standardization of repetitive components (Piroozfar & Piller, 2013, p. 34) that can be configured into a wide variety of end products (Farr, 2013, p. 56). Moreover, The modular approach's advantage promotes the users' emancipatory role as a co-designer, co-planner, or co-creator that determines the end product, not the designer as usual (Farr, 2013, p. 57; Piroozfar & Piller, 2013, p. 4). Besides the modular approach, deployable structures can be another strategy for achieving more variety with a single module (Maurina & Prastyatama, 2018) because it has geometric and spatial transformability. Combining a modular approach and a deployable structure, referred to as a modular deployable structure, will boost flexibility by configuring each module and arranging or organizing some modules. Design flexibility has an advantage deal with uncertainty, such as in post-disaster reconstruction.

In developing countries, resources, i.e., modern construction materials, advanced fabrication tools, and skilled labor, are usually limited and sometimes nonexistent. Thus, the heavy and large-scale prefabrication approach, generally encountered in developed countries, is hard to be adopted in developing countries, specifically in a post-disaster situation. However, prefabrication is "not exclusively based on high technology approaches but is, in fact, appropriate and advantageous to low-income communities and self-help builders." (Davidson et al., 2008, p. 13). The light and small-scale prefabrication approach is preferred as a part of the 'appropriate technology' movement, geared to locally available resources, skills, and needs. The approach not only reduces the construction cost but can also generate employment opportunities, utilize low-skilled labor, and exploit local resources (Stallen et al., 1994, pp. 13–14). Local materials, easily accessible tools, and indigenous construction methods are generally preferable (Anonymous, 2014; Wagemann, 2015) so laypeople can participate in or even lead the reconstruction process. Bamboo is a potential material particularly adapted to modular deployable structures because of its lightweight, exceptional mechanical properties, and local availability, especially in tropical areas of many developing countries. For example, a modular deployable bamboo structure, developed by Maurina and Prastyatama (2020; 2017), can create various shapes and dimensions by configuring within the expandable module and arranging them, as shown in Figure 1 (top). Two community projects (a shelter and a kindergarten),

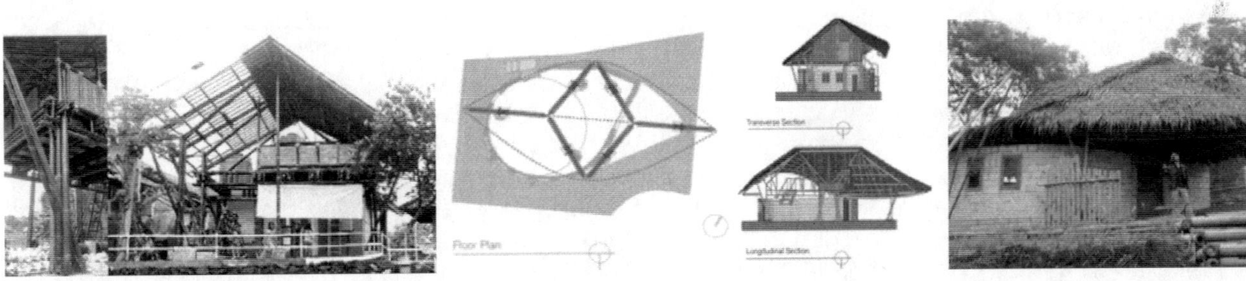

Figure 1: Modular deployable bamboo structure (top); two built projects: a community center in 2017 (left); and a kindergarten in 2019 (right) (2017,2019). Photos by the author.

shown in Figure 1 (bottom left and right), were built with very different forms using the same deployable bamboo structural module. Interestingly, those projects involved the users (laypeople) in the design and construction processes.

This paper is a part of the ongoing study on the structural morphology of modular deployable bamboo structures to achieve design flexibility and constructability. A typical deployable bamboo structure consists of multiple modules made of bamboo poles connected to form scissor-like elements (S.L.E.s). Multiple structural modules are arranged to form the entire building structure and create numerous forms varying in size and shape. This ability to generate various end products is referred to as design flexibility. This paper focuses on testing whether applying modular deployable bamboo structures enables laypeople to participate in the design and construction.

2. DEPLOYABLE BAMBOO STRUCTURES

Deployable structures can transform their shape from a compact configuration to a predetermined configuration (Gantes et al., 1994). One of the most popular deployable structural mechanisms, known as the scissor-like element (SLE) unit, and referred to in this paper as the regular SLE unit (r-SLE),

a) Regular SLE (r-SLE) unit composed of 2 bars and joined by pin connection

b) Modified 1 SLE (m1-SLE) unit composed of 2 bars and joined by a translatable pin connection

c) Modified 2 SLE (m2-SLE) unit composed of 4 bars and joined by a pin connection

Figure 2: Regular SLE (r-SLE), modified 1 SLE (m1-SLE), and modified 2 SLE (m2-SLE) (2021) Illustrated by the author.

is composed of two bars and joined with an intermediate pin connection (De Temmerman & Mira, 2011). The location of the pin connection can differentiate the SLE unit: translational unit (center pin) and polar unit (off-center pin) (Mira et al., 2014). The transformability of this structure provides three remarkable advantages: standardized fabrication, ease of transportation (light and compact), and ease of installation (speed and ease of erection and dismantling) (De Temmerman & Mira, 2011; Mira et al., 2014; Ramos-Jaime & Sánchez-Sánchez, 2019). As a result, skilled laborers are typically not required (Koumar et al., 2017). However, this r-SLE deployable structure cannot offer form flexibility as it can deploy into only one configuration (Brancart et al., 2014; Korkmaz et al., 2012). A flexible structure is expected to have the ability to transform into several predetermined configurations, thus offering form flexibility (Akgün et al., 2007). As shown in Figure 2, there are two modifications of the regular SLE unit (r-SLE) to increase the design flexibility: (1) using a translatable pin connection, referred to as modified 1 SLE (m1-SLE); and (2) using four smaller bars with a pin connection, referred to as modified 2 SLE (m2-SLE). Adding modified SLE units increases the complexity of the design and construction of the modular deployable bamboo structure, leading to decrease constructability. This problem goes against the goal of using deployable structures for vulnerable communities. Thus, the trade-off between flexibility and constructability should be evaluated carefully, specifically regarding the user's experience.

3. PARTICIPATORY DESIGN

A new approach in several Scandinavian countries, known as Scandinavian Participatory Design, involved end-users in the design process even as co-designers (Gregory, 2003); then, this approach was officially introduced at the Design Research Society in 1971 (Lee, 2008). Now, it is also popular as cooperative design or co-design (Sanders & Stappers, 2008). In this approach, users are a critical component in design decision-making (Mirzaean Mahabadi et al., 2014). Based on Hill (2003), Lee (2007), and Vogel (2021), there are three different user participation levels in the design process: design for user/user-centered design, design with users/ co-design, and design by users/ user-generated design (least to most user involvement consecutively). The third level, design by users/ user-generated design, is the goal of developing MDB structures. Users are taught design basics by designers/ social workers in non-government organizations (NGOs). They are given access to tools and resources to create design solutions by themselves (Lee, 2007; Vogel, 2021). Thus, in addition to generating a design aligned with users' needs and desires, actively involving users aims to transfer skills and empower users to create design solutions

(Hussain et al., 2012; Vogel, 2021). Designers or researchers should produce design process tools to allow users to design their own without expert intervention.

The development of methods, tools, and techniques is crucial to involve and transform users in creating products successfully. Every project is unique, and it is necessary to develop method(s), tool(s), and technique(s) according to their form, purpose, and contexts (Sanders et al., 2010). There are three common methods developed for design for users: interview, focus group, and observation (Ulrich, 2003) and Sanders et al. (2010) listed some tools and techniques for design with or by users: (1) making tangible things (2D collage, 2D mapping, and 3D mock-ups), (2) talking, telling, and explaining (stories and storyboarding, diaries, and cards), and (3) acting, enacting, and playing (game boards, pieces, and rules; props and black boxes; participatory envisioning and enactment; improvisation; and acting out, skits, and play-acting). The higher the level of user involvement in making design decisions, the deeper the knowledge that should be transferred through a set of methods. The inappropriate methods, tools, and techniques lead to failures, e.g., a limitation in innovativeness, which is not a failure of the concept of user involvement per se (Holmlid, 2012).

4. RESEARCH OBJECTIVES

Developing modular deployable bamboo structures aims to have a prefabricated-able structure that provides design flexibility and enables laypeople to self-design and self-build. Several modifications from the typical deployable structure composed of scissors-like elements (S.L.E.) are applied to increase the flexibility of deployable structures. However, it has not been thoroughly studied. Increasing flexibility in deployable should be followed by ease of construction, referred to as constructability. The previous experimental research using a mixed-method between computational modeling and physical prototyping (Maurina & Blouin, 2021) compared the flexibility and constructability of typical deployable bamboo structures and several modified deployable bamboo structures. The study stated that modified modular deployable bamboo structures significantly improve design flexibility with a reasonably slight loss in constructability compared to the typical ones. Then, this study's objective is to explore the validity of the previous study's results through user participatory experiments. The research question is whether laypeople users can self-design and self-build applying the modular deployable bamboo structures under particular guidelines.

5. METHODS

This user-participatory experiment has the type of user and modular deployable bamboo structures, referred to as MDB structures, as independent variables and performances of design flexibility and constructability as dependent variables. There are two design flexibility measures related to users' experiences: arrangeability (the user's ability to arrange structural modules in various formal organizations)

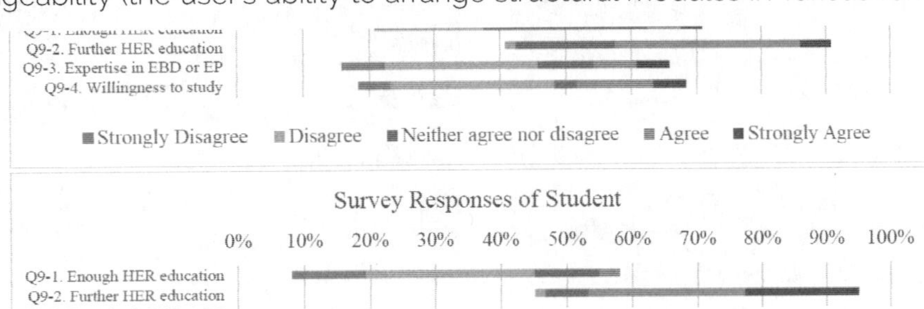

Figure 3: Regular MDB structure (left) and modified MDB structure (right) (2021). Illustrated by the author.

and configurability (the user's ability to configure a structural module in various spans and shapes). While constructability is measured by fabricability (the user's ability to fabricate a structural module), transportability (the user's ability to carry and deploy easily), and installability (the user's ability to install the predetermined configuration of structural modules)

This experiment involved two groups of users: the skilled people, people with a background related to architectural design (as a control group), and the laypeople, people without that background (as a treatment group). Each group tested two types of MDB structures: a typical/ regular MDB structure, composed of multiple regular SLEs (as a control/reference case), and a modified MDB structure, composed of a combination of regular and modified SLEs (as a treatment case) – the modified case is determined by the previous study (Maurina & Blouin, 2021), as shown in Figure 2.

There were three sections of the user-participatory experiment: design workshop, construction workshop, and post-workshop survey and interview. The design workshop had a group of two skilled people and a group of two laypeople. Each group was asked to provide two pavilion design alternatives using each type of MDB structure. Each group got one set of 3D printed MDB structural modules for each MDB structure's type. They were asked to design by configuring and organizing the modules. The expected products of this design workshop were pictures of scaled models, dimensions of the proposed modules, and drawings (if applicable). The whole procedure and duration will be observed. The participant of the construction workshop was the same as the design workshop's participants, aiming to evaluate performances: flexibility and constructability. They fabricated and installed a structural module of two selected alternative designs. As the design workshop, the whole procedure and duration were observed. After each workshop, the participants filled the survey and were interviewed. The survey is designed using Analytic Hierarchy Process (A.H.P.) techniques. This survey aims to get the preference of MDB structure based on flexibility and constructability performances from the user experiences. The survey will use AHP-OS (Goepel, 2018).

6. RESULTS AND DISCUSSION

6.1 Self-Design

Making tangible things, 3D mock-up, help laypeople to imagine the design instead of 2d drawing. Thus, 3D scaled structural models are the provided primary design tools. The design kit comprises 3D printed scaled model structural modules (shown in Figure 4), additional structural elements (pedestals and rafters), and needed tools. Three human figurines (standing, sitting on a chair, and sitting on the ground) were provided as a scale to the model. Besides the design kit, the researcher provided some information about MDB structural concept, objectives, examples, and design guidelines. A particular design

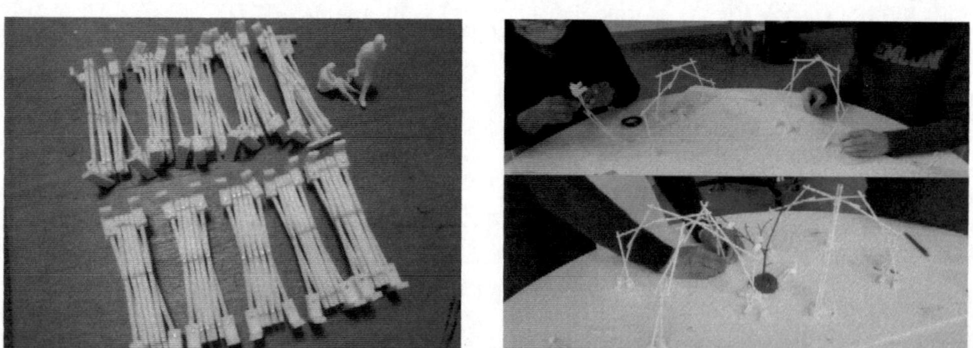

Figure 4: 3D printed scaled models (left), configuring the module (top-right), and arranging the modules (bottom-right). (2021). Photos by the author.

Table 1: The results from the design workshop

Type of MDB	Type of Users	
	Experts Group (Control Group)	Laypeople Group (Treatment Group)
Regular (Reference Case)		
Modified (Treatment Case)		

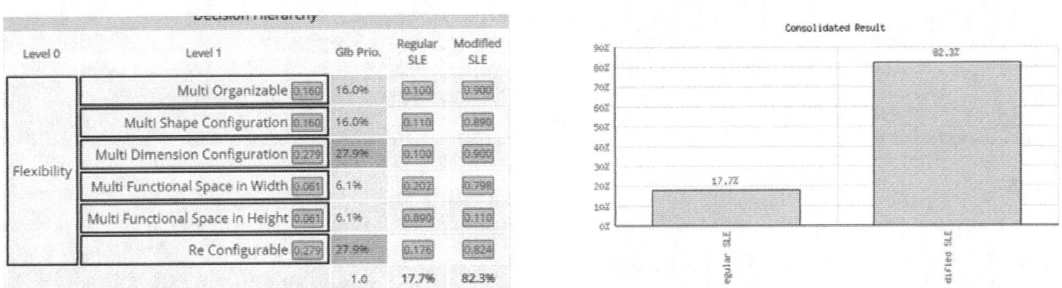

Figure 5: Post-design workshop survey

task is also provided. The design guidelines included three steps, as shown in Figure 4, that is (1) configuring each structural module (defining the span dan the shape of its module), (2) arranging modules in a particular formal organization (linear, centralized, cantilever, or combined), and (3) connecting all modules as a complete building structure using rafters in a certain distance (3-meter maximum).

Based on the design workshop results, as shown in Table 1, both groups of users demonstrated their ability to arrange the modules into different organizations, i.e., linear, centralized, and cantilever. However, one of the laypeople group's results has unclear organization. In terms of configurability, both groups can generate a design that has modules with different spans, although all modules' shapes are symmetrical. Using the modified MDB structure, the participant created more variant designs that cannot be created using the regular MDB structure, such as an inverted configuration (upside down) created by the experts' group and a cantilever configuration created by the laypeople group. The laypeople group also needed a longer time in the design process than the experts' group. However, both groups took a long time to generate their first design, and the duration of the design reduced consecutively until the fourth design alternative. Both groups performed four design alternatives within two hours. Conclusively, the current method has been performed to equip laypeople in designing a structure using MDB struc-

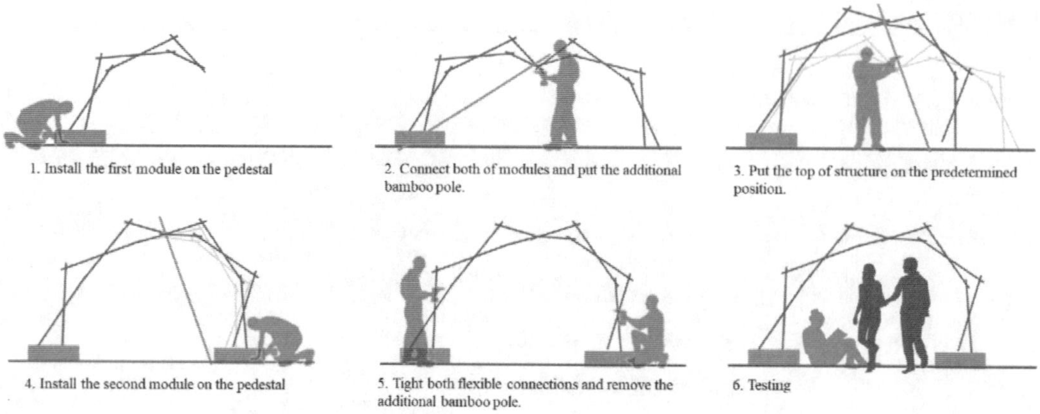

Figure 6 (above): The installation's illustration
Figure 7 (below): The process in Construction Workshop
Measuring (a), Coding (b), Drilling (c), Clamping (d), Assembling (e), Footing (f), Installing (g), Setting the translatable pin connection (h), a cantilever configuration (the prototype vs. the digital model) (i), and the inverted configuration (the prototype vs. the digital model) (j)

tures.

Through the post-workshop survey, the users acknowledged that the modified MDB structures perform more flexibly than the regular MDB (the difference score is 0.64/1.00), as shown in Figure 5. Based on Maurina and Blouin (2021), the modified MDB structures also significantly improve design flexibility (0.7/1.0). Both results respond to each other. Nevertheless, the flexibility also leads to a more complex design process for laypeople.

In conclusion, through the developed design tools, the laypeople perform the self-design ability in terms of arrangeability and configurability. However, more profound design knowledge is needed to be explained and transferred to avoid a misleading design that leads to failure of the concept. More examples are helped their ability to design.

6.2 Self-Built

One modified MDB structural module has been tested to be fabricated and installed in two configurations, resulting from the design workshop: the cantilever and the inverted configuration, as shown in Figure 7. The tool developed for the construction process is a set of construction guidelines for fabrication, transportability, and installation with some illustrations. The design workshop's participants were involved in the construction workshop, and all participants have no background in construction.

Based on the observation, the participants were able to fabricate, transport, and install the modules, as shown in Figure 7. Training is needed, specifically drilling. They were a quiet struggle in assembling the modules: positioning each bar in the module (vertically and horizontally). In terms of duration, the measuring, codding, drilling, and clamping processes took 60 minutes, while the assembling process took 20 minutes. Installing the first configuration needed 50 minutes with footing installations. However, they installed the second configuration. It took 10 minutes to re-setup the translatable pin connections and join two half-modules.

The post-workshop survey was used to quantify the user experience of the constructability of the MDB structure. Based on the user experience, the most challenging processes are assembling the module (66.7%) and installing the predetermined configuration (66.7%). Besides those challenges, they thought that the MDB structure was still constructible.

In conclusion, the laypeople can perform their ability to construct a module with some assistance from the researcher. Structured training and more detailed construction must be developed to reach a self-build goal without expert intervention. Some short movie clips will be helped their ability to understand the detail of each construction process.

7. CONCLUSION

User participatory design and construction workshops are advantageous to evaluate the user's ability to self-design and build. These hands-on workshops are helpful to review the tools for transferring the design knowledge from the experts to the laypeople. Post-workshop surveys and interviews are the critical part of gaining the user's insight.

Conclusively, this study strengthens the previous study that modified MDB structures significantly improve design flexibility compared to the typical ones. Modified MDB structures performed in constructability. Furthermore, using the MDB structures enables laypeople to self-design and build. Making tangible things is a beneficial means to help laypeople. However, it should be followed with a detailed explanation to allow the users to design and build without any aid from experts. The research can be expanded by involving more users and more advanced tools, applying them in actual situations.

Laypeople or NGOs can use this finding to build their facilities according to their specific desires and needs without expert intervention, specifically in post-disaster reconstruction. The designer can use this finding to further develop the modular deployable structures to meet other architectural or structural requirements. Modular deployable bamboo structures also promote the use of local materials to support sustainable development goals.

8. ACKNOWLEDGEMENT

The authors gratefully acknowledge the volunteer students who participated in the pilot study of this research at Clemson University, DIKTI-funded Fulbright Grants for Indonesia Lecturer, AAUW International Doctoral Fellowship, P.E.O. International Peace Scholarship (IPS), and Universitas Katolik Parahyangan for funding this research.

9. REFERENCES

Akgün, Y., Haase, W., & Sobek, W. (2007). Proposal for a new scissor-hinge structure to create transformable and adaptive roofs. *Proceedings IASS 2007 (International Association of Spatial Structures) Symposium.*

Anonymous. (2014, February 25). *Transitional shelter guidelines* [Text]. Humanitarian Library. https://www.humanitarianlibrary.org/resource/transitional-shelter-guidelines-2

Brancart, S., De Laet, L., Vergauwen, A., & De Temmerman, N. (2014). *Transformable active bending: A kinematical concept.* 171–182. https://doi.org/10.2495/MAR140141

Davidson, C., Lizarralde, G., & Johnson, C. (2008). Myths and Realities of Prefabrication for Post-Disaster Reconstruction. 4th International i-Rec Conference 2008-*Building resilience: Achieving effective post-disaster reconstruction.* Christchurch, New Zealand.

De Temmerman, N., & Mira, L. A. (2011). Development of a sustainable construction system for temporary structures. *WIT Transactions on Ecology and the Environment*, 150, 285–296.

Farr, E. R. (2013). Spatial mass customization: Mass-customizable urban spaces and spatial entities. In *Mass Customization and Personalization in Architecture and Construction* (pp. 77–88). Routledge.

Gantes, C., Connor, J. J., & Logcher, R. D. (1994). A systematic design methodology for deployable structures. *International Journal of Space Structures, 9*(2), 67–86.

Goepel, K. D. (2018). Implementation of an Online Software Tool for the Analytic Hierarchy Process (AHP-OS). *International Journal of the Analytic Hierarchy Process, 10*(3), Article 3. https://doi.org/10.13033/ijahp.v10i3.590

Gregory, J. (2003). Scandinavian approaches to participatory design. *International Journal of Engineering Education, 19*(1), 62–74.

Hill, J. (2003). *Actions of architecture: Architects and creative users.* Routledge.

Holmlid, S. (2012). Participative; co-operative; emancipatory: From participatory design to service design. Conference Proceedings ServDes. 2009; *DeThinking Service; ReThinking Design;* Oslo Norway 24-26 November 2009, 059, 105–118.

Hussain, S., Sanders, E. B.-N., & Steinert, M. (2012). Participatory design with marginalized people in developing countries: Challenges and opportunities experienced in a field study in Cambodia. *International Journal of Design, 6*(2).

Korkmaz, K., Akgün, Y., & Maden, F. (2012). Design of a 2-DOF 8R Linkage for Transformable Hypar Structure. *Mechanics Based Design of Structures and Machines, 40*(1), 19–32. https://doi.org/10.1080/15397734.2011.590775

Koumar, A., Tysmans, T., Filomeno Coelho, R., & De Temmerman, N. (2017). An automated structural optimization methodology for scissor structures using a genetic algorithm. *Applied Computational Intelligence and Soft Computing*, 2017.

Lee, Y. (2007). *Design participation tactics: Involving people in the design of their built environment.*

Lee, Y. (2008). Design participation tactics: The challenges and new roles for designers in the co-design process. *Co-Design, 4*(1), 31–50.

Maurina, A., & Blouin, V., (2021). Flexibility and constructability of modular deployable structures. *Proceedings of The 8th International Conference on Architecture and Built Environment with Architecture Awards S.Arch 2021*.

Maurina, A., & Prastyatama, B. (2018). *Bamboo Deployable Structural Systems: An Exploration Study in Responding to Rapid Alteration Challenges*. 56–64. https://doi.org/10.2991/senvar-18.2019.10

Maurina, A., & Prastyatama, B. (2017). *BUMI AWI KABULA KABALE: A PROPOSAL TO ALTER THE FATE OF MANKIND THROUGH ADAPTIVE BAMBOO STRUCTURE*. 714–723.

Maurina, A., Prastyatama, B., & Blouin, V. Y. (2020, November 22). *Approaching Design Flexibility through a Modular Deployable Bamboo Structure for Sustainable Architecture*. The Conference Rapid Cities - Responsive Architectures, Dubai (online). https://youtu.be/8cKhH6zgCoo

Mira, L. A., Coelho, R. F., De Temmerman, N., & Thrall, A. P. (2014). *Evaluation of design parameters for deployable planar scissor arches*. 183–194. https://doi.org/10.2495/MAR140151

Mirzaean Mahabadi, S., Zabihi, H., & Majedi, H. (2014). Participatory design; a new approach to regenerate the public space. International *Journal of Architecture and Urban Development, 4*(4), 15–22.

Piroozfar, P. A., & Piller, F. T. (2013). *Mass customization and personalization in architecture and construction*. Routledge.

Ramos-Jaime, C., & Sánchez-Sánchez, J. (2019). Hyperboloid Modules for Deployable Structures. *Nexus Network Journal, 22*(2), 309–328. https://doi.org/10.1007/s00004-019-00459-y

Sanders, E. B.-N., Brandt, E., & Binder, T. (2010). A framework for organizing the tools and techniques of participatory design. *Proceedings of the 11th Biennial Participatory Design Conference*, 195–198.

Sanders, E. B.-N., & Stappers, P. J. (2008). Co-creation and the new landscapes of design. *Co-Design, 4*(1), 5–18.

Stallen, M., Chabannes, Y., & Steinberg, F. (1994). Potentials of prefabrication for self-help and mutual-aid housing in developing countries. *Habitat International, 18*(2), 13–39. https://doi.org/10.1016/0197-3975(94)90048-5

Ulrich, K. T. (2003). *Product design and development*. Tata McGraw-Hill Education.

Vogel, S. (2021, March 31). Co-Creating a More Equitable World: The Transformative Benefits of Participatory Design |. *MIT D-Lab*. https://d-lab.mit.edu/news-blog/blog/co-creating-more-equitable-world-transformative-benefits-participatory-design

Wagemann, E. (2015). *Transition from shelter to home*.

Nature Integration, Biophilic Design, and Equity in the Urban Interior

Kendra Ordia *(University of Nebraska, Lincoln)*

ABSTRACT

Design is an expression of humanity, a species of and bounded by nature. But "nature" holds many definitions, and the spectrum of connection to nature is as diverse as those experiencing it. As the topic of biophilic design continues to grow and expand, it is vital that designers investigate what biophilia means for the nature deprived; what connection to nature may mean for those without opportunity, access, means, or inclusive spaces to enjoy its documented benefits. Biophilia is a biological theory suggesting humans are innately drawn to nature offering an evidence-based methodology for interior design that derives artistic decisions from a scientific hypothesis. How can design students use their understanding of biophilia and nature-influenced spatial experiences to think about designing more inclusively while considering equity, diversity, and culture? This report of pedagogical and methodological approaches used in upper-level interior design university studio curriculum focuses on established theories, narrative, and designed solutions for increased wellbeing, access, and delight focused on some of the most vulnerable populations - children and youth. By more inclusively and empathetically understanding how human behavior, health, and wellbeing are influenced by connection to nature, designers can begin to propose biophilic design solutions beyond surface level application utilizing the proposed methods of critical thinking, inquiry, and collaboration as future change agents. Through intentional engagement and research-based design, values in nature and contained potential for increased physical, spatial application and integration in built environments can become design tools for not only spatial change but also societal impact.

KEYWORDS

Biophilia; Equity; Nature; Urban; Interiors

1. INTRODUCTION

"Nature" holds many valid definitions from remote, wild landscapes to a single urban street tree—and interactions with nature are as diverse as those experiencing them. However, even when greenspace amenities exist in close proximity, they are less likely to be used by people of color (Mock, 2016). Resulting from systemic racism and complex social and economic factors, the lack of access to benefits of nearby nature for racialized people is far from equitable. People who live in low-income communities and communities of color are less likely than those living in majority white neighborhoods to have a park, playground, or other exercise facility nearby. These vulnerable communities are often sited by disinvestment or design in locations with less tree cover, lower air quality, less access to healthy foods, or places to safely engage in physical activity. Neighborhoods may include locations near brownfields, highways, or various industrial zones (Moore, 2017). This redlining leads to issues of environmental racism among many other health and social disparities. According to Healthy Places by Design, "parks that do exist in these communities are routinely under-resourced, lacking restrooms, drinking water, or safe lighting. And if someone can't afford a personal vehicle and doesn't have access to public transportation, then traveling to parks or healthier place is out of reach" (Moore, 2017). And in situations where ethnic or racial minorities can access a park, their presence within this natural space may be question as we've see from the tragic and deadly scenario of 12 year old Tamir Rice playing with a toy gun in an Ohio park in 2012 to a recorded interaction in Central Park in May 2020 as African American bird watcher, Christine Cooper, engaged in communication with dog walker, Amy Cooper, and subsequently had the police called on him with an emphasis on his race. While access to nature, public parks, or green space may be framed as an accessible opportunity for all, we know this is not the case and we must work to ensure that everyone, regardless of where they live or whom they are, has the same opportunity to access the physiological and psychological benefits of nature.

As Western society becomes increasingly focused on digital and smart technology, many people have seen an increase of time spent indoors – especially related to children and youth - and thus a reduced connection to nature and the inherent benefits of this relationship. Connection to Nature (CTN) is defined as "a stable state of consciousness comprising symbiotic cognitive, affective, and experiential dimensions that reflect a realization of the interrelatedness between one's self and the rest of nature" (Zylstra e al., 2014, p. 126). A growing body of research over the past decade is exploring the topic of connection a person feels with the natural world calling for greater opportunities of interaction, especially in urban contexts, to foster greater CTN and in turn pro-environmental attitudes and behavior (Soga and Gaston, 2018). Additionally, the literature relating to CTN is especially focused on nature access for children and youth whose CTN is in steep decline (Hughes et al. 2018; Larson et al. 2019; Louv, 2005). This loss of nature interactions is often referred to as Nature Deficit Disorder. According to The Center for American Progress, "studies consistently find that children who spend time outdoors in natural environments experience improved health and cognitive functions, strong motor coordination, reduced stress, and enhanced social skills. Students who spend more time in the outdoors, including students from low-income backgrounds, tend to perform better on standardized tests, demonstrate more enthusiasm toward school, and have fewer attendance problems. According to one study, simply having more tree cover in a neighborhood could account for as much as 13 percent of variance in student outcomes; the study found the positive effect to be strongest in schools that faced the most external socioeconomic challenges" (Rowl-Shea et al., 2020, p. 11). Therefore, declining CTN in children and youth is of concern within the contexts of pro-environmentalism and public health since they are some of the most impacted by lack of access to nature's benefits.

2. RESEARCH OBJECTIVES

In the context of equitable connection to nature access in the built environment, this ongoing design studio pedagogy seeks to address the following research and design objectives:

- Investigate what biophilia means for the nature-deprived
- Understand values in nature and the contained potential for physical, spatial application and integration in future built environments for enhanced wellbeing
- Create experiences in the urban interior to enhance awareness, knowledge, and opportunities for meaningful connection to nature for under-represented children and young adults.

The project prompts are framed to address the following research and design questions:

- How do you inclusively design interior nature-influenced spatial experiences considering equity, diversity, and culture, while promoting play, education, and growth?
- How do we create experiences for people, particularly in cities, that foster awareness of the natural world while considering conservation, restoration, and delight?

To further understand some of the context of the research objectives it is vital to also have a common understanding of relevant terminology. The first term is equity which is defined as "being fair such that peoples' needs guide the distribution of opportunities for well-being" (Gispen, 2017b). When considering the definition of wellbeing, it is important to understand the basic definition of health. According the World Health Organization (WHO) and Article I of the 1978 Declaration of Alma-Ata, "health, which is a state of complete physical, mental and social wellbeing, and not merely the absence of disease or infirmity, is a fundamental human right and that the attainment of the highest possible level of health is a most important world-wide social goal whose realization requires the action of many other social and economic sectors in addition to the health sector." Considering aspects of health and wellbeing equity, we must acknowledge that inequity and racial discrimination persist in the foundational level of human needs including shelter, air, water, and food. Inequalities continue as we consider aspects of Social Determinates of Health (SDOH) including economic stability, education access and quality, health care access and quality, neighborhood and built environment, and social and community context (U.S. Department of Health and Human Services, 2020). Therefore, regardless of type of design, policy, or environmental change strategy, it is vital community health initiatives focus on health equity. This begins by acknowledging the systemic inequalities and injustices within spaces for health and wellbeing as well as a focus on the people who are most impacted by these disparities (Moore, 2019).

Prior to social justice movements of the summer of 2020, many non-racialized people likely did not equate nature with sociopolitical structures. Perhaps for the first time, many white Americans began to see and hear narratives of the inequalities our fellow humankind has been dealing with for decades and reexamined their perspective of inequalities, racism, and at the least, where we are all most welcome. In an ideal scenario, the natural world is meant to be inclusive and accessible to everyone, but the issues surrounding this are complex and systemic. As a response to these optimal conditions, the topic of equitable nature integration in urban interiors is explored in this annual interior design studio to explore this concept through specific design prompts, existing urban sites, and to raise awareness in the context of a learning environment. Design students have the power to question historic norms and address these issues as they enter the profession and become future agents of change. In this paper, the pedagogical approach will be discussed with intention to inform others' design processes or methodologies around the topic of equitable children and youth nature connection. Each design problem or prompt the students is tasked with in the semester-long course is meant to promote research and design excellence related to aspects of public health, wellbeing, and equity in the built environment to allow everyone access to the benefits of nearby nature.

3. METHODS

Within interior design curriculum, the studio environment is the crucial academic space allowing students to explore a specific project typology, subject matter, or community. When dealing with concepts of wellbeing or healthy interiors, the topics move more towards concepts of evidence-based design where arts and science merge under research informed creative problem solving. Creative design studios also require students to take an active role in learning through various forms of inquiry and investigation, design proposals, reflection, and visual and verbal communication. Since 2019, a third-year interior design studio at a public University in the US has focused on the future of nature integration in the urban interiors. This experimental and problem-based learning approach is structured around an intention to engage students in systemic inequality issues and to investigate what biophilia means for the nature deprived.

As a designer, it is important to understand one's own perspective and potential biases and for this reason, self-reflective surveys were completed prior to being introduced to a nature-influenced project; the same assessment was utilized for comparison at the end of the project to determine any changes in perspective after research, analysis, and design. The survey utilized two existing scales: Nature Relatedness Scale (NR-6) and Love and Care for Nature Scale (LCN-10) with three additional questions related to nature in built environments (Nisbet et al., 2009; Perkins, 2010). Resulting data was analyzed to understand if design students reported changes in their own connection to nature as they progressed through research and spatial design.

Each design project was introduced through a specific prompt intended to have students respond to a project typology, specific site and thus a specific demographic or community intended to be the primary user group. The design project commenced with a research phase guided by a curated set of resources to expose students to prevalent and supportive research or issues surrounding the larger context of the topic of children and youth nature connection. Students were expected to summarize key points – especially those related to design potential and produce visual representations of these points. Additionally, Through the research phase, students were also required to select specific established educational programming ranging from green and edible school yards, to Nature Explore and established Environmental Education activities with a local/regional foundation.

Project schedules range from three to nine weeks depending on the complexity and scope of the typology. The project typologies also range each year to focus on documenting aspects of urban connection to nature including:

- Nature Lab and Biodesign Makers Spaces *(Focus: Grow, Learn, Sustain)*
- Bio Food Hall and Market *(Focus: Preserve, Restore, Delight)*
- STEM and Nature Play Portable Elementary Education Space *(Focus: Access, Play, Delight)*
- Environmental Education and Work Force Development *(Focus: Education, Conservation, #Natureforall)*
- Environmental Education and Interior Vertical Farming *(Focus: Education, Growth, Sustainable Foods)*

The list of issues for students to be aware of in almost all the project typologies are specific to improving the situation for increased nature connection for children and youth and are further detailed in this section. These include themes of benefits of urban nature contact, topics of environmental and social justice, and aspects of positive youth development. Subjects of play, environmental education, and urban agriculture are explored as models for nature-connection in urban children and youth since access to these programs have historically been met by systemic barriers and involvement varies by race, ethnicity, and socioeconomic status. Finally, by understanding the relationship and benefit of integration of nature (both real and virtual) into our built environment in broader design research topics of connection to nature (biophilia), human behavior, and wellbeing related to indoor environmental quality, opportunities for interior nature inclusion are revealed.

3.1 Benefits of Nature Contact for Children and Youth

The benefits of spending time outdoors are well documented; outdoor time promotes physical and mental health, relieves stress and anxiety, and improves social skills. We also know that time in nature is particularly important for youth development and wellbeing. Yet young people in the US spend an alarming 90% of their time indoors despite the myriad potential health benefits of exposure to nature and green spaces (Youth Outside, 2018; Sefcik et al., 2019, pp. 28–31). Fresh air, light, and open space for movement, as well as the stress-reducing and healing benefits of nature, are aspects of the US park systems designed with goals for public health in the nineteenth and early twentieth century (Spirn, 1984). According to Sefcik at the School of Nursing at the University of Pennsylvania, "research on exposure to or use of parks (as opposed to urban 'nature' or 'green space' in general) has found a positive association with community social relationships, including collective efficacy. Parks have been shown to engender mental health benefits, which could be, in part, due to improved social interactions, increased opportunities for physical activity, or lower stressful exposures" (2019, p.2). While these spaces have been labeled as "parks for all" we know that access to urban parks in not always guaranteed and many existing urban parks are underutilized for various reasons (Boone et al., 2009; Sister et al., 2010). Much of the growing evidence revealing the utilization patterns and inequalities of park access have to do with safety concerns which are primarily tied to lower park use in low-resource neighborhoods (Cohen et al., 2012, 2013; Derose et al., 2018; Park et al., 2018). Studies in Europe and the US show that many in these neighborhoods - low income and ethnic minority families - have less access to urban green spaces in general as well as large, well-maintained parks with amenities (National Recreation and Park Association, 2011; Evans et al., 2012; Wen et al., 2013). The aspect of equitable access to green space, attractive and safe parks, as well as schoolyards or early learning centers that integrate natural elements and play equipment becomes an environmental justice issue – expressly since research provides empirical evidence of the benefits of nature contact for many dimensions of well-being (Chawla, 2015). National and local grass-roots efforts are continually working to create more opportunities for equitable access in communities most burdened by these disconnects. The American Public Health Association called for "a joint action by professionals in public health, parks, recreation, and urban planning and design" in their 2013 policy statement on "Improving Health and Wellness through Access to Nature" (Chawla, 2015 p.434). As this group of professionals consider children and youth populations specifically (and especially in urban areas), joint-use agreements between parks and schools can provide access to natural landscapes on school grounds and allow for community use after hours providing increased opportunities for outdoor learning and play (Chawla, 2015).

3.2 Play and Learning Landscapes

There is nothing frivolous about children's play. It is so important that in 1989 the United Nations Convention on the Rights of the Child (UNCRC) recognized "the right of the child to rest and leisure, to engage in play and recreational activities appropriate to the age of the child and to participate freely in cultural life and the arts." This holistic approach to children's rights identifies play as an important component of their physical and mental health and therefore their wellbeing. In the US, the Growing up in Cities project was revived in the 1990s in response to the UNCRC. Play is vital in all aspects of children's development and consists of several factors (Chawla, 2015). It is typically more about the process of play than the end goal; it is voluntary, spontaneous, and involves engagement of the player. It is flexible combining objects or roles in new ways and can be exaggerated (Garvey, 1990). It also has a positive affect meaning it can insight happiness, pleasure, and joy in a child. Research on play shows these criteria contrast it with exploration "(focused investigation as a child gets more familiar with a new toy or environment, that may then lead into play), work (which has a definite goal), and games (more organized activities in which there is some goal, typically winning the game)" (Zosh, et al., 2018).

Play can be conceptualized as a spectrum taking on different forms and serving different functions. One of the first types of play is "free play" often hailed as the gold standard of play. This play is child-initiated and directed and is not scaffold or guided by adults; there is not a pre-determined learning goal or outcome (Burghardt, 2011). Free play is the focus of the traditional description of play outlined above and is recognized as optimal for promoting social interactions as children engage in play with peers (Gray, 2013; Ghafouri, et al., 2005). As play moves from child-initiated to scenarios where an adult arranges or chooses the context for learning for child-directed play there is a shift to "guided play." This differs from free play in several ways: the activity is centered around a learning goal and is scaffold or guided by adult mentorship. Even within this context of guided play, the child must still have agency and express autonomy within the prepared space to direct the activity. Much research over the last few decades "has repeatedly shown that learning is optimized when adults scaffold an environment or feedback toward a learning goal but the learning environment encourages fun child-led exploration and discovery" (Hirsh-Pasek et al., 2015, p.3). Play is iterative and guided play creates space for independence and self-directed learning exploration of concepts, hypotheses, and contextualization. Guided play "may help to cultivate children's love of learning, promoting their engagement while offering support for knowledge acquisition. In this way, guided play creates the right mise en place—a confluence of environmental and psychological factors that gently shape not only the desired outcomes in learning but also a more positive attitude toward learning itself" (Weisberg, et al., p.179).

Research suggests that children learn best when the learning is "active (minds-on) and engaged (not distracting), meaningful (applied to prior knowledge and transferred to the outside world) and occurring in a socially interactive environment" (Zosh, et al., 2018, p. 3). Additional pedagogical research notes that learning in playful contexts increases educational value due to the positive affect and joy inherent in play. Joy is a central characteristic to play and positive affect or intrinsic motivation; it is essential for an activity to be considered play (Krasnor and Pepler, 1980). The construct of intrinsic motivation is described by experts in the field as a "natural inclination toward assimilation, mastery, spontaneous interest, and exploration that is so essential to cognitive and social development and that represents a principal source of enjoyment and vitality throughout life" (Zosh, et al., 2018, p. 8). The correlation between positive affect and cognition is not new and has been linked to creativity in problem solving as well as both working and long-term memory (Isen, 1984, 1987; Ashby et al., 1999; Zosh et al., 2017). Neuroscience and psychology research also supports theories of the link between emotions and cognition publicizing the benefits for a variety of positive outcomes including leaning (Fischer et al., 2006; Immordino-Yang et al., 2007).

Playful learning is active, engaged, meaningful, iterative, social, and joyful. Active learning is defined as being "minds on" or actively focused and engaged in a task rather than passively learning or observing. Not surprisingly, children learn more when they are paying attention and engaged rather than becoming distracted. They learn more effectively when the activity or material has a meaningful context or connection to previous knowledge or their own lives, as well as in opportunities for interaction with others (Hassinger-Das, et al., 2018). A significant portion of a child's time (80 percent) is spent in a home or community setting while the remaining hours are in school. Community spaces offer opportunities to transform underutilized space while school grounds can increase access to playful learning through the Learning Landscape initiative which involves "crafting carefully planned play experiences that focus on learning outcomes, particularly for children and families from under-resourced communities" (Hassinger-Das, et al., 2018, p. 73). Another goal of Learning Landscapes is to enhance engagement and learning interactions by bringing educational opportunities to urban public spaces as 70 percent of children are projected to live in cities by 2050 (UNICEF, 2012). This focus on public space supports movements for more just cities, public health, and educational equity.

3.3 Environmental Education and Positive Youth Development

Research documents the benefits of time outdoors – especially for children and youth wellbeing and development. It is also documented that young people in the US spend 90 percent of their time indoors (Evans, et al., 1998). While many organizations focused on youth outdoor and environmental education are working to reverse this trend, for many socioeconomic, racial, and ethnic minority youth, systemic barriers compound this problem. Underserved youth may experience a range of barriers including lack of information, not being aware of opportunities, distance and lack of transportation, cost of programs, lack of equipment, safety concerns, parental permission or support, feeling unwelcome and experiences of discrimination, and lack of programming that is relevant to the target youth audience (Youth Outside, n.d.).

One method for children or youth to realize the affordances of nature interactions in cities is urban environmental education (Chawla, 2001, 2006). According to the US Environmental Protection Agency (1996), Environmental Education is a learning process that increases people's knowledge and awareness about the environment and associated challenges, develops the necessary skills and expertise to address the challenges, and fosters attitudes, motivations, and commitments to make informed decisions and take responsible action. In many US cities, these programs are offered through community or non-profit organizations and are offered after-school or during summer. The primary demographic hired as interns for many of these programs is also youth of color from low-resource neighborhoods (Smith, et al., 2015). These programs are beneficial as opportunities or settings for developing youth skills, aspects of sense of place and social capital, and resilience at the individual, community, and social-ecological systems levels (Schusler et al, 2010; Kudryavtsev et al., 2012; Krasny et al., 2013; Dubois and Krasny, 2016). Additionally, these programs can provide affordances for other areas of youth development like cultural and interpersonal competence, sense of purpose, and self-esteem that are linked to success in school and civic life (Schusler et al, 2010; Benson et al., 2011). However, research is lacking in knowledge of how aspects of environmental education programs like social interactions and physical setting present opportunities for positive youth development focused or relevant to urban youth of color including topics of moral stance linked to socio-political action or assisting in developing critical consciousness (Mustakova-Possardt, 1998).

Beginning in the early 1990s, research and programs designed to support children and families shifted from focusing on problematic behavior in youth to consider the context present when these same young adults experience holistic physical, emotional, intellectual, and social development (Eccles et al., 2002; Roth et al., 2003; Catalano et al., 2004; Lerner et al., 2011). A resulting approach of this shift in perspective recognizing youth have the capacity to become successful in their adult lives given appropriate support is referred to as positive youth development (Eccles et al., 2002; Lerner et al., 2005). Types of setting and assets are both considered when discussing the topic; assets include "self-efficacy, prosocial norms, and meaningful relationships with peers and adults, as well as more broadly social, emotional, cognitive, behavioral, and moral competence" (Delia et al, 2018, p. 2). Additional approaches to positive youth development are base on the "Five Cs," defined as 'Competence, Confidence, Connection, Character, and Caring'." Several researchers on the topic also propose a sixth C, "Contributions" relating to civic society and community (Delia et al, 2018, p. 2).

While useful and influential in informing research and policy, concepts of positive youth development have been criticized for lack of attention to systemic barriers and inequalities including racism, poverty, sexism, homophobia, and other forms of injustices (Sukarieh et al, 2011). Many of these issues are addressed through a focus on cultivating critical consciousness and social action within social justice youth development which also contains calls for environmental education in the context of discussions of power inequalities and justice (Ginwright et al, 2002; Bowers, 2002; Gruenewald, 2003). Within an urban environment, it is critical that environmental education is informed by contexts of racial and ethnic diversity and needs a critical perspective discussing aspects of social and ecological justice relates to social and cultural identity as well as systemic oppression (Ceaser, 2012; Cermak, 2012; McKenzie et al., 2017; Cole, 2007). The concept of critical pedagogy of place seeks to integrate aspects of decolonization alongside ecological understanding to disrupt inequitable systems and analyze issues related to power and justice. It places a focus on action that addresses poverty, food security, environmental racism, and equitable access to greenspace through place-restoration, preservation, and transformation – of both human and non-human relationships (Gruenewald, 2003; Gruenewald and Smith, 2008; Smith, 2007). Research has shown that these outcomes are not universal across all urban environmental educational or intern programs. However, they do suggest that "through attention to positive youth development, affordances, authentic care, and critical pedagogy of place, program leaders can foster youth assets that also contribute to socio-environmental affordances for additional youth and the broader community" (Delia et al., 2018, p.12).

3.4 Urban Agriculture

The preceding research related to positive youth development discusses how students' direct interaction with their environment can shape physical affordances that promote learning and action as well as expose their own capabilities. An often cited "development as action in context" program utilized to shape a youth's environment is urban agriculture or community gardening. This activity is useful to enhance community collectivism and increase food access addressing a critical awareness of the food system and related issue of injustice as well as reflecting on aspects of decolonization related to larger issues of waste and nutrition and food access in their community. The research, data, and environmental movements behind rethinking our food systems are well documented and certainly a driver for increased urban agricultural production. However, the focus of this research issue is to explore more of the concepts of food access inequity in urban centers where people are obviously living far from agricultural area as well as lacking green space for connection to nature.

The socio-economic divide in the US continues to widen and influences every aspect of social determinants of health. It also impacts people's ability to afford healthy foods or diets and often leaves low-resource families more susceptible to obesity, diabetes, and other health problems. Geographical access to food – or lack thereof often referred to as "food deserts" – describe areas primarily in low-income neighborhoods without access to a grocery store or supermarket. The term is an over-simplification of the challenges to accessing healthier foods which can also include aspects of public transit, walkability, or other environmental factors to get to the store. Access is not the only concern and research addresses aspects of behavior preferences and affordability related to food. According to the Economist, "Over the last four years, the price of the healthiest foods has increased at around twice the rate of energy-dense junk food. That is the whole problem, in an organic nutshell" (Ghisleni, 2021).

Just like water, shelter, sleep, and breathable air, food is considered a basic human need. It can compete with other essential expenses in many households and is influenced by other factors of food assistance, shelf life, and obviously cost. An additional consideration for food access also needs to address aspects of culturally relevant foods. This is a vital way to preserve health benefits and food traditions for many people. Urban agriculture or community gardening can provide opportunities for access to culturally relevant ingredients as well (Sustainable Food Center, 2020). This is where targeted, and community-oriented design can be especially successful as it directly benefits and integrates and encourages participation in the production of healthy and affordable food. While urban agriculture is not the solution to all issues surrounding food access inequalities or even a wide sweeping solution to reestablish connection to nature, it is one approach that has the possibility to address multiple challenges in many urban environments. It also renders access to nature within its context to be utilitarian, engaging, and potentially symbolic.

3.5 Biophilic Design – More Than Just Plants

Nature Deficit Disorder is described as the loss of children's free-ranging exploration of "wild lands" in cities and suburbs, as children withdrew indoors in front of television and computer screens, parents' fears for children's safety outdoors grew, and bulldozers relentlessly removed wild edges (Chawla, 2015). Biophilic Design is one natural response specifically focused on the built environment and purposeful or intentional nature connection – especially in urban environments. Biophilia, or the innate human predisposition to affiliate with natural systems and processes, especially life and life-like features of the natural environment, was popularized by E.O. Wilson in his book of the same title in 1984. The concept of Biophilic Design was translated as a spatial approach for the built environment primarily by Steven Kellert in the mid-2000s (2005; et al., 2008). And much of the current research on the psychological and physiological response to biophilic design is based in Kaplan's Connection to Nature Theories within the field of Environmental Psychology (1982).

According to Biophilic Design innovator and thought-leader, Jason McLennan "...there has always been a degree of confusion surrounding the implementation of biophilic design into architecture. Though more and more project teams began to discuss the topic of Biophilia, and some project teams did begin to break new ground on nature integration into the built environment, all too often conversations rarely broke through a surface-level understanding" (2018). This surface-level application often stalls at decoration or "green Band-Aid" of small living walls and nature-based visuals or patterns. This veneer of nature is not enough and the mere addition of plants in a space do not fully capture a holistic approach to biophilic design (Browning, 2018). As one of the pioneers of biophilic design, Stephen Kellert, names a "human dependence on nature that extends far beyond the simple issues of material and physical sustenance to encompass as well the human craving for aesthetic, intellectual, cognitive, and even spiritual meaning and satisfaction" (McLennan, 2018). Kellert goes on to establish a typology of human attitudes toward nature including values of humanistic, aesthetic, and symbolic relationships (1993). This value system is crucial in understanding the range and scale of nature connection and can depend on the intensity and character of an urban context. It was also informative in providing evidence to introduce topics of human connection to nature as first seen in sustainable building rating system, The Living Building Challenge. As a leader in holistic sustainability rating systems, the International Living Futures Institute was one of the first to introduce concepts of Equity and Beauty, as well as Biophilic Design, alongside traditionally measure topics of water and energy, recognizing the psychological and physiological benefits of nature access.

The approach to Biophilic Design is not simply "greener is better." It is a far from linear spectrum to determine the quality and quantity of biophilia in an interior space knowing that various types of nature exposure influence various responses. McLennan notes that "the quality is related to the abundance of life present – the diversity and the ecological health – as well as the accessibility, [meaning] any convention that aims to measure relative need for biophilia must address variables that have long been ill-defined: the qualitative difference between a paved courtyard and a park, the amount of time that people spend interacting with nature, and the amount of time that people spend inside or in non-biophilic environments. These variables have long eluded scientific study and will be critical in guiding the conversations to come" (2018).

3.6 Nature Connection: Real versus Virtual

The variables of nature exposure not only play out in the physical and natural environment, but this spectrum of experiences needs to now include a range of virtual or augmented nature exposure. As the dominant leisure activity of children and adolescents, digital electronic media (video games, video streaming social media, etc.), has shifted preferences of the current generation of youth and is considered the primary contributor of Nature Deficit Disorder in their demographic (Larson et al, 2018; Driessnack 2009; Soga et al., 2018).This societal shift from nature to electronic media has oriented generations away from concepts of biophilia to that of videophilia: "the new human tendency to focus on sedentary activities involving electronic media" (Pergams et el., 2006, p. 393). In a 2017 study in the UK, it was reported that children ages 8 to 15 spend an average of six to nine hours per day using electronic media (Ofcom, 2017). The rate of increase over the past decade is largely associated with the increase of portable screen-based devices and the embedded role of digital media in youth and popular culture (Chassiakos et al. 2016). Rachel Edwards, faculty of environment at the University of Waterloo, puts it bluntly, stating, "it is this pervasive extent of digital-media consumption with which efforts to increase children's and adolescents' contact with and interest in nature must compete" (Edwards et al, 2020, p. 952).

The desire for digital media and technology integration in youth needs to be incorporated in scenarios, spaces, or programs striving to foster greater connection to nature. The broader generational reach is appealing to encourage youth to explore more diverse natural settings or spaces subsequently facilitating an expanded environmental interest. This approach to programming can be especially appealing to those from urban environments and underrepresented minorities (Louv, 2005; Gill, 2011). Regardless of basis for program design, it is equally important to ensure the engagement strategies are accessible and appealing to children and youth from a range of ethnic and socio-economic backgrounds. With an exclusionary history, these activities need to be rooted in community and meet the needs or motivations of the local populations participating in nature programming (D'Amore et al., 2017; Kennedy et al., 2018). One of the proposed strategies to enhance integration of nature interaction and digital media is the concept of Gamification. While traditional outdoor activities often require a high level of creativity and imagination, the addition of gamification techniques could facilitate these interactions for those further on the spectrum of videophilia or those who are nature deprived. Gamification offers a more engaging learning environment and is defined as "the use of game design elements in non-game contexts" (Edwards et el,

2020, p. 958). Considering generational preferences and general Nature-Deficit Disorder, more traditional programs or experiences designed with an outdated, romanticized, or Western ideal of what childhood–nature-based experiences will fail to actively engage a larger child or youth proportion. To capture this population of nature-deprived, it is important to ensure an incremental approach to nature expose that is mediated by access to digital media or emerging technology.

4. RESULTS

Each design problem or prompt the students is tasked within the course is meant to promote research and design excellence related to aspects of public health, wellbeing, and equity. Regardless of project typology introduced in the studio, student went through the various phases of research, design, and presentation. As mentioned previously, the research for each project typology is curated to support learning objectives with opportunities for students to dive deeper into topics or issues of interest related to their specific projects. As with any learning activity, there are ways the outcomes are systematically analyzed, but the intention is to scaffold analysis and feedback to inform the next phase of design and ultimately the final inquiry-based design proposal. Students are expected to demonstrate critical thinking through immersive inquiry and proposals of relevant and emerging typologies or spatial solutions to advocate for change for the identified community or partners. In terms of academic benefits, the projects provided opportunity to simultaneously utilize analytical and creative thinking in evidence-based design. Students developed and referenced their design intention to propose innovative spatial solutions elevating the experience of the interior built environment while addressing identified ethical values, aspects of inequality, and wellbeing. Regardless of typology, each project allowed for creative methods of defining spatial conditions simultaneously considering the health, safety, welfare, and delight of the users within

Table 1: *Sample LCN-10 Student Survey Responses*

Survey Question		1 (strongly disagree)	2	3	4	5	6	7 (strongly agree)
I often feel a strong sense of care toward the natural environment.								
	Pre-Assessment	0	0	1	0	8	10	12
	Post Assessment	0	0	0	0	5	16	10
I enjoy learning about nature.								
	Pre-Assessment	0	1	0	2	10	7	11
	Post Assessment	0	0	0	2	6	6	17
I feel that closeness to nature is important for my well-being.								
	Pre-Assessment	0	1	0	4	8	5	13
	Post Assessment	0	0	1	1	5	9	15
I feel a personal sense of interconnectedness with the rest of nature.								
	Pre-Assessment	0	2	2	3	11	8	5
	Post Assessment	0	0	0	3	7	14	7

an existing urban environment. The resulting student proposals demonstrate an awareness and intention for designing beyond surface level applications of "biophilic design" to understand and explain the biological and emotional impact of nature-based spatial design on human behavior and well-being within interior environments. Aspects of place-based narrative and sensory expression became crucial for creating designs that promote positive responses, engagement with place, and the exploration of aesthetic values in nature. In an informal project interview, a student stated: "The first project really changed my outlook and considerations of topics of inclusion in design. As designers we have the ability to do much more than just make things look pretty, we have the opportunity to create justice within design. Moving forward, I plan to always consider this issue while in the design phase."

4.1 Learning from Survey Analysis

At the beginning of the semester, students (n = 31) are given an online survey comprised of existing scales: Nature Relatedness Scale (NR-6) and Love and Care for Nature Scale (LCN-10) with three additional questions related to nature in built environments (Nisbet et al., 2009; Perkins, 2010). The survey is administered online again at the conclusion of their project/semester. A sample of questions from both pre and post assememets are shown in Table 1. Some of the greatest positive shifts in the pre and post survey responses were from the LCN-10 questions: "I feel that a closeness to nature is important for my well-being," and "I feel a personal sense of interconnectedness with the rest of nature." One of the additional questions addressed students' perception of aspects of interior design in terms of their importance when approaching a new project. The perception of importance of health and wellbeing increased from 38.7 to 51.6 percent from pre to post assessment.

4.2 Learning from Self-Reflective Activities

Prior to introduction of the project brief, students complete a self-reflective activity related to a memorable or favorite place. While not required, in all instances, this has been some form of natural environment or one connected to nature. This offers an opportunity of reflective storytelling for students and is produced as a visual and/or written representation of their memory. Eventually, this activity is utilized to discuss aspects of privilege, potentially monolithic experiences, and introduce the following questions:

1. What if you don't have a backyard? Or your own yard?
2. What if it isn't safe to go to the neighborhood park?
3. What if you go to the park and others question your presence there...and the police are called?
4. What if nature is not associated with enjoyment, healing, or wellness?
5. What if you don't really know how (or think you like) to experience nature?

By introducing this set of questions, many students have mentioned they have never stopped to consider a peer's experience of child/youth nature play different than their own. This activity and discussion framed the context for class and small group discussion related to equity, inclusion, and narratives within the natural environment.

4.3 Learning from an Inquiry and Value Based Approach

The interior design department has collectively adopted an inquiry-based approach for design studios resulting in a shift from "design concept" to "design intention." This requires students to propose design of the built environment informed by an intention established and based in purposeful research and analysis. Using their comprehensive understanding of the design problem, students need to identify a unique opportunity they are interested in investing in and declare a design intention that will direct their programming and spatial intervention moving forward. This requires student to embed research and analysis as a core tenant to understanding the complexity of the design problems. The design intention becomes evidence of the student's ability to frame a complex problem in unique and meaningful ways

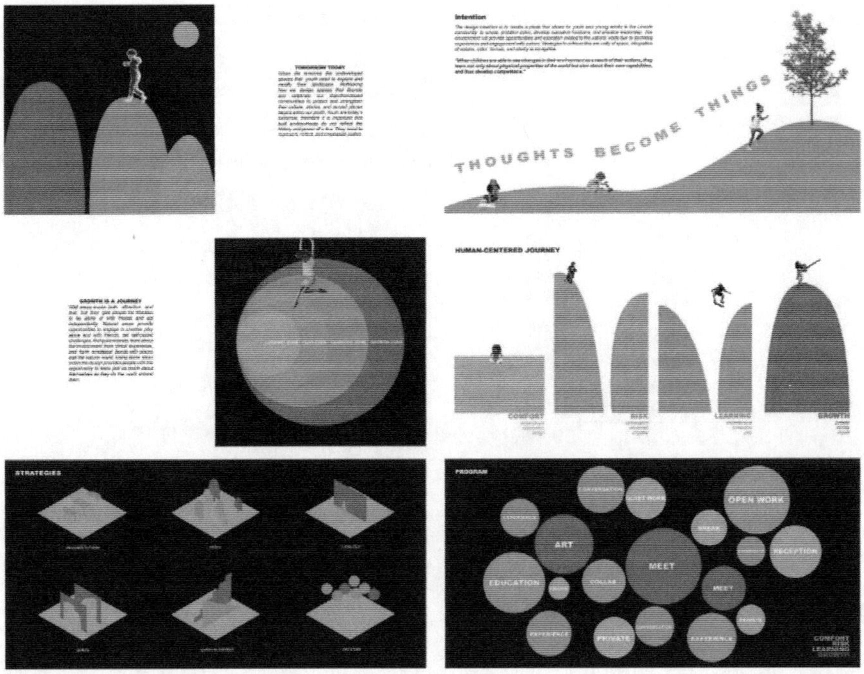

Figure 1 (above): *Design Research and Intention Diagrams for Environmental Education and Work Force Development (Fall 2020). Diagrams by design student, Erin Applegate. Reproduced with permission of student.*
Figure 2 (below): *Nature Play Portable Elementary Education Space (Fall 2020). Drawings by design student, Lauryn Eby. Reproduced with permission of student.*

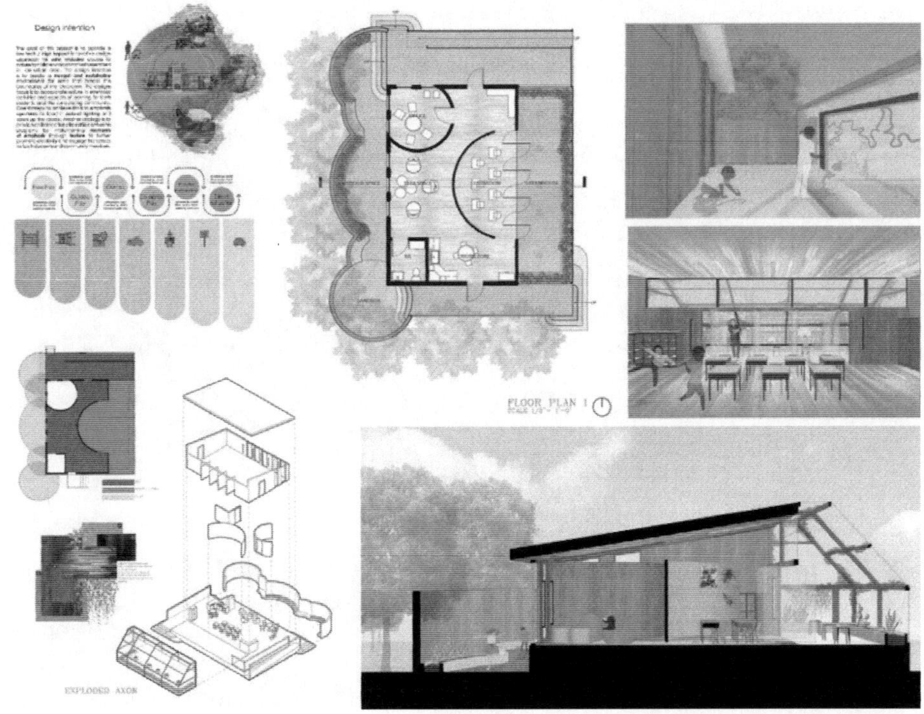

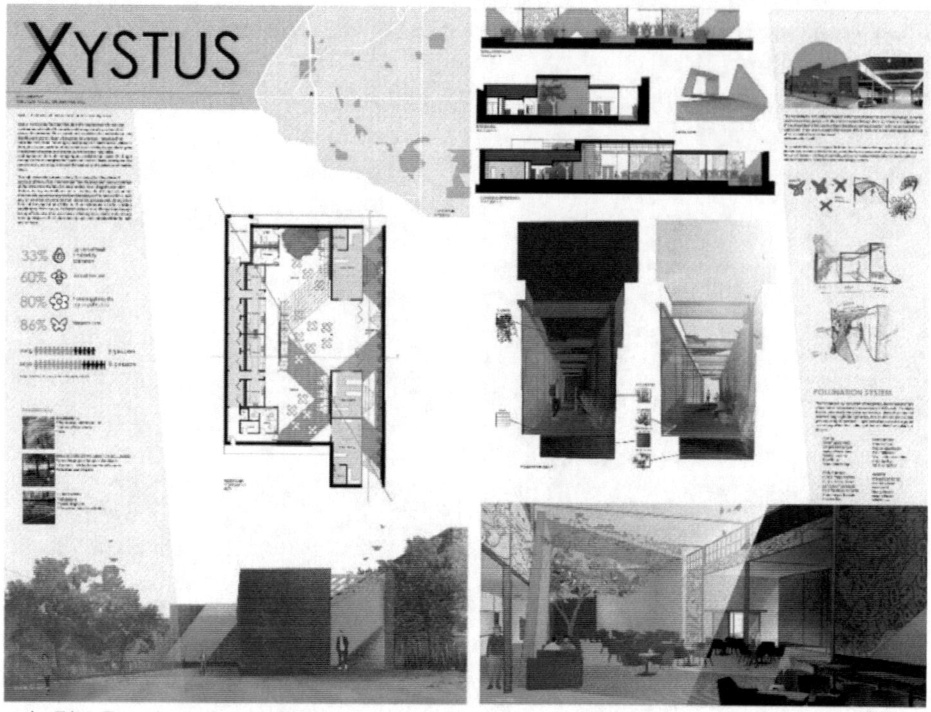

Figure 3 (above): *Bio Food Hall & Pollinator Alley (Fall 2019). Drawings by design student, John Andrews. Reproduced with permission of student.*

Figure 2 (below): *Environmental Education and Work Force Development (Fall 2020). Drawings by design student, Eden Vanarsdall. Reproduced with permission of student.*

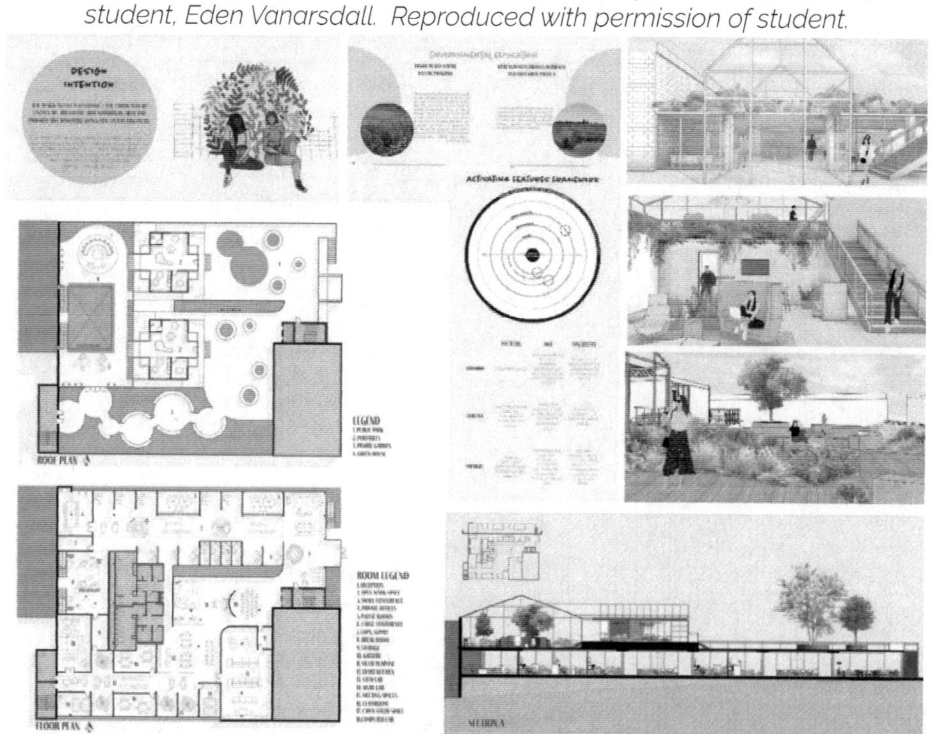

(see Figure 1).

In addition to an evidence-based intention, design ethics are introduced as a toolkit to establish a baseline for framing and terminology within the students' statements (Gispen, 2017a). Values are an important concept in design ethics as students consider translating values to concerns relevant to their design intention and understanding how their design affects others. This also ensured our class understood the definition of terms increasingly used in social justice movements. Since students were organized into peer-groups for discussion and feedback throughout the semester, this allowed for set check-ins regarding intentions and values throughout the design process and became a road map for decision-making.

4.4 Learning from Programmatic Inclusion

In each project, students are expected to explored pre-existing programs for educational, STEM, and nature-based play as activities to design for users that may not have experiences playing in or with nature - or may need various types of guided play to develop their confidence. Resources ranged from Green School Yards – Living Schoolyards Activity Guide, Nature Explore Program activities, Edible School Yards, and state-based conservation and environmental education activities. Students reviewed resources and selected a minimum of three activities to integrate that were in alignment with their intention and values, demographic study of community and surrounding site, aspects of climate or ecosystem, and potentially even culturally relevant activities.

These were used to help build program and function into the space. Positive spatial experiences in the built environment can support growth and comfort with positive experiences in and with nature. They also became meaningful spatial drivers for play and nature-engagement and often reference local or ecological influences within urban environments. The process of meaningful nature integration moved students for surface applications of biophilic design to something with more designed context, access, and scalable levels of connection with nature from passive opportunities to active engagement. This was expressed and analyzed in students written and visual communications (diagrams, design drawings, three-dimensional visualization, etc.) and presented narratives of their design solutions. Overviews of students' design proposals can be viewed in the following student project ranging from three week studies in Figure 2 and nine week studies in Figures 3 and 4.

4.5 Learning from Critique and Feedback

Each project involved a minimum of one feedback session or review with design professionals as well as various points of peer-to-peer feedback. Within the studio environment, the primary means of evaluation is critique of research analysis, case studies, and final design proposals. Studio learning environments are highly collaborative allowing opportunities to engage with the professor/instructor as well as their peers and outside professional designers or community members. The project schedule and required deadlines as checkpoints create opportunities for systemic critique and feedback at various phases of design. Peer-to-peer discussion encouraged students to be proactive, independent learners as well as build skills, knowledge, and confidence as they completed individual assessment tasks. Group critique in class as well as with outside professionals allowed the students the opportunity to verbalize and communicate design intention, proposed solutions, and practice presentation skills. These sessions were met with individual and group follow-up with the professor to address strengths and weaknesses. Additionally, one of the advantages of virtual learning during much of the semesters was access to professional reviewers outside of the region who were able to bring a unique expertise to the topics being explored.

5. CONCLUSIONS

As the topic of biophilic design continues to grow, mature, and expand, it is vital that architects, planners, and designers investigate what biophilia means for the nature deprived - what connection to nature may mean for those without opportunity, access, means, or inclusive spaces to comfortably enjoy its documented benefits. It is imperative it becomes a design tool for not only spatial change but also societal impact. The initial means to moving towards a more equitable biophilic design is increasing exposure to its humanistic and moralistic values. There is danger in a monolithic approach (or in the case of biophilic design, reclaimed wood, natural materials, and tropical plants) to nature integration in the built environment. When approached as such, it is devoid of any reference to identity of place, culture, or local ecosystems. American author and environmental activist, Wendell Berry, speaks against this "rhetoric of nowhere" in conversations about particularity affection declaring, "Even the trees are under this particularizing influence of place and time. Each one, responding to happenstance and circumstance and accident, has assumed a shape not quite like that of any other tree of its kind" (Berry, 2001, p. 44). The concept of avoiding a single identity is eloquently presented in Chimamanda Ngozi Adichie's TEDtalk discussing the danger of a single story (2019). Reinforced in Colors of Nature: Culture, Identity, and the Natural World, "The meaning of the word 'nature' is derived from the Latin nascor, to be born. Perhaps a birth of sorts may yet occur in our ability to re-imagine and re-focus how we think...about nature and environment. Then perhaps all of us might finally begin to resist any mono-identity or mono-culture of mind, self, or knowledge – to celebrate the biodiversity of self and of others" (Savoy and Deming, 2011, p. 8).

An additional way to begin to understand our ability to address this topic is to approach projects through an empathetical lens. Empathy in design is a powerful force, and it is proven that when we are empathetic, we enhance our ability to receive and process information. Empathy is defined as "the ability to be aware of, understanding of, and sensitive to another person's feelings and thoughts without having had the same experience" (Battarbee, n.d., p. 2). The process of mirroring or putting ourselves in "someone else's shoes" is a part of a subconscious behavior. Research also shows this creates measurable changes in our cognitive style and can increase field-dependent thinking. This form of thinking is important as it assists in putting information in context and helps us pick up on contextual cues from the environment – both essential as we seek to understand literal and figurative connections.

If designers are charged with protecting the public's health, safety, and welfare within the built environment, they must look towards concepts of design ethics to make sure they truly act in the benefit of the inclusive public – not just those with access and means. Research and own lived experiences demonstrate that design has a huge influence on how people behave. Education and practice trains designers to solve problems and make people's lives better, but historically they have not considered what 'better' actually is in regard to broader topics of inclusion. It is important to understand that what is designed is not neutral. In fact, design is an inherently ethical activity. Ethics is "the discipline dealing with what is good and bad and with moral duty and obligation." Ethical design is, therefore, design made with the intent to do good. The topics of empathy and ethics not only extend from the environmental and climatic challenges of our day, but also to our fellow humankind who we share, create, and enjoy the built environment and spatial experiences with.

Another aspect of building empathy and responsive, community-based design is to utilize participatory design processes or co-design. Based in Design Justice Principles, co-design is a collaborative, community-based, consentful practice of designing with people and groups committed to building a more just and beautiful future (What is Co-Design – And Also Too, n.d.). Design justice seeks to rethink design processes, works to center people who are traditionally marginalized by design, and uses co-design to address some of the deepest challenges communities face (Read the Principles, n.d.) Prioritizing design impact on the community or those directly impacted supports concepts of everyone being an expert based on their own lived experiences and become valuable contributors to the design process. This is crucial in eliciting design that is sustainable, non-exploitative, and promotes a sense of place while providing aspects of inclusion and equity. Specifically, when it comes to biophilic design, we need to hear, document, and promote other stories of place, nature, and environment.

6. DISCUSSION

One of the greatest challenges of this pedagogical approach for these studio projects is the inherent need for peer and community engagement. As with all in-person and social scenarios during the global pandemic beginning in early 2020, the studio environment was moved to a virtual and digital platform. This required an increase of needing to listen, review, and analyze accounts of environmental education, processes of nature access and anxiety, experiences of injustice or racism, and aspects of narrative through web/blog posts, podcasts, and group discussion. This allowed exposure to certain topics for students but does not replace opportunities for in-person engagement, formal and informal conversations with community partners, and active learning. As the US academic and professional world moves back toward in person learning, work or hybrid engagement, this will be one of the greatest prospects for developing additional learning opportunities, methodologies, and assessments for meaningful student outcomes.

A strategy for increased engagement in communities of need is to investigate programs or groups already embedded or working in the community as well as to consider where children and families without equitable access to nature spend most of their time. One of the primary environments for these encounters, especially children and youth, is educational environments. Identifying existing after-school or environmental education programs, non-profits based on arts, culture, or food access, or even existing program as part of the local school system can provide access to established relationships, trust, and respect for community partners. Collaboration with design and architecture firms can also be an additional way for students to engage in the design process, especially if a firm focuses on educational design or public interest design. An additional strategy is to have design students understand some of the activities and programs that children or youth would participate in if they were part of an environmental education program. For example, during the Fall 2021 semester, students in the design studio are working with a local start-up interior vertical farm to understand our connection to healthy food by seeding, growing, harvesting, and processing fresh lettuce. They are also learning firsthand about ideal spatial layout for efficient workflows, interior environmental conditions, opportunities for outreach, and what makes for successful urban farming. These active-learning and hands on opportunities have helped students develop a deeper understanding of the food systems, environmental education, and scalable opportunities to integrate into their own projects. It is a positive example of biophilic interior design moving beyond surface application to functional and experiential interactions with interior nature

As a collaborative, creative community, designers can advance the potential for designing with nature to one that is more representative, inclusive, and ultimately contributes to people's health and wellbeing. Context and cultural meaning impact our aesthetic experiences; by objectively framing aesthetic judgment through narrative metaphor and multisensory experiences, applying nature-based design to interiors promises to enhance spatial engagement and reduce the distance between users and the natural world; creating opportunities for increased empathy, focus, and mindfulness including reflection, compatibility, and other reflexive aspects of consciousness. Designers can explore how biophilic interior design has the potential to move beyond surface application to functional and experiential interactions with interior nature for increased access, equity, and delight.

7. REFERENCES

Ali, S. (2020, July 21). *Can We Render the Outdoors Truly Inclusive?* Sierra Club. https://www.sierraclub.org/sierra/can-we-render-outdoors-trulyinclusive?fbclid=IwAR0Boc22QQkBna_PDW2Ky-QidzrKaz-3jK6OOIdLJ5OkMEsQRTb7%E2%80%A6

Ashby, F. G., Isen, A. M., and Turken, A. U. (1999). A neuropsychological theory of positive affect and its influence on cognition. Psychol. Rev. 106, 529–550. doi: 10.1037/0033-295X.106.3.529

Battarbee, K., Suri, J., & Howard, S. (n.d.). *Empathy On The Edge: Scaling And Sustaining A Human-Centered Approach In The Evolving Practice Of Design*. IDEO. https://new-ideo-com.s3.amazonaws.com/assets/files/pdfs/news/Empathy_on_the_Edge.pdf

Benson, P. L., Scales, P. C., and Syvertsen, A. K. (2011). The contribution of the developmental assets framework to positive youth development theory and practice. *Adv. Child. Dev. Behav.* 41, 197–230. doi: 10.1016/B978-0-12-386492-5.00008-7

Berry, W. (2001). *Life is a miracle: an essay against modern superstition*. Counterpoint.

Boone, C. G., Buckley, G. L., Grove, J. M., & Sister, C. (2009). Parks and People: An Environmental Justice Inquiry in Baltimore, Maryland. *Annals of the Association of American Geographers, 99*(4), 767–787. https://doi.org/10.1080/00045600903102949

Bowers, C. A. (2002). Toward an eco-justice pedagogy. *Environ. Educ. Res.* 8, 21–34. doi: 10.1080/13504620120109628

Browning, B. (2018, September 27). *Biophilic Design, More Than Just Plants!* Terrapin Bright Green. https://www.terrapinbrightgreen.com/blog/2018/09/biophilic-design-just-plants/

Burghardt, G. M. (2011). Defining and recognizing play. In A. D. Pelligrini (Ed.), *Oxford handbook of the development of play* (pp. 9–18). New York, NY: Oxford University Press.

Catalano, R. F., Berglund, M. L., Jean, A. M. R., Heather, S. L., and Hawkins, J. D. (2004). Positive youth development in the United States: research findings on evaluations of positive youth development programs. *Ann. Am. Acad. Pol. Soc. Sci.* 591, 98–124. doi: 10.1177/0002716203260102

Ceaser, D. (2012). Our school at Blair Grocery: a case study in promoting environmental action through critical environmental education. *Environ. Educ. Res. 43*, 209–226. doi: 10.1080/00958964.2011.637094

Cermak, M. J. (2012). Hip-hop, social justice, and environmental education: toward a critical ecological literacy. *J. Environ. Educ. 43*, 192–203. doi: 10.1080/00958964.2011.633579

Chassiakos, Yolanda R., Jenny Radesky, Dimitri Christakis, Megan A. Moreno, and Corinn Cross. 2016. "Children and Adolescents and Digital Media." *Pediatrics 138* (5): e20162593. doi:10.1542/peds.2016-2593.

Chawla, L. (2001). Putting young old ideas into action: the relevance of growing up in cities to local agenda 21. *Local Environ. 6*, 13–25. doi: 10.1080/13549830120024224

Chawla, L. (2006). Learning to love the natural world enough to protect it. *Barn 2*, 57–78.

Chawla, L. (2015). Benefits of Nature Contact for Children. *Journal of Planning Literature, 30*(4), 433–452. https://doi.org/10.1177/0885412215595441

Chawla, L., and J. Litt. (2013). Improving Health and Wellness through Access to Nature. Policy statement 20137 of the American Public Health Association. http://www.apha.org/advocacy/policy/policy-search/default.htm?id¼1453.

Chimamanda Ngozi Adichie. (2009). *The danger of a single story*. Ted.com; TED Talks. https://www.ted.com/talks/chimamanda_adichie_the_danger_of_a_single_story

Cohen, D. A., Han, B., Derose, K. P., Williamson, S., Marsh, T., Rudick, J., & McKenzie, T. L. (2012). Neighborhood poverty, park use, and park-based physical activity in a Southern California city. *Social Science & Medicine* (1982), 75(12), 2317–2325. https://doi.org/10.1016/j.socscimed.2012.08.036

Cohen, D. A., Lapham, S., Evenson, K. R., Williamson, S., Golinelli, D., Ward, P., Hillier, A., & McKenzie, T. L. (2013). Use of neighborhood parks: does socio-economic status matter? A four-city study. *Public Health, 127*(4), 325–332. https://doi.org/10.1016/j.puhe.2013.01.003

Cole, A. G. (2007). Expanding the field: revisiting environmental education principles through multidisciplinary frameworks. *J. Environ. Educ. 38*, 35–45. doi: 10.3200/JOEE.38.1.35-46

D'Amore, Chiara, and Louise Chawla. 2017. "Many Children in the Woods: Applying Principles of Community-Based Social Marketing to a Family Nature Club." *Ecopsychology 9* (4): 232–240. doi:10.1089/eco.2017.0019.

Delia, J., & Krasny, M. E. (2018). Cultivating Positive Youth Development, Critical Consciousness, and Authentic Care in Urban Environmental Education. *Frontiers in Psychology, 8*. https://doi.org/10.3389/fpsyg.2017.02340

Derose, K. P., Han, B., Williamson, S., & Cohen, D. A. (2018). Gender Disparities in Park Use and Physical Activity among Residents of High-Poverty Neighborhoods in Los Angeles. Women's Health Issues, 28 (1), 6–13. https://doi.org/10.1016/j.whi.2017.11.003

Driessnack, Martha. 2009. "Ask the Expert. Children and Nature-Deficit Disorder." *Journal for Specialists in Pediatric Nursing 14* (1): 73–75. doi:10.1007/BF00861552

Dubois, B., and Krasny,M. E. (2016). Educating with resilience in mind: addressing climate change in post-sandy New York city. *J. Environ. Educ. 47*, 255–270. doi: 10.1080/00958964.2016.1167004

Eccles, J., and Gootman, J. A. (2002). Community Programs to Promote Youth Development.Washington, DC: National Academies Press.

Edwards, R. C., & Larson, B. M. H. (2020). When screens replace backyards: strategies to connect digital-media-oriented young people to nature. *Environmental Education Research, 26*(7), 950–968. https://doi.org/10.1080/13504622.2020.1776844

Evans, G. W., Jones-Rounds, M. L., Belojevic, G., & Vermeylen, F. (2012). Family income and childhood obesity in eight European cities: the mediating roles of neighborhood characteristics and physical activity. *Social Science & Medicine* (1982), 75(3), 477–481. https://doi.org/10.1016/j.socscimed.2012.03.037

Evans, G. W., & McCoy, J. M. (1998). When buildings don't work: The role of architecture in human health. *Journal of Environmental Psychology*, 18, 85–94

Fischer, K. W., and Bidell, T. R. (2006). "Dynamic development of action and thought and emotion," in Theoretical Models of Human Development.*Handbook of Child Psychology*, eds R. M. Lerner and W. Damon (Hoboken, NJ: JohnWiley & Sons), 313–399. doi: 10.1002/9780470147658.chpsy0107

Garvey, C. (1990). *Play*, 2nd Edn. Cambridge, MA: Harvard University Press

Ghafouri, F., and Wien, C. A. (2005). "Give us a privacy": play and social literacy in young children. *J. Res. Child. Educ. 19*, 279–291. doi: 10.1080/02568540509595071

Ghisleni, C. (2021, March 2). From Farm to Fork: How Architecture Can Contribute to Fresher Food Supply. ArchDaily. https://www.archdaily.com/957802/from-farm-to-fork-how-architecture-can-contribute-to-fresher-food-supply?ad_source=search&ad_medium=search_result_all

Gill, Tim. 2011. Sowing the Seeds: Reconnecting London's Children with Nature. London: Sustainable Development Commission. https://www.london.gov.uk/sites/default/files/lsdc_-_sowing_the_seeds_-_full_report_2011.pdf

Ginwright, S., and Cammarota, J. (2002). New terrain in youth development: the promise of a social justice approach. *Soc. Just. 29*, 82–96. Available online at: http://www.jstor.org/stable/29768150

Gispen, J. (2017a, March). *Ethics for Designers — Ethical Skills*. Ethics for Designers. https://www.ethicsfordesigners.com/skills

Gispen, J. (2017b, March). *Ethics for Designers — Moral Agent*. Ethics for Designers. https://www.ethicsfordesigners.com/tools-1/moral-agent

Gray, P. (2013). *Free to Learn: Why Unleashing the Instinct to Play will make our Children Happier, More Self-Reliant, and Better Students for Life*. New York, NY: Basic Books.

Gruenewald, D. A. (2003). The best of both worlds: a critical pedagogy of place. *Educ. Res. 32*, 3–12. doi: 10.3102/0013189X032004003

Gruenewald, D. A., and Smith, G. A. (2008). *Place-Based Education in the Global Age: Local Diversity*. New York, NY: Lawrence Erlbaum Associates.

Hassinger-Das, B., Bustamante, A., Hirsh-Pasek, K., & Golinkoff, R. (2018). Learning Landscapes: Playing the Way to Learning and Engagement in Public Spaces. *Education Sciences, 8*(2), 74. https://doi.org/10.3390/educsci8020074

Hirsh-Pasek, K., Zosh, J. M., Golinkoff, R., Gray, J., Robb, M., and Kaufman, J. (2015). Putting education in "educational" apps: lessons from the science of learning. *Psychol. Sci. Public Interest 16*, 3–34. doi: 10.1177/1529100615569721

Hughes, J., Richardson, M., & Lumber, R. (2018). Evaluating connection to nature and the relationship with conservation behaviour in children. *Journal for Nature Conservation, 45*, 11–19. https://doi.org/10.1016/j.jnc.2018.07.004

Immordino-Yang, M. H., and Damasio, A. (2007). We feel, therefore we learn: the relevance of affective and social neuroscience to education. *Mind Brain Educ. 1*, 3–10. doi: 10.1111/j.1751-228X.2007.00004.x

Isen, A. M. (1984). "Toward understanding the role of affect in cognition," in *Handbook of Social Cognition, Vol. 3*, eds R. S. Wyer Jr. and T. K. Srull (Mahwah, NJ: Lawrence Erlbaum Associates Publishers), 179–236.

Isen, A. M., Daubman, K. A., and Nowicki, G. P. (1987). Positive affect facilitates creative problem solving. J. *Pers. Soc. Psychol. 52*, 1122–1131. doi: 10.1037/0022-3514.52.6.1122

Kaplan, S., & Kaplan, R. (1982). *Cognition and environment : functioning in an uncertain world*. Praeger.

Kennedy, Eric B., Eric A. Jensen, and Monae Verbeke. 2018. "Preaching to the Scientifically Converted: Evaluating Inclusivity in Science Festival Audiences." *International Journal of Science Education 8* (1): 14–21. doi:10.1080/ 21548455.2017.1371356.

Kellert, S.R. (1993). The biological basis for human values of nature in The biophilia hypothesis (Washington DC: Island Press), 42-69.

Kellert, S. R. (2005). *Building for life: designing and understanding the human-nature connection*. Island Press.

Kellert, S.R., Heerwagen, J. H., & Mador, M. L. (2008). *Biophilic design: the theory, science, and practice of bringing buildings to life*. Wiley.

Krasny, M., Kalbacker, L., Stedman, R., and Russ, A. (2013). Measuring social capital among youth: applications in environmental education. *Environ. Educ. Res. 21*, 1–23. doi: 10.1080/13504622.2013.843647

Krasnor, L. R., and Pepler, D. J. (1980). The study of children's play: some suggested future directions. *New Dir. Child Dev. 9*, 85–95. doi: 10.1002/cd.23219800908

Kudryavtsev, A., Krasny, M. E., and Stedman, R. (2012). The impact of environmental education on sense of place among urban youth. *Ecosphere* 3:29. doi: 10.1890/ES11-00318.1

Larson, L. R., Szczytko, R., Bowers, E. P., Stephens, L. E., Stevenson, K. T., & Floyd, M. F. (2018). Outdoor Time, Screen Time, and Connection to Nature: Troubling Trends Among Rural Youth? *Environment and Behavior, 51*(8), 966–991. https://doi.org/10.1177/0013916518806686

Lerner, R. M., and Lerner, J. V. (2011). *The Positive Development of Youth: Report of the Findings from the First Seven Years of the 4-H Study of Positive Youth Development*. Medford, MA: Institute for Applied Research in Youth Development, Tufts University.

Lerner, R. M., Lerner, V., Almerigi, J. B., Theokas, C., Phelps, E., Gestsdottir, S., et al. (2005). Positive youth development, participation in community youth programs, and community contributions of fifth-grade adolescents: findings from the first wave of the 4-H study of positive youth development. J. *Early Adolesc. 25*, 17–71. doi: 10.1177/0272431604272461

Louv, R. (2005). *Last child in the woods: why children need nature, how it was taken from them, and how to get it back*. Algonquin Books Of Chapel Hill.

Lufkin, B. (2020, June 17). *What outdoor space tells us about inequality*. BBC Worklife. https://www.bbc.com/worklife/article/20200617-the-luxury-and-privilege-of-a-balcony-or-yard-during-covid

McLennan, J. (2018, December 13). *Biophilic Design: A New Scale Emerges*. Trim Tab. https://trimtab.living-future.org/trim-tab/issue-36/biophilic-design-a-new-scale-emerges/

McKenzie, M., Koushik, J. R., Haluza-Delay, R., and Corwin, J. (2017). Environmental justice," in *Urban En-*

vironmental Education Review, eds A. Russ, and M. E. Krasny. Ithaca, NY: Cornell University Press, 59–67.

Mock, B. (2016, June 2). *For African Americans, Park Access Is About More Than Just Proximity*. www.bloomberg.com. https://www.bloomberg.com/news/articles/2016-06-02/a-legacy-of-racism-in-america-s-parks

Moore, S. (2017, March 23). *It's Spring. Don't Just #FindYourPark—Defend Parks for Others*. Healthy Places by Design. Retrieved from https://healthyplacesbydesign.org/its-spring-dont-just-findyourpark-defend-parks-for-others/.

Moore, S. (2019, March 27). *Maslow's Hierarchy of Inequity | Healthy Places by Design*. Healthy Places by Design. https://healthyplacesbydesign.org/maslows-hierarchy-of-inequity/

Mustakova-Possardt, E. (1998). Critical consciousness: an alternative pathway for positive personal and social development. *J. Adult Dev. 5*, 13–30. doi: 10.1023/A:1023064913072

National Recreation and Park Association. (2011). *Parks & Recreation in Underserved Areas A Public Health Perspective*. https://www.nrpa.org/uploadedFiles/nrpa.org/Publications_and_Research/Research/Papers/Parks-Rec-Underserved-Areas.pdf

Nesbitt, L., Meitner, M. J., Girling, C., Sheppard, S. R. J., & Lu, Y. (2019). Who has access to urban vegetation? A spatial analysis of distributional green equity in 10 US cities. *Landscape and Urban Planning, 181*, 51–79. https://doi.org/10.1016/j.landurbplan.2018.08.007

Nisbet, E.K., John M. Zelenski, J.M., & Steven A. Murphy, S.A., (2009, September) "The Nature Relatedness Scale: Linking Individuals' Connection with Nature to Environmental Concern and Behavior." *Environment and Behavior 41*, no. 5, 715–40.

O'Neill, M. (2020, July 2). *Why Justice in Design Is Critical to Repairing America*. Architectural Digest. https://www.architecturaldigest.com/story/justice-in-design-america

Ofcom. 2017. *Children and Parents: Media Use and Attitudes Report 2017*. London: Ofcom. https://www.ofcom.org.uk/research-and-data/media-literacy-research/childrens/children-parents-2017

Park, S., Han, B., Cohen, D. A., & Derose, K. P. (2018). Contributions of Neighborhood Parks to Physical Activity in High-Poverty Urban Neighborhoods. *Journal of Urban Health, 95* (6), 881–887. https://doi.org/10.1007/s11524-018-0320-0

Perkins, H. (2010) "Measuring love and care for nature," *Journal of Environmental Psychology, 30*, 455-463.

Pergams, Oliver R. W., and Patricia A. Zaradic. 2006. "Is Love of Nature in the US Becoming Love of Electronic Media? 16-Year Downtrend in National Park Visits Explained by Watching Movies, Playing Video Games, Internet Use, and Oil Prices." *Journal of Environmental Management 80* (4): 387–393. doi:10.1016/j.jenvman.2006.02.001.

Read the Principles. (n.d.). Design Justice Network. https://designjustice.org/read-the-principles

Roth, J. L., and Brooks-Gunn, J. (2003). "What is a youth development program? Identification of defining principles," in H*andbook of Applied Developmental Science: Promoting Positive Child, Adolescent, and Family Development Through Research, Policies, and Programs*, eds F. Jacobs, D. Wertlieb, and R. M. Lerner. (Thousand Oaks, CA: Sage), 197–223.

Rowl-Shea, J., Doshi, S., Edberg, S., & Fanger, R. (2020, July 21). *The Nature Gap*. Center for American Progress. https://www.americanprogress.org/issues/green/reports/2020/07/21/487787/the-nature-gap/

Savoy, L. E., & Deming, A. H. (2011). Colors of nature: culture, identity, and the natural world. Milkweed Editions.

Schusler, T. M., and Krasny, M. E. (2010). Environmental action as context for youth development. *J. Environ. Educ. 41*, 208–223. doi: 10.1080/00958960903479803

Sefcik, J. S., Kondo, M. C., Klusaritz, H., Sarantschin, E., Solomon, S., Roepke, A., South, E. C., & Jacoby, S. F. (2019). Perceptions of Nature and Access to Green Space in Four Urban Neighborhoods. *International Journal of Environmental Research and Public Health, 16*(13), 2313. https://doi.org/10.3390/ijerph16132313

Sister, C., Wolch, J., & Wilson, J. (2009). Got green? addressing environmental justice in park provision. *GeoJournal, 75*(3), 229–248. https://doi.org/10.1007/s10708-009-9303-8

Sivarajah, S., Smith, S. M., & Thomas, S. C. (2018). Tree cover and species composition effects on academic performance of primary school students. *PLoS ONE, 13*(2). https://doi.org/10.1371/journal.pone.0193254

Smith, G. A. (2007). Place-based education: breaking through the constraining regularities of public school. Environ. Educ. Res. 13, 189–207. doi: 10.1080/13504620701285180

Smith, J. G., DuBois, B., and Krasny, M. E. (2015). Framing resilience through social learning: impacts of environmental stewardship on youth in post-disturbance communities. *Sustain. Sci. 11*, 441–453. doi: 10.1007/s11625-015-0348-y

Spirn, A. W. (1984). *The granite garden: urban nature and human design*. Basic Books.

Strife, S., & Downey, L. (2009). Childhood Development and Access to Nature. *Organization & Environment, 22*(1), 99–122. https://doi.org/10.1177/1086026609333340

Soga, M., & Gaston, K. J. (2018). Shifting baseline syndrome: causes, consequences, and implications. *Frontiers in Ecology and the Environment, 16*(4), 222–230. https://doi.org/10.1002/fee.1794

Sukarieh, M., and Tannock, S. (2011). The positivity imperative: a critical look at the 'new' youth development movement. *J. Youth Stud. 14*, 675–691. doi: 10.1080/13676261.2011.571663

Sustainable Food Center. (2020, March 11). *The True Meaning of Food Access*. Sustainablefoodcenter.org. https://sustainablefoodcenter.org/latest/blog/the-true-meaning-of-food-access

U.S. Department of Health and Human Services. (2020). *Social Determinants of Health - Healthy People 2030*. Health.gov. https://health.gov/healthypeople/objectives-and-data/social-determinants-health

United Nations Children's Fund (UNICEF). (2012). *Children in an Urban World*. https://www.unicef.org/media/89226/file/The%20State%20of%20the%20World

United Nations. (1989). *Convention on the Rights of the Child*. OHCHR. https://www.ohchr.org/en/professionalinterest/pages/crc.aspx

Weisberg, D.S, Hirsh-Pasek, K., Golinkoff, R.M., Kittredge, A.K., & Klahr, D. (2016) Guided Play: Principles and Practices. *Current Directions in Psychological Science 25*(3), 177-182. DOI: 10.1177/0963721416645512

Wen, M., Zhang, X., Harris, C. D., Holt, J. B., & Croft, J. B. (2013). Spatial Disparities in the Distribution of Parks and Green Spaces in the USA. *Annals of Behavioral Medicine, 45*(S1), 18–27. https://doi.org/10.1007/s12160-012-9426-x

What is Co-Design? – And Also Too. (n.d.). And Also Too. https://www.andalsotoo.net/what-is-codesign/

Wilson, E. O. (1984). *Biophilia*. Harvard Univ. Press.

World Health Organization. (1978). *Declaration of Alma-Ata*. www.who.int. https://www.who.int/teams/social-determinants-of-health/declaration-of-alma-ata

Youth Outside. (n.d.). *Deepening Commitments: Working Toward Equity and Inclusion When Connecting Youth to the Outdoors - A Case Study. In Justice Outside*. https://justiceoutside.org/wp-content/uploads/general-upload/Cultural-Relevancy-Case-Study-2017.pdf

Zosh, J. M, Hirsh-Pasek, K., Golinkoff, R. M., and Dore, R. A. (2017). "Where learning meets creativity: The promise of guided play," in *Creative Contradictions in Education: Cross Disciplinary Paradoxes and Perspectives*, eds R. Beghetto and B. Sriraman (New York, NY: Springer International Publishing), 165–180. doi: 10.1007/978-3-319-21924-0_10

Zosh, J. M., Hirsh-Pasek, K., Hopkins, E. J., Jensen, H., Liu, C., Neale, D., Solis, S. L., & Whitebread, D. (2018). Accessing the Inaccessible: Redefining Play as a Spectrum. *Frontiers in Psychology, 9*. https://doi.org/10.3389/fpsyg.2018.01124

Zylstra, M. J., Knight, A. T., Esler, K. J., & Le Grange, L. L. L. (2014). Connectedness as a Core Conservation Concern: An Interdisciplinary Review of Theory and a Call for Practice. *Springer Science Reviews, 2*(1-2), 119–143. https://doi.org/10.1007/s40362-014-0021-3

Space Syntax Applications for Window Access and Daylight Design

Sadiqa Al Awadh (University of Oregon); Linda Nubani (Michigan State University); Ihab Elzeyadi (Dept. of Architecture)

ABSTRACT

In office work environments, occupants are often seated in the same workstation for a prolonged period of time. If they do not receive the recommended quantity and quality of light or access to windows, this will be reflected in their decreased wellbeing, satisfaction, and productivity. An isovist, a constructed planar two-dimensional polygon that represents the totality of all visible and potentially visible space from a specific location usually at eye level, can be used to assess spatial compositions and vistas. Space syntax methods have not assessed office interiors from access to windows perspective. This requires designers to pay more attention to isovists and visibility within the indoor building layout to determine if occupants do receive adequate daylight, or whether they do not, despite meeting building performance benchmarks. This paper proposes the use of daylight simulation and isovist analyses methods together as a more holistic approach and method to assess indoor environments from an occupant perspective. An office building was simulated in ALFA for Rhino to run a daylight simulation and the Isovist software was used for the isovist analysis to assess various point perspectives within the building. Several general conclusions were drawn from the analyses that support the use of isovist properties to inform window access and daylight availability. Other more specific recommendations could be applied to the same floorplate types and interior layouts.

KEYWORDS

Daylight; Space Syntax; Isovist; Window

1. INTRODUCTION

An isovist is a constructed planar two-dimensional polygon that represents the totality of all visible and potentially visible space from a specific location, usually at eye level. The term was first coined by Tandy (1967) who focused on natural landscape surveying methods and viewsheds of a site for creating a permanent record of what would be dependent on either memory or upon a number of annotated photographs. The isovist term was subsequently introduced into built environment analysis by Benedikt (1979) who devised many of the isovist measures still in use today. Defining spatial components of the environment by means of isovists will allow for the prediction of trends, optima, and limits on a variety of possible spatial behaviors and perceptions in a given environment. In order to quantify a whole configuration, more than a single isovist is required. The interplay of isovists explains how we experience a space, and how we use it.

This paper introduces space syntax methods that address the importance of determining window availability to predict and measure daylight availability and access to views from an occupant's spatial position and viewshed from within the building interior. From a seated occupant's view, the isovist area and perimeter local measures are important to determine the visibility of windows and access to daylight. From an architectural standpoint, drift will identify regions from which space can be surveyed with a minimum of head-turning which will help assess a zone's performance in terms of how much vertical illuminance can be received by occupants facing specific directions.

Space syntax isovist analyses methods have not previously assessed office interiors from an access to windows for outdoor views or daylight availability perspective. Investigations on the spatial composition of office layouts reflect programmatic requirements for adjacency, clustering, isolation, control, supervision, hierarchical stratification, and functional processes. Similarly, lighting analyses do not necessarily investigate vertical illuminance and occupant access to windows and daylight from their seated positions. Priority is given to light transmittance performance and light distribution in the space.

This paper bridges both lighting design and space syntax fields together to provide a process of assessing building daylight performance. This novel method allows designers from both lighting and interior design fields to understand the considerations to be taken during the design stages and brings awareness to influencing design parameters.

1.1 Windows, Daylight and Biophilia

The vast literature has investigated daylight's role in building design from many angles. It has been historically admired for its architectural and aesthetic complexity, and has been more recently accepted as a driver for sustainable design. Though the field has primarily addressed daylight architecturally in terms of these daylight distribution, visual comfort, and energy efficiency metrics, there has been a recent increased interest in the health and well-being components. This is partly due to the recent discovery of the intrinsically photosensitive retinal ganglion cells (ipRGCs) which are responsible for non-image forming or non-visual functions, both physiological and psychological which include regulating the circadian biological clock and hormones, body temperature, heart rate, vitamin D synthesis, mood, stress, depression, and alertness (Lucas et al., 2014).

With technological advancements, occupants tend to resort to electric lighting for its instrumental benefits as it offers a controlled electric lighting system with uniform illumination to meet visual task needs. It is constant and predictable, whereas daylight is dynamic and can be unpredictable (Haans, 2014). There are common misconceptions that daylight has only an architectural and aesthetic value, and all other daylight functions can be replaced by electrical lighting solutions. From a physiological standpoint, the literature suggests that melatonin suppression, circadian entrainment, and occupant alertness can be stimulated with electric lighting – provided it replicates daylight's characteristics. Luminous characteristics of both daylight and electric light are determined by its spectrum, color temperature, quantity or intensity, and directionality. Other temporal characteristics of light include timing, duration, and history are factors that are mostly dependent on a building's occupancy patterns which vary from one person to another (Khademagha et al., 2016). Based on critical reviews that address the difficulty of replicating daylight, the feasibility of that is questionable. Other psychological benefits such as views and preferences argue for the implementation of daylighting.

A common study observation notes that people will tolerate much lower illuminance levels of daylight than electric light, particularly in diminishing daylight conditions at the end of the day (Baker, 2000). This appeals to our biophilic nature that yearns for a sense of naturalness even in the indoor environment. Building occupants who have a greater connection to nature promoted by sunlight in office environments are noted to have better physical, emotional, and intellectual well-being. Optimal sunlight penetration levels that create maximum degrees of relaxation range from 15%-25% of floor area and sunlight sparkles are generally preferred to large floods when the occupant is sideways to the window (Boubekri et al., 1991).

In a study of windowless offices, Ruys (1970) found that 87% of the occupants indicated that they preferred to have windows in their office and that 47.5% of them thought that the lack of windows affected them physically and/or their work. Among the reasons given for being affected were lack of daylight, poor ventilation, desire to know weather conditions, desire to look in the distance for the view, feeling of being cooped up, isolated and claustrophobic, feeling depressed and tense. It was found that size, office color, lighting level, and the distance to a window had no relationship to the dissatisfaction with the lack of windows. Hence it would seem that the window in its own right performs a unique role, distinct from the provision of light. That unique role may be the ability to be in contact with the external world.

In other studies, it has also been found that lighting quality and views influenced occupant's sick leave where occupants seated in workstations with poor lighting quality and poorer views used significantly more sick leaves (Elzeyadi, 2011, Elzeyadi, 2012). Office workers with the best possible view, as opposed to no view, performed 10% to 25% better on tests of mental function and memory recall (Heschong, 2003).This highlights the necessity of creating a physical and visual connection to nature and the outdoors. This can be achieved by means of manipulating the façade's glazing to provide thoughtful window placement and design.

Creating a human connection to restorative environments can be more challenging than prescribing lighting parameters to achieve energy savings guidelines and minimum quantitative requirements. -Despite the uncertainties and complex human psychological ambiguities, buildings are ultimately designed for people. Thus, designing an indoor environment with an appropriate lighting atmosphere and access to windows should be a critical design consideration.

2. RESEARCH OBJECTIVES

2.1 Space Syntax Software Measures

There are two prominent computer simulation software tools used for isovist analyses 'Isovist' and 'depthmapX'. The measures and fields generated by Isovist have been developed from the isovist literature based on Benedikt (1979) as well as from space syntax literature based on the work of Hillier (2007) and Hanson (1984). The two works of literature overlap, conceptually and in application. Isovist work tends to focus on the building interiors, and on human social and aesthetic experience and perception, whilst depthmapX space syntax tends to focus on the city, behavior, and configurative aspects of space.

The Isovist software is used for this study. The isovist analysis in this software allows basic visual analysis using 'point isovists', 'region isovists', or 'isovist agents'. A 'point isovist', as used in this study, is set by the user moving the cursor or clicking at a point of interest, it identifies the space in plan that falls within the isovist from any given location. The isovist menu controls the parameters of isovist sweep (angle of view cone), direction (heading that the isovist is 'looking' in), far rim (how far the isovist can 'see'), near rim (an internal horizon that sets the nearest visible edges of the isovist).

The software produces twenty-one different field measures, ten are 'local' isovist measures that relate to occupant experience within space; Area (or Connectivity), Perimeter, Compactness, Occlusivity, Vista Length, Average Radial, Drift, Variance, Skewness and Curvature. Five are 'global' space syntax-type measures that characterize configurational relations across a plan as a whole; Choice, Mean Metric Depth, Mean Visual Depth, Mean Angular Depth, and Integration (HH). The remaining six measures are 'semi-local' or relational measures that span between local and global information; Visibility, Control, Controllability, Metric Depth to Location, Visual Depth to Location, and Angular Depth to Location. To help assess when a field analysis is 'complete'. Local isovist measures tend to be statistically stable after 3-5 local cycles, and global space syntax measures after 200+ global cycles.

The measures extracted from the Isovist software analysis that are related to the scope of the study are defined as follows (isovists.org, 2017):

- Area: expresses the area of all space visible from a subject point in the plan. It represents the number of other subject points that a location is directly connected to.
- Perimeter: expresses the length of the edge of all space visible from a location. It represents the geometric isovist perimeter at a location.
- Compactness: expresses the shape property (relative to a circle) of all space visible from a location. In an isovist field, compactness identifies the regions of plan in which an observ-

er's spatial experience is contiguously consistent.

- Drift: expresses the distance from a subject point to the center of gravity of its isovist. It identifies the inherent flow within a series of spaces. High Drift identifies regions from which space can be surveyed with a minimum of head-turning.
- Occlusivity: represents how previously unseen space may be revealed during movement. Occlusivity fields show moments of dramatic visual change as a user passes between spaces.
- Vista: expresses the longest single view available at each location. Vista Length values identify regions of high axial view.
- Visibility: expresses how often any given subject point is seen from a defined sample region. In isovist terminology, it represents how often a space falls within an isovist generated from within said region.

Another important measure that was computed from the data collected is the A/P ratio. This ratio is calculated by dividing the isovist area by the isovist perimeter. If the ratio drops below 1, then the perimeter value exceeds the area value. This indicates a narrow isovist spike. When the ratio is lower than 0.5 then the visual flow is extremely spiky. The A/P ratio has various applications including explaining patterns of crime (Nubani, 2006). For this study's purposes, the ratio is used to indicate visual obstructions that could diminish vertical illuminance transmitted through windows.

3. METHODS

In this study an office building was simulated in ALFA for Rhino to run the daylight analysis and Isovist to run the isovist analysis. "Adaptive Lighting for Alertness" (ALFA), developed by Solemma, deploys spectral calculations that carry out 81-channel renderings. These consider skies using libRadtran, glazing and materials using the international glazing database and is embedded into the Rhinoceros 3d CAD system with the Radiance lighting engine extension.

The Chiat/Day Advertising building located in California was designed by Frank Gehry & Associates in 1991. It has a 22,100 sq ft gross floor area and a 18,700 sq ft net floor area. The building has a wings floor plate type. For the isovist analysis, 30% of the total number of workstations were used as sample point isovist locations. This percentage can be used to ensure a consistent comparison for future studies across all buildings.

The point isovist visual analysis sweep was set to 179 degrees to best depict occupants' cone of vision in stationary positions at their workstations. For visual purposes, in the point isovist diagram (Figure 1) both the accessible (dark blue) and visible (light blue) isovist cones of vision were overlayed to differentiate what can be seen through the window (light blue) and within the building (dark blue). Accessible point isovists are restricted to just inside the building. The software includes the area through the windows when visible point isovists are selected. For the numerical data, only the visible point isovists were used to easily identify which points have window access (thus a much larger isovist area). By triggering the 'extended visibility' option for the area heat map (Figure 2b), it depicts the area through the windows too – which is what is used for the numerical data.

For a general analysis, the visual analysis sweep was set to 360 degrees for all heat maps. This provides an overview from all locations and all view directions within the building. Additionally, the drift heat map (Figure 2c) was overlayed with flow vectors which draw a series of vector lines that indicate the direction and magnitude of the field results at locations throughout the space.

It should be noted that in some buildings there are wall partitions that are only 1.3m high. These are high enough to block visual connections but allow daylight transmittance over them. The other interior walls are 3m from floor to ceiling, these do not allow visual connections or daylight through. The Isovist software does not differentiate between interior partitions and wall heights as it works two-dimensionally.

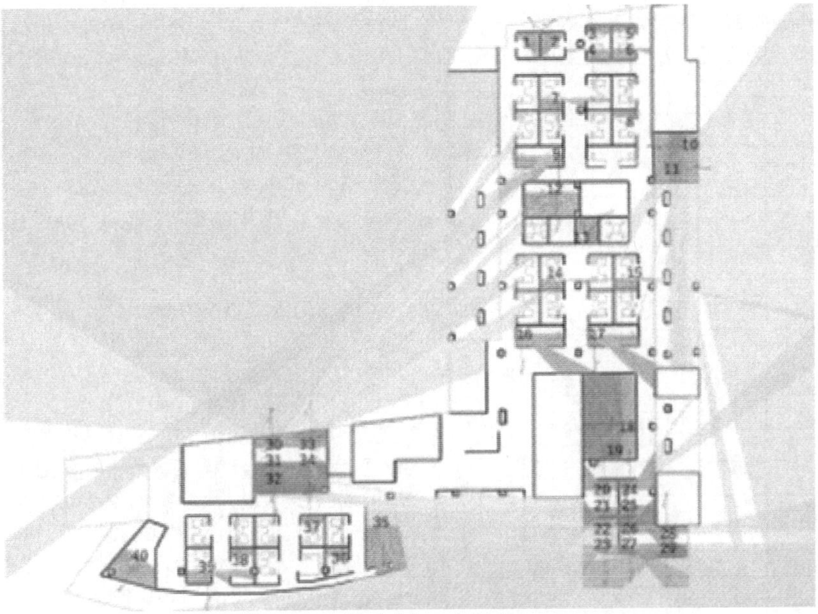

Figure 1: *Point isovist diagram*

For the study's purposes, the isovist analysis remains unaffected since in both partitions and walls cases visual connections are blocked. The daylight simulation address the differences in heights and are visually indicated in the horizontal illuminance isolux plans. Areas in red depict a high value of the respective measure, areas in blue depict lower values of the measure that is being examined.

To check the building's performance, the LEED and WELL credit requirements were benchmarked against the isovist results as follows:

- 75% of all workstations have a direct line of sight to the outdoors, up to 30% may be used as views into interior atria.
- 70% of all workstations to be within 16 ft of the envelope glazing with views to the outdoors.

These benchmarks were used across the 30% of the total number of workstations which were used as sample point isovist locations.

4. RESULTS

With a 0% cellular floor area and a 30.9% open plan floor area, the building's predominant layout is open plan. The L-shaped plot has dictated the shape of the floorplate, while the sculptural entrance and the three atria have affected a rather indented perimeter. Despite having many atria and an open plan, the visual flow is very disrupted in this building. This can be seen in the plan which indicates very low A/P ratios, most below 0.5. The core, despite small in size, joins the perimeter and segregates a narrow zone of the floorplate behind it. The cubicles contradict the openness of the plan. Though the cubicle height permits daylight, seated occupants' views are blocked by the partitions. Pairs of workstations are arranged to form groups of 2x3 and 2x2 in a grid layout.

The disrupted visual flow is also partly due to the wings floor plate type which breaks the plan into two smaller separated areas, rather than one open connected space. The primary circulation consists of two parallel corridors at the periphery of each wing, whereby two of them connect to form an L-shape spine.

The isovist analysis shows that 10 out of 40 workstations have direct views to the outdoors and 3

Point	Area	Perimeter	Area / Perimeter	ompactnes	Drift	Occlusivity	Vista
1	3.33	8.29	0.40	0.61	0.65	0.00	1.90
2	4.27	9.14	0.47	0.64	0.79	0.00	2.17
3	2.83	7.49	0.38	0.63	0.85	0.00	2.16
4	5.18	18.61	0.28	0.19	0.74	0.15	5.82
5	1.64	6.51	0.25	0.49	0.75	0.00	2.11
6	3.08	11.00	0.28	0.32	0.82	0.11	2.35
7	3.86	18.13	0.21	0.15	0.50	0.17	5.72
8	1.66	6.53	0.25	0.49	0.89	0.00	2.25
9	191.42	181.99	1.05	0.07	52.92	0.80	85.04
10	69.83	108.47	0.64	0.07	9.44	0.17	24.07
11	1372.50	262.11	5.24	0.25	22.01	0.49	59.87
12	16.96	17.87	0.95	0.67	1.44	0.00	4.37
13	5.19	9.36	0.55	0.74	0.99	0.00	2.57
14	6.44	19.68	0.33	0.21	1.10	0.11	5.95
15	29.56	76.65	0.39	0.06	18.57	0.74	34.15
16	15.97	25.91	0.62	0.30	3.59	0.25	8.94
17	19.75	27.06	0.73	0.32	3.79	0.21	9.13
18	38.60	26.84	1.44	0.67	2.31	0.00	7.00
19	51.49	29.44	1.75	0.75	4.53	0.00	9.54
20	5.83	12.65	0.46	0.46	1.18	0.11	3.85
21	1267.50	188.44	6.73	0.45	36.87	0.40	69.75
22	99.37	100.94	0.98	0.12	15.14	0.14	37.89
23	1418.61	197.34	7.19	0.46	37.48	0.34	72.47
24	135.88	94.23	1.44	0.19	26.21	0.71	43.16
25	63.94	60.75	1.05	0.22	16.28	0.69	26.36
26	5.84	12.50	0.47	0.47	1.80	0.14	4.25
27	306.21	79.92	3.83	0.60	15.82	0.26	28.10
28	84.94	75.80	1.12	0.19	14.89	0.33	27.29
29	2021.85	220.98	9.15	0.52	28.91	0.31	76.16
30	3924.51	372.79	10.53	0.35	38.84	0.27	77.82
31	24.99	21.99	1.14	0.65	2.44	0.00	6.34
32	8.76	17.77	0.49	0.35	1.65	0.00	5.60
33	4187.70	327.96	12.77	0.49	38.18	0.28	75.96
34	23.84	21.68	1.10	0.64	2.78	0.00	6.87
35	965.76	149.42	6.46	0.54	28.12	0.30	52.39
36	2.55	7.07	0.36	0.64	0.73	0.00	2.07
37	1.42	6.18	0.23	0.47	0.54	0.00	1.82
38	1.93	6.58	0.29	0.56	0.61	0.00	1.91
39	10.20	23.38	0.44	0.23	1.60	0.19	5.47
40	13.81	16.75	0.82	0.62	1.51	0.00	4.05

Table 1 (above): *Building isovist data points*
Figure 2 (below): *Building plotted isovist point measures*

more have views into the internal atria. At 25%, these account for less than the 75% required outdoors views, and the 1% internal atria views does not exceed the 30% internal view maximum, which means the building samples do not meet the benchmarks with an adjusted 26% total. The plans also show that out of 22 out of 40 workstations are within 16 ft of the envelope glazing. At 55%, the 70% benchmark requirements are not met.

4.1 Visual Depth to Location

A 'visual step' is taken whenever a path passes across the threshold of all space visible from the start of the previous visible step. This can be used to assess the visual accessibility of a daylight source. The lower the step depth, the more accessible the location is visually. It can potentially warrant and maximize the potential of a window or atrium location in the early design stages. Figure 4 shows an example of this measure at an atrium location in the building. The results indicate a step depth maximum of 5, minimum 1, and average 3. Figure 5 shows the horizontal illuminance analysis of the building floorplan which identifies areas that lack daylight and need to be addressed with accessible daylight sources.

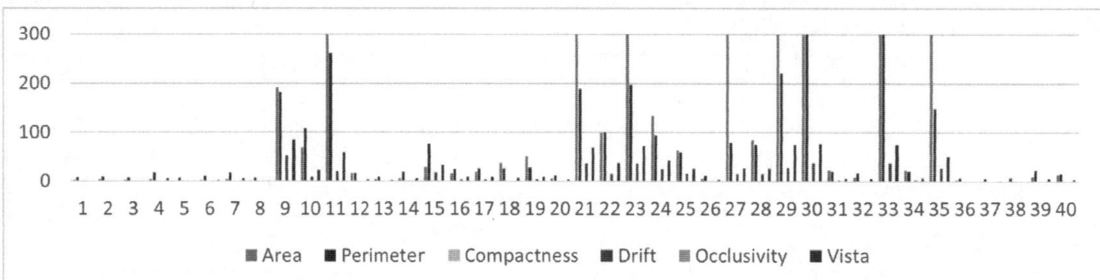

5. CONCLUSIONS

Isovist areas plotted on a bar chart can easily identify workstations that have access to windows. This could be used to calculate the percentage of workstations with window access. Overlaying a daylighting analysis and an isovist area analysis can identify workstations that receive sufficient daylight over the partitions but do not have access to window views. Drift flow vectors overlay can help assess the openness of a design and occupants' ease of surveying the unobstructed space to receive sufficient vertical light. An isovist compactness heat map can easily identify open cubicle and closed office work areas. Visual depth to location can be used to assess the visual accessibility of a daylight source. This could be used to warrant and maximize the potential of a window or atrium location.

Several conclusions were drawn from the isovist analyses that could be applied to the same floorplate types and interior layouts. In the cases where cores were centrally located in the plans, daylight reaches deeper into the buildings, and it provides more potential for workstations to be placed along the envelope to maximize views. In cases where the perimeter is used for closed cellular offices, these block any views and do not permit daylight past the perimeter zone. This could be compromised by either designing lower partitions instead of solid walls or allocating atria that would provide supplemental daylight and allow users to survey the space with internal views for the workstations found deeper into the plan. Open-plan offices with clustered workstations have higher drift and lower A/P ratios, whereas open-plan cubicle offices create spaces with high occlusivity and, smaller vistas, and obstructed lines of sight.

In the end, the design decisions need to be balanced out to enhance occupant wellbeing but also meet requirements for privacy and space allocation based on the culture of the office to prioritize the zones that would be used most.

6. DISCUSSION

This study has been limited to one office floorplate type and a fully glazed curtain wall building. Future works can investigate how various office floorplates and glazing percentages or window to wall ratios perform. With a larger sample and more analyses, they can be classified and measured with isovist components. This approach helps with design predictions of workstations based on architectural design parameters and isovist components at early design stages or can help rectify buildings for post occupancy evaluations.

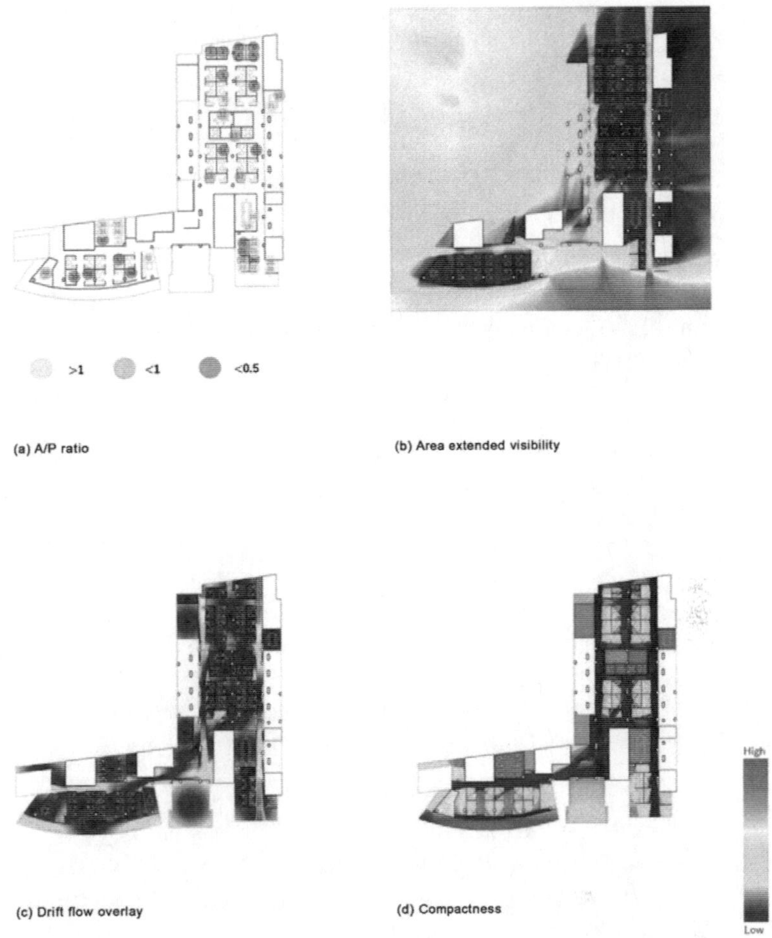

Figure 3 (above): *Isovist results summary compilation*
Figure 4 (below left): *Point analysis of visual depth to location*
Figure 5 (below right): *Building horizontal illuminance analysis*

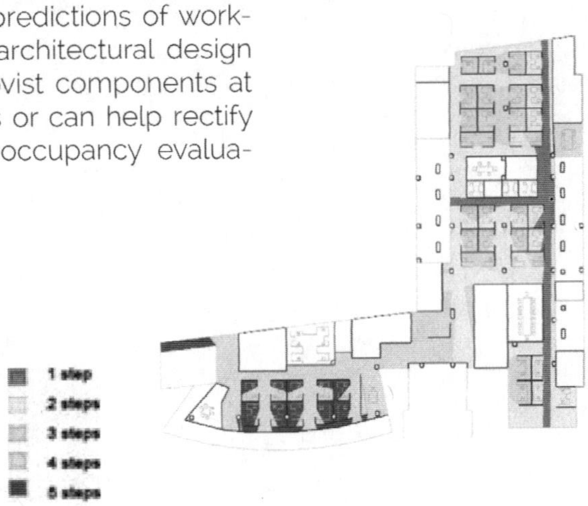

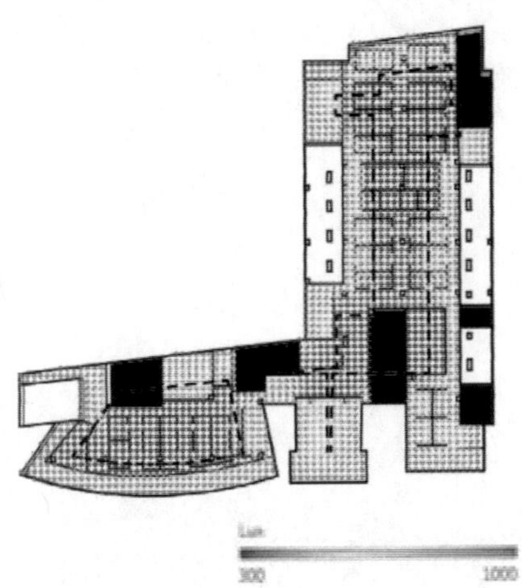

The future direction of this research is to deduce rules of thumb or guidelines to enable designers to meet daylight and view benchmark requirements with ease. The aim is to have an accessible and holistic approach that would tackle more than one issue simultaneously. Designing human-centric environments is still a relatively new concept and not usually the driving force in building design. Though this research has aimed to shed light on its importance and provide strategies for these considerations, it must still be accepted that stakeholders need more incentive and accessible methods to incorporate design for occupant wellbeing.

7. REFERENCES

Baker, N. 2000. We Are All Outdoor Animals. Architecture City Environment, *Proceedings of PLEA, 2000*, 553-555.

Benedikt, M. L. 1979. To Take Hold of Space: Isovists and Isovist Fields. *Environment and Planning B: Planning and design, 6*, 47-65.

Boubekri, M., Hull, R. B. & Boyer, L. L. 1991. Impact of Window Size and Sunlight Penetration on Office Workers' Mood and Satisfaction: A Novel Way of Assessing Sunlight. *Environment and Behavior, 23*, 474-493.

Elzeyadi, I. 2011. Daylighting-Bias and Biophilia: Quantifying the Impact of Daylighting on Occupants Health. *University of Oregon-School of Architecture & Allied Arts*.

Elzeyadi, I. 2012. Health and Healing Impacts of Daylight in the Workplace. *World health*.

Haans, A. A. 2014. The Natural Preference in People's Appraisal of Light. *Journal of Environmental Psychology, 39*, 51-61.

Heschong, L. 2003. Windows and Offices: A Study of Office Worker Performance and the Indoor Environment. *California Energy Commission*, 1-5.

Hillier, B. 2007. *Space Is the Machine: A Configurational Theory of Architecture*, Space Syntax.

Hillier, B. & Hanson, J. 1984. *The Social Logic of Space*, Cambridge Univ. Pr.

Isovists.Org. 2017. *Isovists.Org* [Online]. Available: isovists.org

Khademagha, P., Aries, M., Rosemann, A. & Van Loenen, E. 2016. Implementing Non-Image-Forming Effects of Light in the Built Environment: A Review on What We Need. *Building and Environment, 108*, 263-272.

Lucas, R. J., Peirson, S. N., Berson, D. M., Brown, T. M., Cooper, H. M., Czeisler, C. A., Figueiro, M. G., Gamlin, P. D., Lockley, S. W., O'hagan, J. B., Price, L. L. A., Provencio, I., Skene, D. J. & Brainard, G. C. 2014. Measuring and Using Light in the Melanopsin Age. *Trends in Neurosciences, 37*, 1-9.

Nubani, L. N. 2006. *Targets for Crime: Measuring the Spatial and Visual Attributes of Crime Locations Using Space Syntax*.

Ruys, T. 1970. *Windowless Offices*. University of Washington.

Tandy 1967. The Isovist Method of Landscape Survey. *Symposium: Methods of Landscape Analysis*, 9-10.

The Association Between Urban Environments and Hedonic Well-Being

Asesh Sarkar (IIT Roorkee); Tina Pujara (IIT Roorkee)

ABSTRACT

Studies have established a strong association between urbanization and the rise in mental disorders amongst the urban population. Globally, urbanization is at its peak and hence, comprehending how urbanization may be leading to a rise in mental disorders, is the urgent need of the hour. Literature suggests that urban environments (UE) may be directly impacting mental well-being (MW). It further suggests that these impacts may be either positive or negative, depending on the respective environment. However, research seems to have paid less attention on considering particularly how the physical and social environments may be impacting the hedonic well-being of the urban inhabitants. This paper is an attempt to understand the relationship between UE and MW with particular regard to the physical and social environments and specifically the hedonic well-being (HW). This literature review identified articles particularly related to urban environment indicators associated with well-being and their impact on hedonic well-being, at both urban and neighborhood scale. The selection of the research papers and review papers were based on the relationship of indicators of the PE with HW and the relationship between the urban social environment resulting as the perceived environment with HW. This paper presents the relationship between UE and HW, in form of the UE-indicators identified, with reference to both its positive and negative impacts on HW. The identification of these indicators, particularly focusing on the physical and social environments of the urban scenario is a step towards developing a methodology for assessing the impact of UE on MW. This methodology may further be a contribution towards mentally healthy city design.

KEYWORDS

Urban Environment; Hedonic Well-being; Urban Indicators; Assessment Framework

1. INTRODUCTION

A 2017 study states that 792 million people lived with a mental health disorder which is somewhat more than one in ten people globally (10.7%) (Hannah Ritchie, 2018). It has also been stated that around one in five of the world's children and adolescents have a mental disorder and depression, a type of mental illness is one of the leading causes of disability, affecting 264 million people (United Nations, 2020). According to the report, depression and anxiety cost the global economy around $1 trillion every year in lost productivity. It has been observed people having severe mental conditions tends to die 10-20 years earlier than the normal population. Between 76% to 85% of people with mental health conditions receive no treatment for their condition in low- and middle- income countries and globally there is less than one mental health professional for every 10,000 people (WHO, 2019).

World Health Organization (WHO) has estimated that mental health related problems account for 12% of the global burden of disease. The burden of the mental disorders can be found maximum in young adults and developing countries are going to face a large increase in the burden of mental disorders in coming decades (World Health Organization, 2003). World Health Organization (WHO) is working selflessly to enhance the mental health of individuals and society at large scale; for promotion of MW, the exclusion of mental disorders, guard the human rights and taking care of the people affected by mental disorders.

Studies show that there is a tremendous rise in the urban population worldwide and also indicates direct link between urbanization and mental health. Though there are numerous factors that influence one's mental health, rapid urbanization and the resulting rapid growth of the physical built environment have been connected to an increase in mental health concerns. Mental health is affected by the influence of increased stressors and factors like overcrowding, polluted environment, high level of crime and violence and reduced social support (Kalpana Srivastava, 2009). The increase in the urban population which leads to the demand of new infrastructures, services, facilities is pushing towards a risk of poverty and exposure to environmental affliction, which further decreases social support. Though their relationships are complex, literature confirms significant relationship of UE and MW.

The urban environments which consist of the PE (natural environment and the built environment) and SE, shows a direct impact on the mental well-being. Predominantly the PE is essential as it directly has an effect on the MW and also influences the social behavior which indirectly affects the well-being. A study (Dempsey, 2008) that the condition of the built environment has a direct influence on social cohesion or the social relationships among people within the community. Low quality of the built environment discourages human to human interaction while good quality environmental design, public spaces encourages people to interact, meet and maintain social integrity among themselves.(Ferguson & Evans, 2003) critically analyzed that the characteristics of the built environment can directly influence the mental health in addition to the environmental characteristics of the housing, crowding, indoor air quality and light.

Studies present that the concept of mental well-being incorporates three interrelated types of well-being- hedonic, psychological and social well-being. The psychological and social are two aspects which are collectively termed as the eudemonic well-being. Research has also concluded that hedonic well-being may depend on individually determined positive mental states and hence may be the result of short-lived effects such as the achievement of pleasure and avoidance of pain. However, the eudemonic well-being tends to be linked with lasting effects.

An impressive amount of research on relations between urban environments and, mental well-being as a whole, has been conducted. Notwithstanding this substantial body of literature, little is known about the interaction of the urban environment specifically with each of the three well-being types, the hedonic, the psychological and the social. Social interaction, social networks, sense of community, participation in organized activities, trust and reciprocity, feelings of safety and also, sense of place attachment, all, do find a mention in past studies with regard to the assessment of the quality of built environment. And, the indicators which help assess this quality, have also been categorically listed as, density, mixed land use, attractiveness, connectedness, legibility, accessibility, inclusiveness, maintenance, coverage of natural surveillance and neighborhood character. However, a complete and detailed focus on the urban environment characteristics which may be directly impacting the HW, seems to have been neglected.

This study specifically focuses on HW and presents the identified indicators of the UE for HW, through the conduct of an extensive literature review of selected scholarly articles. It further presents the categorization of these identified indicators under two heads, the physical and the social environment. A total of 15 indicators were identified under six categories of the 'physical environment', namely greenspaces, infrastructure, housing, spatial configuration, outdoor environment quality, urban design. Also, a total of three indicators were identified under one category the 'social environment', namely safety. The study further categorizes the plausible positive and negative impacts of urban environments on the hedonic well-being of its inhabitants, through these identified indicators.

The identification of these indicators, categorized under the physical and social environments of the urban scenario, is a step towards developing a methodology for assessing the impact of urban environments on HW. This methodology may further be a contribution towards mentally healthy city design by developing an assessment framework based on respective contexts. This would also contribute to the achievement of the 'Sustainable Development Goals,' such as health and well-being and the development of sustainable communities.

2. RESEARCH OBJECTIVES

1. To understand the concepts of UE, MW and the relationship between UE and MW.
2. To identify the indicators of the UE that are affecting the hedonic well-being
3. To understand the impact of UE indicators on hedonic well-being

3. METHODS

Around a hundred scholarly articles and review papers on the connection between PE, SE, and HW were studied to establish the theoretical base. The methods include selecting research papers, review papers based on the relationship of indicators of the PE with HW and the relationship between the urban social environment resulting as the perceived environment with HW. This literature review identified articles particularly related to urban environment indicators associated with well-being and their impact on hedonic well-being, at both urban and neighborhood scale. Research papers with terms describing mental health and well-being in the built environment (e.g. urban, built) context were examined. Studies with keywords related to urban environments indicators (e.g., housing quality, social spaces, environment design, green spaces, etc.) associated with terms describing mental health and well-being (e.g., psychological distress, quality of life, anxiety, fear and stress etc.) were reviewed. The studies were chosen based on quantitative and qualitative criteria that revealed either favorable or negative relationship. The literature study helped to understand the concepts of UE, MW and their association between them.

Even there are researches related to the 'built environment and mental well-being'; 'the social environment and mental well-being'; 'the built environment and the social environment' but there are no such studies or research done taking all these three concepts (the physical environment, the social environment and mental well-being) together. The first part of the literature reviews starts with studying the concept of UE and its component; the mental well-being aspects, and the relationship between UE and MW. The second part summarizes different indicators of the PE and SE and their association with the HW.

4. URBAN ENVIRONMENT

The term environment can be broadly, categorized as natural environments, social settings, built environments, ecological environments, cultural environments learning environments, and informational environments. Every indicator and entity of the UE have some effect on well-being. However, few of the features are affecting positively, and few are affecting negatively. Human behavior, reactions, reciprocation, interactions can be altered by changing the quality of the environmental settings. The environment here is more than the aesthetic quality, architectural design and urban landscaping. It's more of a surrounding that can create moments, memory, and experiences that can help develop an emotional connection, thus enhancing the individual's well-being. The urban context or UE can be defined as the characteristics or features of cities that impact both the physical health and mental health. It first emerged in the context of urban and land-use planning, as it was a point of concern for hygienic, reformist or utopian planning movements, which had an impact on how cities were built in the late nineteenth century (Découverte & Cornut, 2019).

Many authors (Ompad, Galea, & Vlahov, 2007) defined urban environment as three distinct concepts: the SE, the PE and the urban resource infrastructure. The urban environment is also believed to be common point for social relations, global and local issues, problems that need solving, and results or impacts linked to human activities (Senecal, 2007). Nevertheless, the concept and context of UE are widely used and differently used in distinctive field of study, the inner components and characteristics of UE remain identical. This paper mainly reflects the impact of UE on MW, UE as broadly divided into two categories a) the Physical Environment and b) the Social Environment.

4.1 Physical Environment

The constructed environment, pollutants, and geological and climate conditions of the city are all addressed in the urban PE (Ompad et al., 2007). The built environment includes "housing form, roads and footpaths, transport networks, shops, markets, parks and other public amenities, public space" as described by (Weich et al., 2001). (Ottawa, Ont.: CIHI, 2011) further elaborated the definition of PE as "the physical design and layout of neighborhoods and communities, including buildings and public spaces" like a) Urban form: the pattern of building and development in a city and the structural elements that form cities, such as natural features, transportation corridors and open spaces, b) Outdoor air pollution: the presence of pollutants harmful to health (Ottawa, Ont.: CIHI, 2011), c) Green space: the presence of green space and vegetated areas within urban settings (Ottawa, Ont.: CIHI, 2011). Another researcher (Anderson et al., 1996) described urban form the foremost component of the PE as patterns of building and development in a city and the structural elements that form cities, such as natural features, transportation corridors and open spaces, or urban form' which purely defines a city's physical characteristics. At the broad city or regional scale, urban form has been expressed as the spatial configuration of fixed elements (Anderson et al., 1996). In this study Greenspaces, Infrastructure, Spatial configuration, Outdoor Environment Quality, Urban Design, and Density are taken into consideration as the main categories of the urban PE that are associated with the HW.

4.2 Social Environment

The urban SE defines the behavior, attitudes and values by members of different social groups alongside the interpersonal relations and interactions shared among urban residents and communities (Kawachi, 2006) and as stated by (Kawachi, 2006) features of the SE can both harm and promote health. Research findings show that several features of quality of the built environment substantially affect dimensions of social cohesion to varying degrees. Overall, the results showed that several elements of the built environment such as high residential density, mixed land uses, accessibility, connectedness and permeability, legibility, attractiveness, inclusiveness, maintenance has a direct effect on the social structure.

The extent of natural surveillance, character, perceived quality, and the attractiveness of the community have a substantial effect on aspects of social cohesion such as residents' perceptions of quality of the neighborhood. (Dempsey, 2008). The PE influences the social activities such as social interactions, Social networks, a sense of community, participation in organized activities, trust and reciprocity, feeling of safety sense of place attachment (Dempsey, 2008). There is prevalent understanding in urban design policy and local authority practice that well-maintained built environments promote positive social activities (Cabe Space, 2013) among the people within the neighborhood thus promoting mental health. The SE is a nebulous and sensitive notion that has developed over time as a result of numerous cross-cultural exchanges, an individual's psyche, local environment, economic circumstances, and community. Overall studies shows that the urban physical has a direct impact or influences the SE which determines the safety, sense of trust and belonging, happiness, social connectedness, life satisfaction, sense of place attachment and overall quality of life. In this study, safety is taken into consideration as the main category of the SE that is associated with the HW.

5. MENTAL WELL-BEING

According to the World Health Organization (WHO), "Mental health is defined as a state of well-being in which every individual realizes his or her own potential, can cope with the normal stresses of life, can work productively and fruitfully, and is able to make a contribution to her or his community" ((World Health organization WHO), 2011). Well-being was considered by different themes and was established differently throughout history in different periods (Janahi, Raman, & Zapata-Lancaster, 2016). While unfolding mental illness implying a wide range of health conditions, cause changes in our thinking, emotions, and/or behavior. With an effect for a long period of time these mental illness later become mental disorders when the changes are related with distress and/or problems in our capability to function in relations, social, school and work settings and so often mental health is associated to behavior (Herman, 2011). Depression, which involves lowered mood, feelings of hopelessness, and lack of interest, is recognized as the most frequent mental problem among older adults (Blazer, 2009). Mental health, mental well-being, mental disorder, and mental illness are all interconnected, interdependent and affects each other.

There are three interrelated types of well-being: a) hedonic (Deci & Ryan, 2008), b) psychological (Huppert, 2009), and c) social well-being (Keyes, 1998). Both psychological well-being and social well-being are part of eudemonic well-being.

MW is more than just the absence of mental illness; it also entails a sense of well-being. Someone with good mental health and high well-being feels good, functions well, and has a higher level of life satisfaction, is growing as a person, and has strong social relationships, whereas poor mental health is a state of low MW that makes it difficult to cope with the daily stresses of life, work productively, or contribute to a community. It Impacts on a person's emotions and thinking, and thus their behavior, limit their ability to reach their full potential. Well-being defines our emotions, our thoughts and feelings, our ability to solve problems and overcome difficulties, our social connections, and our understanding of the world around us (Foundation, Mental Health, 2014). Mostly well-being is well-thought-out as subjective because the idea is for people to calculate for themselves, in a general way, the degree to which they feel a sense of wellness is subjective. As an working definition, Subjective well-being is most often understood to mean experiencing a high level of positive affect, a low level of negative affect, and a high degree of satisfaction with one's life (Deci & Ryan, 2008). The concept of well-being refers to ideal psychological functioning and experience (Ryan & Deci, 2001). In this paper, hedonic well-being is taken into consideration for concluding the impact of the UE.

6. URBAN ENVIRONMENTS AND MENTAL WELL-BEING

City planning and public health works share collective roots and ground (Frank & Engelke, 2001). Certain features of the built environment involve factors that are favorable to the resident's physical and cognitive functioning but it's very rare that we have focused on the planning and design of the built environment with the goal of improving mental health (Hoisington et al., 2019).

Not only the indoor environment affects well-being, but the outdoor environment plays a crucial role in one's development of behavior, attitude and cognitive experiences. The outdoor environment can induce stress and affect poor health, and also it can act as a restorative environment enhancing one's subjective well-being. Good mental health and well-being is of great implication for making a healthy and productive society(Gong, Palmer, Gallacher, Marsden, & Fone, 2016). There is a persuasive and growing body of evidence signifying that severe psychoses are triggered by the repetitive attack of emotionally negative experience which is not only in the SE, but in the physical, designed environment (Bfa, March, & Architect, 2017). The relationship between urban form and mental well-being is complex and, in some situations, contradictory, according to studies. (Fawzi & Ameen, 2017).

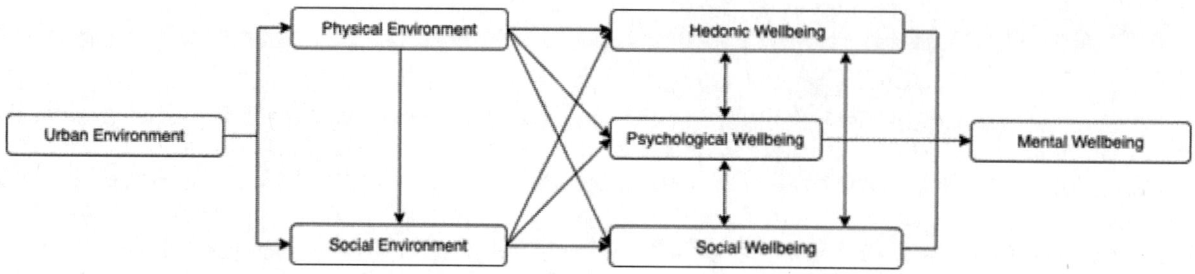

Figure 1 (above): *Relationship between urban environments and mental well-being (Source: Author)*
Figure 2 (below): *Different possibilities of urban environment affecting mental well-being (Source: Author)*

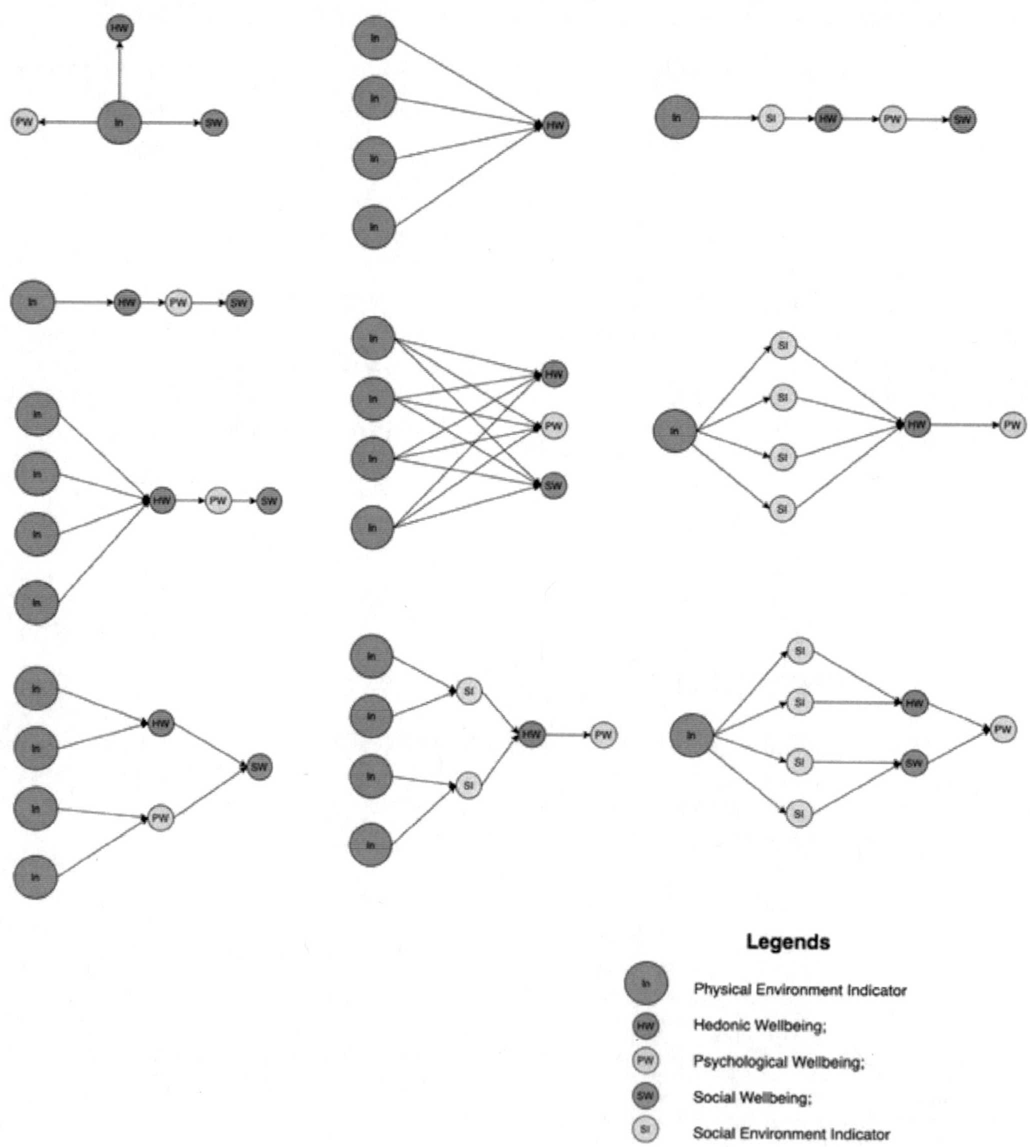

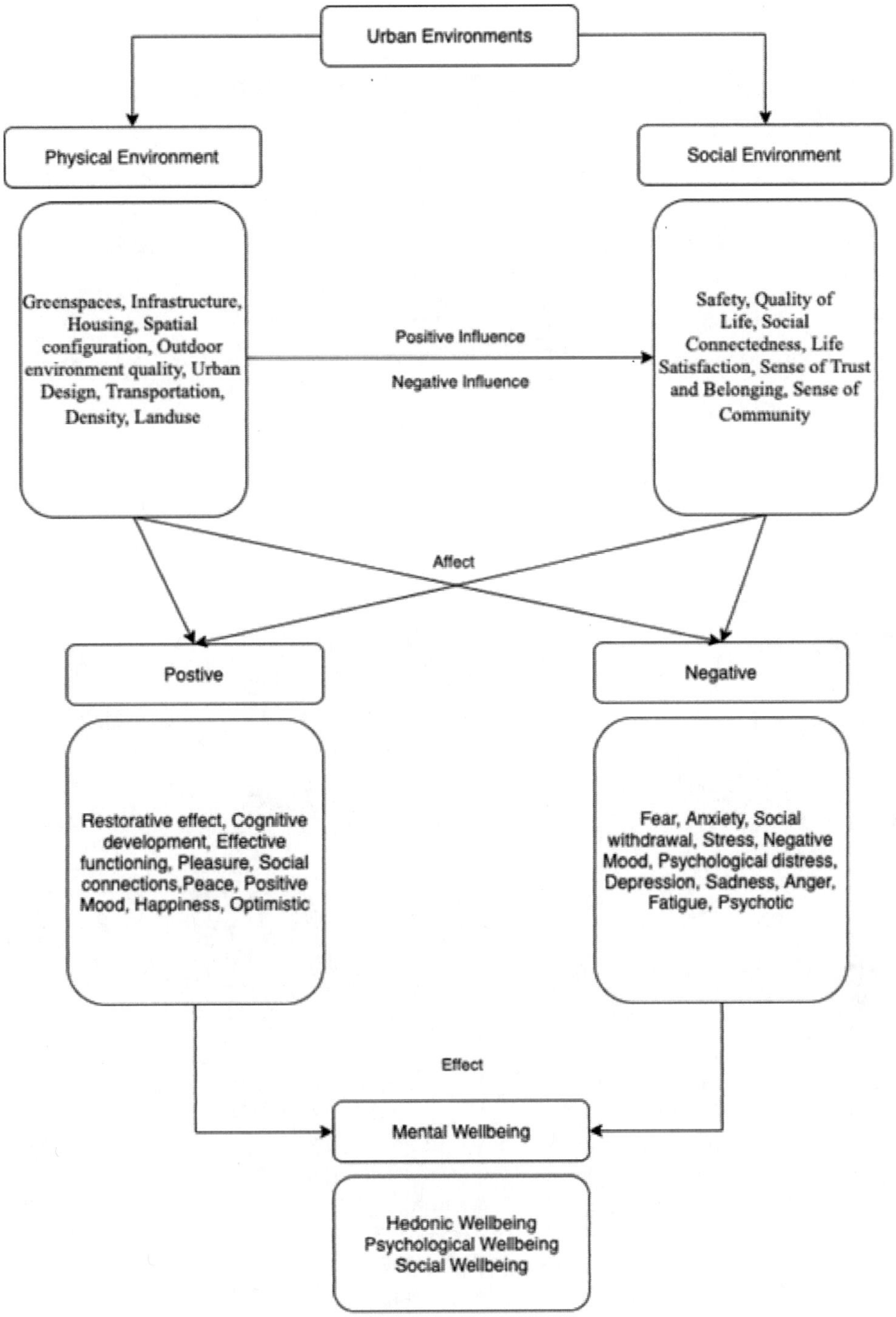

Figure 3: *Effect of urban environments on mental well-being (Source: Author)*

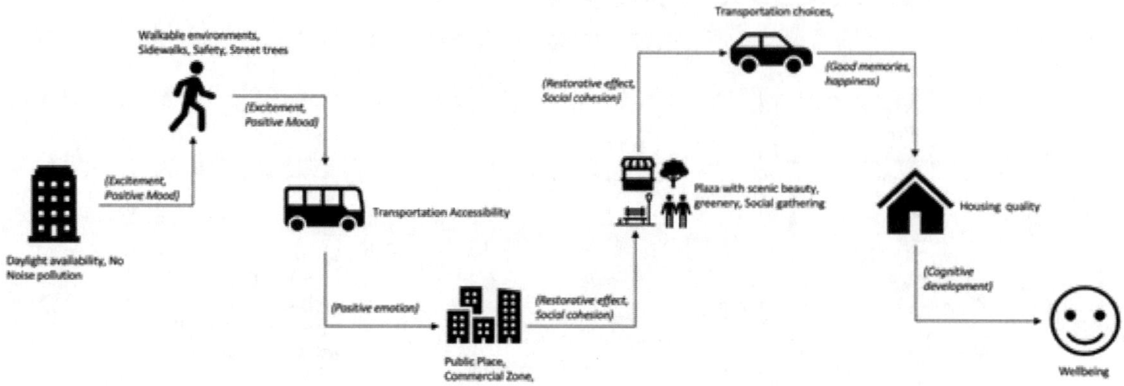

Figure 4 (above): *The plausible impact of urban environments on mental well-being - a representation through the course of the day (Source: Author)*
Figure 5 (below): *Effect of greenspaces on mental well-being (Source: Author)*

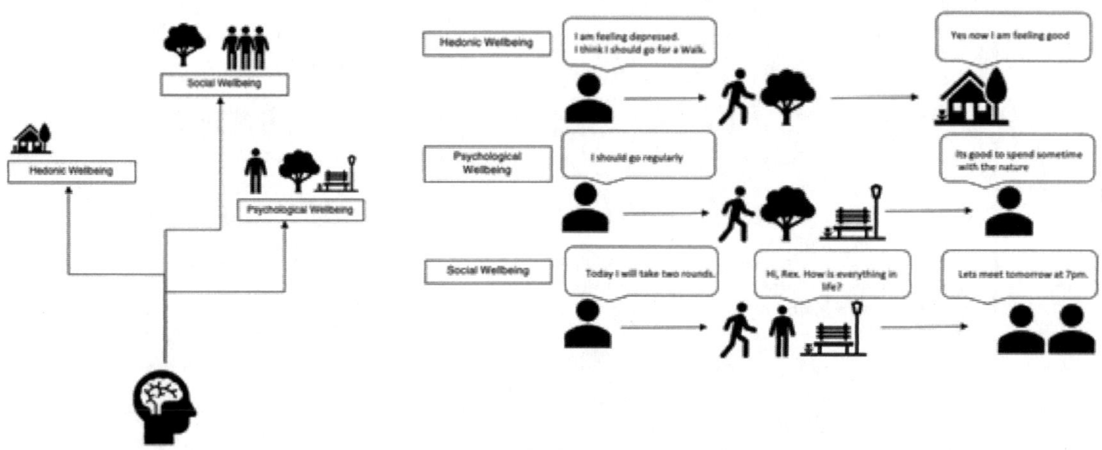

The HW is the instant and short-term effect, which might occur from realizing some pleasure and the absence of pain. The psychological well-being and social well-being (eudemonic) related to experiences that one has and are objectively good for somebody. The eudemonic well-being are connected with long-term and lasting effects (Hajrasoulih, del Rio, Francis, & Edmondson, 2018).

Due to the difference in the socio-cultural context, the degree of effect of the environmental setting would be different. The built environment provides opportunities or provides a favorable condition of how human should interact with each other. In the same way, poor environmental conditions can degrade social interactions and increase crime, altering the perception of safety. The surrounding environment or social spaces with better quality of environmental design also encourages people to have different activities and engagements that involve social interactions and social participation promoting social well-being. How one behaves and responds in everyday life depends on the quality of the built environment, natural environment and social environment. Environmental design can vary from small scale to large scale. For example, it might be a small garden in the courtyard of a residence or a sizable botanical garden with flora and fauna. Through planning and design interventions our built environment could be altered to enhance our MW.

The conceptual relationship between the UE components (PE, SE) and the MW is shown in Figure 1. (HW, PW, SW). It discusses how the PE and SE influence the three MW aspects, as well as how the physical environment influences the MW aspects and how the MW aspects are interconnected. Figure 2 depicts the countless possible UE indicators that influence the MW. It demonstrates that the link is multifaceted, and that the UE can alter the MW in a variety of ways, depending on the context and exposure. Figure 3 shows the complex relationship between the UE and the MW. The urban environment component, the PE categories, such as greenspaces, infrastructure, housing, spatial configuration, outdoor environment quality, urban design of public spaces, transportation, density and land use have a positive or negative influence on the SE categories such as safety, sense of trust and belonging, happiness, social connectedness, life satisfaction, sense of place attachment and overall quality of life.

The indicators of PE and SE categories have a positive impact or negative impact. The positive impact may be in the form of restorative effect, cognitive development, effective functioning, pleasure, social connections, peace, positive mood and happiness. The negative impact may be fear, anxiety, social withdrawal, stress, negative mood, sadness, psychological distress, depression, anger, fatigue. All these have an effect on the overall MW, either the hedonic well-being, psychological well-being, social well-being or on all. MW is a collective state of measure of both hedonic well-being and eudemonic well-being, which further defines subjective well-being or mental health.

Figure 4 depicts a scenario in which the UE has a favorable impact on mental health. It depicts a city dweller's journey from his office to his house, with a social stop in a plaza in between. Walking, transportation accessibility, the public location, the plaza and the social connection, transportation option, and other elements of UE affect them differently along the route from his office to meet his buddy and finally arriving at his home, as shown in the image. The scenario explains the affect such as excitement, positive mood, restorative effect, social connection, happiness at every stage, finally affecting one's MW. Similarly, whether it's indoor or outdoor, the UE, both the physical components and social components, are constantly affecting mental well-being in a certain way.

While Figure 4 explains how various indicators impacts the aspects of MW in different ways, Figure 5 describes the scenario of how a single indicator, ' Greenspaces', concerns the different aspects of MW. Greenspaces can affect both hedonic well-being and eudemonic well-being. A person visiting his own lawn/garden or a local park can have immediate attainment of pleasure affecting the hedonic well-being. Visiting on a daily basis and a long term exposure to greenery can directly affect psychological well-being. (Hajrasoulih et al., 2018). And the visit to the local park would also involve connections with other neighbors, maintain the social relations thus affecting social well-being (Hajrasoulih et al., 2018).

6.1 The Physical Environment and Hedonic Well-Being

The indicators identified through the literature review are categorized under distinctive heads. Table 1 summarizes the indicators of the physical environments and their impact on HW The indicators consist of both objective measures of the physical environment and subjective measures of the social environment. Multiple studies use the same indicator in different contexts, and Table 1 shows this study's outcome as evidence showing association with the HW.

Urban design and aesthetics of public spaces plays an important role in shaping the urban form, city aesthetics, physical features of the city, and also social life. Globally, studies have been done to understand the relationship between urban design and MW. Public art and creative placemaking have been understood as a medium to promote social interaction. As an example, a study of the Boston Chinatown Neighborhood Centre states that this arts-based center is working towards preserving cultural assets and growing connections within the Chinatown residents (Hand & Golden, 2018). Findings from existing research also show that legibility and transparency, are associated with positive mood (Chen et al., 2020). It has the potential to highly influence walking(Ewing & Handy, 2009) and also attract other outdoor activities (Chen et al., 2020) thus impacting the overall mood and social well-being. A study has also concluded that diversified and inclusive public spaces strengthen social connections and hence positively impact social well-being (Ouf & El-Zafarany, 2018). Furthermore, a study at conducted at neighborhood level suggests that the availability of benches along the street, positively enhances the mobility of older adults, the social cohesion and the social capital (Ottoni, Sims-Gould, Winters, Heijnen, & Mckay, 2016). In fact, permeability in public spaces is also known to increase the value of space in terms of physical, functional and the perceptual features and, can be regarded as an essential indicator of environment quality (Yavuz, 2017). At the architecture scale, literature states that buildings made of wood, with fewer edges and squares, creates permeable architecture that encourages public social life (McCay & Lai, 2018). Social connections, not only positively impact social well-being as a long-term effect, but also positively impact hedonic well-being. Immediate relief say from feelings of fatigue, depression or stress may be attained by a visit to the nearby public place which has the natural characteristics such as scenic beauty, fountains or water bodies.

The overall quality of urban public places is determined by the architecture, and the landscape, which may aid the people in spending quality time doing leisure activities, socially interacting, and creating and sharing memories. The design of public spaces should prioritize as it focuses the emotional well-being of the users and contain elements that are helpful to their health and well-being.

Studies present that living near blue spaces promotes physical activity and hence has positive associations with health and well-being (Pasanen, White, Wheeler, Garrett, & Elliott, 2019). Similar studies have also categorically stated that proximity to greenspaces can enhance the HW thereby improving the mental health of the residents. Unplanned areas may often be disorienting and may cause hindrance to one's way finding abilities, leading to stress, and thus impacting an individual's hedonic well-being. Better opportunities, accessibility and proximity to all services and amenities are also interlinked with life satisfaction and thus impact one's MW.

On the whole, data presents that density and subjective well-being have either no association or have a negative association. A cross-sectional and prospective study suggests that higher density triggers social withdrawal and the decline of socially supportive connections (Evans, 2003). Although there is no evidence that optimal population density has a favorable impact on an individual's HW, the fact that density may differ based on context, the relationship between density and HW seems difficult to comprehend.

The pillars supporting the primary goal of enhanced standards of care and well-being include infrastructure for healthcare facilities and services (Luxon, 2015). Infrastructures should be viewed not just as physical structures that provide us with comfort and services, but also as a perception of their presence that has an impact on our subjective well-being. A study states that perception of natural elements, urban public gathering spaces, historic-cultural and recreational open spaces, all have a positive restorative effect on an individual's well-being (Abdulkarim & Nasar, 2014). The architectural characteristics and architectural variation (entropy) helps in promoting psychological restoration (Galindo & Hidalgo, 2005). In fact, cities with access to amenities, leisure facilities, libraries and cultural facilities, transit stops have been noted to have higher level of residents' subjective well-being (Leyden, Goldberg, & Michelbach, 2011). More than one study has revealed that public spaces/plazas and urban squares act a place for social gatherings, interactions and connections. A study conducted in Iran suggests that factors like architectural design, lighting, safety, and accessibility, highly promote the social interaction in public squares (Hajmirsadegh, Shamsuddin, Lamit, & Foroughi, 2013).

Systematic reviews have concluded that there are cross-sectional associations between the elements of the physical environment and psychological health (Evans, 2003). As an example, exposure to natural environments has various health benefits. In fact, even visual contact with nature, just for a small amount of time can have restorative effects. This also holds true for any other activity performed in natural green areas (S. Kaplan, 1995). Recent research has also proven that spending time in open green

Table 1: *Physical environment and its impact on hedonic well-being*

Category	Author(s)	Indicator(s)	Plausible Assessment	Assessment Criteria
Urban Design	(R. Kaplan, 2001),	Urban design quality and landscaping	Restorative effect	Streetscape design, Facade, Color, Texture, building form, Permeability, urban landscape
	(Grahn & Stigsdotter, 2003)			Place based design/Placemaking
				Things to see and do
				Fountains, sculptures, differences in levels with sitting areas with plantations can provide opportunities for adults and children to play and engage with the natural surroundings.
				Places to stop and rest
				Relaxing space
Spatial Configuration	(Wood et al., 2017)	Proximity to green spaces	Effective functioning, Restorative effects, Social Connections	Walkable distance to green spaces and blue spaces, involvement of activities in blue green spaces
	(Pasanen et al., 2019)	Proximity to blue spaces	Effective functioning, Restorative effects, Social Connections	Fishing activities, boating, water games
Density	(Guite, Clark, & Ackrill, 2006)	Overcrowding	Social withdrawl	Crowd management plans
Infrastructure	(Sugiyama & Thompson, 2007)	Recreational spaces	Social Connections, Restorative effects	Provision of recreational spaces within the community or within a walking distance.
				Active urban public spaces, redeveloping unused spaces, architectural installations, public art
	(Abdulkarim & Nasar, 2014)	Attractive spaces for social gathering	Social Connections, Restorative effects	Extensive tree coverage for pedestrians
				A variety of street trees that are hardy, resilient, and low maintenance are planted at regular intervals
				Outdoor activity
				Play space
	(Navarrete-hernandez, Laffan, Urban, Cedeus, & Católica, 2019)	Green Infrastructure	Social Connections, Restorative effects	Community gardens
				Green exercises
				Conserving natural areas
				Small growing spaces

Table 1 (continued): *Physical environment and its impact on hedonic well-being*

Category	Author(s)	Indicator(s)	Plausible Assessment	Assessment Criteria
Greenspaces	(R. Kaplan, 2001)	Parks/ Urban parks, Urban green spaces	Restorative effect, Reducing stress	Traffic calming, trees on street for shades, green spaces within the community apart from parks, fruit trees to attract birds and small creatures, flowers and gardens and regular maintenance, small lawns Infront of residences,
	(R. Kaplan, 2001)	Street Trees	Restorative effect, Effective functioning, Peace	View of greenery from window Percentage of tree canopy coverage Grass walk
	(R. Kaplan, 2001)	Green grass	Restorative effect, Effective functioning, Peace	Park breeze and air quality Flora and fauna in urban fabric
	(R. Kaplan, 2001)	Tree Coverage, Vegetation	Restorative effect, Effective functioning, Peace	Front gardens, window plantation boxes, green walls, plantation hanging baskets – to make more attractive streets and interesting places.
	(R. Kaplan, 2001)	Presence of flowers and gardens	Restorative effect, Effective functioning, Peace	Landscaping at left over or unused spaces, or informal open spaces
Outdoor environment quality	(Evans, 2003) (P Lercher, G W Evans, M Meis, 2003). (Chen et al., 2020)	Daylight Availability	Depression, Sadness, fatigue	Provision of natural lighting Noise buffers Landscaping Acoustic treatments No horn zones Waste management system

spaces may help in reducing the risk of developing stress related ailments (Grahn & Stigsdotter, 2003). Hence, planning for the provision of parks within walking distance, the necessary number of parks and their spatial configurations, are all important factors for positively impacting the mental health of the users through green spaces (Wood, Hooper, Foster, & Bull, 2017).

Exposure to a peaceful street in the viewshed of an apartment, a garden or manicured area, trees, a park, a wide mowed area, a farm or field, a stream or river, and wildlife, have all been linked to effective functioning and peace.(R. Kaplan, 2001). As the accessible studies state, the right quality and quantity of greenspaces are both very crucial in being able to boost an individual's well-being.

It has been established that increase in the ambient temperature has an effect on the emotional well-being. It may be related to reducing positive emotions (e.g. joy, happiness), increasing negative emotions (e.g. stress, anger), and increasing fatigue (feeling tired, low energy)(Clemens Noelkea,1, Mark McGovernb, Daniel Corsic, Marcia Pescador-Jimenezd, Ari Sterne, Ian Sue Winge, n.d.). Similarly, insufficient daylight has also been proven as an influencing factor with regard to emotional well-being. Insufficient daylight positively associates with increased depressive symptoms like sadness and fatigue (Evans, 2003). In fact, ambient neighborhood noise from traffic on roads and trains may also cause psychological

Table 2: *Social environment and its impact on hedonic well-being*

Category	Author(s)	Indicator(s)	Plausible Assessment	Assessment Criteria
Safety	(Guite et al., 2006)	Safety of Public spaces	No Fear, Social cohesion	Lighting and light standards in public outdoor areas, such as in pedestrian walkways, plazas, parks, play lots and parking
	(Lucchesi, Larranaga, Ochoa, Samios, & Cybis, 2020)	Security by Design	No Fear, Social cohesion	
	(Cho & Kim, 2017)	Lack of Privacy in Space	Fear, Negative emotion, Negative mood	Community gardens

distress and negatively affect particularly the children's mental health (P Lercher, G W Evans, M Meis, 2003).

Studies conducted in China and UK have concluded that neighborhood cleanliness or hygiene may affect mood (Chen et al., 2020), and uncleanliness may be associated with lower levels of neighborhood satisfaction and poor mental health (Gale, Dennison, Cooper, & Sayer, 2011).

6.2 The Social Environment and Hedonic Well-Being

Existing literature has concluded that the quality and design of the built environment influences the social cohesion and residents gain from high-quality built environments in terms of social advantages. The literature review indicates that environmental factors related to activity participation which involve land-use diversity, connectivity, access to shops and recreational facilities, pavement quality, aesthetics, and safety from traffic and crime, influence the social behavior of the people. Social interaction encouraged by the use of open space can improve people's sense of community safety (Sugiyama & Thompson, 2007). Furthermore, it is suggested that indicators measuring features of quality of the built environment such as density, mixed land use, attractiveness, connectedness, legibility, accessibility, inclusiveness, maintenance, extent of natural surveillance and neighborhood character, highly influence the social cohesion characteristics such as social interactions, social networks, sense of community, active participation, trust within the community, feelings of safety and sense of place attachment (Dempsey, 2008).

Neighborhood characteristics have been proven to determine the safety of the residents. Poor neighborhood design and quality can influence crime and fear of crime, and these are identified as prospective mediators affecting MW (Jenkins et al., 2008). A study also infers that high prevalence of trees in a neighborhood are perceived to be safe and may lead to an increase in social cohesion (Bjornstrom & Ralston, 2014). Privacy is also an essential factor that may affect the user experience. A user having a negative experience due to lack of privacy, or the experience of comfortable personal space, the distance between personal space, minimizing of sharing space, minor space for doing individual work etc., directly affect the MW (Cho & Kim, 2017). As an example of a daily life plausible experience, a couple not being able to get the experience of an intimate comfortable space to spend a nice evening, may negatively impact their hedonic well-being.

7. CONCLUSION

Elements of the urban built environment and the characteristics of the built form are directly or indirectly associated with mental well-being. The existing research dominantly focuses on aspects urban environments, such as 'green spaces' or 'housing quality' and their impact on mental health. The emphasis on the urban environment, the physical and social environment as a whole and their impact, appears to be limited. Developing a unified 'Urban Environment Mental Well-being Framework' could fill this void and aid in analyzing urban environments to forecast their impact on mental well-being. The study will contribute to the development of a framework for assessing urban environments which takes into account all the three, the environmental, the economic, and the social contexts. The framework may aid in building safe and healthy cities which promote mental wellbeing across the globe.

Cities have always attempted to focus on healthcare facility design to be able to contribute to a better quality of life, but it now seems time to take a step ahead and look at health, also from the particular perspective of mental well-being at an urban design and planning level. Most of the Smart City plans seem to focus on achieving a good quality of life through technological innovations and energy efficiency through provision of state of art services for the residents, but less is focused upon the subjective well-being of the people. The dire need of the hour is 'healthy city plans' which look into the current and future requirement of positively impacting mental health of the citizens. Healthy City Plans require to prioritize focus on the social environment and the subjective measures of the built environment. Subjective perceptions of mental well-being and life satisfaction may differ among individuals but that must not negate the established facts about the plausible positive and negative influences of the urban environment on mental health of all. As an example, it has been well established that noise pollution negatively impacts mental health, while greenspaces universally have proven to have a calming influence on mental health. Taking on from this well-established objective understanding, it may be plausible to assume that a focus on the subjective environment can work positively towards hedonic well-being. The design of an environment which positively impacts hedonic well-being must allow people to 'sit and talk', 'see and feel', must resemble a 'thoughtful ambiance', must be, 'quiet and relaxing', a space where people can be 'alone but not lonely', and most importantly, a geography where one may feel completely 'free and at peace'. Such a space and it's qualities would elicit certain types of activities, further leading to social connection. These activities may be individual activities or activities in the guise of social interactions. And these immediate consequences with regard to the environment may influence hedonic well-being, further impacting the other two types of well-being, the psychological and social.

It may be concluded that the quality of the physical built environment influences the social environment and further hence, a strong focus on the environment-behavior studies must be engaged in the making of 'healthy city plans'. Interdisciplinary studies in the field of urban design and psychology may be a must for the making of these plans. Furthermore, to be able to generate new ideas and understand the environmental parameters impacting people's welfare, local governments require to focus on 'local area planning' and/or micro-level actions. Data on mental health of a large sample size at a local area level, requires to be gathered to understand, the urban design perspective and it's spatial linkage.

It is time for the built environment professionals to rethink people's well-being with particular regard to the subjective, the emotional and the psychological well-being, rather than only with regard to, the citizens' satisfaction with governance, urban services, and facilities. The quality of life "motto" must engage a focus on comfort, emotion, feeling, need, preferences and the subjective well-being of the residents. In the current era, which calls for a focus on 'health for all,' the environmental perception, the behavior, the attitude, cognition, and the idea of personal space, all must hold high significance for environmental psychologists, urban designers and planners, to be able to build a better city for tomorrow. Stakeholder investigations at the local area level to determine the relevance of parameters affecting mental well-being may be the way forward. These investigations would bring to the forefront the priorities of the citizens, which further maybe a way towards the development of an assessment system [of the urban environment for mental well-being] aided by this priority-based designation. Global urbanization calls for immediate measures to be taken with reference to spatial planning and design, for mitigating the surge in mental health-related challenges. Interdisciplinary studies require to be conducted in the times to come, to better achieve a holistic understanding of the interactions and relationship between the urban environment and mental well-being. A bottom-up strategic planning method maybe the best route to 'healthy cities'.

8. REFERENCES

(World Health organization WHO). (2011). No Title. Retrieved from Mental health: strengthening our response. Retrieved from Mental health: strengthening our response (Fact Sheet) website: https://www.who.int/news-room/fact-sheets/detail/mental-health-strengthening-our-response

Abdulkarim, D., & Nasar, J. L. (2014). Are livable elements also restorative? *Journal of Environmental Psychology, 38*, 29–38. https://doi.org/10.1016/j.jenvp.2013.12.003

Anderson, W. P., Kanaroglou, P. S., Miller, E. J., Anderson, W. P., Kanaroglou, P. S., & Miller, E. J. (1996). Linked references are available on JSTOR for this article : Urban Form , Energy and the Environment : A Review of Issues , *Evidence and Policy. 33*(1), 7–35.

Bfa, J. G., March, B., & Architect, R. (2017). Architecture, the urban environment and severe psychosis: *Aetiology*. 1–12.

Bjornstrom, E. E. S., & Ralston, M. L. (2014). *Neighborhood Built Environment , Perceived Danger , and Perceived Social Cohesion*. https://doi.org/10.1177/0013916513503833

Blazer, D. G. (2009). Depression in Late Life: Review and Commentary. *Focus, 7*(1), 118–136. https://doi.org/10.1176/foc.7.1.foc118

Cabe Space. (2013). The Impact on Physical and Mental Health. *Exchange Organizational Behavior Teaching Journal, 19*.

Chen, C., Luo, W., Kang, N., Li, H., Yang, X., & Xia, Y. (2020). Study on the impact of residential outdoor environments on mood in the elderly in Guangzhou, China. *Sustainability (Switzerland), 12*(9). https://doi.org/10.3390/su12093933

Cho, K., & Kim, C. (2017). Design for privacy in public space. *Proceedings of the International Conference on Engineering Design, ICED, 5*(DS87-5), 239–248. Retrieved from https://www.scopus.com/inward/record.uri?eid=2-s2.0-85029781899&partnerID=40&md5=3cd376023c3397b08fc59f1fb19f6571

Clemens Noelkea., Mark McGovernb, Daniel Corsic, Marcia Pescador-Jimenezd, Ari Sterne, Ian Sue Winge, L. B. (n.d.). *Increasing Ambient Temperature Reduces Emotional Well-Being*

Deci, E. L., & Ryan, R. M. (2008). Hedonia, eudaimonia, and well-being: An introduction. *Journal of Happiness Studies, 9*(1), 1–11. https://doi.org/10.1007/s10902-006-9018-1

Découverte, L., & Cornut, P. (2019). Berdoulay V . & Soubeyran O ., *L ' écologie urbaine et l ' urbanisme : aux fondements des enjeux actuels*. 1–3.

Dempsey, N. (2008). Does quality of the built environment affect social cohesion? *Proceedings of the Institution of Civil Engineers - Urban Design and Planning, 161*(3), 105–114. https://doi.org/10.1680/udap.2008.161.3.105

Evans, G. W. (2003). The Built Environment and Mental Health. *Journal of Urban Health, 80*(4), 536–555. https://doi.org/10.1093/jurban/jtg063

Ewing, R., & Handy, S. (2009). Measuring the unmeasurable: Urban design qualities related to walkability. *Journal of Urban Design, 14*(1), 65–84. https://doi.org/10.1080/13574800802451155

Fawzi, R., & Ameen, M. (2017). *A Framework for the Sustainability Assessment of Urban Design and Development in Iraqi Cities By*. (September).

Ferguson, K. T., & Evans, G. W. (2003). The built environment and mental health. *Encyclopedia of Environmental Health, 80*(4), 465–469. https://doi.org/10.1016/B978-0-12-409548-9.11009-7

Foundation, Mental Health, N. Z. (2014). *Mental health and well-being definitions. 2014*. Retrieved from https://www.mentalhealth.org.nz/assets/Working-Well/FINAL-Working-Well-FS-Mental-health-and-well-being-definitions-approved.pdf

Frank, L. D., & Engelke, P. O. (2001). The built environment and human activity patterns: Exploring the impacts of urban form on public health. *Journal of Planning Literature, 16*(2), 202–218. https://doi.org/10.1177/08854120122093339

Gale, C. R., Dennison, E. M., Cooper, C., & Sayer, A. A. (2011). Neighborhood environment and positive mental health in older people: The Hertfordshire Cohort Study. *Health and Place, 17*(4), 867–874. https://doi.org/10.1016/j.healthplace.2011.05.003

Galindo, M. A. P., & Hidalgo, M. A. C. (2005). Aesthetic preferences and the attribution of meaning: Environmental categorization processes in the evaluation of urban scenes. *International Journal of Psychology, 40*(1), 19–26. https://doi.org/10.1080/00207590444000104

Gong, Y., Palmer, S., Gallacher, J., Marsden, T., & Fone, D. (2016). A systematic review of the relationship between objective measurements of the urban environment and psychological distress. *Environment International, 96*, 48–57. https://doi.org/10.1016/j.envint.2016.08.019

Grahn, P., & Stigsdotter, U. A. (2003).

Guite, H. F., Clark, C., & Ackrill, G. (2006). The impact of the physical and urban environment on mental well-being. *Public Health, 120*(12), 1117–1126. https://doi.org/10.1016/j.puhe.2006.10.005

Hajmirsadegh, R. S., Shamsuddin, S., Lamit, H. Bin, & Foroughi, A. (2013). Design's factors influencing social interaction in public squares. *European Online Journal of Natural and Social Sciences, 2*(4), 556–564.

Hajrasoulih, A., del Rio, V., Francis, J., & Edmondson, J. (2018). Urban form and mental well-being. *Journal of Urban Design and Mental Health, 5*, 10. Retrieved from https://www.urbandesignmentalhealth.com/journal-5---urban-form-and-mental-well-being.html

Hand, J., & Golden, T. (2018). Arts , Culture , and Community Mental Health. *Community Development Innovation Review*, 41–49.

Hannah Ritchie, M. R. (2018). *"Mental Health."* Retrieved from OurWorldInData.org

Herman, H. (2011). Promoting mental health. *The SAGE Handbook of Mental Health and Illness*, 405–429. https://doi.org/10.4135/9781446200988.n20

Hoisington, A. J., Stearns-Yoder, K. A., Schuldt, S. J., Beemer, C. J., Maestre, J. P., Kinney, K. A., ... Brenner, L. A. (2019). Ten questions concerning the built environment and mental health. *Building and Environment, 155*(January), 58–69. https://doi.org/10.1016/j.buildenv.2019.03.036

Huppert, F. A. (2009). Psychological Well-being: Evidence Regarding its Causes and Consequences. Applied Psychology: *Health and Well-Being, Vol. 1*, pp. 137–164. https://doi.org/10.1111/j.1758-0854.2009.01008.x

Janahi, H., Raman, S., & Zapata-lancaster, G. (2016). *Understanding the impact of the residential built environment design on inhabitants ' well-being*. 2(2003).

Jenkins, R., Meltzer, H., Jones, P. B., Brugha, T., Bebbington, P., Farrell, M., ... Knapp, M. (2008). Foresight Mental Capital and Well-being Project. Mental Health: Future Challenges. *LSE Research Online*, 1–93. Retrieved from https://core.ac.uk/download/pdf/17341.pdf

Kalpana Srivastava. (2009). *Urbanization and mental health. 18*(2). https://doi.org/10.4103/0972-6748.64028

Kaplan, R. (2001). The nature of the view from home psychological benefits. In *Environment and Behavior* (Vol. 33). https://doi.org/10.1177/00139160121973115

Kaplan, S. (1995). The restorative benefits of nature: Toward an integrative framework. *Journal of Environmental Psychology, 15*(3), 169–182. https://doi.org/10.1016/0272-4944(95)90001-2

Kawachi, A. C. (2006). The urban social environment and its effects on health. *Cities and the Health of the Public.*

Keyes, C. L. M. (1998). Social Well-Being Author (s): Corey Lee M . Keyes Source : Social Psychology Quarterly , Vol . 61 , No . 2 (Jun ., 1998), pp . 121-140 Published by : American Sociological Association Stable URL : http://www.jstor.org/stable/2787065 Accessed : 17-06-2. *American Sociological Association, 61*(2), 121–140. Retrieved from https://www.jstor.org/stable/2787065

Leyden, K. M., Goldberg, A., & Michelbach, P. (2011). Understanding the pursuit of happiness in ten major cities. *Urban Affairs Review, 47*(6), 861–888. https://doi.org/10.1177/1078087411403120

Lucchesi, S. T., Larranaga, A. M., Ochoa, J. A. A., Samios, A. A. B., & Cybis, H. B. B. (2020). The role of security and walkability in subjective well-being: A multigroup analysis among different age cohorts. *Research in Transportation Business and Management*, (May), 100559. https://doi.org/10.1016/j.rtbm.2020.100559

Luxon, L. (2015). Infrastructure – the key to healthcare improvement. *Future Hospital Journal, 2*(1), 4–7. https://doi.org/10.7861/futurehosp.15.002

McCay, L., & Lai, L. (2018). Urban design and mental health in Hong Kong: a city case study. *Journal of Urban Design and Mental Health*, (4), 9. Retrieved from https://www.urbandesignmentalhealth.com/journal4-hk-case-study.html

Navarrete-hernandez, P., Laffan, K., Urban, S., Cedeus, D., & Católica, P. U. (2019). Landscape and Urban Planning A greener urban environment : Designing green infrastructure interventions to promote citizens ' subjective well-being. *Landscape and Urban Planning*, *191*(July), 103618. https://doi.org/10.1016/j.landurbplan.2019.103618

Ompad, D. C., Galea, S., & Vlahov, D. (2007). *Chapter 3 Urbanicity, Urbanization, and the Urban Environment.* (May 2014). https://doi.org/10.1007/978-0-387-70812-6

Ottawa, Ont.: CIHI, 201. (2011). *Urban Physical Environments and Health Inequalities : A Scoping Review of Interventions Factors Influencing Health.* Retrieved from https://sph.umd.edu/sites/default/files/files/UrbanPhysicalReport2012EN_web.pdf

Ottoni, C. A., Sims-gould, J., Winters, M., Heijnen, M., & Mckay, H. A. (2016). Social Science & Medicine " Benches become like porches " : Built and social environment in fl uences on older adults ' experiences of mobility and well-being. *Social Science & Medicine*, *169*, 33–41. https://doi.org/10.1016/j.socscimed.2016.08.044

Ouf, A. S. E.-D., & El-Zafarany, N. A. (2018). Diversity and Inclusion in the Public Space As Aspects of Happiness and Well-being. *Journal of Urban Research*, *28*(1), 109–129.

P Lercher, G W Evans, M Meis, W. W. K. (2003). Ambient neighborhood noise and children's mental health [5]. *Occupational and Environmental Medicine*, *60*(2), 146. https://doi.org/10.1136/oem.60.2.146

Pasanen, T. P., White, M. P., Wheeler, B. W., Garrett, J. K., & Elliott, L. R. (2019). Neighborhood blue space, health and well-being: The mediating role of different types of physical activity. *Environment International*, *131*(June), 105016. https://doi.org/10.1016/j.envint.2019.105016

Ryan, R. M., & Deci, E. L. (2001). On Happiness and Human Potentials: A Review of Research on Hedonic and Eudaimonic Well-Being. *Annual Review of Psychology*, *52*(1), 141–166. https://doi.org/10.1146/annurev.psych.52.1.141

SÉNÉCAL, G. (2007). *URBAN ENVIRONMENT : 1*(2004).

Sugiyama, T., & Thompson, C. W. (2007). Outdoor environments, activity and the well-being of older people: Conceptualising environmental support. *Environment and Planning A*, *39*(8), 1943–1960. https://doi.org/10.1068/a38226

UNITED NATIONS. (2020). Policy Brief : COVID-19 and the Need for Action on Mental Health EXECUTIVE SUMMARY : COVID-19 and the Need for Action on Mental Health. *World Health Organization, Geneva, Swithzerland*, 3–10.

Weich, S., Burton, E., Blanchard, M., Prince, M., Sproston, K., & Erens, B. (2001). *Measuring the built environment : validity of a site survey instrument for use in urban settings. 7*, 283–292.

WHO. (2019). *Mental health*. Retrieved from https://www.who.int/news-room/facts-in-pictures/detail/mental-health

Wood, L., Hooper, P., Foster, S., & Bull, F. (2017). Public green spaces and positive mental health – investigating the relationship between access, quantity and types of parks and mental well-being. *Health and Place*, *48*(July), 63–71. https://doi.org/10.1016/j.healthplace.2017.09.002

World Health Organization. (2003). Mental Health Policy and Service Guidance Package: The Mental Health Context. *Mental Health Policy and Service Guidance Package*, 1–46. Retrieved from http://www.who.int/mental_health/resources/en/context.PDF

Yavuz, A. (2017). *World Journal of Permeability as an indicator of environmental quality : Physical , functional , perceptual components of the environment.* (January 2014).

The Positive Impact on Individuals' Sustained-Attention Level of Micro Interactions with Natural Green Elements in Low-Income Communities

Hossein Saedi *(North Carolina State University);* ***Arthur Roy Rice*** *(North Carolina State University)*

ABSTRACT

Theories such as attention restoration theory (ART) and other research suggest that interaction with nature can improve an individual's attention level. Research has shown that individuals in low-income urban housing have disproportionately less access to natural environments and, therefore, lack benefits from encounters with nature. This research examines the possibility of utilizing natural green elements in the design of low-income residential buildings' interiors to compensate for the lack of natural environments in low-income urban areas.

The researchers compared the results from a Sustained Attention to Response Task (SART) for one hundred and eighty-two residents of a high-rise residential building. During an experimental study, participants were randomly selected to experience one of two versions of a building's lobby modeled in a 3D immersive virtual reality environment. One model included natural green elements and the other did not. Participants completed the SART twice. Once before experiencing the lobby and once after. The results indicate that those who interacted with natural green elements in the building lobby for less than a minute demonstrated significant improvement in their attention level. They received higher scores in the SART post-test and demonstrated fewer cognitive errors. These results support the potential positive effect of short-term interaction with natural green elements on an individual's sustained attention level.

KEYWORDS

Low-income Housing; Attention Restoration Theory (ART); Natural Green Elements, Virtual Reality (VR); Sustained Attention to Response Task (SART)

1. INTRODUCTION

Many factors impact an individual's health and well-being. Some of these factors are access to health care, the availability of adequate and healthy foods, and the social and physical environments they interact with on a daily basis. Research in the fields of environmental psychology and landscape architecture has indicated that exposure to natural environments can play an essential role in restoring depleted cognitive resources (Pilotti et al., 2015, p. 947-969; Wang et al., 2016, p. 112-122; Jenkin et al., 2018, p. 315-328; Saedi & Rice, 2019, p. 96-99; Pascoe et al., 2017, p. 156-178). Research has demonstrated that both physical and visual contact with natural elements has the ability to increase attention levels and therefore may have a positive impact on an individual's mental well-being (Romero-Martínez & Moya-Albiol, 2013, p. 515-522). The goal is to create living environments for all that enable an individual to experience, on a daily basis, places that have restorative benefits.

The exposure to natural or "green" environments is something all people benefit from, but some people have far fewer opportunities for such interactions in their daily life and are therefore often deprived of the restorative effect of these interactions. Higher-density urban environments that are usually where less economically advantaged individuals live lack the natural/green elements or environments that have been shown to be of benefit (Astell-Burt et al., 2014, p. 292; Hamedani Golshan & Saedi, 2017, p. 18-27). Besides, this group frequently has less mobility and more difficulty visiting natural areas (Phinney,

2013, p. 780-815). These limitations make them more dependent on their local environment to provide day-to-day interactions that enable them to restore their cognitive resources.

One of the ways that the restorative effect of an environment has been measured is the assessment of an individual's ability to maintain sustained attention. Attention Restoration Theory has suggested that the ability to sustain attention is a critical factor in an individual's ability to maintain focus, ignore distractions, and participate in constructive human interactions (Kaplan, 2001, p. 507-542, Baycan-Levent et al., 2009, p. 193-213, Keniger et al., 2013, p. 913-935). Research has shown that one way to restore an individual's ability to sustain attention is for that individual to interact with "green" or "natural" environments. The exact nature of that interaction varies significantly. Factors such as the physical nature of the "natural/green" environment, the type of interaction (physical or visual) (van den berg et al., 2003, p. 135-146; Calogiuri et al., 2018, p. 2321), the frequency of the interaction, and the duration of the interaction are just a few of the variables that may impact the restorative effect (Mitchell & Popham, 2008, p. 1655-1660, Dean et al., 2018, p. 1371).

The research effort reported on in this article focuses on learning more about the specific characteristics of visual interactions with natural/green environments and how these Interactions impact restorative benefits. This more detailed understanding will enable architects and landscape architects to incorporate cost-effective natural/green elements into lower-income housing in a way that has the most positive impact on health and well-being. This research documents the effect of individuals' visual interaction with natural elements in a housing entry situation. The studied interaction took place in an immersive virtual reality environment of an entry to a high-density housing environment. Both pre and post-testing were conducted to determine the extent of a short-term interaction with a limited selection of plants in an interior space on an individual's ability to sustain attention.

Research has proven that retaining attention is a cornerstone for ignoring distractions (Posner, 2012; Schwartz & Kaplan, 2006, p. 242-277), focusing on duties (Lee et al., 2014, p. 504-514), and having positive interpersonal interactions and behaviors (Podsakoff, Whiting, Podsakoff, & Blume, 2009). Maintaining an attention level over time requires effort and cannot be sustained over a prolonged period of time (MacLean et al., 2010, p. 829-839; Sarter et al., 2001, p. 146-160). When individuals put themselves under pressure to remain focused and sustain their attention level, they may put their mental and physical health at risk (Jett & George, 2003, p. 494-507; Sonnentag et al., 2010, p. 965-976).

The Attention Resource Model suggests that sustaining attention depletes individuals' mental resources (Maclean et al., 2010). Maintaining attention control consists of two separate processes occurring in two separate parts of the brain. External distractions are processed through the ventral attention network located in the subcortical part of the brain (Corbetta & Shulman, 2002, p. 201-215; MacLean et al., 2009, p. 1042-1058); while efforts to maintain attention control are processed thorough the dorsal attention network in the cortical part (Paus et al., 1997, p. 392-408; Sturm & Willmes, 2001, p. S76-S84). The brain areas that are associated with attention control become less active after executing demanding tasks (Lim et al., 2010, p. 3426-3435). Even the blood flow decreases in these areas with an increased task load (Hitchcock et al., 1999, p. 365-372). Different types and forms of alerts and warnings, including tones, lighting signals, and cues, can be used in working environments or during experiments to compensate for this attentional decay (MacLean et al., 2009, p. 1042-1058; O'Connor et al., 2011, p. 535-543). The use of those alerts is not feasible in most cases in real-life situations.

The Sustained Attention to Response Task (SART) was used by researchers to measure the participants' tendency for frequent lapses in sustained attention (Robertson et al., 1997, p. 747-758). The brain networks involved in maintaining concentration and ignoring external distractions contribute to successfully performing the SART test (Manly et al., 2003, p. 340-349). Lower variability in performing the sustained attention to response task demonstrates that participants are more able to sustain their attention (Barkley, 1997, p. 65-94, Hester & Garavan, 2004, p. 11017-11022). The researchers employed the fast Fourier Transform neuroscience analysis technique to measure sustained attention to examine if the brain networks mentioned above were affected by a short and informal encounter with natural/green elements in the residential building lobby. In this research, these types of interactions are referred to as "micro-restorative" interactions.

The fast Fourier transform technique separates response variability into two categories: Fast Frequency and Slow Frequency (Johnson et al., 2008, p. 927-37). As can be understood from the suggested names, the fast frequency demonstrates the rapid alternation in an individuals' reaction time during the task execution. The Attention-resource model argues that the fast frequency indicates changes in the brain's cortical activities that are associated with attentional control (Johnson et al., 2007, p. 630-638; Johnson, Kelly, et al., 2008) or, as attention restoration theory suggests, changes in participants' voluntary attention (Kaplan & Kaplan, 1989). On the other hand, the slow frequency illustrates a gradual increase or decrease in individuals' reaction time throughout the task execution. The gradual change suggests changes in sub-cortical arousal, or in Attention Restoration Theory language, oscillation in non-voluntary attention (Kaplan, 2001, p. 507-542). Based on what the Attention Restoration Theory suggests, researchers expected to detect some degree of arousal in the participants, who experienced the lobby with the natural/green elements, sub-cortical part of the brain, and enhance cortical attention control. Research suggests that the demonstration of those effects represents lower fast frequency and slow frequency variability (Lee et al., 2015, p. 182-189) among those who experience the lobby with the natural/green elements compared to those experiencing the lobby with no natural green elements.

Attention Restoration Theory suggests that the presence in nature or visual interaction with nature can boost voluntary attention through engaging non-voluntary attention that frees up room for depleted voluntary attention to refresh and replenish (Kaplan & Kaplan, 1989). Considering both the Attention Restoration Theory (Kaplan & Kaplan, 1989) and the Attention-Resource Model (Davies & Parasuraman, 1982; Warm et al., 2008), the researchers anticipated that interaction with natural green elements in a residential building lobby would stimulate sub-cortical arousal processes to a degree that can be detected through less fast frequency variability and, amplify cortical attention control that can be verified through less slow frequency variability.

The research explores the validity of the hypothesis that an individual's interaction with natural/ green elements for a short period in high-density residential buildings can replenish exhausted mental resources. The goal is to provide policymakers and designers with the information they need to create living environments that meet everyone, both physical and psychological needs.

2. RESEARCH OBJECTIVES

This paper examines the possible effect of utilizing natural/green elements in indoor spaces' design to restore an individual's sustained-attention level. Researchers are exploring some of the impacts that interaction with these elements could have on an individual's cognitive functioning. The research strives to determine, by adding natural/green elements experienced through *micro-interactions*, if minor changes in the design of a space can reduce mental resource depletion.

3. METHODS

This exploratory research examines the impact of the presence of natural green elements, as the independent variable, on participants' sustained-attention level, as the dependent variable. The researchers used a cross-sectional research approach to compare the quantitative data obtained from two groups. One group experienced the intervention while a second group did not. Experimental research helps researchers to find causal relationships between changes in the independent and the dependent variable(s) being studied. However, in some cases, there are also other characteristics or features that can affect the relationship. These factors are intervening variables, such as mental pressure, workload, and the lack of sleep or breaks (Abbott et al., 2016), and researchers have no control over them. Such

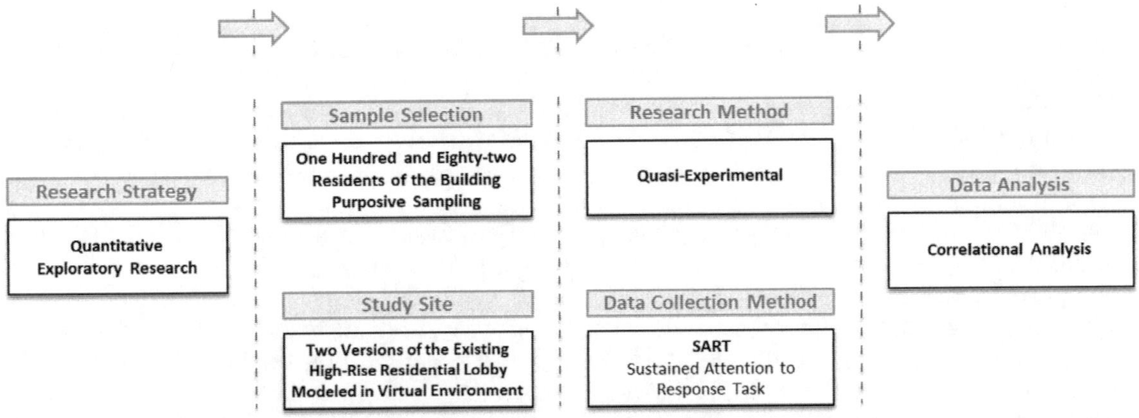

Figure 1: *Research methodology overview (Diagram by the Authors)*

Figure 2: *Two versions of the residential building lobby as the study sites (Renderings by the Authors)*

variables make it harder for researchers to establish a causal relationship between the dependent and independent variables. As a result, quasi-experimental research was conducted to address the research question, and a correlation analysis was done to interpret the data. The overview of this research is illustrated in Figure 1.

3.1 Study Site

As Figure 2. Illustrates, the study site for this research was the two virtual versions of an existing residential building's lobby, one with and the other without natural green elements. Two versions were modeled in Auto Desk Revit 2020 and were then rendered using Lumion for Revit. The models were then exported to the Unity game engine to enable participants to spend time in one of the two versions through an immersive virtual reality experience.

3.2 Participants

One hundred and eighty-two residents of the residential building, the lobby of which was modeled in a virtual reality environment as the study site, volunteered to participate in the experiment through purposive sampling. The population distribution was 63% female and 37% male with a mean age of thirty-five. During a break, each participant was randomly assigned to experience one of the two treatment conditions explained in 3.1. as shown in Figure 3.

3.3 Measures

A Sustained Attention to Response Task (SART) was utilized to measure the possible change in participants' sustained attention level before and after experiencing the building lobby (Saedi et al., 2021, p. 5-21). Two hundred and twenty numbers were presented to the participants in two separate sections during the experiment. One hundred and ten numbers were displayed before experiencing one of the two versions of the lobby and one hundred and ten after experiencing the lobby. The series of numbers were shown to participants using the E-prime software.

The numbers were viewed on an iPad Air 2 display. Participants clicked on the black arrow that existed on the bottom of the screen after seeing any number but the number "7." Fifteen instances of "7" appeared on display during the pre-test and twelve appeared in the post-test. Researchers created a series of one hundred and ten numbers for the pre-test and a different series of one hundred and ten numbers for the post-test. All participants responded to the same pre and post number sequences. Participants were asked to respond to each number's appearance on the display after a response cue of "⊗" disappeared. This method was used to control the reaction speed and tighten the error margin due to very fast or prolonged reaction times (Lee et al., 2015, p. 182-189). Figure 3. illustrates the process individuals went through and successfully finished in order for their data to be included in the data analysis.

3.4 Procedure

The end of a regular workday was selected by researchers as the time frame for conducting the experiment. Activities such as driving a car, fulfilling job responsibilities, and running daily errands consume an individual's mental resources; therefore, it is more likely to maintain low/limited attentional resources at the end of the day (Austria, 2014). The goal was to increase the possibility of detecting changes in the participant's cognitive performances before and after experiencing the design intervention.

Some environmental characteristics such as room temperature, surrounding noise, lighting luminosity, visual access to outdoor spaces, etc. can impact individuals' performance when it comes to tasks that require maintaining higher levels of attention, in this case, the Sustained Attention to Response Task. Participants were moved to a room in which the air conditioning, lighting level, noise level, etc. were kept constant to minimize the impact of such factors. To begin the participation in the study, participants were asked if they had an unusual day; for example, if they had a car accident, they had an argument with their boss or a client, as those incidents deplete mental resources much faster. The data from those participants that experienced an atypical day was then removed from the data set.

Researchers then taught the participants how to take the SART test, and they were given a sample test with a series of ten English letters and they had to react to all but the letter D. Following the SART trial round, participants practiced working with the VR device to learn how to maneuver while experiencing one of the two building lobbies in a virtual environment.

Once done with all familiarization processes, each individual took the pre-test to establish a baseline for their attention level. After the pre-test, participants were given a one-minute break while researchers randomly assigned them to one of the two lobby experiences, one with and the other one without

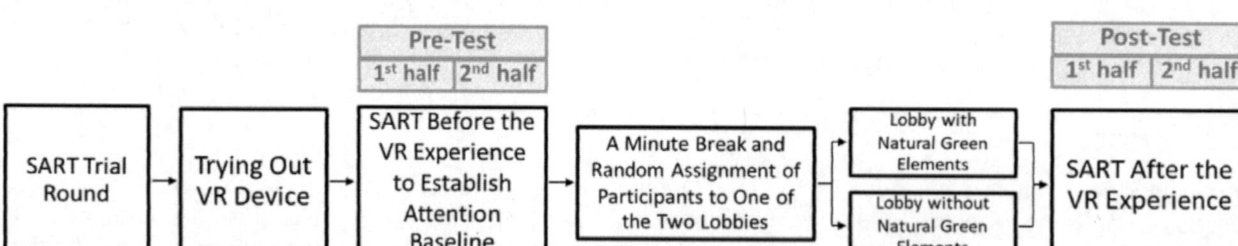

Figure 3: *Overview of the experiment process (Diagram by the Authors)*

natural/green elements. Participants were advised to walk through the lobby from the building entrance to the elevators at a normal pace with no stop, turn around, or pause.

The HTC VIVE Pro-Eye VR gear was used in this research. Participants could start the VR environment's immersive experience by pressing any key on the VR controllers. They had to press any key again to finish the process and have their data recorded. Modeling the lobby in the VR settings, rather than changing the real lobby, made it possible for researchers to try out various iterations and create the intended version more rapidly and at a lower cost (Saedi & Boone, 2018, p. 60).

3.5 Data Analysis

One hundred and seventy-one out of one hundred and eighty-two participants performed the SART test correctly. Twelve other participants were eliminated from the data analysis due to various reasons such as having experienced an unusual day with extra mental pressures, spending more time and/or engaging with the lobby designs, failing to maneuver in the immersive virtual environment using VR devices, or being an outlier to the standard deviation to response time. Ultimately, data from one hundred and fifty-nine participants were used in the final data analysis.

The overall response time was measured for all participants in the two groups alongside the standard deviation of each individual's response time. Drawing on fast Fourier transform, fast frequency variability was considered as the variability within one SART cycle. Each part of the SART test consisted of one hundred and ten numbers created by eleven cycles of ten numbers. The slow frequency variability captured all variabilities in more than one SART cycle (Johnson et al., 2007, p. 630-638).

Following the method used by Johnson and her colleagues in 2007 to measure the fast frequency variability for each individual, the response times on the SART were translated to time-series data, de-trended, and separated into seven segments. Each segment comprised of seventy-five data points with fifty points overlap. These data points were then hamming-windowed and zero-padded for the total length of four hundred and fifty points. The separate Fourier transform's amplitude was squared to create the periodogram for each segment, which was then distributed across the full seven SART blocks to create the one power spectrum for each individual during each SART block (Johnson et al., 2007, p. 630-638).

The data for the fast frequency variability and standard deviation to response time was calculated for two halves of the pre-test and the two halves of the post-test to measure possible changes in the participants' sustained attention level during this experiment. In contrast, the slow frequency variability was only calculated for the pre-test and the post-test as a whole and was not divided into two halves. The mean response time and the standard deviation to response time were normally distributed and analyzed using analysis of variance and the pairwise adjusted Bonferroni comparison. The fast frequency and slow frequency variability data were non-normally distributed; therefore, the Mann-Whitney U test was used to measure changes or differences between the two groups. Friedman's analysis of variance was utilized to detect meaningful differences in performance among the same group members.

4. RESULTS

Analyzing the results measured by the standard deviation demonstrated a more uniform response time pattern among participants who experience the lobby with the natural green elements, as reflected in Table 1. These results suggest that a higher level of sustained attention was maintained by the people of that group $F(1, 159) = 12.56$, $p < .001$. Data collected demonstrated no meaningful difference in the performance for individuals in two separate groups at baseline $F(1, 159) = 0.00$, $p = 0.939$, $r = 0.00$. However, there was a significant difference in the participants' performance after experiencing the two different versions of the lobby $F(1, 159) = 5.44$, $p = 0.031$, $r = 0.18$. Participants who walked through the lobby with natural/green elements demonstrated less response variability $F(1, 159) = 5.00$, $p = 0.023$, $r = 0.18$. In con-

	Pre-Test								Post-Test							
	1st Half				2nd Half				1st Half				2nd Half			
	M.E.	IQR	M	S.E.	M.E.	IQR	M	S.E.	M.E	IQR	M	S.E	M.E	IQR	M	S.E
andard Deviation of response time																
obby with Natural Elements			95.20	4.33			102.38	4.90			89.54	3.67			94.14	3.99
obby without Natural Elements			92.48	3.78			108.88	4.65			103.11	6.01			114.13	6.32
oment-to-moment variability																
obby with Natural Elements	127,888	121,693			122,839	130,020			114,859	127,934			137,838	119,009		
obby without Natural Elements	131,884	124,522			148,138	162,841			136,987	142,638			182,348	188,748		
adual variability																
obby with Natural Elements	137.13	168.14							117.80	152.78						
obby without Natural Elements	161.11	282.2							193.28	242.86						
ean response time																
obby with Natural Elements			581.71	17.23			621.16	18.33			623.37	18.61			517.80	20.0
obby without Natural Elements			539.53	16.34			619.92	18.63			618.72	20.10			499.88	18.1

Table 1: The Mean (M) ± Standard Error (SE) for Response Time and Standard Deviation of Response Time provided in Seconds. Median (M.E.) and Interquartile Range (IQR) are Presented for the fast frequency and slow frequency variability on the sustained attention to response task SART test in power

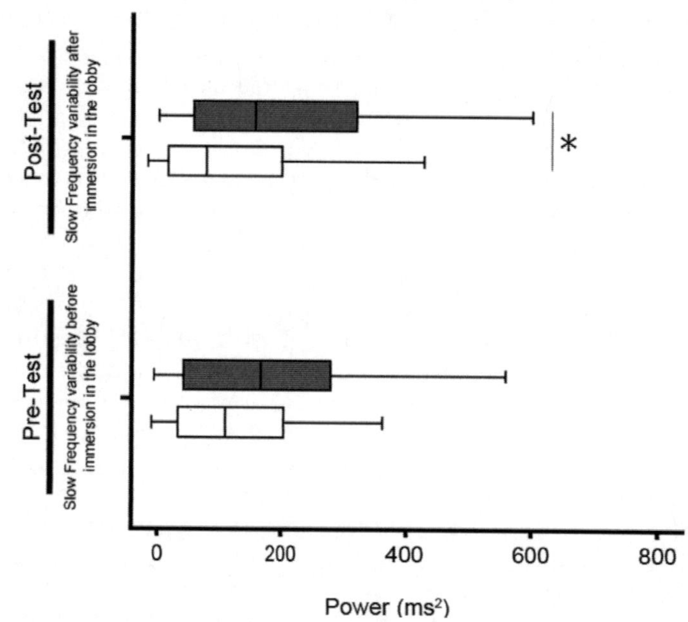

Figure 4: Boxplot of the median and variance of slow frequency changes in response variability. Results for performance at pre-test and post-test obtained from participants who experienced the lobby without natural/green elements (black boxes) and the lobby with natural/green elements (white boxes). The asterisk indicates a significant difference between participants who walked through the lobby with natural/green elements compared to those who experienced the lobby with no natural/green elements at post-test (p=0.008). No meaningful difference was observed at pre-test (p=0.143).

trast, a significant increase was observed among participants in the other group after walking through the lobby with no natural/green elements $F(1, 159) = 7.59$, $p = 0.007$, $r = 0.27$. Results also revealed that both groups performed with lower response variability in the first half of the pre-test compared to the second half. The same performance result was observed in the first half of the post-test compared to the second half of the post-test $F(1,159) = 4.57$, $p = 0.041$.

Data obtained from the SART test, as illustrated in Figure 4., demonstrated that there was not a meaningful difference between participants in the two different groups at baseline [$U = 2231$, $p = 0.148$, r

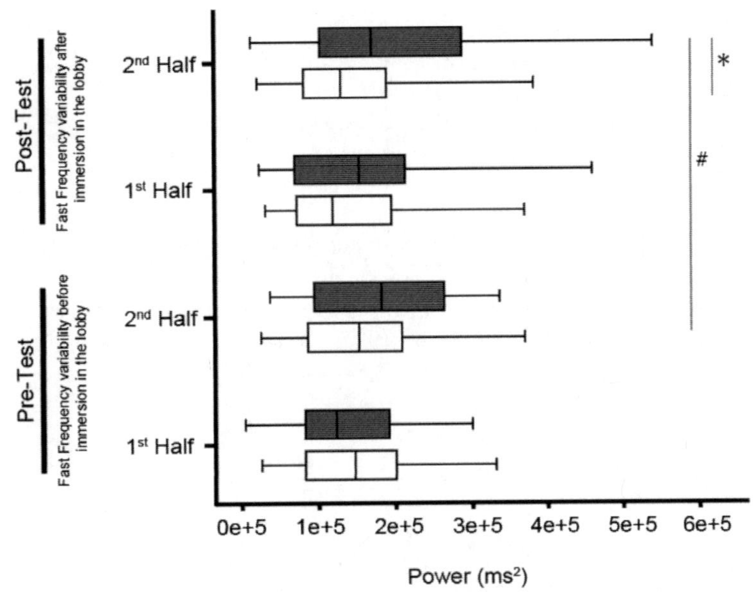

Figure 5: Boxplot of the median and variance of fast frequency response variability (reported as power). Participants experienced the lobby without natural/green elements (gray boxes) or with natural/green (white boxes). Data shown for the 1st and 2nd half of the pre-test, and the 1st and 2nd half of the post-test. The asterisk indicates a significant difference between participants exploring the lobby with and without natural/green elements (p=0.014). The hash sign indicates a significant increase in variability for participants experiencing the lobby with and with no natural/green elements in the 2nd half of the SART task from pre-test to post-test (p=0.041).

= -0.12]. However, after experiencing the lobby design, the slow frequency variability for the participants who experienced the lobby with natural/green elements during the test was significantly lower compared to the other group [U = 1971, p = 0.008, r = -0.21]. But Figure 4. shows no meaningful change in slow frequency variability among participants of each group separately [Lobby with natural/green elements, z = -1.37, p = 0.090, r = -0.09, Lobby without natural/green elements, z = -0.74, p = 0.232, r = -0.05].

Also, as illustrated in Figure 5., results of the fast frequency variability for two halves of the pre-test indicated no meaningful differences between the participants of the two groups [1st half, U = 2450, p = 0.376, r = -0.03, 2nd half, U = 2322, p = 0.165, r = -0.08]. Similar results were observed in the 1st half of the post-test. There was no meaningful difference in the fast frequency variability between the members of the two groups [U = 2450, p = 0.336, r = 0.04]. In contrast, in the second half of the post-test, those who experienced the lobby with no natural green elements demonstrated more significant fast frequency variability. These results suggest that after immersion in the lobby without natural/green elements, participants' attention control was significantly worse than the members of the other group [U = 1989, p = 0.013, r = 0.18].

As it can be seen on Figure 5. the fast frequency variability deteriorated over time, only among participants who experienced the lobby with no natural/green elements [Lobby with no natural/green elements, x^2 (3) = 29.05, $p < 0.001$; Lobby with natural green elements, $x^2(3)$ = 2.11, p = 0.533]. The decline in the fast frequency variability was more significant between the two halves of the post-test compared to two halves of the pre-test [z = -1.75, p = 0.034, r = -0.14].

During this experiment researchers observed that interacting with natural/green elements in the lobby was associated with less slow frequency and fast frequency variability. These results suggest a higher-subcortical arousal and better attention control for participants who experienced the lobby with natural/ green elements (Johnson et al., 2007, p. 630-638).

One of the factors that can affect the fast and slow frequency \variability was the participants' response time to the displayed numbers during the SART test (Johnson et al., 2007, p. 630-638). Therefore, researchers had to make sure that the response rates were similar in both groups in order to compare the SART test results, and neither of the group replied to the data significantly faster than the other; the data were therefore comparable.

No significant difference was observed in the mean response time between the two groups [$F(1,159) = 0.10$, $p = 0.759$]. This result suggests that participants followed the reaction cue "⊗" signal to react to the numbers displayed on the screen which resulted in reduction of the trade-off between accuracy and reaction speed. All participants in the second part of the test performed faster than the baseline [$F(1, 159) = 5.33$, $p = 0.021$, $r = 0.19$]. Overall, participants responded faster in the post-test compared to the pre-test. They performed faster in the second half of each part of the test, a typical outcome which can be attributed to the participants' having more experience with the way the test is conducted [$F(1,159) = 14.88$, $p < 0.001$, $r = 0.35$] (Lee et al., 2015, p. 182-189).

5. DISCUSSION

The outcomes of this study were in line with Attention-resource Model (Warm et al., 2008) and Attention Restoration Theory (Kaplan & Kaplan, 1989) that suggest people find presence in nature and contact with natural/green elements have a positive effect on individuals' attention level and mental resources (Abbott et al., 2016, p. n/a).

The Attention Restoration Theory puts forward that physical or visual interaction with nature nurture attentional capacities and resources (Hartig et al., 2003, p. 109-123). The outcomes of this research also show that walking through a building lobby with natural elements can improve participants' sustained attention level and attention control. In this research, fast frequency and slow frequency variability in response time were assessed as indicators of the sustained-attention level measured by the SART test. Participants who walked through the building lobby with natural elements maintained significantly less fast and slow frequency response time variability than those walked in the lobby without natural/green elements. Therefore, the outcomes of this research support the research hypothesis.

Multiple studies have verified the positive impact of presence in and visual interaction with nature on attention level (Berto, 2005, p. 249-259; Kaplan & Kaplan, 1989). The current study expands on the former research and suggests that the positive effect can result from visual contact with only a few natural elements. This study provides evidence that suggests the positive consequences of contact with natural/green elements could occur in a much tighter time frame than previously expected, less than a minute in this case. Previous studies have verified the positive outcomes of that interaction for more extended periods, from hours to days (Bratman et al., 2015, p. 8567-8572). In contrast with former studies that emphasized the abundance of natural elements for positively impacting an individual's attention, the study's results confirm the value of using limited natural/green elements in indoor spaces.

Natural/green elements have multiple features and characteristics such as color, shape, height, and more that were not considered in this research. Future research can focus on any of those properties as the independent variable and measure the possible impact of any changes in those properties on the individuals' attention level. In line with other recent studies (Berman et al., 2008, p. 1207-1212, 2008; Berto, 2005, p. 249-259; Bailenson, 2018), this experiment used the immersive VR technology to explore the role of natural/green elements on restoring people's attention and possibly promoting their mental health status. This research's outcomes can be further examined by comparing the impact of interacting with natural/green elements in both virtual and real-world experiences. Since there are still some disagreements over the extent to which a virtual environment can induce the same psychological and physiological responses that are similar to real-life situations (Daniel & Meitner, 2001, p. 61-72; de Kort, Y. A. W. et al., 2006, p. 309-320). This research was exploratory research focusing on detecting any major changes in people's attention level after interaction with limited natural/green elements in an indoor setting. What this research did not focus on was the persistence of such an impact.

One of the factors that can affect people's engagement with an environment is the level to which people find new and novel elements in that space and find them interesting (Bagot et al., 2007, p. 124-127). This research used an existing residential building where the participants were living and added natural/green elements to its design. People's familiarity with the unvegetated lobby might have made the natural/green elements stand out more. Therefore, studies that measure the impact of natural/green elements on people's attention restoration, after a more extended existence of those elements in the lobby, might reveal more about the extent and persistence of positive benefits.

6. CONCLUSIONS

This research demonstrated that micro visual interaction with natural green elements in a residential building could have a meaningful positive impact on residents' sustained-attention level. Usually, people who live in low-income housing often face mentally depleting circumstances and have fewer options and opportunities to replenish their attentional resources. Therefore, this study suggests that using natural/green elements in designing housing entrances has the potential to play a role in improving their sustained attention level, especially in high-density communities and low-income housing.

The results of this research suggest that by utilizing natural/green elements in interior spaces, in this case, a building lobby, designers can offer more equal access to green environments to those who do not have access to natural environments and green spaces. This access may allow those individuals to gain benefits similar to those who live in more green neighborhoods. The research also indicates that, in addition to larger natural areas, such as parks and greenways, much smaller localized green environments that can be experienced on a daily basis may also have significant value. The authors contend that guidelines and policies related to natural/green environments are needed for all scales and paying more attention to the inclusion and maintenance of natural/green elements in high density, low-income housing may significantly impact residents' quality of life.

7. REFERENCES

Abbott, L., Taff, D., Newman, P., Benfield, J., Mowen,A. (2016). The Influence of Natural Sounds on Attention Restoration. *Journal of Park and Recreation Administration, 34*(3) https://10.18666/JPRA-2016-V34-I3-6893

Ashbullby, K. J., Pahl, S., Webley, P., & White, M. P. (2013b). No title. *Health & Place, 23*, 138.

Astell-Burt, T., Feng, X., Mavoa, S., Badland, H. M., & Giles-Corti, B. (2014). Do low-income neighborhoods have the least green space? A cross-sectional study of Australia's most populous cities. *BMC Public Health, 14*(1), 292. https://10.1186/1471-2458-14-292

Austria, D. (2014), How Can Workplaces Restore the Mind and Support Employee Wellbeing A Seven-Mode Restorative Workplace Typology (Mater Thesis M.I.D.), University of Florida, Gainesville, U.S

Bagot, K. L., Kuo, F. E., & Felicity C.L. Allen. (2007). Amendments to the Perceived Restorative Components Scale for Children (PRCS-C II). *Children, Youth and Environments, 17*(4), 124-127. http://www.jstor.org/stable/10.7721/chilyoutenvi.17.4.0124

Bailenson, J. (2018). *Experience on demand : what virtual reality is, how it works, and what it can do*. New York : W. W. Norton & Company, 2018].

Barkley, R. A. (1997). Behavioral inhibition, sustained attention, and executive functions: Constructing a unifying theory of ADHD. *Psychological Bulletin, 121*(1), 65-94. https://10.1037/0033-2909.121.1.65

Baycan-Levent, T., Vreeker, R., & Nijkamp, P. (2009). A Multi-Criteria Evaluation of Green Spaces in European Cities. *European Urban and Regional Studies, 16*(2), 193-213. https://10.1177/0969776408101683

Berman, M. G., Jonides, J., & Kaplan, S. (2008). The cognitive benefits of interacting with nature. *Psychological Science, 19*(12), 1207-1212. https://10.1111/j.1467-9280.2008.02225.x [doi]

Berto, R. (2005). Exposure to restorative environments helps restore attentional capacity. *Journal of Environmental Psychology, 25*(3), 249-259. https://https://doi.org/10.1016/j.jenvp.2005.07.001

Bratman, G. N., Hamilton, J. P., Hahn, K. S., Daily, G. C., & Gross, J. J. (2015). Nature experience reduces rumination and subgenual prefrontal cortex activation. *Proceedings of the National Academy of Sciences, 112*(28), 8567-8572. https://10.1073/pnas.1510459112

Cackowski, J. M., & Nasar, J. L. (2003). The restorative effects of roadside vegetation: Implications for automobile driver anger and frustration. *Environment and Behavior, 35*(6), 736-751. doi:10.1177/0013916503256267

Calogiuri, G., Litleskare, S., Fagerheim, K. A., Rydgren, T. L., Brambilla, E., & Thurston, M. (2018). Experiencing Nature through Immersive Virtual Environments: Environmental Perceptions, Physical Engagement, and Affective Responses during a Simulated Nature Walk. *Frontiers in Psychology, 8*, 2321. https://10.3389/fpsyg.2017.02321

Corbetta, M., & Shulman, G. L. (2002). Control of goal-directed and stimulus-driven attention in the brain. *Nature Reviews Neuroscience, 3*(3), 201-215. https://10.1038/nrn755

Daniel, T. C., & Meitner, M. M. (2001). Representational validity of landscape visualizations: The effects of graphical realism on perceived scenic beauty of forest vistas. *Journal of Environmental Psychology, 21*(1), 61-72. https://10.1006/jevp.2000.0182

Davies, D. R. (., & Parasuraman, R. (1982). *The psychology of vigilance*. London ; New York : Academic Press, 1982.

Dean, J. H., Shanahan, D. F., Bush, R., Gaston, K. J., Lin, B. B., Barber, E., Franco, L., & Fuller, R. A. (2018). Is Nature Relatedness Associated with Better Mental and Physical Health? *International Journal of Environmental Research and Public Health, 15*(7), 1371. https://10.3390/ijerph15071371

Fridel, E. E., & Fox, J. A. (2019). Gender Differences in Patterns and Trends in U.S. Homicide, 1976–2017. *Violence and Gender, 6*(1), 27-36. https://10.1089/vio.2019.0005

Hamedani Golshan, H. & Saedi, H. Nanotechnology and Green Building: The Effect of Nanotechnologies on Optimal Use of Environmental Resources in Building, *Payam e Mohandes Magazine, No.69*, 18-27

Hartig, T., Evans, G. W., Jamner, L. D., Davis, D. S., & Gärling, T. (2003). Tracking restoration in natural and urban field settings. *Journal of Environmental Psychology, 23*(2), 109-123. https://https://doi.org/10.1016/S0272-4944(02)00109-3

Hester, R., & Garavan, H. (2004). Executive dysfunction in cocaine addiction: evidence for discordant frontal, cingulate, and cerebellar activity. *The Journal of Neuroscience : The Official Journal of the Society for Neuroscience, 24*(49), 11017-11022. https://24/49/11017 [pii]

Hitchcock, E. M., Dember, W. N., Warm, J. S., Moroney, B. W., & See, J. E. (1999). Effects of Cueing and Knowledge of Results on Workload and Boredom in Sustained Attention. *Hum Factors, 41*(3), 365-372. https://10.1518/001872099779610987

Jenkin, R., Frampton, I., White, M. P., & Pahl, S. (2018). The relationship between exposure to natural and urban environments and children's self-regulation. *Null, 43*(3), 315-328. https://10.1080/01426397.2017.1316365

Jett, Q. R., & George, J. M. (2003). Work Interrupted: A Closer Look at the Role of Interruptions in Organizational Life. *Amr, 28*(3), 494-507. https://10.5465/amr.2003.10196791

Johnson, K. A., Kelly, S. P., Bellgrove, M. A., Barry, E., Cox, M., Gill, M., & Robertson, I. H. (2007). Response variability in Attention Deficit Hyperactivity Disorder: Evidence for neuropsychological heterogeneity. *Neuropsychologia, 45*(4), 630-638. https://https://doi.org/10.1016/j.neuropsychologia.2006.03.034

Johnson, K., Kelly, S., Robertson, I., Barry, E., Mulligan, A., Daly, M., Lambert, D., McDonnell, C., Connor, T., Hawi, Z., Gill, M., & Bellgrove, M. (2008). Absence of the 7-repeat variant of the DRD4 VNTR is associated with drifting sustained attention in children with ADHD but not in controls. *American Journal of Medical Genetics.Part B, Neuropsychiatric Genetics : The Official Publication of the International Society of Psychiatric Genetics, 147B*, 927-37. https://10.1002/ajmg.b.30718

Kaplan, R. (2001). The nature of the view from home: Psychological benefits. *Environment and Behavior, 33*(4), 507-542. https://10.1177/00139160121973115

Kaplan, R., & Kaplan, S. (1989). *The experience of nature: A psychological perspective*. New York: Cambridge Univ Pr.

Keniger, L., Gaston, K., Irvine, K., & Fuller, R. (2013). What Are the Benefits of Interacting with Nature? International *Journal of Environmental Research and Public Health, 10*, 913-935. https://10.3390/ijerph10030913

Lee, J. M., Nouri-Mahdavi, K., Morales, E., Afifi, A., Yu, F., & Caprioli, J. (2014). Comparison of regression models for serial visual field analysis. *Japanese Journal of Ophthalmology, 58*(6), 504-514. https://10.1007/s10384-014-0341-5

Lee, K. E., Williams, K. J. H., Sargent, L. D., Williams, N. S. G., & Johnson, K. A. (2015). 40-second green roof views sustain attention: The role of micro-breaks in attention restoration. *Journal of Environmental Psychology, 42*, 182-189. https://https://doi.org/10.1016/j.jenvp.2015.04.003

Lim, J., Wu, W., Wang, J., Detre, J. A., Dinges, D. F., & Rao, H. (2010). Imaging brain fatigue from sustained mental workload: An ASL perfusion study of the time-on-task effect. *NeuroImage, 49*(4), 3426-3435. https://https://doi.org/10.1016/j.neuroimage.2009.11.020

MacLean, K. A., Aichele, S. R., Bridwell, D. A., Mangun, G. R., Wojciulik, E., & Saron, C. D. (2009). Interactions between endogenous and exogenous attention during vigilance. *Attention, Perception & Psychophysics, 71*(5), 1042-1058. https://10.3758/APP.71.5.1042 [doi]

MacLean, K. A., Ferrer, E., Aichele, S. R., Bridwell, D. A., Zanesco, A. P., Jacobs, T. L., King, B. G., Rosenberg, E. L., Sahdra, B. K., Shaver, P. R., Wallace, B. A., Mangun, G. R., & Saron, C. D. (2010). Intensive Meditation Training Improves Perceptual Discrimination and Sustained Attention. *Psychol Sci, 21*(6), 829-839. https://10.1177/0956797610371339

Manly, T., Owen, A. M., McAvinue, L., Datta, A., Lewis, G. H., Scott, S. K., Rorden, C., Pickard, J., & Robertson, I. H. (2003). Enhancing the sensitivity of a sustained attention task to frontal damage: convergent clinical and functional imaging evidence. *Neurocase, 9*(4), 340-349. https://10.1076/neur.9.4.340.15553 [doi]

Mitchell, R., & Popham, F. (2008). Effect of exposure to natural environment on health inequalities: an observational population study. *The Lancet, 372*(9650), 1655-1660. https://10.1016/S0140-6736(08)61689-X

National Coalition Against Domestic Violence (2020). *Domestic violence*. Retrieved from https://assets.speakcdn.com/assets/2497/domestic_violence-2020080709350855.pdf?1596811079991.

O'Connor, C., Robertson, I. H., & Levine, B. (2011). The prosthetics of vigilant attention: Random cuing cuts processing demands. *Neuropsychology, 25*(4), 535-543. https://10.1037/a0022767

Pascoe, M. C., Thompson, D. R., Jenkins, Z. M., & Ski, C. F. (2017). Mindfulness mediates the physiological markers of stress: Systematic review and meta-analysis. *Journal of Psychiatric Research, 95*, 156-178. https://https://doi.org/10.1016/j.jpsychires.2017.08.004

Paus, T., Zatorre, R. J., Hofle, N., Caramanos, Z., Gotman, J., Petrides, M., & Evans, A. C. (1997). Time-related changes in neural systems underlying attention and arousal during the performance of an auditory vigilance task. *Journal of Cognitive Neuroscience, 9*(3), 392-408. https://10.1162/jocn.1997.9.3.392

Phinney, R. (2013). Exploring Residential Mobility among Low-Income Families. *Social Service Review, 87*(4), 780-815. https://10.1086/673963

Pilotti, M., Klein, E., Golem, D., Piepenbrink, E., & Kaplan, K. (2015). Is Viewing a Nature Video After Work Restorative? Effects on Blood Pressure, Task Performance, and Long-Term Memory. *Environment and Behavior, 47*(9), 947-969. https://10.1177/0013916514533187

Posner, M. I. (2012). *Cognitive neuroscience of attention*. New York : Guilford Press, 2012].

Rice, A. & Saedi, H. (2021). Modes Matter! A Methodological Framework for Studying Restorative Impact of the Human interaction with Nature, *2021 Annual Conference of the Council of Educators in Landscape Architecture (CELA) Virtual Conference*, March 17–19, 2021, (ID:1142)

Robertson, I. H., Manly, T., Andrade, J., Baddeley, B. T., & Yiend, J. (1997). 'Oops!': Performance correlates of everyday attentional failures in traumatic brain injured and normal subjects. *Neuropsychologia, 35*(6), 747-758. https://https://doi.org/10.1016/S0028-3932(97)00015-8

Romero-Martínez, Á, & Moya-Albiol, L. (2013). Neuropsychology of perpetrators of domestic violence: the role of traumatic brain injury and alcohol abuse and/or dependence. *Revista De Neurologia, 57*(11), 515-522. http://europepmc.org/abstract/MED/24265146

Saedi, H. & Boone, K.M (2018), Virtual Reality and Student Understanding of the Third Dimension in the Landscape Architecture, *2018 Annual Conference of the Council of Educators in Landscape Architecture (CELA) at Virginia Tech, Blacksburg, Virginia*, March 21–24, 2018, (ID:289)

Saedi, H. & Rice, A. (2019) Minor Change for Major Impact: How Can Minor Changes in the Daily Urban Environment Impact an Aspect of Psycho-Physiological Health?, *Prometheus, No.4*, 96-99

Saedi, H. & Rice, A. (2021). Towards a More Just Design: The Potential Mental Health Benefits of Natural Green Elements, *2021 Annual Conference of the Environmental Design Research Association (EDRA) at Detroit, Michigan*, May 19–23, 2021, (ID:10318)

Saedi, H., & Einifar, A., & Barati, N. (2021). The Impact of Micro Interaction with Natural Green Elements Through Virtual Reality on Attention Restoration In a High-Rise Residential Building's Lobby. *Journal of Architecture and Urban Planning, 13*(30), 5-21. https://www.sid.ir/en/journal/ViewPaper.aspx?id=821171t

Saedi, H., & Rice, A. (2022). The Importance of Both: Competing Factors That Impact Attention Level Restoration and Mental Health. *Research Record*, 135-149.

Sarter, M., Givens, B., & Bruno, J. P. (2001). The cognitive neuroscience of sustained attention: where top-down meets bottom-up. *Brain Research Reviews, 35*(2), 146-160. https://https://doi.org/10.1016/S0165-0173(01)00044-3

Schwartz, D. A., & Kaplan, S. (2006). Concentration and attention: new directions in theory and assessment. In D. Clements-Croome (Ed.), *Creating the productive workplace* (2nd ed.). (pp. 242e277). New York: Taylor & Francis.

Sonnentag, S., Binnewies, C., & Mojza, E. J. (2010). Staying well and engaged when demands are high: The role of psychological detachment. *Journal of Applied Psychology, 95*(5), 965-976. https://10.1037/a0020032

Sturm, W., & Willmes, K. (2001). On the Functional Neuroanatomy of Intrinsic and Phasic Alertness. *NeuroImage, 14*(1), S76-S84. https://https://doi.org/10.1006/nimg.2001.0839

van den berg, A., Koole, S., & Van der wulp, N. (2003). Environmental preference and restoration: (How) are they related? *Journal of Environmental Psychology, 23*, 135-146. https://10.1016/S0272-4944(02)00111-1

Wang, X., Rodiek, S., Wu, C., Chen, Y., & Li, Y. (2016). Stress recovery and restorative effects of viewing different urban park scenes in Shanghai, China. *Urban Forestry & Urban Greening, 15*, 112-122. https://10.1016/j.ufug.2015.12.003

Warm, J. S., Parasuraman, R., & Matthews, G. (2008). Vigilance requires hard mental work and is stressful. Human Factors: *The Journal of the Human Factors and Ergonomics Society, 50*(3), 433e441.

Using a Post-Use Evaluation to Study Chinese Station Square Under Transit-Oriented Development Mode

Yingjun Zhao (Beijing Jiaotong University); *Chunfang Li* (Office@Csadi.Cn); *Li Wang* (Central-South Architectural Design Institute co;Ltd); *Yi Yang* (Beijing Jiaotong University); *Bo Zhang* (Oklahoma State University)

ABSTRACT

In China, with the increase in population and the integrated development of transportation and cities, most railway-integrated transportation hubs adopt the Transit Oriented Development (TOD) development model that uses urban multi-functional integration with the station as the core. The authors collect user comment data on social media platforms using python technology in the square in front of Hangzhou East Railway Station. The investigators use Anaconda and Excel software to divide the word frequency of the comment data and Gephi software to visualize the data to obtain the usage characteristics of the station square. Through their analysis, the authors determine:

1. The user's attention and satisfaction;
2. The usage characteristics of the station square;and
3. The accessibility of transportation transfer.

These findings are further analyzed to study the success of the development of the station plaza under the TOD model.

KEYWORDS

Data visualization; Hangzhoudong Railway Station; Post-use evaluation; TOD; Integration of station and city

1. INTRODUCTION

Social media has become a platform people reference for travel and a medium for expressing their emotions. People can follow their own wishes to publicly comment on the platform (which contains information such as their feelings of use, behavior, time of use, pictures, videos, etc.) (Zhao, 2020). Social media comments are characteristically numerous, diverse, spontaneous, and authentic, making them data for quantitative analysis (Zhou, 2013; Yu, 2015).Therefore, social media platform data is not only a travel reference and a medium for expressing emotions, but also brings new research methods. The current research using social media data involves the following fields: landscape design (Yang,2020); technology communication (McGuire, 2015); medical care (Wolska, 2011); transportation planning (Lock, 2020); people in the natural environment (Sinclair, 2019); sports activities (Liu, 2016);and so on. While these studies are solving problems, they also illustrate the effectiveness of big data analysis. This study uses the advantages of social media data to conduct a post-use evaluation of the station square under the TOD model.

1.1 Development Status of Railway Integrated Transportation Hub

In China, railway-integrated transportation hubs often adopt the TOD (Transit Oriented Development) station-city integration model (Zhao, 2020), forming a trend of urban multi-functional integration with stations as the core. At the same time, the function of the station square has also changed from a single station square to an urban square (Li,2009). The current research on railway integrated transportation hubs mainly explores development models and post-use evaluation (Liang, 2021; Li, 2021).

1.2 Current Status of Big Data Research on Railway Comprehensive Transportation Hub

Currently, the post-evaluation of the use of railway integrated transportation hubs mainly uses traditional data collection methods, such as observation, questionnaire surveys and behavioral graph analysis (Bi, 2018;Yang, 2021; Zhu, 2020; Lou, 2020). Compared with traditional data collection methods, social media comment data has spontaneous characteristics and can more genuinely reflect passengers' experiences. This research hopes to obtain passenger experience and station square usage characteristics through social media comment data analysis. It also seeks to provide an empirical basis for designing and constructing comprehensive railway transportation hubs.

Figure 1: *Hangzhoudong Railway Station (Photo by CSADI)*

2. RESEARCH OBJECTIVES

Hangzhoudong Railway Station is a comprehensive railway transportation hub designed under the TOD model and is one of China's largest railway hubs. Designed by CSADI and put into use on July 1, 2013, the railway platform consists of 15 stations and 30 lines (Li, 2015; Li, 2010). It covers an area of 720,000 square meters -the square covers an area of 320,000 square meters, and the station covers an area of 400,000 square meters. The total building area is 1.098 million square meters-the square building area is 810,000 square meters, the east square building area is 160,000 square meters, and the underground building area is 210,000 square meters (Li, 2018). The west square is 110,000 square meters above ground and 330,000 square meters underground. In 2019, Hangzhoudong Railway Station served 71.9 million passengers (China News Service, Hangzhou, December 31).

We chose Hangzhoudong Railway Station as a case study for the following reasons:

1. It is a comprehensive railway transportation hub developed under the TOD model;
2. It delivers a vast passenger flow;
3. The underground development level of the square in front of the Hangzhoudong Railway Station is relatively high, and the square in front of the station is transformed into an urban square (Li, 2019).

The main objective of the study is to determine the characteristics of the use of the station square:

1. What do passengers do in the station square?
2. Does the environment of the station square have an auxiliary effect on the station building?

3. What are the means of transportation connected to the city?

3. METHODS

This study uses Python to collect social media platform comment data on the square in front of Hangzhoudong Railway Station. Anaconda and Excel software are used to clean the comment data and determine the word frequency. Finally, Gephi software is used to visually analyze the collected comment data, study the usage of the square in front of the station, and provide an empirical basis for the builders. The data analysis flow is summarized in Figure 2.

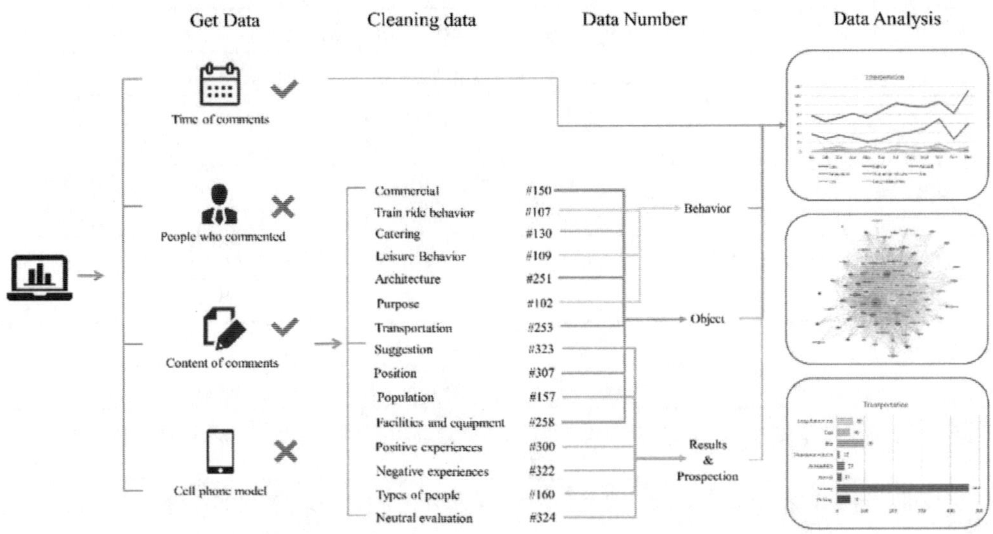

Figure 2: *Data analysis flowchart (Diagram by Authors)*

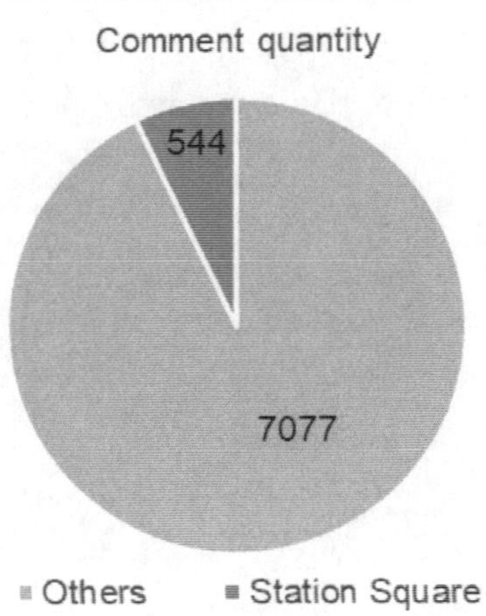

Figure 3: *Quantity comparison (Diagram by Authors)*

3.1 Database Construction from Social Media

Python technology was used to collect 7,621 points of data from social media platforms, including: Dianping, Sina; Mafengwo and Ctrip. The data covered the period from February 25, 2014 to October 31, 2020. There are 544 articles related to the station square, with a total of 839,19 words. The data includes information such as who posted the review, time, content and the poster's mobile phone use.

3.2 Data Analysis

Cleaning up the raw data required deleting useless information, such as: advertisements, mobile phones used by commenters, etc. Excel's search function was used to find keywords such as "outside the station,""outdoor,""square,"etc., to filter out the comments to only those made in front of the station, resulting in a total of

Table 1: Class words

Category	Subclass	Project & Active
Behavior	Purpose	Travel, Return home, Work
	Train behavior	In&out&Transfer, Ticket Checking, Departure, Lead, Passenger pick-up, and drop-off, By train, Ticketing behavior, Peripheral behavior, Manage
	Leisure behavior	Photo, Movement, Play, Shopping, Chat, Rest, Walk, Sit, Run, See, Inquiry, Entry & Exit, Eat,
Object	Square	Square
	Architecture	Architecture, Building Exterior, Landscape
	Catering	Fast food restaurant, Chinese restaurant, Bakery, Coffee shop
	Commercial	Store, Speciality Shop, Hotel, Mall, Convenience Stores, Company, Bookstore
	Transportation	Parking, Traffic, Train, Subway, Taxi, Bus, Aircraft, Automobiles, Non-motor vehicles, Long-distance bus
	Facilities and equipment	Seat, Elevator, Vending machine, Facilities, Signage
	Position	Here, Underground, Location
Results & Prospection	Population	Large populations, Few populations
	Types of people	Staff, Elderly, Children, The disabled, Passenger
	General positive experiences	Fast and efficient, Spacious, Orderly, Clean, High level, Quiet, Praise
	General negative experiences	Own problems, Slow and inefficient, Lost, Noisy, Traffic congestion
	Neutral evaluation	Not enough, General
	Suggestion	Approach, Suggestions, Measures

544 comments (Figure 3). Anaconda software was used to preliminarily divide the comment data according to the part of speech and delete the meaningless words, such as: "very,""etc."Excel software then helped to integrate and summarize the words.
The acquired words are classified and coded into three categories (Table 1):

1. Behavior category
2. Object category
3. Results and emotion category.

3.3 Data Visualization Analysis

The process used for visual analysis involved the following steps:

1. Add the number of words per month to get the total frequency of the comment data, and conduct a visual analysis of the frequency of the comment words.
2. Calculate the comment data on a monthly basis, use Excel to obtain a line graph of the word frequency of similar words in different months of the year, and visually analyze the monthly trend of word frequency.
3. After the words are numbered and classified, use Gephi software to visually analyze the correlation between words.

4. RESULTS

4.1 Whole Word Frequency Analysis

There is a certain connection between the number of word frequencies and social phenomena, and social changes will affect the fluctuation of word frequencies (Zhang, 2011). In this study, by categorizing the word frequency, passengers can quantitatively analyze the comment data of Hangzhoudong Railway Station, and compare the number of word frequencies and the fluctuations of the word frequency to reflect the characteristics of the use of the square in front of the station and the passenger's perception of the square in front of the station. Use evaluation.

1. Behavioral

Taking mainly the ride behavior and square leisure for comparison, the ride behavior word frequency is 1219 times, the square leisure behavior word frequency is 369 times, and the word frequency number ratio is about 3.3:1. At present, the activities taking place in the square in front of the Hangzhoudong Railway Station primarily revolve around taking a bus.

The ride behaviors are further subdivided into 9 items, sorted by word frequency from most to least: Departure(266 times) > in & out &transfer (226times) > Ticket checking (149) > Train (142) > Peripheral behavior (117times) > Ticket behavior(111 times) > Guide (57 times) > Management (38 times) > Pick-up and drop-off (20 times). Among the ride-related behaviors, Arrival and Transfer in and out of the station are the main functions of the station square.

The leisure behavior in the square continues to be subdivided into 12 items, sorted by word frequency from most to least: Space entry and exit (139 times) > Walk (92 times)>See (39times) >Rest (26times)>Shopping (21times) > Inquiry(20times) > Photo (12times) >Movement (7times) >Communication(6 times) > Sit (4 times) > Play (2 times) >Run (1 time). The word frequency of the two categories of Space entry and Exit tags was 231 times, accounting for more than half of the total leisure activities in the square.

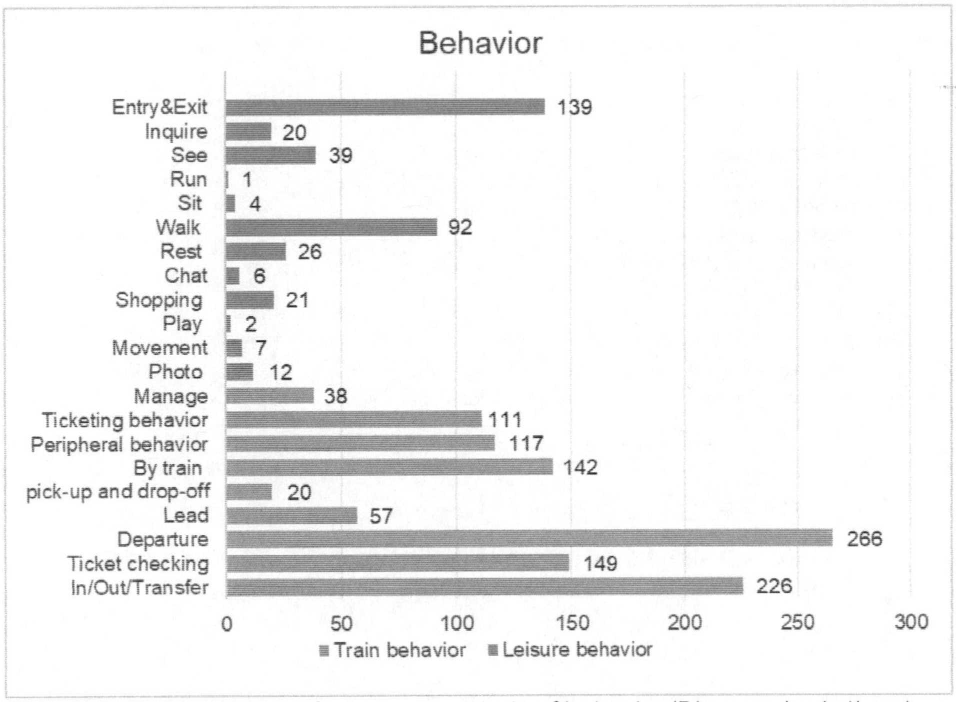

Figure 4: Overall word frequency analysis of behavior (Diagram by Authors)

and the "Sitting" tag was mentioned only 4 times. It shows that passengers are mostly walking in the station square, which means that the station square has strong mobility. It can be analyzed from the number of word frequencies that passengers are more inclined to spend their waiting time through shopping.

2. Transportation

The main analysis is to compare connection from railway to external transportation, a total of 8 items. The order of word frequency from most to least is: Subway (464 times) > Bus (99 times) > Long-distance Bus (59 times) > Taxi (48 times) > Automobiles (29 times) > Aircraft (17 Times) > Non-motor vehicles (12 times). See also Figure 5. Among them, subways, buses, and buses rank the top three, which reflects that the current connection between Hangzhoudong Railway Station and the city is mainly public transportation.

The subway accounted for half of the total word frequency of transfers. Airplanes are mentioned more than motor vehicles. This is related to the city terminal building in the square in front of Hangzhoudong Railway Station that strengthens the connection between the railway comprehensive transportation hub and the airport. The word frequency of the "Park" tag is 50, and people are more concerned about the parking problem in the square in front of the station.

3. Facilities

The facilities and equipment are subdivided into 5 categories, from which 4 types of specific facilities are extracted for comparison. The order of word frequency from high to low is: Signage (81 times)> Elevator (79 times)> Seat (28 times)> Vending machine (11 times). Passengers pay more attention to signs than other infrastructures and pay more attention to how to reach other places in the railway complex through the square in front of the station.

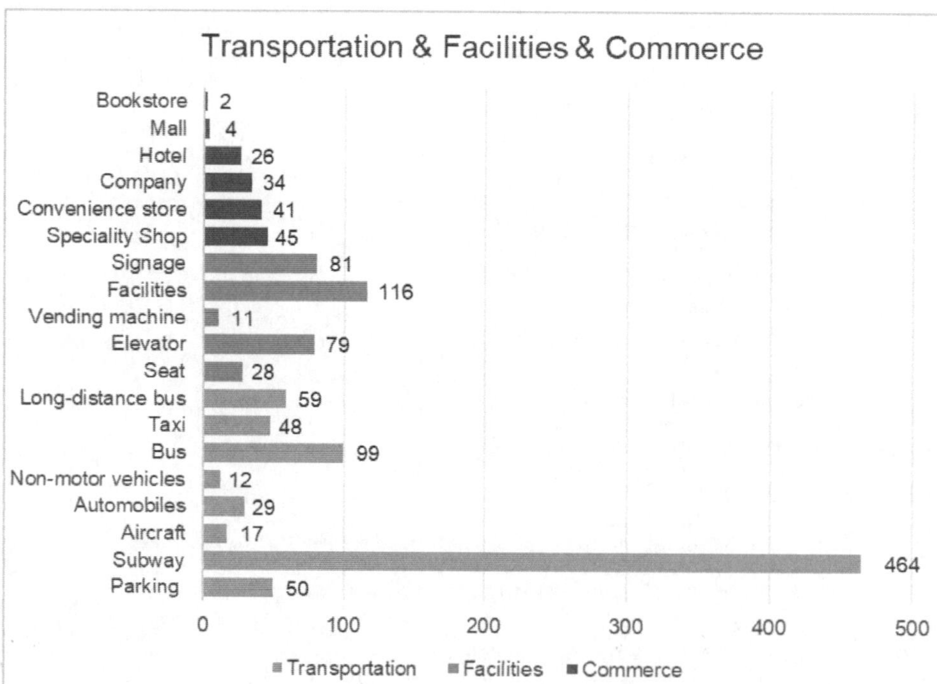

Figure 5: *Overall word frequency analysis of transportation, facilities, and commerce (Diagram by Authors)*

4. Commercial

Here mentions of different types of businesses are taken out for comparison: specialty stores, convenience stores, companies, hotel accommodations, shopping centers, and bookstores. In the commercial category, passengers paid the most attention to specialty shops, with a total of 45 mentions,while shopping malls mentioned 4 times. This has something to do with the incomplete construction of shopping centers around Hangzhoudong Railway Station. Currently, the Wanxianghui Shopping Center is only built in the East

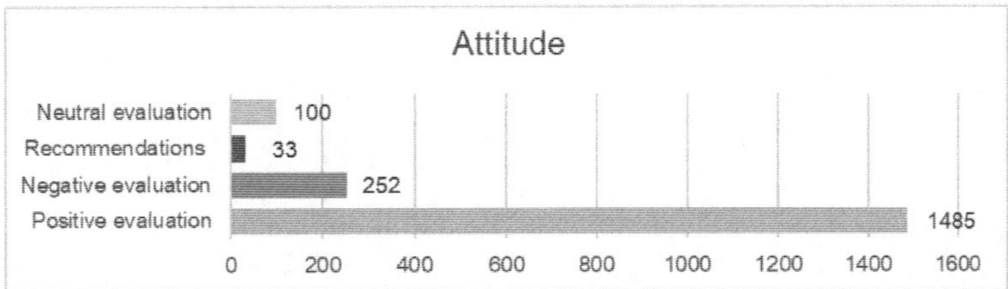

Figure 6 (above): *Overall word frequency analysis of attitude (Diagram by Authors)*

Figure 7 (below): *Contrast analysis of positive and negative evaluation word frequency (Diagram by Authors)*

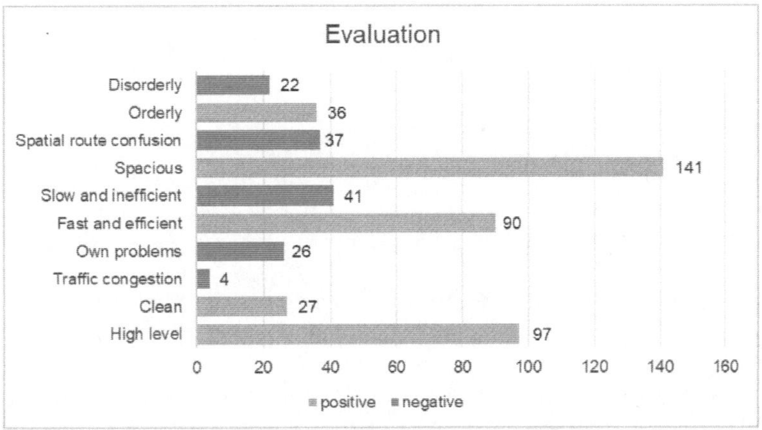

5. Results and Emotions.

The evaluation attitude of passengers is divided into four aspects: positive evaluation, negative evaluation, neutral evaluation,and suggestions. The maximum number of positive evaluations is 1485, which indicates that passengers are satisfied with the construction of Hangzhoudong Railway Station Square. The least number of suggestions is mentioned, reflecting that those passengers have not made more suggestions for the optimization of the square in front of the station. Comparing the speed efficiency category, the spatial order category, and the spatial feeling, the number of positive evaluations for each item is greater than the negative evaluations.

In the positive evaluation, five specific evaluations were extracted: Spacious, High level, Fast and Efficient, Orderly and Clean. Among them, passengers mentioned the space as "Spacious" most (141 times), and "Quiet" the least (27 times). Passengers pay more attention to the overall space experience.

Among the negative evaluations, five specific evaluations were extracted: Slow and Inefficient, Disorderly, Own Problems, Confusion and Traffic Congestion. The proportion of the five items is: 10:9:6:5:1, among which the Negative evaluation caused by people's own problems are mentioned 26 times.

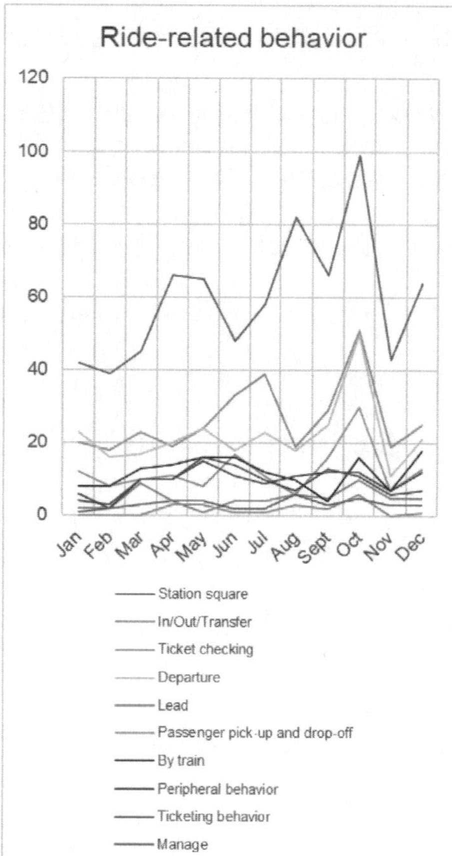

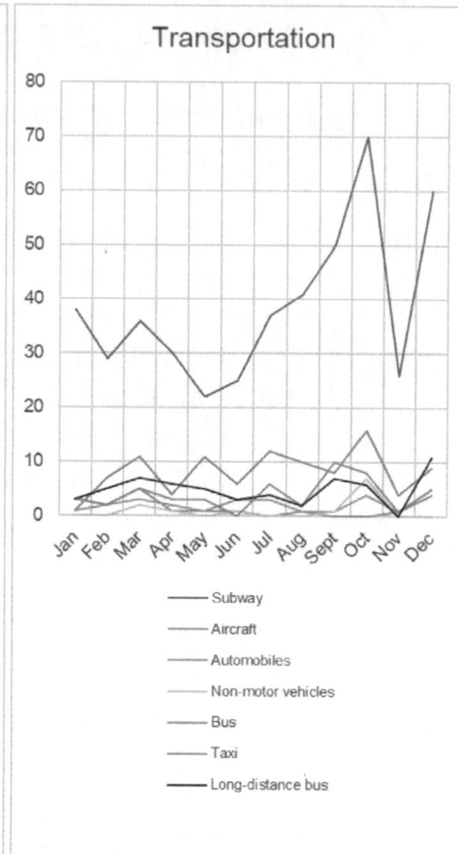

Figure 8: *Monthly distribution of ride behavior and transportation hashtags in categories (Diagram by Authors)*

4.2 Monthly Distribution

Overall, the number of comments on the square in front of the station increased significantly in spring and autumn. The peak occurred in October and the trough was in February. The outdoor temperature in winter was low and affected passengers' activities in the square in front of the station. The station square is basically consistent with the monthly trend peak of ride behavior. The peak of several labels in October were: Take the train,Transfer in and out of the station, Passengers Pick-up and drop-off; Ticket checking; Lead and Departure. The peak of the "ticket buying behavior" and "peripheral behavior" labels appeared in May, which is related to the longer days of holidays on Labor Day and National Day.

Transportation word frequency: The subway peaked in October and reached the bottom in March. It is consistent with "Taking the train";"In & out & transfer";"Passenger pick-up and drop-off"; "Tickets checking", "Lead"and "Departure"several ride-related behaviors. Therefore, the subway is a means of transportation that is closely connected with riding behavior.

4.3 Gephi Network Connection Analysis

Gephi is a visual analysis software that reflects the relationship between data through points and lines. Among them, the size of the point indicates: the number of times this tag appears in the database, the larger the point, the more times the passenger mentions it. The position of the point indicates the position of this label in the visual network. The closer the label is to the center, the more important the

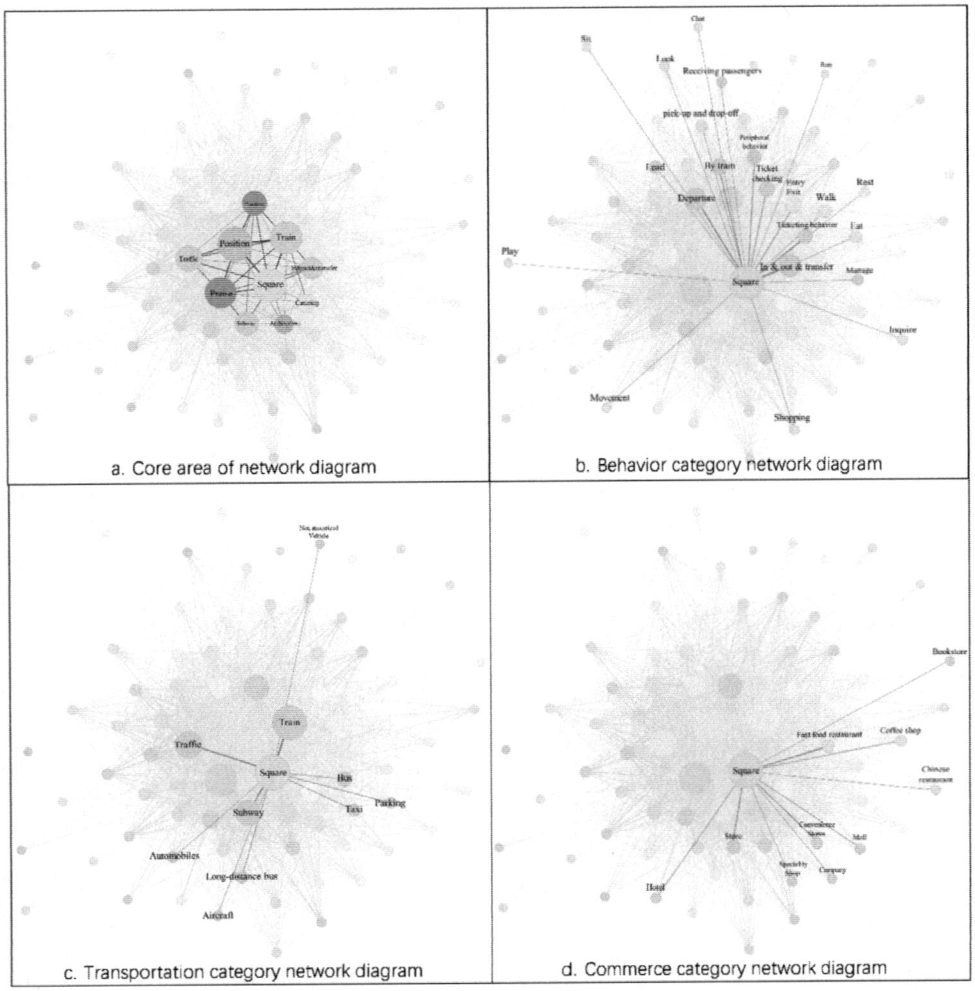

Figure 9: Gephi network diagram (Diagram by Authors)

label, and the higher the connection with other labels in the network. The width of the line indicates the strength of the connection between the labels. The wider the line, the stronger the relationship between two nodes. In Gephi software, the network relationship diagram mainly shows the importance of node labels, which can analyze which factors affect passengers' experience.

According to the central area of the network diagram, we can know:

1. Passengers are more concerned about the position, and this label is very closely related to the square. Therefore, the layout of the square is a key factor affecting passenger experience.
2. Through other label nodes that are closely connected with the Square we can determine that the main function of the square is to transfer to other transportation, get in and out of the station, set off the station building, and meet the catering needs of passengers.
3. The Praise label has a high correlation with the square and Position. Currently, the station square of the Hangzhoudong Railway Station can meet the needs of passengers.

The Behavior label node in the Gephi network diagram, we can know:

1. The location of the tag node of the riding behavior class is closer to the central area. "Departure" is larger than the label node of "In&Out& Transfer", but in terms of location, "In &Out & Transfer"is closer to the square, and"In &Out & Transfer"is more closely connected with the station square.
2. In the leisure behavior, "Sit" is the label of the node farthest from the "Square", which is located at the edge of the network relationship graph. In the station square, passengers do not pay much attention to the behavior of "sit".And there is no continuity between "Play", "Movement", "Shopping"and other entertainment activities. The node label of "In & Out& Transfer" is the closest to the station square and the node is the largest, indicating that passengers mention "In & Out& Transfer" the most times.

The Transportation label node in the Gephi network diagram, we can know:

1. The connection line between the Subway and the station Square is the thickest and the label node is the largest among the transfer vehicles. Passengers choose the subway as the most transfer method, and the station square has the closest connection with the subway.
2. In the car category, the taxi node is larger than the Automobiles node and is located closer to the square. Passengers tend to choose taxis instead of automobiles.
3. Passengers mentioned airplanes in their comments on the station square. Hangzhou East Railway Station builds an urban terminal in the square in front of the station, which can provide passengers with services such as ticket exchange and airport buses.

In the commerce label node in the Gephi network diagram, we can know:

1. Node of "stores"are closely connected with the node of"square", followed by "Convenience store;" "Specialty store;" "Shopping-mall;""Companies"and "Hotel".
2. Catering commercial: The "fast food" node is similar in size to "Coffee shop"nodes, but the node of "fast food restaurants"are more closely related to the node of "Square".

5. DISCUSSION

The basic features of the station square

Through this analysis it was possible to determine that passengers mainly carry out ride-related behaviors in the station square, most of which are transfers in and out of the station, and a few are related to leisure and entertainment activities. Compared with leisure activities, passengers tend to pass the waiting time through shopping. The "architecture" label node is located around the "square" in the Gephi relationship diagram and is in the most closely connected circle, indicating that the square in front of the station has the function of setting off the building. In terms of transportation transfers, passengers choose public transportation to account for 85% of the total transfer methods. Although the number of long-distance buses is higher than taxis, the degree of correlation between taxis and squares is higher than that of long-distance buses.

Advantages of the research system

This study collected 7,621 data on social media platforms from February 25, 2014 to October 31, 2020. Among them, there are 544 articles on the square in front of the station, with 83919 words. The huge data sample basically represents the passenger experience in the square in front of the station in TOD mode. The collected data is analyzed by word frequency, Gephi, Excel software is used for data visualization analysis, and a complete set of research system is formed to study the passenger experience of the station square in TOD mode. Provide a practical basis for designers.

The feasibility and effectiveness of big data methods

Compared with traditional data collection methods such as questionnaire surveys, social media platform big data has the advantages of large data volume, diverse information, and spontaneity. It truly starts from the passenger's perspective and supplements the information neglected from the professional perspective. Provide new inspiration for research content and direction.

Through the word frequency division, classification and sorting of the collected data, the data has been quantitatively analyzed. It objectively reflects the passengers' experience of using the square in front of the station, as well as the characteristics of the square in front of the station, and other information, and provides designers with a practical basis for construction based on the experience of passengers.

Gephi visual analysis of word frequency is performed to form a network relationship diagram, which intuitively reflects the distance between node labels and the size of nodes, to analyze the degree of association between the two. The network relationship graph can directly reflect the label of the node with the highest degree of association with the square in front of the station.

6. CONCLUSIONS

Functional changes in the station square: the sum of the frequency of "space in and out" and "walking" accounts for 62% of the total word frequency of leisure activities, and the number of words in "sitting" is 4 times, which is also reflected in the Gephi diagram, "space in and out" and "Walking" are all located near the square in front of the station, which can reflect that current passengers are more often going to other spaces through the square in front of the station.

Passengers have a relatively high degree of satisfaction with the current Hangzhoudong Railway Station construction: through the analysis of the frequency of evaluation words, the number of positive evaluation words is 1,485 times, and the number of negative evaluation words is 252 times. Among them, whether it is spatial experience, square order or speed efficiency, the positive evaluation is higher than the negative evaluation.

Relevant factors affecting satisfaction: In the positive evaluation, the wide spatial scale, modernization level, and speed efficiency of the station square are the key factors that make up the positive evaluation.

In addition to taking trains and transportation transfers, satisfying passengers' catering needs and setting off the building are factors that need to be considered in the construction of the square in the future. In the Gephi diagram, although the catering and building nodes are not as large as the nodes of traffic, ride behavior, and positive evaluation, they are all in a position comparable to the station square.

The high degree of compatibility between public transportation and railway transfer: Comparing the overall word frequency, it is found that public transportation transfer methods (metro, bus, long-distance bus) account for 85% of the total transfer methods, and public transportation transfers have been realized.

The guiding role of the station square is more important: Passengers pay much more attention to the signs than other sub-categories under the category of facilities and equipment, and most of them are positive evaluations. In the Gephi network relationship diagram, compared to other facilities and equipment, the correlation between signs and positive evaluation is higher than that of other subcategories.

Comparison between taxi and long-distance bus: Although the word frequency of long-distance bus is higher than that of taxi, the label of taxi node in the Gephi network diagram is closer to the square in front of the station.

Through the crawling and sorting of social media comment data and Gephi visualization analysis, research results can be drawn on the necessity, space usage, and basic usage characteristics of the station square in TOD mode. The feasibility and effectiveness of big data collection methods are summarized as follows:

7. LIMITATIONS

The age of passengers in transportation buildings is high. Compared with young people, the elderly are slightly less active on social media platforms. Therefore, the age level of the publishers of the comment data about the station square is relatively clustered. But with the popularity of social media, the user hierarchy will expand to a wider range. The research results will be more accurate.

In the future, social media comment data can be tested with traditional surveys (questionnaires, interviews) to more accurately analyze passenger experience.

8. REFERENCES

Bi, L. (2018). *The Research Of Post Occupancy Evaluation In Station Square Of Optimizing And Design In The North Square Of Changchun Railway Station*. Jilin Jianzhu University

Li, C., Yuan, P. and Qi, G. (2010). Hangzhou East Railway Station Design. *Urbanism and Architecture, 04*.https://doi.org/10.19892/j.cnki.csjz.2010.04.017

Li, C. (2018). CreativeDesign Practice of Modern Railway Transportation Hub.*Architecture Technique, 09*, 20-35.https://doi.org/10.3969/j.issn.1674-6635.2018.09.004

Li, C.(2019). Station-City Integration: Design Strategy of Hangzhoudong Railway Station. *Architecture Technique, 07*,64-69.https://doi.org/10.3969/j.issn.1674-6635.2019.07.011

Li, C.and Wang,L.(2015). Hangzhou East Railway Station, China. *Urbanism and Architecture, 13*, 56-63. https://doi.org/10.3969/j.issn.1673-0232.2015.13.013

Li, Q. (2021). Discussion on the Integrated Development of Railway Terminal Station and City. *China Plant-Engineering, 08*.

Liang, Q. (2021). Exploration and reflection on the integrated development modelof station-city (TOD). *Construction Enterprise Management, 03*, 92-95.

Liu, S., and Young, S.D. (2018). A survey of social media data analysis for physical activity surveillance. *Journal of forensic and legal medicine, 57*33-36. https://doi.org/10.1016/j.jflm.2016.10.019

Luo, Z. (2020). *Old City Railway Station In Shijiazhuang City Based on Multi-source Data Study on Regional Renewal*. Hebei University Of Engineering

McGuire, M.and Kampf,C. (2015). Using social media sentiment analysis to understand audiences: A new skill for technical communicators? *IEEE International Professional Communication Conference: 2015 IEEE International Professional Communication Conference (IPCC), 12-15 July, 2015*. Limerick, Ireland.: Institute of Electrical and Electronics Engineers

Lock, L.andPettit, C.(2020). Social media as passive geo-participation in transportation planning-how effective are topic modeling & sentiment analysis in comparison with citizen surveys?*Journal of Geospatial Information Science (Chinese Edition) 23*(4):275-292.https://doi.org/10.1080/10095020.2020.1815596

Sinclair, M., Ghermandi, A., Moses, S.A., et al.(2019).Recreation and environmental quality of tropical wetlands: A social media based spatial analysis. *Tourism management, 71*(Apr.):179-186. https://doi.org/10.1016/j.tourman.2018.10.018

Song, Y. andZhang, B. (2020). Using social media data in understandingsite-scale landscape architecture design: taking Seattle Freeway Park as an example. *Landscape Research*, 627-648.https://doi.org/10.1080/01426397.2020.1736994

Wegrzyn-Wolska K., Bougueroua, L. Dzickowski, G. (2011).Social media analysis fore-health and medical purposes *//2011 International Conference on Computational Aspects of Social Networks.: IEEE*, 2011:278-283

Yang, J. (2021). *Multi-source Data-based Spatial Evaluation of the Station Area of Hefei Station Walkability Evaluation Study*. Anhui Jianzhu University.

Yu, J. (2015). *Research on the Timely Changes of Tourist Emotion Based on Weibo Big Data——Taking Xi'an as an Example*. Shanxi Normal University.

Zhang, Q. (2011). Review on the Word Frequency Analysis Employed to Discover the Development of Science research in China. *Documentation,Information & Knowledge, 02*.https://doi.org/10.13366/j.dik.2011.02.021

Zhao,P.,Lv,D.,Hu, H., Cao, Y.,Xie, J.,Pang,L.,Zeng,L.,Zhang, T., andYan, D. (2020). The population-development-orientedcomprehensive modern transport system in China. *Acta Geographica Sinica, 75*, 2699-2715. https://doi.org/10.11821/dlxb202012011

Zhou, S., Zhai, W., Shi, Y., Shi, X. and Sun, Y. (2013). Overview on Sentiment Analysis of Chinese Microblogging *Computer Applications and Software, 30*. https://doi.org/10.3969/j.issn.1000-386x.2013.03.043

Zhu, L.(2020). *Post Occupancy Evaluation of Handan Railway Station Square and Optimization Strategies*. Hebei University of Engineering.

Figure 1. Hangzhoudong Railway Station. Photo by CSADI
Figure 2. Data analysis flowchart(2021).Diagram by the authors.
Figure 3. Quantity comparison(2021). Diagram by the authors.
Figure 4. Overall word frequency analysis of Behavior(2021). Diagram by the authors.
Figure 5. Overall word frequency analysis of Transportation & Facilities & Commerce(2021). Diagram by the authors.
Figure 6. Overall word frequency analysis of Attitude(2021). Diagram by the authors
Figure 7. Contrastive Analysis of Positive andNegative Evaluation Word Frequency(2021). Figure by the authors.
Figure 8. Monthly distribution of Ride behavior & Transportation hashtags in categories(2021). Diagram by the authors.
Figure 9. Gephi network diagram(2021). Diagram by the authors.
Table 1. Class words(2021). Table by the authors.

Abstracts: Individual Presentations

This track examines how we generate knowledge to address the great challenges of our time that influence intersections across human, community, and planetary health. Examples of topics include public health issues, an increasingly digital society, climate change, social inequities, overpopulation, stewarding tangible and intangible heritage, an increase in both waste and pollution (soil, air, noise, water), natural resource depletion, access to affordable housing, access to food and water, loss of bio-diversity, loss of cultural diversity, and urban sprawl. How do we rely upon simultaneity and adjustability to manage these challenges both locally and globally?

Design for a Sustainable Urban Outdoor Environment: An Investigation of the Daylight Availability and Building Energy Efficiency of Urban Forms

***Qingqing Sun** (Clemson University); **Vincent Blouin** (ASHREA)*

Climate change and the COVID-19 pandemic have altered how people interact with the built environment, which results in significant impacts on public health and well-being. It has been shown that the lack of daylight availability in the working and residential built environment can increase the risk of depression and circadian rhythm disorders (Beute & deKort, 2018), on the other hand, energy efficiency plays an important role in the future urban design process for many cities with net-zero climate goals. To create a more healthy and sustainable urban environment, many urban researchers examined the urban morphology from different performance perspectives (Chokhachian et al., 2020). Yet the synergetic impacts of urban forms on daylight availability and energy efficiency have not been explored completely.

This study proposes a simulation-based approach for investigating daylight availability (DA) and energy efficiency of urban forms. A series of iterative simulations were conducted to evaluate the daylight performance and energy efficiency of theoretical urban design scenarios for the climate in Atlanta, GA. As the third fastest-growing city in the USA, improving public health and environmental sustainability is a major challenge for Atlanta in the post-pandemic climate-changing world. Existing urban design studies based on Atlanta fall short of leveraging daylight availability and energy efficiency.

Our research findings show that the urban form attributes, including the building density and orientation have significant effects on daylight availability and energy efficiency. With regards to the interaction between daylight availability and energy efficiency, we analyze the trade-off between the annual energy consumption and the Spatial Daylight Autonomy(sDA) when assessing the impacts of selected urban form attributes. This study focuses on enhancing the understanding of the urban morphology and urban design strategies used by planners, urban designers and architects, to properly balance daylight availability and energy efficiency considerations in urban design practices.

References

Beute, F., & de Kort, Y. A. W. (2018). The natural context of wellbeing: Ecological momentary assessment of the influence of nature and daylight on affect and stress for individuals with depression levels varying from none to clinical. *Health & Place, 49*, 7–18.

Chokhachian, A., Perini, K., Giulini, S., & Auer, T. (2020). Urban performance and density: Generative study on interdependencies of urban form and environmental measures. *Sustainable Cities and Society, 53*, 101952.

Geriatri-City: Aging Playfully in Seoul

Lisa Lim *(KAIST);* ***Hyun-Young Jin*** *(Seoul National University)*

The world is aging. By 2050, more than 20% of the world's population will be over 60 years. With such population aging, the health of the elderly population becomes a critical factor determining their quality of life and contribution to society.

Health is defined as "a state of complete physical, mental, and social well-being and not merely the absence of disease or infirmity" by the World Health Organization. While a significant number of studies provide ways to improve the health of the elderly population, many of them focus on the physical activities and health of the individuals. While improved physical activities and health are critical for their health, mental health and social well-being of the elderly population are also critical to support healthy aging. Furthermore, a significant proportion of aged 65 and older Americans are considered socially isolated and report feeling lonely, emphasizing the importance of mental and social health along with the physical health of the elderly population.

Leisure activities, such as hobbies, sports, socializing, and volunteering, are found to have physical, mental, and social health benefits by a growing body of research. According to a recent framework, leisure activities improve the health of individuals through psychological, biological, social, and behavioral processes at multiple levels (Fancourt et al., 2021). For instance, leisure activities support cognitive learning, biologically activate individuals' physical conditions, promote individuals to be socially active, and to be engaged in healthy behaviors. However, unfortunately, a significant proportion of the elderly population does not have awareness and access to healthy leisure activities in our communities.

This study addresses the following questions: are communities providing various types and spaces to perform healthy leisure activities to the elderly population? How can we design healthier communities where the elderly population can be physically, mentally, and socially active through healthy leisure activities?

To answer such questions, this study investigates the city of Seoul in South Korea where the aging population is highly populated, as a case study of a fast-aging metropolitan area. This study analyzes and evaluates the distribution and accessibility of leisure facilities in urban settings of Seoul using GIS and Space Syntax methods. Also, to understand the patterns of leisure activities of the elderly population, National Leisure Activity Survey is analyzed. Furthermore, the relationships between spatial attributes of the leisure facilities and leisure activity patterns will be provided.

The results of this study will provide preliminary design strategies that could promote healthy leisure activities of the elderly population through the design of the communities in the context of a high-density metropolis area. As the World Health Organization states, physical and social environments of communities can provide more opportunities for the elderly population to be active physically, mentally, and socially. The results of this study are expected to illustrate ways to provide such opportunities through the design of the communities.

References

Fancourt, D., Aughterson, H., Finn, S., Walker, E., & Steptoe, A. (2021). How leisure activities affect health: a narrative review and multi-level theoretical framework of mechanisms of action. *The Lancet Psychiatry.*

City-Wide Park Use before and during COVID-19: A Case Study of Atlanta, Georgia

Katherine Melcher *(University of Georgia);* ***Jessica Fernandez*** *(University of Georgia);* ***Yang Song*** *(Texas A&M University)*

Research indicates that access to parks and other outdoor greenspaces are important to physical, mental, and social health (for an overview, see Van den Berg et al., 2019). These health benefits became especially critical during the COVID-19 pandemic: when indoor activities were limited, stress rates were high, and gyms and other means of exercise such as team sports declined. Anecdotal evidence suggests that, after the start of the pandemic, more people were going outside, exercising, and using parks (Boston University, 2020).

Given the potential value that parks could have to people's health, it is important to inquire whether park use did or did not increase during the pandemic. Also important to ask is which populations accessed parks during this time as compared to before the pandemic. This study employs SafeGraph Places data to study 122 parks in Atlanta, Georgia for an in-depth analysis of visitation patterns and core points of interest information. Descriptive statistics and pairwise correlations provide initial significance for further exploration, and multiple regression analysis compares park use by different populations over time with variables such as park typologies, tree coverage, amenities, and location demographics.

On a city-wide level, preliminary results showed no significant change in park use when comparing park usage data from March through February of each year from 2018 through 2021. However, park use by people who rent housing and do not own a vehicle decreased during the pandemic 7% from the year before and 8% from two years prior, showing a concerning decline in park use for this population. Additionally, median dwell time in parks during the pandemic was down by 7.6% from the year before and 11% from two years prior, signifying less time spent in parks since the COVID-19 shutdown. Our findings that park use remained relatively the same pre and post pandemic contradicts the general impression that outdoor recreation increased significantly during the pandemic. However, perhaps people were using streets and sidewalks for recreation rather than visiting parks. The lack of change in park use could also be explained by a decline in use of certain types of parks, such as playgrounds, basketball courts, and recreation centers, while others, such as passive parks and trails, might have had an increase in use. The decline in use of parks for renters without cars and the reduced time spent in parks are cause for concern and need further study.

References

Boston University Initiative on Cities. (2020). 2020 Menino survey of mayors: Urban parks and the public realm: equity and access in post-COVID cities.

Safegraph Core Places (2021). Available from safegraph(dot)com.

Van den Berg, A.E., Joye, Y., & de Vries, S. (2019). Health benefits of nature. In L. Steg & J.I.M. de Groot (Eds.), *Environmental psychology: An introduction* (pp. 55-64). John Wiley & Sons.

Beyond Bazalgette: Pandemics and Public Health Based Urban Design

Anirban Adhya *(Lawrence Technological University)*

From the medieval plague to the recent COVID19, cities have evolved with public health crises (Fisher, 2010). The goal of this project is to study and analyze cities through the lens of diseases, their urban responses and their consequences - both planned and unintended. Pandemics, public health, and urban infrastructure are the drivers of this study focusing on how diseases and their spread affect city form and urban life. Using the case of cholera in London and plague in Genoa and Venice, the research highlights specific design decisions and infrastructural planning. Findings from literature review and analytical map studies allow us to develop design guidelines for healthy and resilient cities. The study includes pioneering works, prior to advent of modern architecture and planning, fundamental to monumental urban infrastructures.

The project employs a case-study-based methodology involving historiography of a disease, its response in a specific city, and analysis of the responses to study their implications for development of cities, urban design and urban life. Specifically, the methodology includes four key steps. First, literature review of pandemics and their urban responses in cities across history and geography is undertaken. Second, within the content of diseases and their urban responses, cholera in London is identified as the pandemic urban case study for this project. Third, analysis of map and documents in architecture, planning, and sociology is undertaken to study the extent and nature of urban responses, especially in terms of infrastructure planning and design. Finally, the analytical findings are used to prompt questions and discussions to understand the imperative for development, sustenance, and resilience of urban infrastructure in the face of pandemics.

The urban history of disease also revolves around how aspects of modern urban planning like centralized infrastructure networks and contemporary urban design elements like formal open spaces have evolved (Chandra, 2020). The development of sewer and storm-water systems have been critical in the rise of safe and healthy cities. Similarly, green spaces and urban parks have played an important role in quality of urban life and experiences. Even certain elements of modern architecture have partly emerged in responses to disease outbreaks and measures to contain them. Disease outbreaks have always been drivers for new innovations in architecture and urban design. Pandemics often lay bare spatial inadequacies and highlight the need for broader changes in how societies are spatially conceptualized and organized.

The historical analysis highlights the challenges and limitations of large centralized engineered solutions in sustaining resilience against pervasive existence of virulent pathogens and in the face of climate change - rising water level and extreme storm-water events. Beyond Bazalgette, the current London Super Sewer efforts and even its vulnerability reinforces the need for hybridization, where large centralized engineered systems are coupled with local site-specific de-centralized systems.

References

Chandra, S., Kassens-Noor, E. (2020). 5 ways the world is better off dealing with a pandemic now than in 1918. The Conversation, June 2020. Accessed 14 Nov 2021.

Fisher, T. (2010). "Viral Cities," *Places Journal*, October 2010. Accessed 14 Nov 2021.

The Impact of Place Identity on Social Resilience in Time of a Disaster

Saeideh Sobhaninia *(Clemson University);* ***Melika Amirzadeh*** *(University of Art, Tehran)*

Experiencing a disaster and losing family and friends are challenging by themselves. Imagine being forced to live in a temporary shelter for a while, being detached from friends and family, and not knowing when you can return to your place.

Due to recent climate change, vulnerability to disruptions has increased (Aldrich & Me yer, 2015) and what makes the effects of disasters worse and recovering from them harder is community vulnerability (Roque et al. 2020). Environmental disasters create acute vulnerabilities that must be addressed by making communities more robust and resilient to future shocks.

Moreover, based on past experiences, many people have difficulties with forced relocation in times of disasters (Brown and Perkins, 2003) that have caused profound anxiety for people. According to Diaz and Dayal (2008), one of the most catastrophic impacts of disasters is people's feeling of 'loss of place'. In the recovery process, residents try to reshape their individual and shared identities that are dependent on environmental and social characteristics of the place in which they live (Cox and Elah Perry, 2011) to counterbalance the feeling of loss. Thus, place identity is an asset and a cultural resource after a disaster (Fields et al., 2015)

Therefore, this research aims to identify how place identity can affect social resilience to help communities better prepare, cope with, adapt to, and recover from a disaster, which eventually leads to a faster and stronger return of the forced relocated population to their homes. To achieve the study's goal, we should answer the question of "what is the relationship between place identity and social resilience?" To answer these questions, we need to deeply analyze the past literature and experiences to identify the indicators of place identity and social resilience. Then, we need to see how these concepts affect each other in the context of neighborhoods. This research is an exploratory cross-sectional survey design. Data gathering is via questionnaire, and the method of analysis is multi-variable linear regression.

References

Aldrich, D. P., and M. A. Me yer (2015). "Social Capital and Community Resilience." *American Behavioral Scientist, 59*(2): 254–69

Brown, B., Perkins, D. D., & Brown, G. (2003). "Place

attachment in a revitalizing neighborhood: individual and block levels of analysis." *Journal of Environmental Psychology, 23*, 259e271.

Cox, R.S., Elah Perry, K. (2011). "Like a Fish Out of Water: Reconsidering Disaster Recovery and the Role of Place and Social Capital in Community Disaster Resilience", *Society for Community Research and Action*

Diaz, J., & Dayal, A. (2008). "Sense of place: A model for community based psychosocial support programs." *The Australasian Journal of Disaster and Trauma Studies, 1*, 1174–4707.

Fields, B., Wagner, J., Frisch, M. (2015). "Placemaking and disaster recovery: targeting place for recovery in post-Katrina New Orleans", *Journal of Urbanism: International Research on Placemaking and Urban Sustainability, :1*, 38-56

Roque, A. D, Pijawka, D., Wutich, A. (2020). "The role of social capital in resiliency: disaster recovery in Puerto Rico", *Risk, Hazards, & Crisis in Public Policy.*

The Neighborhood-Scale Heat Risk Assessment to Reduce Heat-Health Vulnerability in Persian Gulf Cities with a Particular Focus on Climate Justice (Case Study: Bandar Abbas City, Iran)

Marzieh Rezaei Ghaleh *(Arizona State University);* ***Maryam Rezaei Ghaleh***

The impacts of global warming will be more intense across the Middle East and North Africa (MENA), characterized by a hot and arid climate (Ahmadalipour and Moradkhani 2018). The rising temperature trend in MENA increasingly affected human health. Most of MENA's population (about 65%) lives in cities, which is projected to double by 2050 (Worldbank 2021). This issue could amplify the exposure to heat and health vulnerability. Thus, the heat-related mortality risk in MENA without implementing suitable actions in climate change adaptation will increase 8 to 20 times more in the future (Ahmadalipour and Moradkhani 2018). Among the MENA cities, urban areas in the coastal regions in the Persian Gulf are much more at risk of heat-health risks because they will be affected by extreme heatwaves and elevated wet-bulb temperatures by the end of the 21st century (Salimi and Al-Ghamdi 2020). Some studies also indicate a substantial increase in the Persian Gulf's heat-related mortality risk (Ahmadalipour and Moradkhani 2018), leading to climate and Health injustice. As a result, the Persian Gulf's inhabitants in the hottest neighborhoods face the most significant heat-health risks and suffer from extreme inequality. Thus, this research aims is to find possible solutions for reducing health vulnerability and enhancing resilience to urban heat by managing green infrastructure (GI). In other words, the primary focus is on strategies for mitigating the urban heat effect and increasing thermal comforts by implementing GI on a neighborhood scale, providing new solutions to tackle some of the health problems Persian Gulf's cities face. As a result, the research method for this study is the case study, including statistical methods and numerical modeling. We evaluate and compare differences in size, shape, connectivity, composition, and configuration of GI on outdoor microclimates and human thermal comfort by simulating different scenarios in the same neighborhood to find optimal options. Finally, a conceptual framework for future cities was outlined once patterns classification and modeling techniques are identified. Modeling the neighborhood and simulating GI indicators for cooling urban neighborhoods with ENVI-met in adaptation scenarios are done to find the best option for maximum temperature reduction and Validate ENVI-met simulations with T (air) and LST map.

Consequently, heat vulnerability mapping in this research identifies health and heat exposure disparities on a neighborhood scale and helps to target interventions at the community level. Moreover, proposed Green Infrastructure (GI) as a nature-based solution to climate change adaption reduces these consequences. However, improving this infrastructure in the urban areas, especially in high-density cities, cannot be done without considering limitations. Thus, the optimal spatial pattern of GI is critical for decision-makers and climate change adaption. The optimal proportion varies from city to city depending on the climate background. Also, this issue is more important in hot spots because they lack green spaces, and the opportunity to create them is low. Finally, the result of this research can be applied to other similar regions in MENA and serve as a catalyst for mitigating urban heat island effects and improving heat-related health.

The Role of Mobility Behavior in the Relationship of Greenness and COVID-19 Incidence: An 80-Week Nationwide Study

Tong Liu *(Clemson University),* ***Matthew Browning*** *(Clemson University),* ***Winifred Elysse Newman*** *(Clemson University)*

The COVID-19 pandemic and related quarantine policies (i.e., social distancing) radically changed how people interact with their neighborhoods. In particular, the closure of public facilities (i.e., recreation centers) decreased people's opportunities for physical exercise and leisure. Many people therefore turned to nearby nature (i.e., parks and tree-lined streets) for outdoor recreation as well as other health-promoting behaviors, such as social interaction.

A mounting number of studies have examined the association between greenness and COVID-19 incidence at national scales and in relationship to mobility/usage patterns. However, little is known about the role of mobility behavior between the relationship of greenness and COVID-19 vulnerability. In a larger context, building capabilities (i.e., promoting physical activities) is one of the major pathways through which greenness can affect health. Yet the evidence of whether green space contributed to mobility behavior (i.e., walking and park visiting) during the COVID-19 pandemic is neither consistent nor generalizable.

Thus, this paper investigates the linkage between the "greenness-mobility-health triad" from the perspective of COVID-19 vulnerability, including both infection and mortality. We posit that the COVID-19 pandemic led to trends in higher levels of nature appreciation and exposure as well as associated mobility behaviors as a result of bringing indoor activities outdoors. This change in public attitudes and behaviors may amplify "greenness-mobility-health" linkages.

Data used for this study is from February 16, 2020, to June 26, 2021, an 80-week period. The variables include county-level greenness, mobility behavior, and COVID-19 cases and deaths. Structural equation modeling (SEM) is applied to examine relationships between each category.

This research is currently in the pilot study phase using two selected states – South Carolina and Massachusetts. Preliminary results suggest mobility behavior plays a mediating role in the association between greenness and COVID-19 vulnerability. The higher the greenness level in a county, the less vulnerable its residents were to COVID-19 cases and deaths. In the next phase, we will pair all U.S. counties with similar conditions into sixteen groups according to four dimensions: (1) low/high percentage of aging population; (2) low/high urbanicity; (3) low/high percentage of race minority population; and (4) low/high vaccination rate. We will run SEMs for all paired groups to analyze the hypothesized dependent pathways between "greenness-mobility-health" within each of these stratified samples.

The research project is expected to be completed by May 2022. This will be one of the first studies to consider the effect of both greenness and spatiotemporal mobility behaviors on COVID-19 vulnerability at the national level. We also expect this project to advance understandings of mobility behavior as an important mediator in the greenness-health relationship outside of the COVID-19 pandemic context.

The Watershed House: A Prototype Microhome and Small Business Space Dedicated to Vulnerable Communities with a Lack of Access to Clean Water

Martín Paddack *(Howard University);* ***Dahlia Nduom*** *(Howard University)*

Equitable access to clean water is one of the greatest challenges that vulnerable communities face around the globe in the 21st Century. According to research conducted by Dig Deep and the US Water Alliance in the report Closing the Water

Access Gap in the United States: A National Action Plan, in the United States alone, over 2,000,000 people lack access to running water, indoor plumbing, or wastewater services (Roller, 2019). African American and Latinx households are twice as likely to lack complete plumbing than white households, and Native American households are 9 times more likely (Roller, 2019). In many minority communities across the United States, people travel significant distances to access clean water and transport it back to their homes.

The Watershed House is a low-cost prototype design for an adaptable, modular home that is projected to be self-sustaining and designed to serve vulnerable communities. The design incorporates several sustainable strategies, including rainwater harvesting and solar power generation. In addition, the house proposes a biomimetic design based on the Namib beetle, which uses the structure's envelope to create a "drinking skin" that can harvest over 100 gallons of drinking water per month through atmospheric water generation.

The prototype house will be sited in the Texas Colonia of La Presa, in Webb County. Colonias communities are located along the US-México border in Texas, New Mexico, Arizona, and California, with over 2,300 Colonias communities located in Texas alone. The majority of the over 500,000 Colonias residents are Latinx, (96%), and the poverty rate in Colonias sits significantly higher than the national average at 42% (Roller, 2019). In a survey of conditions in 2014, 337 Colonias did not have access to drinkable water (Federal Reserve Bank of Dallas, 2015).

The Watershed House also addresses the family unit by creating a modular design that can be connected via a porch space, which fosters both privacy and community. This design aspect is of significant cultural importance since many families occupy the same land on narrow but deep lots, which the design can accommodate to create family micro-communities.

Of further importance, each module (designed for two to five people) is also equipped with a workspace with outdoor access. Many families in the Colonias communities subsist in the informal economy, with small businesses such as food stalls, handicrafts, and textile work. Providing a workspace for residents of these homes is of primary importance.

Situated in a dry climate region, La Presa is an ideal case study location to test design solutions that could translate to communities in similar, water-deficient areas of the world. The goal of the Watershed House is to create meaningful, healthy, well-designed spaces that are not only sustainable but are family-oriented and provide an equitable platform for communities that need it.

References

Roller, Z. (2019). Closing the Water Access Gap In the United States: A National Action Plan. Retrieved from US Water Alliance: http://uswateralliance.org

Federal Reserve Bank of Dallas Community Development (2015). Las Colonias in the 21st Century: Progress along the Texas-Mexico Border. Retrieved from texascolonias.org

The Public Realm: Open Streets and Shared Spaces in Post-COVID Cities

Celen Pasalar *(North Carolina State University);*
George Hallowell *(North Carolina State University)*

The COVID-19 pandemic has altered the way that people socialize, travel, and experience their neighborhoods and public spaces in high to low-density urban areas. The use of outdoor space has gained significant focus during COVID, particularly as cities have shut down, providing limited access to public green spaces for healthy activities, or required social distancing measures for social gathering. Many cities in the US are now reclaiming streets, squares and plazas for public life with an emphasis on the creation of shared activity spaces. Certain streets have been converted into shared corridors that encourage improved safe travel and healthy activity during the stay-at-home period and through reopening. In varying cases applied shared street strategies are generating and promoting corridors that have limited or no-car access with increased activities for distanced outdoor dining, biking, recreation, exercise, and walking. Streets, as outdoor spaces, have a new meaning, but how are they changing, and will they become more accessible to all citizens post-pandemic?

Now, more than two years into the COVID-19 global pandemic, we can take stock of the impacts of this pandemic on our cities, and begin to imagine a post-COVID urban landscape. This presentation will focus on lessons learned from the pandemic, and underscore what should be improved in the design and operation of the North American urban communities. The goal of this study is to examine recent efforts to convert urban streets and plazas into a more sustainable network that enables walking, rolling, biking and transportation within neighborhoods to inspire healthy activity, physically-distanced engagement, and safe travel during the pandemic. These converted corridors and public spaces also offer new social equity benefits for wheelchair users and access to community amenities and healthy food sources for residents who do not own a car, particularly in neighborhoods with no, or limited sidewalks. We examine on-going efforts in multiple cities, including Chicago, Boston, New York, and Oakland to describe their open street and shared space programs, review the implementation history, and explore ways that physical distancing can be integrated into future urban planning efforts. Using crowdsourced data, literature review and current reporting from these case cities, we assess the short- and long-term benefits of these projects, as well as identify useful design and planning strategies for shared street efforts in the post-COVID age.

Framing Political-Environment Dynamics of Coupled Human Health and Social Equity in the Chesapeake Bay Watershed

Stephen Mainzer *(The Pennsylvania State University);* **_Emily L. Pakhtigian_** *(The Pennsylvania State University)*

The United Nations lists Good Health and Well-being (#3) and Reduced Inequalities (#10) among its top goals for sustainable development. Yet intersecting these goals requires a place-based understanding of complex socio-environmental systems. The current COVID-19 pandemic has reinforced longstanding signals of inequity across the policies, plans, and decisions that have shaped the well-being of disadvantaged populations, particularly those among the Global Majority. We suggest that identifying socio-environmental linkages is necessary to address the long-term health of a place. The purpose of our study is to explore how 1) environmental-political-health interactions vary based on characteristics such as race, ethnicity, and socioeconomic status, specifically among underrepresented communities, 2) environmental and political conditions vary along with population health outcomes, and 3) environmental attitudes vary among areas with stark environmental differences.

We use the Chesapeake Bay Watershed (CBW) frame as a proof-of-concept product. In nearly 35 years, the poor ecological health of the CBW has not meaningfully improved. However, during this same period, political and environmental sentiment has grown increasingly divisive through affect polarization. While this has led to stark differences in health behaviors between groups that often share common social, political, demographic, and/or place-based characteristics, it is unclear how interactions among these characteristics in the CBW are driving risks to communities' well-being. We aim to deepen our understanding of how individuals in the CBW define and understand their environments and consider how these environmental framings affect policy positions, priorities, and the health of individuals across sociodemographic characteristics.

Our approach maps, explores alignments, and statistically summarizes a breadth of readily available NSF-supported data networks in the Chesapeake Bay Watershed, including the American National Election Studies, the General Social Survey, the Multi-resolution Landcover Database, and the National Historical Geographic Information System. We expect this process will identify novel environmental-political-health interactions research questions, produce pilot data, and test the validity of our interdisciplinary approach.

Enhancing Youth Energy Literacy through Green Building Education: Lessons from Multiple Research Interventions

Laura Cole *(University of Missouri);* ***Laura Zangori*** *(University of Missouri);* ***Sepideh Fallahhosseini*** *(University of Missouri, Columbia)*

Improving unsustainable energy systems and reducing energy consumption can substantially decrease environmental degradation and increase public health. However, youth and adults alike struggle to make sense of energy ideas, understand how energy is used within buildings, and make informed decisions regarding energy use (DeWaters & Powers, 2011). Despite the sizable environmental impact of buildings, learning about how energy systems intersect with the built environment is rarely available within science lessons. Without this knowledge, it is challenging to advance public understanding of the need for green infrastructure. To address these gaps, our interdisciplinary team has spent the last six years working at the intersection of sustainable architecture and science education, leveraging green building technologies to teach standards-aligned science lessons in K-8 classrooms. In this presentation, we offer an overview of our projects and summarize insights across projects to address the question: How do youth conceptualize energy systems and the intersection of energy systems with built infrastructure? We identify the key misconceptions that youth have about energy and the built environment.

We have been developing curricular units for grades 4-8 that address energy literacy, or the knowledge, attitudes and behaviors that students have about energy systems (DeWaters & Powers, 2011). Our work has featured a local eco-schoolhouse, a renewable energy unit, lessons on green roof technologies, and an NSF-funded curricular unit that focuses on the energy impacts of lighting and heating/cooling systems. Each educational intervention was evaluated with a mixed-methods research design that utilized surveys, student drawings, student interviews, student learning artifacts, teacher focus groups, and classroom observations. While previous reporting and ongoing data analyses uncover the efficacy of our interventions, this presentation will focus specifically on the pre-intervention data collected across studies (largely student interviews, drawings and writings) to identify youth patterns of thought, including misconceptions and gaps in understanding, prior to receiving formal sustainability education. These gaps include confusion about what "energy" really is, since the term is used broadly to refer to human energy, fossil fuel energy, light energy, sound energy, and the list continues. Our data additionally reveal confusions about green building technologies, such as the notion that the lights go off when the sun goes down when a house utilizes solar panels. Our presentation features an organized content analysis of such findings to reveal consistent patterns across four studies.

Outlining youth conceptions of energy systems and green building technologies provides foundational information for both educational and architectural interventions. This work can inform energy education efforts by revealing the baseline understanding into which future knowledge can be integrated (Linn, 2006). This work also informs designers who create youth environments and aspire to use green design to teach sustainability.

References

DeWaters, J. E., & Powers, S. E. (2011). Energy literacy of secondary students in New York State (USA): A measure of knowledge, affect, and behavior. *Energy policy, 39*(3), 1699-1710.

Linn, M. C. (2006). The Knowledge Integration Perspective on Learning and Instruction. In R. K. Sawyer (Ed.), *The Cambridge handbook of: The learning sciences* (pp. 243–264). Cambridge University Press.

Framing Community Health for Regional Transportation Planning

Adam Yeeles *(HDR);* ***Jeffrey Arms*** *(HDR);* ***Jeri Brittin*** *(HDR);* ***Sarah Larsen*** *(MetroPlan Orlando);* ***Nick Lepp*** *(MetroPlan Orlando);* ***Megan McGinley*** *(HDR)*

Transportation, health, and sustainability are deeply intertwined, but regional transportation planning has often focused solely on building more roads to meet traffic demand. However, incorporating knowledge of the bidirectional linkages between transportation and health into the planning process is increasingly of interest to metropolitan planning organizations (MPOs). MetroPlan Orlando, the federally mandated transportation-planning organization for the Central Florida region, is an example of one such organization pushing the boundaries of regional transportation planning by integrating health into their efforts to move people and goods safely and efficiently. While there is significant empirical work linking different aspects of the transportation system and health, a holistic framework that integrates both transportation planning and public health perspectives is needed to guide this integration process. In this presentation, we describe MetroPlan Orlando's collaborative development of the PATHS (Planning and Analysis for Transportation-Health Strategies) framework for understanding the linkages between community health outcomes, the social and physical determinants of health, and the different intervention points in the transportation system where changes may ultimately lead to downstream benefits for community health. The PATHS framework was co-produced with regional public health stakeholders, transportation planners, and researchers using literature review as research methodology, a structured visioning session, and conceptual testing workshops. Once the framework was developed, an Analytic Hierarchy Process approach was then used to prioritize transportation-health pathways within the PATHS framework for addressing regional public health needs. Finally, the information from these efforts was used to inform an organizational health strategic plan for MetroPlan Orlando. Our presentation covers the development of the PATHS framework, translation from conceptual framework into formal organizational strategic plan for MetroPlan Orlando, a broad overview of the plan that provides the organization with strategic guidance for pursuing health-oriented transportation goals, and concludes with a discussion of additional use cases for the framework.

Engaging Jacksonville's Watershed Communities through Health, Housing, and Environment

Jeffrey Carney *(University of Florida);* ***Lisa Platt*** *(University of Florida);* ***Carla Brisotto*** *(University of Florida)*

Weakness in even one measure of health, environment, and housing (HEH) outcomes can manifest through chronic illness, housing insecurity, and other critical vulnerabilities (Agyeman, Bullard, & Evans, 2003) and lead to persistent spatial inequity. The project "Resilient Jax: Engaging Jacksonville's Watershed Communities" focuses on vulnerable populations in the creek adjacent neighborhoods within the 5 square mile Hogan's and McCoy's Creek Watersheds in Jacksonville, FL. Concurrent to the recent State and Federal funding of a watershed plan and building from community partnerships currently focused on the building of a bike trail network, Resilient Jax is conducting a series of interlocking research and engagement efforts to determine areas of overlap and correlation between measures of HEH that can be positively affected through watershed restoration.

Intersectionality is a qualitative analytic framework that identifies how interlocking systems of power affect those who are most marginalized in society (Cooper, 2016) and takes these relationships into account when working to promote social and political equity (IWDA, 2018). This research project, through the intersectional study of HEH, uses quantifiable measures to model relationships across HEH, as well as qualitative measures through interviews and design-based case studies to consider factors that could contribute to equity restoration and resilience measures. The effort works to consider HEH in combination, instead of measuring impacts in isolation.

Research questions driving the project including the following will frame the presentation: What are the comparable measures of health, housing, and environment in urbanized watershed that improve health and wellbeing? Can watershed improvements be developed to measurably increase resilience across these measures and lead to greater equity across stakeholders? What design processes and partnerships are most effective to achieve multiple benefits measured through housing, environment, and health outcomes?

This session will review the research findings by the interdisciplinary faculty team through a discussion of the following outcomes and planned future efforts including: A review of the completed socio-ecological model developed to measure combined factors of HEH (Completed Winter 2021). A discussion of methods of stakeholder engagement through a completed transect analysis (Completed Spring 2022). A discussion of planned "co-designed" studios (planned for Fall 2022 and Spring 2023).

References

Agyeman, J., Bullard, R., & Evans, B. (2003). *Just sustainabilities: Development in an unequal world*. Cambridge, MA: MIT Press.

Cooper, B. (February 1, 2016). Intersectionality. In Disch, L., Hawkesworth, M. (eds.). *The Oxford Handbook of Feminist Theory*. DOI: 10.1093/oxfordhb/9780199328581.013.20

International Women's Development Agency. (IWDA) (May 11, 2018). "What Does Intersectional Feminism Actually Mean?" https://iwda.org.au/what-does-intersectional-feminism-actually-mean/

What We Practice Vs What We Preach: Comparison between the 19th Century Asylum Related Literature and Asylum Design

Intisar Ameen Tyne *(University of Kansas)*

Aim: This study examines how the gallery space was designed in the 19th century asylums, and what were the scholarly prescriptions about those spaces. Through the analysis of gallery spaces, the aim is to understand the gap between scholarly design guideline and the built space in the 19th century asylums.

Background: Gallery, which was a unique feature of asylums, was introduced after the invention of moral therapy and became a social space shared by the patients and staffs. Single rooms opened into the multipurpose, wide 'gallery' spaces. Gallery became a space for socialization because in this space mixing could be allowed without losing control over segregation (Markus, 1993; p. 131). This space was used by patients for dining, socializing, and other recreational activities. Many 19th century authors (architects, physicians, and asylum superintendents) like Samuel Tuke, W. A. F. Browne, John Conolly, Robert Reid, John Arlidge, and Dr. C. Lockhardt Robertson preach about the therapeutic effects of gallery space in the wellbeing of insane patients.

Methodology: This study analyses a set of chronological asylum case studies constructed between 1851 to 1914, to track the changes of gallery spaces in asylums. Guidelines from a set of scholarly articles published between 1806 to 1866, are also examined to identify the prescriptions of designing gallery spaces. The case studies are selected from a well-known British journal, 'The Builder', whereas the scholarly articles are selected by cross-referring current literature related to the 19th century asylum design. The selected 19th century scholars are Phillippe Pinel, William Stark, Robert Reid, Samuel Tuke, W. A. F. Browne, Gardiner Hill, John Conolly, Maximilian Jacobi, Kirkbride, W. Sankey, John Arlidge, Dr. C. Lockhardt Robertson, and E. Toller.

Findings: Overtime the multipurpose gallery spaces were replaced by purpose driven spaces like dayrooms, dormitories, dining spaces and corridors. Among the nine, only two asylums (Middlesex County Lunatic Asylum, Essex County Lunatic Asylum)had gallery spaces, whereas one asylum (Eglinton Lunatic Asylum) had a wider corridor instead of the gallery. In two other asylums (Lunatic Asylum at Abergavenney, Carmarthen Lunatic Asylum) a narrow corridor and dormitories replaced the gallery space. In the other four asylums (Middlesex Fourth Asylum at Claybury Essex, Bethlehem hospital, Exeter Asylum, The Norwich Lunatic Asylum) gallery spaces were completely replaced by dormitories, dayrooms, and dining halls.

Conclusion: The 19th century scholars supported and encouraged the use of gallery space in patient ward, yet the gallery spaces were constantly disappearing from the case studies. That represents, a huge gap between the scholarly prescriptions and actual design in the 19th century asylums. Elimination of the gallery space also significantly reduced the scope for patients' socialization. Patients were only allowed to use the purpose driven spaces at a fixed time as specified by their timetable. Duration of using each space was also pre-decided by the asylum authorities. All the patients had to occupy the same space at the same time and perform the same activity as enforced by the authorities. As a result, patients had neither the time nor the space for socialization.

Young People, Open Space & the Pandemic

Patsy Eubanks Owens *(University of California, Davis)*

The restrictions due to the COVID-19 pandemic effected young people's ability to participate in activities in public open spaces. These constraints impacted their physical, emotional, and social development opportunities and experiences. Youth populations in urban areas and those from marginalized populations were particularly impacted due to more limited availability of nearby recreational and natural setting in their neighborhoods and at their homes (e.g., Geary, R. S., 2021). This presentation focuses on adolescents' disruptions and the community coping strategies in San Francisco, California (Phillips, D. & Gramstorff, C., 2021) and places these findings in the context of reporting from the other Pacific Rim settings of New Zealand, Australia, and western Canada (Bishop, et al., 2021).

While the repercussions of mobility restrictions and in-person communications were numerous, this paper focuses on those relating to social and recreational engagement. A context focused on the roles that these activities play in adolescent development sets the stage for understanding the importance of these interruptions to a young person's daily life. In example, access to open space is needed for physical activity and for mental healing while interactions with friends and others are needed for developing social skills and a sense of community belonging. This presentation shares how some communities adapted to address these needs and how these lessons can inform the future design of public spaces. As shown by the examination of the San Francisco Community Hub program and youth responses, this presentation illustrates how reclaiming of streets by pedestrians and cyclists, providing community-based recreation and education hubs, and encouraging informal neighborhood actions can contribute to healthier and more supportive environments for young people.

References

Bishop, K., et al. (2021). The Impacts of COVID-19 on children, youth and their environments in Canada, the USA, New Zealand, and Australia. Working Paper. Association of Pacific Rim Universities.

Geary, R.S., Wheeler, B., Lovell, R., Jepson, R., Hunter, R., & Rodgers, S. (2021). A call to action: Improving urban green spaces to reduce health inequalities exacerbated by COVID-19. *Preventative Medicine 145*.

Phillips, D. and Gramstorff, C. (2021). *Showing Up while Everything is Shutting Down: A story of cooperation in San Francisco.* San Francisco Department of Children Youth and their Families. Retrieved from www.dcyf.org/chicasestudy.

Therapy Dogs in Design Studios: A Case Study of Feasibility and Efficacy

Lara Browning *(Clemson University);* ***Matthew Browning*** *(Clemson University);* ***Olivia McAnirlin*** *(Clemson University);* ***Kailan Sindelar*** *(Clemson University);* ***Colby Parkinson*** *(Oregon State University);* ***Dina Battisto*** *(Clemson University)*

Students majoring in design are vulnerable to poor mental health. Public design critiques of student work may lead to exceptionally high expectations. Studio culture can promote working both day and night. Such psychological and physical stressors increase the risk of anxiety and depressive symptoms as well as mental disorders, self-harm, and suicidal ideation (Block, 2019). Mental health interventions are needed now more than ever given the additional burdens that the COVID-19 pandemic has caused.

Therapy dogs joining design studios are a promising, but understudied, mental health intervention. Therapy dogs have been shown to increase contentment, happiness, and energy levels, while decreasing cortisol levels, heart rate, blood pressure, stress, anxiety, and irritability in as little time as 15 min (Brisson et al., 2021). However, most of this research has been conducted with general student populations and immediately before exams. We are unaware of previous research examining the feasibility or efficacy of therapy dogs interventions that occur over the course of a semester or therapy dog programs associated with design studios, an area where this intervention could be particularly useful.

To address this gap in the literature, we conducted a case study in the School of Architecture (SoA) at Clemson University. All 472 undergraduate students and 109 graduate students were eligible to participate. Therapy dogs visited studios once a week during a designated period over the lunch hour. Students were encouraged to pet and interact with the dogs as they walked through the studios. Efficacy was preliminary examined with anxiety and depressive symptoms (DASS-21) measured at the beginning of the program (October 2021) and after the program was implemented for 6-months (April 2022). Interviews and focus groups will take place in April 2022 to understand student perceptions of efficacy, satisfaction, and suggested improvements for the program. Interactions with the therapy dogs will also be calculated. Our presentation will report the preliminary findings of the program's efficacy as well as the lessons learned on the feasibility of implementing a therapy dog intervention in the SoA design studios. These findings are expected to contribute to a growing body of literature that addresses how to improve mental health in design studios through student-centered interventions.

Acknowledgments: The therapy dogs time and training were generously provided by volunteers of the Alliance of Therapy Dogs.

References

Block, I. (2019, July 16). Architecture students "considered suicide" over long hours, say #dezeenchat participants. *Dezeen*. https://www.dezeen.com/2019/07/16/burn-out-design-education-mental-health/

Brisson, S., Davis, T., Sanders, T. & Young, K. (2021). The Impact of a Therapy Dog Team on Medical Students' Physiological Stress and Perceived Anxiety Prior to an Exam. *Journal of Creativity in Mental Health*, 1–15. https://doi.org/10.1080/15401383.2021.1986186

Teachers' Preferred Behaviors to Improve Indoor Air Quality in Elementary Schools: Benefits and Drawbacks

Helia Taheri *(North Carolina State University);* ***Traci Rose Rider*** *(North Carolina State University)*

Schools are the second most important space in children's lives after their homes (Baki-Biro et al., 2012). Indoor air quality (IAQ) and ventilation rate in schools have a noticeable impact on improving children's comfort, health, and learning performance (HaverinenShaughnessy et al., 2011). People's awareness of the impact of IAQ and the built environment on their health has been noticeably increased due to COVID-19 (Gupta et al., 2020). All leading agencies agreed on the importance of adequate ventilation rate and outdoor air ventilation to safely reopen schools during the pandemic. Suggestions include using operable windows and air filtration to provide adequate and clean outdoor air in the classrooms, leading to a higher IAQ that improves students' learning performance based on the existing literature. Despite the benefits of these suggestions on improving IAQ, some drawbacks might keep stakeholders from considering those behaviors or using them effectively. This paper provides a comprehensive and holistic understanding of the benefits and drawbacks of using operable windows, fans, and air purifiers which are recommended by leading agencies to improve IAQ during the pandemic. It is an exploratory mixed-method case study that includes surveys and interviews with teachers and engineers focused on their preferred behaviors to improve IAQ in classrooms before and during the pandemic. Four elementary schools in the United States participated in this research - a total of 27 survey respondents and eight interviewees. Moreover, since different stakeholders play a role in effectively using operable windows, fans and air purifiers, several strategies were suggested to each stakeholder group to mitigate the drawbacks of each behavior while enhancing their benefits. Also, considering the limitations of this study - the low number of participants - this paper suggested conducting more interdisciplinary mixed-method research on this subject by including more stakeholders and schools to have a comprehensive understanding of the classroom conditions and how to effectively improve students' experience a whole in classrooms.

References

Baki-Biro, Zs, Clements-Croome, D. J., Kochhar, N., Awbi, H. B. and Williams, M. J., 2012. Ventilation Rates in Schools and Pupils' Performance, *Building and Environment 48*: 215-223.

Gupta, M., Abdelmaksoud, A., Jefferany, M., Lotti, T., Sadoughifar, R., Goldust, M., 2020, COVID-19 and Economy, *Dermatol Ther.*, e13329.

HaverinenShaughnessy U, Moschandreas D, Shaughnessy R (2011) Association between substandard classroom ventilation rates and students' academic achievement. *Indoor Air 21*(2): 121–131.

Towards a Causal Relationship - the Role of Micro Interactions with Natural Green Elements in Recovery from Mental Fatigue

Hossein Saedi *(North Carolina State University)*

Attention Restoration Theory (ART) indicates that interaction with natural green elements in indoor spaces can foster attention restoration, rehabilitation from mental fatigue, and improve cognitive functions. Researchers have used different methods of assessing one's interaction with vegetation to measure the effect on people's attention level. However, studies have not established a causal relationship between the existence of natural green elements and a higher attention level due to the potential impact of other variables and the difficulty in determining the precise nature of an individual's interaction with the environment.

This study is exploratory research that aims to examine if the existence of natural green elements in indoor environments affects people's attention levels. Also, do those elements receive more visual attention, or do they cause other elements in the space to stand out more visually? 182 residents of a high-rise residential building were randomly assigned to experience one of two versions of a 3D virtual reality(VR) environment, via VR goggles, of a building lobby, one with and one without natural green elements. The two versions were modeled in Autodesk Revit 2020, and the natural green elements were then added to the model using Lumion for Revit. Lastly, final models were exported to the Unity Game Engine for the immersive VR experience. Participants completed the Sustained Attention to Response Task(SART) twice to assess the possible improvements in their attention level. Once before experiencing the lobby to establish a baseline of attention and once after. Also, the amount of visual attention that each element received in the environment was calculated through gaze tracking.

The results indicated that participants who experienced the lobby with vegetation showed meaningful improvement in the SART score. The gaze tracking heat maps revealed that vegetation received significantly higher attention than all other elements. The analysis of the data obtained from this group demonstrated those who gained the highest scores paid the highest amount of visual attention to natural green elements. These findings suggest a positive causal relationship between the duration of visual attention and attention restoration level. This research indicates that green elements capturing non-voluntary attention may be among the major factors that positively impact attention restoration.

References

Chung, K., Lee, D., & Park, J. Y. (2018). Involuntary attention restoration during exposure to mobile-based 360° virtual nature in healthy adults with different levels of restorative experience: Event-related potential study

Kurzhals, & D. Weiskopf. (2013).Space-time visual analytics of eye-tracking data for dynamic stimuli. IEEE Transactions on Visualization and Computer Graphics, 19(12), 2129-2138.

Saedi, H. & Rice, Art. (2019), Minor Change for Major Impact: How Can Minor Changes in the Daily Urban Environment Impact an Aspect of Psycho-Physiological Health?, *Prometheus*, No.4, 96-99

Saedi, H., & Einifar, A., & Barati, N. (2021). The Impact of Micro Interaction with Natural Green Elements Through Virtual Reality on Attention Restoration (In a High-Rise Residential Building's Lobby). *Journal Of Architecture And Urban Planning*, *13*(30), 5-21.

Saedi, H., & Rice, A. (2022). The Importance of Both: Competing Factors That Impact Attention Level Restoration and Mental Health. Research Record, 135-149.

Agriculture and Architecture: Wisely Designing Housing for Large Scale Food Production in Rural Developing World

Magdalena Wallhoff-Lamprecht *(VALDE)*

As food production continues to be consolidated and scaled, labor patterns change in rural communities. When a large corporate entity comes into rural communities and swiftly builds up operations, locals often do not have sufficient labor numbers. Outsiders are either bussed in daily, or they need to settle in the community which often lacks extra housing. The rapid changes require not mere more roofs overhead, but sensitive housing designs at low costs.

Drawing on examples from Honduras and Mexico, the discussion will focus on the housing needs in rural communities in the developing world; what factors affect the level and type of need; the dynamics of communities; lenders; lawmakers; and international employers. Far from suggesting quick solutions or building crude urban structures in gentle rural landscapes, this discussion proposes the opportunity for large scale employers in rural areas to not only tick some supposed sustainability checklists, but to genuinely examine how architectural and communal designs can effect a healthier impact in agricultural communities around the world.

Monitoring the Culture of Sustainability: An Overview and New Initiatives Reflecting the Growing Importance of Carbon Neutrality

Robert W. Marans *(University of Michigan);* ***John Callewaert*** *(University of Michigan);* ***Noah Webster*** *(University of Michigan)*

Since 2012, The University of Michigan has been measuring and tracking environmental sustainability indicators reflecting levels of awareness and behaviors among its students, faculty and staff.[1] Annual surveys as part of the Sustainability indicators Program (SCIP) covered themes of the University's sustainability goals dealing waste prevention, energy conservation, sustainable foods, and protection of the natural environment. With the advent of the worldwide pandemic resulting campus shutdowns in 2019, efforts to measure changes in the culture of sustainability on the University's main campus were deferred. In the fall 2021, the SCIP surveys were re-established with two major modifications. One was the addition of questions covering carbon neutrality. The other expanded the surveys to U-M's satellite campuses in Dearborn and Flint Michigan. Following an overview of SCIP, its importance and uses by the University, an overview of U-M's recent Presidential Commission on Carbon Neutrality, the impetus for the new carbon neutrality questions is discussed.[2] The presentation then presents findings covering levels of awareness and thoughts about carbon neutrality among students, faculty and staff on U-M's three campuses. The implications of these findings for educational programming and campus operations including planning and marketing on each campus are then reviewed.

References

1. Marans, R. W. & J. Callewaert 2018. Measuring Sustainability Culture: An Overview from a Multi-Year Program of Evaluation Research. In T. Sanchez (Ed.) Planning Knowledge and Research. New York: Routledge, Taylor & Francis.
2. https://news.umich.edu/u-m-commits-to-universitywide-carbon-neutrality/

Sustainable Design Research of Natural Light Environment in Green University Campus

Mengqi Li *(Tongji University);* ***Shaoying Mi*** *(Pioneer Architects);* ***Lila Cai*** *(Zhongdu Engineering Design Co.Ltd)*

Every country in the world attaches great importance to the construction of green campus. Since the 1970s, the United States and Britain have taken the lead in putting forward the concept of green campus. By comparing the evaluation standard weights of green campuses in the United States, Britain and China, it is found that the United States, Britain and China all focus on energy conservation, planning and site, indoor environment. The design stage is an important stage of green campus construction. The earlier the design is considered in combination with environmental and climatic factors, the higher the impact on green campus construction is. Then it is easier to meet the relevant green evaluation standards.

Energy saving and sustainability run through the whole process of green campus design. Through literature investigation, field research, comparative analysis and other methods,and through the analysis of design strategies from planning, architecture and landscape, it can be concluded that the use of renewable resources, energy conservation, and the creation of a healthy campus building and environment are important parts of green campus design. The use of natural light for indoor lighting is more conducive to energy conservation and the creation of a healthy light environment. At present, there is a general lack of sufficient attention to the natural light environment of university campus classrooms. It is an important part of green campus design that how to ensure good and homogeneous natural lighting in classrooms to achieve the purpose of effectively ensuring the comfort of the eye environment and saving energy.

The author takes the natural light environment of a university classroom in Guangzhou University as an example, investigates on the spot, and analyzes the factors affecting the natural light environment of the classroom. Then the questionnaire data is analyzed by SPSS. And the relevant model is established to predict the subjective evaluation results with the data, so as to verify the relevant problems existing in the current university classroom design. The analysis shows that the plane form of the building, the form of lighting windows, the shading of the building, and the decorative materials of the interior wall have a significant impact on the natural light environment of the classroom. Finally, combined with the case, the design strategy of natural light environment in the classroom is further analyzed. It is concluded that the design of small depth, large windows, high side windows, skylights and external shading can reduce artificial lighting. Making full use of natural light and adjusting the uniformity of light, which is an effective measure for energy saving.

This paper provides a meaningful reference and guidance for our country. Achieving a sustainable campus environment requires holistic design to achieve a low-carbon, ecological campus environment.

Furniture Embodied Carbon Calculator for Interior Design Projects

Javkhlan Nyamjav *(University of Minnesota)*

Current whole building life cycle assessments (LCA) primarily focus on structural and major architectural elements to measure building embodied carbon. Most of the interior finishes and fixtures are available on digital tools (such as Tally), however furniture is still left unaccounted for. According to previous studies furniture can be major contributors to interior design due its repeated refreshments and its complexity (Huang et al. 2018). This paper presents a method to calculate the Global Warming Potential (GWP) of furniture elements in commercial buildings. The calculator uses the quantity takeoff method with GWP averages gathered from Environmental Product Declarations (EPD). The data was collected from EPD databases and furniture manufacturers from North America to Europe. A total of 48 GWP numbers were collected, with 16 GWP coming from alternative EPD. The finalized calculator shows the average GWP of typical commercial furniture and helps the decision-making process to reduce embodied carbon. The calculator was tested on MSR Design projects and showed furniture can account for more than half of the interior embodied carbon. The calculator highlights the importance of adding furniture to overall conversation. However, the data collection process showed a) acquiring furniture EPD is not straightforward as other building materials; b) there are extremely limited furniture EPD, which can be explained from many perspectives including the EPD price; c) the EPD themselves vary in terms of units, LCA scopes, and timeframes, which makes it hard to compare the products. Even though there are current limitations, the emerging focus on interior embodied carbon will create more demand for furniture EPD. It will allow manufacturers to represent all their efforts on reducing embodied carbon. In addition, the study concludes with recommendations on how designers can reduce furniture embodied carbon through reuse and closed loop systems.

References

Huang, M., Simonen, K., Ditto, J. (2018) *Life Cycle Assessment (LCA) for Low Carbon Construction: Tenant Improvements in Commercial Office Buildings, Final Report.* http://www.carbonleadershipforum.org/projects/lca-of-mep-and-ti/

In Situ Seeding Strategies for Roadside Meadow Success and Ecosystem Health in the Southeastern US

***Brad Edward Davis** (University of Georgia); **Chris Robey** (University of Georgia)*

A growing body of work lies at the intersection of planning, ecology, engineering, landscape architecture, and horticulture, and points to need for economically viable, low maintenance planting solutions that meet human aesthetic needs and provide greater ecosystem services. Reliance and preference for human and turf dominated landscapes of artificial conditions has damaged ecosystems and caused decreasing biodiversity worldwide (Tallamy, 2014).

This paper outlines the methods and results of three years of a five-year research study of designed seed mixes for the southeastern Piedmont of North America. Following protocols for in situ seeding methods developed by Hitchmough and others (Hitchmough, 2004; Hitchmough et al, 2006). This study details three unique seed mixes featuring native forbs and grasses. The approach is novel in that the conventional grass dominance has been reversed with forbs composing 80% of the seed mix to meet public aesthetic goals. Season two data is reported for meadow trials in phase one, installed January of 2020, in which three seed mixes are trialled on two soil types: Mix A on clay, Mix A on clay plus mineral fines blanket; Mix B on clay, Mix B on clay plus mineral fines blanket, and Mix C on clay, and Mix C on clay plus mineral fines blanket. Phase 2 installed December of 2020, season one data is shared, and Phase three mixes were installed in November of 2021, on compost plus clay. Results thus far favor seed mixes applied on mineral fines for weed suppression and successful establishment of desirable species. Challenges remain to achieve the public's desire for the level of roadside color provided by annual species plantings.

The results of this study are significant in building a set of successful protocols for establishment of low meadow like plantings for use in public green infrastructure projects to reduce costly maintenance, increase habitat and ecosystem support, while also providing aesthetic beauty for people. Establishment methods and species mixes must be tested and developed for each specific ecoregion across the globe leading to unique place honoring approaches that meet human and ecological needs.

References

Dunnett, Nigel, and James Hitchmough. *The dynamic landscape: Design, ecology and management of naturalistic urban planting*. New York; London: Spon Press, 2004.

Hitchmough, James, Marcus de la Fleur, and Catherine Findlay. "Establishing North American prairie vegetation in urban parks in northern England: Part 1. Effect of sowing season, sowing rate and soil type." *Landscape and Urban Planning 66*, (2004): 75-90.

Hitchmough, James, and Marcus de la Fleur. "Establishing North American prairie vegetation in urban parks in Northern England: Effect of management and soil type on long-term community development." *Landscape and Urban Planning 78*, no. 4 (2006): 386-397.

Tallamy, Douglas, and Rick Darke. *The living landscape: designing for beauty and biodiversity in the home garden*. Portland, OR: Timber Press, 2014.

Post-Disaster Housing : Design Considerations

***Jennifer Smith** (Auburn University)*

This presentation critiques post-disaster housing strategies by examining design considerations influencing a project's successes. While design considerations for relief and recovery housing have been published by FEMA and UNHCR, they have not been represented through drawings and connected to international case studies. This investigates fourteen design considerations gathered through analysis of more than twenty international case studies. These case studies are selected based on their relationship to the recovery timeline, scalability, and flexible adaptation to local conditions. They include rural and urban housing typologies as well as historic and contemporary examples. The fourteen design considerations include: 1) Timeline to Occupancy, 2) Ease of Deployment, 3) Ease of Construction, 4) Ease of Disassembly, 5) Cost of Construction, 6) Economic Catalyst, 7) Owner-Driven Growth/ Owner Agency, 8) Strategic Footprint, 9) Expandability, 10) Connection to Grid, 11) Off-the-Grid Operation, 12) Environmental Appropriateness, 13) Durability, and 14) Resilience. It is important post-disaster housing to strategically prioritize design considerations that meet specific project goals based on schedule, local conditions, and emergency management processes.

The fourteen design considerations are derived from FEMA bid requirements and analysis of post-disaster case studies. After a brief introduction explaining design considerations and methods for selecting these parameters, the paper elaborates on each. Each consideration discusses: 1) how the design consideration aids post-disaster housing; 2) examples of how the consideration may be implemented; 3) limitations regarding its implementation. For instance, steel moment connections resist seismic loads; however, this particular detail may require welding or extensive bolting. This may drive up material and labor costs and extend the project schedule, which are not ideal following a disaster event. Steel moment connections may be more appropriate for long-term housing or prefabricated components stored prior to an event.

Research developed from case study analysis, student design work, conversations with disaster survivors, discussions with emergency management personnel, and interviews with architects and manufacturers. There is the undeniable fact that disaster events are a part of our future. According to the National Centers for Environmental Information (NCEI) major disaster events in the U.S. have risen from 2.9 events from 1980-1989 to 11.9 events from 2010-2019. That amounts to an increase of 90 major disaster events per decade, an additional $630 billion cost-burden, and almost double the fatalities (Smith, 2021). This presentation explores how post-disaster housing, specifically, is a substantial part of recovery and mitigation. As outlined by Wagemann, post-disaster housing frequently fails to meet family needs, despite ongoing efforts of diverse disciplines (Wagemann, 2017). There must be more flexible housing typologies that work top-down and bottom-up as they adapt to local conditions and occupant needs. While this approach requires more resources and planning, it can reduce impact, save lives, and reallocate resources toward resiliency efforts.

References

Smith, A. B. (2021, January 8). 2020 U.S. billion-dollar weather and climate disasters in historical context: NOAA climate.gov. 2020 U.S. billion-dollar weather and climate disasters in historical context | NOAA Climate.gov. Retrieved October 1, 2021, from https://www.climate.gov/news-features/blogs/beyond-data/2020-us-billion-dollar-weather-and-climate-disasters-historical.

Wagemann, E. (2017). From Shelter to Home: Flexibility in Post-Disaster Accommodation

(Doctoral thesis). https://doi.org/10.17863/CAM.43234

Planning for Community Resilience in Detroit Neighborhoods

Ceara O'Leary *(Detroit Collaborative Design Center)*

The last two years have both highlighted and exacerbated inequities built into our cities and environment. In Detroit, infrastructural disparities impact residents' abilities to lead healthy thriving lives and access resources contributing to community resilience. This is particularly acute in neighborhoods with high levels of vacancy, where the social fabric has a loose weave and resources are geographically disparate. This proposal focuses on a research, community engagement and planning effort working to define and plan for resilience and health equity at the neighborhood level in two Detroit neighborhoods. The author and her university-based community design center are working with community development organizations and in two distinct neighborhoods on the eastside and in southwest Detroit to unpack these issues and plan for a more resilient and equitable future. This highly collaborative project centers health equity outcomes in neighborhood planning, focusing on strategies for responsive and resilient planning, community connections and access to resources in neighborhoods of varying density. This work focuses on supporting thriving communities that are self-reliant and resilient in the face of future hardships. The identification and amplification of existing community hubs as spaces that support larger resilience goals is central to this effort, as is an emphasis on social networks as tethers of resilience. The work also focuses on policy implications and lessons for other communities citywide ranging from resident organizing to green infrastructure. This presentation will focus on the first year of research, engagement and planning in a two year effort, with an emphasis on models of community networks that support resilient neighborhood structures, engagement processes informing the definition of resiliency and health equity, and the in-progress planning framework in both neighborhoods, drawing from planning case studies in the field.

Exploring the Impact of Furniture on Individuals Who Transitioned from Homelessness

Linda Nubani *(Michigan State University);* ***Alaina De Biasi*** *(Michigan State University);* ***Marie Ruemenapp*** *(Michigan State University);* ***Lisa Tams*** *(Michigan State University Extension);* ***Robert Boyle*** *(Furniture Bank of Southeastern Michigan)*

Research on place theories have made critical contributions to the relationships between people and places. However, very little research exists on the lives of those who have transitioned from homelessness. In this study, we conducted semi-structured interviews with twenty individuals who recently transitioned from homelessness. Each of our participants was placed into a permanent unfurnished housing and lived there for a period of time within little or no furniture. All our participants were later qualified to receive furniture from the Furniture Bank. Given the study's exploratory nature, our interview questions were purposefully broad to allow themes to naturally emerge and were analyzed using an open-coding methodology in NVivo. Our findings demonstrate that receiving furniture had a positive impact on achievement of goals, health and place attachment.

Exploring the Relationship between Greenspace Accessibility and Adult Obesity in Rural Appalachia

Udday Datta *(West Virginia University);* ***Shan Jiang*** *(West Virginia University)*

Accumulating studies have identified a positive relationship between the amount of greenspaces in people's living environments and the perceived health status of urban dwellers in multiple studies (Jiang et al., 2020; De Vries et al., 2003; Zhang et al., 2018). However, the relationships between various greenspace metrics and the health of residents in rural communities are inconclusive (Alt, 2008; Jennings & Gaither, 2015). The rural population, which makes up nearly 20% of the U.S. population, has been influenced by the spatial disparities in the distribution of public greenspaces and inequitable access to health care (National Rural Health

Association, n.d.; Wen et al., 2013). We intend to explore the relationship between greenspace accessibility and people's physical health in rural Appalachia regions.

The study intends to investigate the relationship between the obesity rate among adults living in small-area census geographies and indicators of the neighborhood greenspace environment in 420 counties across 13 states in the rural Appalachian region. Obesity is a multi-factorial disorder related to many other significant diseases such as diabetes, hypertension, cardiovascular diseases, osteoarthritis, and certain cancers (Bray, 2004; Hu, 2008). Behavioral Risk Factor Surveillance System (BRFSS) is a large-scale survey conducted by state health departments to assess health-related risk factors. County-level data from the BRFSS with a particular focus on disadvantaged areas of the country will be analyzed to create maps of obesity prevalence in Appalachia.

The green accessibility index (GAI) will be used to assess the accessibility of various types of greenspaces at the county level (Fan et al., 2017; Comber et al., 2008; Higgs et al., 2012). The index will indicate the overall green cover area, the size of accessible open spaces, tree density around residential addresses, and pedestrian accessibility within 300 m of any greenspace. Using the ModelBuilder workflow in ArcPro, we will rank existing greenspaces according to their accessibility index. ModelBuilder is a visual programming language represented in diagrammatic formats (Chaaban et al., 2012). The diagrams chain together sequences of processes for building a geoprocessing workflow. The National Land Cover Database (2016) will be used to identify accessible greenspaces in the rural Appalachian counties. By modeling the spatial characteristics of existing greenspace provision within a Geographic Information System (GIS) based framework, we will use the landscape metrics to quantify the connectivity and accessibility of existing greenspaces in the rural Appalachian region. The number and location of the accessible greenspaces in each county will be further analyzed concerning the obesity prevalence among adults within residential areas. The study findings will reveal the spatial disparities and inequitable access to quality greenspaces among rural populations within the framework of social determinants of health (U.S. Department of Health and Human Services, n.d.).

Housing, Social Life and Relational Heath. Lesson from the LIVE Learning-By-Living Initiative at 'Solidarity Village'

Deni Ruggeri *(University of California, Berkeley);* ***Marco Vanoli*** *(Merchant Logo Villaggio Solidale)*

According to the United Nations Economic Commission for Europe (UNECE), 100 million low and middle-income people spend more than 40 percent of their disposable income on housing. For many, this is not only a quantitative issue. With the provision of affordable and livable housing options for the diversity of people living in our community, there is also an issue of quality, which revolves around creating environments to guarantee everyone's effective participation in society, and the fulfillment of Nussbaum's "human capabilities" (1997). This can only be the result of the synergies between goal 11 of the United Nations Goals for Sustainable development, which calls for safer, more resilient and sustainable cities and human settlements, and many of the other 16 goals.

Access to home–both intended as shelter and as the provision of landscapes that support a sense of insideness and belonging-- is fundamental to achieving landscape democracy. Health is a state of complete physical, social and mental wellbeing over time, and it should be a critical goal for environmental designers and community development professionals. This involves providing home and community landscapes that serve as affordances for community activities, social interaction, and a sense of attachment and belonging that invites people to steward their landscapes. The challenge in contemporary society is to fulfill the human right to a home and a landscape to call their own and fulfilling community life. This is particularly important to the most fragile in our society: senior citizens, children, nontraditional families, transients, and those at risk of abuse.

This paper illustrates how design can set into

motion processes that promote relational health. It focuses on the "Villaggio Sociale" (translated as Solidarity Village, or SV). Nestled in the small rural community of Laureano, in Northern Italy, SV is an architectural and social project occupying an area of 7,500 square meters (1.8 acres) in which domestic spaces, residents' services, collaborative spaces, and green areas coexist to support well being. SV is home to the project called "LIVE," a co-housing effort for youth and adults with disabilities, seeking to help them learn and practice skills that can help them in a potential future without parents.

The LIVE project is currently performing an impact assessment. Through a Social Return on Investment approach (SROI), the project partners seek to uncover the changes experienced by stakeholders and identify which practices and landscapes have had the most impact. The assessment includes a storytelling dimension to supplement statistical information with users' perceptions and emotional responses. Residents appreciate the physical access to the surrounding woods and water springs as activators of biophilia and their beauty. They also point at courtyards and play spaces as activators of dialogue with residents of the surrounding community. They also appreciate the housing integration with the workshops, libraries, and food processing facilities regarding chance encounters and social interactions they afford. The lessons learned at SV may offer insights into new forms of collective living and working and new practices that can nurture a renewed connection with the landscape and each other.

"Come As You Are": Attachment to Islamic Third Spaces in the United States

Hassnaa Mohammed *(University of Wisconsin, Madison)*

Today, there are more than 3.4 million Muslims living in the United States (PEW, 2017). There is an everlasting demand on serving the need of a more acculturated generation of U.S. Muslims. Islamic third spaces are hybrid socio-religious spaces. They are different from mosques- the traditional worship space of Muslims. This study aims to (1) conceptualize Islamic third spaces in relation to mosque, and (2) examine the psychological processes that bonds occupants to two third spaces located in the D.C. and Northern Virginia areas using data from a purposeful sample of 26 interviews.

The study differentiates mosques from third spaces based on the categorization of essentialist versus anti-essentialist places put forward by (Lewicka et al., 2019). The majority of U.S. mosques are seen as a bounded space, while third spaces are seen as open and dynamic. The study also engages with the concept of religious place attachment (Mazumdar, 2009) to understand the complex relationship between people and their places. It focuses on the importance of the nested context in which the population exists in contributing to this process.

Findings suggest that occupants' attachment to the physical and social dimensions of the place was not only motivated by religion, but a deeper level of identity formation process in a nested socio-political context. The brand of the space, reflected in the physical and social environment, positively impacted women, youth, and young adults. People from various racial and ethnic background felt included and represented. Overall, members of third spaces indicated that the space afford a balanced American-Muslim identity.

Elderly, Living in Poverty and the Absence of Health, Safety, and Welfare

Shelby S Hicks *(Western Carolina University)*

As the design professions continue the commitment to health, safety, welfare, and the support of social justice; there is the stark reality happening around us; 40 million people live in poverty in the United States, 18.5 million in extreme poverty, and 5.3 million live in third world conditions of absolute poverty. (Human Rights Council, Philip Alston, 2018) Health issues are many when living in poverty. The recent pandemic has solidified the stark contrast between vulnerable and marginalized populations, their resilience to a health crisis and their access to health care compared to those not within these populations. Social Determinates of Health contain five key areas that are identified as economic stability, education, social and community context, health and health care, and neighborhood and the built environment. (World Health Organization, 2010) This puts interior and environmental designers in a key position to potentially change the trajectory of persons living in poverty and health issues related to the built environment.

Healthy housing has long been an environmental justice issue. Low access to quality food, chronic illness, and poor housing conditions are endemic to those living in poverty. For example, according to HUD, 42.9% of residents in the rural southeast in rental households experience at least 1 of 4 housing problems including incomplete kitchen facilities; incomplete plumbing facilities, more than 1 person per room; and a cost burden greater than 30%. Add to this 28.5% of rental households experience at least 1 or 4 severe housing problems, and cost burden that is greater than 50%. (U.S. Department of Housing and Urban Development, Office of Policy Development and Research, 1998) Socioeconomic status is strongly associated with poor IAQ and exposures to airborne particulate matter, radon, and volatile organic compounds.

This study is an ongoing multi-disciplinary project that investigates the current housing conditions of elderly community members living in poverty in the rural South East, U.S.. Results of a literature review, data collected from local nonprofits for housing repair requests, and further analysis will be presented. The challenges of working on a service outreach project during a pandemic will also be discussed. In conclusion, I will examine the possibilities of initiating change.

References

Human Rights Council, Philip Alston. (2018). *Report of the Special Rapporteur on extreme poverty and human rights on his mission to the United States of America.* United Nations General Assembly .

U.S. Department of Housing and Urban Development, Office of Policy Development and Research. (1998). *Resident Assessment of Housing Quality: Lessons from Pilot Surveys.* Retrieved from www.huduser.gov.

World Health Organization. (2010). *A Conceptual Framework for Action on the Social Determinates of Health.* Geneva: WHO.

Access to Neighborhood Green Space Influences Health Outcomes for Different Racial and Income Groups: A Case Study of Urban Areas in the Southeast Region of USA

Jiaying Dong *(Clemson University);* ***Dina Battisto*** *(Clemson University)*

Background: Green space in residential neighborhoods, such as parks, forests, gardens, trails, and other vegetated open space, provides precious amenities that benefit public health. Considerable research supports the idea that nature has therapeutic and restorative effects on health. However, several studies show that populations living in US urban areas do not have equal access to green space (Jennings et al., 2017). In particular, the literature suggests that people from racial minorities or low-income groups are more likely to live in neighborhoods with limited access to green space (Boulton, Dedekorkut-Howes & Byrne, 2018). In addition, this disparity could also apply to the elderly population, who is found to be more vulnerable to health risks and hence might benefit more from green space. However, there is still no clear evidence or explanation on the protective effects of green space on older adults. Thus, this research aims to conduct a nationwide assessment to investigate the correlations between green space and mortality of the elderly group, and the role of race and income as mediators within U.S.

Methods: A case study of the southeastern region of the USA utilizes secondary datasets from 8 states and one state equivalent to investigate if access to green space contributes to health disparities by race and income. The southeastern region was selected because there is a higher percentage of minority populations by race and income. Relationships are studied across three research constructs, including the elderly, green space coverage, and mortality rates. Multilevel regression models are built to examine the associations between two variables among older adults: green space and mortality rate, while controlling for other extraneous factors like education attainment, per capita income, etc. The Palma ratio is introduced to measure the extent of green space and mortality inequalities for the elderly.

Findings: Findings show that mortality rates of the elderly population vary by access to green space in urban areas across 9 southern states. Furthermore, results display that there are individual heterogeneities between states and regions. Palma ratios indicate that the inequalities of green space and health outcomes are more serious for the elderly in African Americans and other minority groups. Empirical evidence from this case study analysis reveals that there are green space and health disparities for minority populations based on race and income. This study suggests that policymakers and city planners should consider green space as a fundamental urban planning strategy for public health.

References

Boulton, C., Dedekorkut-Howes, A., & Byrne, J. (2018). Factors shaping urban greenspace provision: A systematic review of the literature. *Landscape and urban planning, 178*, 82-101.

Jennings, V., Floyd, M. F., Shanahan, D., Coutts, C., & Sinykin, A. (2017). Emerging issues in urban ecology: Implications for research, social justice, human health, and well-being. *Population and Environment, 39*(1), 69-86.

Equity Prescription: Addressing Gender-Based Occupational Health in Architecture

Stacy Scott *(Clemson University);* ***Dina Battisto*** *(Clemson University);* ***Adriane McGillis*** *(SSOE | Stevens & Wilkinson);* ***Jiaying Dong*** *(Clemson University)*

Despite a decades-long dialogue on the importance of gender parity in the industry, measurable change has remained elusive within the architecture profession. Unfortunately, initiatives that have resulted in the significant advancement of diversity throughout the profession continue to remain rare. The marginalization of women is a significant area where this is still visible through the inequity present in the field's character and demographic makeup. This marginalization is seen somewhat inconclusively through the disparate evidence of workplace discrimination faced by women in general.

There is a paucity of research on the impact of the architecture profession on the occupational health of women. In response, a case study of one southeastern state utilized a state-wide survey to explore gender disparities in the architecture profession. The purpose of the research was to gather a consensus on where the state stands on issues of equity and explore the barriers and facilitators for advancement in the workforce or profession. [The University's] faculty, in collaboration with American Institute of Architects (AIA) [Name of state], developed and administered an online survey in 2018 using Qualtrics to collect demographic information about [The state's] population of licensed and unlicensed architectural professionals working in the state or region (N=380).

Findings from this survey illuminate gender differences from the voices of men and women, what successful components already exist in practice and some of the challenges that need to be addressed concerning diversity and equity goals. In particular, three themes are highlighted in this session with respect to gender and occupational health and equity, including Licensure and involvement with the American Institute of Architects (AIA) organization, job roles, and salary and compensation. Finally, this session seeks to situate equity within the context of occupational health and the avenues meant to implement them, such as architecture education, current practice, and organizations. Recent research suggests that women in architecture are at risk for lower job satisfaction, occupational health, and overall wellness compared to their male counterparts. This study indicates that the architectural profession should identify ways to translate the intention to diversify architecture into action.

Housing the Working Class

Dennis Antonio Chiessa *(The University of Texas at Arlington)*

The Northside of Fort Worth is home to the Fort

Worth Stockyards and to a Latinx community with a strong Mexican American identity that sits at the center of a city trying to accommodate unprecedented population growth. This study and project presentation focuses on the analysis of the housing stock of a 100+ years old neighborhood and subsequent design proposals that were informed by that analysis. Situated in central Fort Worth, the research area/community is in danger of gentrification and displacement of the historically marginalized and underserved Latinx community members.

Understanding the housing stock of the neighborhood is critical to developing appropriately scaled and appropriately priced housing to meet current and future demands while slowing down displacement and creating minimal disturbance to the urban fabric of the neighborhood. By documenting, through drawing and models, ten existing homes within the study area that range in size, styles, and location we were able to create a catalog that identifies key architectural elements commonly found in the neighborhood. From that catalog it was determined that scale/size, roofs, porches, and parking conditions are the main building elements that determined the character of the built environment within the Northside.

These building elements were then used to develop new infill housing. As one of the oldest neighborhoods in the city and as a neighborhood that, historically, provided the workforce for the Stockyards, the Northside was segregated along racial lines and the housing stock reflects it. Our research reveals how parcels of land that were subdivided almost one hundred years ago to allow for the construction of multiple houses (typically shotgun houses) on a single lot are no longer buildable lots according to current zoning ordinances. This study identifies the 'nonconforming' lots in the neighborhood to use as sites for the new infill prototype houses.

This study proves that these 'nonconforming' lots are viable options for reintroducing smaller scaled, affordable houses that cause minimal disruption to the existing urban fabric. The projects presented will show new house prototypes that increase density by using a contextual approach that takes advantage of infill vacant land and residual nonconforming properties.

Ultimately, this study aims to contribute to existing scholarship pertaining to affordable housing design and zoning policy by examining the detrimental effects that zoning ordinances may have by requiring minimum lot and home sizes and provides alternatives based on existing conditions for developing infill houses.

Study on Tourist Experience of the Comprehensive Rural Tourism Based on Big Data - a Case Study of NAPA Valley

Pang Shaojie *(Beijing Jiaotong University);* ***Yi Yang*** *(Beijing Jiaotong University);* ***Bo Zhang*** *(Oklahoma State University)*

The comprehensive rural tourism refers to the participation of the whole community residents, which is guaranteed by the design of planning and policy, and provides tourists with the experience of the whole process, time and space. In recent years, the development pattern of American comprehensive tourism has entered a stage of mature development and caused a research upsurge of scholars. However, the existing research lacks in-depth research on the design of the comprehensive rural tourism tourist experience and its planning.

Taking advantage of the big data, of fast, convenient and macroscopic, this study takes the Napa Valley as an example to exemplify the research method of comprehensive rural tourism tourist experience based on social media. Napa Valley, in the northern California, has a history of more than 180 years of wine industry development. With wine culture tourism as a link, it develops a series of business arts, leisure and health, education and other industries, forming a comprehensive tourism destination, attracting nearly 5 million tourists from home and abroad each year. Therefore, using python technology, we can quickly obtain 5609 reviews and about 180,000 words of data on the TripAdvisor website from June 2002 to September 2020,along with the comment time, satisfaction level, and other information. Using

Rost and Excel, the textual data was categorized to five elements related to comprehensive planning and design, such as comprehensive space planning, rural landscape integration, characteristic architectural style, supported public services and winery culture, aiding our understanding of tourist motivation, activities, attentions, perceptions in rural tourist destinations. We then use gephi to conduct the data visualization. From these analysis, we reveal more understandings about:1)the design method of organic combination of comprehensive space planning mechanism and characteristic resources;2)the importance of landscape design and infrastructure planning in comprehensive rural tourism;3)what are the supporting public services in the theory of comprehensive rural tourism and what are the focuses of tourists;4)the seasonal patterns of the popularity of rural destination programs;5)research on the specific methods of comprehensive rural tourism design. This study creates a comprehensive rural tourism tourist experience research system, provide theoretical guidance for the construction and development of comprehensive rural tourism in the United States.

Understanding Flood Risks to Brownfields in Florida's Marginalized Communities to Create Public Space and Flood Secure Toxic Waste Remediation Design Guidelines

Eliza Breder *(The University of Florida)*

Sea level rise and an increase in frequency and magnitude of hurricanes has multiplied vulnerability in places facing pre-existing challenges. Neighborhoods across the United States that were historically redlined by the Homeowners Loan Corporation (HOLC) are currently majority minority neighborhoods and face an increased risk of adverse health outcomes, flooding from disasters and sea level rise, are disproportionately closer to toxic waste sites, and overall lack green space (Mitchell, 2018). It is necessary to understand the relationship between these variables to assist in resiliency planning for coastal marginalized communities. This research reviews the history of redlining, current definitions of social vulnerability, and present-day related challenges marginalized communities face.

The present challenges focus on toxic waste, or Brownfield sites and risks to surrounding communities in flooding scenarios. Florida has many coastal cities, and with sea level rise that leaves 15 million people at risk (Florida, 2021). Additionally, toxic waste sites are located disproportionately closer to marginalized communities (Richter, 2018). This research examines the areas in Florida that will experience long term inundation such as sea level rise and periodic floods. Using an overlay analysis in GIS the number of brownfield sites in and near marginalized communities and their relation to sea level rise and flood zones were quantified.

Marginalized Communities have experienced historic discrimination through redlining, rank high on CDC's social vulnerability index, and continue to experience adverse health effects and physical risks in their communities due to discriminatory land use decisions (Sevelius, et al., 2012). For the purpose of this research, the redlining and high social vulnerability data sets were merged to create a marginalized community dataset, as 84% of the historically segregated communities are currently within highly vulnerable areas. Understanding the flood risks to Brownfield remediation techniques can enable designers to create public spaces that anticipate various flood types, plan for toxic waste sites, and are sensitive to underserved communities. Analyses found that 77% of brownfield sites are within a mile of marginalized communities, 30% of brownfield sites are within global average sea level rise of 6ft for 2100, and 55% of Florida brownfield sites are within areas that experience storm surge from a category 5 hurricane. This research details best management practices and designs for existing brownfield remediation techniques that account for rising seas and temporary floods. These flood safe brownfield design typologies can be complimented by community sensitive public parks.

References

Florida. NOAA Office for Coastal Management. (n.d.). Retrieved March 31, 2021, from https://coast.noaa.gov/states/florida.html.

Mitchell, B., & Franco, J. (2018). HOLC "redlining"

maps: The persistent structure of segregation and economic inequality.

Richter, L. (2018). Constructing insignificance: Critical race perspectives on institutional failure in environmental justice communities. *Environmental Sociology, 4*(1), 107-121.

Sevelius, Jae M., Luis Gutierrez-Mock, Sophia Zamudio-Haas, Breonna McCree, Azize Ngo, Akira Jackson, Carla Clynes et al. Research with marginalized communities: challenges to continuity during the COVID-19 pandemic. *AIDS and Behavior 24, no. 7* (2020): 2009-2012.

Use Post-Use Evaluation to Study Chinese Station Square Under Transit-Oriented-Development Mode

Yingjun Zhao *(Beijing Jiaotong University);* ***Chunfang Li*** *(Office@Csadi.Cn);* ***Li Wang*** *(Central-South Architectural Design Institute co;Ltd);* ***Yi Yang*** *(Beijing Jiaotong University);* ***Bo Zhang*** *(Oklahoma State University)*

In China, with the increase in population and the integrated development of transportation and cities, railway integrated transportation hubs mostly adopt the TOD (Transit Oriented Development) model. Form the development trend of urban multi-functional integration with the station as the core. At the same time, the station square is evolving into a city square. The current post-use evaluation system for the station square is not perfect. Therefore, there is a lack of empirical research on the construction of station squares under the new development model. The builders cannot make accurate judgments on the nature of the station square.

This study takes advantage of social media include: the large amount of comment data; diversified information and spontaneity. Visual analysis of the collected data. Take the Hangzhoudong Railway Station as an example.

Hangzhoudong Railway Station is a comprehensive railway transportation hub under the TOD model. In 2019, a total of 71.9 million passengers were sent, which has a strong data foundation.

This research uses python technology to collect 544 comments on social media platforms (Dianping, Sina, Mafengwo, Ctrip) from 2014 to 2020 Hangzhou East Railway Station square (the station square was put into operation on January 1, 2014). The date including the following Information: The person who commented, the time and content of the comment.

Use Anaconda and Excel software to divide the comment data into parts of speech. According to the characteristics of the use of the square, it is divided into three dimensions: behavior type; object type; result and emotion type. And use Gephi software to visually analyze the data. Get the current usage characteristics of the station square.

Through the above analysis, we can get: 1. User attention and satisfaction. 2. How the station square is used. 3. The accessibility of transfer, and then study the development direction of the station square under the TOD mode.

This research uses social media comments. Visually analyze the collected data. Provide a new research perspective for the study of station squares under TOD mode. The evaluation of passengers after use will be transformed into the basis for the construction of the station square. Provide methods of big data collection and analysis for research in other disciplines.

Uses and Functions of Green Areas and Public Spaces in Mexico City in the Face of the COVID-19 Pandemic

Eric Jimenez *(Universidad Nacional Autónoma de México)*

The Covid-19 pandemic has dramatically affected the world's population. Various strategies have been taken in order to prevent contagion and reduce the multiple consequences generated by this disease. In Mexico, one of the most pronounced measures, at various times during the pandemic, was to recommend that the population remain, as much as possible, in confinement. However, there is a robust body of literature that points to the multiple benefits in physical and mental health of visiting urban green spaces (WHO, 2016). On the other hand, green areas and public spaces have been used previously, as means to attend to various complications and strategies associated with social emergencies, such as floods and earthquakes (Pizzo, B., di Salvo, G., Giuffré, M ., & Pellegrino, P., 2013). Based on this, we ask ourselves the following question: What are the uses and functions that green areas and public spaces have had during the COVID-19 pandemic in Mexico City? To answer this question, the research was carried out through 3 methodological approaches: a) Review of scientific and demographic literature; b) More than 2,000 surveys to the general population of Mexico City; C) Interviews with specific groups, such as social organizations, athletes and children. Using the Atlas Ti software, the information obtained was analyzed and different dimensions of the uses and functions of green areas and public spaces during the pandemic, were identified . We were able to develop a conceptual model whose dimensions are consistent with the empirical evidence that we collected. The conceptual model reflects that green areas and public spaces have been used for different purposes, including:

- Preservation and promotion of physical and mental health
- Prevention of contagion
- Disease care, for example to carry out virus detection tests and vaccination
- The dissemination of information
- The social organization
- Managing various strategies for the pandemic
- Personal and family socio-emotional restoration
- Access to economic resources
- Carrying out physical activity

In respect to people's perception of green areas and public spaces during the pandemic is ambivalent. On the one hand, they are perceived as safe places, that provide benefits to physical and emotional health and that it is desirable to visit them. On the other hand, they are perceived as potential sources of contagion, risky and that should be avoided.

We consider that the findings obtained are a solid empirical basis that can provide relevant information for the management of green areas and public spaces during pandemics. These spaces are potentially valuable as they provide multiple uses and useful functions to deal with the complicated situations of pandemics.

References

WHO (2016). *Urban green spaces and health. A review of evidence*. Copenague: United Nations

Pizzo, B., di Salvo, G., Giuffré, M., & Pellegrino, P. (2013). Earthquakes, public spaces and the social construction of environmental disasters. *Italian Journal of Planning Practice, 3*(1), 4–41.

Where I Pray: A Pilot Participatory-Action Study on Muslim Students' Experience in a Midwestern Campus

Hassnaa Mohammed *(University of Wisconsin, Madison)*

There is a wide push on U.S. campuses to serve students from diverse backgrounds (Gates, 2021). While there is plethora of research on Muslim students campus experience (Foster, 2020; Gibbs, 2021), there is little exploration of their spatial experience. One of the main rituals of practicing Muslims is praying five times at different times during the day.

This participatory action study explores the experience of 68 Muslim students through a survey questionnaire and a photovoice activity on a Midwestern campus. It seeks to understand the impact of (1) availability, (2) distribution, and (3) affordances of spaces suitable for prayer on campus on their mental wellbeing. The photovoice activity prompts students to take pictures and add a description to them of places their pray on campus.

Findings indicated that students' well-being and sense of belonging to the campus community were negatively impacted by the lack of accommodation for an integral part of their practices. While the requirement for prayer is simple, a clean space that can accommodate the physical movements of the canonical prayer, students struggle with various other issues such as the need for privacy and the fear of being judged.

In addition to this paper, the study resulted in an interactive map that students could use to identify suitable prayers near them and an infographic to be used by the Muslim student association to apply for prayer spaces on campus.

Adaptation Strategies in Food-Related Activities Among Older Indonesian Women

Widya Ramadhani *(University of Illinois at Urbana-Champaign);* ***Lynne M. Dearborn*** *(University of Illinois at Urbana-Champaign)*

Independent conduct of food-related activities is central to older adults' health. However, declining physical and cognitive capacities, along with decreases in overall health in old age can lead to restricted mobility, increasing the risk for food insecurities (Wolfe et al., 1996). This potential risk is more likely among older women, as activities related to food provision have generally been considered women's work in the household (Sidenvall et al., 2001). For older women who choose to age in place in their own homes, the spaces to conduct food-related activities should match their changing needs (Maguire et al., 2014). This study looked at the range of food-related activities – food preparation, cooking, eating, and cleaning – and the spaces in the home environment to examine older women's personal and environmental adaptation strategies employed to maintain their health and independence. We focused on older Indonesian women – a less studied population group – to develop a culturally sensitive understanding of adaptation strategies when aging in place at home.

This study employed the person-environment interaction lens, a temporal process that influences the dialectic of autonomy and support (Lawton, 1980; Lewin, 1936; Nahemow & Lawton, 1973). Additionally, we observed the relation of culture and environment through observation of 'systems of settings and systems of activities' (Rapoport, 1990). It was grounded in activity-driven observation to assess human behavior through systems of activities to understand the people-environment mechanisms in food-related activities in the systems of settings within the home environments (i.e., kitchen, dining room). Participants' personal capacity (sensory, motor, and cognitive function) and architectural features (design, fixtures, and appliances) of their home settings were examined to identify personal and built environmental factors that hinder successful engagement in food-related activities.

Participants were 25 community-dwelling Indonesian older women (ages 60+) who did not need assistance to carry out basic daily activities. We conducted photo- and video-elicitation followed by interviews to analyze physical spaces and the experience of food-related activities. As a grounded theory study, data collection and analysis took place simultaneously (Charmaz, 2014). To date, we discovered that reduced personal capacities (e.g., strength, agility) impact individuals' adjustment on the complexity of their food preparation, cooking, and cleaning routine. Furthermore, external factors, for instance, changes in household size, work, and roles in the community, also contributed to adaptations of food-related activities. Such adaptations were reflected in the modification of their methods of conducting the activities (systems of activities) or the food-related activity spaces (systems of settings).

The preliminary findings showcase adaptation strategies that involve multifaceted aspects: personal, environmental, and social. These aspects interact with each other, creating an inseparable transactional relationship that influences individuals' activity engagement. Integrated support through modification of the built environment and development of support programs that meet older women's needs, abilities, preferences, and their sociocultural context can improve older women's food-related activities engagement and their sense of independence and wellbeing. Findings from this study will set a foundation for developing future housing designs, intervention programs, and policies to better support older women's health and independence.

Measuring Inclusivity: Development of a Survey Instrument to Assess Perceived Social Cohesion Among Racially and Ethnically Diverse Park Users

Raaga Bhandari *(North Carolina State University)*

The aim of this study is to review the current range of post-occupancy evaluation (POE) methods used for assessing public spaces, provide a critical evaluation of their efficacy, and develop a dynamic survey instrument that can effectively measure the degree of social cohesion among park users. With cities becoming more diverse than ever before, the general population of urban park users encompasses more racial and ethnic minorities, making them increasingly significant social actors in the public realm (Dwyer, 1994). Although there are several established post-occupancy evaluation (POE) methods in place that investigate the public life and performance of public spaces, there is a lack of standard protocol that particularly includes the experiences and preferences of racial and ethnic minorities. Consequently, these methods not only fail to draw sufficient numbers of minority respondents but also fall short of providing detailed insight specific to minority users and their preferences within a public park setting (Floyd, 1999). A further intent of this study is to develop a POE survey instrument that allows design practitioners to measure the performance of public parks, and that will produce data that is reliable and representative of all users (i.e., majority users as well as ethnically diverse user groups).

References

Dwyer, J. (1994). *Customer diversity and the future demand for outdoor recreation (General Tech. Rep. RM-252)*. Fort Collins, CO: USDA, Forest Service, Rocky Mountain Forest and Range Experiment Station.

Floyd, M. (1999). Race, ethnicity and use of the National Park System. *Social Science Research Review, 1*(2), 1–24.

Identifying Adolescents' Hangouts: Leveraging the Construct of 3rd Places to Discover "Public Space in Practice" in Three Low-Income Communities in Hyderabad, India

Lyndsey Deaton *(University of Oregon)*

Cyberabad is a large urban development intended to make Hyderabad an international hub of the information technology industry following the design precedents of Malaysia's Cyber Corridors and San Francisco's Silicon Valley. In the process of progress, however, eighteen heritage villages were dispossessed of their land through displacement and encroachment resulting in a lack of access to city amenities such as formal public space. These environmental changes raise important questions about the residents who most depend on these public spaces, namely children.

It is known, for example, that women and children are more seriously affected by a decline in the quality of their built environment than other groups, and that low-income adolescents in particular are susceptible to developmental risks if their access to public space is inhibited. The criticality of public space for adolescents' developmental needs is firmly established. Indeed, such access is so dire that the United Nations sustainable development goal (UN SDG) 11 has specifically called out the need for quality public space in cities. And its Target 7 specifically points to the necessity, by 2030, to "provide universal access to safe, inclusive, and accessible, green and public spaces, in particular for women and children, older persons and persons with disabilities."

Following the work of Louise Chawla (2002) and Angela Kruetz (2015), this research focuses on adolescents' (12-16 years) (n=42) perspectives in three dispossessed communities impacted by the social and environmental changes brought about by the production of Cyberabad. I use photovoice, behavior mapping, and observations to answer questions about where and how adolescents hang out when public spaces are not accessible.

I found that Oldenburg's (1989) concept of 3rd places to be a useful tool to conceptualize hang outs when traditional definitions of public space do not apply as typical in dispossessed communities. By broadening the definition of public space, designers and planners may realize the importance of transitory and threshold spaces to the spatialities of children. In the paper, I evaluate adolescents' 3rd spaces within a human context framework and expand upon the affordances of the built environment while asking questions about the social changes in these communities as brought about by Cyberabad.

This work was sponsored by the Ryoichi Sasakawa Young Leaders Fellowship Fund (SYLFF), the Julie and Rocky Dixon Foundation, and the University of Oregon.

References

Chawla, L. (2002) *Growing up in an urbanizing world.* London: Earthscan.

Kruetz, A. (2016). *Children and the environment in an Australian indigenous community: a psychological approach.* London: Routledge.

Oldenburg, R. (1989). *The great good place.* New York: Paragon House.

Just Design: A Vision to Reconstruct Gaza Airport and the Architecture of Hope

Ahmad Nour Turani *(Jordan University of Science and Technology);* ***Bushra Obeidat*** *(Jordan University of Science and Technology)*

This research is founded on the concept of "Architecture of Hope" and aims to examine the link between the current and continuous war in the Gaza Strip, Palestine, and its population's changing socio-economic demands. Gaza is an area fraught with significant difficulties and possibilities and serves as a laboratory for scarcity engineering, which may address the location's complex social dynamics unprecedentedly. The purpose of this project is to envision and depict a paradigm for post-conflict rehabilitation for vulnerable communities in the Gaza Strip using participatory design principles. Gaza has been isolated from the rest of the world by land and air due to the fighting there. In 1998, Gaza opened its international airport. For two years, the airport was operational, but Israeli troops bombarded the airport during the second intifada, which was progressively reduced to ruins after that. This project aims to identify unique conceptual architectural alternatives for the renovation of Gaza International Airport. More precisely, this study project intends to address and account for citizens' requirements and views of their future airport, as well as viable, inexpensive materials and self-construction processes, through Design by Participation. By allowing contact with everyone participating in the future airport's design, it was possible to guarantee that the participatory design sessions that generated the data for this prototype design took place in natural settings. The terminal design process and judgments on the suitability of design ideas for a particular airport remain not well defined. This article discusses a way to include Gaza locals in developing a conceptual design concept for the airport and other project demands and functional spaces. Finally, critical aspects impacting the final design ideas selection are stated and examined in light of the suggested expert system decision-making technique. The interrelationships between these numerous requirements are examined side by side to allow airport planners to make an "ideal" choice - the optimum option for a given airport.

Health, Equity, Resilience and Sustainability - Outdoor Environments

Gisou Salkhi khasraghi *(1989);* ***Aynaz Lotfata*** *(Chicago State University)*

Walking as a healthy mode of transportation plays a crucial role in the livability/sustainability of college cities. Many studies from different disciplines have documented Walking's importance to urban sustainability, including urban planning, health, safety, security, and environmental viewpoints. Primarily because of pandemic-related health concerns in indoor environments, a holistic assessment of the urban outdoor environment is needed to understand whether it is socio-spatially appropriate for physical activities. Improved walkability can promote public health and make the urban environment more pleasant, safer, and less polluted.

This study explores how built environments' features in micro-scale has an impact on pedestrian tendency to walk. This paper aims to figure out the walkability of the university neighborhood in the college city of Lubbock. This study explores how built environments' features (e.g., greenery, shading, infrastructure, safety) in microscale impact pedestrian tendency to walk. In order to do that, the selected main routes in the university neighborhood will be evaluated as a case study.

First, the physical characteristics of the neighborhood walking routes will be evaluated using Google Street View and on-site audit. Secondly, an interactive GIS-web map will be designed to collect the sampled individuals' environmental perceptions of walkability. Finally, we will examine the relationship between participants' perceptions with routes' physical characteristics. Based on the results, this paper will suggest the design and planning guideline framework according to Complete Street policies to help policymakers and urban planners to increase the public tendency towards walking by assessing and improving built environments infrastructure and attributes.

Nature Integration, Biophilic Design and Equity in the Urban Interior

Kendra Ordia *(University of Nebraska, Lincoln)*

Design is an expression of humanity, a species of and bounded by nature. But "nature" holds many definitions, and the spectrum of connection to nature is as diverse as those experiencing it. As the topic of biophilic design continues to grow and expand, it is vital that designers investigate what biophilia means for the nature deprived; what connection to nature may mean for those without opportunity, access, means, or inclusive spaces to enjoy its documented benefits. Biophilia is a biological theory suggesting humans are innately drawn to nature offering an evidence-based methodology for interior design that derives artistic decisions from a scientific hypothesis. How can design students use their understanding of biophilia and nature-influenced spatial experiences to think about designing more inclusively while considering equity, diversity, and culture? This report of pedagogical and methodological approaches used in upper-level interior design university studio curriculum focuses on established theories, narrative, and designed solutions for increased wellbeing, access, and delight focused on some of the most vulnerable populations - children and youth. By more inclusively and empathetically understanding how human behavior, health, and wellbeing are influenced by their connection to nature, designers can begin to propose biophilic design solutions beyond surface level application utilizing the proposed methods of critical thinking, inquiry, and collaboration as future change agents. Through intentional engagement and research-based design, values in nature and contained potential for increased physical, spatial application and integration in built environments can become design tools for not only spatial change but also societal impact.

Multifunctionality of Public Play Spaces

Weishunhua Zhang *(University of Florida)*

The development of public play spaces in marginalized communities often faces a lot of challenges, including financial constraints. Therefore, improving the multifunctionality of public play spaces becomes a necessity to satisfy the diverse community needs and to use resources for maximum benefit (Mohammed et al., 2020; Nagapan et al., 2012). This study contrasts the landscape performance and multifunctionality of two public play spaces namely Seattle Children's play garden and Yanaguana Garden at Hemisfair.

This study uses secondary literature review and case-study method. Seattle Children's play garden and Yanaguana Garden at Hemisfair public spaces are designed to accommodate various public functions and serve as a playground for children. These two projects have been the subject of the Landscape Architecture Foundation Case-study and thus have a wealth of data regarding landscape performance.

The study determined that the two public playgrounds have a high landscape performance across different categories. Seattle Children's Play Garden's environmental benefits include capturing and infiltrating a significant amount of stormwater which saves the city a cost of about $300 in stormwater management (Seattle Children's PlayGarden, 2021). It also provides outdoor education, recreational activities, and therapeutic condition for many children while taking into consideration those with disabilities (Seattle Children's PlayGarden, 2021). Similarly, the Yanaguana Garden helps the city capture and infiltrate stormwater and provides a cool microenvironment for the visitors (Yanaguana Garden at Hemisfal, 2021). It allows all visitors, especially children to visit and enjoy all recreational activities and encourages interaction (Yanaguana Garden at Hemisfal, 2021). Additionally, it has restaurants and businesses that attract visitor spending.

This study sheds light on how public play spaces can be enhanced to increase their multifunctionality in the community. Such work can help landscape architects better understand how spaces can achieve more as they seek to serve as children's play spaces while still helping conserve the environment, improve the socio-economic status of the community, and foster social interactions. Notably, there is a need for additional study to evaluate the sustainability of the play spaces, especially in less resource-rich parts of the world. It is also indispensable to ensure that infrastructures achieve their intended landscape objectives observed through careful monitoring and regular maintenance.

References

Mohammed, M., Shafiq, N., Abdallah, N.A.W., Ayoub, M. and Haruna, A. (2020). April. A review on achieving sustainable construction waste management through application of 3R (reduction, reuse, recycling): A lifecycle approach. In *IOP Conference Series: Earth and Environmental Science, 476*(1), p. 012010.

Nagapan, S., Rahman, I.A., Asmi, A., Memon, A.H. and Latif, I. (2012). December. Issues on construction waste: The need for sustainable waste management. In *2012 IEEE Colloquium on Humanities, Science, and Engineering (CHUSER)*. pp. 325-330.

Seattle Children's PlayGarden. (2021). *Landscape Performance Series.*

Yanaguana Garden at Hemisfair. (2021). *Landscape Performance Series.*

Let's Connect Parks to Connect and Empower People

Noura Bishay *(NPB Design Studio)*

When most people hear San Diego, they think of sunny beaches, ample tourism, and green parks, but ignore the historically marginalized communities of Barrio Logan and Southeast San Diego. These diverse communities carry the weight of their rich culture, impoverishment, disenfranchisement, and environmental toxicity; it is here where we see the interplay between racism, urban planning, and politics rear its ugly head. Cultural suppression, social injustice, economic inequality, health disparities, and pollution are eating us alive.

Based on the evidence below San Diego needs more parks; however, it is critical to strategically add parks and trees which are walkable in low-income colored communities, with the highest pollution levels and burden of chronic diseases. The report entitled Healthy Parks, Schools, and Communities: Mapping Green Access and Equity for Southern California, clearly explains the need. The authors stated that "the most park poor areas of the region are also the areas with the highest concentrations of low-income households and people of color". Plenty of people, especially children in San Diego, suffer from health issues such as asthma, depression, obesity, diabetes, and heart problems which are the symptoms of a disconnected city as explained in CalEnviroScreen 3.0. The truth is, we do not have enough walkable parks. The Nation Recreation and Park Association explained the critical necessity of adding walkable parks. They stated that "Research demonstrates that people who have easy access to parks are 47 percent more likely to walk at the daily-recommended level than those who do not have easy access. Moreover, when the distance from a park double, the likelihood of park usage decreases by almost 50 percent" (NRPA 2014). The lack of walkable parks in low-income colored communities is critically affecting the community's health and causing the poverty cycle. The way we are designing our city is making us sick and dividing us. We must stop fixing the apparent symptoms and start fixing the core problem.

To sum up, parks are critical to human survival. Having accesses to a walkable park should be a basic human right, just as breathing clean air, to maintain a healthy, safe, and happy life. The dignity of humanity starts by adding nature to park-poor and low-income areas, which are severely in de-stress. It is time to heal, inspire and empower our communities to be more resilient via social-impact urban design as employed in the Park-to-Bay (P2B) Project.

The P2B model is centered around walkability, connecting parks to connect people. We share the community story by creating a multi-destination, inclusive, safe, and sustainable green corridor with a double-aisle of trees, community gardens, art corners, farmers' markets, pop-ups, street vendors, and more. P2B fosters job creation & cultural preservation while nurturing innovators and entrepreneurship. This is a plan to rebirth, re-imagine, and renew our city image that communities everywhere should implement now. Through thoughtful urban design, we can make a difference!

Modular Outdoor Learning Environments at a Title 1 Elementary School during the COVID-19 Pandemic

Carla Delcambre *(North Carolina State University);* ***Spencer Stone*** *(North Carolina State University);* ***William Stanton*** *(North Carolina State University)*

In January 2021, landscape architecture students at North Carolina State University (NCSU) began a 16-week design/build studio with the goal to enhance an outdoor learning environment at a Title 1 elementary school in Princeville, North Carolina. Princeville Elementary has a minority population of 93% and provides free lunches to 98% of its students (IES, 2021). Through stakeholder meetings, informal interviews, and a survey administered by the Coastal Dynamics Design Lab at NCSU, students were able to better understand the needs and desires of teachers and administrators to connect existing curriculum with outdoor learning environments. Teachers expressed an interest in hands-on structures that could support the existing curriculum and an opportunity to embed aspects of environmental education, such as local ecologies and resilience. Globally, the COVID-19 pandemic brought to light the connection between open spaces and health and well-being. As a result, K-12 schools placed a greater emphasis on providing outdoor learning environments so that children could be socially distanced in a safer environment and to have access to fresh air. Outdoor learning environments have also been shown to support environmental stewardship (Chawla, 2014) as well as intellectual, social, and physical growth in children (Sanoff, 1995; Cosco et al., 2014; Boldemann et al., 2015). With this understanding, landscape architecture students at NCSU designed and constructed a series of modular and moveable "ed-YOU-cation stations", pollinator habitat structures, and scrim installations that featured self-portraits from the children. The "ed-YOU-cation stations" are designed to prioritize the students' social and learning experiences through flexible seating and planters that teachers can easily incorporate into curriculum-based activities. In August 2021, landscape architecture students delivered the built structures to the school to coincide with the school's reopening to resume in-person learning. Since reopening, teachers have begun to incorporate the outdoor learning structures into their daily lesson plans. This hands-on, service-learning project provided an opportunity for landscape architecture students to partner with at a STEAM elementary school during the pandemic. By implementing a flexible, outdoor workspace for teachers and students, this new classroom is being used to advocate for a safe learning environment that promotes health and wellness at work and school.

What the Pandemic Has Highlighted: Built Environment Interventions to Address Pre-Pandemic Health Inequities

Debarati "Mimi" Majumdar Narayan *(The Pew Charitable Trusts)*

Nothing has made existing inequities in society clearer than the pandemic. From highlighting the importance of healthy housing when stay at home mandates were put in place; to the need for safe public transit for essential workers; to the importance of access to healthy, affordable foods as food outlets shut down and worker shortages slowed delivery and created food scarcity in stores; to the dire necessity for access to outdoor places for social connection and physical activity as we learnt that outdoor environments had lower chances of transmission; and more.[1] Throughout the pandemic, low-income people and people of color have disproportionately faced the negatives effects of not having these components (healthy housing, affordable food, etc.) that are critical to good health.[2] How our built environments are designed drives the long-term solutions that address the needs of people and places that have been pushed into the lowest quartiles of health, well-being, and economic measures due to systemic injustice.

At the Health Impact Project (Project), a collaboration of the Robert Wood Johnson Foundation and The Pew Charitable Trusts, we saw this time as an opportunity to galvanize community coalitions and decision-makers around shared visions for long-term improvements to address persistently unaddressed inequities. Through funding and technical assistance to communities in four US regions already facing significant inequities and hardest hit by COVID-19, the Project is supporting the use of Health in All Policies approaches to help advance health equity through changes to promising, evidence-informed built-environment practices and policies. The partnerships between community-based organizations and local decision-making entities tackle issues such as driving water and waste-water infrastructure investment to disadvantaged unincorporated communities that are often left out of jurisdictional decisions, supporting residents in community-driven vacant lot revitalization efforts, developing guidance that promotes the use of school and community-based infrastructure to feed children when schools are closed, and applying water conservation policies to support home gardening in remote Native American communities living on water-poor tribal lands. In addition to the individual projects in each of these jurisdictions, the project is also engaging national partners to lift these issues to a broader audience and scale and spread these evidence-informed promising built environment practices and policies.

This presentation will elaborate on the promising policies/practices each team is tackling and how these projects can advance health equity. While these projects are still ongoing, we will discuss some preliminary lessons learned and highlight how environmental designers and researchers can be a part of built environment solutions to ensure healthy and equitable outcomes for all.

References

1. E.M. Abrams and S.J. Szefler, "Covid-19 and the Impact of Social Determinants of Health," *The Lancet 8*, no. 7 (2020): P659-61, https://doi.org/10.1016/S2213-2600(20)30234-4.
2. *Healthy People 2030, U.S.* Department of Health and Human Services, Office of Disease Prevention and Health Promotion. Retrieved [November 1, 2021], from https://health.gov/healthypeople/objectives-and-data/social-determinants-health

Hospital Emergency Department Adaptations and Resilience in Response to Respiratory Outbreak Events: The Case of SARS-COV-2 (COVID-19)

Seyedmohammad Ahmadshahi *(Clemson University)*

As of September 2021, nearly 220 million cases and 4.5 million casualties have been reported worldwide, resulted by COVID-19 pandemic. The United States with 42 million cases and over 700,000 deaths have been one of the epicenters of the outbreak. In major cities, the pandemic has put a significant strain on hospitals with a considerable portion of the patients requiring critical care. The pandemic has forced a major impact on Emergency Departments (ED) across the world, changing the ED patient population and disrupting the usual functioning as the front line of response. These changes and challenges have required immediate adaptations in operational workflow and the built environment of the EDs (Uppal et al. 2020).

During the peak of the pandemic, the patient flow

in major city hospitals (i.e. New York) far exceeded the capacity of the EDs and created backlogs of infectious patients in waiting areas (Uppal et al. 2020). The sheer volume of the patients has necessitated changes in staff deployment, workflow, and supply management, resulting in adaptations in the ED to support the operational adaptations. Overall, there has been a significant variation between the EDs' responses and adaptations during the pandemic, and due to the unique structure of each ED it is impossible to provide a blanket strategy to address these issues (Gopinathan et al. 2020). In this study, we are trying to explore the role of the ED built environment in supporting the changes and adaptation necessitated by the COVID-19 pandemic. In this context, we aim to answer the following questions:

- How have different EDs responded to the changes required in response to the pandemic?
- What types of strategies were employed to cope with changes required in response to COVID-19 (Operational, resource management, built environment, etc.)?
- What are the built environment adaptations that may be required by hospital based EDs in response to future pandemics?

These research questions are addressed through an in-depth literature review. In this presentation, the key findings of this literature review and a framework for evaluation of the ED readiness against pandemic is shared. A range of external factors impacted the ED response, including the location of the ED, disease prevalence rates, and disaster preparedness is taken into consideration.

References

Uppal, A., Silvestri, D. M., Siegler, M., Natsui, S.,... & Wei, E. K. (2020). Critical Care And Emergency Department Response At The Epicenter Of The COVID-19 Pandemic: New York City's public health system response to COVID-19 included increasing the number of intensive care units, transferring patients between hospitals, and supplementing critical care staff. *Health Affairs, 39*(8), 1443–1449.

Gopinathan, V., Kunju, S. A., Krishnan S, V., Sirur, F. M., & Balakrishnan, J. M. (2021). Assessment of the Preparedness and Planning of Academic Emergency Departments in India During the COVID-19 Pandemic: A Multicentric Survey. Disaster Medicine and Public Health Preparedness, 1–6.

Care in Place: New Approaches to Community Clinic Design to Reduce Disparities and Develop Resilience in Baltimore

Caitlin DeClercq *(Research Design Connections);* ***Mohammad Gharipour*** *(Morgan State University);* ***Salman Mohagheghi*** *(Colorado School of Mines)*

In the state of Maryland, USA, one-third of the population is Black, yet the rate of COVID-19 infections was disproportionately higher among the African American community, accounting for almost half of all infections and 53% of COVID-19 deaths in the state's most populous city, Baltimore (MDOE, 2020). Though the pandemic made these disparities more visible, in fact, this is only the most recent manifestation of a post-industrial urban landscape whose outcomes such as income, investment, access to healthcare, and social vulnerability (De los Santos, et al., 2021; Foster et al., 2019) are divided among racial lines. Dr. Lawrence Brown describes this bifurcation as the "black butterfly" of east and west Baltimore. These patterns provoke an urgent question: where does health happen, why, and for whom?

The twin pandemics of COVID-19 and entrenched racism uncovered the need for and possibility of new paradigms for and spaces of health care for vulnerable populations, including those living in substandard housing, without sufficient income or access to care, and/or in areas with lower-than-average life expectancy rates. In the midst of COVID-19, we saw vacant lots, open spaces, grocery stores, museums, and other institutions used as centers for testing and vaccination. Indeed, as Thomas Fisher (2021) has observed, healthcare is increasingly moving out of the hospital to homes, communities, and spaces of daily life. Community clinics in particular have a long history of creative adaptation and reuse of existing or interstitial spaces to accommodate forms of care not accessible via mainstream healthcare (Bronston, 2021). How might we envision and work toward such spaces for the most vulnerable communities in Baltimore?

This session focuses on an innovative NIH project undertaken by an interdisciplinary team of researchers to design an evidence-based tool to identify the best location for temporary community clinics in high-need neighborhoods in Baltimore. Once ideal sites are selected, vacant houses in these locations can be converted into temporary clinics to provide underserved residents and vulnerable communities with easy accessibility to community healthcare resources. In particular, this paper will showcase a three-pronged methodology to identify locations that are: both physically and relationally proximal and accessible to served communities (Cummins et al., 2005); that are currently vacant or underused; and that could be renovated to be temporary or "warm site" clinics to respond to COVID or future disasters and offer necessary services and resources. Ultimately, by working with this tool, we identified five sites within Baltimore's most vulnerable neighborhoods that would be ideally suited to be renovated into a community clinic.

The paper will conclude with a discussion of the implications of this work not only in providing urgent health services and resources to underserved communities within Baltimore but also in serving as a model for proposing new paradigms of healthcare design and community-based interventions. Such a model is useful not only in times of crisis such as pandemics but also can help to intervene in and build resilience against other epidemics currently facing American cities such as racism, chronic disease, and climate change.

Visibility in Intensive Care Units and Its Role in Enhancement of Teamwork, Collaborative Communication, and Safety- a Qualitative Study

Arsalan Gharaveis *(Jensen Partners);* ***Denise McCall*** *(Cinco Ranch ECC, Infusion Center);* ***Ahmad E Alansari*** *(College of Basic Education)*

Aim: This study explores the effects of visibility for promoting teamwork, collaboration, and safety in hospital Intensive Care Units (ICUs). The researcher's explored the contributing factors associated with visibility in ICUs and how teamwork, collaborative communication, and security issues are impacted.

Background: Visibility has been addressed as one of the significant factors in improving teamwork and collaboration, while reducing security issues in healthcare facilities.

Methods: A developed semi-structured sets of questions was used to interview nurses and physicians from a critical care unit—which covered four major topics: visibility, teamwork, collaborative communication, and security. Direct observations and behavior mapping were also used as the second qualitative method.

Results: The findings address a significant association between visibility in ICU and teamwork and collaborative communication among the medical staff members. Additionally, the interview participants emphasized that the rate of safety issues would decrease by improvement of visibility.

Discussion/Conclusion: As one of the few studies focusing on the relationship between visibility and other behavioral factors, this study findings are in alignment with the existing literature about favorable impact of visibility. Also, this study provides a valuable model for future research to investigate observed reactions and subjective perceptions of medical staff in relation to environmental variables.

Building Awareness: A Mixed-Methods Study of Green Building Communications in the Green Residence Hall

Laura Cole *(University of Missouri);* ***Erin M Hamilton*** *(Texas Tech University);* ***Lindsay McManamon*** *(Sandhills Community College)*

The urgent challenge of global climate change demands holistic responses coupling technological innovation with human agency. Green buildings – with goals to promote resource conservation – are venues where technology and human action intertwine. Yet, few green buildings bridge technological solutions with occupant knowledge and behaviors. Conservation psychology research to date suggests the potential of promoting occupant eco-behaviors through strategies such as signage, behavioral prompts, environmental feedback, and amplifying communications around social norms within the building (Abrahamse & Matthies, 2018). Other emerging scholarship frames green buildings as informal teaching tools and examines the capacity for green buildings to support environmental knowledge acquisition and promote environmentally responsible behaviors (ERBs) (e.g., Wu et al., 2017), but this work is still in the early stages of providing evidence-based guidance on green building communications.

This exploratory, mixed-methods project aims to increase environmental awareness and eco-behaviors for undergraduate students in a case study LEED Gold residence hall at a large Midwestern state university. This project began with approximately 2-years of creating an interdisciplinary framework for "mindful green building communications" [adapted from eco-tourism work by Woods & Moscardo (2003)], which informed the design of a multi-media signage system for the residence hall. The intervention was designed to be easily perceptible, legible, cognitively engaging, and appeal to a variety of behavioral motivations (personal, social, ecological) to promote green building awareness and specific eco-behaviors (e.g. shorter showers and taking the stairs). These outcomes and motivations were the basis for a survey instrument adapted from previously validated instruments. The signage intervention was installed in Fall 2021 and data collection included a pre/post online survey and interviews. The survey was disseminated to students in two different residence halls, one green (with intervention) and one non-green (no intervention), which allows us to compare the post intervention green hall to their own baseline and to the non-green hall. Pre-intervention results analyzed to date (n=80) demonstrate that students were only aware of green building features with which they regularly interacted (e.g., water bottle stations and recycling). Despite existing informational signage, few residents report being aware of these features or noticing the existing signage. Post-intervention survey data and walk-through interview data with residents will be collected and analyzed in late 2021.

The work here will result in evidence-based, open-access green building communications together with a framework for creating signage interventions. The work contributes to research in conservation psychology that provides guidance for informational interventions. The work makes practical contributions to designers of student eco-housing by testing an intervention that could improve environmental learning and behavior change.

References

Abrahamse, W. and Matthies, E. (2018). *Informational Strategies to Promote Pro-Environmental Behaviour. In Environmental Psychology* (eds L. Steg and J.I.M. Groot).

Woods, B., & Moscardo, G. (2003). Enhancing wildlife education through mindfulness. *Australian Journal of Environmental Education, 19*, 97–108.

Wu, S. R., Kim, S.-K., Park, H., Fan, P., Ligmann-Zielinska, A., & Chen, J. (2017). How do green buildings communicate green design to building users? A survey study of a LEED-certified building. *Journal of Green Building, 12*(3).

Indoor Air Quality As Influenced By Common Building Materials: Empirical Testing in the Classroom

Aditya Jayadas *(Oklahoma State University);* ***Paulette Hebert*** *(Oklahoma State University);* ***Hebatalla Nazmy*** *(Oklahoma State University)*

Background: Indoor air quality (IAQ) is a very important issue to consider when designing any building. The plethora of available building materials can each pose different risks. A building's IAQ can be compromised by microbial contaminants, chemicals, allergens or other factors that can negatively impact health of individuals who use a building (Spengler et al., 2000). Though different studies have explored a myriad of factors related to IAQ no studies were found exploring CO_2, total volatile organic compounds (TVOC), particulate matter 2.5 (PM2.5) and overall IAQ levels of commonly used building materials. No studies were found which utilized empirical tests to educate college students.

Purpose: The purpose of this study was to utilize empirical testing to document and assess CO_2, TVOC, PM2.5 and overall IAQ level for commonly used building materials as measured in an interior design classroom in a mid-western University.

Methodology: Students examined 16 different building materials for assessment. Temperature and relative humidity were recorded at the beginning of the study, followed by the CO_2, TVOC, PM2.5 and overall IAQ levels at 10 second intervals for 1-minute using the AWAIR IAQ meter. Descriptive statistics, including averages, minimums, maximums and standard deviations, were reported.

Results: Temperature and relative humidity values were 720F and 48% respectively. Average CO_2 values exhibited minimal variance amongst the 16 variables. The lowest recorded value was for the oriented strand board at 803.80 and the highest value was for interior paint at 976.50. The average TVOC values did show significant variability across the 16 variables with values recorded as ~20.00 for plywood, carpet and wool materials, 52.67 for interior paint, 82.33 for bleach wipes, 250.67 for oil-based stain-blocker, 319.67 for wood finish, 341.50 for latex paint, 8,223.17 for enamel neutral base and 31,738.67 for spray paint. PM2.5 values, on the other hand, were higher for different plywood materials, ranging from 168.67 to 778.67. Stain blocker, enamel neutral base, nylon stain, interior paint, paint thinner, wood stain and latex paint all had PM 2.5 values under 10.00. Bleach wipes and particle board had values between 15.00 and 25.00. Oriented strand board had a value of 254.20 and spray paint resulted in the highest PM 2.5 value at 853.00. Lastly, spray paint was the only material with an IAQ total value lower than 70 (56.33) which is within the range posing significant risks to individuals.

Discussion: Findings suggest that CO_2, TVOC, PM2.5 and overall IAQ levels should all be considered when designing buildings as materials can contribute differently to buildings' IAQ levels. Using empirical test protocols in the classroom may help students to connect more viscerally to IAQ concepts when using real-world building materials and seeing outcomes first-hand. Students may be more likely to share material selection best practices or IAQ assessments with other practitioners in the future.

Implications: Creating interior design students' awareness and understanding of empirical IAQ testing for different building materials could potentially influence the materials they decide to specify or avoid in their future professional careers, potentially making buildings healthier for their occupants.

Preparing for the Inevitable: How Diligent Design Can Mitigate Climate Threats to Hospitals

Lauren Seydewitz *(Gresham Smith);* ***Corie Baker*** *(Gresham Smith);* ***Skip Yauger*** *(Gresham, Smith)*

Natural disasters often disable healthcare facilities at the precise time their services are needed the most, posing a major threat to healthcare providers. And, with a rapidly changing climate that continues to elevate the threats and level of damage from natural disasters, there's only one solution: design for the future.

During climate disasters, health care facilities often function as safe havens. But, failures in building systems that require changes in operations have a direct impact on financials and the quality of care delivered to patients. Research estimates that severe weather events can cost hospitals anywhere from $600,000 to $2 billion per occurrence.

However, there is no monetary value that can be placed on the negative impact of deficient care. It's also very important to remember that the same low-income, racially diverse communities repeatedly feel the worst impacts of climate disasters and require more health care services in times of crisis, making it imperative that equity is a critical part of the design. Healthcare providers and designers must incorporate future climate projections into their planning.

Baptist Health Care is building a new hospital and medical campus in Pensacola, Florida, and Gresham Smith is providing architecture, engineering, and planning services for the project.

When designing this project, our team had to acknowledge the severity of Pensacola's weather events. Baptist Health looked to assess how the new location could be impacted by the changing climate conditions, as they wanted to make sure the facility could last for 75 to 100 years. Gresham Smith had the right tool available: a climate risk assessment.

The firm's team of environmental scientists, architects, engineers, and designers worked with Baptist to gather data on climate predictions and determine which climate hazards would most threaten the project site in the future. These included hurricanes, inland flooding and water scarcity, to name a few. Then the team then systematically identified which of the hospital's assets were most critical to keep online during an extreme weather event, and, using modeling software, the team estimated the level of damage that could possibly occur to specific systems, and calculated the resulting financial impact.

Using the data from the climate risk assessment and working with our environmental scientists, the design team implemented strategies that will safeguard the medical campus' assets and help Baptist Health Care avoid or minimize service disruptions. For example, the climate risk assessment simulated 100-, 200-, 500-, and 1,000-year storms to understand flood depths and routing pathways for water on the site, which enabled the design team to make strategic decisions about right-sizing stormwater infrastructure and grading. Additionally, the team performed a detail analysis on the structure and building envelope to understand the effects of a Category 5 hurricane.

During this presentation, members of the Gresham Smith team will use this project as a case study to discuss why and how a facility would conduct a climate risk assessment, including the background data and research, as well as why facilities should utilize resilient design strategies in general.

Life-Cycle Cost Analysis (LCCA) of Outpatient High Touch Contact Surfaces

Xiaoyu Chen *(University of Florida)*

Introduction: The sustainability of the high touch contact surface system can be an essential factor in outpatient clinics, as closing the department will interfere with the daily operations of building users (Ulrich et al., 2004). However, the time required to replace the surface system depends on many factors, such as the type of surface material and the installation method. Currently, there is limited research on the life cycle cost analysis (LCCA) of high touch contact surfaces.

Methodology: The protocol to perform a LCCA is defined by the National Institute of Standards and Technology (NIST). The steps of LCCA include defining problems, identifying viable alternatives, establishing common assumptions and parameters, and obtaining financial information. The data is designated for typical high touch contact surfaces used in outpatient clinics. These materials comply with the following standards and guidelines: The General Design and Construction Requirements Guide (2014) from Facility Guidance Institution (FGI), WELL v2 Material Standard (2021) administered by the International WELL Building Institute (IWBI), and the Bloodborne Pathogen Standard (2000) from the Occupational Safety and Health Administration (OHSA). These standards and guidelines provide basic surface design and construction requirements, the health and safety criteria, cleaning methodologies separately. This study uses the LCCA calculation model that incorporates the time value of a currency and 50-year period use discounts to predict future high touch contact surface value. Based on the service life and maintenance of the system, the future value (FV) is calculated and expressed of present value(PV) dollars to determine the replacement cost (Harris, 2015).

Utility: The use of LCCA provides a valuable tool for predicting the long-term cost of healthcare interior surfaces to plan the operating and maintenance costs associated with long-term ownership investments. Results show that outpatient high touch contact hard surfaces are more cost-effective in terms of initial purchase and installation and long-term maintenance of equipment assets and facilities. Therefore, this study evaluated the life cycle cost of the high touch contact surfaces and allowed decision-makers to understand the long-term cost of ownership and other key factors such as infection prevention safety, durability, and aesthetics.

Conclusion: In conclusion, when choosing high touch contact surfaces for healthcare settings, the sustainability of the materials is an important factor. Specifically, cost, infection prevention safety, durability, and aesthetics should be considered to achieve an overall return on investment.

References

Fuller., S. (2016, September 19). *Life-cycle cost analysis (LCCA)*. WBDG. Retrieved November 15, 2021, from https://www.wbdg.org/resources/life-cycle-cost-analysis-lcca

Harris, D. D. (2015). *ORIGINAL ARTICLE A life-cycle cost analysis for flooring materials for healthcare facilities. 4*(4), 92–100. https://doi.org/10.5430/jha.v4n4p92

Ulrich, R., Quan, X., Systems, H., Architecture, C., & Texas, A. (2004). The Role of the Physical Environment in the Hospital of the 21 st Century : A Once-in-a-Lifetime Opportunity. *Environment, 439*(September), 69. http://www.saintalphonsus.org/pdf/cah_role_physical_env.pdf

Thresholds of Nature-Based Solutions for Adaptation to Sea-Level Rise

Yuang Sun *(Cornell University)*

There are growing interests in nature-based solutions as strategies for sea-level rise adaptation, but as designers and planners, we often don't know how well these systems perform over time, especially after a big disaster like a hurricane and flooding. We emphasize the importance of planning dynamic coastal management to implement responses to sea-level rise over time and to manage adaptively for uncertainty. However, the problem is: how well can nature-based systems survive different kinds of events? As time pass by, what are the thresholds or limits to their effectiveness under multiple conditions?

Nature-based strategies for the sea-level rise include dunes, oyster and coral reefs, mangrove barrier forests, coastal wetlands, etc. Given nature-based solutions' properties to grow, develop, evolve and change over time (as dynamic living systems), they should be reinforced and embody this temporal multi-scalar process (Bush & Doyon, 2019). At the same time, with the evolvement of ecosystems, there is another iteration that these living systems become affected by the rate of sea-level rise, which influences by extreme climate disasters such as hurricanes.

The monitoring and evaluation should be continued on coastal projects to understand if they were indeed performing the way we thought, or have they kept pace with the climb for the sea-level rise, or if there are any disjuncts. To support this, I conduct a literature review of coastal nature-based strategies and identify the key metrics of its performance, such as the persistence of ecological ability, the function for biodiversity purposes or human protection, and the ability to rebuild. Then I identify case studies under threats such as sea-level rise rate or extent, human activities, habitat change, etc., and assess them using these metrics. By comparing these two, I finally conclude what are the thresholds of each strategy in multiple extents of coastal challenges and the tradeoffs among them.

From small to large scale nature-based solutions, oyster reefs appear to be in dynamic equilibrium with short-term moderate fluctuations in sea-level rise, but with a huge drop in effectiveness during extreme flooding. Medium-scale solutions such as coastal wetlands, mangrove barrier forests, are unlikely to achieve maximum desired performance without considering the context of the greater landscape setting. The thresholds of coastal wetlands rely on the water level and salt marsh plants system. A higher rate of sea-level rise could make the plants' system intolerant to salt, which takes a long time to rebuild and return to balance. Mangrove barrier forests have secondary benefits such as carbon sequestration and habitat provision, but their performance is affected by the accretion of soil sediment, constrained by context characteristics. Dunes, on a city-scale or even regional scale, the threshold mainly lies in water level and human intervention. The rising water levels will increase erosion. If they are caught between the sea and the built environment, lacking the natural conditions enabling them to move.

References

Bush, J., & Doyon, A. (2019). Building urban resilience with nature-based solutions: How can urban planning contribute? *Cities, 95*, 102483. https://doi.org/10.1016/j.cities.2019.102483

Placemaking through Storytelling

Jennifer Smith *(Auburn University)*

In an Alabama town there is a bottom-up movement to communicate under-represented, African-American history through a series of "sacred sites" in the landscape. This under-represented history includes: former slaves engaged in early city development, Black land owners, redlining practices, and racial injustice. History education presently does not have the capacity to fully discuss these truths, and there is a movement to make them apparent in our cities. Rosenwald Schools, lynching sites, cemeteries, and formerly segregated schools are considered sacred due to their significance in the African-American and simply, American experience. In The Power of Place Dolores Hayden argues that we are fascinated with the past when touring historic sites but miss opportunities to translate this to our neighborhoods imbued with place-making potential. She states, "If Americans were to find their own social history preserved in the public landscapes of their own neighborhoods and cities, then connection to the past might be different" (Hayden, 46). This connection to place and history exists for local African-American families and has potential to engage a collective city. While some histories are painful, all should be evident for united progress. As stated by a Community Remembrance Project member, "There can be no reconciliation and healing without remembering the past" (2021).

These ideas are explored through a local, historic African-American cemetery dating back to Emancipation, and those buried were key figures in early city development. While a prominent landmark sited at the terminus of a historic road, its past is scarcely known. In fact, the cemetery has been poorly maintained over the past century compared to other cemeteries in the city, despite being one of the oldest. Additionally, due to erasure and lack of equitable agency, this African-American landmark is one of a few remaining in the town, and there is a movement to protect these assets and communicate their stories.

For this project students and I are working with stakeholders to envision public space that provides storytelling and placemaking opportunities. Stakeholders include: cemetery descendants, researchers, city representatives, and more. By elongating the schematic design schedule, we can gather stories from community members, host participatory design sessions, and increase bottom-up advocacy. We are exploring placemaking and storytelling through a number of design considerations including: physical markers in the landscape, vernacular building typologies, and local materials. Presently, the project has land for development adjacent to the cemetery, has the interest of city officials, and has gone through initial participatory designs. Looking forward, we aim to continue participatory design sessions, and research grant opportunities to match city funding.

As with many U.S. cities, African-American assets have largely been erased. This erasure is more than the loss of building infrastructure. It represents who has a voice and who is excluded in urban development. It furthermore provides opportunity for neighborhoods to communicate history representative of all past, present, and future residents.

References

Hayden, Dolores. *The Power of Place*. The MIT Press, 1995, 46.

Eji's community remembrance project. Equal Justice Initiative. (2021, October 22). Retrieved October 26, 2021, from https://eji.org/projects/community-remembrance-project/.

Sensory Engagement in Design: A Path to Stress Mediation

Lisa Phillips *(Jefferson University)*

Rising levels of stress have continued to draw attention in the last several decades, with rates climbing globally. This is especially true since 2020 due to the COVID-19 pandemic, which has had an ongoing impact on the physical and mental health of families, workforces and communities in general. Now, more than ever, designs for well-being should be urgently considered and integrated into the built environment.

In fall 2020 and 2021, interior design juniors investigated how they could mitigate stress through multisensory designs for hypothetical tranquility pods. Each student selected unique users from within the local community, groups they felt were under considerable pressure. These ranged from nurses, firefighters and policeman, to religious figures and public transportation workers. Each student conducted an interview with a member of their user group and then chose sites based on density studies. Sensory site analyses were subsequently created that included recording the sights, smells, sounds, and user behaviors in the area. The pod itself was a prefabricated box of approximately 15'x15'x15' that was intended to be utilized by one individual in the user group at any given time.

The class had no formal training in either designing for stress relieving environments or designing multisensory spaces so this project acted as an introduction to both. As such, the group began by discussing the writings of Juhani Pallasmaa, and the work of architect, Peter Zumthor to learn about sensory design, atmosphere, and how a designer can affect the mood and emotions of users in interior environments. Other early discussions included examples of spaces utilized for stress alleviation, meditation, and contemplation. Case studies included Tadao Ando's Meditation Space for the UNESCO headquarters and Meditation Hall in Eastern China by Hil Architects.

In tandem with research into stress relieving methods, sketching and models were used in the early stages of the process. As space planning evolved, students began working with physical materials and 3D software walkthroughs as well. Through this multi-faceted approach, students were able to experiment with light, color, and materiality, testing multiple options rapidly. Sounds, tastes, smells, textures, materials, thermal properties, the play of light and shadows, and contrasts of colors were intricately considered.

During the final critique for this five-week project, students presented their work to professionals in the field. Utilizing both the jurors' comments and observations throughout the term, a rubric was utilized to determine their level of success on the project. The mean the class achieved for the criteria "perceived stress relief of user group" was 4.03 on a 1-5 scale, with 1 being low and 5 being high. For the criteria of "multisensory usage," the mean was a 3.92, with the largest issue being incorporating taste and authentic sound in many cases. This presentation will discuss the role sensory design can contribute to stress mitigation and how students, educators, and design professionals can implement these concepts to alleviate stress in their own projects in the built environment. Examples of student work and external research will be utilized to describe these methods.

Relinking Nature and Health: Perspective on Design and Integration of Green Spaces in Healthcare Facilities

Samuel Charlebois *(UQAM)*

As acknowledged by the World Health Organization, urban green spaces (UGS) constitute essential urban infrastructures for citizen's physical, mental and social health. Decades of research on the effects of green spaces in healthcare facilities (HF) demonstrate significant positive effects on the quality of given services, healing process, and provision for social and emotional needs (Weerasuriya 2018). From the evidence based design approach, multiple studies have identified environmental qualities related to these physical, mental and social salutary effects.

Nevertheless, accessibility to qualitative UGS in HF has proven to be difficult. Lack of available space due to urban density and poor adaptation to winter conditions constitute major setbacks (Marcus & Sachs 2013).

Consequently, the integration of UGS to architectural settings is perceived as an innovative strategic response. This thesis aims to clarify the potentials of UGS integration in HF to offer salutary effects and give perspective on two main questions:

- How do we define environmental qualities that are linked to UGS's salutary effects;
- How can the integration of UGS in HF promote desired environmental qualities and enhance accessibility.

The methodology unfolds in three parts. First, a literature review clarifies salutary effects obtainable from UGS usage by four mechanisms: stress reduction, attention restoration, increase in physical activity, and social capital enhancement.

Next, a comparative study identifies recurring environmental qualities discussed in three scientific publications in order to establish a table of common attributes: Urban Green spaces and Health (WHO, 2016), 14 Patterns of Biophilic Design (Browning et al, 2014), and Therapeutic Landscapes (Marcus & Sachs 2013).

The third part, based on a case study method, analyzes five different HF to highlight practical applications of integrated UGS and their correlations to previously identified environmental qualities: the Montreal Neurological Institute, the Massachusetts General Hospital, the Lurie's Children Hospital in Chicago, as well as the Khoo Teck Puat and NG Teng Fong Hospital in Singapore. These facilities were chosen because of their context - characterized by urban density and/or winter conditions - and because they exhibit multiple UGS integrative strategies - rooftop gardens, atriums, interior courtyards, green walls and green corridors.

The comparative study identified 28 common attributes to consider when planning the integration of UGS in HF, distributed into 6 attribute categories: systemic, accessibility, programmatic, natural, psychological, and social. The case studies identified practical applications for those 28 attributes through photographic evidence, schematic drawings, and textual descriptions. In conclusion, this research provides perspective supporting the potential for integrated UGS in HF to enhance their accessibility and provide important environmental qualities linked to short and long term health benefits.

References

WHO Europe (2016). *Urban green spaces and health: A review of evidence. World Health Organization regional office for Europe*, Copenhagen, Denmark

Marcus, C. C., & Sachs, N. A. (2013). *Therapeutic Landscapes: An Evidence-Based Approach to Designing Healing Gardens and Restorative Outdoor Spaces* (1 edition). Wiley.

Weerasuriya, R., Henderson-Wilson, C., & Townsend, M. (2018). Accessing Green Spaces Within a Healthcare Setting: A Mixed Studies Review of Barriers and Facilitators. *HERD: Health Environments Research & Design Journal*

Rural Resiliency in the Public Realm: A Collective Case Study Analysis of Land-Grant Design Impacts on Rural Main Streets

Ole Sleipness *(Utah State University);* ***David Evans*** *(Utah State University);* ***Jake Powell*** *(Utah State University);* ***David Anderson*** *(Utah State University)*

Purpose: This study provides a comparative case study analysis of how a University Extension Design program in the US has empowered local communities through design engagement at the intersection of rural community health and transportation.

Background: Globally, urbanization has resulted in population increases in metropolitan areas, while many rural communities have experienced depopulation (Travis, 2013). Rural population decline has been exacerbated by changes in traditional agricultural and natural resource industries, labor mechanization, and fewer employment opportunities. Concurrently, urban areas have seen rapid population increases, as people have migrated to urban areas seeking education, cultural, and economic opportunities.

Over several decades, many rural communities have struggled to attract young professionals, retain young families, or compete with the allure of urban environments.

However, the COVID-19 pandemic disruptions have led many to reconsider the resilient value of exurban and rural life. As the pandemic limited access to recreational amenities, social interaction, and cultural amenities, many urban inhabitants sought exodus to exurban and rural environments. Due to their relative affordability and direct access to ample green space, rural communities became suddenly attractive to urbanites newly empowered with a capacity to work remotely from virtually anywhere with a sufficient internet connection. For many, this exodus has been a temporary reprieve. For others, the move is long-term.

In most rural communities, Main Street has traditionally been the hub of local economic activity, historic identity, and sense of place. As core to daily activity, the form and composition of this public realm plays a profound role in social activity, human health and wellbeing, and community resilience. Qualities of this built environment—including tree canopy, fixtures, furnishings, and general design qualities—greatly impact its walkability, alternative transportation connectivity, and human comfort. In many rural communities, Main Streets are also under the jurisdiction of state or federal DOT. State transportation policies have the potential to both constrain or enhance the potential health and resilience of the Main Street environment.

Methods: This study documents and evaluates how a University Extension Design program has empowered local communities through design engagement of enhancing rural community health through design improvements in the public realm of rural Main Streets. Through a comparative case study analysis of completed rural transportation-focused design projects (Yin, 2013), we compare and contrast how the policy environment can both constrain and provide opportunities for viable design proposals, and the role of university design programs in building local capacity for improving social connectivity, health, and resilience.

Significance: Many smaller rural communities do not have the capacity to propose substantive design improvements while successfully navigating policy environment, jurisdictional issues, and political limitations. To meet this need, University Extension programs in the US often engage local community partners in co-creating innovative design solutions for local problems, as a fulfillment of their land-grant mission.

References

Travis, W. R. (2013). *New geographies of the American West: land use and the changing patterns of place*. Island Press.

Yin, R. K. (2013). *Case study research: Design and methods*. Sage publications.

Autonomous Vehicles as a Force Reshaping Cities - a Comprehensive Observation of the Impacts of Autonomous Vehicles on Urban Design and Everyday Living Environment

Jun Wang *(Georgia Institute of Technology)*

Transportation systems and mobility modes are two of the major forces shaping our cities. In the 20th century, the invention of the inner combustion engine-powered vehicle gave birth to the highway system and changed the way we perceive and organize the city ever since. The creation of suburban garden neighborhoods and the spaghetti roads are the witnesses of the power transportation modes had on changing the cities. Autonomous vehicles (AVs), already stepped into our daily lives from science fiction, with different operating systems and on-road behavior compared to the previous generations of cars, are bound to have an impact on urban designs and everyday living environments.

This paper will make observations and predictions on topics of:

- AVs as a new model of vehicle and platform;
- AVs' impact on urban networks, including traffic flows and parking spaces;
- AV's impact on urban form, including land use pattern, neighborhood structure, and the intensity of concentricity;
- and AVs' impact on infrastructure systems, including the new facility locating problems

and streetscape design.

Together these observations will lead to a comprehensive prediction of how AVs will reshape the cities, in a "better" way to a more livable and more sustainable environment or a more jammed yet sprawled future, and a brief discussion about the methods and actions to facilitate the "brighter" future is included at the end.

Drawing actual conclusions is hard without the mass adoption of AVs among transportation systems. However, predictions could be given with the observation of existing studies and pilot programs around the world. AVs have unprecedented benefits compared to conventional human-driven vehicles, in that they provide higher mobility to the disabled or people who are unable to drive, which promotes equity in the transportation system, and AVs consume less energy and generate fewer pollutants per vehicle. AVs could also be new developing opportunities for the long lost areas both in the city and suburbia. However, AVs may also lead to a more inequitable and less sustainable future since AVs could result in more traffic flow, higher traffic speed, more intense urban sprawl and waste of rides due to unregulated public-used AVs, the higher average price of private AVs could as well make it harder to acquire for the underrepresented population.

Considering AVs as an important driving force in shaping cities, in either possible way, and as an even more vital role in this process, using various means to facilitate the future with a living environment that is more sustainable and more equitable is crucial. Regulations and law enforcement are essential and policymakers should carefully make the judgment and use proper legislation methods to promote a more walkable, livable future.

Carbon-Neutral Adaptive Reuse through Community Outreach in the Shaw Neighborhood of Washington, DC

Robin Puttock *(Catholic University of America)*

"The world today is facing broad and complex challenges that threaten every aspect of our lives. The architect's call to protect the health, safety, and welfare of the public has a new and broader meaning amid challenges such as increasing climate extremes and social inequity."[1] These words served as the inspiration for the Fall 2021 XX University's Net Zero Design Studio in which students worked in teams and partnered with the Washington DC Office of Planning to examine carbon-neutral, equitable solutions for adaptive reuse of a one-block site in the historic Shaw neighborhood. In an effort to sustainably address the current clash between equity and gentrification in this swiftly-developing area, and contrary to most design studios today, a design program was not provided to the students. Instead, students were encouraged to implement multiple research methodologies such as interviews, observation and surveys, gleaning feedback from several hundred local community leaders, residents and visitors to learn, first-hand, what the community needed.

The data collected by the students served as the inspiration for 5 unique programs addressing the top needs of the community, both on the local and global scale. Focus areas include: modular construction to address resiliency and incremental funding sources, community aquaponics to combat the existing food desert, preserving place as a path for equity, considering a combination of reuse and infill to minimize operation and embodied carbon emissions, and finally, serving the youth of the neighborhood with after school and weekend programming.

In addition to these research methodologies, several pedagogical methodologies were introduced in the studio to prepare the students for the 2022 AIA/ACSA COTE Top Ten for Students Competition. These methodologies included over twenty subject-based mini-lectures, participation from over twenty professional firms nation-wide and the introduction of a wide variety of building analytic software including Tally, Sefaira and EC3. The course framework also included an emphasis on precedent study and case study analysis of Living Buildings and professional COTE Top Ten winners.

This presentation will include an examination of the final student design projects from both a carbon neutrality perspective, using reuse as the primary sustainable strategy, and from an equity viewpoint, emphasizing the methodology of community outreach. The health and well-being of humans will be shown to be the unifying inspiration between these two critical topics. Finally, the presentation will include a segment based on Discovery, one of the 10 principles in the AIA Framework for Design Excellence, which will reveal the intersections and balances required to achieve carbon neutrality, support human well-being and begin to address the equity issues evident in the current development of the Shaw neighborhood of Washington, DC.

References

1. *Framework for design excellence.* The American Institute of Architects.

Alabama Grasslands: Designing Plant Species Corridors for Biodiversity

Kelly Homan *(Auburn University)*

East of the Mississippi River Alabama ranks first in species diversity and many scientists believe with more exploration Alabama could one day come in at number one across the entire United States (Duncan, 2013). This rich diversity is a product of the state's unique climate, geological formations, yearly rainfall, and evolutionary trends and provides crucial ecosystem services and recreational beauty for the people of Alabama. While the depth of Alabama's biodiverse landscapes and waters are just beginning to be fully understood, the state also currently comes in at number two, surpassed only by Hawaii, for total species extinctions to date (AWAP, 2015). Loss of the state's grassland communities has played a significant role in Alabama's overall biodiversity loss. These native landscapes, highly rich in species diversity, are in steep decline due to urbanization, land use conversions to agriculture, and climate change factors. Grasslands in Alabama include the Black Belt Prairies, the Coosa River Valley Prairies, the almost completely extinct Jackson Prairies, and the lower Alabama Coastal Prairies. Along with prairies, the barren grasslands in the rocky northern portion of the state contain some of the most biodiverse land on earth (Duncan, 2013). The bogs, fens, and coastal grasslands in the southern portion of the state are so rich in diversity that in 2017 lower Alabama was designated as part of biodiversity hotspot #36. Biodiversity hotspots across the globe cover only 2.4% percent of land but contain 60% of the world's plants and animals including many endemics (CEPF, 2020).

Plant species corridors are a spatial strategy to both reestablish Alabama grassland communities and protect vulnerable plant species at risk of extinction. As with many states across the country, Alabama does not include specific plant species in the states wildlife action plan giving most conservation funding to animal species and their habitats. Using newly released GIS data sets and research by design methodologies, this research study spatially defines plant species corridors at the state scale with a goal of connecting crucial areas of biodiverse lands through a network of protected areas. The research seeks to place 30% of Alabama's lands into easements, public land trusts, parks, reserves, and other forms of protection.

References

Alabama Wildlife Action Plan 2015-2025. *Division of Wildlife and Freshwater Fisheries*, 2015, Alabama Wildlife Action Plan 2015-2025.

Critical Ecosystem Partnership Fund (2020). (rep.). *CEPF Impact Report 2001-2020.*

Duncan, R. S. (2013). *Southern wonder: Alabama's surprising biodiversity.* The University of Alabama Press.

Duncan, S. (n.d.). *Biodiversity in Alabama. Encyclopedia of Alabama*. Retrieved November 11, 2021, from http://encyclopediaofalabama.org/.

A Study of Green Infrastructure Education for Promoting Its Acceptance

Joowon Im *(University of Texas at Arlington)*

Green infrastructure (GI) is a holistic and sustainable development strategy that treats stormwater runoff concerning its quality and quantity and flooding issues of urban ecology in our built environment. While GI is useful in mitigating urban flooding issues, there are still challenges in accepting and implementing GI in a community since its approach is still "new and different". The challenges and barriers include issues with public awareness, technical difficulties in construction, obtaining funds, multiple stakeholders, maintenance, and setting priorities in its planning. These challenges defer GI implementation and communities that can be beneficial by having GI miss the opportunity for environmental improvement.

Among those challenges, this study focuses on raising public awareness through providing GI education to promote more acceptance and successful implementation based on empirical research. Various forms of public outreach and involvement in the process of planning and design can help to draw more attention and awareness toward it, which helps the successful promotion and application of GI. Further, the study will explore how the landscape architecture discipline, as a profession that emphasizes a holistic understanding of the environment and comprehensive approaches of art & science, can play a role in creating effective education to better promote GI.

The target subjects are secondary teacher candidates who have great potential to extend the effect of GI education and knowledge to their future students. If they pass down their knowledge to their future students at an early age, there will be more chances and greater impact to have an open mind to a GI approach as they grow up. This interdisciplinary approach allows teacher candidates to learn the opportunities that students identify problem situations and control science and technology for their communities. The authors first provided the subjects with a GI education session that was developed with the 5E (engage, explore, explain, elaborate, evaluate) learning cycle model and then, conducted a survey to measure the changes in the level of understanding of GI and to ask the subjects to evaluate the education session as teacher candidates.

The survey revealed that the education session had a positive impact in increasing the subjects' understanding of GI and increasing their intention to incorporate GI education in their future curricula. The subjects found the use of graphics and local examples was helpful to understand the importance of GI because they have more understanding of site contexts. This study is meaningful in measuring the actual effectiveness of GI education to plan the improvement and better utilization of the educational materials. The study is also useful in suggesting the implications regarding the effectiveness of developing educational materials through the lens of landscape architecture.

A Green Network Plan for the Greater Baybrook, Baltimore, MD

Bridget Stokes *(University of Maryland, College Park);* ***Byoung-Suk Kweon*** *(University of Maryland)*

The Goal of the Green Network Plan is to enhance and strengthen the community of the Greater Baybrook by connecting the area's green infrastructure into a unified network. It has been widely researched that communities with green infrastructure have increased economic, environmental, and social benefits. This increased exposure to the natural environment promotes physical health (McCurdy, 2010), mental well-being (Kaplan, 1995), and social connectivity (Jennings, 2019). In particular, green network plans in poor minority neighborhoods provide many opportunities to transform vacant lots into green open spaces, and to support sustainable redevelopment of vacant lands. In summary, green network plans can improve health and well-being of residents, create safer and vibrant communities as well as enhance environmental sustainability.

In a coordinated effort, the Maryland Department of Natural Resources, the Greater Baltimore Wilderness Coalition, the University to Maryland, and EnviroCollab LLC have been working together with the Greater Baybrook to design a plan that would transform the fragmented greenspaces into a system of interconnected parks and trails. The Greater Baybrook is located on the peninsula south of downtown Baltimore. The racial composition is 33% African American and 15% Hispanic with a median household income of about $54,000, 36% lower than the Maryland average. The park system is fragmented and only makes up 5.7% of the land, a very low percentage compared to Baltimore overall, at 9.6%. Of those parks, the majority are not well maintained and lack necessary amenities like lighting and trashcans, which severely limits positive activity and perception of safety. Curtis Bay, one of the three neighborhoods within the Greater Baybrook has a staggering percentage of only .05% parkland, a true environmental injustice for the residents living there.

The Green Network Plan was designed by determining ongoing investment strategies in the neighborhood, evaluating opportunities and constraints, and analyzing demographics, park equity, environmental justice, and other current site conditions. The Greater Baybrook Green Network Plan will revitalize the community and provide residents with more equitable access to nature. The Green Network Plan will connect local & regional green infrastructure and provide residents with better access to nearby amenities. The plan will provide residents with greater access to the waterfront and other underutilized waterways, will improve existing greenspaces, and will increase park acreage and tree canopy. Utilizing green infrastructure, the currently fragmented neighborhoods of the Greater Baybrook will become a thriving and connected system of trails, parks and greenspaces while controlling flash flooding and decreasing stormwater runoff. This green network plan is a long-term vision plan that creates an interconnected network of green space within the neighborhoods and expand to other surrounding communities. This is just the beginning of many changes that may improve the quality of life among the residents and create more sustainable environments.

The Effects of Environmental Degradation on Residents' Quality of Life

Byoung-Suk Kweon *(University of Maryland);* ***Christopher D. Ellis*** *(University of Maryland)*

This paper explores how perception of environmental degradation such as the loss of natural areas, wildlife habitat, and discharge of wastewater as well as concerns for air pollution relate to self-reported quality of life and neighborhood satisfaction. Environmental degradation is an important issue affecting quality of life. Environmental degradation is defined as any change or disturbance to the environment perceived to be deleterious or undesirable (Johnson, 1997). These can include air, soil and water pollution, disturbance or elimination of habitat, declines in biodiversity and significant changes in climate leading to extreme weather events. The UN Millennium Ecosystems Assessment (2005) states that "humans have changed ecosystems more rapidly and extensively over the past 50 years than in any comparable period of time in human history" (p. 1). It points out that while these changes led to economic gains, they also resulted in degradation to fresh water, land and air, and biodiversity. The negative impacts can have measurable effects on human wellbeing. The Intergovernmental Science-Policy Platform on Biodiversity and Ecosystem Services (IPBES, 2018) estimates that 3.2 billion people worldwide are negatively affected by environmental degradation. In addition, past research on the effects of air pollution on human health has found significant negative relationships with well-being, life-satisfaction, and overall quality of life. Luechinger (2009) found that living downwind from a power plant (SO2) can have a negative effect on life satisfaction. Similarly, Orru and colleagues (2016) showed that both PM 10 and SO2 concentrations were negatively related to life satisfaction.

Data for the analysis are drawn from a survey questionnaire (n=4077) and face-to-face interviews (n=315) in the Detroit metropolitan area consisting of seven counties including the City of Detroit. To determine how much of a problem environment degradation causes in nearby living environments, participants were asked to indicate how much of a problem each of the following environmental issues is in their county: 1) loss of natural areas, 2) loss of natural places for fish and wildlife to live, 3) discharge of waste into lakes, rivers, and streams, and 4) air pollution.

Environmental degradation, as reported by respondents in metro Detroit, effects neighborhood satisfaction and quality of life. Hierarchical regression analyses revealed that four-question environmental degradation index negatively affects quality of life and neighborhood satisfaction after controlling other individual characteristics. Specifically, habitat loss and air pollution significantly affected respondents' quality of life while air-pollution significantly affected neighborhood satisfaction. Identifying the relationships between subjective measures of environmental degradation and quality of life helps to reveal the perceptions people have about their living environments, and how they are affected by them. Future studies should continue to refine these factors and explore other potential negative influences in an effort to improve the human condition. Emphasis should be given to the impact of environmental degradation on people of lower socioeconomic means who often live in the less desirable parts of a city or region.

References

Millennium Ecosystem Assessment. (2005). *Ecosystems and human well-being: Synthesis.* Island Press, Washington, DC.

Armourdale Master Plan: Comprehensive Master Plan for the Armourdale Neighborhood in Kansas City, Kansas

Andrew Moddrell *(University of Kansas)*

Armourdale Context: Following the United States Civil War, Kansas City became a national railroad and livestock distribution hub located primarily in the wide and flat floodplain at the confluence of the Kansas and Missouri Rivers. In 1879, Armourdale was platted on approximately 2000-acres of Kansas River floodplain land adjacent to downtown Kansas City, MO to become a new company town for workers in the nearby stockyards and meat packing plants. Although Armourdale grew to almost 18,000 residents by 1900, escalating Kansas River flooding events in the early 1900's devastated the area, leading many residents to seek higher ground, while those that stayed behind endured regular flooding, declining living conditions, neglected infrastructure and minimal municipal services.

A substantial population of Mexican immigrants moved to the neighborhood in beginning in the 1910's, leading to the segregation of the neighborhood, followed by enforcement of redlining and discriminatory lending practices. In 1951, the most extreme flood event in Kansas City's history devastated Armourdale. Following the flood, significant levee and flood control projects were implemented primarily to protect Armourdale's high-value railroad and industrial businesses. While these same flood control measures have protected Armourdale's neighborhood core for the last 70 years, it has endured decades of neglect and disinvestment. Today, Armourdale consists of a 350-acre residential neighborhood core comprised of cottages and bungalows surrounded by 1500-acres of industry, warehouses and rail yards. Its current population of 2,500 residents is 70% Hispanic, 38% of whom are foreign-born. Public health indicators show Armourdale residents suffer worse health outcomes by almost every measure than both Kansas and the United States as a whole.

2021 Armourdale Master Plan: In 2020, the Unified Government of Wyandotte County and Kansas City, Kansas commissioned the presenter's planning practice and consultant team to develop the first master plan for Armourdale since 1979. In order to identify community priorities and goals for the master plan, the planning team conducted an extensive community engagement effort that included: recruiting, hiring and training neighborhood residents to engage their friends and neighbors in the planning process; initiating regular meetings with community-based organizations, local experts and a stakeholder steering committee; and hosting several community events, workshops and focus groups.

The 10-month planning process culminated in a master plan document focused on actionable strategies to strengthen Armourdale's neighborhood core and improve the quality of life for its residents. These strategies range from infrastructure improvements, municipal service upgrades, affordable housing, rent assistance, and job training, to expanding community-focused development and locally owned business initiatives. The plan also calls for mitigating the environmental impact of industrial uses on the neighborhood core, expanding recreational access to the Kansas River, and strategies to improve the river's ecological health by restoring native ecologies in the existing floodplain.

This project presentation will share an overview of the planning team's historical research and existing conditions analysis; community engagement methods and outcomes; and the recently adopted final master plan for Armourdale.

Seeing Green, Doing Green: A Mixed-Methods Study of Eco-Behaviors and Occupant Perception of Building Sustainability

Erin M Hamilton *(Texas Tech University);* ***Anne Herndon*** *(Lake|Flato);* ***Ashley Grzywa*** *(Lake|Flato);* ***Heather Holdridge*** *(Lake | Flato)*

The challenge of global climate change necessitates interdisciplinary problem solving. In the built environment sector, the pursuit of sustainability requires not only constructing and maintaining a green building, but considering how best to support the green behaviors of occupants within these buildings. On the university campus, green buildings serve as places of environmental education, and in turn, occupant awareness of green building features supports environmentally responsible behaviors (ERBs). While previous literature has examined strategies for explicit green building communication through signage, behavioral prompts, and feedback (Wu et al., 2017), recent work has also suggested that the overall perception of a building as "green" through the use of biophilic elements (e.g., views to nature, natural materials, and nature motifs) also supports ERBs. Drawing from the literature, this project suggests biophilic environments provide behavioral support via two pathways: 1) through occupant interpretation of biophilic elements as "green" building features, and 2) through the creation of restorative environments, which are supportive of ERBs (e.g., Hartig, Kaiser, & Bowler, 2001).

This project explores how occupants interpret the sustainability of two LEED certified university buildings in the Northeast United States. Both buildings house a variety of assigned faculty and staff spaces, classrooms, and multiple spaces for unscheduled student use (e.g., studying and socializing). Green building communication is limited in both buildings, mostly confined to the display screens in lobbies. The chief observable difference between the two buildings is that the LEED Platinum building was designed with biophilic intent, and the LEED Gold building was not. In short, the LEED Platinum building looks like a sustainable building, whereas the sustainability of the LEED Gold building could easily be missed.

This mixed-methods study involves an online survey of building occupants (faculty, staff, and students) in both buildings conducted in November 2021. Variables of interest include participants' self-reported building related ERBs (e.g., recycling, taking the stairs), assessment of social norms, values, environmental concern, green building awareness, and perceived environmental restorativeness. Photograph-based methods involving a heat map analysis will be used to determine the environmental features that occupants identify as sustainable and/or restorative. Follow-up interviews will be completed with select survey participants in January 2022.

The anticipated outcomes of this work contribute theoretically to our understanding of how to support and promote ERBs within green buildings. As environment and behavior scholars, we have long acknowledged the human benefits of contact with nature. The integration of nature and natural analogues into the built environment through biophilic design promotes both physical and psychological well-being. This project aims to further the conversation around biophilic design in promoting both personal and planetary well-being.

References

Hartig, T., Kaiser, F. G., & Bowler, P. A. (2001). Psychological restoration in nature as a positive motivation for ecological behavior. *Environment and Behavior, 33*(4), 590–607.

Wu, S. R., Kim, S.-K., Park, H., Fan, P., Ligmann-Zielinska, A., & Chen, J. (2017). How do green buildings communicate green design to building users? A survey study of a LEED-certified building. *Journal of Green Building, 12*(3).

This track focuses on how we design environments that recognize the needs of a diverse population shaped by people's unique perspectives, life experiences, socio-demographics, cultural influences, identities, geography, preferences, and more. What impacts do our buildings, communities and natural environments have on vulnerable populations including children, ethnic minorities, young adults, the elderly, people with mental health disorders, and people with physical disabilities during the pandemic? How will the lessons learned during the pandemic shape the design of future environments to better support all people?

Typologies of Spread

Douglas Pardue *(University of Georgia),* ***Jon Calabria*** *(University of Georgia);* ***Sungkyung Lee*** *(University of Georgia);* ***Alison Smith*** *(University of Georgia)*

Designers construct and use models to understand, describe, and test essential characteristics of landscapes and systems (Leitao and Ahern, 2002, Verboom and Wamelink, 1999). Through this process, models invite exploration and understanding of diverse perspectives, measurement and manipulation in creative and critical ways (Corner, 1999; Cooper, 2019), and increased cognitive empathy through active consideration of other perspectives (Davis, 1983; de Waal, Preston, 2017). Categorical types, used to examine and curate diverse concepts such as landscape and public, (Meinig, 1979, Iveson, 1998), can be communicated through beautiful evidence to foster clarity, reflection, and comparison of perspectives in design (Tufte, 2006; Mostafavi, 2016).

Typologies of Spread is a conceptual model that describes the essential landscape conditions, relationships, and changes provoked by the arrival of the Joro spider, Trichonephila clavate, a controversial orb weaver that hitched a ride in a shipping container from Asia to the southeast US in 2014 (Hoebeke, Huffmaster, Freeman, 2015) and has been spreading exponentially ever since. The wide range of opinions toward the Joro, from embrace to execution, parallels design's own discourse of evolution and expansionism, and allows probing and provoking of perspectives related to types and rates of change (Nash, 1989; Weilacher, 1999).

Within this context, the model takes on three goals: 1) measure and describe landscape conditions, changes, and relationships related to Joro; 2) foster cognitive empathy through reflection and sharing of deviating attitudes toward Joro; and 3) invite informed, imaginative discussion of potential changes to landscape design and practices. Methods used to address these include change maps to identify patterns and rate, typological cross sections to describe and compare conditions and change, and a question framework to relate perspectives. Resulting Typologies of Spread will be presented, with findings and lessons for modeling, cognitive empathy, and landscape metrics.

Understanding and Engaging Diverse User Groups in Higher Education Occupancy Evaluation

Oshana Reich *(HGA);* ***Renae Rich*** *(HGA)*

Higher education facility design is complex and involves many, and sometimes competing, voices of opinion and influence. The physical learning environment must enhance evolving pedagogies; support learning, administrative, and social functions; and serve institutional strategies. Higher education institutions strive to meet diverse student demands and accommodate ever-transforming technology to promote student success and ensure institutional relevance. Most recently, pandemic effects are of pressing interest in technology-rich learning environments, and accommodating new pedagogical challenges, such as hybrid learning, remains largely unsolved (Clay & Johnson, 2021). Especially now, physical campus relevance and function is under examination. Students, faculty, administrators, campus or community members, and facilities personnel each engage and invest in buildings differently, offering unique and important perspectives. To develop a holistic approach for the evaluation of facility planning, all user needs must be considered.

A national architecture and engineering firm's research team engaged in an exploratory study to guide the development of a systematic and standardized tool for evaluation and comparison across higher education facility projects. This research sought to identify different user groups of higher education facilities, develop relevant and consistent constructs across campus facility types, and appropriate methods for reaching various user groups. A mixed-method approach was developed that entailed a literature review, interviews with nine project teams, and thematic synthesis. This presentation will focus on the findings from the study that helped frame the constructs of a holistic evaluation and tool development.

The literature review identified theoretical frameworks that define learning environment components, their physical dimensions, and related learning outcomes (Baars et al., 2021; Radcliffe, 2008). Methodological precedents in higher education building evaluation included processes for engaging occupants, measures for evaluation, and definitions of building success. Interviews with higher education project teams were used to classify common goals and areas of interest among within the sector. Seven common themes were identified, including student experience and success, accommodation for pedagogies, and integration with the campus and community. With the literature review insights, these themes were further developed into specific constructs for targeted user groups with tailored evaluation tools to inform a general evaluation framework to be integrated into higher education project timelines.

Examples of higher education design strategies that have been associated with occupant outcomes through previous research will be discussed. Study results, along with the evaluation process and tools will be presented. Lessons learned for future research across the industry, current gaps in knowledge, and recommendations for relevant journals and resources will also be shared.

References

Clay, M., & Johnson, M. (2021). Flexing Beyond the Pandemic. P*lanning for Higher Education, 49*(3),17-28.

Baars, S., Schellings, G. L. M., Krishnamurthy, S., Joore, J. P., den Brok, P. J., & van Wesemael, P. J. V. (2021). A framework for exploration of relationship between the psychosocial and physical learning environment. *Learning Environments Research,24*,43-69.

Radcliffe, D. (2008). *A Pedagogy-Space-Technology (PST) framework for designing and evaluating learning spaces.* In D. Radcliffe, H. Wilson, D. Powell, & B. Tibbetts (Eds.), Learning spaces in higher education: Positive outcomes by design (pp. 9–16). The University of Queensland.

Research on the Design Strategies of Agritourism Park Based on Beijing Tourists' Comments

Qingchen Zhu *(Beijing Jiaotong University)*

The tense working atmosphere in first-tier cities and the long-term work make urban residents in a sub-healthy state both mentally and physically. Therefore, many urban residents choose to go to agritourism parks to relax and entertain. Agritourism parks serve tourism with the help of agricultural, natural and cultural resources, and carry out innovative planning and design with the help of science and technology, related auxiliary facilities, etc., then forming a collection of scientific and technological demonstration, tourism, popular science education, leisure and entertainment and other functions. Since the development of China Agritourism park in 1970s, the designers of the agritourism park paid more attention to the theoretical design of the agritourism park, ignoring the needs of tourists, resulting in some tourist parks being poorly managed and on the verge of bankruptcy. So design strategy of agritourism park should be improved to make the designer's design more practical.

Before studying the needs of tourists, collects 82 design cases of agritourism parks from CNKI(China National Knowledge Infrastructure), mass media, and so on, and integrates the case analysis to obtain a preliminary design strategy. After that, in order to study the needs of tourists, this paper selects Beijing, which has the most diversified development of agritourism parks in China, as a sample, and uses PYTHON (a computer Languages used to crawl data from tourism websites) to collect data on the website Dianping. The tourist data of 70 tourist parks with more than 200 comments were collected, they totally have 29,104 comments and 3,025,985 words. After collecting the data and clean the irrelevant comments, we use ROST (a software that divides sentences into words and counts word frequencies) to segment sentences and count word frequencies, then we classify and integrate the data according to word frequencies and meanings. So we got the demands of tourists: The main group of people in the agritourism parks are mainly families with children, followed by elders and friends; tourists focus on characteristic agricultural products, agricultural experience activities in the park, as well as the environment and architectural style of the park. According to the demands of tourists, the preliminary design strategy of the agritourism parks is deepened and perfected into a design strategy with practical significance.

This paper answers the following questions: (1) the types of agritourism parks in design; (2) the portrait of tourists' demands for agritourism parks ; (3) the construction process of agritourism parks in China; (4) the agritourism parks design strategy based on tourists' demands.

Developing Post-Occupancy Evaluation Method Using Social Media to Reveal Usage Pattern of High-Speed Railway Stations

Yi He *(Beijing Jiaotong University);* ***Chunfang Li*** *(Office@Csadi.Cn);* ***Li Wang*** *(Central-South Architectural Design Institute co;Ltd);* ***Yi Yang*** *(Beijing Jiaotong University);* ***Bo Zhang*** *(Oklahoma State University)*

After nearly 20 years of development, China's railway technology has reached a relatively mature stage. As of December 2020, the railway operating mileage in China has reached 146,300 kilometers, of which high-speed rail has reached 38,000 kilometers, ranking first in the world. There are currently more than 5,000 railway stations in China, including more than 500 high-speed railway stations. According to the statistics of the National Railway Group, the volume of railroad passengers sent in China reached 357.86 million. China now has a mature and advanced railway system. Yet the usage of these high-speed railway stations has not been attracted much scholarly attention, as not many empirical studies on this topic is available, partly because the difficulty of long-term on-site observation and survey. Hence, this study develop an post-occupancy evaluation method using social media to reveal the usage pattern of high-speed railway stations in China.

Hangzhoudong Railway Station was a case selected to study the user experience of the large-scale high-speed railway station in China. The massive data sources, in terms of the large data volume, multiple types, rich content, authenticity and other characteristics of big data suffice the content under study. Using Python technology to mine data from Dianping, sina, Ctrip, Mafengwo platforms from January 1st 2019 to December 31st 2019 for analysis. Several analysis were conducted, such as word frequency analysis, monthly trend analysis, and Gephi network analysis to reveal the passenger behaviors, space functionality, experiences, and the causal relationships between the designed elements and their environmental impacts.

The results show that Hangzhoudong Railway Station gave rise to positive passenger experience.

Various behaviors were codified from the data indicated the order and efficiency of the building complex. The pair analysis also helped to suggests the issues with flow, management, sign design, and other issues.

Taking Hangzhoudong Railway Station as the research object, this an post occupancy evaluation method using social media.. Different from traditional data collection methods, it broke through limitations of quantity, type, time, and regional scope. This method puts forward thoughts on the future TOD prospects and improvement strategies of large-scale railway comprehensive transportation hubs in China and other regions. The results provide a new way for designers to study the current usage of public transportation complex from the available social media data.

The Chipping of Chocolate Cities: Designing "Intentional Spaces" to Build Community

Jacqueline Carmichael *(Howard University)*

Many urban African American "Chocolate Cities" have undergone prolonged disinvestment and increasing cost-of-living expenses. Consequently, lower-income residents' supply and access to affordable housing have decreased significantly. As a result, many of these municipalities switch to private developers to increase their affordable housing stock through inclusionary zoning (IZ) measures by converting government-funded public housing supportive through market rate mixed-income developments. But how does mixed-income housing build a diverse community while addressing the notion of rich and poor residing in harmony without deploring one another? It will take careful interior design spatial analysis and implementation to create "intentional spaces"- mindful of individual differences, shared experiences, societal power dynamics, and privilege to encourage a more inclusive sense of community.

This visual essay, through photo-elicitation, uses photographs, photographic case studies, and other visual mediums to generate verbal discussion to develop data and knowledge by interviewing and observing methodologies to assess residents of mixed-income public housing conversions. In addition, we seek to compare and analyze any layers of meaning that evoke memories, behaviors, and ideas through photo-elicitation. Finally, organize the data from the interviews to validate the rigor of the findings through participant verification and interpretative analysis to create themes for a case study write-up.

We review project outcomes concerning interior design concepts impacting government-funded lowcost housing conversions into fair and equitable mixedincome housing. Observe how the design community addresses indigenous black communities' historical and cultural vibrancy with former, current, and incoming residents. And address how diverse communities move toward alliances while respecting, preventing housing displacement, and allowing the indigenous black residents to remain and thrive in their established community. In addition, examine black creative agency and best practices to avoid cultural erasers (Summer 2020). Evaluating a person's lived-experienced day-to-day engagement facilitates inclusion, wellness, and belonging while preventing othering and micro-segregation (Blackburn, Traynor, Avent 2018). And assessing the use of cultural aesthetics in shared community areas to respect the native African American communities and their culture, promote social equity, and build consensus encourages open engagement across race and class (Summer 2019).

The results indicate that the topic of "Intentional Spaces" is absent in design literature that analyzes the efforts to support cultural histories and displacement prevention of Black communities. Therefore, this paper seeks to create a design tool for future IZ housing models to create "intentional spaces" to bring diverse groups together to discuss and work out differences to reject hierarchy. And further generate a tool for the ease of access, the maintenance of generational wealthbuilding, and social justice for the most vulnerable groups as models for the future.

References

Blackburn, F., Traynor, B., and Avent, Y., (2018).

"Practical Ideas for Addressing Micro-Segregation in Mixed-Income Communities."

Summers, B. (2019). *Black in Place: The Spatial Aesthetics of Race in a Post-Chocolate City.* Chapel Hill: University of North Carolina Press.

Summers, B. (2020). "Authenticity a "Post-Chocolate" Cool in a Rapidly Gentrifying Washington, DC How the marketing of Blackness as a prized aesthetic often leaves the city's Black residents behind." NextCity.org.

Triple Aim Impact Consulting. https://case.edu/socialwork/nimc/services/triple-aim-impact-consulting (ND).

Effects of the Physical Environment on Children and Families in the Emergency Department: A Systematic Literature Review

Monica Gripko *(Clemson University);* ***Anjali Joseph*** *(Clemson University);* ***Soheyla MohammadiGorji*** *(Clemson University)*

Every year, millions of children seek care in emergency departments. In 2018, almost 20% of children under the age of 18 in the United States (approximately 14.5 million) visited an emergency department (ED) at least once in the previous 12 months (National Center for Health, 2019). In the ED setting, patients may receive care for various circumstances: life-threatening emergencies, complications from chronic conditions, acute illness and injury, and mental health disorders. However, the ED also serves as an alternative to primary care for many children and families, especially those in low-income or minority populations (Moore et al., 2017).

The physical environment of the ED provides the context and setting for care delivery, influences workflows, and shapes interactions between clinicians, staff, patients, and families. The ED environment can be counter-therapeutic to patients and families due to the often noisy and highly stimulating nature. Sterile furniture, wires, and life-saving equipment may also intimidate or disorient children, especially those with mental and behavioral health conditions. Furthermore, while some pediatric patients seek care in specialized pediatric emergency departments, most children receive care in general EDs not explicitly designed for children, which may increase anxiety and negative perceptions and decrease satisfaction with the environment and care.

Because of the prevalence and importance of emergency department care for pediatric patients, researchers and designers must understand the complex relationships between the physical environment and patient outcomes. The purpose of this study is to examine the state of existing research regarding the effects of the physical environment on children and their families seeking care in hospital-based emergency departments. Following methods for systematic literature review, outlined by Preferred Reporting Items for Systematic Reviews and Meta-Analyses (PRISMA), we will identify articles using PubMed, Web of Science, CINAHL, PsychInfo, and a hand search. The central research question driving this systematic literature review is "How does the built environment of emergency departments affect children and their families?" We broke down the research question using a PEO framework to develop keyword "buckets" for constructing database searches: relating to the Populations (e.g., children/adolescents, parents), Exposures (e.g., terms for the ED and its built environment/design), and Outcomes (e.g., terms relating to behaviors, perceptions, and mental states) of interest. Only original research papers published in peer-reviewed journals between 1996 and 2021 focusing on physical environment effects on children and families in hospital-based ED settings will qualify for a full review.

Through this process, we anticipate gaining a better, more comprehensive understanding of the current state of knowledge concerning relationships between pediatric patients, families, and the physical environment of emergency departments to identify gaps in existing knowledge and assess avenues for future research.

References

Moore, B. J., Stocks, C., & Owens, P. L. (2017). Trends in emergency department visits, 2006–2014. *HCUP statistical brief*, 227.

National Center for Health, S. (2019). Table 36:

Emergency department visits within the past 12 months among children under age 18, by selected characteristics: United States, selected years 1997–2018. In *Health United States, 2019*. Hyattsville (MD): National Center for Health Statistics (US).

From Sheltered in Place to Thriving in Place: Investigating Dimensions of Aging in the 'Right' Place during the COVID-19 Pandemic

Valerie Greer *(University of Utah)*

While aging in place involves supporting older adults to live as long as possible in their homes and communities (Center for Disease Control, 2009), aging in the "right" place recognizes that where an older person lives impacts their ability to age optimally and must match their unique lifestyles and vulnerabilities (Golant, 2015). COVID-19 has created a unique set of challenges related to aging and place, including increased home confinement, limited social interaction, and a growing reliance on digital technologies. With the global population aging at an unprecedented rate, it is critical to understand how the pandemic has transformed attitudes and perceptions of what constitutes aging in the "right" place from the lived experiences of older adults. There is additionally a need to better understand how different place types—e.g., places where people live, work, worship, recreate, etc.—can be adapted to support perceptions associated with the "rightness" of place.

This presentation focuses on a research study which utilizes photovoice methods to collect data on what aging in the "right" place has meant to older adults in the context of the pandemic. Data was collected through photos and stories from community dwelling older adults who were asked to identify environmental factors that support "rightness" of place. Distinct from pre-pandemic discourse on aging in place, which has evolved from traditional domains of place such as housing, safety, social support and technology into emergent issues such as community advocacy, immigration and moving issues (Weil, 2019), data collected during the pandemic points to a need to focus on components in the built environment that enable older adults to thrive, such as opportunities to pursue goals and hobbies, and to stay socially connected. Findings that were generated through a thematic analysis of the data suggest that through transformative experiences of the pandemic, older adults may assign new values to elements in the built environment that support interests, passions, activities and goals.

The research prioritizes the voice, views, and lived experience of older adults, encompassing diverse narratives to yield insight on myriad dimensions that reexamine the question of what it means to be aging in the "right" place. Given that place is known to be an important factor in health outcomes, it is crucial to reconcile how the pandemic has radically transformed experiences and perceptions of place. Understanding narratives of what aging in the "right place" has meant to older adults during the pandemic has the potential to inform future research, policy, and design practices that support the health and resilience of older adults and communities.

References

Centers for Disease Control. (October, 2009). *Healthy Places Terminology*, Centers for Disease Control and Prevention.

Golant, S.M. (2015) *Aging in the Right Place*. Baltimore, MD: Health Professions Press, Inc.

Weil, J. (2019) Developing the Person-Place Fit Measure for Older Adults: Broadening Place Domains. *The Gerontologist*, Volume 60, Issue 8, December 2020, Pages e548–e558.

Evidence-Based Design in a Geriatric Ward

Minou Afzali *(Bern University of the Arts);* ***Jimmy Schmid*** *(Bern University of the Arts);* ***Jean Odermatt*** *(Bern University of the Arts);* ***Ramona Tschuppert*** *(Bern University of the Arts);* ***Rahel Inauen*** *(Bern University of the Arts);* ***Alexa Blum*** *(Design Alexa Blum GmbH)*

Background: The pandemic brought problems to the fore, that were part of our lives long before the global outbreak of COVID-19. Such being the case in the present project, which started in

2019. The research team was commissioned in September 2019 to optimize the interior design of a newly occupied geriatric university clinic in the German-speaking part of Switzerland. Many aspects of the award-winning building, which had been operational for five months, were criticized by patients, their relatives as well as employees. Patients, many of whom suffering from dementia, had difficulties, orienting themselves within the building. Relatives and staff found the modern building not very homely. The building, hailed as an architectural marvel by design specialists, was deemed rather useless by its occupants.

Methods: In a first step, the research team - consisting of signage and interior design experts - carried out room inspections on site and documented them. In a second step, the spaces were analyzed using literature from the field of evidence-based design. In a workshop, 14 employees from different areas of the clinic, identified particularly problematic hotspots with regard to their design. It became clear, that the existing signage needed to be optimized and that the employees wanted a warmer atmosphere in the building for themselves and for their patients. This also became evident in focus group interviews with representatives of the geriatric psychiatry and the admission ward. Based on these results, the research team developed recommendations on how to improve the interior design. These included a new design concept where signage, images and colors serve to improve orientation and increase well-being. Before these concepts were implemented, the first lockdown took place in March 2020, which rendered the clinic inaccessible to external people, which included the research team.

The lockdown posed a great challenge and burden for the clinic staff. The number of patients infected with COVID-19 increased, and entire wards had to be isolated to prevent transmission of the virus to other patients. During these challenging times, it became all the more clear where the weak points of the interior design lay. Patients got lost in wards that were not supposed to be accessible to them and lacked clear directions. In addition, the isolation from the outside world increased the desire for a homely interior design that promoted the well-being of patients and staff.

Outlook: After the lockdown was lifted, the research team was able to resume its work. In this second phase of the project, the design researchers are working with a practice partner who is responsible for developing the color concept. With a strongly participatory approach, the team has since been working on the development of concepts for signage and images as well as on a color concept. In close exchange with the users, the concepts are tested and optimized in an iterative process. The implementation of the interior design is planned for spring 2022. The evaluation will take place a few months after the implementation through focus group interviews.

Pediatric Intensive Care Unit (PICU) Patient Room Design: Identifying Safety Risks in Mirrored Rooms through a Graphical Systems Analysis

Nora Colman *(Children's Healthcare of Atlanta);* ***Sahar Mihandoust*** *(Clemson University);* ***Anjali Joseph*** *(Clemson University);* ***Kiran Hebbar*** *(Children's Healthcare of Atlanta)*

Objective: The objectives of this study are to graphically depict specific clinical challenges encountered in a mirrored pediatric intensive care unit patient room and to represent potential solutions to address these challenges using a systems approach.

Background: The intensive care unit (ICU) is a complex environment, where the design of the patient room must support patient care delivery safely and efficiently. ICU patient room design is difficult to study, and there is a lack of research examining how ICU design elements impact patient care. The design of same-handed inpatient room configurations versus mirrored rooms is a controversial topic in healthcare design. It remains unclear as to which configuration affords safer care. Clinicians are unlikely to be able to make an informed design decision regarding room configuration options based on two-dimension renderings.

Methods: In the design of a new children's hospital,

ICU rooms were configured in the mirrored orientation with in-board bathrooms. High fidelity simulations were conducted to elucidate clinicians' perspective and identify safety. An observational case study method utilizing a systems approach was used to observe and graphically depict clinical challenges with mirrored room configurations and to identify potential solutions. Video recordings of the three clinical scenarios were analyzed in detail in conjunction with three rounds of interviews with a clinical expert.

Results: A graphical depiction of the simulated patient room plan was created based on simulation videos and expect interviews. Latent conditions related to room configuration included impact on provider workflow, positioning of respiratory equipment, challenges to surgical approach during emergent bedside surgery, positioning of emergency equipment, and impact of lack of standardization on team cognitive load. Key challenges, safety risks and potential solutions to address challenges in the mirrored room configuration were represented graphically.

Conclusion: A range of built environment, equipment, training, tasks, and organizational adaptations have to be considered to facilitate safe and effective care in a mirrored room configuration. If these problems and their possible solutions are not identified during the design process, teams will have to address them during transition planning before the building is occupied. Solutions to the challenges presented in mirrored room configurations are multifaceted and require simultaneous and ongoing changes to multiple systems elements, while others must addressed through process improvement, operational adaptions, technology, or staff education.

A Framework for Co-Designing with Cognitively Impairment Individuals

Jennifer DuBose *(Georgia Institute of Technology);* ***Leila Aflatoony*** *(Georgia Institute of Technology)*

The best home environments are those that fit the needs, expectations and ability of the occupants. One successful strategy for accomplishing this is to include the intended users in the design process so that they can bring their deep knowledge and expertise developed out of their lived experience to find solutions that fit their unique situations. Participatory design (also called co-design) is a collaborative process that engages end-users as active participants in design decision-making processes (Sanders & Stappers, 2008). However, many well-established participatory design toolkits are not appropriate for engaging people with cognitive impairment in design activities as they require certain levels of abstraction, conceptualization, or creative thinking (Lindsay et al., 2012). Yet, people with cognitive impairments have a great need for creative design solutions that can help them create home environments that enable them to remain independent in the community for longer.

Engaging people with cognitive impairment in cognitively demanding activities is challenging due to their limitations in expressing their opinions, expectations, and skills. People with cognitive impairments may have difficulties with verbal comprehension, word-finding, working memory, auditory/speech comprehension, and social and practical skills. In the context of research, traditional user involvement methods (e.g., interviews) require adequate cognitive-verbal communication abilities, posing challenges to people with cognitive impairments. There is an ongoing need for researchers to develop, adapt, and tailor participatory methods that support the inclusive and active engagement of people with cognitive impairment to facilitate their meaningful participation in/contribution to design activities (Hendriks et al., 2015).

In this presentation, we provide an overview of four participatory workshops conducted with people with Mild Cognitive Impairment (MCI) in the context of the built environment over two years. For each workshop, we developed a set of toolkits to explore and support the cognitive-verbal communication abilities of individuals with MCI. The primary aim of this project is to facilitate the engagement of people with MCI in design research activities by introducing a set of novel participatory/co-design toolkits tailored for co-developing interventions in the home environment. The outcomes of this study underline the active, meaningful, and long-term engagement of people with MCI in built environment research through inclusive and participatory activities. Also, the built environment researchers collected firsthand/insightful information from people with MCI on aspects of the built environment. Based on these workshops and literature review findings, we provided a design guideline for developing co-design toolkits to engage people with MCI in home-specific research activities. We anticipate implementing participatory activities and associated toolkits to enhance collaborative efforts among individuals living with MCI and design researchers.

References

Hendriks, N., Slegers, k., and Duysburgh, P. (2015). Codesign with People Living with Cognitive or Sensory Impairments: A Case for Method Stories and Uniqueness. *CoDesign, 11* (1), 70–82.

Lindsay, S., Brittain, D. Jackson, C. Ladha, K. Ladha, and P. Olivier. (2012). Empathy, Participatory Design and People with Dementia. *Proceedings of the SIGCHI Conference on Human Factors in Computing Systems: ACM*, 521–530.

Sanders, Elizabeth B.-N., and Pieter Jan Stappers. (2008). "Co-creation and the New Landscapes of Design." *Co-design 4*(1): 5–18.

The Impact of Design Decisions in a Cancer Infusion Center: Comparing Results from a Pre and Post-Occupancy Evaluation

Mahshid Jalalian *(HGA Architects & Engineers);* ***Kara N Freihoefer*** *(HGA Architects & Engineers)*

Cancer infusion centers are among the least studied healthcare environments with limited studies that have performed an in-depth investigation on this treatment area. The purpose of this study is to evaluate workflow of staff, and staff and patient satisfaction in a new cancer infusion center and compare that to the results from a pre-occupancy evaluation that was conducted in 2018. The new cancer infusion center opened in 2020 and replaced two previously existing infusion centers on a medical campus in northern Kentucky.

One of the previous infusion centers had a traditional open bay design with infusion chairs and the other center included semi-private bays. The pre-occupancy study was conducted on these two infusion centers and established a baseline dataset to compare to the new infusion center. The pre-occupancy study collected 34 hours of nurse shadowing data from both infusion centers along with data from staff and patient questionnaires on their satisfaction with different aspects of the infusion centers.

The current study is applying the same methodology including staff shadowing along with staff and patient questionnaire and is intended to gather post-occupancy evaluation (also known as POE) data through a mixed-method approach in the new infusion center. More specifically, the current research will be centered around five areas including staff workflow and room visits, staff and patient satisfaction with design, patient privacy, staff communication and collaboration, and delivery of medication. Data collected around these metrics will then be compared to the results from the pre-occupancy evaluation to understand how design decisions in the new center have influenced the efficiency of staff workflow and staff and patient experience.

The pre-occupancy study revealed patient and staff had higher satisfaction with patient privacy in the semi-private bay design. It is expected that the POE study shows an increased satisfaction with privacy, considering the design decision to increase patient privacy through dividing the infusion center into five pods and locating semi-private bays in each pod. The new bays are also larger compared to the older bays, which is expected to increase patient satisfaction with room size and staff satisfaction with amount of space to perform task in the patient bays. The new infusion center also includes an embedded pharmacy in the center of the five pods, which is anticipated to increase satisfaction with medication delivery and reduce travel time and distance to retrieve medication.

Considering that this research involves human subjects, the study was submitted for review by an Institutional review Board (IRB) and was determined exempt from review with no or minimal risk to the subjects. The POE data collection was scheduled to take place in Fall 2021, however had to be delayed due to the COVID-19 pandemic surge in the area. It is expected that the research team can go back to the site and collect data in January 2022. The POE data that will be collected will therefore shed light on how design decisions in the new cancer infusion center have impacted care delivery and perceptions.

Outdoor Learning Environment Activity Settings: Identifying the Most Validated Settings across Theory, Policy and User Preference

Lori Guerrero *(Texas Tech University);* ***Sharran Parkinson*** *(Texas Tech University);* ***Kristi Gaines*** *(Texas Tech University)*

Childhood well-being may be at risk due to societal trends separating children from nature. Outdoor learning environments (OLE) are intentionally designed natural playscapes to increase exposure to nature and promote well-being. There are many intervention programs with individual sets of guidelines supported by varying levels of empirical evidence. As of yet, there has not been a literature review to constitute a singular set of guidelines reflecting the whole body of knowledge.

A meta-analysis of literature aims to understand the most validated behavior settings. This review synthesizes the interdisciplinary literature guided by a conceptual framework which specifies three types of literature to compare: 1) theory, 2) policy and 3) user preference. Comparing these three types of literature is important, because it gives a broader perspective of the total influences of OLE design, build and implementation. For this analysis, theory is defined as validated theoretical frameworks and empirical research; policy is defined as regulations developed by government agencies or intervention programs; and user preference is defined as the preferences of parents, children and teachers concerning OLE. The literature review searched eight databases, used twenty-one keywords and analyzed seventy-six articles.

The results reveal the top nine OLE activity settings validated by the conceptual framework: 1) water, 2) loose parts, 3) looping pathway, 4) structures for gross motor skills, 5) vegetable and fruit garden, 6) nature art, 7) plants, 8) refuge/restoration and 9) sand. This list of recommended behavior settings offers OLE designers, educators and administrators an evidence-based list that reflects the entire body of knowledge provided by theory, policy and user preference. It aims to provide a holistic set of guidelines to child-care centers and early childhood development centers, if they are unsure of which intervention program to follow.

A Mixed-Method Approach to Understanding User Experiences in the Built Environment: Case Study of an Art Center

Mahshid Jalalian *(HGA Architects & Engineers);* ***Adaheid Mestad*** *(HGA Architects & Engineers);* ***Jonathan Bartling*** *(HGA Architects & Engineers);* ***David Goldstein*** *(Walker Art Center)*

Providing a welcoming and intuitive experience for visitors is imperative to the success of buildings. This is especially important in the case of museum buildings and a key element in fulfilling the goal of actively engaging audiences. The purpose of this study is to use mixed methods to evaluate visitors experience in the case of an art center in Minneapolis, Minnesota. This study specifically aims to understand key touch points in a first-time visitor's experience that support or hinder a sense of welcome, inclusion, and confidence in wayfinding and orientation during their visit to the museum. This study specifically wants to understand the motivations and triggers for visitor behaviors and perceptions. Another goal of this study is to understand how the building configuration plays a role in visitor experiences through the visibility and accessibility patterns that it provides.

The study is seeking to gather data through a mixed-method approach in the building. The mixed-method approach leads to triangulation of findings and helps inform conclusions. The methods in this study include tracking visitors, using an indoor tracking device to capture visitor's travel patterns, time spent in different areas of the art center, galleries visited, etc. Participants in the tracking activity will also be asked to take part in a digital ethnography activity as they navigate through the art center and will be asked to record their voice answering a series of questions. The main purpose of this activity is to understand visitors' feeling of how welcoming and inclusive the museum is. Finally, participants will be asked to fill out an online questionnaire at the end of their visit to the art center, the primary intent of which is to understand visitors' satisfaction with their ability to navigate through the different areas of the art center. Considering that the research will involve human subjects, documentation for the review of the research by an Institutional Review Board (IRB) has been submitted and the data collection will start in mid-November 2021 upon review of the research by the IRB institution.

The results of this research will help the art center make data-driven decisions to update wayfinding and mapping resources to improve visitor experience. It will also inform design attributes that support or hinder visitor experience and a sense of welcome throughout built environment. Finally, through comparing behaviors with the results from analysis of the layout, the study provides insights on the implications of layout for providing or inhibiting wayfinding in museum settings.

Developing a Conceptual Model: Play-Space to Foster Liveware Brain Changes in Trauma-Informed Design (TiD) Approaches

Davis Harte *(Paradigm Spaces, LLC/Boston Architectural College);* ***Janet Roche*** *(Janet Roche Designs, LLC);* ***Alina Osnaga*** *(Lawrence Technological University)*

The trauma-to-health in designed environments' knowledge base is growing. Recently, multiple Trauma-informed Design (TiD) conceptual frameworks, both by academics and practice-based groups (Bassetti, 2021), have been developed. These frameworks suggest means to minimize spatial triggers and increase resiliency, for those with acute or persistent traumas, including chronic stress. We seek to build and grow this scholarship, by proposing a novel iteration: trauma-informed designers first adopt a play-space lens, to elevate neuroscientific trauma-informed understandings, to more robustly apply a TiD approach. Our research aims to understand where TiD and play-spaces share similar characteristics and highlight their presence within architectural features.

Play is the main facilitator for human experimentation and learning needs. Humans leverage discoveries to both adapt brain structures and also mature skills for engagement, flexibility, and health-promotion. However, with traumatized populations, negative experiences cycle emotionally into a 'stuck'-state; whereas we argue play can help dissolve this pattern and reroute the nervous system towards adaptive learning. Clinical studies in which participants who suffered serious adversity were observed, support the premise that play enables strength and flexibility capacities (Brown, 2019), therefore, a TiD approach must also incorporate play, as both conceptually and applied. Play, which helps regulate emotions, may be the missing link in the TiD approaches, as it can help us gather information for design as well as influence and model behaviors. Thoughtfully designed spaces, using TiD that also prioritizes play from the beginning of both the design process and the arrival at the site, may more quickly and effectively move the traumatized nervous system to a state of resilience and wholeness.

We agree with Eagleman (2020) that instead of 'brain plasticity', the process be termed 'livewiring': the ability for our brain to "reconfigure itself, that adjusts and adapts to whatever is going on around it to optimize its function." Realizing the brain can heal, we outline two conceptual tracks: trauma-informed design and play-space, with early findings suggesting a connection with spatial design, with the objective to develop a novel and more robust TiD iteration. It is suggested graduated play opportunities that prompt first the sense of safety, can then lead to states of trust and alert calm, moving towards states of curiosity, awe, and wonder. Brain territories that had been occupied with trauma/stress, once now more engaged in meaningful play, will become overrun with feelings associated with resilience (Eagleman, 2020). Can designers transform the five learning characteristics of play (joyful, meaningful, actively engaged, iterative and socially interactive) into architectural features that will support traumatized individuals? Can we adapt socio-spatial concepts and make them more appealing for traumatized people, based on the neuroscience research on trauma and play?

References

Bassetti Architects/Architects of Achievement (2021). *Trauma informed design checklist: Version 20211007v3.0*. http://www.bassettiarch.com/index.php/tid/.

Brown, S. (2019). *The science of play: How play helps us develop resilience*. Playcore - Building communities through play and recreation, www.playcore.com/news/how-play-helps-us-develop-resilience.

Eagleman, D. (2020). *Livewired: The inside story of the ever-changing brain*. Pantheon Books.

Place Meaning and Social Identity: Mapping Significant Places on University Campuses

Brian Schermer *(University of Wisconsin, Milwaukee);* ***Mahshid Jalalian*** *(HGA Architects & Engineers)*

Universities have been called upon to address demands for equity and inclusion for marginalized and underrepresented student groups. Student protests have made headlines over unfair policies, physical threats and slurs, and the naming of buildings and other places after slave owners, members of the Confederacy, and racists. There are numerous efforts underway on campuses to remedy systemic and implicit racism and bias that are both inherent in university policies and in the built environment. Universities are creating new facilities and revising policies to ensure that students from marginalized and underrepresented groups have access to safe places that allow them to bond, study, relax, and cultivate a sense of belonging. Assessing the inclusiveness and sense of welcoming afforded by physical places on college campuses has been the subject of recent studies (Jessup-Anger et al. in publication; Trawalter et al. 2021, Cheryl et al. 2009). The present study explores the significance that students from different racial, ethnic, gender, sexual orientations, and other identities attribute to physical place on campuses. The findings are based on an online participatory mapping study of over 5,000 students at six universities across the United States. The studies took place over four years, from 2016 to 2019. Students used an online participatory mapping tool to locate places on and near their campuses according to four different categories: social, intellectual, symbolic, and restorative. The survey also asked for demographic information to investigate potential correlations between mapping results and participant social identities. Campuses vary widely in the number of places students identified, from a low of 1.81 places per student at the University of Nevada-Las Vegas to a high of 4.43 places at the University of Wisconsin-Madison. There are minor differences in the number of mapped places between women and men at all the campuses. There are racial and ethnic differences at some campuses. At the University of Illinois at Urbana-Champaign, Black, Asian, and Latinx students identified fewer significant places than their White counterparts. However, at Purdue University and the University of Wisconsin-Madison, there were relatively minor differences in the number of mapped places by students from different races and ethnicities. At Georgia Tech, Asian students lagged behind their peers. There were stark differences between International students and their US peers on most campuses. International students identified far fewer places, and while the places they mapped overlapped to a degree with US students, they also included places not mapped by their US peers. Some student groups appeared to exercise different levels of agency when it comes to attaching significance to campus places. For example, students at Georgia Tech who identify as members of the LGBTQ community identified more than twice as many places per student than the campus as a whole. These disparities among campuses and identity groups suggest that a more nuanced understanding is necessary to explain the differences in mapping results. Additional quantitative and qualitative analysis gathered through these surveys furthers understanding of the connections between place meaning and social identity on campuses.

The Influence of Classroom Design on Children with Autism Spectrum Disorder (ASD)

Anthony Asher *(Clemson University);* ***Dina Battisto*** *(Clemson University);* ***Matthew Siegel*** *(Maine Behavioral Health);* ***Jon Boyd*** *(E4H - Environments for Health);* ***Vincent Blouin*** *(ASHREA)*

In 2020, the Center for Disease Control (CDC) reported approximately 1 in 54 children in the U.S. had been diagnosed with Autism Spectrum Disorders (ASD) (CDC, 2021). ASD affects core human traits and behaviors such as social interactions, the ability to communicate, share feelings, express imagination, and create relationships with others (NRC, 2001). Those with ASD are susceptible to their environment and may exhibit abnormal responses due to sensory processing deficits to noise, light, and textures (Iarocci, 2006). Children with ASD tend to cope with their stressors in a manner that often appears as an "inappropriate tantrum" to those unfamiliar with ASD. These "tantrums" are typically triggered by an "imbalance between the environment and the individual's ability to adapt to it" (Sanchez et al., 2011).

Early intervention through education is vital to the treatment and growth of children with ASD. Problem behaviors in the classroom and educational environment become distractors and barriers to effective social and educational development (NRC, 2001). Creating well-designed classroom environments that consider sensory issues of children with ASD help teachers and caregivers support each student in reaching their goals (Clouse et al., 2020). However, there are no uniformly accepted and recognized guidelines for the built environment of early education and intervention environments for children with ASD.

This presentation reports on findings from a pre- and post-occupancy evaluation using multiple data collection methods to explore how classroom design features contribute to behavioral outcomes for children with ASD. Ten children, ages three to five years older with ASD, were observed over four months as they transitioned from their current classrooms into their newly built classrooms based on evidence-based design for children with ASD. For a two-month period in each setting, environmental conditions were tracked continuously in both classrooms. In addition, interviews were conducted with the special education teachers in both settings to gain insight into the functionality of the classrooms. This collaborative study between the [Center name here] and [University name here's] program clearly shows that classrooms design features (natural lighting, daylighting, noise levels, temperature, and interior furnishings) are all essential factors for creating supportive teaching and learning environments for children with ASD. Findings suggest when there is an incongruity between the demands posed by the classroom design and a child's ability to process environmental stimuli, then problem behaviors increase, whereby disrupting a child's educational growth potential.

Neighborhood Streets and Older Adults' Behavior for Active Living in an Ancient Town

Zhe Wang *(Henan University);* ***Guoxiang Li*** *(Henan University)*

Background: Neighborhood streets in ancient areas aren't suggested for car traffic due to their advanced ages and narrow sizes. These are convenient places for older adults to engage in behavior for active living, such as active travel (e.g., walking or cycling) and social engagement (e.g., chatting with neighbors).

Aims: This research aims at 1) identifying the most popular types of active-living behavior among the older adults on neighborhood streets in an ancient town, and 2) clarifying the difference in social engagement among older adults on the streets with different levels of environmental friendship to active travel.

Methods: Taking Daokou ancient town in China as an example, data on street environments and active-living behavior and were collected through on-site observation. The observation was conducted on two neighborhood streets for four weekdays. Of street environment, the typology, motivation, functionality, and safety were measured in terms of active-living promotion. A total of 350 older adults' active travels and social engagements were recorded. One-way ANOVA tests were applied to identify the differences in social engagement, after controlling for a significant confounding variable.

Results: Among the older adults, independent walking (67%) and 2-wheel or 3-wheel cycling (17% or 18% by street) were the most popular types of active travel. Of their social engagement, staying and chatting (61%), group walking, and chess or card playing were popular. On the street considered more friendly to active travel, older adults had significantly higher levels of social engagement ($p < 0.05$).

Conclusion: Of older adults in Daokou ancient town, walking, cycling, staying and chatting, and chess or card playing are popular behaviors for active living on neighborhood streets. The friendship of street environments to active travel influenced their social engagement. To promote older adults' active living, environmental design and practice on neighborhood street intervention should be refined.

Participatory Design to Develop Neighborhood Spaces That Will Improve Mental Wellbeing for All

Natasha Yeo *(Singapore University of Technology and Design);* ***Keng Hua Chong*** *(Singapore University of Technology and Design)*

Singapore's context of high-density urban living, an aging population and increasingly insular lifestyles due to the COVID-19 pandemic presents a particular pain point and need to introduce neighborhood spaces that are more inclusive especially of vulnerable seniors, and to improve the mental wellbeing of every citizen.

On the dementia front, 1 in 10 people in Singapore above the age of 60 suffers from dementia. For a small city state with 4 million residents, this corresponds to approximately 82,000 people in 2018 and this number is projected to almost double to 152,000 by 2030. There is thus a crucial need to consider the design of neighborhood spaces and facilities to be inclusive of Persons living with Dementia (PLWD). PLWDs are often confined to their own homes due to social stigma and problems with neighborhood way-finding, which limits their contact to the outdoors and nature. Community spaces should be designed to welcome PLWD to keep socially, mentally and physically active in their neighborhoods, whilst ensuring safety in navigation and confidence in their environment.

With regards to mental health, the high-density built environments often manifest different forms of stress, depression and anxiety. Exacerbated with COVID-19, social isolation and constant disruptions have shown to greatly heighten anxiety and sense of helplessness. With our local neighborhood spaces becoming ever more important due to the default mode of working from home, there is an urgent need to re-examine how neighborhood spaces can be designed to cater to the mental health of general residents as well.

This paper presents diverse methodologies to engage PLWDs and community members towards these goals. To understand the spatial preferences of PLWDs and their cognitive perception of neighborhood wayfinding in high-density urban context, our research develops innovative hands-on interactive tools including a jigsaw mood board and shadow walk audit toolkit to collect such data. This is done to cater to the range of conditions of PLWD whose varying cognitive abilities may affect their communication and verbal clarity. With these game-like tools, they are encouraged to communicate their thoughts through non-verbal means and using a sensorial experience to unlock memories.

To ensure seamless assimilation into neighborhoods and adoption by other community members, we are also conducting a large-scale survey in selected neighborhoods to uncover their perceptions of inclusivity of PLWD in their neighborhoods, as well as their needs for spaces that promote mental wellness.

By comparing these data, we will then engage PLWDs to work alongside community members through a participatory design process to ideate design principles that will guide the design of wayfinding strategies and new typology of inclusive neighborhood spaces. The inclusion of PLWDs in the process will require a highly sensitive approach to ensure a safe space to express their thoughts and for community members to gain a deeper understanding of inclusivity. Findings from the data collection and the prototyping process will then contribute to the existing universal design guideline to guide future development of Dementia Friendly Neighborhoods.

Introducing Home Environment Features Associated with Environmental Mastery for People Living with Mild Cognitive Impairment

Herminia Machry *(Georgia Institute of Technology);* ***Fatemeh Motamed Rastegar*** *(Georgia Institute of Technology);* ***Maureen Burke*** *(Emory University);* ***Craig Zimring*** *(Georgia Institute of Technology)*

Background: For people living with mild cognitive impairment (MCI), functional independence and the degree of control over the physical environment contribute to environmental mastery, which influences the capability of these individuals to age at home and avoid or delay moving into assisted living (Burton, et al., 2009). Increased environmental mastery is associated with an improved sense of self and is a key factor for the well-being of older adults living with MCI (Ong & Bergeman, 2004). Studies have emphasized that appropriate home design can support and enhance both control and functional independence, by creating a safe, enabling, and predictable home environment (Ruggiero and Lachini, 2018). However, the mechanisms through which the design of home environments can provide MCI-specific supportive environments are still unknown, with studies around this topic usually focusing on normal aging or more advanced cognitive impairments such as Alzheimer's disease and Dementia (Marquardt et al., 2011).

Purpose: We designed a study aimed at identifying properties of the home-environment that promote functional independence and control as the main components of environmental mastery for older adults living with MCI.

Method: We conducted focus groups and interviews with patients and staff members from a cognitive empowerment program (CEP) focused on providing therapeutic services for those living with MCI and their care partners. Interview and focus groups were semi-structured, audio-recorded, and lasted approximately 1 hour each, including questions informed by a review of the literature on MCI, aging-in-place and universal design. Questions asked about environmental factors contributing to any difficulties in activities such as physical activity, cooking, housework, and gardening for people living with MCI. Questions also elicited about environmental features influencing their ability to choose, evaluate or plan their home activities, as well as find their way or personal items around their home. The first phase of the study comprised of focus groups and interviews with staff working closely with CEP members and care partners, sometimes using an online platform (zoom) and other times in-person. The second phase focused on interviews with members and their care partners, using a narrowed down set of questions informed by phase one. Qualitative data was transcribed verbatim and thematically analyzed to identify spatial properties that can facilitate or hinder environmental mastery for people living with MCI.

Findings: Results suggest that environmental qualities of homes like visibility, accessibility, flexibility, and furniture ergonomics can promote environmental mastery at home for people living with MCI.

Conclusions: Our study findings build on the aging in place literature by informing design strategies that help prolong the time spent at home by people living with MCI, supporting environmental mastery despite cognitive deficits. By investigating ways to ameliorate typical environmental challenges at home, the results of our study inform further research on home modifications and design interventions to promote control and independent functioning for people living with MCI.

Where Hotdesking and Hoteling Work and Where They Do Not: Towards a Context-Sensitive Implementation of Hotdesking and Hoteling in Academia

Manju Adikesavan *(City University of New York)*

Office-based work is on the cusp of change. Workers are no longer required to congregate in a centralized 'office' since mobile internet and portable devices such as smartphones, laptops, and tablets, have made it possible to work from anywhere and at any time. It is now common to work at variable times of day and night from diverse settings such as co-working spaces, the home, third places such as coffee shops, parks, and public spaces, while commuting, or when traveling. The function and size of the office are changing due to hybrid (a combination of office-based and off-site work), remote (work performed fully out of an office), and mobile (work performed at diverse locations by a worker on the move) ways of working that leverage the flexibility to work from anywhere and at any time. These changes have been intensified by the widespread adoption of hybrid and remote working during the COVID-19 pandemic. Recent studies show that workers no longer prefer to spend every workday at the office; offices are, instead, preferred for strategic meetings and collaborative work (Katsikakis et al., 2020; Lund et al., 2020; Salon et al., 2021). Thus, offices in the hybrid working context are likely to be visited no more than 2 to 3 days a week. This has led to a shift from fixed or assigned workspaces for workers to nonterritorial workspaces which are temporarily available to workers on a day to day or session by session basis. Hoteling (temporary workspaces only available upon prior reservation) and hotdesking (temporary workspaces available on a first come first served basis) are commonly encountered examples of nonterritorial approaches. These practices, however, are not limited to commercial offices and are being adopted in faculty and staff offices in universities.

This study examines the drivers of the shift toward hotdesking and hoteling underway in various US universities. It identifies the positive and negative impacts of hotdesking and hoteling on faculty teaching and research practices based on popular and gray literature, online discussions, and interviews with researchers, designers, and campus planners. The study concludes by identifying the contexts in which hotdesking and hoteling work and do not work, and developing policy and design recommendations that facilitate a context-sensitive implementation of hotdesking/hoteling in academia.

References

Katsikakis, D., Rodriguez, M., Smith, D. C., Leinberger, C., Rockey, R., & Bitner, D. (2020). *Workplace Ecosytems of the Future. Cushman & Wakefield; Center for Real Estate and Urban Analysis*, The George Washington University. https://info.cushmanwakefield.com/l/263412/2020-12-15/3bmdfp

Lund, S., Madgavkar, A., Manyika, J., & Smit, S. (2020, November). *The future of remote work: An analysis of 2,000 tasks, 800 jobs, and 9 countries* | McKinsey. https://www.mckinsey.com/featured-insights/future-of-work/whats-next-for-remote-work-an-analysis-of-2000-tasks-800-jobs-and-nine-countries

Salon, D., Conway, M. W., Capasso da Silva, D., Chauhan, R. S., Derrible, S., Mohammadian, A. (Kouros), Khoeini, S., Parker, N., Mirtich, L., Shamshiripour, A., Rahimi, E., & Pendyala, R. M. (2021). The potential stickiness of pandemic-induced behavior changes in the United States. *Proceedings of the National Academy of Sciences, 118*(27), e2106499118. https://doi.org/10.1073/pnas.2106499118

The Usage and Experience of Bed and Breakfasts in the Suburbs of Beijing (2017-2021): Evidences from Bigdata from Travel Websites

Hefan Wen; Yi Yang *(Beijing Jiaotong University);* ***Bo Zhang*** *(Oklahoma State University)*

Rural B&Bs in Beijing's suburbs are in a phase of transition. 20 years ago, rural B&Bs attracted urban tourists mostly because they were inexpensive and offered an authentic rural living experience, which is similar to many other countries around the world. In the last five years, however, the newly built B&Bs have diverged from the traditional farmhouse

B&Bs, similar to the sociological characteristic of "rural gentrification," which is reflected in the higher prices, design quality and style of the B&Bs that cater to urban tastes. These new B&Bs are attracting attention both online and in reality because of their visually appealing spaces.

Previous researchers have conducted research on the satisfaction of B&B tourists through big data of online evaluations, but few researchers have also used spatial typology methods to purposefully explore tourists' perceived characteristics of B&B design. This study uses big data research method, which has advantages over the traditional questionnaire method in terms of data volume, speed of access, and spontaneity of evaluation content. At the same time, local residential forms and characteristic space placement are combined to summarize the derived B&B space types and explore the relationship between tourists' emotions, tourists' behavior and B&B design.

The researchers use 76 B&Bs in Beijing suburban area as case studies. Employing Python, 11571 Qunar textual reviews from 2017 to 2021 are mined. The textual data of 725,925 words were categorized into 68 themes. B&Bs with design among them are the main objects, and B&Bs without design are used as auxiliary comparisons, with tourist behavior, B&B architecture, and positive and negative tourist reviews as the main analysis aspects .

This study includes five research questions: (1) The B&Bs in two famous ancient villages in western Beijing show a typical differentiation, what is the difference between the tourist reviews of these two places? (2) What are the basic spatial types of rural B&Bs in Beijing's suburbs? (3) How do tourists evaluate different spaces of rural B&Bs differently? (4) How do the characteristic spaces of B&B design influence tourists' behavior? (5) What are the differences in tourists' demand for B&B design among rural B&Bs of different price levels? This study reveals tourist attention characteristics of rural B&Bs in suburban Beijing, which helps to enhance positive tourist experiences and provides a theoretical basis for the design of rural B&Bs with an experiential perspective.

The Design Artifact As a Mediator of Race Conversations: Case Study of an Interdisciplinary Studio

Newton D'souza *(Florida International University);*
Roberto Rovira *(Florida International University)*

Nationwide protests in response to the death of George Floyd have sparked explicit conversations about race, justice, policing and politics in our everyday lives. It has created an urgency to galvanize equity and inclusion in the design fields and to examine practices that structurally harm the participation of Black populations. As architects, interior architects, and landscape architects, and, in our role as creative problem solvers, we can bring about positive change in our society, our environment, and our shared public space, particularly through the design studio.

The design studio is unique in higher education, as it is at the same time a pedagogical method and a spatial concept (Cornell AAP, 2021). The studio model inherited from French Beaux Arts and the German Bauhaus School has both its advocates and critics. On one hand it holds vast potential as a model for the integration and application of learning (Boyer & Mitgang, 1996). The studio culture aspires to be a creative and inclusive space, and a healthy studio culture is recognized to promote essential values such as optimism, respect, sharing, engagement, and innovation (AIAS, 2002). Criticisms nevertheless express how the studio system can privilege a narrow section of students and act as a social filter, ensuring that only students with the right sort of cultural capital are successful (Stevens, 2002). There is also the power difference between instructors and students that impedes a culture of collaboration, often in the absence of voices outside the design disciplines.

Given these challenges, how can the studio become a mediator of race conversations?

This paper describes an interdisciplinary studio that included the departments of Interior Architecture and Landscape Architecture in Southeast US University. The studio was to design a rehabilitative place for the victims of the Rosewood Massacre, which destroyed a thriving and economically self-sufficient African American community in 1923.

The project provided a setting to explore race conversations through the lenses of social justice, decarbonization, and economic opportunity.

The studio began by asking students to internalize oral histories of Rosewood through an exploration of concepts such as "whole/fragment," "presence/ absence," "rest/action," "continuity/ discontinuity" and "isolation/ unity." These first principles were to be expressed through design artifacts, which were loosely defined as any material/ non-material that had cultural, contextual and historic interest in Rosewood (for e.g. a quote of oral history, a house piano, or natural elements such as fire). These artifacts were used as a critical first step to frame race conversations and the violent events that led to Rosewood's destruction. They provided an anchor to have difficult conversations between students, community members, museum curators and creative economist studio consultants. The artifacts were both an analytic and synthetic tool that challenged fundamental basis of "memorialization" and "commemoration" within that context of Rosewood and continues to play a role in discussions with grant organizations and museum curators as we aspire to make the project tangible.

Modular Deployable Bamboo Structures: Enabling User Participation to Self Design and Build in Developing Countries

***Anastasia Maurina** (Clemson University); **Vincent Blouin** (ASHREA)*

Post-disaster reconstruction requires rapid building on a large scale. The prefabrication approach is often used to fulfill these requirements while maintaining quality. Most of the time, this approach is used to generate uniform designs that lack 'flexibility to adapt to various users' desires and needs. In developing countries, resources, i.e., modern construction materials, advanced fabrication tools, and skilled labor, are usually limited and even sometimes inexistent. Local materials and adapted technologies are generally preferred so laypeople can participate or even lead the reconstruction process. This paper focuses on the study of modular deployable structures using bamboo as a local material. A typical deployable bamboo structure consists of multiple modules made of bamboo poles connected to each other to form scissor-like elements (S.L.E.s) and referred to as S.L.E. units. Multiple structural modules are arranged to form the entire building structure and create numerous forms varying in size and shape. Several types of S.L.E. units are considered in this research to investigate their impact on various measures such as structural performance, design flexibility, and constructability. This paper describes the result of user participatory experiments in designing and constructing a pavilion using modular deployable bamboo structures. Two groups, i.e., one group of experts and one group of laypeople, were involved in the experiments to evaluate the ability of laypeople to design, fabricate, and install modular deployable bamboo structures and identify which type of S.L.E. unit induces the highest chance of success. The results show that modified modular deployable bamboo structures provide better design flexibility than the typical ones and perform in constructability. Through this study, the laypeople can perform their design-and-build ability with additional aids from researchers/experts. However, using the MDB structures is very potential to enable laypeople to self-design and build.

Keywords: bamboo, deployable structures, user participation, self-design and build

Live-Learn Fellow: A Retrospective Account of My Experience As a Participant Observer

***Elinor Oren** (University of California, San Diego)*

Coalitions at the intersection of academia and practice promise new modes of research collaboration to inform the design of healthier environments. I have served as one such mode of formalizing those partnerships as a Live-Learn Fellow for the Center for Advanced Design Research and Evaluation (CADRE). I am an undergraduate Real Estate Development major at UC San Diego (UCSD) connecting Salk Institute Neuroscientists, UCSD Administration, and HKS researchers to study UCSD's newly constructed mixed-use neighborhood, North Torrey Pines Living Learning Neighborhood (NTPLLN). With a focus on physical and mental wellbeing, a connection to community, and a commitment to the environment, NTPLLN is a living and learning neighborhood where all aspects of student life are intertwined at every scale of the built environment. Over the past year, I have conducted mixed-methods research on how the built environment impacts student life, through ongoing participant observation, digital/physical artifact analysis, behavior mapping, photo diaries, and multi-participant interviews. The purpose of this presentation is to explore the methodologies that I participated in and conducted to support a longitudinal pre-post longitudinal study on how the built environment influences the health and wellbeing of college students.

As an undergrad and former resident of the dorms, I am uniquely positioned to bridge the diverse stakeholders involved in the NTPLLN. My 24/7 access to the space as a resident-researcher allowed me to observe evolving and unexpected space utilization throughout the pandemic, enabling me to "gut-check" designers' assumptions about student preferences and behavior. My findings on privacy and everyday student life have already been incorporated into the ongoing development of an additional UCSD dorm building. Most immediately, in the implementation of less transparent blinds in response to students' privacy concerns at NTPLLN. My status as a student grants me the sense of agency to identify synergies between our coalition members and advance further inquiries into the relationship between people and place.

At present, I am supporting HKS-UCSD collaborations by analyzing interview data to create a holistic understanding of student wellbeing and supporting HKS-Salk collaborations by assisting the development of an NSF grant proposal addressing the limitations of spatial analytics in omitting sensory experiences – starting from the behavioral data I collected in Winter 2020-2021.

This opportunity to engage in design research has been pivotal in my personal growth, professional aims, and sense of belonging to UCSD, functioning as an intermediary between research and industry silos. It is inspiring when my Green Associate Certification Class references my immediate environment for examples of design strategies that meet LEED Certification while positively influencing wellbeing. In addition, I am both an ambassador for UCSD and effectively represent my peers by providing the UCSD administration with research insights on students' perspectives of their actual and ideal living and learning spaces. My contributions have had a tangible impact on ongoing campus development and operation through my role as a participant observer and this novel role of a Live Learn Fellow could be applied in future work investigating how the built environment influences health.

Trans* Inclusive Restrooms: A Study of Best Practices

Edward Steinfeld *(University at Buffalo)*

Public restrooms have become the major locus of conflict over trans* rights. But this is only the latest manifestation of cultural conflicts related to restrooms. Historically, the restroom has been studied through four aligned, but ultimately separate, lenses: gender studies, public health, ergonomics, and proxemics. These four lenses are both interdependent and intersectional. The author and his colleagues are engaged in a long range initiative to advance inclusive public restroom design. One activity in this initiative is the identification of best practices and documentation, using interviews and a case study approach. Methods include a screening interview, documentation of projects using photography and video, and in-depth interviews with stakeholders on site. The study examines how projects originated, barriers to and facilitators of implementation, the outcomes as viewed by building owners, managers, designers and users. Documentation is intended to advance policy, advocacy, education and practice. This paper will present the findings of a literature review that addressed the four lenses above, a method for identification of best practices based on current knowledge, and selected case studies that demonstrate how best practices are being introduced effectively in practice. Recommendations for policy, advocacy and design will be included. The research creates a holistic picture of the public restroom and positions the contemporary conflict as the result of polarized public opinion. These opinions are driven by demographic, ideological, and geographic factors. While the public restroom is the primary site of interest, this research improves our understanding about the larger issues of how our built environment might adapt in response to a more nuanced view of gender and how key spatial practices might serve as catalysts for social change.

A Framework to Locate Tiny Home Communities for Unsheltered Individuals That Respect Their Preferences and Leverage Existing Supportive Services & Municipal Infrastructure

Poorna Patange *(University of Waterloo)*

In response to the growing number of unsheltered individuals, municipalities across North America are considering tiny homes — self-contained structures with extremely small building footprints — as an alternative to traditional emergency shelters, community housing and tent cities. However, little is known about how to effectively leverage an existing urban context to respect the needs and preferences of unsheltered individuals moving into a tiny home community. Although cost-effective, rapidly constructible, and mobile when necessary, the tiny home can only provide a small provision of private space that does not offer much room for activities outside the bare essentials of being sheltered in an enclosure. Thus the urban context of the home must provide the supports and spaces for the complex and diverse needs of tiny-home inhabitants. This study developed a framework to utilize open space within a mid-sized city to locate tiny home shelter-or-housing communities based on the needs and preferences of unsheltered individuals accessing specific types of shelter.

The experience of homelessness has been theorized as an exclusion from society (Deutsche, 1996). As such, many activists and experts on the housing rights of marginalized unsheltered people advocate for housing and shelter in central spaces within a city. However, there is a gap in research that explicitly addresses the urban dimensions of the needs and preferences of individuals seeking shelter (Brallier, Southworth, & Ryan, 2019). The problem of locating a tiny home community effectively is complicated by the wide range of potential sites that can accommodate tiny homes and the diverse needs of unsheltered individuals who may inhabit them. We performed a semi-systematic literature review of research from multiple disciplines engaged in observing the preferences and needs of unsheltered people as they seek housing solutions. A semi-systematic review was used because it is better suited to topics that have been studied and conceptualized differently by various disciplines (Snyder, 2019). Studies were selected only if first-person accounts, interviews, and surveys with unsheltered people were the primary methods for uncovering the preferences of unsheltered people. The spatial framework produced by this research extrapolates an urban condition — whether that be in the heart of a residential neighborhood or at the edge of the city — from the social and service conditions that are desirable for individuals accessing specific types of housing and shelter as described in the reviewed literature. This research provides a framework to insert tiny home communities within appropriate urban contexts to address the needs and preferences of unsheltered individuals in a complex and politicized system of service providers and services.

References

Brallier, S., Southworth, S., & Ryan, B. (2019). Rolling forward: addressing needs in the homeless community. *Journal of Social Distress and the Homeless, 28*(2), 186-192.

Deutsche, R. (1996). *Evictions: Art and spatial politics.* Cambridge, MA: MIT Press.

Snyder, H. (2019). Literature review as a research methodology: An overview and guidelines. *Journal of Business Research, 104*, 333-339.

Creating a Workable Workspace - Office Design Strategies for Individuals with Autism Spectrum Disorder

Farzane Omidi *(Texas Tech University);* ***Kristi Gaines*** *(Texas Tech University)*

The unemployment rate of adults with autism spectrum disorder (ASD) in comparison with other adults that suffer from other disabilities is high in the United States (Ohl et al., 2017). People need to participate in some activities in order to transition from childhood to adulthood. Some of these identified activities include graduating from high school, financial independence through having a job and income, and leaving their parental home and establishing a family (Anderson et al., 2014). This shows the importance of having a job to provide independence for individuals, but in general, 85% of adults with ASD are unemployed which is roughly two-thirds of this population. One potential reason for this high unemployment rate is that the design of most workplaces does not consider the needs of these individuals. Since those with ASD are sensitive to sensory and visual input, some design characteristics, such as high auditory levels in open-plan offices or harsh lighting conditions, can cause problems (Lorenz et al., 2016). Since there is a broad spectrum of sensitivities, creating appropriate adaptive workspaces that address these individuals' needs is crucial. For example, lighting, access to nature or quiet places, audio conditions, proper materials, and colors, are some of the sensory needs that should be addressed through special physical design. Some common designs such as open-office plans are not appropriate as they may increase tension and prevent individuals with ASD from concentrating on their works. Thus, controlling the light and noise, establishing an environment that makes wayfinding easier, and providing spaces that allow individuals to concentrate or offer natural views can all contribute to creating productive workable places for people with ASD.

This study examines the main issues that people with ASD are facing in indoor environments and identifying the factors that contribute to their negative experience. These issues cause some challenges in workspaces for them, and this study identifies possible design solutions for maintaining a workable workspace for these individuals. These strategies can reduce the sensitivity of people with ASD in workplaces and it can help them to engage with their work, and finally increases their self-confidence and independence. Also, a conceptual design is included that shows the implementation of these strategies in physical design. In the presentation, researcher outlines the aspects of this design and discuss these potential solutions.

References

Anderson, K. A., Shattuck, P. T., Cooper, B. P., Roux, A. M., & Wagner, M. (2014). Prevalence and correlates of postsecondary residential status among young adults with an autism spectrum disorder. *Autism, 18*(5), 562–570. https://doi.org/10.1177/1362361313481860

Lorenz, T., Frischling, C., Cuadros, R., & Heinitz, K. (2016). Autism and overcoming job barriers: Comparing job-related barriers and possible solutions in and outside of autism-specific employment. *PLoS ONE, 11*(1). https://doi.org/10.1371/journal.pone.0147040

Ohl, A., Sheff, M. G., Little, S., Nguyen, J., Paskor, K., & Zanjirian, A. (2017). Predictors of employment status among adults with Autism Spectrum Disorder. *Work, 56*(2), 345–355. https://doi.org/10.3233/WOR-172492

Design Thinking: Rediscovering the Social Value of Co-Creating Environments for Multicultural University Students in the Pandemic

Seo Young Kim *(Inje University);* ***Jinkyung Paik*** *(Inje University)*

The COVID-19 pandemic has presented the broader health perspectives of social isolation for university students including ethnic diversity in campus populations. The long-term and unexpected circumstance of a lack of contact between students has given rise to questions about how to 'care' for them socially and mentally in terms of social connectedness. Based on the background, the researchers' challenge was to help to solve the problem by applying the key idea of co-design to the on-campus environment. The study is currently in the initial phase of research and will focus on building a substantial framework from which to develop further stages. In the study, the conceptual definition of 'design' implies: create program guidelines for environmental resilience. The aim of the research is to explore the role of design in developing a student-centered community for a culturally diverse population within the environment of universities during the pandemic. The research proposal opens up a discussion of 'how students' collaborative designs can create better and feasible solutions for their care and satisfy their individual and/or collective needs due to the pandemic?' In doing so, a design thinking theory will help to build a strategic outline by following five stages, including empathize, define, ideate, prototype, and test. The two stages of 'define' and 'ideate' will be the pivotal process in conducting the project. The methodology will be based on a qualitative approach to determine the problems of selected students. For data collection and analysis, two types of methods will be underpinned. First, interviews and a focus group will be used to provide detailed content to shape the scope of the findings from the research. Open coding will be applied to mapping the essence of the findings from the qualitative surveys. Next, workshops with the students will be used to create distinctive themes to shape a co-design program to identify answers to the research question. The expected result of the research is a programmatic approach to reflect the cross-cultural values of students in the form of a contemporary exhibition.

Keywords: Co-design, Design thinking, Multicultural environment, Social interaction, Student-centered community

References

Britton, G. (2017). *Co-design and social innovation: Connections, tensions and opportunities.* Routledge.

Fisher, T. (2022). *Space, structures and design in a post-pandemic world.* Routledge.

Taekleves, E. et al. (2021). *The little book of global health / design & COVID-19.* Imagination Lancaster, Lancaster University.

Including Children in the Design of Urban Play Spaces: A New Framework for Participatory Design

Sara Eslamzadeh *(Clemson University);* ***Matthew Powers*** *(Clemson University)*

Many young people, especially those living in urban areas, do not have sufficient daily access to nature. This leads to various health and play implications. As new landscapes are built, children can become disconnected from the design process. This paper examines participatory design in urban areas and the role of children in the design process. This study presents new strategies for integrating children's ideas and criteria into the design of nature-based, urban play spaces that support children's health and wellness.

Childrens' connection with nature has been declining, resulting in many adverse health outcomes (Louv, 2008). Recent studies suggest a connection between children's participation in the design process and their health (Derr & Rigolon, 2017). Sharp population growth and increased urbanization-industrialization in recent decades make this connection more critical (Özdemir, 2019). Just as children are getting less exposure to nature, a growing body of research says that children's physical and emotional health is strongly dependent upon nature. As Louv (2008) wrote, a lack of exposure to nature or "nature deficit" is a fundamental design and planning issue because the absence of green areas can be associated with different mental and physical health problems in children and adults. The participatory planning process has been shown to be an effective tool for citizen involvement in the design process and is directly connected to community health. However, very little research exists about the role of children in the design process. Therefore, this research contributes to the body of knowledge related to children's participation in the design of nature-based, urban playscapes.

In this study, an extensive literature review of existing studies about play spaces, design process, and participatory design is presented. This review focuses on children's participation in the design process, and how participation affects subsequent engagement. The purpose of the literature review is to create an analytic framework illustrating the child's role in participatory design related to issues like privacy, recruitment, and other subjects affecting youth involvement. Early findings suggest that designers may be reticent to integrate children into projects because they do not know how to do it or may be concerned about the legalities. Some evidence suggests that children are able to perceive their role as active and effective participants in the urban planning process. Future findings are expected to show how participating in the design process can boost engagement in play, thus enhancing learning outcomes and supporting health.

References

Derr, V. L., & Rigolon, A. (2017). *Participatory Schoolyard Design for Health and Well-Being: Policies that Support Play in Urban Green Spaces.* https://doi.org/10.1007/978-981-287-035-3_2110.1007/978-981-287-035-3

Louv, R. (2008). *Last child in the woods: Saving our children from nature-deficit disorder.* Algonquin books.

Özdemir, A. (2019). An approach on children's experiences of participatory planning. *Cities, 93*, 206-214.

The Challenge of Creating Play-Supportive Environments for Children: Perspectives from Practitioners of the City of Montreal, Canada

Ipek Epikmen *(Université de Montréal);* ***Juan Torres*** *(Université de Montréal);* ***Gabriella Tavernese*** *(Université de Montréal)*

Play is internationally acknowledged as a right, embedded in the 1959 Declaration of the Rights of the Child and the 1989 Convention on the Rights of the Child. Access to outdoor free play is determinant for children's wellbeing and healthy development, enabling socialization, acquisition of skills, and opportunities for daily physical activity, to mention only some benefits (Brussoni et al. 2012, WHO, 2016). Nevertheless, creating play-supportive environments remains a challenge, especially from the perspective of municipalities, where outdoor free play is often considered an activity limited in space and time to the private realm or the use of specific equipment, such as parks and playgrounds. Labeled as Child friendly, the City of Montreal committed in 2016 to "Offer children an urban environment that promotes play and discovery [...]". Five years after the adoption of this policy, how is play understood by the practitioners concerned? How is this understanding informing transformations in the urban environment?

The goal of our exploratory research was to bring a better understanding of the challenges and the opportunities for creating play-supportive environments from the point of view of practitioners working in a municipality. To do this, we followed a three-step method: 1) Preparation, including a literature review; 2) Data collection and analysis, based on 15 interviews with a variety of stakeholders from the municipality; 3) Validation and synthesis, through a workshop with 9 participants from different circles (interviewed practitioners, academics, community associations).

Our results confirm a very sophisticated understanding of play among participants. They consider the play opportunities as a combined effect of actions from a) parents, b) schools, c) community organizations, and d) the municipality. Participants view municipal action as key for maintenance, animation of the urban space, and management, especially when multiple users share the same public spaces or equipment. Beyond this system of actors, our results reveal a profound mismatch between play, understood as a multidimensional phenomenon, and the restrictive framework from which municipal action is supposed to promote it. This mismatch generates insufficient actions and frustration. Lack of flexibility in regulations and administrative structures, excessive specialization (of services, of spaces), scarcity of public spaces, stereotypes concerning play and children, social inequalities, and variability of resources between boroughs, were identified as challenges. However, participants agreed on the existence of many opportunities: the recent implementation of pilot projects, the availability of spaces with a potential for transformation (streets, alleys, wastelands, etc.). The ongoing implementation of traffic-calming measures, the institutionalization of an equity-diversity-inclusion approach, the existence of a strong community organizations network, and the interest of the various sectors about play-supportive partnerships.

References

Brussoni M, Olsen LL, Pike I, Sleet DA. (2012) Risky play and children's safety: balancing priorities for optimal child development. *International Journal of Environmental Research And Public Health, 9*(9):3134-48.

WHO - World Health Organization (2016) *Report of the commission on ending childhood obesity.* WHO. https://apps.who.int/iris/bitstream/handle/10665/204176/9789241510066_eng.pdf?sequence=1

Lessons to be Learned: Children with ASD and the Development of Transition Zones for Learning-Ready Home Environments

Fatemeh Marzban *(Texas Tech University);* ***Sharran Parkinson*** *(Texas Tech University);* ***Jennifer Hamrick*** *(Texas Tech University);* ***Jennifer Hixson*** *(Texas Tech University);* ***Janet Stockton Parker*** *(Texas Tech University)*

The COVID-19 pandemic resulted in unexpected effects on the daily lives of neurodiverse populations, specifically children with ASD, who thrive on routine, coherence, and structure. Transitioning from a school to a home setting is an ongoing and difficult challenge for these children and their families, especially if it is not learning-ready. While several design considerations can aid in this process, one of the most important is the implementation of transition zones (Mostafa, 2018), areas that separate environmental space from another and signal to the user the affordance of that space. Here, transition refers to a change in an activity, location, or routine that requires children to adjust. Transition zones provide predictable daily changes to help reduce unexpected schedule changes (Hume, 2008). Furthermore, these zones allow users to recalibrate their senses when moving between sensory spaces defined as either high or low-stimulus (Mostafa, 2021, 2018). These zones are often utilized in schools and universities, but they are less prevalent in home environments, and there is limited research concerning the design of transition zones for home learning environments. Drawing from research that establishes an initial set of guidelines for designing supportive home learning environments that help engage children and hold their attention, this presentation outlines the importance of transition zones between non-learning areas (eating, sleeping, playing, etc.) and areas established for learning within the home. Specifically, the purpose of such research is to offer designers and practitioners examples of how these transition zones might be applied to the interior and structural design of homes with the expressed purpose of decreasing transition times for children as they move from areas designated for activities such as play or eating to areas that are expressly purposed for learning. As more and more families, having children with autism, choose not to transition back to the school setting (Pachner, & Aranyi, 2021), the need for more studies and research concerning design and environmental features in the home has increased. This work contributes to this need and is intended as a foundation for continued research into solutions for those families with children with autism who are turning to home schooling for the foreseeable future.

References

Hume, K. (2008). Transition time: Helping individuals on the autism spectrum move successfully from one activity to another. *The Reporter, 13*(2), 6-10.

Mostafa, M. (2018). Designing for autism: an ASPECTSS™ post-occupancy evaluation of learning environments. *Archnet-IJAR: International Journal of Architectural Research, 12*(3), 308-326.

Mostafa M. (2021). *The autism friendly university design guide.* Dublin City University Press.

Pachner, O., & Aranyi, G. (2021). Challenges for Children and Adolescents with Autism and Their Families during the COVID-19 Pandemic. *Journal of Global Awareness, 2* (1),1-21.

Portraiture for Environmental Design: Giving Voice to Subject

Anne C Godfrey *(SUNY College of Environmental Science and Forestry)*

Though our subject matter is the landscape, how we design, plan, manage and restore places, is also always about people. In working with the landscape, we use photography to document and investigate qualities of these places to help us make choices about the changes we propose. These photographs present the physical characteristics of a place, and often indicate the presence and actions of larger systems (cultural, ecological, economic, etc.). This discussion presents another option for a type of photography that can be used in these environmental design endeavors – portraiture.

People express the landscapes in which they live. Their gaze, posture, clothing, and demeanor indicate the impact their home landscape has upon them. In certain ways, we can say that people hold the landscape within them.

Iconic examples come to mind, Dorothea Lange's photographs made during the Dust Bowl (1930's), Richard Avedon's In The American West (1985), and even Brandon Stanton's Humans of New York (2010 - present). Yet, quickly following these examples is the question of objectification. Were these portraits made because these people were different, and considered objects of interest? Is this a process of othering? This is a complex question, with no single answer. The presentation will touch upon this issue to create ground for a more holistic approach.

Several contemporary photographers engage in portraiture that combines photography with a narrative written or spoken by the subject as a way to create a more holistic relationship between the viewer and the subject. The subject tells their own story, giving the viewer a more specific and unique understanding of the person before them. The author proposes this way of working can be a method for engaging with community during the process of design. This can lead to understanding instead of objectifying.

A primary example will come from photographer Dawoud Bey's ongoing work Class Portraits. Bey photographs teenagers in their school settings and interviews them or asks them to write about themselves. These narratives are shown with the photographs, to be viewed equally. Bey created this work to give voice to the interior lives of teenagers, who he believes are often treated in stereotypic ways (he cites, similar to the lack of interior life granted to Black people).

Other examples to be discussed are: photographer Sarhar Coston-Hardy's work for Agency's design for the AT&T building in Columbus, Indiana, which combines portraiture with recorded interviews; Barnabas Crosby's work with the Design Trust for Public Space for their Photo Urbanism Program; Naima Green's photo project Jewels From the Hinterland which photographs Black people enjoying green spaces as a disruption of common stereotypes.

Through looking at these examples, a set of techniques and methods will be presented on how to approach portraiture of community members for environmental design projects. Key to this is combining the voice of the person being photographed with the photograph itself. Also discussed will be options for composition that help demonstrate the impact of the person's landscape upon their lives.

Those Marginalized By Design: Research + Prototype + Pedagogy

Tina Patel *(Kent State University)*

Context: Marginalized populations are groups and communities that experience discrimination and systematic exclusion because of unequal power relationships across economic, political, social, and cultural dimensions. Who is considered marginalized by design? What impact have designers had on their living situations? What are the responsibilities of designers to improve the lives of those who are still marginalized?

The legislation in the USA dictates that children with disabilities should be educated in the same school environment as children without disabilities if the classroom meets their needs (Individuals with Disabilities Act, 2004). Children with disabilities (visible or invisible) are often served in a specialized learning environment in public schools called resource rooms or self-contained classrooms. A survey of K-8 public schools in the region indicated that in most cases, these classrooms are typically not designed with consideration for the sensory needs of the children served within them. For children with exceptionalities who attend public schools, further inequalities based on race, ethnicity, socioeconomic status, and location of residence can make it difficult for them to reach their full potential for life in the community. Classroom environments must meet the sensory needs of students to provide them with the opportunity to feel physically comfortable, encourage self-regulation, and focus on the learning tasks. This calls for designers, researchers, educators, and the community at large to explore interior design as a tool to understand the world and represent all voices. This presentation focuses on how to use design to empower children with special needs who are disadvantaged by designing a prototype for their special need classroom based on research and then offering it as a design project studio project to raise awareness among students.

Research and Prototype: A thorough literature review, indicates that there are no holistic design guidelines in place to meet the sensory needs of students with exceptionalities. Sensory design guidelines were established utilizing a qualitative method, providing a foundation for the development of the prototype of the special need classroom. The resulting prototypes provide a basis for the further development of design standards and take designers closer to creating more conducive and inclusive environments. This study reinforced the belief that these recommendations should be considered in the school-wide design.

Pedagogy: The second part of the presentation describes a pedagogical approach that was employed to help students explore users' experience, research, and develop conceptual approaches to a 4,200 sf, learning center to serve students with ASD from early childhood through high school.

Implications: Through the research, development of the prototype, and design pedagogy, we had an opportunity to study the sensory needs of children with exceptionalities and how these sensory needs interact with the built world. We developed empathy for this user group, bringing them more intentionally into the design processes and imagine a future that will better meet the extraordinary range of their collective sensory needs. As designers, we must move beyond the perfunctory retrofitting of spaces and consider how can purpose-built design dignify and fully support ones marginalized by design?

How Popular Is the Internet Celebrity Building? Research on the Relationship between Architectural Behaviors in the Red Brick Art Museum Based on Network Open Data

Luo Moxin *(Beijing Jiaotong University);* ***Yi Yang*** *(Beijing Jiaotong University);* ***Yingying Hou****;* ***Bo Zhang*** *(Oklahoma State University)*

With the rise of major online social media, architecture has also become a "net celebrity" product. Because of the lack of big data research support, research on the relationship between diverse viewer behavior and architectural space characteristics seems to be limited. This research takes the Red Brick Art Museum in Beijing as an example, the social media posts, which cover a wide range of topics and ages of visitors in various comment forms. The architect Dong Yugan uses the Tang Dynasty poets "make tools according to the shape" and "unchanged according to things" as the concepts throughout the design and use red bricks as the basic construction material. At the same time, the concept of "ecological experience museum" was proposed, and outdoor installations by masters were introduced, which opened up a new model of "art wetland" for the public.

We manually crawled 925 tour reviews, including the pictures taken, the release date and other information on Dianping platform from 2016 to 2019. The age groups of tourists are classified into three intervals of 18-28, 29-40, and 41-65 years. And further record the humanities and environmental elements that each age group pays attention to during the activities, and extract the emotion and aesthetic perception data generated by the users. From the study, we discovered (1) From a behavioral perspective that the spontaneous action accounts for the highest proportion among the nineteen tourist behaviors. And the public has increased awareness of aesthetic concepts such as the structure and material of the building. (2) From the perspective of architectural elements ,Visitors between the ages of 18 and 28 are particularly sensitive to the acoustic environment, and the building materials have the highest degree of correlation with necessary behaviors. Visitors between the ages of 29 and 40 are less concerned about the building itself, and their visiting behavior is more closely related to natural elements. (3) From the perspective of tourist perception ,the internal acoustic environment of the museum brings negative emotions of loneliness and fear, but the composition of red bricks also provides visitors with positive and warm emotions and aesthetic feelings. (4) The occurrence of social activities such as meditation, weddings, and group building shows that the Internet celebrity building is not just a backdrop for tourists to gain attention after taking pictures, but a comprehensive place that combines dynamic and static to accommodate the space needs of multiple age groups. This article attempts to use the system of "behavior-building elements-perception evaluation", using visual data results to provide suggestions for the design of diverse crowds in public buildings.

Bringing the Disability Lived Experience to Residential Design: Learning from COVID-19

Neda Norouzi *(UTSA);* ***Melanie Cawthon*** *(disABILITYsa)*

The housing crisis for people with disabilities includes affordability and accessibility. Without affordable and accessible housing, many of these individuals are at risk of institutionalization or homelessness (Burns et al., 2021). The COVID-19 pandemic has disproportionately affected the lives of people with disabilities (NCD, 2021). Recognizing the need for designing and building affordable and accessible housing, this article is aimed at identifying important design criteria for architectural design of houses that serve people of different ages and abilities.

A study conducted in collaboration by the city and two non-profit organizations focused on identifying critical areas of concerns for individuals with disabilities, their family members, and their caregivers during COVID-19 in the City of San Antonio. Data collected from 415 respondents with the majority being middle-and older-age adults presented the residents top concerns to be on (1) personal/family health, (2) social experience, , and (3) food security.

The findings of these surveys were shared with 15 graduate students taking an architectural design studio with the first author. The students were tasked to design Universally Designed residential buildings for individuals with disability. In addition to incorporating the survey findings, the architecture students conducted a narrative literature analysis (Baumeister & Leary , 1997) of 150 peer-reviewed articles published in the last five years. The findings of these literature analysis combined with the results of the survey included a set of design criteria that must be incorporated in residential design of building for individuals with disabilities. These criteria are: (1) multi-sensory design and incorporation of light, texture, smell, and sound (2) clear circulations and line of sight, (3) respecting autonomy and independence (4) offering opportunities for different levels of social interactions.

These design qualities were then incorporated in designing residential buildings for five individuals with different disabilities or needs (1) a father with a blind son, (2) a deaf mom and a 12-years old son, (3) a woman and her husband who uses an electrical wheelchair and works from home, (4) a mom pregnant with twins and her husband who works night shifts as a physician, and (5) a couple in their late 40's and their 14-year old daughter with autism.

Fifteen design solutions were created and presented to architects, interior designers, professional experts in each disability category, and individuals who live with a disability or care for a person with a disability.

This article provides examples of specific architectural features to be integrated in designing and building affordable and accessible housing for individuals with different disabilities.

References

Baumeister, R. F., & Leary, M. R. (1997). Writing narrative literature reviews. *Review of General Psychology, 1*, 311–320. https://doi.org/10.1037/1089-2680.1.3.311.

Burns,S. P., Mendonca, R., Pickens, N. D., & Smith, R. O. (2021). America's housing affordability crisis: perpetuating disparities among people with disability. *Disability & Society, 36*(10), 1719–1724. https://doi.org/10.1080/09687599.2021.1960276

The Impact of COVID-19 on People with Disabilities. (2021, 10). National Council on Disability. Retrieved 02, 2022, from https://ncd.gov/progressreport/2021/2021-progress-report

This track focuses on the various ways planning and design professionals, researchers and educators define health and apply the concept to their practice. How does the concept of health affect their philosophy toward design, approaches, methods and tools used to design for health and wellbeing? What is the theoretical foundation for research and practice focused on the built environment and health? What are the emerging design tools (data, simulation, virtual) and how are they being deployed in design projects? What are the ways researchers are studying communities, landscapes, buildings, spaces, and products in relation to health-related outcomes?

Examining the Users' Perception of Privacy: Personal Space and Proximity in the Waiting Rooms of Doctors' Offices

Suining Ding (Purdue University, Fort Wayne)

Lack of privacy has been reported to be a long-standing problem in situations related to patient information. Most of the waiting rooms in doctors' offices are designed as open plan configurations. The waiting rooms are adjacent to the check-in desks, where other people often hear conversations between patients and medical staff. Therefore, patient information might be revealed through conversations. Thus, it is crucial to have a better understanding of patients and medical staff's perceptions of privacy and their behavioral preferences in the waiting rooms. Little studies that examine patients' preferences regarding personal space and proximity in the waiting rooms have been found. Thus, to fill the void in the current research by investigating privacy, personal space, and proximity from environment-behavior (EB) studies perspective in waiting rooms makes this study significant. How do the physical configurations of the waiting room in a doctor's office affect users' perception of privacy? How does the furniture layout in the waiting room affect patients' preferred personal space and proximity? These research questions have been investigated through this study.

In environment-behavior studies, privacy is commonly described as the ability of an individual to seclude themselves or information about themselves and thereby express themselves selectively. Physical privacy is closely related to the concepts of personal space and territoriality, and it is described to have personal space as a precondition. Personal space is the bubble around a person shaped by cultural or background experiences. Proxemics is an area of study of the relationship and interactions between humans in a particular culture and their use and perception of space. Thus, the research design of this study was based on these EB studies' theoretical concepts.

This study took a qualitative approach with grounded theory methodology. The method used for this research was a triangulation method that multiple sources of data were collected through observations and interviews. Before the study started, the researcher secured IRB approval. A total of three waiting rooms in doctors' offices were randomly selected to conduct observations and interviews. A total of fifty patients were observed in three different waiting rooms using behavior mapping to record the patients' seating preferences and trace their performance. A total of three receptionists were interviewed using the interview protocol.

Based on the behavioral mapping and interview data, the findings show that patients prefer a more visible seat in the waiting room, not necessarily the most private seating. Thus, privacy preference might not be a significant concern; instead, visibility for nurses is a top preference. It was confirmed by the interviews with the receptionists, who do not think that privacy is a significant concern. However, personal space and proximity are still a consideration for patients. Patients selected the seats that were further apart from other patients. It can be explained by patients' preference for a bigger personal space and the social distancing because of the COVID pandemic. Future research can confirm this explanation. The implications of this research provide practical applications to the waiting room design in doctors' offices.

Understanding Anesthesia Workflow Challenges during Medication Related Tasks

Sahar Mihandoust *(Clemson University),* ***Anjali Joseph*** *(Clemson University);* ***Soheyla Mohammadi-Gorji*** *(Clemson University);* ***Kenneth Catchpole*** *(Medical University of South Carolina);* ***James Abernathy*** *(Johns Hopkins);* ***David Neyens*** *(Clemson University)*

The workspace for the anesthesia providers (AN) in the OR is prone to interruptions and distractions (Pape & Dingman, 2011); these events can increase the occurrence of medical errors especially while performing medication related tasks such as medication preparation, documentation or administration (Savoldelli et al., 2010). According to previous research, anesthesia providers were involved in 45% of all observed minor flow disruptions and 35% of all major flow disruptions in the OR. Also, 37% of all minor FDs and 32% of all major FDs took place in the anesthesia area (Palmer et al., 2013). Previous research has investigated the frequency of distracting events and the causes for these disruptions/interruptions, and people involved in flow distributions. However, there is a paucity of research investigating the relationship between anesthesiologist medication tasks and flow disruptions.

The purpose of this study is to understand whether anesthesiologists might experience flow disruptions while performing medication activities and the type of flow disruptions experienced by them. Understanding these flow disruptions and the sources of these disruptions will help us identify potential solutions to support safer anesthesia medication tasks.

Video recordings of 25 pediatrics surgeries were coded for type of anesthesiologist medication tasks (medication administration, medication preparation, recording information, seeking and gathering information and other) being performed and flow disruptions in the OR utilizing Noldus Observer XT.

The type of surgery, frequency of information gathering, medication administration had a significant impact on flow disruptions in the OR ($p < .05$). This study found that disruptions were more likely to happen when AN were seeking information and doing medication administration followed by medication preparation and other non-medication related tasks. Among anesthesia team, there was a higher rate of disruptions for medication administration and lowest rate related to other and recording information. Layout related disruption and environmental hazards were the most frequent type of disruptions that happened when anesthesiologist was conducting medication tasks.

The study findings suggest that the organization of the equipment in the OR and specially in the anesthesia zone can impact flow disruptions. Future design should test and implement an equipment configuration for different medication tasks to reduce layout and environmental hazard related disruptions during anesthesia medication activities.

References

Palmer, G., Abernathy III, J. H., Swinton, G., Allison, D., Greenstein, J., Shappell, S., . . . Reeves, S. T. (2013). Realizing improved patient care through human-centered operating room design: a human factors methodology for observing flow disruptions in the cardiothoracic operating room. *Anesthesiology, 119*(5), 1066-1077.

Pape, T. M., & Dingman, S. K. (2011). Interruptions and distractions during anesthesia induction: a pilot study. *Plastic Surgical Nursing, 31*(2), 49-56.

Savoldelli, G. L., Thieblemont, J., Clergue, F., Waeber, J.-L., Forster, A., & Garnerin, P. (2010). Incidence and impact of distracting events during induction of general anaesthesia for urgent surgical cases. *European Journal of Anaesthesiology| EJA, 27*(8), 683-689.

Evaluation of Cohort Isolation Strategy in Emergency Department in Response to COVID-19 Pandemic

Marzia Chowdhury *(The University of Kansas);* ***Hui Cai*** *(The University of Kansas);* ***Frank Zilm*** *(The University of Kansas);* ***Bryan F. Imhoff*** *(Clinical Assistant Professor)*

Background: The COVID-19 pandemic has presented severe challenges to emergency departments (EDs). Cohort-isolation strategy has been identified as an important intervention in maintaining the regular treatment capacity for non-infected patients and providing surge capacity for infected patients during earlier infectious disease surges (e.g., SARS-CoV and H1N1). However, little is known about the impact of a pandemic on ED visit trends, cohort patient groups' operational performances, and cohort-isolation strategy effectiveness.

Aim: This study investigates COVID-19 impacts on the ED visit trends, operational performance and evaluates the cohort-isolation strategies at different waves of the pandemic.

Methods: This retrospective empirical study combines both qualitative and quantitative research methods. Firstly, researchers collected the de-identified patient-level data (from March-2020 to December-2020). The ED visit trends, cohort patient groups' length of stay (LOS) during COVID-19 were evaluated from an academic tertiary hospital ED. A two-way ANOVA analysis was conducted to comprehend the impact of arrival months and disposition groups on their LOS.

Secondly, on-site walk-through-interview and in-depth semi-structured interviews were conducted to gather information about the operation models (patient-flow, staff-movement) and space adaptions as an evolving response to different waves of the COVID-19 pandemic.

Results: Operational metrics analysis revealed that the distinct differences in LOS during different phases of the pandemic evolution. Different waves of the COVID-19 pandemic influenced ED visit trends; in particular, weekly visits significantly dropped during the first wave in April-2020 and moderately during the third wave in November-2020. In the first and third wave strikes, all four patients received faster care than in the previous month, except for COVID-19 admitted patients in the first wave. Two-way ANOVA analysis revealed statistically significant interaction effects between arrival months and disposition groups. Compared to the other three groups, discharged non-COVID-19 patients experienced shorter LOS, while admitted non-COVID-19 patients experienced significantly longer LOS.

The interview revealed multiple strategies, including a) negative pressure rooms b) split-flow, and cohort-isolation strategy (separate zone for COVID-19 risk patients), were implemented as infection control strategy and surge capacity. As knowledge of infection risk advanced, COVID-19 patients were no longer geographically separated after May-2020. More importantly, flexible use of treatment and non-treatment areas within and adjacent to ED is key to addressing the unique challenges of evolving nature of pandemic waves.

Findings and Significance: This research revealed the importance of a flexible cohort-isolation strategy in adapting to the evolving stages of pandemics. Designing with built-in-flexibility and adaptability is essential to be better prepared for future pandemics. Filling a current knowledge gap of ED design will benefit front-line staff in clinical settings, hospital administrators, architects, and others.

Rehabilitation Facilities for Substance Abuse: A Healing Approach to Design for Treatment Affordability

Cullen Moser *(Kansas State University);* ***Mariana Junqueira*** *(Kansas State University)*

It is no secret that the abuse of substances such as alcohol and illicit drugs is an ongoing public health concern in the United States. The latest National Survey on Drug Use and Health, estimated that 21.6 million Americans needed substance use treatment in 2019 to address problems associated with their use of alcohol or illicit drugs (Substance

Abuse and Mental Health Services Administration - SAMHSA, 2020). However, many of these individuals do not get or seek the treatment they need. In 2019, only 2.7 million received treatment at a rehabilitation facility (as an inpatient or outpatient). Financial limitations are one of the major barriers that prevent people from receiving treatment, as most substance abuse victims are impoverished. For instance, 15% of addicts do not seek treatment due to financial barriers and 17% left treatment early due to treatment costs (Hardey, Thomas, Stein, Kelley, & Ackermann, 2021). Focusing on the role of design in treatment affordability this study asks, "How can the design of rehabilitation facilities improve treatment access to impoverished populations?" An adequately designed rehabilitation facility is one that provides individuals with the needed treatment for their problems associated with substance abuse in an environment that is conducive to their mental health and well-being. Supporting this idea is a healing design approach. Described as designing a physical environment that supports patients and families through the anxieties experienced during the healing or bereavement processes (Nugraha, Rajendra, & Manik, 2018). In this way, the effectiveness of treatment improves and its duration is reduced, along with its cost (Devlin & Arneill, 2003). Consequently, an adequately designed facility should be more affordable, and thus, more accessible to impoverished populations who are the most affected by substance abuse. Through an evidence-based design approach via qualitative case studies, this study proposes the design of a rehabilitation facility in Detroit, Michigan. The proposed design optimizes treatment services by integrating technology into the space and reduces treatment duration by creating environments that are conducive to improved mental health and well-being. These two design goals (i.e. technology-based service and healing environments) were evidenced from the comparative analysis of precedent facilities around the world (e.g., in the U.S., the Netherlands, and Canada). A content analysis of anonymous online testimonials and interviews with designers who specialize in healthcare environments contributes to further understanding of the experiences individuals have in facilities of this type. Preliminary findings show that rehabilitation facilities, especially those with more affordable treatments, do not provide spaces that support mental health and well-being. Further, these facilities are often designed in ways that make the patients feel trapped, depressed, and isolated. The proposed design addresses these issues through strategies, such as, the use of spatial layouts that reduce stress and anxiety, the application of colors that promotes a sense of security and comfort, and the organization of a program that provides the patients with various spaces that adapt to fit their needs in order to make the recovery process more positive, efficient, and, therefore, more affordable.

Cluster-Formations and Typologies in Radiotherapy Departments Developed from Comparative Floorplan-Analysis

Carolina Kolodziej *(Technische Universität Dresden)*

Cancer treatment is an individualized therapy with the possibility of chemotherapy, surgery and/or radiotherapy. Radiotherapy is an essential part in cancer treatment and is the forefront of effective treatment therapies offered to cancer patients. (Abshire & Lang, 2018) The implementation of evidence-based design in health care facilities can positively influence workflow, travel paths, well-being and quality of stay. (Mahmood, 2021) Transferred to radiotherapy, an optimized architecture and built environment of radiotherapy departments is a prerequisite for treatment. This study establishes typologies and spatial criteria of cluster formations and room organization by analyzing floorplans of radiotherapy departments in German hospitals.

With the current lack of planning requirements of radiotherapy departments, the configuration of room clusters was approached. With the implementation of evidence-based typologies, the workflow and patient-stay in radiotherapy departments can be positively influenced. „By comparing a wide range of building layouts for similar organizations one may achieve a good understanding of the ways in which goals and values can be expressed in spatial solutions. It offers the opportunity to develop a spatiofunctional typology of design solutions." (van der Voordt et al., 1997)

For developing typologies and planning requirements a comparative floorplan-analysis from 25 radiotherapy departments in Germany was conducted. As a first step a list of rooms was drafted and clusters were categorized to structure the complexity of radiotherapy departments. The cluster-formations were further analyzed by their relation, distance and arrangement towards each other. The analysis was inspecting differences and similarities in patterns of spatial relationship for clusters and rooms. In addition, the comparability of different sized departments, measured by the number of therapy rooms, was investigated

With this comparative floorplan-analysis a classification of radiotherapy departments based on organizational and spatial characteristics was developed. 6 cluster-formations were conducted: Outpatient, Imaging, Planning, Therapy, Personnel and Service with each dedicated rooms. Typologies and spatial characteristics were derived and visualized.

The comparative analysis of floorplans shows a spectrum of built environment and cluster arrangements, of which typologies were derived. Further research will be conducted by combining these typologies with workflow, individual travel paths, environment-behavior and requirements of all user groups and expert knowledge. With this multilayered study, design recommendations and planning requirements for radiotherapy departments will be developed.

References

Abshire, D., & Lang, M. K. (2018). The Evolution of Radiation Therapy in Treating Cancer. *Seminars in Oncology Nursing, 34*(2), 151–157. https://doi.org/https://doi.org/10.1016/j.soncn.2018.03.006

Mahmood, F. J. (2021). The role of evidence-based design in informing health-care architects. *Journal of Facilities Management, 19*(2), 249–262. https://doi.org/10.1108/JFM-09-2020-0062

van der Voordt, T. J. M., Vrielink, D., & van Wegen, H. B. R. (1997). Comparative floorplan-analysis in programming and architectural design. *Design Studies, 18*(1), 67–88. https://doi.org/https://doi.org/10.1016/S0142-694X(96)00016-6

A 'Flip-Book' Approach for Documenting Walking Preference in Rural Communities

David Spooner *(The University of Georgia)*

Researchers have identified significant linkages between public health and the design of the built environment. The impact the form cities and suburban communities have on physical activity, walkability, social and mental health is well documented. However, research focused on rural communities (pop. < 5000) is not as prevalent and research methodologies tailored to measure rural environments have not been developed and tested on a similar level. One of the complicating factors is the lack of GIS data and a 'rural' process to analyze the opportunities and constraints related to health and the built environment (Lee, 2014). Organizations such as the American Planning Association and Centers for Disease Control have developed resources to inform rural communities how to collect baseline data for health assessment, but unlike the 'macro' variables used to measure urban contexts, rural data is often unavailable, and/or it does not inform the design of the built environment to reach healthy outcomes on a 'micro' site scale (Reid, 2009).

To help fill this void, this study tests a methodology that strives to collect site specific data and assess the functional and experiential quality of walking in rural communities. A 'flip-book' tool was created and used to record motion and movement sequences that highlight known issues associated with proposed walking routes. The method is based on Photovoice, which is a local community-based qualitative data collection method that allows rural residents to photograph physical and metaphorical barriers that limit their decision to engage in walking activity (Catalani, 2010). The method was tested in the rural communities of Crawfordville (pop. 516) and Vienna (pop. 3,664) Georgia. Two specific walking routes, one in each community, was identified as a key connection between residents and services, yet were under utilized as walkable routes. To understand why this was the case, residents were asked to view a 'flip-book' photo sequence of the route and comment on it.

Findings indicate community members were able to identify positive and negative aspects of the walking route and were successful in voicing concerns related to the functional sequence and experiential quality of the route. The results were subsequently used during a conceptual design effort to recommend future improvements.

References

Catalani, Caricia and Meredith Minkler. (2010) Photovoice: A Review of the Literature in Health and Public Health. *Health Education and Behavior*, 37:3, 424-451.

Ewing, Reid and Susan Handy. (2009) Measuring the Unmeasurable: Urban Design qualities Related to Walkability. *Journal of Urban Design*, 14:1, 65-84.

Lee, Sungduck and Emily Talen. (2014) Measuring Walkability: A Note on Auditing Methods. *Journal of Urban Design*, 19:3, 368-388.

Green Skins for Gray Cores: The Impact of LEED Building Envelope Retrofits on Occupant's Health and Well-Being

Ihab Elzeyadi *(Dept. of Architecture)*

Employers, developers, and designers are persuaded, in response to an increasing marketing campaign by the green building industry, that LEED-certified buildings affect the health and well-being of occupants in many ways. With staff accounting for 90% of business operating costs, a 1% improvement in productivity can have a major impact on the bottom line and competitiveness of any business. Building developers are also discovering the business value of delivering healthy and green buildings to their markets, which are tied to increasing rent and competitiveness in office buildings real estate. Despite the favorability of these hypotheses, most recent studies have failed to systemically prove these linkages leading to non-conclusive evidence of green building performance. In addition, the current trend of open-office plans and glazed facades in work environments to achieve LEED certification credits resulted in mixed perceptions of favorability of this design strategy by the building occupants. The specific question of this presentation answers is whether a well-planned evaluation study with pre-post occupancy analysis of a retrofitted, green-certified building could lead to more conclusive findings related to the impacts of green buildings, in general, and those with specific high IEQ on occupant's well-being, health, and productivity.

A late 1960's commercial office building was transformed into a state-of-the-art double platinum-rated LEED® (USGBC LEED v3 Core and Shell and Commercial Interiors) corporate headquarters over an extensive 18-month renovation period. Approximately eight-hundred employees work within 270,000 square feet of open-concept office space with an additional 116 meeting rooms available to promote cross-collaboration. The traditional floor plan with perimeter offices and central workstations was reconfigured into an open-concept office space with central workstations, perimeter hallways, and collaborative space. The existing building was stripped down to the steel and concrete structural core and enclosed in a high-performance building envelope and glass façade. The interior open-plan office space was designed to maximize occupant comfort, as well as improve the health and well-being of the employees.

The presentation describes the extensive improvements to green the existing building envelope, interior space, and mechanical systems. A comprehensive PrePost Occupancy Evaluation protocol (PPOE) was employed to assess and analyze multi-comfort parameters and metrics of the thermal, visual, acoustical, and air quality environment over one year, both before and after occupancy. Results of a systematic indoor environmental quality (multi-comfort) assessment and pre-post occupancy evaluation for the building and its occupants pre-and post-retrofit, using continuous and intermittent measurements to quantify indoor thermal, visual, and acoustical comfort, as well as air quality, will be presented and correlated with the occupant's surveyed experience. The presentation will provide evidence-based guidelines for implementing successful design strategies to improve the IEQ of an all-glass building. Most important, is the application of an integrated design and post-occupancy evaluation process that would act as a replicable methodology to the design and operation of the future all-glass building.

Place-Based Health Uncertainty: A Bayesian Approach to Heuristics

Michelle Ossmann *(Herman Miller)*; ***Eric Ossmann*** *(Prisma Health)*

Place-based health uncertainty associated with the COVID-19 pandemic drove millions to avoid needed care, stymied educational pursuits for a generation of children and young adults, and upended nearly every economic enterprise. While SARS-CoV-2 appears to be moving to endemic status such that we will become immunologically and psychologically accustomed to this coronavirus, we would be remiss to ignore the health communication lessons of this recent scare: it will not be our last.

Generations ago were familiar with place-based health uncertainty, associating stagnant air, poor environmental cleanliness, and lower socioeconomic class, among other characteristics, with risk. These heuristics – however accurate or not – provided a key element for a sense of safety, namely, control. In contrast, the constant place and behavior-related COVID-19 updates from national and international public health bodies have resulted in citizen confusion, frustration, and mistrust, expressed humorously via social media and dangerously through disregard. While updates reflect the novelty of the current threat and desired transparency, that is, 'learn and do', the confusion amongst the general public is only heightened by the known challenges associated with making decisions related to risk.

No doubt future contagions will carry their own set of unknowns, dos and don'ts. To effectively participate in an ongoing mitigation strategy, the general public needs to understand the relationship between place-based activity and risk to develop reasonably accurate heuristics. Using a COVID-19-based mitigation model (Rivers, Martin, Watson, et al., 2020), we present the development of a Bayesian, yet distinctively human-centered framework – the Risk Journey Map (RJM), towards the development of such a mindset.

The RJM is grounded in three core tenets: visualization, co-production, and adaptation. Visual aids have been shown to improve risk comprehension and promote risk-avoidance behaviors across international samples and most pertinently, the vulnerable. Such visualization is also associated with trust and willingness to participate in decision-making, which we suggest is the basis for co-production. The notion of co-produced public and healthcare services are well-described (Batalden M, Batalden P, Margolis P, et al., 2016) and especially relevant for developing resiliency by empowering citizens and communities to adapt as new information becomes available. Such tools are commonplace for personal and public health but have not yet been extended to include place. A Bayesian approach to heuristics is but one potential avenue to alleviate place-based health uncertainty, restoring a modicum of control to the individual, organization, and society.

References

Rivers, C., Martin, E., Watson, C., Schoch-Spana, M., Mullen, L., Sell, T. K., Gottlieb, S., Warmbrod, K. L., Hosangadi, D., Kobokovich, A., Potter, C., Cicero, A., & Inglesby, T. (2020). *Public Health Principles for a Phased Reopening During COVID-19: Guidance for Governors.* The Johns Hopkins Center for Health Security. https://www.centerforhealthsecurity.org/our-work/publications/2020/public-health-principles-for-a-phased-reopening-during-COVID-19-guidance-for-governors

Batalden, M., Batalden, P., Margolis, P., Seid, M., Armstrong, G., Opipari-Arrigan, L., & Hartung, H. (2016). Coproduction of healthcare service. *BMJ Qual Saf, 25*(7), 509–517. https://doi.org/10.1136/bmjqs-2015-004315&domain=pdf&date_stamp=2015-09-16

Mediation Effects of Travel Satisfaction and Social Relationship on the Association between Built Environment and Subjective Well-Being: Preliminary Findings from Singapore

Natasha Yeo *(Singapore University of Technology and Design)*; **Yohei Kato** *(Singapore University of Technology and Design)*; **Kanchana Devi Sokkalingam** *(Singapore University of Technology and Design)*; **Keng Hua Chong** *(Singapore University of Technology and Design)*

In light of rapid urbanization across the world, concerns for the mental and physical health of urban populations have grown recently. The COVID-19 pandemic brought further attention to the health and well-being of urban dwellers and highlighted urgent needs to design healthy built environment. In examining the role of the built environment to promote well-being of urban residents, environmental determinists tend to claim the deterministic role of the physical environment on human behaviors and perceptions, often ignoring non-physical factors (e.g. social demographics and personal values) on social life (Dempsey, 2009).

As a more holistic approach examining the relationship, recent studies have proposed several frameworks that link built environment and non-physical factors with health and well-being. Mouratidis (2021) synthesized several models from earlier studies and proposed the seven pathways through which built environment affects subjective well-being (SWB). This framework aims to understand the mechanism in which built environment, in relation to non-physical factors, influences SWB of urban populations. The framework also offers a basis for urban planners and policymakers to improve SWB through urban planning strategies. However, there is limited empirical evidence to support the proposed pathways. For example, little is known about the strength of associations among the proposed variables in the pathways (e.g. public transportation, travel satisfaction, and perceived well-being).

Therefore, this study examined the pathway model, focusing on the associations between physical environment (access to public transportation and pedestrian-friendly design), perceived health, and well-being mediated by satisfaction with public transportation and walkability, and social relationship. The study used cross-sectional survey data collected from residents of Punggol Town (n = 991), Singapore, through a systematic random sampling procedure. Mediation analysis was employed to understand the mechanism of built environment that influence resident's perceived health and well-being through the selected mediators. Standardized effects of mediators were estimated by Bootstrap confidence interval method, using PROCESS version 4.0 (model number 4 in PROCESS; Hayes 2017) for R software (version 4.0.3). The results indicated that travel satisfaction (satisfaction to accessibility to public transportation and perceived walkability) and social relationship mediate the effects of accessibility to public transportation and pedestrian-friendly design on perceived health and SWB. This implies that better access to the nearest train station is associated with the higher perceived satisfaction with public transportation, which in turn is associated with the higher perceived health and well-being of residents. The preliminary findings from this study highlight the potential contribution of mediation analysis in examining the under-studied mechanism of built environment associated with SWB through non-physical factors. The findings also suggest that urban planning strategies targeting to improve travel satisfaction, walkability satisfaction, and social relationship among residents can lead to better well-being and health of residents. Suggestions for future studies include employing a strong research design (experimental design and longitudinal study) and causal inference approaches (e.g. propensity score matching, instrumental variable method).

Exploring the Walkability of Three Urban Hospital-Anchored Neighborhoods

Xiaowei Li *(Clemson University)*; **Dina Battisto** *(Clemson University)*

Background: The field of healthcare design is embracing the concept of healthy communities as a model for planning and designing hospital-anchored neighborhoods. Walkability is a key indicator of creating healthy, vibrant, and livable communities. The urban design qualities of streets contribute to walkability by accommodating a comfortable and safe walking environment, supporting active street life with diverse programs, and providing a pleasant outdoor experience. Limited research exists on how to apply the concept of walkability to connect hospital campuses to surrounding neighborhoods.

Research Objectives: The research has four objectives:

- To assess neighborhood-level walkability across three urban hospital-anchored neighborhoods using National Walkability Index, as measured by four neighborhood-level design dimensions, density, diversity, design, and distance to transits.
- To propose and test a Street-level Walkability Framework by documenting street design features in one hospital-anchored neighborhood related to walkability (Ewing & Clemente, 2013).
- To test data collection methods and procedures in one hospital-anchored neighborhood, as measured by the types of activities on the streets, how pedestrians use the streets, and how they experience walking.
- To present design recommendations for creating walkable streets based on lessons learned from the case study.

Methods: A qualitative case study approach is used to explore walkability patterns in three urban hospital-anchored neighborhoods. The neighborhood-level walkability of three cases was assessed using GIS archival data. The Street-level Walkability Framework was used to collect data through a pilot study on one neighborhood among the three. First, street design characteristics were collected from GIS archival data, Google views, and field photos. Second, ethnographic observations were collected to generate behavioral maps that track the street use, the pedestrians' locations, and activities from snapshots of the streets during the morning, noon, and evening hours. Third, the pedestrian walking experience was studied from 40 semi-structured interviews with people familiar with the pilot neighborhood.

Results: The neighborhood-level walkability of three neighborhoods are indicated by the ranking of their National Walkability Index. The street-level walkability pattern of one studied neighborhood is revealed by the integration of street features, behavioral mapping, and interviews. Street segments with the highest and lowest number of pedestrians were compared according to the street design qualities and neighborhood contextual factors. In addition, interviews provided insights into pedestrians' perceptions of which streets are more walkable in the neighborhood and why. Findings from one neighborhood study indicate some revisions to the Street-level Walkability Framework. Evidence-based design guidelines for planning and designing walkable urban hospital-anchored neighborhoods will be presented based on lessons learned. Methods and procedures tested in the one studied neighborhood will be applied to all three neighborhoods.

References

Ewing, R. H., & Clemente, O. (2013). *Measuring urban design: Metrics for livable places*. Island Press.

US EPA (2014, February 27). *Smart Location Mapping*. US EPA.

Urban Corridors: A Healthy Asset for the City. University Heights Corridor Planning Intervention

Ana Karinna Hidalgo (University of Saskatchewan)

North American suburbs have brought many non-solved planning issues to cities. Subsidized infrastructure, sprawl, commuting times are among the top negative characteristics of these areas. However, people are still looking at renting and ownership opportunities in the suburbs. Among the reasons are affordability, privacy, oversized lots, and a sense of community reclaimed by inner-city and downtown areas. With few opportunities to redo what is designed, developed, and implemented, this project is aimed at giving suburbs the opportunity to be a positive asset to the city.

The pandemic and the post-pandemic world are reclaiming nature. Native species, urban biodiversity, edible gardens, and green and blue landscapes are well-known for their environmental, physical, mental health, and food security benefits. Unfortunately, downtown and inner-city areas have few vacant spaces designed for these purposes. However, the public and private areas of the suburbs would be ideal locations to promote urban biodiversity and, therefore, health, economic, environmental and social benefits attached to it.

Biodiversity in cities is well-known for the various ecosystem services and physical and mental health benefits that it can provide. There is a strong connection between nature and health that involves air quality, physical activity, social cohesion, and stress reduction (Hartig et al., 2014). However, nature is not considered a priority for most city planning and design endeavors.

The Corridor Planning project at the City of Saskatoon, Canada, incorporates some of these concepts. The city's proposed scenario considers these corridors as places for people and destinations and not only roads (City of Saskatoon, 2021). Although this transformation will significantly improve people's urban landscape and living conditions using these corridors, there is an opportunity not yet included.

This planning studio project was developed during the PLAN490 Senior Planning Studio at the University of Saskatchewan (Winter 2022). Using site planning analysis, observation, surveys and map and data analysis, students proposed a sustainable, vibrant, and healthy design for the University Heights corridor segment that connects the suburban west side of the City of Saskatoon.

In a joint effort with city planners and the public, students designed a corridor proposal based on the 'comprehensive street functions framework.' This framework considers four functions for streets: channel, container, social and health artifact. The current corridor planning includes channel and social artifact functions. However, the 'container' function (biodiversity, urban design elements) and health artifact were not included.

A report demonstrating the economic, social and mainly health benefits of this urban design intervention is the outcome of this project. In addition, the multi-dimension benefits of this vision are worth replicating for transit corridors.

References

City of Saskatoon (2021). *Corridor Planning*. Retrieved from https://www.saskatoon.ca/business-development/planning/growth-plans/plan-growth/corridor-planning

Hartig, T., Mitchell, R., De Vries, S., & Frumkin, H. (2014). Nature and health. *Annual Review of Public Health, 35*, 207–228. https://doi.org/10.1146/annurev-publhealth-032013-182443

Implications of a Flexible Work Model on Corporate Design

Kara N Freihoefer *(HGA Architects and Engineers);*
Sarah Berseth *(HGA Architects and Engineers)*

Employees of most corporate companies have spent the last 1.5 plus years in a virtual and remote work environment because of the COVID-19 pandemic. Most of these employees previously worked in an open office setting with dedicated workstations that were often found to be highly exposed to distractions and lack environmental control. Remote working has completely flipped these experiences as employees have minimal disruptions and more choice over preferred conditions while working remotely. As corporations are starting to plan for their employees to the return to office post-pandemic, employees are expecting a different type of work environment that offers similar accommodations experienced while working remotely.

A national architecture and engineering firm has been studying the impact of the pandemic on workplace strategy and design with their clients and among themselves. This presentation will detail results of a multi-method research approach that applied findings to the renovation of the firm's largest office located in the mid-west. The findings helped to shape the firms flexible work policy and to inform the office redesign.

First, a company-wide employee questionnaire was issued in the Summer of 2021 (n = 223, 69.7% response rate). The questionnaire had four sections: demographics, pre-pandemic, remote work, and post-pandemic. Questions were centered around employees' overall satisfaction with work environmental qualities, perceived productivity, desired workplace attributes, and motivating factors for visiting the office. Furthermore, eight semi-structure focus groups were conducted, each hosting roughly ten employees from various departments. Questionnaire findings helped to develop focus groups questions around collaboration and conferencing spaces, individual work areas, and workplace amenities. Other aspects of importance were discussed, including how to best foster mentorship and encourage spontaneity within a flexible work model.

According to studied participants, 91% have indicated the pandemic has made them think differently about how they can work, while 80% are satisfied with their remote work experience during the pandemic. The top benefit of remote work selected among participants was not having a commute which, in turn, enables a more flexible work schedule. Ergonomic discomfort was the top negative impact of remote work. Overwhelmingly, participants signified that collaboration, face-to-face meetings and socialization are the top three reasons they will come into the office post-pandemic.

The data was synthesized into a design success criterion that outlined four return to the office themes. The themes include support a collaborative, studio-like work environment; organize space to showcase work and to encourage spontaneity, mentorship, and socialization; provide flexibility and variety for individual work; and design an aesthetic and appealing environment reflective of the company's core values. Each theme details several attributes to consider for design, procedure/policy, and technology responses. For example, to support a collaborative environment, the design team must provide solutions that supports an equitable experience for all meeting attendees whether they are in-person and/or virtual. Designers must ideate to create flexible collaborative spaces with multi-technology solutions, such as dual displays to simultaneously show documentation or boards and the speaker. Concurrently, specific conference procedures are being developed to foster a respectful and equalized experience for all employees.

Why Hand Hygiene in Nursing Homes Matters? Built Environment's Impact on Compliance

Hao Huang *(Texas A&M University);* ***Wenjin Wang*** *(Texas A&M University);* ***Seokyung Park*** *(Texas A&M University)*

Nursing homes have been hit hard by the COVID-19 pandemic, with more than 134,000 COVID-related resident deaths. Although less than 1% of Americans live in nursing homes, they accounted for 20% of all U.S. COVID-19 deaths during this time period (The Centers for Disease Control and Prevention [CDC], 2021a). As nursing home residents are very vulnerable to infectious disease, including COVID-19, infection prevention and control is crucial to minimizing the spread of infectious diseases. Unfortunately, before the pandemic, infection control was not a paramount issue in nursing homes, compared with hospitals and other acute care settings, so nursing homes were less prepared for the COVID-19 pandemic.

Infectious diseases are caused by microbes such as viruses, fungi, etc. The diseases may be transmitted from person to person or through another medium. Scientists have developed a model to help understand infectious diseases - Epidemiologic Triangle. The triangle is comprised of three sides: agent, host, and environment (CDC, 2021b). To prevent the spread of infectious disease, at least one side of the triangle must be broken. Hand hygiene is a widely accepted method to break the triangle and prevent infections in healthcare facilities. The hand hygiene compliance of healthcare workers and staff members plays a crucial role in infection control (Cai et al., 2020; Hamilton, 2013).

Research in the healthcare industry has focused on developing various interventions to improve hand hygiene compliance, such as training sessions and rewards to care workers. However, few studies have focused on the effect of built environment on hand hygiene compliance, and very few studies were found that specifically addressed environmental aspects of hand hygiene in nursing home settings. The goal of this research is to address this gap. This study has explored the role of environmental design in improving nursing home staff hand hygiene compliance.

The pandemic has exposed significant infectious disease-related challenges experienced in nursing homes. This research will broaden our understanding of how nursing home facility design might facilitate lower levels of infectious disease transmission. This study has the potential to impact the future of the healthcare architecture industry by using design strategies to increase hand hygiene compliance.

References

Cai, H., Tyne, I. A., Spreckelmeyer, K., & Williams, J. (2020). Impact of Visibility and Accessibility on Healthcare Workers' Hand-Hygiene Behavior: A Comparative Case Study of Two Nursing Units in an Academic Medical Center. *Health Environments Research & Design Journal, 14*(2), 271–288 https://doi.org/10.1177/1937586720962506

CDC (2021a, September 30). *Nursing Home COVID-19 Data Dashboard*. https://www.cdc.gov/nhsn/covid19/ltc-report-overview.html

CDC (2021b, April 10). *Understanding the Epidemiologic Triangle through Infectious Disease*. https://www.cdc.gov/healthyschools/bam/teachers/epi-triangle.html

Hamilton, D. K. (2013). Facility Design to Reduce Hospital-Acquired Infection. *Health Environments Research & Design Journal, 6*(2), 93–97. https://doi.org/10.1177/193758671300600208

Using Design to Keep the Frontline Healthcare Workers Safe during a Pandemic: A Research-Based Approach

Yeinn G Oh *(Georgia Institute of Technology);* ***Zorana Matic*** *(Georgia Institute of Technology);* ***Lisa Lim*** *(KAIST)*

As the current outbreak of Coronavirus Disease continues to affect the countries worldwide, addressing the needs of frontline healthcare workers (HCW) has become a high priority. During the 2014 Ebola outbreak, the doffing of personal protective equipment (PPE) and activities in the doffing area were identified as one of the biggest challenges for HCW's safety. In response, the importance of environmental design has become more evident. In response to the 2014 Ebola outbreak, the CDC updated their guidance on PPE donning and doffing, in which they emphasized the importance of BCU design. Recent studies have found that the doffing area's design can support a safer process by reducing self- and cross-contamination risk. However, as many patient-care sites are often adapted for biocontainment use to address the patient surge, there is significant variability in the doffing area's design. The efficiency of such various design layouts remains unclear.

In this presentation, we will provide examples of doffing area design and illustrate ways to evaluate the various design layouts from the users' perspective and implications to their safety. We will define the different roles of healthcare workers in the doffing area, namely the doffing healthcare workers (DHCW) and the Trained Observer (TO), and discuss their specific spatial requirements. We will then explain how different configurations may impact DHCWs' doffing performance. For instance, the DHCW needs to have access to critical items within arm's reach, but at the same time enough maneuvering clearance around their designated doffing spot to minimize the risk of unexpected cross-contamination to the environment. On the other hand, the trained observer needs to have visibility of the DHCW at all times and a designated working area.

Our findings reveal performance scores of several doffing area configurations and demonstrate the method that can be used for design, evaluation, and comparison of layouts when choosing between options. Finally, we will discuss the design strategies that designers can employ to improve communication between HCWs, reduce the cognitive and physical load, and, ultimately, enhance the HCWs' safety during the doffing process. These strategies should be considered for implementation in both current and future doffing spaces and non-traditional patient-care sites where PPE doffing occurs.

The Importance of Walking As a Design Strategy for Post-Pandemic Living

Sarah Trautvetter *(Morgan State University)*

Walking became a method many used to help themselves cope with the stresses of solitude and isolation at the height of the pandemic in the Spring of 2020. Some people have always found walking a beneficial way of dealing with loneliness or being free to think without distraction. Others have never considered walking as anything more than "merely practical, the unconsidered locomotive means between two sites." (Solnit, p. 3) Many of those in the practical corner will keep on walking long after we have come out the other side of COVID 19 and it is up to Landscape Architects to continue to design spaces that inspire regular walking, in both cities and suburban areas.

The word walking as a noun is defined by Merriam-Webster as "1: the action of one that walks; 2: the condition of a surface for one going on foot." The fact that both the physical action required for the movement and the ground's surface condition are included in the definition highlight the two main prerequisites for a successful walk: mobility and a smooth, unobstructed surface. The act of physically putting one's foot to the ground brings an experience that is not replicated by bike, bus, or car. As Solnit writes in Wanderlust, "The rhythm of walking generated a kind of rhythm of thinking, and the passage through a landscape echoes or stimulates the passage through a series of thoughts." (Solnit, p. 6) A walk through leaves is a very different experience than a walk in the sand or a walk down a brick sidewalk. The haptic experience of each walk's condition generates a unique primitive reaction in the walker. Walking allows us to remain connected to the landscape (whether urban neighborhood or rural meadow). Landscape Architect, James Corner, describes the importance of walking, this physical touch with the land: "Landscape is best understood not as scenery, object or thing, as if external to the human body, but more as a deeply visceral milieu within which the body is fully and completely immersed." (Mind Landscapes (2020): 62)

This paper presentation will explore the cultural and literary history of walking, its beneficial impacts on our physical health, and its psychological effects. It will demonstrate how walking played an important role in keeping people of all ages and demographics healthy and sane during the long months of isolation. And it will argue that the continued creation of walking trails that are both ecologically functional and accessible to all users, while also providing four-seasons of color and texture is a challenge. But this is a challenge that we, as Landscape Architects, are particularly skilled to tackle and for which we are ethically responsible.

The Association between Urban Environments and Hedonic Well-Being

Asesh Sarkar *(IIT Roorkee);* ***Tina Pujara*** *(IIT Roorkee)*

Studies have established a strong association between urbanization and the rise in mental disorders amongst the urban population. Globally, urbanization is at its peak and hence, comprehending how urbanization may be leading to a rise in mental disorders, is the urgent need of the hour. Literature suggests that urban environments (UE) may be directly impacting mental well-being (MW). It further suggests that these impacts may be either positive or negative, depending on the respective environment. However, research seems to have paid less attention on considering particularly how the physical and social environments may be impacting the hedonic well-being of the urban inhabitants. This paper is an attempt to understand the relationship between UE and MW with particular regard to the physical and social environments and specifically the hedonic well-being (HW). This literature review identified articles particularly related to urban environment indicators associated with well-being and their impact on hedonic well-being, at both urban and neighborhood scale. The selection of the research papers and review papers were based on the relationship of indicators of the PE with HW and the relationship between the urban social environment resulting as the perceived environment with HW. This paper presents the relationship between UE and HW, in form of the UE-indicators identified, with reference to both its positive and negative impacts on HW. The identification of these indicators, particularly focusing on the physical and social environments of the urban scenario is a step towards developing a methodology for assessing the impact of UE on MW. This methodology may further contribute towards mentally healthy city design.

User Journey Mapping: A User-Product Interaction Method to Evaluate and Inform Solutions to Improve Medication Adherence for Older Adults with Dementia

Anne Cramer *(Cornell University);* ***Rana Zadeh*** *(Cornell University);* ***Elizabeth Capezuti*** *(City University of New York)*

As part of a large research project entitled Home Opioid Prescription Education and Smart Storage (HOPES), a novel research and community outreach engagement initiative designed to improve medication adherence and minimize medication mistakes among community-dwelling older adults with early-to-moderate levels of dementia and cognitive impairment, the research team employed the methodology of user journey mapping to understand and document the experience of searching for, purchasing, and using a purpose-built medication management system. The journey mapping method is widely used in customer and user experience design, wherein all aspects of a user's experience with a product or service are mapped in a visual medium. Presenting the holistic user journey allows researchers to find potential pain points and moments of truth for the user, thus allowing for opportunities to improve product or service design. For the HOPES project, the journeys of both the older adults and their caregivers are presented in a map that highlights all interactions, pain points, and moments of truth along the user life cycle stages, including searching for a medication management system, reading reviews and assessing the best options for their specific needs, selecting a system, purchasing and using the system, and either fully adopting or rejecting it. As Funded by the National Institute of Aging of the National Institute of Health, the goal of HOPES is to achieve a significant reduction in negative health outcomes due to medication mismanagement and support safety among a growing geriatric population. This journey mapping effort, informed with service design and user-product interaction methodologies, can reveal the ways that evidence-based solutions are feasible and adaptable for the end user.

The Role of the Built Environment in Surgical Ergonomics and Interactions in the Operating Room

Sara Kennedy *(Clemson University)*

Background: Ergonomics and the built environment play a significant role for surgeons operating in the operating room (OR) and can influence factors like the mental and physical health of surgeons, surgical performance, and patient safety. Outcomes like fatigue, physical pain, eye strain, cognitive health, and ability to complete tasks are caused by ergonomic failures in the OR related to monitor placement, noisy work conditions, inadequate lighting, and challenging OR layouts (Lee et al., 2014).

Method: This study is an in-depth, narrative literature review conducted to understand the surgeon's ergonomic experience in the OR, their primary tasks, and the equipment they interact with, in various types of surgical procedures. A key objective was to understand and identify built environment features that contribute to poor ergonomic environments in the operating room, and how layout, noise, lighting, and monitor placement impact outcomes related to surgeons' health, performance, and patient safety. Through the literature search, 31 articles were found to be relevant for full review and were cited in a summary of findings.

Findings: By evaluating the scope of the literature, surgeons were found to experience musculoskeletal pain in their neck, back, and shoulders related to work tasks (Yu et al., 2016). The physical pain and fatigue surgeons experience from poorly designed display equipment, inadequate lighting environments, and excessive noise in the OR can lead to more severe outcomes like sleep deprivation and burnout for surgeons, increasing chances of surgical errors and risks for patient safety (Koshy et al., 2020). The literature showed that outcomes like task performance, patient safety, surgeon's health can be alleviated through design solutions like increasing the size of the OR and implementing flexible lighting systems. As well as applying sound-dampening surface materials, and correct placement of the monitor. These evidence-based design applications showed improvement in the ergonomic conditions, viewing angles, and eased physical pain and mental strain in the OR.

Conclusions: It is important to consider ergonomic environments in the operating room since they directly impact staff and patient outcomes. The literature shows a clear understanding of the cost of poor ergonomics, but there is limited research of the OR layout related to surgical ergonomics. Disruptions near the surgeon, crowding of equipment, or interactions with clinicians, and how these factors impact a surgeon's ergonomic environment, also need more exploration.

Keywords: Surgical ergonomics, Surgeon, Human factors, Operating room, Ergonomics

References

Koshy, K., Syed, H., Luckiewicz, A., Alsoof, D., Koshy, G., & Harry, L. (2020). Interventions to improve ergonomics in the operating theatre: A systematic review of ergonomics training and intra-operative microbreaks. *Annals of medicine and surgery, 55*, 135-142.

Lee, G. I., Lee, M. R., Clanton, T., Sutton, E., Park, A. E., & Marohn, M. R. (2014). Comparative assessment of physical and cognitive ergonomics associated with robotic and traditional laparoscopic

Yu, D., Green, C., Kasten, S. J., Sackllah, M. E., & Armstrong, T. J. (2016). Effect of alternative video displays on postures, perceived effort, and performance during microsurgery skill tasks. *Applied Ergonomics, 53*, 281–289.

Impact of Exposure to Virtual Tours of Healthcare Facility on Child and Parent Anxiety

Swati Goel *(Clemson University);* ***Soheyla MohammadiGorji*** *(Clemson University);* ***Sahar Mihandoust*** *(Clemson University);* ***Matthew Browning*** *(Clemson University);* ***Anjali Joseph*** *(Clemson University)*

Pediatric outpatient procedures have risen sharply over the past decade. These procedures can be extremely anxiety-provoking for children and their companions. Nearly 75% of children report feeling anxious prior to their operation. Preoperative stress can negatively impact post-operative physical health outcomes such as length of anesthesia induction and wound healing. Most surgical environments are unfamiliar institutional spaces with intimidating medical devices that may contribute to anxiety prior to a procedure. Exposing patients to the environment in which care will be provided prior to the actual experience may help in decreasing preoperative anxiety. A few studies used simulated video tours of operating rooms to orient children and their parents to surgical procedures. While reported results showed the pre-exposure to surgical environments in VR can help to reduce preoperative anxiety, existing studies focused the tours on operating rooms without adequate consideration of other spaces that children will see throughout surgery day. Additionally, these studies used self-reported measures along with cost-prohibitive method to create the video tours.

In this project, we created a highly realistic virtual models of all spaces (entry lobby, corridors, waiting room, preoperative exam rooms, operating rooms and post-operative room) that children and parents will experience during the day of surgery, so that they can see the exact environment prior their surgical procedure. The overall goal is to help pediatric patients and their parents overcome the environmental triggers of anxiety prior to surgery. The specific aim is to evaluate the impacts of this exposure on anxiety on the day of surgery using established survey and physiological measures (i.e., heart-rate and electrodermal activity).

We recruited 20 children between ages 6-17 and their caregiver/parent at an outpatient surgical center in the Southeastern part of the US. Participants were randomly assigned to a control or intervention group at the time of recruitment. The researchers contacted the parents by phone, text, or email to confirm the parent's and child's interest in participating in the study, and to schedule a second (synchronous) meeting with them. During the second meeting, informed consent was administered to parents and informed assent to children, and demographic and trait-level (generalized) anxiety data was collected using a validated measure. Participants in the intervention group engaged with the virtual tour and participated in a semi-structured interview after the tour. On the day of the procedure, researchers collected data on anxiety in each of the key clinical spaces experienced by participants using objective and subjective measures as well as participant impressions about each space. In this presentation, we will present our findings from the comparison of control and intervention groups with regard to the anxiety levels of children and their caregivers on the day of procedure.

Exploring Nurse Burnout between Nurses in COVID-19 and Non COVID-19 Units and the Role of Break Area Support in the Hospital

Sahar Mihandoust *(Clemson University);* ***Anjali Joseph*** *(Clemson University);* ***Jamie Roney*** *(Covenant Health)*

Burnout is highly prevalent among nurses (Ribeiro et al., 2014). More than forty percent of hospital nurse staff in the US are reported to have high levels of burnout. Nurse burnout has negative impacts both on nurses' physical and mental health, and organizational productivity, service quality, and patient outcomes (Lerner et al., 2004). COVID-19 has intensified burnout among nurses and clinicians (Ross, 2020). A high-quality break area for nurses can enhance job satisfaction and reduce retention (Nejati, Rodiek, & Shepley, 2016), however, there is paucity of research exploring how perceived support from access to a nurse break area can impact burnout.

This study explores the relationship between the perceived support from having a break area and measures of burnout between nurses working in two units for COVID-19 patients and two units dedicated to non-COVID-19 patients. This study also explores the features of the break areas utilized by the nurses in the two types of units to understand whether there is a difference between break area utilization between nurses who experience higher levels of burnout.

This study collected data from 52 nurses working in COVID-19 units and 38 nurses working in non-COVID-19 units. Data was collected on demographics, burnout scores, break areas support and utilization of break area from both day and night shift nurses.

Study findings show that nurses in the COVID-19 units had a significantly higher score for emotional exhaustion and depersonalization compared to nurses working in non-COVID-19 units. Nurses in COVID-19 units who thought the break area location supported their use of the break area had significantly lower emotional exhaustion compared to other nurses in this group. A higher percentage of nurses in COVID-19 units took their breaks in their workstation. Nurses in COVID-19 units had windows in their break area but they demonstrated they needed access to fresh air and relaxation station and nurses in non-COVID-19 units noted the need for additional space and windows to nature views.

The study findings suggests that perceived support in the break area can be related to the nurse burnout. Positive features such as access to fresh air and nature view were the top listed features deemed necessary by nurses. Nurses provided with windows in the break area suggested also the need for fresh air. Integrating balconies or gardens in break area design may ameliorate the negative impact of burnout intensifying events such as COVID-19.

References

Nejati, A., Rodiek, S., & Shepley, M. (2016). The implications of highquality staff break areas for nurses' health, performance, job satisfaction and retention. *Journal of nursing management, 24*(4), 512-523.

Ribeiro, V. F., Ferreira Filho, C., Valenti, V. E., Ferreira,

M., de Abreu, L. C., de Carvalho, T. D., . . . Leão, E. R. (2014). Prevalence of burnout syndrome in clinical nurses at a hospital of excellence. *International archives of medicine, 7*(1), 22.

Ross, J. (2020). The exacerbation of burnout during COVID-19: A major concern for nurse safety. *Journal of PeriAnesthesia Nursing, 35*(4), 439-440.

Research on Outdoor Living Environment of Rural Elderly Community in China

Menghan Liu *(Beijing Jiaotong University);* ***Yi Yang*** *(Beijing Jiaotong University);* ***Bo Zhang*** *(Oklahoma State University)*

With the acceleration of China's urbanization and industrialization, the elderly population in urban and rural areas continues to grow. Compared with the previous 10 years, the population aged 60 and over and the population aged 65 and over have increased by 2.51% and 2.72% respectively. The aging trend in China is becoming more and more severe, and the social pension pressure is increasing year by year, and it will reach its maximum in 2051. Therefore, some old people with a certain economic foundation and good physical conditions choose to go to rural areas with beautiful surroundings for the elderly. At present, most domestic scholars are studying the service system, supporting infrastructure, and aging design of the internal space in the rural elderly care community, and lack of discussion and excavation on the outdoor living environment of the rural elderly care community.

Empirical research can provide researchers with first-hand information, and the results obtained are more accurate and objective, and can be used for reference. This paper takes the rural elderly care communities in the suburbs of Beijing as the research object, and conducts a questionnaire survey on the elderly living in them. First, the elderly living in it are divided into urban elderly and rural elderly, the survey data is visualized, and the survey results of two different groups of people are compared to explore 1. Existing problems of the outdoor living environment of rural elderly communities in China. 2. The difference and identity of the urban and rural elderly's needs for the outdoor living environment of the rural elderly care community. 3. The degree of satisfaction of the urban and rural elderly with the outdoor living environment of our country's rural elderly care community. These three issues also explain 1. Strategies for improving the living environment of the rural elderly in China. 2. The weighting ratio of various indicators of the outdoor living environment evaluation system of the rural elderly care community. 3. The construction strategy of the outdoor living environment evaluation system of the rural elderly care community. Provide a theoretical basis for the construction of the outdoor living environment of the rural elderly community.

Evaluating Daylight in Nursing Homes: An Analysis of Three Small House Case Studies

Jana Stojanovska *(Ryerson University);* ***Terri Peters*** *(Ryerson University)*

Exposure to daylight in residential environments has been proven to support healthy sleep patterns, reduce stress, and improve physical and psychological wellbeing (Veitch and Galasiu 2012). In typical nursing homes, resident rooms are arranged along a double loaded corridor, and social spaces and amenities are centralized, requiring residents to socialize and eat together in larger groups. COVID-19 increased people's awareness of the challenges of healthy nursing home design and the need for incorporating biophilic design and natural lighting (Peters and Verderber 2021). Numerous studies have shown that daylight is an important part of therapeutic environments for the elderly (Day et al., 2000). This research project examined floorplan layouts of designs that follow 'small house' design principles, a generic name for elder care environments that focus on creating non-institutional and 'home like' designs, where residents live in 8-12 room clusters, have decentralized living and dining areas and other specific staff and facility requirements. A number of small house projects were considered and typology-specific daylight challenges were identified in these environments. This study then evaluated three case studies in more depth, and these floorplans were modeled and simulated for daylight autonomy (to identify spaces with adequate light levels), annual solar exposure (to assess glare and over-lit conditions), and useful daylight illuminance (considering more variety in light levels) using environmental simulation software. The case studies represent different small house designs: a double loaded corridor design in Vancouver, British Columbia, with ten individual residential rooms and shared living spaces on the southeast side; 2) an L-shaped facility consisting of both single and double loaded corridors in Saskatoon, Saskatchewan, with six individual residential rooms and central living spaces, and; 3) a clustered floorplan arrangement in St. Catherines, Ontario, with eight individual residential rooms and central living spaces. The private rooms, social spaces, and staff spaces of each case study was compared, to understand which interior layouts allows for the best daylight conditions. As expected, the L-shaped facility in Saskatoon had the best results, whereas the double-loaded corridor in Vancouver had the worst overall performance. All three projects had resident rooms that had enough daylight based on annual daylight autonomy simulations, but all experienced high levels of glare and over-lighting, which is known to cause discomfort. In all cases, the shared resident social spaces and all staff spaces did not receive sufficient daylight autonomy. The design of social spaces should be reconsidered to promote the comfort and wellbeing of the residents by improving daylighting in these areas. The lack of daylight in staff spaces also highlights another concern of nursing homes which is staff burnout and poor staff satisfaction. The results of this preliminary study will be extended with on site measurements in a more comprehensive analysis of non-renovated and newly renovated nursing homes. A main conclusion of this study is that the use of environmental simulation to evaluate how daylight is experienced in the different spaces can be a powerful tool for predicting future designs and identifying areas for future renovation.

Integrating Research into Design Practice: An Occupancy Outcomes Evaluation of an inpatient Medical Tower Pre and Post Move

Rutali Joshi *(HKS Inc.);* ***Upali Nanda*** *(HKS Inc.);* ***Camilla Moretti*** *(HKS Inc.);* ***Martyna Falloni*** *(HKS Inc.);* ***Parsa Aghaei*** *(Kent State University)*

Objective: When embarking on the design of new inpatient medical tower, a leading Midwest healthcare organization knew that they wanted to utilize an evidence-based design approach. To support this vision, a fully integrated team comprised of designers, health leadership, facility staff, and researchers came together to develop an innovative design that would provide the best possible patient, family and staff experience in a patient-centered care environment.

Methods: A Design Diagnostic was conducted by the research team in the Surgical Intensive Care unit (SICU) and Med-surg units of the existing facility in 2015 to understand challenges in the current state and inform key design and operational innovations to be implemented in the proposed Tower. The design diagnostic is a study method that uses on-site observations, interviews, and off-site spatial analysis using parametric modeling tools. Findings from the research revealed 1) long walking distances for staff for relatively minor tasks; 2) limited point-of-use access to meds and supplies; 3) low visibility/ connectivity impacting care coordination; 4) under-utilized Spaces; 5) spillover staff areas due to unaccommodated WoWs; and (6) excessive noise levels. The design innovation resulting from the research included acuity blocking and service line tracking, blended acuity staffing model, setting up units as pods, shared family and staff zones, dual access nurse servers in each patient room for point-of-care supplies, decentralized nursing stations, nourishment room and collaboration hubs. Following construction, phased move-in and occupancy of the new Tower between 2019-2020, an Outcomes Evaluation study was conducted in 2021. This entailed collection and analysis of reported data (staff interviews, leadership focus groups and staff surveys), observed data (shadowing, behavior mapping, noise measurements, photo essays) and operational data including Hospital Consumer Assessment of Healthcare Providers & Systems (HCAHPS) and other metrics like fall rates identified as Key Performance Indicators.

Results: The Occupancy Outcomes evaluation provided the opportunity to celebrate success as well as identify additional areas for improvement. The unit layout and integration of nurse servers reduced staff walking distance by about 50% (compared to the existing unit), allowing more available time for patient care. In addition, reduction in daytime noise levels, improvement in HCAHPS scores, staff satisfaction around design and size of patient rooms, utilization of sunrooms, minimized clutter are some of the key successes that came to the forefront which reflect operational and design innovation. Additionally, inability to operationalize the Pod model as envisioned, inconsistent stocking of nurse servers, differences in utilization of decentralized care team stations between the ICU AND Med-surg units, as well as repurposing of space came to the forefront.

Conclusion: While several strategies were effective in achieving the pre-defined performance targets, some of the design and operational intent was lost in transition. A check-in between the design team and operational team could have enabled a smooth transition from the old tower to the new tower. It is important that an operational handbook and functional narrative accompany the documented design intent so that the units are operated the way they are planned.

Use of Virtual Tours to Inform Healthcare Facilities Design through the Recognition of Anxiety Triggers

Shuai Yuan *(Clemson University);* ***Matthew Browning*** *(Clemson University);* ***Swati Goel*** *(Clemson University);* ***Anjali Joseph*** *(Clemson University);* ***Sahar Mihandoust*** *(Clemson University);* ***Jonathan Markowitz*** *(Prisma Health);* ***Joseph Heritage*** *(Prisma Health)*

Surgical environments should be designed to minimize perioperative anxiety and thus promote fast recovery. However, "cold" highly functional designs and intimidating medical devices can cause patients and their caregivers to feel anxious. For children, s can even negatively impact post-operative physical health outcomes, including chronic pain, medication use, delirium, and sleep problems (Kain et al., 2006). Previous studies have found that preoperative anxiety can be predicted by children characteristics, presence of parents, music use, and healthcare facility management. Less is known about built design features that impact children's preoperative anxiety. One narrative review of surgical and nonsurgical environments identified nature images, art, spacious rooms, and sunlight could help with patient's pain and anxiety (Vetter et al., 2015), but this review also reported a scarcity of studies on built environmental factors. Interactive virtual tours represent a promising and convenient tool to identify anxiety-inducing (and anxiety-buffering) features in healthcare facilities prior to surgery.

The of this pilot study is to identify anxiety triggers and anxiety-buffering features in pediatric surgical facilities through virtual tours. We used 360-degree images with audio guides to create an interactive virtual tour for phones, tablets, laptops, or head-mounted displays either off- or online. We used established anxiety survey instruments and semi-structured interviews to identify relevant built environment features while pediatric patients experienced the tour and discover factors that influenced satisfaction with the virtual tour. We developed an interactive, environment using the Insta360 Evo and Pro II cameras, as well as 3DVista Virtual Tour software. Tours included all rooms in the Patewood pediatric surgical facility that patients and their parents saw prior to, during, and after their procedure. These included the entry lobby, corridors, waiting room, preoperative exam rooms, operating rooms, and post-operative room. We recruited 20 children aged 6-17 and their caregivers/parents and asked them to experience the virtual tour over Zoom for 15 min. After experiencing the tour, children and caregivers/parents reported anxiety level using the State-Trait Anxiety Inventory for Children (STAIC) and the State-Trait Anxiety Inventory (STAI). Children also participated in semi-structured interviews to evaluate the virtual tour and identify features that induced/buffered against anxiety in each room.

This pilot study will contribute to human-centered healthcare design. It will discover the features in pediatric surgical facilities that impact patients and their parents, and test the use of virtual tours as a novel yet simple approach to evaluate surgical environment. Such an approach may be applied to identify and/or evaluate mental health-related features in a variety of physical environments, such as other types of healthcare facilities, therapy gardens, workplaces, school campus, and classrooms.

References

Kain, Z. N., Mayes, L. C., Caldwell-Andrews, A. A., Karas, D. E., & McClain, B. C. (2006). Preoperative Anxiety, Postoperative Pain, and Behavioral Recovery in Young Children Undergoing Surgery. *Pediatrics, 118*(2), 651–658. https://doi.org/10.1542/peds.2005-2920

Vetter, D., Barth, J., Uyulmaz, S., Uyulmaz, S., Vonlanthen, R., Belli, G., Montorsi, M., Bismuth, H., Witt, C. M., & Clavien, P.-A. (2015). Effects of Art on Surgical Patients. *Annals of Surgery, 262*(5), 704–713. https://doi.org/10.1097/sla.0000000000001480

Exploring Feasibilities of SPACE Syntax Analysis As a Tool to Measure the Risk for Patient Aggression Against Healthcare Providers and Opportunities to Intervene in Emergency Department Settings

Soheyla MohammadiGorji *(Clemson University);* ***Linda Nubani*** *(Michigan State University);* ***Sheila Bosch*** *(University of Florida);* ***Shabboo Valipoor*** *(University of Florida)*

Although healthcare workers comprise a relatively small percentage of the U.S. workforce, they sustain nearly 75% of workplace assaults. Poor environmental design has been identified as an antecedent to aggression by patients or their companions. This study aimed to 1) investigate whether space syntax analysis is an appropriate method for identifying risks of aggression and opportunities to intervene; and 2) identify environmental design strategies that may reduce the risk of aggression and improve interventional opportunities. Guiding theories for this study included Rational Choice Theory and Criminal Opportunity Theories (Lifestyle Exposure Theory and Routine Activity Theory). Five measures were selected, based on their linkage to the theoretical framework, which were helpful in identifying vulnerable spaces. Research was conducted at three different hospital-based emergency departments. Two methods were utilized. First, visibility graph analysis of the entire layout was conducted, examining mean visual depth and control measures. Secondly, visibility graph analysis was conducted within specific zones, including key patient and staff areas. Results suggested that zone size, distance, and visual blockages created by architectural features may affect visual access and exposure. This study demonstrated that space syntax analysis is a useful tool for identifying risk of aggression and opportunities to intervene. For example, providing centralized staff workstations in smaller zones typically affords better control of patient spaces. Small changes in the location of visual obstructions (e.g., columns) may have a large effect on the level of control of surrounding spaces. Alcove-style spaces (e.g., registration or workspaces) are often associated with limited control of neighboring areas. In this presentation, we will present our findings on the feasibilities of space syntax for identifying the risk of aggression and opportunities to intervene.

Seasonal Changes in Virtual Natural Landscapes and Pain Reduction: Piloting Virtual Reality Assisted Guided Imagery (VR-AGI) for Patients with Advanced Cancer

Fredric Mau *(Watermark Counseling, LLC)*

Now more than ever, it is crucial to explore at-home solutions to all-consuming health problems. For advanced cancer patients, it's imperative that these solutions are accessible, efficacious, and above all, safe. Patients with advanced cancer often experience debilitating pain and pain-related psychological distress. A recent meta-analysis showed that pain was reported in 64%

of patients with advanced cancer and unrelieved pain greatly affected patients' comfort, activities, motivation, interactions with family and friends and quality of life (1). Although there is increasing evidence that non-pharmacological strategies are needed to treat pain in advanced cancer patients, pharmacologic modalities remain the preferred strategy. The National Comprehensive Cancer Network (NCCN) guidelines recommend that practitioners consider referring patients to a licensed mental health professional trained in cognitive behavioral therapy (CBT), hypnosis, biofeedback, mindfulness-based stress reduction (MBSR), or guided imagery. Accessibility to these powerful pain relief processes increases individual resilience and promotes sustainability as these processes engage natural body functions and increase wellbeing. Challenges to deliver these non-pharmacologic treatments for pain include training personnel to administer the treatment, the noisy healthcare environment which can be disruptive for patients trying to relax with the processes, and transportation issues for patients in accessing the treatments.

Guided imagery (GI) has already been shown to significantly improve cancer pain (2). Virtual reality (VR)-based interventions are also emerging as evidence-based treatment modalities for cancer pain and numerous recent studies have shown that VR use is safe and associated with improvements in cancer related symptoms including pain, fatigue, anxiety, depression, and cognitive dysfunction (3). However, VR studies in cancer pain have been limited to short-term clinical trials, have small sample sizes, and suboptimal research designs, limiting the interpretability and generalizability of the findings. Most studies are done in a hospital or acute care setting. To date, there have been no studies reporting the use of VR-based interventions in a home setting for cancer patients.

To bridge these gaps, we propose an innovative and novel non-pharmacologic approach, using three seasons (winter, spring, fall) of natural landscapes in VR to augment GI and help treat cancer pain. This study seeks to: (1) assess the efficacy of VR-AGI in reducing pain, anxiety, and opioid use among patients with advanced cancer; and (2) measure the feasibility, acceptance, and safety of VR-AGI in a home setting. Participants with significant symptoms are invited to participate in three VRAGI processes based on the three seasons, in the comfort of their homes. The home environment offers easy access to the processes and familiar surroundings conducive to facilitating healing. We predict patients will report reduced pain, anxiety, depression, fatigue, and require lower doses of opioids compared to the control group. If proven effective, nature-based VR interventions coupled with GI could be widely broadcast at low-cost in-home settings for patients with advanced cancer and possibly other diagnoses. With its emphasis on promoting health, equity, sustainability, and resilience, EDRA provides the optimal environment for collaborative brainstorming and feedback from researchers as we explore this exciting approach to pain relief.

The Analysis of Community Health Centers in Terms of Spatial Configuration, and Functional Distribution

Shermineh Afsary *(The University of Kansas);* ***Mahbub Rashid*** *(The University of Kansas)*

In the USA, Community Health Centers (CHCs) provide affordable primary healthcare services to all patients including the uninsured, low-income ones, or those living in remote areas (NACHC, 2015). The main purpose of this research is to systematically analyze CHCs in terms of spatial configuration and functional distribution. The focus of spatial configuration is overall layout configuration; decentralized/ centralized organization of main functional spaces including nursing stations, clinicians' offices, registration offices, as well as the spatial visibility within the spatial configuration. This study is needed since there is a lack of rigorous studies on the design of CHCs. Studies in other healthcare settings have already shown that spatial efficiency can improve the quality of healthcare, but only a few studies of these studies involve CHCs. This research will contribute to a better understanding of typological variation, spatial configuration, functional distribution, and visibility within the building of CHCs. This study will include several large CHCs from different parts of the USA. These CHCs have different layouts, and their floor areas vary between 35'000 sq.ft and 68'000 sq.ft. The methodology of this research will involve a systematic spatial analysis. Firstly, using the evidence-based healthcare design literature, the study will provide an assessment of the spatial attributes of these CHCs. In addition, using systematic spatial analysis of layout plans, the study determines layout typology, and decentralized/centralized organization of main functional spaces, space allocation, and functional distributions and their relationships within the CHCs. As one of the method, Space Syntax Analysis (SSA) is conducted to evaluate the spatial visibility in different spatial configuration of the CHCs. For visibility analysis, visual attributes of connectivity, integration will be analyzed. As one of the findings and contribution of this research, to fill the gap of the current literature on different layout configurations, this research has defined 6 new different typology of layout configurations and functional distributions in CHCs. Another contribution of the research is to develop new indexes of design. Based on the findings, the study will provide guidelines for better CHC design.

Developing Design Guidelines for Anesthesiologist Workspace to Support Safe Medication Practices and Workflows

Seyedmohammad Ahmadshahi *(Clemson University);* ***Anjali Joseph*** *(Clemson University);* ***Sahar Mihandoust*** *(Clemson University);* ***David Neyens*** *(Clemson University);* ***James Abernathy*** *(Johns Hopkins);* ***Kenneth Catchpole*** *(Medical University of South Carolina);* ***Soheyla MohammadiGorji*** *(Clemson University)*

Anesthesia providers (AN) experience numerous difficulties while performing critical medication tasks such as medication preparation and administration due to their workspace poor ergonomics, cluttered and crowded layout, and limited available space. It is important to improve the design of the anesthesia workspace in the operating room to support safer medication practices.

The purpose of this study was to develop a set of evidence-based guidelines to support the design of anesthesia work environments that enable AN to conduct medication tasks safely. This study involved an extensive literature review and comprehensive observation and coding of more than 30 surgical pre-recorded videos of pediatric outpatient surgical procedures.

We found that the ANs are required to perform within an ergonomically flawed workspace, conducting a range of medication-related tasks including constant patient monitoring, documentation, medication preparation, and administration tasks. The AN zone is confined and prone to workspace clutter, tangling the team members in a web of cables and tubing attached to the equipment or the patient, which can cause physical barriers to workflow and also impact patient safety (Boquet et al., 2017).

The current standard anesthesia workspaces force the ANs to work with multiple bulky pieces of equipment with numerous cords and connections from every direction that require them to constantly rotating to cover different angles (Seagull et al., 2004) causing disruptions and safety issues along with fatigue and musculoskeletal problems. The ANs have insufficient available worksurfaces for medication preparation tasks increasing the chance of clutter, contamination, and errors . Moreover, due to an inappropriate positioning and accessibility of the equipment, ANs are also challenged with other team members movements into and through their workspace causing distraction, and contamination (Taaffe et al., 2018).

To overcome the challenges, we have channeled the observations and literature findings into 7 design guidelines, through which we may categorize the problems, and direct the potential design solutions while considering trade-offs between different guidelines. The key evidence-based guidelines that were developed in this study include:

- Locate critical tasks within a dominant field of view
- Eliminate travel into and through the anesthesia zone (for other staff)
- Identify and demarcate a distinct anesthesia zone with adequate space for the anesthesia provider

- Optimize the ability to reposition/reconfigure the anesthesia workspace
- Minimize Institutional Clutter
- Provide adequate and appropriately positioned surfaces for medication preparation and administration
- Optimize task and surface lighting

References

Boquet, A., Cohen, T., Diljohn, F., Cabrera, J., Reeves, S., & Shappell, S. (2017). A theoretical model of flow disruptions for the anesthesia team during cardiovascular surgery. *J Patient Saf*(00), 1-6.

Seagull, F. J., Ward, R., Mills, J., Goodrich, C., & Xiao, Y. (2004). Measuring awkwardness of workplace layout: Dispersion of attentional and psychomotor resources within the anesthesia workspace. *Proceedings of the Human Factors and Ergonomics Society Annual Meeting*.

Taaffe, K., Lee, B., Ferrand, Y., Fredendall, L., San, D., Salgado, C., Shvorin, D., Khoshkenar, A., & Reeves, S. (2018). The influence of traffic, area location, and other factors on operating room microbial load. *Infection Control & Hospital Epidemiology*, 39(4), 391-397.

Adverse Outcomes of Excessive Sensory Stimuli in Trauma Rooms: Staff's Perspectives

Hossein Mirzajani *(Kent State University);* ***Sara Bayramzadeh*** *(Kent State University)*

Background: Multidisciplinary medical teams conduct a rapid assessment in the trauma room to treat patients in a timely manner and help prevent deaths. High noise levels, excessive light intensity, and uncontrolled temperature can be sources of disruptions and contribute to adverse healthcare outcomes in trauma rooms. Excessive sensory stimuli can hinder efficient patient care and impact patient safety.

Objective: This study aimed to explore sensory stimuli as a byproduct of the physical environment in trauma rooms and their impact on healthcare delivery from staff's perspectives.

Method: A convenience sampling method was used to recruit participants for semi-structured focus groups. Trauma team members with different roles from six Level I trauma centers in the United States participated in 20 focus groups. Each focus group was one hour long, and 64 trauma team members participated in this study.

Result: Findings were divided based on three categories: noise, lighting, temperature. Several themes and sub-themes were identified for each category. According to findings, the physical environment at some point negatively impacts sensory stimuli in trauma rooms. For example, open wards, open doors, and room location can impact temperature fluctuations in these rooms. Light intensity might cause glare issues. Therefore, staff declared having control over lighting facilitates their work. Environmental features like layout design and materials can increase noise levels in trauma rooms and lead to disruptions, miss-communication, and gaps in the care delivery process.

Conclusion: Having control over the physical environment could improve outcomes in trauma rooms. Sensory overload in trauma rooms can impact staff communication, leading to fatigue, burnout, and medical errors.

Trends in Health Environments Research: An Analysis of Five Years of Research Articles from the Health Environments Research and Design (HERD) Journal

Dina Battisto *(Clemson University);* ***Xiaowei Li*** *(Clemson University);* ***Jiaying Dong*** *(Clemson University)*

Objective: This study aims to explore trends in research methodology from an analysis of 157 research articles published in the Health Environments Research Design (HERD) Journal in the last five years (2016 – 2020).

Background: The field of healthcare environments research is a complex field comprised of research from various disciplines worldwide. Consequently, there are variations in the ways research studies are crafted, conducted, and written up. No systematic study exists to uncover trends in

EBD research concerning the types of research published, people engaged in research, and the research methods employed. Understanding the nature of health environments research performed can help researchers, practitioners and students situate their work within an evidence-based design research methodology.

Methods: This study used a qualitative design, particularly case study research, where 157 articles published in one scholarly journal, the HERD journal, devoted to evidence-based design and research. Secondary data were extracted from the articles and inductively analyzed using content analysis to generate research categories and study themes that emerged from the data. The design and outcome categories for the analysis were structured around Ulrich et. al's (2010) Evidence-Based Design Framework and the Center for Health Design's Knowledge Repository.

Results: Findings were reported from the analysis on the following categories commonly found in empirical research articles: (i) keywords, (ii) disciplines from authors (iii) settings studied, (iv) populations studied or sampled, (v) research approach and study design (vi) research strategies, (vii) data collection methods, (viii) data analysis procedures, (ix) design categories and variables, (x) outcome categories and variables.

Conclusions: The analysis of 157 articles in HERD highlighted the research methods most frequently used in health environments research. Findings revealed several inconsistencies across articles regarding keywords and how research studies are framed. Findings from this analysis suggest that there should be an overarching research taxonomy with a set of acceptable terms used consistently across articles. Having an existing taxonomy would help authors frame a research study and organize published studies in a database for more effective literature searches.

Patient Needs for Retail Services in Large General Hospitals in Zhengzhou

Zhe Wang *(Henan University);* ***Yahong Zhu*** *(Henan University)*

Introduction: The strategy of developing an interior 'Hospital Street' has been applied in China to facilitate wayfinding in large general hospitals. It is a spatial design strategy of organizing functional zones and service areas horizontally and vertically along a center corridor or multi-story space. The streets are supposed to address patient needs for care and shopping while waiting for care. What kind of retail services should be regulated along the streets to meet patients' needs?

Methods: Taking two large general hospitals (at the tertiary level and with about 3,000 beds) in Zhengzhou as examples, we collected data on the needs and use of existing retail spaces on the streets through field observation and questionnaire survey. Based on two weekday observations, the diagrams of customers' visits to the retail spaces were developed. Focusing on the needs and reasons for shopping in a hospital, questionnaire data were collected from patients and their families on the streets. ANOVA tests were applied to identify the differences in needs and use between hospitals.

Findings: Retails on the street in Hospital A included nutrition canteens, restaurants, a café, and supermarkets. In Hospital B, more services were provided besides those in Hospital A, including pharmacy, maternity and baby care supplies, gift shop, bank, and book store. In both hospitals, nutrition canteens and restaurants were the most popular. Regarding the needs, message chairs and bookstores were mentioned the most. The top reasons for people to shop in a hospital is time saving and convenience.

Conclusion: Patient needs for retail services on an interior hospital street may vary. Catering services should be regulated on the street to address people's eating needs during hospital stay. The planning of retail services should also consider patients' and families' needs for stress reduction and help to develop positive distraction.

Le Corbusier's Four Compositions Viewed through the Lens of Positive Psychology

Phillip Mead *(University of Idaho)*

Le Corbusier's urban ideas and "Five Points for a New Architecture" are vilified because of their inability to encourage social interaction and connect with the existing urban fabric. However, his lesser-known "Four Compositions" outlined in Oeuvre Complete are minimally covered or explained briefly in form-based texts. This essay argues that his preferred compositions appear to be overlooked as sound pattern generators for promoting well-being. They approach Christopher Alexander's patterns in Pattern Language (Alexander, C. 1977) for creating spaces that enhance life experiences. Although Alexander's ideas appear to work well at the component level for the promotion of comfort, light, air, and social interaction (i.e., "Six Foot Balcony" and "Courtyards Which Live"), they are limited in their ability to express cultural meanings beyond the use of local building materials and applied ornament. Like Alexander's patterns, Le Corbusier's preferred compositions promote higher qualities of comfort, light, air, views of nature, and social interaction. Additionally, they can potentially express cultural meaning: existential and semiotic. Existential meaning is derived from Norberg-Schulz's conception of an architecture that provides an 'existential foothold.' Semiotic meaning is less value-driven and more informative. This study uses Positive Psychology's PERMA elements for well-being (Positive Emotions or Pleasure, Engagement, Relationships or Community, Meaning and Achievement) (Seligman, M. 2011) to evaluate the potential effectiveness of Le Corbusier's preferred compositions. Like Pattern Language, Corbu's compositions appear to allow for more opportunities for the formation of Positive Emotions, Engagement, and Relationships, which may be due to the fact that the compositions allow for a greater range of outdoor comfort zones in most climates. From the perspective of meaning, the compositions also allow for meaningful expression in the roof, wall, and component level (stair tower, important rooms, etc.) due to their relative independence from the structure and functional wall configuration. In short, Le Corbusier's planning strategies can liberate elements that have the ability to express meaning independent of the building's functional obligations. The author will examine a selection of Le Corbusier's buildings and more recent buildings that appear to be influenced by these compositions and how they potentially accommodate today's ever-increasing demands for overall well-being, for which meaning plays a critical part.

References

Alexander, C. (1977) *A Pattern Language*, Oxford, Oxford Press

Le Corbusier (1965) *Le Corbusier Oeuvre Complete 1910-29*, Zurich, Les Edmond d' Architecture

Norberg-Schultz, C. (1980) Genus Loci, *Towards a Phenomenology of Architecture*, New York, Rizzoli

Seligman, M. (2011) *Flourish*, New York, Free Press

Sensorial Dimensions of Nature: An Analysis of Benefits for Human Wellbeing

Nisha A. Fernando *(University of Kansas)*

Beginning from the seminal the Attention Restorative Theory(ART), many rigorous research has established that exposure to natural environments provide restorative therapy and relieve physical and mental stress, (Kaplan & Kaplan, 1989). This concept has become even more apparent during the recent pandemic; when people were mostly confined to indoors, natural environments provided safe havens for change of scenery, much needed relief from monotony and for reducing mental fatigue. Design research literature continues to provide abundant evidence on benefits of natural air, light, and visual scenes on everyday human productivity and wellbeing (Stevenson et al. 2018). However, one unfilled gap in the research literature is an in-depth understand of which specific characteristics of a given natural environment may generate therapeutic effects, and what role non-visual senses plays in such positive experiences. This paper presents the results of an empirical research study that focused on the above gap. Thirty-two adults (age range

19-60 years) were anonymously surveyed who provided detailed narratives with photographs on an everyday experience of a natural environment that contributed to any restorative affect and relief from mental fatigue. The narratives included the type of natural environment (garden, park, lake, riverfront, forest, etc) and particular details of personal experiences (a) type of activity – walking, jogging, biking, etc., and length of time; (b) descriptions of the affects (feelings, emotions, somatic and psychological changes, and so on); (c) descriptions of the detailed physical characteristics of the natural environment that led to these affects; and (d) the nature of the respective affective components. A qualitative content analysis using thematic grouping the data was utilized for the data analysis. Several new themes emerged from the results, in addition to the well-known positive correlation nature and psychological wellbeing: (a) the length of outdoor exposure were extremely important to release stress but depended on the type of activity, (b) the type of natural environment was insignificant overall positive experience but only when not repeatedly experienced, and most importantly, (c) both visual and other sensory experiences (i.e. auditory, olfactory, tactile, kinetic experiences) of natural environments were important for positive restorative affects, while (d) non-visual sensory experiences were especially critical for a more holistic experience of nature, thus for fuller restorative affect. This paper will present the expanded results of (d) above, to illustrate how specific non-visual sensory characteristics of a given natural environment become significant catalysts for more complete restorative affects and towards uplifting and rejuvenating human experiences.

References

Kaplan, R., and Kaplan, S. 1989. *The Experience of Nature: A Psychological Perspective*. New York, NY: Cambridge University Press.

Lee, K. E., Williams, K. J. H., Sargent, L. D., Williams, N. S. G. and Johnson, K. A. (2015). 40-second green roof views sustain attention: The role of micro-breaks in attention restoration. *Journal of Environmental Psychology 42*:182–89.

Stevenson, M.P., Schilhab, T. & Bentsen, P. (2018). Attention Restoration Theory II: a systematic review to clarify attention processes affected by exposure to natural environments. *Journal of Toxicology and Environmental Health*. 21/4: 227-268.

Interior Wayfinding Theoretical Framework: A Synthesis of Wayfinding Related Theories Identified in the Literature

Saman Jamshidi *(University of Nevada, Las Vegas);* ***Debajyoti Pati*** *(Texas Tech University)*

Purpose: The purpose of this presentation is to examine the interconnections between wayfinding-related theories that have been used in isolation in the literature and to synthesize them to form a more holistic picture of the wayfinding process.

Background: Wayfinding is a multifaceted process involving cognitive (e.g., spatial memory, planning, and problem solving), behavioral (e.g., navigation, locomotion), and environmental factors (e.g., floorplan complexity and landmarks). Multiple theories have been used in isolation to explain different components of the wayfinding process in the empirical literature on wayfinding. However, the interconnection between these theories and the implications of each in the overall process of wayfinding have not been discussed in depth. A lack of a holistic perspective may prevent environmental designers from (1) recognizing gaps in their approach to addressing wayfinding issues and (2) seeing new opportunities.

Methods: This study is the second stage of a larger investigation. In the first step, a literature review was undertaken by searching four databases systematically (PsychINFO, JSTOR, ProQuest, and EBSCO). A list of theories was constructed from the 81 included articles. In the current study, information processing theory was adopted as the framework to synthesize the identified theories in the previous stage. The interconnections between identified theories were examined to create a holistic picture with the aim of identifying conflicts, compatibilities, and gaps between wayfinding-related theories.

Finding: The identified theories were classified into four classes: (1) environment, (2) perception, (3) cognition, and (4) execution. Using information processing theory, a framework was created to fit the four classes of theories into the wayfinding process. Each class of theories explains a broad step of the wayfinding process. The environment is the first step from which people receive sensory inputs. The environmental factors that Lynch (1960) proposed (e.g., landmarks, paths, edges) pertain mainly to this step. However, his legibility and imageability concepts seem to bridge this step to the next one. In the second step (i.e., perception), environmental information is perceived through the sensory system. The theories of perception specifically explain how people pick up and perceive information from the environment. The third step is the cognitive process which consists of attention, memory, learning, reasoning, problem-solving, decision making, etc. The theories that are categorized under spatial knowledge development and mental representation describe some part of the cognitive process (step 3). In the fourth step, the wayfinder executes the decision that was made in the previous step. Generally, the theories classified in spatial cognition can explain this step. These theories essentially explain the loop of information gathering, decision making, action, and feedback; hence, they typically cover several steps in the proposed framework.

Implications: This study can provide a more holistic framework for designers to find more innovative design solutions to address wayfinding issues by taking the systems thinking approach. Also, the gaps that were identified in this study can direct future empirical research on the role of environmental design on wayfinding.

Promoting Physical Activity through Zoning Code Reform – Assessing Longitudinal Changes in the Adoption of Code Reform Zoning and Characteristics of Code Reform Jurisdictions

Lindsey Realmuto *(The New York Academy of Medicine);* ***Jamie Chriqui*** *(University of Illinois at Chicago);* ***Meg Fredericks*** *(University of Illinois at Chicago);* ***Henry Siegel*** *(University of Illinois at Chicago);* ***Julien Leider*** *(University of Illinois at Chicago)*

Background: Local land use regulation plays a key role in defining the built environment. Zoning reform efforts, such as form-based codes, new urbanism, and smart growth, have emerged in recent years to combat sprawl, single use development, high-reliance on automobiles, and limited opportunities for physical activity, including active commuting. (Chriqui et. al., 2011; Schilling & Mishkovsky, 2005; American Planning Association, 2006) Zoning reforms seek to create pedestrian-friendly neighborhoods with increased street connectivity, mixed-use and higher density, open space, public transportation infrastructure, and a traditional neighborhood structure (e.g., grid street patterns).

Purpose: This presentation will examine longitudinal changes in the adoption of zoning reform efforts between 2010 to 2020 in over 2,000 U.S. jurisdictions as well as municipal characteristics associated with code reform zoning.

Methods: This study builds upon a previously conducted NIH-funded study that involved the largest nationwide evaluation of active living-oriented provisions in zoning and land use codes in effect as of 2010. For the present study, we are compiling and evaluating zoning codes in effect as of 2020 for 2,117 municipal jurisdictions located in the 186 largest US counties (covering 55% of the US population) that were also included in the prior study. Zoning codes are being compiled and coded by trained, Master's level (or higher) urban planners using a systematic audit tool developed by the study team. The following measures are being used to assess the active living orientation of the zoning codes: the adoption of code reform/

new urbanist-type zoning (and the type of code reform); any references to requirements or encouragement of sidewalks, crosswalks, bike-pedestrian connectivity, street connectivity, bike lanes, bike parking, bike-pedestrian trails/paths, mixed use development, active recreation, passive recreation, plazas, and public transit (12 measures). We will link the zoning data with municipal-level data from the American Community Survey to examine the prevalence of zoning code reforms and variability in zoning code reforms by municipal-level characteristics including, but not limited to, median household income, population-level race/ethnicity, % of households in poverty, public transit use, and urban/rural locales.

Results: Data collection is completed and coding is scheduled to be completed by January 2022. Linked data analyses will occur in January-April 2022.

References

Chriqui JF, Nicholson LM, Thrun E, Leider J, Slater SJ. (2016). More active living–oriented county and municipal zoning is associated with increased adult leisure time physical activity—United States, 2011. *Environment and Behavior 48*: 111-130. doi:10.1177/0013916515611175.

Schilling J, Mishkovsky N. *Creating a Regulatory Blueprint for Healthy Community Design: A Local Government Guide to Reforming Zoning and Land Development Codes. E-43346*. 2005. Washington, D.C., ICMA.

American Planning Association. *Planning and Urban Design Standards*. 1st ed. Hoboken, NJ: John Wiley & Sons, Inc., 2006.

Effects of the Outdoor Time Versus Screen Time on Sleep Health of Adolescents and Young Adults

***Sohail Sadroleslami** (Cornell University); **Mardelle McCuskey Shepley** (Cornell University)*

Objective: Sleep health affects almost all areas of human health and well-being including mental health, social life, longevity, and the immune system (Eanes, 2015). However, we are experiencing a global crisis in sleep health as both the Center for Disease Control (CDC) and World Health Organization have declared poor sleep health as a public health epidemic (Chattu et al., 2018).Young adult and particularly adolescents are among the mostly commonly overlooked populations in health studies and are also very vulnerable to sleep health problems (Illingworth, 2020). Important parts of human brain, especially the prefrontal cortex, are still developing in the critical and transitory years of adolescence, in which sleep plays a pivotal role. This study examines how outdoor time versus screen time affect sleep health among adolescents.

Methods: The design of this study is based on the results from a pilot study that involved interviews with 18-year-old students. The study applies mixed methods. Participants are undergrad students at Cornell of 18 and 19 years old. To examine the subjective quality of sleep health, participants (n = ~100) are given diary-based surveys. Participants reply to online questions for seven consecutive days each morning. The questions rate their sleep quality and are also a measure of their outdoor time and screen time. In the second part of the study, the objective quality of the sleep health is measured using biometric watches (n = 6). Participants are randomly assigned to wear the watches for another seven consecutive days.

Results: Results from the pilot study suggest that the negative effects of screen time are greater than the positive effects of outdoor time. In spite of this finding, we hypothesize that additional qualitative and quantitative data will suggest that adolescents and young adults have a higher quality of sleep if they spend more time outdoors relative to screen time. The data from the main study will be analyzed in Fall 2021

References

Chattu, V., Manzar, M., Kumary, S., Burman, D., Spence, D., & Pandi-Perumal, S. (2018). The Global Problem of Insufficient Sleep and Its Serious Public Health Implications. *Healthcare, 7*(1), 1. doi.10.3390/healthcare7010001

Eanes, L. (2015). The potential effects of sleep loss on a Nurse's health, CE. *AJN, American Journal of Nursing, 115*(4), 34-40. doi:10.1097/01.naj.0000463025.42388.10

Illingworth, G. (2020). The challenges of adolescent sleep. *Interface Focus, 10*(3), 20190080. doi.10.1098/rsfs.2019.0080

Assessment of Student Comfort and Stress Levels in Traditional Classrooms Versus Biophilic Classrooms

***Alyssa Oates** (Oklahoma State University); **Payton Losh** (Oklahoma State University); **Aditya Jayadas** (Oklahoma State University)*

Background: The classroom is a place that many people know very well; on average, we spend over thirteen years in schooling, so it is important for students to build a positive connection with their classrooms. Though studies have explored the design of classrooms, there has been a lack of understanding on how biophilic design could affect student behavior and performance in a classroom setting.

Purpose: The purpose of this study is to discover how the design of classrooms on the campus of Oklahoma State University, compared to classrooms designed with biophilic design elements, impacts the comfort and stress levels of students utilizing those classrooms.

Methodology: Ten participants were recruited for the study using convenient sampling. Participants were randomly assigned to one of two environments - Environment A (traditional classroom without biophilic elements) and Environment B (Redesigned classroom with biophilic elements). The two classrooms were designed using Sketchup and Enscape. Participants were required to use a virtual reality headset to experience both spaces while also wearing a heart rate monitor. The resting heart rate was recorded and used as a baseline measurement prior to experiencing the two environments. The heart rate measurements in the two spaces were normalized to the baseline measurement. In addition, an interview with open-ended questions and a survey with closed-ended questions were administered after experiencing each space. A content analysis and a paired t-test was used for the qualitative and quantitative analysis respectively.

Results: Based on the qualitative analysis, the themes identified for Environment A (traditional classroom) included lighting (feeling enclosed and feeling sterile), work (less productive and isolating) and energy (stressed and no excitement). As for environment B (the classroom with biophilic environments) the themes included views (natural lighting and views to exterior), environment (comfort from materials and finishes, feeling of community) and work (more productive and more creative). For the quantitative results, there was a statistically significant difference between the two environments for perceived comfort ($p < 0.05$), stress levels ($p < 0.05$) and normalized heart rates ($p < 0.05$). While perceived comfort was rated higher for Environment B (the biophilic classroom), stress levels and the normalized heart rates were higher for Environment A (the traditional classroom).

Discussion: The findings suggest the need for more biophilic design in classrooms. In future studies, it is recommended that studies be carried out in physical settings over a longer period of time to study the benefits of biophilic design.

Implications: As shown by findings in this study, biophilic design in classrooms would be beneficial to students in the classroom, as the biophilic elements would increase comfort, decrease stress, and promote the health and well-being of students. There is an opportunity for interior designers, architects, practitioners and researchers to learn which biophilic elements produce greater benefits in a virtual environment before implementing them in a physical setting such as a classroom.

Creating Supportive Environments for Caregivers in Mental Health Facilities: Three Cases from Kansas

***Sara Hadavi** (Kansas State University); **Madison Quincke** (Kansas State University)*

With an increase in mental health diagnoses across the world, and a new wave of healthcare design interests, evidence-based design of such spaces based on interdisciplinary studies is necessary. Green outdoor settings can greatly contribute to stress reduction, clear-headedness, and feelings of being integrated into one's living environment (Kaplan & Kaplan, 1989; Franco et al., 2017). Although meeting the needs of patients in such healthcare settings is a priority to designers, the staff's wellbeing and needs are as important and crucial to the well-functioning of such facilities. This study aims to integrate two theoretical frameworks that help designers create restorative and supportive environment; therapeutic landscape guidelines based on the Stress Reduction Theory and the Reasonable Person Model (Kaplan & Basu, 2015). The goal is to offer a set of evidence-based guidelines to create more supportive environments for those who spend long hours in mental health facilities and are in direct contact with patients. Survey data was collected from 140 staff members of three mental health facilities that provide services to severe and persistent mental illnesses (SPMI) in Kansas, including Larned State Hospital, Parsons State Hospital, and Osawatomie State Hospital.

Six objectives for supportive environments were included in the photo-survey with five-point rating scale including fascination, wayfinding, privacy, social connection, exercise, and meaningful action. Participants responded to three different types of simulated environments that met each of the six objectives of supportive environments (total of 18 images). Self-reported mental wellbeing was also asked through questions on stress level, mental fatigue, social connectedness, and moods. The results showed that community park with large trees was the most preferred space that encouraged meaningful action and helped with clear-headedness, followed by outdoor learning environment and farmer's market. In many of the examined themes, statistically significant association was not found between preferences and the self-reported wellbeing. Art space was the most favored social space followed by outdoor lounge. Walking trails with large trees were the most favorite elements that encouraged exercise and clear-headedness. Among the fascination images, garden gazebo got the highest rating score for clear-headedness. The participants seemed to like the idea of implementing more integrated activities and spaces between the hospital and the local community. Comfortable outdoor seating, socializing opportunities, more sunlight, safety, abundance of plants, and views to green and water features were among the participants' needs. This study offers insights to design of outdoor spaces in mental health facilities where long working hours may lead to mental fatigue and decreased effective functioning in caregivers who are in direct contact with patients.

References

Kaplan, R., & Kaplan, S. (1989). *The experience of nature: A psychological perspective*. Cambridge university press.

Franco, L. S., Shanahan, D. F., & Fuller, R. A. (2017). A review of the benefits of nature experiences: more than meets the eye. *International journal of environmental research and public health, 14*(8), 864.

Kaplan, R., & Basu, A. (2015). *Fostering reasonableness: Supportive environments for bringing out our best*. Michigan Publishing.

Future Tools for Mental Health (How Virtual Reality and Artificial Intelligence are redefining the perception of Clinical Environments)

Tina Giorgadze (Perkins and Will))

In a time when Demand for Mental Health treatment is at its highest ever when the shortage of providers and access to treatment remains an obstacle, what new tools, treatment methods, and technological advancement aid the deficit and allows better access to care? Are Virtual Reality, Artificial Intelligence, and Telemedicine an answer? And if so, how do new advancements affect the built environment?

The research aims to assess the current state of Mental Health demand, identify future projections,[5] how COVID Era transformed care.[6] Consider how newly introduced Treatment methods that utilize Virtual Reality, Artificial Intelligence, and Telemedicine[1,2,3,4] are transforming Mental Health treatment. But most importantly, what are the implications on the Built Environment. The study's goal is to explore newly introduced VR, AI, or Telemedicine technologies and Identify critical considerations for designing a Physical Environment for Hybrid settings.

A literature review revealed the current state of Mental Health demand, provider shortage, future predictions, and recommendations. We examined new tools coming to market and how they integrate into the physical environment. The study also explored the Gaming industry and how they incorporate technology into the physical world. Organized data identifies current demand, obstacles, recommendations, and relevant industry knowledge to find critical considerations while designing future Mental Health facilities.

Research revealed promising advancements in treatment methods using Virtual Reality and AI;[1,2,3,4] however, VR Therapy is still practiced in the physical environment. The merger of VR and telehealth capabilities is still an issue, and there is a need for creative solutions to take full advantage of technology.

There is a void in the design industry to create a safe environment where various VR/AI technologies are integrated into Healthcare, especially in the Mental Health environment. Architects have an opportunity to develop well-thought-out guidelines and case studies that address space requirements to allow the proper functionality of technology, safety, and welfare of its users.

Case Study scenarios identify critical considerations in designing a physical/virtual environment that can address the immediate demand for Hybrid integration, as demonstrated in this study.

References

1. Rizzo, A. S., Koenig, S. T., & Talbot, T. B. (2018). Clinical virtual reality: emerging opportunities for psychiatry. *Focus, 16*(3), 266-278.
2. Lucas, G. M., Rizzo, A., Gratch, J., Scherer, S., Stratou, G., Boberg, J., & Morency, L. P. (2017). Reporting mental health symptoms: breaking down barriers to care with virtual human interviewers. *Frontiers in Robotics and AI, 4*, 51.
3. Górski, F., Buń, P., Wichniarek, R., Zawadzki, P., & Hamrol, A. (2016). Effective design of educational virtual reality applications for medicine using knowledge-engineering techniques. EURASIA *Journal of Mathematics, Science and Technology Education, 13*(2), 395-416.
4. Atwood, B., Greenleaf, W., Kessler, D., Nordberg, S., Rizzo, S., Vogl, M. (2020). 4. The Big reset: why COVID-19 presents a blue Moon Moment for Mental Health technology [White Paper]. Oxford VR. https://hitconsultant.net/wp-content/uploads/2020/04/OVR-The-Big-Reset.pdf
5. *Behavioral Health workforce projections, 2017-2030*. (n.d.). HRSA Health Workforce. https://https://bhw.hrsa.gov/data-research/projecting-health-workforce-supply-demand/behavioral-health
6. Substance Abuse and Mental Health Services Administration (SAMHSA). *Telehealth for the Treatment of Serious Mental Illness and Substance Use Disorders*. SAMHSA Publication No. PEP21-06-02-001 Rockville, MD: National Mental Health and Substance Use Policy Laboratory. Substance Abuse and Mental Health Services Administration, 2021.

Creating Healing Environment: Toward Designing a Healthcare Room That Supports Patients' Psychological Health and Circadian Rhythm

Mansoureh Sadat Jalali *(Virginia Tech);* ***Sara Saghafi Moghaddam*** *(Virginia Tech)*

Prolonged hospitalization carries a risk of sleep disorder and circadian rhythm disruption for patients. Following recent findings in lighting studies that demonstrated the key role of lighting in adjusting the circadian rhythm, many studies have investigated how lighting design properties, such as color, timing, intensity, duration, and wavelength impact human circadian rhythm. Besides, people of different ages, genders, nationalities, and other personal characteristics have varied color associations and preferences. Some studies report that psychological reactions to color can also trigger a physiological response. Patient rooms in healthcare buildings are critical spaces in which people with special needs spend time. Due to financial constraints, it is impractical and costly to tailor the color and lighting design of the room to each patient's preferences and health constraints. This paper focuses on lighting color and wavelength and proposes a design process for architects and interior designers to determine design strategies that support a healthy mood and circadian rhythm. To employ this new technique, LED hidden light sources throughout the room will consider a patient's preferences while also adapting to the color recommendation by the circadian rhythm guidelines. In this simulation-based case-study research, Rhinoceros 6 is used for 3D modeling. The Alfa Solemma plugin is used to calculate the effect of light on human circadian rhythm by indicating changes in the amount of room average melanopic lux.

The findings indicate that moving from warm to cold hues, melanopic lux increases and exceeds 50, the WELL Building Standard threshold for rooms at night. These numbers aid in determining appropriate hues and light levels for different times of the day. This suggests that changing the color of a room with hidden LED light sources can help create a flexible and vibrant environment that potentially promotes a healthy circadian rhythm.

Evaluation of Outpatient Pharmacy Designs for Improved Workflow: The Use of Virtual Reality to Compare Design Alternatives

Ghayda Fahed Awad *(Jordan University of Science and Technology);* ***Khaled Obeidat*** *(Jordan University of Science and Technology);* ***Ibrahim Abdallah; Bushra Obeidat*** *(Jordan University of Science and Technology)*

The interior design of outpatient pharmacies in hospitals is a critical component of the medication administration process since it impacts staff and patients' experiences. Thus, pharmacy design research focuses on workflow optimization to decrease errors, accessibility to medication, equipment placement inside the pharmacy, and waiting periods. However, there has always been a dearth of thorough testing methods for effective pharmacy planning and workflow verification. This study aims to evaluate the effectiveness of a hospital outpatient pharmacy's workflow and provide recommendations about the pharmacy layout and furniture arrangement. The evaluation utilizes a virtual reality platform and surveys to compare design alternatives and capture user feedback. The hospital pharmacists and pharmacy students assess the design of an existing pharmacy and three modified and virtual pharmacy models. The survey results and the objective VR data converged in terms of identifying the highest-performing design option. Survey data showed that Design 2 performed best in terms of perceived physical access to shelves and unobstructed movement. VR data showed variations among the designs regarding participants' visibility to computer screens and medication shelves throughout their simulated interaction. The evaluations will allow hospital officials to assess the workflow and accessibility associated with various solutions and validate the efficacy of the proposed designs.

Perceived Importance of Wellness Features to Improve End-User Experience at Cancer Centers: Patient and Staff Perspectives

Hossein Mirzajani *(Kent State University)*

Background: Due to the consistent nature of cancer treatments, building features that promote wellness is of increasing interest to the stakeholders, designers, and end-users.

Conducted research indicates that the physical environment can significantly improve the overall healing process and the quality of care-delivery. Having long-term and frequent treatment process makes the cancer patients more exposed and sensitive to the physical environment. Building features such as natural light, thermal comfort, noise control, and privacy levels are considered wellness features that promote wellness and productivity. Given the diverse population in cancer care facilities, wellness features vary in importance and preference to different end-users depending on their experience with a cancer care facility.

Objective: This study aims to distinguish the end-users' preferences of wellness features at cancer centers and its impact on the quality of deliver/receive quality care for patients and caregivers.

Method: This study performed multiple evaluation surveys of two user groups, including staff and patients. A couple of online questionnaires were developed and distributed in cancer care facilities and social media platforms to provide a snowball sampling of diverse cancer populations. The questionnaires mostly focused on end-users' preferences in specific areas such as break areas, waiting zone, and treatment areas.

Result: Findings indicated that wellness features were viewed favorably by two groups, with access to natural light/view, thermal comfort, and ease of movement were found for three top categories for both target populations. Wellness features related to sensory stimuli such as thermal comfort, natural lighting, and access to quiet space were highlighted by the participants as being effective in improving the interaction between patients and caregivers, as well as significantly supporting the mental health of both groups.

Conclusion: The results of this study emphasize the impacts of wellness features on the overall healing process and can inform the design of future cancer care centers.

Hospice Care Facility Design in the COVID-19 Era

Sharmin Kader *(Kent State University)*

Hospice design plays a great significance to a dying patient and their families, because the place experience has an imperative impact on the patient "quality of life" (Cohen et al., 2001) and the possibility of a "good death" as defined by Tong and his colleagues (2003). The physical environment is a part of the entire care milieu which also includes personal, social, and organizational dimensions. COVID-19 is an unprecedented situation that has created many challenges for any healthcare facilities including hospice or end-of-life care facilities. Generally, hospice facilities face unique challenges during times of disasters as their patient populations are particularly vulnerable due to terminally ill conditions with decreased mobility and dependence on medical technology. Additionally, hospice care facilities accommodate patients' family and provide spaces for social interactions, and the interdisciplinary care model deals with many volunteers and social workers. So, there is a risk of spreading infection among patients, family members, and staff. In addition, the restriction of family visitation, constrain of social interaction, control over shared activities (spiritual care), and wearing of personal protective equipment by staff all create an extra level of mental stress, depression, and dissatisfaction. This study has considered a systematic literature review and has identified six major design-related challenges of hospice care facilities: a) improving infection control, b) accommodating COVID-19 patients along with regular patients, c) accommodating patients' families in the facilities, d) creating a safe and supportive place for healthcare workers, e) providing palliative therapies and spiritual or grief support, and f) increasing in-house surge capacity. Considering these challenges, this study has analyzed eleven therapeutic goals of hospice environment: continuity of self, access to nature, privacy, social interaction, safety and security, autonomy, sensory stimulation, spiritual care, family accommodation, support after death, and support for staff. This study plows new territory in attempting to identify the gaps and issues created by COVID-19 pandemic to achieve the eleven salient therapeutic goals of hospice environments and, in so doing, challenges architects and society to create more enabling and inspiring environments to support a high-quality dying experience for all involved. In the era of an increasingly aging population, the expansion of designing new hospice care facilities and remodeling the old ones is predictable. Additionally, the COVID-19 pandemic has forced to figure out how to make emergency changes with limited supplies and resources. In the coming years, hospice facilities need to adjust their operations for future pandemics and need to be rewritten design guideline to safely encounter these new situations.

Traditional Vs. Co-Designed Classrooms: Impact on Student Learning

***Payton Losh** (Oklahoma State University); **Alyssa Oates** (Oklahoma State University); **Aditya Jayadas** (Oklahoma State University)*

Background: An interior environment can positively or negatively impact physical and mental health of individuals who use that environment. Thus the design of interior environments should be carried out while understanding the needs of individuals who use that space with the primary focus on health and wellbeing. Specifically for students, it is vital that they have a space where they do not feel stressed and overwhelmed, and at the same time be productive.

Purpose: The purpose of this study is to assess how the design of a traditional classroom compares to a co-designed classroom's impact on students' learning and stress levels.

Methodology: A total of 40 participants were recruited using convenient sampling. 10 of the 40 participants participated in a focus group with seven open ended questions about their perception of classrooms at Oklahoma State University. The responses from the focus group were used to create a co-designed classroom using Sketchup and Enscape. Following this, a survey was administered to 30 participants who compared images of the traditional classroom and the co-designed classroom environments. The survey used a Likert scale with five questions on stress, comfort, feeling overwhelmed, ability to learn and satisfaction. Participants were required to answer each of these questions for the traditional classroom as well as for the co-designed classroom. For the analysis of the focus group data, a content analysis was used. A paired t-test was used to analyze the data from the survey.

Results: Based on the qualitative analysis, the themes identified for the traditional classroom were environment (the space feeling old and bland), work (not creative and less productive), and energy (tiresome and stressed). As for the co-designed classroom, these are themes that were identified for what students want to see in the co-designed classroom such as environment (color and the layout of the space), lighting (more windows and natural light), and energy (calmness and engagement). For the quantitative results, there was a statistically significant difference between the two classrooms based on stress ($p < 0.05$), comfort ($p < 0.05$), feeling overwhelmed ($p < 0.05$), ability to learn ($p < 0.05$) and satisfaction ($p < 0.05$).

Discussion: The findings suggest that the co-designed classrooms were perceived as better environments for students. In the future this study should be replicated in a physical classroom involving students who would be learning and engaging within that classroom. Studies should not be limited to comfort and stress, but also include performance based tests.

Implications: This study shows that involving students in the co-design of classrooms can have a positive impact on students' ability to learn, stress levels, and comfort. Interior designers, architects, and other practitioners should consider integrating co-design when they design spaces like classrooms.

Spatial Composition and Student Well-Being: Student Accounts of Pandemic-Related Campus Modifications

***Caryn Brause** (University of Massachusetts)*

In March 2020, the World Health Organization declared COVID-19 a global pandemic. Immediately, higher education institutions modified their campuses to reduce the potential for viral spread (CDC, 2020). However, for many colleges and universities, financial stability is connected to the quality of in-person experience (Fishman 2020). Thus, decisions about COVID-related campus protocols involved balancing conflicting objectives of safety and interaction.

For the college student population, mental health and well-being are critical components to effective learning and development. Even before the pandemic, undergraduates had mental health and well-being concerns that they reported were significant impediments to their academic performance, including the interrelated impacts of stress, anxiety, depression, loneliness, and sleep difficulties (American College Health Association, 2019). Students come to post-secondary education with significant societal and financial stressors, which have been exacerbated this year (Healthy Minds Network, 2020). While there are many dimensions to student well-being, including physical, spiritual, and economic, one critical component of student thriving is social connectedness (Schreiner, 2010).

A diverse body of research has considered the relationship between social ties and spatial contexts. While historically, interacting socially in shared physical space were both considered essential for forming social ties, this view has been challenged with the rise of social networking and ubiquitous connectivity (Rainie & Wellman, 2014). However, the mechanisms of spatial propinquity, composition, and configuration remain important to understanding how space contributes to social tie formation (Small & Adler, 2019).

This presentation shares findings from a qualitative interview study documenting student accounts of their experience of COVID-related campus modifications. During Spring 2021 semester, data was collected using a semi-structured interview protocol to interview undergraduates living in on-campus residence halls. Qualitative data analysis employing a grounded approach (Charmaz, 2014) underscored the importance of spatial propinquity and composition to the development and maintenance of undergraduates' social networks. Findings show students were able to develop (or maintain) small numbers of close relationships due the trust built up through spatial proximity. Reliance on strong ties during a pandemic is a healthy adaptation to crisis; close relationships are known to support social wellbeing. However, the findings also show that students greatly reduced their social networks in response to COVID protocols, a form of behavior known as "turtling up" in which close relationships are strengthened at the expense of more distant ones (Romero et al., 2016).

Disruption of the campus' spatial composition significantly diminished the opportunity for casual interactions that expand students' social networks. Research has shown that students who have casual daily interactions with acquaintances experience greater feelings of campus belonging (Sandstrom & Dunn, 2014). This spatio-social deficit, along with other pandemic-related challenges, wreaked havoc on students' well-being. While the reopening of campuses in Fall 2021 may mitigate some systems shocks, others require longer term attention, coupled with a recognition that mental health, and other, impacts of the pandemic are unevenly distributed across student populations. (Soria & Horgos, 2021). This study's findings advance our understanding of the ways in which campus spaces contribute to students' mental health and well-being.

The Third-Place Concept for Transitional Space Design in the Academic Setting, Under the Pandemic

Sabeen Durrani *(Yonsei University);* ***Suk-kyung Kim*** *(Michigan State University)*

People are usually in three places: their home, their workplace, and a third site that is generally associated with sociability and leisure. Ray Oldenburg (1989), a sociologist, came up with the concept of "third places." The third-place is very essential in our lives because it acts as a social meeting place, a place to share ideas, and a place to create empathy for people from all walks of life (Spooner, 2020). We've lost our 'third-places' during the pandemic: places that are neither home nor work, but someplace in between. The third-place is a sociological and urban planning concept that emphasizes the importance that semipublic and semiprivate spaces play in creating social interaction, community identity, and civic participation (Weseluck, 2021). They foster "place attachment"–the tie between a person and a place–by providing a familiar setting for social interaction among regulars (Henshall, 2021). Recognizing the necessity of social distance, our varied daily-life settings will inevitably alter. The design of architecture and how we move between spaces will need to adapt to the new reality COVID-19 and social distancing.

This research focuses on the revision of

transitional space design in an academic setting in Korea by incorporating the third-place Concept. It argues for a common space, separating the largely uncontrollable external environment from the internal threat-reduced space, and for the separation of visitor areas and private areas. The methodology for the current research includes initial observation of user behaviors in transitional spaces, which was carried out amidst COVID19 in July 2020, for three days, three times per day i.e., morning (9:00~9:20), afternoon (12:00~12:20), and evening (17:00~17:20) respectively. This helped the researcher to finalize the space to study further with the concept of the third-place. Central Library at University is selected as it had more frequent users and is accessible to outsiders as well. The methodology employed for this research is the design charrette with thirty-two participants in May 2021. The design charrette is further divided into three sections; questionnaire survey, to give an overview of the study to the participants as researcher and participants had a language barrier, A1 sheets with current layout plans, and participants were asked to write their opinions on post-its and lastly revised transitional space design images designed by the researcher, based on the initial observations. To ensure social distancing the design charrette was conducted multiple times with five to eight people per session.

The results showed that participants showed dissatisfaction with the current transitional space design for the library, and they encouraged the idea of transitional space as a third-place which will serve as a buffer between the public and the private as well as a common space for the visitors and regulars. Participants showed satisfaction with the transitional space design proposed by the researcher along with certain changes that can help the research further in creating a better transitional space for the users.

Redefining Proxemics in a Post-COVID Classroom: A Case Study

Marwa Abdelmonem *(Virginia Commonwealth University, Qatar);* ***Sherin Karawia*** *(Virginia Commonwealth University, Qatar)*

Introduction: Despite a global effort to increase COVID-19 vaccination to limit the spread of coronavirus, considerable hesitancy remains an obstacle to creating COVID-free environments. The effectiveness of non-vaccine preventative measures such as social distancing and face covering in interior environments has been largely examined. However, their effects on communication in interior environments are inadequately addressed.

Purpose: To examine the impact of social distancing on classroom interactions among college students. The study sheds some light on the emerging proxemics in the socially distanced setup. The goal is to understand how social distancing affects the classroom means of communication (e.g. verbal and non-verbal communication), and student engagement.

Method: This study follows a case study methodology. A review of literature was conducted to establish a theoretical framework derived from Hall's Proxemics and Resource-based Learning theories. Methods used are semi-structured interviews and non-participant observation. Thematic and mapping analyses are utilized for interviews and observations, respectively. This study is conducted over a two-month period of time.

Results: Preliminary results include: 1) non-verbal cues such as body language and angulation play a significant role in facilitating verbal communication and student engagement, 2) the use of technology such as zoom and/or speakers is inevitable depending on the size and layout of a classroom, 3) the location of the instructor's workstation impacts the level of engagement, 4) the locus of control of students contributes to their level of engagement, and 5) specific environmental factors such as lighting and acoustics enhance non-verbal communication.

From Design to Health Outcomes: A COVID Era Pre-Post Study on Student Wellbeing on College Campuses

Renae Mantooth *(HKS, Inc.);* ***Upali Nanda*** *(HKS, Inc.);* ***Evie Guo*** *(University of California, San Diego)*

According to the latest National College Health Assessment (NCHA, 2021), anxiety, depression, loneliness, physical inactivity, and poor eating habits are all common among college students. External stressors include concerns with factors such as food, housing, and transportation which limit a college student's ability to concentrate on the academic environment (Astin, 1999; Lundberg, 2014; Wood & Harris III, 2013; Wood & Williams, 2013) and are a negative predictor of college student persistence (Mason, 1998; Wood & Williams, 2014). To that end, health and wellbeing are influenced by many environmental factors. Walkable amenities, available greenery, convenient public transportation, and safety can influence the amount and the types of physical activities that students engage in (Gehl, 2010; Saelens, Sallis, Black, & Chen, 2003). College students are developing lifestyles on their own that may last beyond college, contributing to their wellbeing in the long run.

Designed with an understanding that college years are formative for building healthy habits, North Torrey Pines Living and Learning Neighborhood (NTPLLN) incorporates evidence-based design strategies to improve physical, mental, and social wellbeing. Leveraging the Point of Decision Design framework (CADRE, 2017), the design team sought to make healthy choices available, accessible, affordable, and appealing. Each building in the neighborhood offers scenic coastal views and connections to the tropical climate, to improve mental wellbeing. Bicycle-friendly streets and prominently located staircases throughout the neighborhood encourage mobility and exercise. Communal areas such as a rooftop vegetable garden provide opportunities for healthy habit development and physical activities including gardening and fitness classes, and community kitchens on each residence hall floor encourage cooking and socializing.

In an effort to link design intent to student outcomes, this study first surveyed students in their current residential environments (Camp Snoopy, $n = 134$) in the Spring of 2020, and then a year later in their new environments (NTPLLN, $n = 174$) in the Spring of 2021, to understand if there were any key changes in their perceptions and behaviors pertaining to mental and physical health and wellbeing in relation to their physical environments. Mental health and wellbeing was measured by two validated instruments, the Satisfaction with Life Scale (SWLS; Diener et al., 1985) and Center of Epidemiology Studies-Depression, 10 item version (CES-D; Andresen et al., 1994). Physical health and wellbeing was measured with the International Physical Activity Questionnaire (Craig et al., 2003) and fruit and vegetable consumption time usage (Dibsdall et al., 2007). Environmental satisfaction was measured with an internal tool that assesses overall and environmental attribute specific items for social, classroom, and private residential spaces.

Results indicate an 8.2% reduction in depression while no significant change in life satisfaction. We observed an 11% increase in satisfaction with diet, no significant change in frequency of cooking behaviors, but significant improvements in satisfaction with cooking facilities across multiple metrics. Students reported an 11% increase in satisfaction with transportation which is driven by the improvement in safety of scootering and biking, and the accessibility and availability of driving. Implications for designing residential and student life spaces will be discussed.

A Theory-Driven Investigation into the Affordances of the Built Environment and the Impact on Child Development

Lori Guerrero *(Texas Tech University);* ***Debajyoti Pati*** *(Texas Tech University);* ***Kristi Gaines*** *(Texas Tech University)*

This theory-driven investigative study, grounded in Gibson's Ecological Theory of Perception (1979), explores affordances in child environments. A literature review reveals a common methodology for studying affordances in outdoor learning environments: 1) assess an existing site, 2) create a site-specific taxonomy of affordances and 3) identify the behaviors connected to the affordances. This study proposes reversing the methodology and starting with the desired outcomes first. The proposed methodology is: 1) identify desired outcomes, 2) create a taxonomy of affordances required for the desired outcomes and 3) ideate design considerations that provide the required affordances. For the purpose of this study, the desired outcomes are defined as the developmental milestones developed by the Centers for Disease Control and Prevention (2019).

Literature explains that nature improves childhood development, but there hasn't been a study that focuses on specific design features, their affordances and how that relates to child development. Moore and Cosco of Natural Learning Initiative emphasize the importance of progressing past generalized constructs such as "exposure to nature" and identify specific features related to health outcomes (2010). This is in accordance with the purpose of the proposed methodology which aims to discover the relationships between physical design features and specific developmental outcomes.

This study proposes the question: What design considerations are revealed when developmental milestones are assessed as the required affordances to support physical, cognitive, and social/emotional development in children ages 18 months to 3 years? The results demonstrate a detailed taxonomy of design considerations and eight overarching themes to guide design: 1) adjacencies, 2) auditory, 3) challenges, 4) mystery, 5) scale, 6) spacing, 7) variety, and 8) visibility. If selected for presentation, the methodology and results will be explained and illustrated. It is implicitly hypothesized that following the proposed methodology may lead to innovative design solutions that better promote child development.

Play in 'the Backyard': Environmental Features and Conditions of a Natural Playspace Which Support Diverse Outdoor Play Types

Janet Loebach *(Cornell University);* ***Adina Cox*** *(University of Kentucky)*

Engagement in play has been definitively linked to the healthy development of children across physical, social, cognitive, and emotional domains. The enriched nature of high-quality outdoor play environments can afford a greater diversity of opportunities for play than indoor settings. To more effectively design outdoor play settings, we must better understand how the physical environment supports, or hinders, the different types of play which suit children's needs and interests. This study examines seeks to identify specific environmental features and conditions which support specific forms of outdoor by examining differences in children's outdoor play patterns before and after a renovation to an outdoor nature playspace. Researchers carried out an extensive behavior mapping protocol (Cox & Loebach, 2019) for 7 days in 'The Backyard', a natural outdoor play and learning space at the Santa Barbara Museum of Natural History just before a significant environmental renovation and again several months after its completion. Outdoor play types were captured using the Tool for Observing Play Outdoors (TOPO), a new typology of outdoor play (Loebach & Cox, 2020) for more than 800 individual play events at both time 1 and Time 2; additional play and environmental data were recorded for each play event including physical activity levels, peer and adult interactions, and environmental interactions. In this presentation, findings from quantitative and spatial analyses will highlight the environmental features and interactions found to support each of the eight primary play types outlined in the TOPO: physical play, exploratory play, imaginative play, play with rules, bio play, expressive play, restorative play and digital play. Patterns in each outdoor play type by age group will also be presented, highlighting play environment features which support diverse ages. Findings will not only highlight the value and efficacy of the TOPO for capturing outdoor play type patterns, but will provide insights on specific outdoor play environment features which afford high-quality play interactions for diverse child users and interests.

References

Loebach, J. & Cox, A. (2020). Tool for Observing Play Outdoors (TOPO): A new typology for capturing children's play behaviors in outdoor environments. International Journal of Environmental Research and Public Health; Special Issue: *The Environment and Children's Health, 17*(15), 5611. https://doi.org/10.3390/ijerph17155611.

Cox, A., Loebach, J. & Little, S. (2018). Understanding the Nature Play Milieu: Using Behavior Mapping to Investigate Children's Play in Outdoor and Nature Playspaces. *Children, Youth and Environments Special Issue: Unleashing the Power of Play, 28*(2), 232-261. doi:10.7721/chilyoutenvi.28.2.0232

Contact with Nature in Childhood and Sensory Characteristics in Adulthood

Dongying Li *(Texas A&M University);* ***William C. Sullivan*** *(University of Illinois at Urbana-Champaign)*

Objective: Children's use of digital media has increased rapidly, and their outdoor time has dropped significantly over the past decade. Nature deficit poses critical developmental challenges to the present and future generations. Compared to the integrated multi-sensory stimuli one can find in nature, digital media often provides distorted and pre-calibrated sensory input. Although Louv (2008) suggested that nature deficit may cause problems in sensory processing and other developmental disorders, no empirical research has examined the relationship between nature exposure in childhood and sensory processing patterns in adulthood. This research aims to examine 1) the extent to which childhood nature exposure is associated with adulthood sensory profiles, and 2) whether sensory profiles explain the relationships between nature exposure in childhood and nature-relatedness and creativity in adulthood.

Design and Method: We conducted a cross-sectional survey with retrospective measures of perceived childhood exposure to investigate the gaps in research on nature exposure, sensory processing, nature-relatedness, and creativity. 700 young adults (18-25 years old) were recruited from a comprehensive university. Participants' childhood residences showed diverse geolocations and vegetation coverage. Sensory Profile was measured using the Adolescent/Adult Sensory Profile (AASP); Creativity measured using the Alternative Uses Task (AUT), and nature-relatedness measured using Nature-relatedness (NR) scale. Perceived childhood nature exposure was calculated as a cumulative score based on the perceived nature in residential surroundings from up to three childhood home locations weighted by duration of residence. Ordinary Least Square (OLS) and structural equation models (SEM) were fitted to examine the direct and indirect relationships.

Results: After adjusting for socio-demographic characteristics, higher childhood nature exposure was associated with the lower scores on the low registration sensory quadrant. Regarding the relationship between childhood nature exposure and adulthood nature-relatedness, we identified both a significant direct path and a significant indirect path through the low registration sensory quadrant. Similarly, for creativity, childhood nature exposure is directly related to creativity, and also through the low registration sensory quadrant as an indirect pathway.

Conclusions: The results provide empirical evidence that childhood nature exposure is associated with sensory patterns. Children who had lower levels of nature exposure grow up to exhibit a high tendency to miss subtle sensory stimuli (low registration), and this sensory processing pattern in turn is associated with lower levels of affinity to nature and creativity. Therefore, sensory processing patterns may be the mechanism through which childhood nature experiences influence other developmental outcomes. These findings offer implications for designing child-friendly cities that facilitate sensory explorations and cognitive development.

References

Louv, R. (2008). *Last child in the woods: Saving our children from nature-deficit disorder*. Algonquin books.

The Impact of Physical Design Features in Outdoor Learning Environments on Play

Lori Guerrero *(Texas Tech University);* ***Kristi Gaines*** *(Texas Tech University);* ***Debajyoti Pati*** *(Texas Tech University);* ***Malinda Colwell*** *(Texas Tech University);* ***Charles Klein*** *(Texas Tech University)*

Utilizing the repertory grid technique in a survey sent to members of the National Coalition for Campus Children's Centers, this study collected beliefs about physical design features of nine outdoor learning environment (OLE) behavior settings that promote solitary, parallel and cooperative play in preschool-aged children. The nine behavior settings and independent variables of the study are: 1) water, 2) loose parts, 3) looping pathway, 4) structures for gross motor skills, 5) vegetable and fruit garden, 6) nature art, 7) plants, 8) refuge/restoration and 9) sand. According to the beliefs of 32 Early Childhood Educators at Campus Children's Centers across the United States, there are physical design features that are more critical than others for each type of play. The findings demonstrate that the following physical design considerations may impact the types of play children choose to engage during outdoor learning: 1) materials of the behavior setting, the size of the space allocated for the setting, the orientation of the child's body influenced by the physical design and layout, amount and type of manipulatives provided to the children, visibility and/or seclusion, proxemics, and anthropometric considerations of a child's body. The findings may guide the design and implementation of OLEs that provide an environment which affords children solitary, parallel and cooperative play, which is important for children's development, health, and well-being.

A Landscape Language for Health: Improving Human Resilience through Design

Anne Spafford *(North Carolina State University)*

One in five Americans experience some kind of mental health condition. With the ongoing Pandemic, racial reckoning, and the recent political landscape, depression and anxiety are on the rise—42% of U.S. adults recently reported experiencing symptoms, an 11% increase from previous years (Leonhardt 2021, n.p.). The National Alliance on Mental Illness (NAMI) states that 20.8% of people experiencing homelessness in the U.S. have a serious mental health condition (NAMI.org). Long lasting mental health issues can lead to serious chronic health problems such as heart disease, hypertension, and diabetes (Ibid.). Mental health treatment and services reached a staggering $225 billion in 2019, up 52% since 2009 (Leonhardt 2021, n.p.). Mental illness also affects the economy with lower workforce participation rates and decreased productivity (Ibid.). Surprisingly, only 20% of good health is based on actual health care, while 80% is based on social and environmental determinants (Mangan 2017, n.p.). This should catapult designing for a health a priority into the design of everyday landscapes. However, a disconnect exists between the wealth of published environment-behavior research across disciplines, and the application of that research by design practitioners.

I am advocating for designing for human resiliency and the power of the built environment—the everyday landscape—to mitigate mental health issues. More than simply reducing human stress response (a pathogenic approach), resiliency implies that humans can adapt to cope better when stressful events occur (a salutogenic approach). Current psychology research (Fredrickson 2004) suggests that when people experience joy, gratitude, serenity, interest, hope, pride, amusement, inspiration, and awe, it encourages new actions which in turn promote skills for showing care, creating social bonds, increasing knowledge, motivation, and creating new worldviews. My research investigates the intersection of positive psychology, the neuroscience behind sensory stimulation, and opportunities for improving human resiliency through the design of everyday outdoor spaces accessible by all. This is an environment-behavior study with two parts: 1. a landscape assessment of 5 public landscapes to analyze possible emotive qualities pertaining to layout, spatial characteristics, garden elements and sensory aspects; and 2. Behavior mapping of participants in the landscapes and self-evaluation surveys of visitors' emotional state and perceived resiliency. Together, these data will be valuable in designing to elicit positive emotions and/or assist in processing other emotions. The research will culminate in the creation of a landscape language for health guidebook for practitioners, and future professionals. It will also be a valuable tool for project stakeholders to articulate better their programmatic needs at project outset. This landscape language for health will act as a prescription for designers to become health agents.

References

Fredrickson, B.L. (2004). The broaden and build theory of positive emotions. Philosophical Transactions of the Royal Society B: Biological Sciences

Leonhardt, M. (May 10, 2021). What you need to know about the cost and accessibility of mental health care in America. CNBC Make it website, n.p.

Mangan, S. (October 9, 2017). Social determinants of health 101 for health care: five plus five. National Academy of Medicine Website, n.p.

National Alliance on Mental Illness. Website homepage, n.p.

Continuing Care Retirement Communities: Social Engagement, Wellbeing, and Life Satisfaction in Geriatric Settings

Caitlyn Barry *(Kansas State University)*

By the year 2050, the United States elderly population is expected to reach over 81 million with an increased dependency ratio of 72 dependents per 100 working age adults (Passel, 2008). As of 2010, about 6.5% (2.5 million) of older adults (65+ years old) in the United States lived in care facilities (Pray, Boon, Miller, Pilsbury, and Rapporteurs, 2010), this number is expected to rise with the growing older population. These older adults require facilities to house and care for them as their medical, physical, and mental care needs increase. Continuing Care Retirement Communities (CCRC) typically include varying levels of care in a campus-style setting and accommodate for independent, assisted, and skilled nursing care living (Shippee, 2010). Most care facilities are successful at meeting the basic human needs of physical nourishment, shelter, protection, and medical care; but secondary needs like social engagement, wellbeing, and life satisfaction are easily forgotten (Shippee, 2010). With an increasing population, quality of care in these facilities is expected to be strained and design solutions are needed to use care space more efficiently while improving quality of care.

Following an extensive literature review, a case study analysis was completed for one chosen facility. Due to the contagious nature of the novel coronavirus, in-person data collection was not feasible, so qualitative observations were conducted virtually, through video tours, photographs, and social media postings. The data was analyzed via visual methods, and spaces were categorized in three main groups: social spaces, private spaces, and transition spaces. Informed by the conclusions drawn from the literature review, these three areas were then evaluated on the following criteria: seating and arrangement, size and space planning, lighting, color, and materials and finishes. Results of the case study and literature review were summarized into actionable design solutions and applied to the proposed project: a CCRC that focuses on wellness, socialization, and life satisfaction.

Therefore, this evidence-based design proposes a CCRC model that serves as a precedent for existing and new facilities that aims for the promotion of a holistically healthier aging in place.

References

Passel, J. S., & Cohn, D. V. (2008, February 11). *U.S. Population Projections: 2005-2050*. Washington, DC; Pew Research Center.

Pray, L., Boon, C., Miller, E. A., Pillsbury, L., & Rapporteurs. (2010, January 1). *Size and demographics of aging populations. Providing Healthy and Safe Foods As We Age: Workshop Summary*. Retrieved September 18, 2021, from https://www.ncbi.nlm.nih.gov/books/NBK51841/#:~:text=Only%204.5%20percent%20(about%201.5,million)%20live%20in%20the%20community.

Shippee, T. P. (2010, December 16). On the edge: Balancing health, participation, and autonomy to maintain active independent living in two retirement facilities. Minneapolis, MN: *Journal of Aging Studies*.

Wrublowsky, R. (2017). *Design Guide for Long Term Care Homes*. FGI Guidelines. https://www.fgiguidelines.org/wp-content/uploads/2018/03/MMP_DesignGuideLongTermCareHomes_2018.01.pdf.

Spatial Distribution Characteristics and Influencing Factors of Rural Tourism Based on Poi: A Case Study of Agritainment in Beijing

Rui Shi *(Beijing Jiaotong University);* ***Yi Yang*** *(Beijing Jiaotong University);* ***Bo Zhang*** *(Oklahoma State University)*

Most of the current studies on the spatial distribution of agritainment are based on the traditional survey data. With the development of online electronic maps, POI (point of interest) data provide new big data sources, yet there are a few examples of this kind of big-data-based study on spatial distribution of agritainment at the city level. By 2021, there are more than 2,000 agritainment in Beijing.In order to understand the spatial distribution characteristics and influencing factors of agritainment in Beijing, 647 agritainment points of interest (POI) captured from AutoNavi Map were taken as the research objects, using GIS spatial analysis tool and mathematical statistical analysis method, the nearest neighbor index, K-function, kernel density estimation, Getis-ORD Gi* hot spot analysis and Moran's I index were used. The results indicate: (1)The distribution of agritainment in Beijing is not balanced, showing an overall trend of aggregation, and the spatial autocorrelation is significant. (2)The agglomeration degree of agritainment in urban area increased with the increase of spatial scale, and the characteristic spatial scale of main urban area was 13.49 km. (3)The hot spots of agritainment distribution in Beijing are concentrated in the southwest of the city, while the main city is scattered and the main city is outside the city. (4) 65.7% of the agritainment were distributed within 7km of a-level scenic spots, and tended to be distributed around nature scenic spots and high-level scenic spots. It is found that the supply orientation of regional policy is the driving force for the spatial agglomeration of agritainment, high economic level, income and consumption ability are the basis for the expansion of agritainment scale, and perfect facilities supply is the external dependence of spatial distribution of agritainment. The influencing factors also include topography, vegetation coverage, traffic conditions and tourism resources. Based on the analysis of the data, the paper puts forward some suggestions to optimize the layout of agritainment industry, to promote the full integration of rural tourism development and ecological civilization construction, and to promote the revitalization of rural areas.

The Positive Impact on Individuals' Sustained-Attention Level of Micro Interactions with Natural Green Elements in Low-Income Communities

Hossein Saedi *(North Carolina State University);* ***Arthur Roy Rice*** *(North Carolina State University)*

Theories such as attention restoration theory (ART) and other research suggest that interaction with nature can improve an individual's attention level. Research has shown that individuals in low-income urban housing have disproportionately less access to natural environments and, therefore, lack benefits from encounters with nature. This research examines the possibility of utilizing natural green elements in the design of low-income residential buildings' interiors to compensate for the lack of natural environments in low-income urban areas.

The researchers compared the results from a Sustained Attention to Response Task (SART) for one hundred and eighty-two residents of a high-rise residential building. During an experimental study, participants were randomly selected to experience one of two versions of a building's lobby modeled in a 3D immersive virtual reality environment. One model included natural green elements and the other did not. Participants completed the SART twice. Once before experiencing the lobby and once after. The results indicate that those who interacted with natural green elements in the building lobby for less than a minute demonstrated significant improvement in their attention level. They received higher scores in the SART post-test and demonstrated fewer cognitive errors. These results support the potential positive effect of short-term interaction with natural green elements on an individual's sustained attention level.

Refugee Housing in Support of Health, Well-Being, and Self-Reliance

Hannah Nicole Bidigare-Curtis *(Cornell University);* ***Nancy M. Wells*** *(Cornell University)*

The movement of refugees often triggers the creation of emergency-style settlements where housing is typically low-quality. . Due to the prevalence of protracted global violence in the last few decades, these settlements have become increasingly permanent for their residents. This research explores associations between refugee housing characteristics and desired refugee outcomes, namely health, well-being, and self-reliance, as well as plausible mediating mechanisms that may explain the associations between these variables. A sample of 82 participants was randomly selected in three zones of Bidibidi Refugee Settlement in Uganda, where residents are largely responsible for constructing and maintaining their own earthen housing. Residents were surveyed and their housing was both photographed and diagrammed. Demographic variables including age, gender, settlement zone, hut tenure and marital status were used as statistical controls. Results indicate the importance of crowding, household security, food storage, and presence of indoor pests as predictors of health and well-being. Sleep quality was the most relevant health variable to self-reliance. This cross-sectional research is one of the first studies to directly examine the relationship between refugees' housing and self-reliance, in alignment with Housing First models. Ultimately, these findings help to identify potential points of intervention for settlement housing in terms of both aid and construction processes and the quality of the final product, thereby informing the policies and design of refugee settlements going forward.

Time Spent Playing Outdoors in Community Environments: Gendered and Seasonal Differences in Outdoor Play Patterns Among Children in Canadian Communities

Janet Loebach *(Cornell University);* ***Tara Elton-Marshall*** *(Center for Addiction and Mental Health);* ***Marcos Sanches*** *(Center for Addiction and Mental Health)*

Outdoor play and independent, neighborhood activity, both linked with healthy childhood development, have declined dramatically among Western children in recent decades. A number of previous studies have also reported that male children tend to spend more time playing outdoors than females, however some studies have shown few differences in outdoor play or physical activity by gender. In countries like Canada which experience significant seasonal differences in climatic conditions, factors influencing outdoor play patterns differ by season. This study examines how social, cultural and environmental factors may be hindering children's outdoor and community-based play, with a particular focus on gender differences and seasonal differences in time spent outdoors. A comprehensive survey was completed by 826 children (aged 10–13 years) and their parents from 12 schools (four each urban, suburban and rural) from a large county in Ontario, Canada. In addition to examining differences in time spent outdoors between male and female child participants, as well overall and gendered differences in outdoor play, regression models (after controlling for school clustering effects) examine associations between outdoor play time per week and variable sets representing prevalent factors cited in the literature as influencing children's outdoor play. Analyses show that boys spent more time outdoors on average per week than girls, but that socio-environmental factors influencing this time outdoors differed by gender. Not surprisingly, time spent outdoors in winter was lower than in spring, summer, or fall seasons for both boys and girls, but girls on average still spent proportionally less time outdoors. Factors influencing outdoor play not only differed for winter versus other seasons, but different factors influenced girls' winter outdoor time than boys. Findings suggest that in some communities there remain gendered differences in both outdoor time and barriers, and that these differences are also affected by seasons differences. These analyses suggest that environmental or program interventions focused on increasing time spent outdoors and reducing barriers to outdoor play may be more effective if they account for differences in barriers, interests and motivators across genders, and across seasons. Study findings have important implications for targeting environmental, cultural and policy changes to foster child-friendly communities which effectively support healthy outdoor play for all children, year-round.

Campus Crowdsourcing: A Tool to Amplify Students, Staff and Faculty Experiences of Welcoming, Inclusivity and Safety on Higher Education Campus

Milagros Zingoni Phielipp *(University of Tennessee);*
Bethany Morris *(ASLA)*

Students, staff and faculty, as human beings, are a system in frequency: resilient and flexible. We evolve and adapt continuously through self-awareness, which is the ability to perceive, process, and manage one's system. This implies re-evaluating emotions to make them explicit, understanding that there are many ways to portray an idea, and that the problem framing and problem solving will be different depending the user. The social and political unrest of the past few years, have encouraged higher education campuses to develop more inclusive, safe and welcoming experiences for students, faculty and staff. However, most efforts have been related to freedom of speech and academic freedom, with very little attention towards how the built environment supports experiences of feeling inclusive, welcoming and safe (or not). As members of a grant land university, our dimensions of citizen expand to work with and for communities. We approach problems by thinking about multiple contexts in shorter and longer terms. This research presents a pilot study carried out in a Research I public Institution in the southeast of the United States, using crowdsourcing as a means to amplify the voices of different higher education campus users. It summarizes higher education users' perspectives of environmental settings that provides safe, welcoming and inclusive experiences.

The research employed crowdsourcing as a data collection. Crowdsourcing is the use of digital technologies to gather crowd wisdom to solve a problem (Manzano et al, 2019) that is often not available to researchers, and decision-making leadership. Similar to "urban crowdsourcing" (Zambonelli 2011) and "citizensourcing" (2008), this study used digital technologies to gather and organize contributions from everyday users in order to improve the diversity of voices and experiences on higher education campus. Although there is a gap in the literature on crowdsourcing in higher education campus, several investigations and various experiments have recently been conducted with the goal of engaging citizens in order to gather information about their cities and their communities employing urban crowdsourcing/citizensourcing.

What are the elements and methodology of campus crowdsourcing to amplify the voices of users on higher education campus?

The researchers developed a platform using GIS survey as a means to quickly and affordably recruit multiple perspectives with diverse backgrounds (Rea et al 2021). The tool was available as an open source for four weeks, and received over 200 entries.

The data analysis of this pilot study reveals that the crowdsourcing tool provided data to generate significant statistical findings across the selected site.

Do Evidence-Based Biophilic-Designed Environments Promote Mental Health and Well-Being during the COVID-19 Pandemic?

***Ruba Nooman Khalaf** (Jordan University of Science and Technology); **Bushra Obeidat** (Jordan University of Science and Technology)*

The COVID-19 pandemic has altered people's interactions with nature, which is expected to intensify the pandemic's psychological effects. The purpose of this research is to determine if biophilic design attributes may benefit mental health even when there is inadequate outside exposure during periods of physical seclusion from the outdoors. We used the Patient Health Questionnaire's nine-item and the Generalized Anxiety Disorder's seven-item scales to assess depression and anxiety symptoms in 210 students. We used a self-reported questionnaire to assess a set of ten biophilic attributes that are particularly rooted in daily experience: visual connections with nature, non-visual connections with nature, non-rhythmic sensory stimuli, thermal and airflow variability, water presence, dynamic and diffused light, complexity, and order, prospect, refuge, and mystery. We used generalized linear regression and logistic regression to examine the associations between Biophilic design features and mental health. Students expressed clinically significant symptoms of mild sadness and anxiety. This study establishes a favorable association between the presence of visual biophilic design attributes in the environment and students' psychological condition, including emotions of enjoyment and enthusiasm. However, determining the causal significance of these correlations is not straightforward. Additionally, this research indicated that user inputs might be a viable method for testing the notion of the biophilic design prior to implementation, allowing designers to assess the psychological impacts on users.

Green Infrastructure and Campus Health: Examining the Characteristics of College Campus Users

***Galen Daniel Newman** (Texas A&M University); **Ryun Jung (RJ) Lee** (Texas A&M University); **Chanam Lee** (Texas A&M University); **Yang Song** (Texas A&M University); **Zhicheng Xu** (Michigan State University); **Won Min Sohn** (Michigan State University); **Yizhen Ding** (Texas A&M University); **Dongying Li** (Texas A&M University)*

Purpose: Green infrastructure can bring many public health benefits by encouraging physical activities and promoting mental health. Many studies have indicated the importance of campus green space for university students who spend most of their time on campus (van den Bogerd, etc., 2020; Gulwadi, et al., 2019; Ibes & Forestell, 2020). This study analyzes the compositional and configurational characteristics of green infrastructure and its relationship with College campus users' health outcomes by examining areas with a high number of campus users.

Methods: We focused on three campuses of large public universities in Texas: Bryan-College Station, Lubbock, and Austin (which are the home of Texas A&M University, Texas Tech University, and the University of Texas at Austin, respectively). We measured the quantity and quality of green infrastructure of the surrounding communities and their community characteristics. Health outcomes in this study include the census tract level health conditions (e.g., physical and mental health) and healthy behaviors (e.g., regular workouts, drinking habits, etc.) obtained from the Centers for Disease Control and Prevention (CDC)'s Place dataset. The quantity and quality of green infrastructure were measured using land cover, imperviousness, tree canopy, normalized difference vegetation index, and FRAGSTATS variables. To measure campus users, the number of people from each census tract who visited the "campus tracts" (census tracts overlapping the university campus) were calculated using the place-based mobility data (SafeGraph, 2021) . ANOVA was conducted to test if the difference in health outcomes is significant between campus tracts and non-campus tracts. Further, OLS and logit models are estimated with spatial lag variables to capture the spatial interdependency between census tracts.

Results: ANOVA results indicated that campus tracts showed a significantly higher level of mental health issues compared to non-campus tracts, suggesting that campus users may be more exposed to potential stressors. Regression results further suggested that a higher number of campus visitors (calculated with SafeGraph) is associated with increased mental health problems. For physical health conditions, no meaningful differences between campus and non-campus tracts are found. Tree canopy and imperviousness showed significant associations with both positive health conditions and healthy behaviors. Our preliminary findings offer initial insights on (1) the importance of green infrastructure on both healthy behavior and health conditions and (2) the potential mental health threats to which campus users such as students, faculty, and staff may be exposed. This stresses the importance of a campus environment where the users would spend most of their day time and suggests potential for green infrastructure interventions to encourage their healthy behaviors and outcomes.

A Social Identity Perspective to Understand How Living Learning Community (LLC) Environment Matters for the Student Residents' Social Well-Being

Yaoyi Zhou *(Virginia Tech);* ***Elif Tural*** *(Virginia Tech)*

Living Learning Community (LLC) is a common way to encourage social interaction and foster a sense of belonging among college students. Although the concept of community building has been acknowledged as a significant area of research in design literature, how the LLC environment influences the student residents' social well-being has remained unclear. Extant studies lack a firm theoretical underpinning.

Social identity refers to the sense of self that people derive from their membership in a social group (e.g., family, work, community.; Tajfel, 1978). In recent years, a social identity perspective of well-being has received more attention in social psychology and public health (Haslam et al., 2018). This theoretical thread suggests that a desire for meaningful social identification helps the individual to make sense of his/her environment and to function effectively within it. Empirical evidence was found in a plethora of recent studies (Jetten, Haslam & Alexander, 2012).

The goal of this project is to unravel theoretical and conceptual threads in social identity literature and use them to explore relationships between the LLC environment's design and the student residents' social well-being. To inform the conceptual framework, we first conduct a systematic literature review of studies related to "social identity" and "place identity" in design and environment & behavior literature. Then we propose a case study of a global LLC on a public university campus, applying a mixed-method design involving data collection comprised of semi-structured interviews and a survey study. The primary research question is: which aspects of the LLC environment's design may affect the extent that how student residents identify with that LLC? We also propose two hypotheses for statistical analyses of the survey results: a) the extent that the student residents identify with the LLC is associated with the levels of engagement in the LLC's organized activities; b) the extent that the student residents identify with the LLC is associated with the levels of social support that they receive.

Overall, this presentation addresses the theoretical foundation for research focused on the LLC environment's design and the residents' social well-being. We believe that the social identity approach would help us further study the instrumentality of space, and contribute to the understanding of higher education facility design.

References

Haslam, C., Jetten, J., Cruwys, T., Dingle, G. A., & Haslam, S. A. (2018). *The new psychology of health: Unlocking the social cure*. Routledge.

Jetten, J., Haslam, C., & Alexander, S. H. (Eds.). (2012). *The social cure: Identity, health and well-being*. Psychology Press.

Tajfel, H. E. (1978). *Differentiation between social groups: Studies in the social psychology of intergroup relations*. London, UK: Academic Press.

Systematic Review on Color Research and Design Implications for Interior Spaces

Jin Gyu Park *(University of North Texas)*

Purpose: The purpose of this presentation is to provide evidences from color impacts and design implications for interior spaces through an extensive literature review on color research studies and the presenter's color research experiences.

Problem Statement: Color is taken for granted since people often consider our response to color as instinctive and simple, but it actually involves a very complex interaction between light, the eyes, and the brain. Color has a great impact on our psychological and physiological responses. While previous studies on color are informative; those studies are typically conducted by using small color chips or papers which are different from seeing a color applied on one or more wall surfaces. In addition, they failed to control confounding variables such as brightness and saturation while investigating hue effect. Many designers have sought empirical evidence of color application to room design, but the investigation of design guidelines on color application for environmental design based on empirical research studies is particularly non-existent.

Significance: This presentation addresses the above issues by summarizing literatures about color studies from the 1920s up to present and exploring the PI's color research projects. The presentation will facilitate design professionals in color applications for the spaces they design.

Methodology: A critical literature review is conducted by using key search terms, including but not limited to "color, color, wall color, room color, built environment, physical environment", within several academic databases. Color studies in social science, psychology, and environmental design, and the presenter's empirical color studies using physical model simulation are considered. Each chosen study is reviewed in terms of its significance, appropriateness of the research methods utilized, strengths and limitations of the study, and suitability of the conclusions.

Summary of Results: From the literature review, the arousal effect of red was supported (Kwallek, Lewis, & Robbins, 1988) by several studies measuring physiological responses and psychological responses. Emotional associations with colors were also suggested. Brighter colors have a positive relationship with positive emotions; in contrast, darker colors elicit negative feelings (Boyatzis & Varghese, 1994; Hemphill, 1996). Age effect on color preferences was found despite subject characteristics, variables controlled for, measures used, and type of statistical analysis. Slight gender differences were observed; females tend to prefer warm colors, whereas males tend to prefer cool colors. Cultural differences in color preferences are not widely studied, though culture does seem to impact color preferences. The presenter's research projects identified color preferences for patient room design from healthy children, pediatric patients, and design professionals. As a conclusion, the presenter proposes design implications for interior spaces based on evidences of color effects from literature and future research considerations.

References

Boyatzis, C. J., & Varghese, R. (1994). Children's emotional associations with colors. *Journal of Genetic Psychology, 155*, 77-85.

Hemphill, M. (1996). A note on adults' color-emotion associations. *Journal of Genetic Psychology, 157*, 275-280.

Kwallek, N., Lewis, C., & Robbins, A. (1988). Effects of office interior color on workers' mood and productivity. *Perceptual and Motor Skills, 66*, 123-128.

Designing for Patient Safety; Simulation-Based Hospital Design Testing

Nora Colman *(Children's Healthcare of Atlanta);* **Kiran Hebbar** *(Children's Healthcare of Atlanta);* **Caitlin Ivie** *(Children's Healthcare of Atlanta)*

Background: The ability to address safety and mitigate risk in the design development period is imperative, practical, and cost effective (1). If safety is not a focus of design prototypes, it is likely that the design will not support safe care delivery, requiring need for costly retrofitting and design enhancements later (2). There is opportunity for institutions to engage in activities that improve clinical care, optimize safety, and maximize investment. This is a prospective investigation of the cost avoidance associated with Simulation-based Hospital Design Testing.

Method: Simulation-based Hospital Design Testing, conducted in a cardboard city, was identified latent conditions to mitigate safety concerns related to the proposed schematic and detail design of 15 distinct clinical areas. Architectural modifications were made to the proposed design to resolve latent conditions and address safety concerns. Cost associated with each design modification was estimated and categorized by clinical area, evidence-based design principle, and detectability. Detectability was defined as items that would be addressed in design meetings, items that would be missed in design meetings and were cost prohibitive or impossible to change post-construction, and items that may be missed during design development but required renovation or retrofitting post-construction.

Results: During SbHDT, 722 latent conditions were identified and 456 of those latent conditions required architectural design modifications, resulting in a cost savings of $90 million. Design modifications ranged from minor renovations such as changes to millwork or relocation of mounted fixtures (sharps containers, gloves boxes, hand foam) to major reconfiguration of clinical areas. 14% of the latent conditions were design elements that would have likely been missed during design development and required renovation or retrofitting post-construction. Examples include addition of equipment rooms, enlarging storage areas to accommodate equipment, addition of windows, sinks, medical gasses, removal of fixed wall elements that impeded workflow, or positioning of code blue buttons. Major design modifications included addition of sinks in the bed tower, redesign of care teamwork areas, reorientation of adjacencies (supply, equipment, medication, and clean storage rooms), addition of soiled utility rooms to improve OR workflow, redesign of the nurse server, complete redesign of the MRI induction area, scan room, and control space, and total reconfiguration of operating rooms to optimize surgical bed positioning.

Conclusion: SbHDT was a deliberate activity that harnessed evidence-based design to improve clinical care, optimize safety and maximize investment. Application of SbHDT to optimize architectural design as a means to mitigate risks to safety was financially effective. Using simulation early during design development was optimally positioned on the cost-influence curve. The return on investment following SbHDT demonstrates the value of this activity as significant costs were avoided with early detection of design inefficiencies.

References

1. Taylor E, Hignett S, Joseph A. The environment of safe care: considering building design as one facet of safety. *International Symposium on Human Factors and Ergonomics in Health Care: Advancing the Cause 2014*:123-7.
2. Joseph A, Rashid M. The architecture of safety: hospital design. *Curr Opin Crit Care. 2007;13*(6):714-9.

Design Factors Affecting Millennial New Employees' Job Satisfaction in Workplace: A Focus Group Study

Huili Wang *(Texas Tech University);* **Michelle Pearson** *(Texas Tech University);* **Kristi Gaines** *(Texas Tech University);* **Erin M Hamilton** *(Texas Tech University)*

Background: Millennials are the largest generation in the U.S. workforce today and they are thought to have significantly different working preferences compared to previous generations (Pew Research

Center, 2018). Previous research has documented increased rates of turnover among millennials, with most turnover occurring in new employees who work less than two years (Kuron, Lyons, Schweitzer, & Ng, 2015). Job satisfaction is the most important predictor of employees' outcomes, such as productivity, absenteeism, turnover, and well-being. Moreover, studies show evidence that physical work environment satisfaction has a positive relationship with job satisfaction (Vischer, 2008). However, the relationship between physical work environment satisfaction and millennial new employees' job satisfaction remains largely unexamined.

Methodology: A descriptive and exploratory qualitative study was conducted to answer the research question: what physical work environment factors affect millennial new employees' job satisfaction. The qualitative research is motivated by the need to deeply understand how millennial new employees experience the new work environment. Two online focus groups were held via Zoom with six participants in the first group and five in the second group. All participants were millennial and identified themselves as IT industry employees. Nine participants stated that they experienced a new work environment within the last two years. After the completion of two focus groups, the moderator and the assistant moderator agreed that no new information was being collected, therefore, the sample size was large enough to obtain data saturation. The data used in the analysis of the focus group discussion included the audio and video recordings, online chat, verbatim transcripts, and the assistant moderator's notes. The transcripts were reviewed several times to gain an overall understanding of the data and then analyzed in NVivo.

Results: After open coding, axial coding and selective coding, six office design factors were identified which are important for increase millennial IT newcomers' job satisfaction. They are 1) Socializing and relaxing space, 2) Ergonomic furniture, 3) Nature and windows, 4) Technology, 5) Personalize surroundings, 6) Lighting. Each factor was analyzed and discussed in the paper.

References

Fry, R. (2018, April 11). *Millennials are largest generation in the U.S. labor force*. https://www.pewresearch.org/fact-tank/2018/04/11/millennials-largest-generation-us-labor-force/

Kuron, L. K. J., Lyons, S. T., Schweitzer, L., & Ng, E. S. W. (2015). Millennials' work values: differences across the school to work transition. *Personnel Review, 44*(6), 991–1009. https://doi.org/10.1108/PR-01-2014-0024

Vischer, J. C. (2008). Towards an environmental psychology of workspace: How people are affected by environments for work. *Architectural Science Review, 51*(2), 97–108. https://doi.org/10.3763/asre.2008.511

Opportunities for Transformation in Peri-Operative Services: Nursing Perceptions of Clinical Efficiency

Laurie Waggener *(EYP Architecture & Engineering);* ***Apoorva Rane*** *(EYP Architecture & Engineering);* ***Alan Hedge*** *(Cornell University)*

Objective: This research-in-practice study examined the supportiveness of the physical working environments through medical practitioners' perception after moving to a newly renovated peri-operative unit.

Background: The recent literature reveals substantial evidence regarding operating suite design, process flow, and clinical efficiency from the surgeon's and patient's standpoint. However, the physical design responses supporting the clinical processes of Pre-op, PACU, and Recovery II departments require additional scrutiny for architecture practice.

This session will focus on the facility performance evaluations of the new peri-operative unit located in a Planetree-certified hospital in the northeast region of the United States. Prioritizing evidence-based literature, a participative design approach, and field studies are some commonly holistic design practices harnessed at the participating architecture firm.

This new construction was driven by the need to replace an outdated physical environment. Client goals included enhancing human-centered care and transforming the culture of the unit through a commitment to Planetree principles. The goal for the hospital was to strike a unique balance between the level of quality care and service for patients while offering an equally uncompromised commitment to staff's well-being. The key design goals of this project were to (a) incorporate Planetree philosophy values, (b) facilitate clinical efficiency and patient safety, and (c) embrace a team approach to evidence-based design.

Method: This pre-test-post-test research implemented a multi-methods approach, and the quantitative data were collected using the Practitioners Perception Survey (Cronbach's Alpha = 0.882; FIRO LLC.,], 2013). Similarly, qualitative data was documented with semi-structured focused group interviews, photography, annotation. The pre-move surveys were administered in September 2016. The peri-operative team moved into the new unit in October 2016. The post-move surveys were administered in December 2017 – January 2018, followed by the qualitative data collection in March 2018.

A total of 32 and 51 practitioners participated in the pre-move and post-move practitioners' surveys, respectively. Over 16 practitioners participated in the qualitative process. Quantitative data were analyzed using chi-square tests and t-tests. The content analysis of the qualitative data revealed a thematic analysis of emerging clinical and physical design challenges. The floor plan annotations and photo documentation supported the narrative.

Results: The results will discuss the statistically significant findings and frontline practitioners' expectations of supportiveness of their workplace. Similarly, noise and equipment-related challenges in the operating rooms will be briefly discussed. This deep-dive exploration will further guide future peri-operative unit configuration.

Conclusion: This study articulates the changing needs of peri-operative services due to the transforming clinical expectations. Front-line practitioners' responses to the open comments portion of the survey as well as focus group interviews will enlighten the architect and the interior designer for future innovative design responses in this fast-paced, often, critical care environment.

Student Health and Well-Being in Design Education

Dina Battisto *(Clemson University);* ***Katherine Price*** *(Clemson University);* ***Michael Ureta*** *(Clemson University);* ***Julia Blouin*** *(Clemson University);* ***Xiaowei Li*** *(Clemson University);* ***Jiaying Dong*** *(Clemson University)*

Background: The American College Health Association surveyed 96,489 college students from a hundred thirty-seven colleges and universities across the U.S. in Spring 2021. According to the survey, 80.8% of students reported moderate to serious levels of stress within the last 12 months (70.2% men, 85% women, and 88.7.5% trans/gender, non-conforming). The survey further revealed that stress and anxiety are the greatest academic impediments for students: 43% of college students reported that stress negatively impacted academic performance and 35% reported anxiety negatively impacted academic performance. Even more troubling, these numbers jump higher for minority populations.

According to the Counseling and Psychological Services (CAPS) program at one University, architecture students have the highest stress and anxiety rates compared to all students on campus and the highest severity of mental health issues. Students in under-represented categories are at an even higher risk for stress and retention in college programs, which may be why architectural practices lack the diversity found in the U.S. population. Some research uncovers the mental health challenges college students face overall. However, very little research exists about architecture and landscape architecture students. We do know that stress should be addressed since numerous research studies show that prolonged stress compromises physiological and mental health outcomes (McEwen 2008; Ribeiro et al., 2018).

Research Objective and Methods: A mixed-methods research approach, utilizing three data collection tools, was used to investigate the health of architecture and landscape architecture students during fall 2021. First, an existing screening tool, the Depression and Anxiety Stress Scale (DASS-21), was administered to all students to measure the emotional states of depression, anxiety and stress (n = 399 or 68% response rate). Second, a health questionnaire was developed and administered through Qualtrics to explore factors that elevate stress, the adverse effects of stress, and strategies to cope with stress (n = 301 or 51% response rate). Third, 44 interviews were conducted with students to gain an in-depth perspective of the stressors students experience and the consequences of this stress.

Findings: By all indicators, mental health can be a severe threat to some architecture and landscape students. This presentation reports on findings from the study to (1) reveal a quantitative snapshot of the emotional states of depression, anxiety, and stress among students, and (2) shed light on the most common stressors voiced by students and the negative consequences. Administrators, professors, and counselors have been witnessing an increase in the number of students with mental health disorders, and this research offers empirical evidence. The next phase of this research is to seek pathways that can lead to higher levels of student wellness in design programs.

Rethinking Design Education for Student Wellness

Dina Battisto *(Clemson University);* ***Katherine Price*** *(Clemson University);* ***Kristian Baber*** *(Clemson University);* ***Michael Ureta*** *(Clemson University);* ***Lara Browning*** *(Clemson University);* ***Julia Blouin*** *(Clemson University);* ***Gregg Ussery*** *(Clemson University);* ***Annie Steele*** *(Clemson University)*

Background: Educational demands in Schools of Architecture, stemming primarily from the design studio, often result in students neglecting some of the essential ingredients to maintaining health and wellness – adequate sleep, regular physical activity, a balanced nutritional diet, and meaningful social interactions. Does the journey to earning a degree in architecture and landscape architecture have to compromise health? Can design programs explore avenues to restore the joy of being a design student and serve as a model for student wellness across college campuses? This session explores these questions and presents how a School of Architecture is working to improve student wellness following a research study that revealed students are struggling with balancing mental health during their studies.

Research Objectives & Methods: The purpose of the research study was to capture an in-depth understanding of the mental health of architecture and landscape students and strategies to promote health and well-being. This presentation will present strategies for promoting student health following a case study research strategy utilizing interviews and open-ended questions for an online questionnaire. First, a total of 44 architecture and landscape architecture students across year levels were interviewed to gain an in-depth understanding of the triggers that exacerbate stress and anxiety and possible solutions to help promote well-being. Second, an online questionnaire was administered to all students in the School of Architecture to solicit feedback on one burning question: "What recommendations could you offer to the School of Architecture to promote student health and well-being as well as lower stress?" (n = 299 or 68% response rate). Content analysis was used to explore themes and patterns from the two data sources collected in fall 2021.

Findings: Six themes emerged from the student voices and will be discussed, including (1) scheduling, coordinating due dates and communication, (2) health promotion and environmental therapeutics (2) support groups, mental health check-ins, and mentorship programs; (3) recognizing the diversity among the student population; (4) sensitivity training for students and awareness training for faculty; (5) practical skills to survive design studio – e.g., time management, overcoming procrastination and navigating team dynamics and (6) improvements in the facilities. Findings from this study are being advocated by the School of Architecture's Student Health and Wellness Task Force with a goal of introducing actionable strategies to encourage change. Several activities are being piloted, including student and faculty meet and greets, social events, weekly walks in the local botanical garden, therapy dogs, light yoga and meditation, and an away space with comfortable furniture for students to relax during long hours spent in the studio.

Exploration of Human Perceptions to Interiors of a Coffee Shop for Enhancing Social Interactions Using Virtual Reality

Kyoungmee Kate Byun *(Northern Arizona University);* ***Min-Kyoung Kim*** *(GwangJu University);* ***Shandiin Lake*** *(Northern Arizona University)*

Many researchers have addressed the importance of the community to the human social, emotional, and cognitive experiences (Waxman 2006; Campbell 2014). Socializing in a space affects the lives of people positively by creating a sense of community, belonging, and attachment. Thus, environmental psychologists and interior designers have proposed social and physical factors to enhance social interaction in gathering places. However, it does not indicate detailed applications such as what degree and/or level of interior physical factors could have an influence on social interactions. Additionally, present studies have explored participants' perceptions on 2D images of proposed spaces for data collection which is less credible than 3D virtual experiences. In this study, participants will be exposed to 3D virtual coffee shops and their emotional responses to the proposed physical settings will be measured.

In order to measure emotional responses, Mehrabian and Russell's model on approach and avoidance behavior is applied (Mehrabian & Russell 1974). According to Mehrabian and Russell, approach and avoidance forces are present in every interpersonal encounter and socialization is derived from approach behavior (Mehrabian & Russell 1974). Emotional dimensions of pleasure, arousal, and dominance are positive mechanisms for approach behavior; thus, those dimensions are evaluated in this study.

The 3D virtual coffee shops are designed for the study. Controlled empirical experiments of 3D virtual coffee shops are conducted in a VR lab at Western University. Top four physical factors of interiors (e.g., appealing aroma, adequate lighting, comfortable furniture, and a view to the outside) are chosen as independent variables from Waxman's suggested top five physical settings for the coffee shop (Waxman 2006). Voluntary university student subjects (a defined group of 30 students) of 3 groups are selected to participate in an anonymous VR experiment and answer 7-point Likert scale survey questions in terms of feeling of pleasure, feeling of arousal, and feeling of dominance. Beyond sense of vision, participants are exposed to sense vision, olfaction, and spatiality. Likert scale scores will be analyzed for each setting and a repeated measures ANOVA will be used to evaluate the data to find significant differences for each setting.

As a result, this study will address the design of gathering spaces, especially coffee shops, to enhance social interaction for creating a sense of community, demonstrate 3D virtual reality as a valid means of conducting research of environmental perceptions, and contribute future research in interdisciplinary approach between interiors and environmental psychology.

Mental Health and the Panopticon: Environmental Factors Affecting Work from Home Situations

Gregory Galford *(Virginia Tech)*

The global pandemic has altered the way in which the managed employee produces work. From a strictly on-site situation that enables those employees to be visually controlled, to one where they are working independently at home, new strategies of control are now employed by management to ensure workers are present which indirectly refine methods of capitalism (Hirst, 1982). These systems of surveillance engage worker mental health in a new way and establish a new type of panopticon (Bauman & Lyon, 2013). The purpose of this study is to glean insight into the environmental effects upon behavior for people who choose to work from home as their primary employment, and this paper focuses on those whose jobs are managed by an outside employer through surveillance software. Within those work-from-home environments, the research question seeks to know the behavioral effects of controlled environmental factors using data from residential correctional research as a foundation for the study. The research design is qualitative in character and uses coded data from all stakeholders in a two-step interview process with male inmates in two medium security state prisons. Grounded theory was used as an analytic method. Findings were that time and routine operate uniquely within residential correctional environments, sound becomes dominant when vision is controlled, views to nature are important for mental health, and trust is a dominant behavior for officers. The implications of this research for a controlled residential work environment are that spaces of acoustic privacy are important for productivity, visual connections to nature enhance mental health, and that spaces that promote routine and visual privacy promote discipline within the home when it is used as an office space.

References

Bauman, Z., & Lyon, D. (2013). *Liquid surveillance.* Polity Press

Hirst, P. (1982). Constructed space and the subject. In R. Fardon (Ed.), *Power and knowledge: Anthropological and sociological Approaches: Proceedings of a conference held at the University of St. Andrews in December 1982* (pp. 216). Scottish Academic Press, Ltd.

Neighborhood Design and Holistic Health: A Literature Synthesis

Sara Khorshidifard *(Drury University)*

Numerous comprehensive recent studies have explored connections and impacts of neighborhood formations and health. Nevertheless, there is inadequate synthesis considering some of the more nuanced qualities, for instance, intersections with themes such as environment-related boredom. After a brief overview of previous wide-ranging studies, this presentation will offer a methodical and conceptual visual mapping and clustering of some holistic-health-related neighborhood traits characterized by subtle and complex qualities, with promoting or deterring effects. Beginning by accentuating essential premises regarding all individuals' deserved rights to live, work, and play in holistically healthy neighborhoods, the presentation will next re-ask long-enduring questions such what makes healthy neighborhoods and how neighborhood-scale design and planning can better facilitate or hinder health. Ensuing contents will then interrogate and share summative cross-disciplinary examinations on current states of studies, where subsequent outcomes may also suggest knowledge gaps for future explorations.

Fostering personal, public, physical, and mental health in the built environment as a constituent of architecture and urban design discourse aligns with essential holistic-health awareness and intents of care for the whole person's physical, emotional, social, spiritual, and mental health. Furthermore, formulated by the USDHHS' Healthy People Initiative, 'neighborhood and built environment' is amongst the five 'Social Determinants of Health' categories. There is a growing recognition for the health significance of place and vicinity, alongside the emerging wealth of research into whether/how their physical and social attributes can shape and impact health outcomes. Attending overarchingly to neighborhoods' diverse compositional, contextual, and collective effects, current studies have likewise drawn on detailed factors such as physical inactivity, unhealthy eating, and environmental hazards, to name a few. Some research syntheses have conjured critical associations between people living in disadvantaged neighborhoods, and inferior physical and mental health while consequentially-positive physical and mental health effects are confirmed based on quality and quantity of social relationships.

A fascinating and mystifying psychological concept with neighborhood-health connections hitherto insufficiently examined, ennui is a trait with imperative human-functioning consequences generally emerging where engagement is difficult. Some studies diverge on its all-time negative consequences, considering how boredom may also motivate the pursuit and exploration of new/alternate goals and experiences resulting in positive realizations. Known to us is how poorly designed cities and neighborhoods largely built around cars, lacking access to walking, biking, or public transport can also be conditioned to the consequences of locational boredom. The psychic limbo of the COVID-19 pandemic has since shed further light on neighborhood shortcomings, some being breeding grounds for boredom. Rather gravely felt following earlier shelter-in-place orders when workplaces, schools, downtowns, and businesses had to shut down, people's homes and immediate localities became one and only go-to retreats to quench social needs while dealing with pandemic blues. This presentation will scan the literature and display synopses of this and similar nuanced traits for laying foundational understandings on neighborhood environments in relation to holistic health.

Evaluating Grassland Tourist Usage and Perception Based on Social Media Data- Taking Nalati Grassland As a Case Study

Darman Abulaiti *(Beijing Jiaotong University);* ***Yi Yang*** *(Beijing Jiaotong University);* ***Bo Zhang*** *(Oklahoma State University)*

With the popularity of domestic grassland scenic tourism and the universalization of network technology, tourism websites have become a platform for people to share their feelings and experiences. Yet the empirical studies on grassland experiences are scarce. Part of the reason could be the difficulty of on-site questionnaires and observation, given visitors scatter. The open-sourced social media data shed new light to study people's visit patterns. The voluntarily posted and ever-growing data has a huge quantity (always at least 100 times greater than a normal survey) and multiple facets (not only post contents, but also post time, date, geographical information, reviewer age, etc.), which provides a data collection method of greater efficiency and reliability to study grassland tourism.

This study takes the Nalati Grassland Scenic Area (equal to a state park in US) in Xinjiang, China as an example. This 960-square-kilometer scenic area is the only 5A-level grassland scenic area in Xinjiang. In 2019, it received 1.15 million tourists, with a maximum of 20,000 in a single day. Using Python as a major tool, 6,387 reviews from August 2013 to September 2020 are mined from the three social media platforms of Dianping, Ctrip, and Mafengwo. After cleaning, 6358 valid reviews with a total of 180,000 words are obtained. The research explores three research questions: (1) What scenes and objects do tourists pay attention during their visit? (2) What are the tourist experiences that relate to different grassland programs in ? (3) What are focuses of negative reviews? (4) What are the seasonal patterns in grassland tourism? The textual data was categorized into six dimensions, such as scenery, food, living, travel, shopping, and entertainment, and then further into 102 sub-dimensions. A subdimension text frequency analysis and a text network analysis are conducted to unveil the popularity of sceneries, activities, and perceptions, as well as their relationships.

This study contributes to the understanding of people's tourist experiences of grassland. More specifically, these four issues are explained (1) the influencing factors of grassland tourism satisfaction; (2) the perceived values of grassland; (3) the tourist complaint mechanism; (4) the seasonal changes of grassland visit and perception. In practice, these conclusions could provide guidance for the development of grassland tourism.

Research on the Aging-Adaptability Strategies for the Retrofitting of Existing Residential Buildings Under Green Building and Healthy Building Standards

Chenhui Wu *(Dalian University of Technology);* ***Guopeng Li; Zhou Bo*** *(Dalian University of Technology)*

According to the report of the seventh national census in 2020, China's population over the age of 60 increased by 5.44 percentage points compared with than in 2010. It can be seen that China's aging issue has further deepened. Regardless of national policies, traditional culture or living habits, home-based care is always the most common for the elderly in China. However, the existing residential buildings were not designed for aging population in the design and construction stage, thus there are many problems for the elderly living in. Moreover, there is still no national standards of residential building retrofitting for aging adaptability in China. Therefore, it is imminent to retrofit existing residential buildings for aging-adaptability under home-based care model. In the context of comprehensively promoting healthy China, people are also paying more and more attention to the health of living environment. However, to improve the health performance of existing residential buildings and the living quality of the elderly, the price should not be energy consumption. Under the requirements of China's overall promotion of the green and low-carbon transformation of urban and rural construction, Green and Healthy as the goal of Aging-adaptability should be taken at the same time. Therefore, this study is divided into three steps. Firstly, starting with a comparative study of national and local design specifications and assessment standards in terms of Green, Health, and Aging-adaptability, combined with the investigation of the behavior mode of the elderly, this paper summarized the construction standards of aging adaptability for residential buildings retrofitting. Secondly, the existing residential buildings in typical cities in Northeast China built from 2000 to 2010 were investigated, and the summing-up was compared with the summarized construction standards. Finally, the paper summarized retrofitting strategies in view of Green, Healthy and Aging-adaptability of existing residential buildings, expecting to provide theoretical and practical references for the design and construction of residential buildings.

Revisiting Doxiadis' Balance of Nature and Society in a Mega Mass-Housing Project

Nadia Shah *(Illinois Institute of Technology)*

The Greek architect and planner of the 1950s and 1960s, Constantinos Doxiadis, emphasized the environmental impacts of the twentieth century rapid industrialization, and urbanization. He proposed holistic planning to create a balance between nature and society. He named this holistic approach Ekistics, his self-proclaimed science of human settlements. Like other modernists of his time, he also saw the profession of architecture and planning as a vehicle for socioeconomic reform, however, in his mega housing projects around the globe, he rejected the functional rationality of high-density planning with high-rise buildings. On the contrary, learning lessons on the coexistence of man and nature from past settlements, he proposed housing typologies that incorporated passive cooling systems in low-rise residential buildings. This research paper examines the environmental design solutions proposed by Doxiadis in his mass housing project (Korangi Town) for the hot climatic region of Karachi, Pakistan. The paper examines the proposed design solutions for the housing units and planning of the settlement followed by a current evaluation of the design features. The evaluation will give an understanding of the success of the holistic approach to the environmental issues. The changes made by the residents to the single story courtyard designs over the past sixty years will be documented along with Doxiadis' proposals for the preservation of green and open spaces along the coast of Karachi.

References

Mahsud, A. Z. K. (2010). Rethinking Doxiadis' Ekistical Urbanism. *Positions, 1*, 6–39. http://www.jstor.org/stable/25835100

Doxiadis, C. A. (1975). Action for human settlements. *Ekistics, 40*(241), 405–448. http://www.jstor.org/stable/43618611

Moving Places: Design Analysis of Halprin's Spatial Choreography to Create an Expanded Topology of Movement

Judith Wasserman *(West Virginia University)*

Creating places for movement, community events, performance, and urban joy was an essential goal of landscape architect Lawrence Halprin. Halprin employed spatial choreography to inspire creative physical engagement with his designed sites. Lawrence Halprin's ideas were developed both in conjunction with the investigations of his contemporaries, Gordon Cullen and Kevin Lynch, as well as through the close collaboration with his wife, dance innovator Anna Halprin. Anna focused her work on investigating how movement is informed by environmental site characteristics, both urban and natural. Her dance experimentation enhanced Lawrence's understanding of the movement potential of placemaking. Anna challenged standard ideas of performance by investigating how complex choreographic ideas could engage performer, space, and spectator as equal partners. Lawrence was closely connected to her work, and they collaborated on joint architecture and dance workshops as well as in the invention of the RSVP Cycles (Halprin, 1969).

Motation (Movement + Notation) was a key aspect of Lawrence Halprin's methodology. In his article "Motation" (Halprin, 1966) Halprin developed a sophisticated framework for urban design through spatial choreography. Motation and The RSVP Cycles were two processes that informed both of their creative works. In his public space design, Lawrence employed these tools to invite diverse physical engagement. While Lawrence's ideas of design choreography have been extensively researched, there has been limited inquiry to understand if his design process has been successful in producing work that achieved its goal: The design of places that inspire physical motion.

This study focuses on Halprin's Portland Open Space System (Portland, Oregon) and is tested by examining its use during a 2008 performance event, The City Dance of Lawrence and Anna Halprin. Research methodology includes: Graphic analysis of choreographic process of site design; Visual design analysis to confirm how the choreographic process resulted in the intricacies of the complex spatial sequence, including assessing types and qualities of spaces, levels, use of water, and other factors of the built forms; Visual analysis of performance photography and video footage to understand the impact of how the site informed the dancers body and movement choices; Development of a topology of movement, categorizing the type and quality of motion, speed, parts of the body employed to navigate the site, the degree in which the body is in motion or rest, the spatial planes the body navigates, the degree of danger evoked in the movement, and other movement analysis as it relates to the built form.

Testing how dancers employ diverse spaces in body movement provides a framework for determining how the choreographic process of design has the potential to create a deeper and more complex sequence of places that promote whole body physical engagement for movement and delight. This study offers a framework to understand how the Motation choreographic design tool is still a relevant process to inform the design of form complexity for health, wellness, and expanded performance possibilities.

References

Halprin, L. (1966) *Motation. Impulse, 1966*. pp. 26-33. Illus, Diagrs.

Halprin, L. (1969) *The RSVP Cycles: Creative Processes in the Human Environment*. George Braziller.

Community for Life in Beijing: Designing a Dementia-Friendly Urban Environment for People with Dementia

Martin Holland *(University of Guelph)*; ***Xuejin Zhuge*** *(University of Guelph)*

Background: Dementia is an umbrella term for describing progressive neurological disorders which affect senior groups. The prevalence of dementia is increasing in the areas with higher levels of urbanization (>70%; Northam, 1979) within China, which performance differs from the findings in the west countries (Cassarino, et al.,2018). The researchers presumed environmental problems might be one of the reasons to increase the prevalence of dementia within China. Over ninety percent of seniors with dementia will remain at home. However, no community-based plans and designs in high urbanized areas in China have been concerned about this empirical research and correlated practices on creating a dementia-friendly community to support these vulnerable groups in living independently longer.

Aims: This study aims to offer and contribute to comprehensive design recommendations and relevant solutions to establishing piloting community-based interventions when building a dementia-friendly community.

Methods: This study focused on an individual senior with early-stage dementia, his daily activities within his everyday places and networks within the Fangzhuang community, Beijing, China. Employing a mixture of qualitative approaches that included procedures for collecting observations of participant's behaviors and testing his spatial cognitive capabilities, investigating abnormal behaviors caused by overstimulated urban environments, and details the difficulties of mentally and physically navigating chaotic in an unfamiliar area, the potential environmental risks of fall-related injury due to sensory impairments. The research planned an inclusively and friendly community intended for seniors with early-stage dementia.

Results: The research shows and analyzes problematic situations people with dementia experienced when doing daily tasks and errands, including formal grid street patterns, monolithic architectural styles, insufficient facilities servicing for high level of population aging, unfamiliar street features, low-maintenance paths, complex traffic conditions, unpredictable level changes and obstacles, and missing or ambiguous environmental cues. The findings analysis identified strategies at all scales from urban design to landscape details for considering in improving an aging neighborhoods to be a piloting dementia-friendly community in Beijing: a) designing a completed and integrated service system and sufficient facilities for all seniors within a 15-minutes walking distance with frequency rest spots, well-maintained, leveled paths considering issues of physical frailty- creating a 15-minutes walkable life service circle for dementia; b) customized design recommendations and solutions for people with dementia by associating with theories and users' engagement; c) inclusive outdoor environmental design; d) focusing on design details to support and make daily life easier and more convenient for people with mild stage dementia in the community.

Conclusions: These strategies and relevant design recommendations enable to guide for evaluating and creating dementia-friendly communities in Beijing or even in the large cities of northern China. Understanding the community plans and designs need to respond to the specific cultural contexts and geographical changes for dementia-friendly communities in different regions of China. The differences between China and the western countries need to be further explored and developed, such as color preferences and font styles.

A Mini Systematic Review of the Influences of Diverse Virtual-Environment Interventions on the Emotional Change of Older Adults

Pai Liu *(Dalian University of Technology);* ***Mofei Lin*** *(Dalian University of Technology);* ***Yuxuan Wang; Qi-annan Wu*** *(Dalian University of Technology);* ***Xinxue Guo*** *(Dalian University of Technology);* ***Yuan Meng*** *(Dalian University of Technology)*

The living environments of older adults were relatively isolated due to their declined body functions, which limited their access to the natural and social environments, causing emotional problems a general issue for this group(Barnett et al., 2018). Researchers started to explore the use of virtual reality (VR) in promoting the emotional health of older adults two decades ago, but the VR technology have never been widely accepted in eldercare industry. COVID-19 expedited the use of VR to change the eldercare modes as the virtual technology reduced the needs of physical environments to provide natural and social experiences, which fits the needs of older adults with declined mobility. By adopting a systematic review method(Foster, 2013), we aims to explore the effects of virtual environments on the emotional change of older adults with a question of "What are the differences of diverse virtual environmental influencing the emotions of older adults?" We found 279 studies published between 1998 and 2021 by searching PudMed database with the key words of "older adults [Title/Abstracts]", "virtual reality [Title/Abstracts]" and "emotion [Title/Abstracts]. Two independent researchers conducted the evaluation process, and 12 articles were included in qualitative synthesis. Natural, social, and reminiscent environments were the three main categories of environments used in the examined VR studies. The results illustrated positive influences of the three types of environments on promoting the emotions of older adults by wearing head-mounted display (n = 12) though some participants reported uncomfortable with the VR equipment (n = 1) . The VR experiences reduced the symptoms of apathy, anxiety and depression. Considering the different sample size and research design, there were no significant differences between the effects of the three types of environments. Further research should explore the effectiveness of different virtual-environment interventions on promoting the emotional health of older adults. We suggest further studies in healthcare environments assess the effects of virtual environments with an evaluation of the current conditions of the older adults. Linking their needs of environments, for example, natural, social, and reminiscent environments, with virtual study support to create a database in developing a framework explaining the effects of diverse virtual environments in enhancing the emotional well-being of older adults.

References

Barnett, A., Zhang, C. J. P., Johnston, J. M., & Cerin, E. (2018). Relationships between the neighborhood environment and depression in older adults: A systematic review and meta-analysis. *International Psychogeriatrics, 30*(8), 1153–1176. https://doi.org/10.1017/S104161021700271X

Foster, M. J. (2013). Introduction to systematic reviews for healthcare design. *Health Environments Research and Design Journal, 7*(SUPPL.1), 143–154. https://doi.org/10.1177/193758671300701s11

Connecting the Dots: Inter-Generational Community Engagement to Build Social Health in Older Adults in Low-Income Housing

Sai Saranmegha Parimi *(University of Michigan);* ***Eliza Beird*** *(University of Michigan)*

In 2017, the United Nations released reports describing the increasing population of individuals around the world 60+ years of age will be doubled by 2050 (United Nations, 2017). However, this increase is not met with increased focus on this population. In fact, the trend observed is the increase of devaluing the aging population within society and also experiencing and reporting higher rates of loneliness and social isolation (Federici, 2012, Healthy Aging Poll, 2019). These trends are concerning as they can all negatively impact the physical and mental well-being of all individuals but especially older adults. Social connectedness, especially intergenerational connectedness, is extremely beneficial to the wellbeing of aging adults as it encourages ideas of self-worth, improves cognitive functioning, and much more (Dinkins, 2019). Despite being in proximity to community resources, Woodbridge Manor, a low-income senior resident facility in Detroit, remains isolated from the greater community, with its residents mostly staying on site due to lack of transportation and other obstacles. This barrier to community engagement is concerning due to research on the importance of social connectedness in both physical and mental health. By working with different entities and organizations (such as schools, churches, transportation, parks etc.) in the surrounding community, the proposal aims to establish relationships and bridge gaps between the senior residents of Woodbridge Manor and the greater community. This intervention aims to connect the senior residents with the community, but also must incentivize the community to become involved with the senior residents and how they would benefit from the involvement and partnership. By community mapping and establishing relationships with local resources and programs, it is hypothesized that Senior Residents at Woodbridge Manor will have higher levels of social connectedness and public space engagement which will act as a protective factor to both physical and mental well-being among aging adults and other individuals in the community. In this presentation, we will share a research-based design solution, along the design continuum, that addresses how urban planning and information design solutions can be brought together to improve social health for older adults in low-income housing.

The Power of Play: Improving Brain Health in Affordable Retirement Communities

Zoe Elliott *(The University of Michigan)*; **Sophie Jackson** *(The University of Michigan)*; **Maya Fraser** *(The University of Michigan)*

Older adults experiencing loneliness are at a much greater risk of death and severe disease than those who frequently interact with others. This includes an 50% increase in the risk of developing dementia (NASEM). More than one third of older adults in the United States report feeling lonely, and the COVID-19 pandemic has only exacerbated this trend (NASEM). Play can greatly improve health outcomes among older adults. It is associated with increased physical activity, reduced stress, engagement in cognitive activities, and social bonding, all of which are known to prevent significant health decline (Bherer et al, Menec). This makes it a promising intervention for improving the brain health of older adults experiencing isolation during the pandemic. Our project, "The Power of Play", proposes a hybrid in-person/digital games competition and traveling pop-up "fun bus" for the Presbyterian Villages of Michigan, a network of affordable retirement communities. A digital application will allow residents of different communities to compete against each other remotely and connect to a digital leaderboard, and the fun bus will travel between different communities to offer in-person experiences. The sides of the bus will flip up and awnings will extend, creating a well-ventilated, "indoor-outdoor" area that reduces the risk of COVID-19 spread. Potential games already popular with the residents of these communities include balloon volleyball, beanbag toss, badminton, and Wii-bowling, though the programming could be flexible.

We would evaluate the impact of the gaming program using several different methods: 1) usage statistics would be collected on the digital and in-person components and 2) surveys before and after the intervention would measure residents' loneliness, how often they socialize in the community, their perceived health, and satisfaction with the games program (after the intervention only). Our talk will discuss the design criteria for this intervention, what might be possible at different budgets, and our evaluative scheme. We will pay special attention to how this scheme would apply to our study site, the Presbyterian Villages of Michigan at St. Martha's. By creating impactful networks that physically and digitally connect the greater Presbyterian Villages, our intervention offers options to socialize safely during the ongoing COVID-19 pandemic and motivates residents to engage with their communities.

References

Bherer, L., Erickson, K. I., & Liu-Ambrose, T. (2013). A Review of the Effects of Physical Activity and Exercise on Cognitive and Brain Functions in Older Adults. *Journal of Aging Research*, 2013, e657508. https://doi.org/10.1155/2013/657508

National Academies of Sciences, Engineering, and Medicine. 2020. *Social Isolation and Loneliness in Older Adults: Opportunities for the Health Care System.* Washington, DC: The National Academies Press. https://doi.org/10.17226/25663.

Menec, V. H. (2003). The Relation Between Everyday Activities and Successful Aging: A 6-Year Longitudinal Study. *The Journals of Gerontology: Series B, 58*(2), S74–S82. https://doi.org/10.1093/geronb/58.2.S74

The Effects of Vacant Land on Mental Health in Flood-Disaster Impacted Communities

Galen Daniel Newman *(Texas A&M University)*; **Dongying Li** *(Texas A&M University)*

Excessive amounts of neighborhood vacant land and abandoned structures can significantly lower community and outsider perceptions, and ultimately impact the mental health conditions of inhabitants. While depopulation, economic conditions, and land use dynamics can all play a role in the amount of neighborhood-scaled vacancies and structural abandonment, natural disaster events such as flooding can also exacerbate the ratio of vacant to non-vacant properties in cities and neighborhoods through resultant building damage and resident relocations. Examinations on the association between post-disaster mental health are limited, and even less is known about the extent of vacant and abandoned properties on mental health, especially within the disaster recovery context. Using survey responses (n = 257) from Houston, TX, USA, from Hurricane Harvey stricken neighborhoods, this study quantitatively examines how vacancy and abandonment are associated with mental health in disaster-effected communities. Post-traumatic stress disorder (PTSD) was measured using the PTSD Checklist for DSM-5 and health-related quality of life was measured using the Health-Related Quality of Life (HRQOL) scale. Vacancy rates and perceived vacancy were used to predict PTSD and HRQOL in generalized mixed linear models while adjusting for covariates. Findings indicate significant relationships between higher neighborhood vacancy and elevated risks of PTSD and HRQOL. Further, while the average rate of abandonment in Houston stayed relatively flat, it increased considerably in hurricane impacted communities until two years after Harvey. The outcomes of this study suggest a link between hazard mitigation-recovery and urban regeneration planning to prevent neighborhood deterioration and improve mental health outcomes after disaster events.

The Building Edge As a Restorative Design Feature of Healthy Residential Buildings

Mina Sufineyestani *(Heriot-Watt University);* ***Harry Smith*** *(Heriot Watt University);* ***Sarah R Payne*** *(Heriot-Watt University)*

The home is one of the most important places to support people's health and well-being. It both meets basic needs like shelter while also offering opportunities to rest, relax and recover. The home and its surrounding environment, whether private or shared, is even more important as a restorative environment for those who may not have access other nearby environments due to limited mobility, time, job requirements, or safety and health concerns. Thus, providing restorative environments within cities which are next to and within residential areas is critical.

On the one hand, the lack of minimum standards in the design and construction of residential buildings in the UK has prompted a call for legislation in the form of a Healthy Homes Act in order to ensure decent standards of UK home design. The ongoing COVID-19 pandemic, on the other hand, has brought these issues to light by challenging the way homes are used.

As a result, designers, planners, governments, and community members are becoming more aware of how our living environments affect our health and well-being. In response to these needs, design guidelines prioritizing resident health and well-being are emerging, but they are not yet comprehensive and easy to implement. These guidelines must be updated to reflect the current needs of various groups of urban dwellers and the potential of housing development projects.

However, little is known about how the architectural features and natural characteristics of residential environments, particularly at the building edge, act as a restorative home design feature.

This research aims to understand how natural characteristics, design elements, and architectural features at the building edge of various housing typologies relate to the Restoration Outcome Scale (ROS) and help residents live in a healthy and restorative environment.

Data was collected from urban residents in Edinburgh, UK, using an online questionnaire (n > 300). Latent Class Analysis (LCA) was used in this study to first identify latent housing clusters in the sample and then to relate housing cluster membership to variables such as use circumstances of outdoor spaces and individual characteristics of respondents.

The data was best fit by a three-cluster model, with membership in housing clusters distinguished by dwelling built form, type of connection, type of garden, the floor level and restoration outcome scale of outdoor space. The clusters were labeled as follows: (1) upper and middle floor flats with relatively restorative shared gardens, (2) lower floor in detached houses with high and very high restorative private garden, and (3) middle floor in semi-detached houses with higher than the average restorative private garden. LCA identified that housing cluster membership was significantly related to four use circumstances: use frequency and duration, social preference, and motivation to use outdoor spaces. According to our findings, the restorative opportunities at home and in nearby areas vary according to different housing clusters.

We conclude that the design and construction of our residential environments have a significant impact on our restorative experiences, and it is crucial to build more healthy and resilient homes through increasing indoor-outdoor connections.

Designing Mentally Healthy Industrial Sectors. Saskatoon's Riel Industrial Sector Studio Project

Ana Karinna Hidalgo (University of Saskatchewan

Industrial sectors in cities are often designed with transportation and practicality in mind. Large parcels of land, massive warehouses and box-like buildings are part of the urban landscape of these spaces. Moreover, most of these sectors have a poor walkability index due to the lack of sidewalks and pedestrian amenities that reduces users' physical health. This situation is the reality of thousands of workers that use these spaces daily. In addition to the physical problems these environments create, mental health should be considered. According to the Canadian Health Association (2021), 1 in 5 people in Canada experience mental health issues each year, and half of the population experienced mental illness by the age of 40. Thus, mental health issues affect all Canadians indirectly.

This project combines the industrial landscape design and health issues. It looks at improving users' mental health at the Riel Industrial Sector, located in northwest Saskatoon, SK, by redesigning its urban landscape. The majority of heavy industrial development of Saskatoon is located in this area. The location has easy access to the railway, airport and highways. On the contrary, public transit is infrequent with limited coverage. According to the Areas Employment Study of Saskatoon (2016), 24% of the city's job is allocated in this area, projected 30% by 2044.

An urban design framework that integrates health, equity, climate change, and the environment looks at elements contributing to health in this winter city. Several studies have shown that green and well-designed landscapes, mainly green vegetation and biophilic design (Beatley and Newman, 2013), positively contribute to mental health, which in turn help individuals to work productively and contribute to their communities. In addition, street trees and vegetation can promote well-being even during the winter season by reducing mental fatigue and restoring psychological health (Hidalgo, 2021).

This project was developed during the PLAN446 Advanced Urban Design Studio (Winter 2022) at the University of Saskatchewan. Students were in charge of the fieldwork, gathering users' perceptions, conducting computer-aided and data analysis. Then, urban design alternatives with computer software were developed based on site characteristics and the proposed framework.

An outcome of this project is a comprehensive report for socialization and discussion with stakeholders. This report includes visual proposals and analyses on mental health improvements and thus public health benefits. An industrial sector could be an area of constant psychological restoration from stress and mental fatigue and could contribute positively to all individuals and the city design in general. The benefits of green areas within the city go beyond the area's physical boundaries. These areas should be the greenest in both the landscape and the infrastructure used.

References

Beatley, T., & Newman, P. (2013). Biophilic cities are sustainable, resilient cities. *Sustainability, 5*, 3328–3345. http://doi.org/10.3390/su5083328

City of Saskatoon (2016). *Employment Areas Study*. Saskatoon. Retrieved from https://www.saskatoon.ca/sites/default/files/documents/community-services/planning-development/integrated-growth-plan/growing-fwd/employment-areas-study_march-2016.pdf

CMHA. Canadian Mental Health Association. (2021). *Mental illnesses in the workplace*. Retrieved from https://cmha.ca/brochure/fast-facts-about-mental-illness/#_edn1

Hidalgo, A. K. (2021). Mental health in winter cities:

The effect of vegetation on streets. *Urban Forestry and Urban Greening, 63*(September 2020), 127226. https://doi.org/10.1016/j.ufug.2021.127226

Behavioral Needs Assessment for Healthy Precinct Design to Combat Non-Communicable Diseases

Sofia Foo *(Singapore University of Technology and Design)*; **Kanchana Devi Sokkalingam** *(Singapore University of Technology and Design)*; **Keng Hua Chong** *(Singapore University of Technology and Design)*

COVID-19 has illustrated that people with underlying health conditions and compromised immune systems are at a higher risk of getting severely ill. (CDC, 2020). According to reports worldwide, Non-communicable diseases (NCDs) like heart disease, stroke, asthma, and diabetes were the most common comorbidities identified among COVID-19 patients hospitalized, and almost 90% of patients who died of COVID-19 had NCDs. NCDs also form part of the underlying health conditions that account for 71% of deaths worldwide. (WHO, 2021) NCDs tend to arise as a result of physical inactivity, under-nutrition, and stressful lifestyles. (Lachat et al., 2013) In 2019, NCDs accounted for 80% of the total disease burden in Singapore. (MOH, 2020) As we transit from a pandemic to an endemic world, it is becoming paramount to nudge citizens towards a healthier lifestyle to reduce the strain on healthcare resources and falling severely ill due to COVID-19.

Once termed as a disease of affluence, NCDs can now affect anyone. (WHO, 2011a) Recent reports have also described NCDs as a global burden in terms of mortality and disability-adjusted life years (DALYs) (WHO, 2005), increasing the need for healthcare resources adding a strain to the economy. (Suhrcke et al, 2006) In Singapore, low-income and high-income households can be found within the same precinct, often sharing the same physical environment. Studies have shown that the physical environment plays a drastic impact on an individual's health and wellbeing. (Ohrnberger, Fichera, & Sutton, 2017) However, the ease of access to green and social spaces or fresh and quality food products may not be equal depending on one's level of affluence and preference despite sharing the same physical environment. Therefore, there is a need to investigate how physical, environmental, and social factors influence the behaviour and overall health of individuals from different socioeconomic groups.

This paper presents the findings from a Behavioral Needs Assessment conducted in a selected town, Boon Lay, using Q-methodology (n = 200). Q-methodology is a quantitative method that explores issues related to human subjectivity (Brown, 2008). Factor analysis is performed based on data collected through Q-methodology to capture the sentiments of three main socioeconomic groups: Vulnerable (low-income earners), Heartlanders (middle-income earners), and Executives (high-income earners). In addition, programmatic and environmental audits were also conducted. By combining quantitative and qualitative methods, our framework provides deeper insights into the perceptions and behaviors of different socioeconomic groups and uncovers their respective latent factors. These would be substantiated by the spatial characteristics identified via environmental and programmatic audits, assessing the role of the built environment and the community in supporting or inhibiting different health behaviors, namely physical activity, diet, and rest.

For example, a farming hawker center could improve the accessibility to healthy food by providing healthy yet tasty and affordable meals using fresh ingredients sourced directly from the community farm above, fostering sustainable healthy eating habits, reversing the rise of NCDs in the longer run. Redesigning neighborhoods and precincts could ensure residents with equal opportunities to stay motivated, connected, active, and safe, preparing us for future health crises.

Transforming Emergency Care to Combat Coronavirus: The Role of the Physical Environment

Xiaobo Quan *(University of Oklahoma)*

Background: On the frontline against the pandemic, emergency departments (EDs) are facing challenges around efficiency and safety, including the cost-effective management of COVID and non-COVID cases while maintaining a safe environment for staff and patients, the turnovers and shortages of healthcare workers due to concerns over safety and prolonged working hours, and the increases of mental health issues in staff and patients related to the pandemic. In responding to the challenges, many EDs have reorganized their operations and made extensive modifications to their physical environments. Given the evolving nature of the pandemic, healthcare organizations need to continuously track the disease, predict its impact on healthcare services, and implement measures to effectively respond to the dynamic conditions. However, it is not clear how well the various physical environment strategies worked for individual emergency care facilities and what lessons can be learned and applied to create better emergency care facilities that are more efficient in managing similar crises in future.

Purpose: The purpose of the study is: 1) to document and empirically evaluate the physical environment strategies used by emergency care facilities in addressing the challenges posed by a national crisis; and 2) to develop recommendations to improve the effectiveness and efficiency of ED's in managing future crises and disasters.

Methods: A mixed-methods case study approach is used to gain an in-depth, multi-faceted understanding of the effectiveness of physical environment strategies implemented in a major emergency department. First, semi-structured interviews are conducted with representative stakeholders and staff members involved in the decision-making, implementation, evaluation, and utilization of the physical environment strategies. The various perspectives of administrators as well as frontline staff members would contribute to a more comprehensive view. The sample is expected to include about 15 individuals in various roles: administration, facility management, building design/construction, healthcare delivery (doctors, nurses, technicians, etc.), and environmental services. The interviews are conducted on-site or virtually through online meetings. The transcripts and notes are analyzed to identify common themes related to the research questions. Second, the implementation of the physical environment strategies is documented through observing the ED spaces and examining the existing drawings and photos. Third, relevant information such as ED volume, throughput, infection rates, and costs will be extracted from medical and other records and analyzed to answer research questions. In addition, literature reviews will be conducted on the implemented environmental strategies for the purpose of benchmarking.

Results: The triangulation of data from multiple sources would highlight the environmental strategies implemented to support emergency care during the pandemic as well as the decision-making process along the way. By identifying high-performing design strategies and lessons learned, the study would produce recommendations for EDs to respond effectively and efficiently to possible crises in future.

ORsmart: Design to Understand and Improve Workspace Design and Safety Culture to Influence Anesthesia Medication Selection and Delivery

Kassandra Landvay *(Clemson University);* ***Anjali Joseph*** *(Clemson University);* ***Sahar Mihandoust*** *(Clemson University);* ***David Neyens*** *(Clemson University);* ***James Abernathy*** *(Johns Hopkins);* ***Kenneth Catchpole*** *(Medical University of South Carolina);* ***Seyedmohammad Ahmadshahi*** *(Clemson University);* ***Mina Shokrollahi Ardekani*** *(Clemson University);* ***Devi Soman*** *(Clemson University)*

Operating rooms are complex spaces that come with a range of challenges, many of which are heavily influenced by poor design. As a result of a six-year multidisciplinary research project looking into improved patient care outcomes through human-centered design within the operating room, the anesthesia (AN) work zone was recognized as a space to experience a multitude of design challenges that create an ineffective, suboptimal environment for clinician workflow, especially as they engage in critical medication tasks such as information gathering, medication preparation, administration, and documentation.

In this study, we used an evidence-based design process to develop concepts for an AN work zone that supports safe medication practices for anesthesia providers. The research team worked closely to gather and analyze AN workflow data from video observations of surgeries as well as from an in-depth literature review. Based on this information, a set of guidelines paired with sets of visual illustrations documenting AN provider workflow as well as AN spatial organization while performing medication tasks during surgery were developed to inform a series of design solutions. These observations and design guidelines were used to identify anesthesia related poor practices of which ultimately contributed to the research team's development of future best practice design recommendations.

The design process was a collaborative effort at every stage. When it came to formulating design solutions, multiple teams were defined: two design teams and two consult teams. Each team developed their own design solutions over a multitude of meetings and proposed their designs to the consult teams. As the process progressed, these solutions underwent a series of iterations and refinements in order to ensure addressment of all identified guidelines. The design teams then combined their solutions in order to create one optimal design recommendation framework for the AN work zone which then underwent the same process of consult and iteration refinement.

The result of the design process is a framework of recommendations that includes AN work zone spatial reconfigurations both internally and in relation to the larger operating room, a rethinking of traditional AN and operating room structured systems, and implementation of identified efficient and effective medical equipment. Each of these solutions are projected to allow for better AN provider workflow and less medication task disruptions and errors. Providing these specific AN work zone design recommendations based on prior research and published studies will help facilitate better workspace design practices for AN providers, designers, and clinicians and help create spaces that are safer for patients.

The Impacts of Healthcare Lighting Design on Elderly Settings Quality of Care and Performance – a Bibliometric Analysis

Nasrin Golshany *(University of Oregon);* ***Ihab Elzeyadi*** *(Dept. of Architecture)*

Healthcare Lighting Design (HLD) of elderly environments has attracted significant attention from researchers in both architecture and medical sciences. While an increasing body of knowledge exists within this rapidly growing field of research, there is still a lack of a systematic conceptual framework that highlights the parameters and variables essential to quantify the structure and evolution of the field. In addition, the literature in this field of study is challenging to manage because of its multidisciplinary approach and wide range of studies that approached this topic through the specific disciplinary lens of architecture, medicine, and gerontology. The main goal of this presentation is to conduct a bibliometric analysis of research studies from 1990 to 2021 specific to healthcare lighting design for elderly people. The presentation reports on a compiled database of over 335 publications that were analyzed and screened using a theoretical targeted framework. VOSviewer is a science mapping software tool that was utilized to identify major topic areas and detect influential publications, authors, countries, and prominent journals through various network analysis techniques such as term co-occurrence, co-citation, and bibliographic coupling. In addition, SciMAT was used to identify major themes of each period and the evolution of the parametric variables database of the field over time. For this purpose, three different periods were identified (1990-1999; 1999-2013; 2014-2021). Results show that this field of study initially focused on the relationship of light and sleep quality yet has thus diversified to investigate the impact of light on both visual and non-visual outcomes of elderly people. While Circadian rhythm and sleep quality are still dominant topics in the field, light therapy cognitive impairment, and Alzheimer's disease therapy are the emerging trends in these domains of studies.

Understanding How Social Spaces Support Social Engagement for People Living with Mild Cognitive Impairment

Raha Rastegar *(Georgia Institute of Technology);* ***Ye-inn G Oh*** *(Georgia Institute of Technology);* ***Yasaman Gholami*** *(Georgia Institute of Technology);* ***Craig Zimring*** *(Georgia Institute of Technology)*

Background: Studies suggest that higher social engagement contributes to improving cognitive function, and to delaying the development from mild cognitive impairment (MCI) to more severe cognitive impairments such as dementia (Kuiper et al., 2015). On the other hand, people living with MCI often tend to engage in less social activities considering their decline on functional abilities such as hearing, attention, speech, and mobility. The built environment has the potential to positively impact social engagement, with evidence suggesting that the layout of spaces and furniture impact the likelihood of individuals to engage in social interactions (Dempsey, 2008). Additionally, research on older adults with advanced cognitive impairment (e.g., Dementia and Alzheimer's patients) shows physical and visual connections between social spaces helping control stimulations and distractions during social interactions, and thus influencing the way people engage in and maintain a conversation.

Purpose: Recognizing the lack of studies investigating these relationships in the context of MCI, we developed a study to understand how the built environment of social settings can encourage social interactions for people living with MCI. We aimed at identifying specific environmental features regulating privacy, control and choice are perceived or preferred by people living with MCI.

Methods: In a qualitative approach based on photo elicitation, we conducted virtual interviews with members of a cognitive empowerment program (CEP) that were diagnosed with MCI, asking them questions about their perceptions of built environment features determining privacy, choice and control in social settings, during hypothetical social interactions. The research team interviewed members individually or with their care-partner for approximately 30 minutes, using an online platform. Meetings were video recorded and followed a three-step process; scenario introduction, questions about photo-pairs depicting social settings differentiated by privacy features (e.g., space with/without internal partitions), and follow-up questions about spatial preferences for social interactions. Qualitative data from interviews' open-ended questions were thematically coded using a pattern matching strategy. Resulting patterns relating environmental features to social behaviors and perceptions were compared in terms of photo-pairs to capture spatial factors associated with participants' preferences.

Findings: Themes included visual awareness of social stimuli and shielding from negative distractions, indicating vertical partitions, natural light and furniture ergonomics as relevant environmental factors to members' preferences, mostly due to balancing privacy with spatial awareness.

Conclusions: Findings from this study inform the design of social areas in therapeutic settings focused on providing care for people living with MCI, and ultimately contribute to their cognitive functioning by supporting social engagement in these spaces. Furthermore, this study directly informs future design interventions at the cognitive empowerment center to test a set of environmental features in a natural setting.

References

Dempsey, N. (2008). Does quality of the built environment affect social cohesion?. *Proceedings of the Institution of Civil Engineers-Urban Design and Planning, 161*(3), 105-114.

Kuiper, J. S., Zuidersma, M., Voshaar, R. C. O., Zuidema, S. U., van den Heuvel, E. R., Stolk, R. P., & Smidt, N. (2015). Social relationships and risk of dementia: A systematic review and meta-analysis of longitudinal cohort studies. *Aging research reviews, 22*, 39-57.

This track focuses on critical conversations to seek ways to improve advocacy for better designed environments that promote health and wellbeing for all people, communities, animals, eco-systems and living systems. We are especially interested in magnifying how to create equitable design practices, improve diversity within our design community, and identify best practices that can transform local practice and global movements toward higher-quality environments. This track will cover the methods, conversations, and outcomes for those researching and designing under the auspices of design activism, action research, public service, and public education. We encourage not only success stories but also critical discussions of pitfalls and "failures" that serve as learning opportunities for this work.

Facilities Planning as a Nexus of Politics and Opportunities for Democratic Participation

Lubomir Popov *(Bowling Green State University);* ***Ivan Chompalov*** *(Edinboro University of Pennsylvania)*

Buildings are spatial resources for accommodating people, their activities, and their needs. From a very abstract perspective, the building includes quantitative aspects (size, square footage) and qualitative aspects (features and qualities of the built spaces). These resources are allocated to people according to established practices created over long periods of time under the influence of social groups that have enough power and privilege to impose their agendas. Considering the competition for resources, we understand that the production and allocation of space involve conflict, negotiation, and politics. Furthermore, these processes embody all systemic traits, including injustices, inequalities, and oppression.

Our long-term goal is to explore directions for democratic practices to foster fair, just, and balanced process of specifying and allocating spatial resources. In this part of the project, our goal is limited to the realm of the facility planning process. Our objective is to identify the steps in this process where democratic activities are most productive and efficient.

Our project is theoretical and has a multidisciplinary methodology. It combines the pragmatism of a facilities planning approach with the social production of space perspective and Activity Theory approach in order to explore the social aspects of decision making. The facilities planning approach guides the articulation of the stages that involve decisions regarding the preferred qualities of designed spaces and the allocation of spatial resources. The Activity Theory approach is used to explore the social dynamics, influences, conflicts, and negotiations in the planning process. From this position, we focus on the steps where the most important decisions are made regarding the allocation of spatial resources.

We use an articulation of the facilities planning process that includes needs assessment, feasibility studies, master planning, and programming. Very often programming must start from scratch and needs to cover all these stages. Our analysis indicates that the decisions at the initial stages define the solution "space" for subsequent stages. However, the initial stages involve more abstract subject matter and require user-group consultants to interpret and advise constituents. Also, at the initial stages, politics involve very powerful players, up to the level of senior elected officials and political representatives. Regarding the democratic process, this has significant implications. At these levels, the most important factor is the political organization of the action. When we go to the level of programming, the playing field becomes more comprehensible for stakeholder populations. However, even at this stage, user groups need much technical guidance in addition to political organization. At this stage, we see the need not only for political organization, but also for capacity building regarding stakeholders who can competently negotiate and defend their requirements and interests.

We will limit our presentation to the facility planning process. The analysis of democratic representation in the process of design and in post-occupancy evaluation are tasks for the next phases of our project. We also hope that this presentation will initiate collegiate collaboration and additional projects.

Landscape Architecture as Democratic Practice: Methods and Rationale

Nan Yang *(Pennsylvania State University)*; **Mallika Bose** *(Pennsylvania State University)*; **Paula Hurley Horrigan** *(Cornell University)*

While the convergence of democratic professionalism and community-engaged design in landscape architecture practices has been occurring for decades in some quarters, additional academic changes are warranted to further facilitate and establish the democratic turn in landscape architecture academia and practice (Horrigan & Bose, 2018). Democratic professionalism is "situated squarely within the public culture of democracy" and pursues "the public good with and not merely for the public" (Dzur, 2008, p. 130). It refers to a democratic model of the profession that shifts professionals from task monopolists to task sharers by "encouraging lay participation in ways that enhance and enable collective action and deliberation about major social issues inside and outside professional domains" (Dzur, 2019, p. 14). In landscape architecture, the theories and practices of participatory community design have been important contributors to the democratic turn (Horrigan & Bose, 2018). To embed the practice of democratic professionalism in landscape architecture, this study investigates the methods utilized in landscape architecture practice through community-engaged design under the auspices of democratic professionalism and the reasoning driving such practice.

Using a snowball technique through professional networks, we identified academics involved in community-engaged design and planning. From these identified practitioners, we conducted semi-structured interviews with 16 architecture, landscape architecture, and planning scholars/practitioners (via Zoom) whose practices are rooted in participatory and democratic means (May 2015-July 2016). The interviews were transcribed, and the data were qualitatively analyzed (using NVivo-March 2020 release) through open-coding. The qualitative analysis of their experiences and insights reveals patterns regarding methods of and rationale for landscape architecture and other related design fields realized through the principles of democratic professionalization and community-engaged theories.

The findings include methods and strategies used for democratic landscape architecture and design practice categorized into the different stages of typical projects: i) site analysis/data collection, ii) design, and iii) delivery/post-delivery. We discuss two emergent themes that characterized the methods used by the democratic scholar-practitioners: a focus on deep communication and relationship building. Besides, a convergence of objective and subjective methods to adapt to uncertainty and individualized community situations. Our analysis indicates that the motivations driving democratic design scholar-practitioners are – empowerment and advocacy, community engagement ethics, and skill-building for democratic practice.

Through this study, we develop an expanded toolbox of essential methods and strategies for landscape architecture as democratic practice. The findings also contribute to validating landscape architecture as a profession that can foster empowerment and advocacy, ethical, democratic, and participatory design practices - all hallmarks of democratic professionalism (Dzur, 2008).

References

Dzur, A. W. (2008). *Democratic professionalism: Citizen participation and the reconstruction of professional ethics, identity, and practice.* Pennsylvania State University Press.

Dzur, A.W. (2019). *What Is a Democratic Professional?*

Kettering Review.
Horrigan, P., & Bose, M. (2018). Towards democratic professionalism in landscape architecture. In Egoz, S. (Ed.). *Defining landscape democracy: A path to spatial justice*. Edward Elgar Publishing.

Designing for Social Impact Along and Across the Scale of Design Action

Peter Aeschbacher *(Pennsylvania State University)*

Designers and planners often make rhetorical claims about the impact of their work across scales. "Small scale, big change!", solving homelessness through architecture, community issues by constructing community gardens, or the ills of capitalism via better doorhandles. Design history is full of ambitions: the comradely objects of Russian Constructivists; the stadiums, museums, and convention centers of urban redevelopment. While measuring impact in complex systems may prove impossible, evaluating designers' arguments for impact is possible - if delineated with logos alongside pathos and ethos. Connections drawn from intent to design strategy across scales to intended outcomes can improve design processes and communication. This presentation will tackle a crucial aspect of this larger project: an integrative definition of scale that accommodates physical and 'invisible' design, has a broader definition of designed 'things', and is legible for designers.

Taxonomies of scale tend to be drawn from disciplines, size, or activities rather than things. Focusing on disciplines - graphic, product, building, landscape, urban – sidelines designed artifacts. However, spotlighting artifacts omits plannerly activities, policies and institutions. Buchanon (1992) proposed four domains: symbolic and visual communications; material objects; activities and organized services; and, complex systems or environments. He demonstrates overlapping 'placements' generates new opportunities but the operative words are "and" and "as" rather than "along" or "across." A building as a sign is not equivalent to one attempting 'upward' social change. A complementary 'downward' effect is described in Winner (1980). Winner sees artifacts as technological constructs whose physical properties enact authority and political will. His explanations are ex post facto: running 'backwards'. But social change designers work 'forward' through propositions and 'upward' in scope.

Complexity provides another question: does it simply increase with scale? Campuses are more complex than teapots, yet the sheer number of design issues is not definitive. Rather, entanglement across scales causes complexity. A teapot designed to midwife social transformation requires consideration of more than materials, form, and production. Jones (2014) ties complexity to scale in four domains. The lower two are material but the latter are goal-based, becoming blind to a wider definition of design that includes plans, policies, and institutions as design artifacts.

Each framework favors design as activity over artifacts as autonomous agents. Without attention to design products, their intended actual impact across scales becomes easily conflated with the domain of work. This presentation presents a revisiting of the scales of design that consistently reframes attention on the products of design action. Building on Buchanon, Winner, and Jones, the scalar framework includes the domain of design (information; communications; simple artifacts), its overlap with the domain of planning (complex artifacts and environments; activities and organized services) and planning's targets of institutions and society. Herein both physical design and planning are accommodated (and distinguished), allowing proper definition of links and leaps.

References
Buchanan, R. (1992). Wicked Problems in Design *Thinking. Design Issues*, Vol8No2 (Spring).
Jones, P. (2014). Systemic Design Principles for Complex Social Systems. In: *Metcalf, Social Systems and Design*, vol1. Springer, Tokyo.
Winner, L. (1980). Do Artifacts Have Politics?. *Daedalus* (Winter).

Rural Park Classification Systems: Outside the Ownership Bubble

Hans Klein-Hewett *(Iowa State University)*

Iowa parks, especially rural parks, have a naming

problem. There, most currently describe parks based on their ownership (state parks, county parks, city parks), not their amenities. As an example, the names Joe Sheldon County Park and Dolliver Memorial State Park, found in Humbolt and Webster counties, respectively, do not give any indication of amenities or programming found in those spaces. That opaque naming system clouds the ability for the public—especially the underserved and rapidly changing rural public—to understand what outdoor recreation amenities are available in their region (Johnson, 2006). Parks are essential in rural areas, as they contribute heavily to the overall quality of life for rural residents (Allen, et al., 1987; Long & Stiehl, 1984). For example, there are around 6,100 acres of public recreation land in Greene County, Iowa. However, around 29% of that public recreation space is primarily used for hunting or trapping. When looking at the acreages of those parks, they represent 83% of the public recreation space in the county. That means that only 0.2% of land in the county is dedicated to all other forms of public recreation (e.g., aquatic centers, trails, playgrounds, sports fields, skate parks, dog parks, etc.).

To rectify that naming problem, this session will propose a new rural park classification system that focuses on park amenities, not ownership. The classification system was developed by chronicling the amenities and use of rural parks in an eight-county case study region in central Iowa. As an example, in the Greene County example above, the recreation spaces dedicated to hunting or trapping are considered Nature Extraction Parks. The resulting classification structure allows the public to find park spaces that meet their programmatic needs, regardless of ownership. Additionally, it allows researchers to consider park amenities and uses when understanding spatial relationships, not just their location. That will hopefully illuminate if there are park class deserts or densities in a region and how park classes are distributed around urban areas and transportation corridors.

References

Allen, Lawrence B., Patrick T. Long, and Richard R. Perdue. (1987). The Role of Leisure. *Journal of Physical Education, Recreation & Dance*. 58:4.

Johnson, Kenneth. (2006). *Demographic Trends in Rural and Small Town America*. Carsey Institute's Reports on Rural America, Vol 1, No 1.

Long, Patrick T. and Jim Stiehl. (1984). Recreation and Rural Families. *Journal of Physical Education, Recreation & Dance*, 55:8.

Architectural Programming as a Major Arena for Activism and Advocacy

Lubomir Popov *(Bowling Green State University;* ***Franklin Goza*** *(University of Wisconsin, Whitewater)*

Social inequalities affect the distribution of environmental resources in multiple ways, both in terms of quantity and quality. From this broad situation, we have focused on the ubiquitous exclusion of underserved and underrepresented social groups from participating in important decisions about their own built environment that affects their health, wellness and quality of life. This exclusion is one of the major factors for environmental injustice. One way to alleviate this problem is to facilitate built environment activism and advocacy that will provide opportunities for voicing underrepresented citizen's needs and requirements.

The goal of our project was to search for the best solution space for incorporating activism and advocacy in the project delivery process. Our objective was to find the stages and phases for the most efficient inclusion of underrepresented user groups—the place where user participation makes the biggest difference. In the process of this study, as mentioned below, we limit our scope to the architectural programming process. Although programming is a well-known architectural activity, our intent is to emphasize its importance for effective activism and advocacy in the building delivery process.

This project is theoretical. Our methodology was influenced by the location of the problem in the intersection of environmental and social problems. The focus on justice, inclusivity, and service for disadvantaged populations tipped the methodological balance to the social science side. In particular, we used a sociological perspective on social problems and an Activity Theory approach to investigate processes and actions. We create a transdisciplinary platform as a foundation for investigating available solutions within the domain of the project delivery process, from inception to post-occupancy evaluation. We scrupulously analyze every step in this process with the objective of uncovering which stages or phases are most productive for activism and advocacy, thus empowering the disadvantaged user group.

The results of our study lead us towards the pre-design processes. This appears to be the most intensive time when important decisions about allocation of resources, user needs, and stakeholder requirements are made. After these decisions are negotiated and approved, they shape the "core" design process and the rubrics for evaluation the design alternatives. This proved to be wide and requires many intellectual resources to finalize the project. To make the project manageable, we gradually limited the scope of this study to the programming phase.

Programming involves fundamental decisions that shape the equitable social functioning of the future building, community, or town. Programming involves researching all stakeholders, including building users, immediate community, and many other concerned parties. Our research shows that from all stages in the project delivery process, programming is most heavily loaded with research, politics, and decision making regarding stakeholder groups. The programmatic decisions presuppose to a large extent a just and fair consideration of user needs, as well as protection of environmental rights and interests of all stakeholder groups.

Collaborative Activism: Essential Partnerships and Practices in Responding to Neighborhood Crime and Violence

***Maren King** (SUNY College of Environmental Science and Forestry); **Alexandrea Samoray** (SUNY College of Environmental Science and Forestry)*

College and University planning and design programs, and associated community design centers, provide valuable assistance to the communities and regions in which they are located. Service learning and funded research projects accomplished through these partnerships can benefit all involved through shared learning, hands-on experience, useful outcomes and increased capacity in the community to advance projects to next steps. (Angotti, et al. 2011)

In our community engagement activities over the past 20 years, public safety related to fear of crime and violence has been raised as a concern in many of our city's neighborhoods. While physical design solutions have been proposed, the social and community responses to these concerns seemed to be kept insular and private, with a desire to address them from within the community. More recently, these events have become more public and our design center has collaborated on projects that through process and outcomes bring light and attention to issues of crime and violence in which residents, including teens and children are being seriously injured or killed. Two of these projects in particular - a student capstone to design a healing and memorial space for lives lost to violence and a youth participatory action research project through which the team investigated how crime and violence affects the lives of neighborhood residents - have caused us to reexamine our own biases and roles as we hear the emotions and personal stories of loved ones who have been lost to violence; see the longer terms effects of poverty, racism, inequity, segregation and disinvestment; and experience the pervasive impact these are having on the sense and reality of safety, social cohesion and trust. (HUD 2016).

This presentation provides an overview of these recent projects as well as findings from interviews with our local partners and community members. We reinforce the negative effects that crime and violence have on the lives of neighborhood residents (McIntrye 2000), as well as underline the critical importance and effect that physical conditions have on the mental health and outlook of neighborhood residents, especially as COVID has affected community connections and access to familiar resources. We examine the role of community design and academic design research in acknowledging and addressing these complex issues and describe ways to be more effective members of diverse partnerships so that our skills and experience can contribute to lasting changes in public safety and other public health challenges.

References

Angotti, Tom, Cheryl Doble & Paula Horrigan (Eds.) (2011). *Service-Learning in Design and Planning: educating at the boundaries.* New Village Press

HUD Office of Policy Development and Research. (2016) Neighborhoods and Violent Crime. *Evidence Matters*, Summer 2016.

McIntyre, Alice. (2000). Constructing Meaning About Violence, School, and Community: Participatory Action Research with Urban Youth. *The Urban Review 32*(2), 123-154.

Mapping Water Shutoffs and the Early Spread of COVID-19 in Detroit

Emily Kutil *(Lawrence Technological University);* ***Monica Lewis-Patrick*** *(We the People of Detroit);* ***Nadia Gaber*** *(University of California, San Francisco)*

Detroit, Michigan was particularly devastated in the first months when COVID-19 spread throughout the United States. By mid-April, Michigan had the third-highest number of confirmed cases in the country; by June 13, there had been almost 11,000 cases of COVID-19 in Detroit. When the pandemic struck, the city was in the midst of a mass water shutoff crisis: about 170,000 families have had their water shut off by the Detroit Water and Sewerage Department (DWSD) for nonpayment of bills in the past ten years. This practice is not only cruel and inhumane, but it also puts the health of the entire city at risk (see Plum et al., 2017). CDC guidelines recommend frequent hand washing and sanitation as a key defense against infection by COVID-19. In 2019 DWSD shut off water to over 23,000 households; in January 2020, about 9,500 homes remained without water (Kurth et al., 2020). Detroit Mayor Mike Duggan and Michigan Governor Gretchen Whitmer announced a water restart plan to restore water to those who had been shut off on March 9, 2020, but the city's water shutoff practices had already made its residents vulnerable to the spread of COVID-19. For some residents, the water restart process took over a month to complete.

While researchers have documented the effectiveness of water shutoff moratoria on lowering infections and deaths from COVID-19 in the United States (Zhang et al., 2021), there has been little research on the relationship between water shutoffs and COVID-19 in particular US cities. This paper discusses research conducted during Summer 2020 to investigate potential relationships between water shutoffs and the spread of COVID-19 in Detroit. We further refined this research with new data obtained from DWSD in Spring 2021. Using COVID-19 data obtained from the City of Detroit COVID-19 data portal, water shutoff data obtained from DWSD, and demographic data obtained from the US Census Bureau, we mapped relationships between zip codes heavily impacted by water shutoffs, zip codes with high concentrations of COVID-19 cases, and zip codes with high concentrations of residents over age 65. In order to focus specifically on potential impacts of residential water shutoffs on the spread of COVID-19, we controlled for cases occurring in nursing homes and assisted living facilities, which do not experience water shutoffs. Our research revealed significant overlaps between areas of the city with the most residents over age 65, areas heavily impacted by water shutoffs, and areas where COVID-19 spread most rapidly outside of nursing homes in the early days of the pandemic.

References

Alexander Plum, Kyle Moxley, and Marcus Zervos. "The Impact of Geographical Water Shutoffs on the Diagnosis of Potentially Water-Associated Illness, with the Role of Social Vulnerability Examined." *Henry Ford Health System* (2017).

Joel Kurth and Mike Wilkinson. "I hate to complain, but I haven't had water in a year. A Detroit story." *Bridge Magazine* (Feb 17, 2020).

Xue Zhang, Mildred E. Warner, and Mary Grant. "Water Shutoff Moratoria Lowered COVID-19 Infection and Death Across U.S. States." *American Journal of Preventive Medicine* (Sept 10, 2021). DOI: https://doi.org/10.1016/j.amepre.2021.07.006.

Beyond the Object: Redefining Success and Failure in Public Interest Design

Ann Yoachim** (Tulane University); **Maggie Hansen

This work engages emerging discourses on design process and assessment through evaluation of a university-based design center's 15 years of work. Founded in 2005 in a mid-size city, the Center is committed to building capacity and coalitions to address inequity in the built environment and focuses on expanding access to high quality design services to those who have been under-resourced by the design professions. Developed in partnership with community based organizations, the Center's projects fall into five categories: design/build, architectural visioning, urban design, graphic design advocacy, and public programming/exhibitions. The Center's work is also embedded in the School of Architecture's curricular and co-curricular programming, with most projects engaging undergraduate and graduate students. At the core of all the Center's research, teaching and practice is deep community engagement. The Center is recognized as a leader in the field of public interest design and has received a range of awards: traditional design (AIA), socially engaged post-occupancy evaluations (SEED, Rudy Bruner) and engaged design and research efforts (ACSA).

Public interest design serves different clients and works toward outcomes beyond formal or material innovations, and yet success is still measured through images of physical forms and statements of concept. (Wilson, 2018:27) The research reflects how we might expand design evaluation to consider impacts of equitable design practices and results provide an opportunity to better understand impacts of collaborative design processes. Conducted between 2019-2021, the research design was based on grounded research theory (GT), a method of research that uses iterative comparative analysis to generate results that are abstracted directly from the data gathered. Qualitative in-person and on-line interviews and site visits were conducted for 50 projects across the Center's fifteen-year history and representative of all five categories of work. Interviewees represented the diversity of Center's partners across race, gender, age, sexuality, and position within their organization's hierarchy. Participation was voluntary and interviews were anonymized and then coded using setting-specific codes, which are 'faithful to and capture the central elements of the setting in the language and category schemes of those who populate and negotiate the setting on an everyday basis' (Lofland et al, 2006:205). Study results provide an expanded view of success and failure that goes beyond traditional metrics and detailed insight on collaborative design processes and power dynamics. The interviews also highlight the importance of reflexive design practice in addressing historical inequities in design and architecture, bridging campus-community dynamics, and changing public understanding of design more broadly.

This track focuses on the different ways of working that have proven to be effective during and following a post-pandemic world. Armed with new perspectives gained from an awakening during the pandemic, this track will highlight how professionals and academics are crossing boundaries to address emerging issues that compromise health, equity, sustainability and resilience in a post-pandemic world. The intersections between academia and practice that offer new modes of collaborating to create better environments that promote health are covered. What are the means for embarking on productive collaborations and partnerships? What are the benefits and challenges? What critiques emerge when blurring and/or borrowing from multiple disciplines?

Utilizing Genetic Algorithms to Optimize Space Syntax Values in Emergency Department Layouts

Brick McMenomy *(Perkins Eastman Architects)*; **Alexandra Nelson** *(Perkins Eastman Architects)*; **Linda Nubani** *(Michigan State University)*; **Gustavo Pardo** *(Perkins Eastman Architects)*

Space Syntax researchers have produced various computational tools to quantify the relational and visual properties of space. A growing body of literature documents the use of these tools in understanding the impact of architectural layouts on facilitating positive health outcomes in healthcare settings. However, from a practical perspective, meeting multiple requirements to develop an optimum layout for the healthcare facility has been both challenging and time-consuming for architects and designers. The purpose of this study is to examine methods that use generative design in emergency departments and present a model that brings together space syntax measures that were shown to enhance patients' and staffs' experiences. The outcome of the proposed process is to employ a multi-objective evolutionary algorithm to optimize the internal layout of a typical emergency department; improving the experience and utilization of space from the perspectives of both patients and staff through quantifying metrics that include intelligibility, nurse surveillance, targeted visual connectivity, and spatial navigation. The presented research further demonstrates the opportunity to bridge the gap between the generative use of space syntax research and practice in real world applications.

Envisioning, Enacting, and Experiencing Innovative Learning Environments: Process and Perspectives

Raechel French *(DLR Group | University of Melbourne)*

Innovative Learning Environments (ILEs) are being constructed throughout the globe in response to an increased focus on achieving student deep learning. These designs replace the historically double-loaded corridor of classrooms with a variety of space types intended to support multiple teaching and learning activities. Intended operations within these ILEs differ from what is expected in traditional learning spaces, resulting in a range of experiences in their implementation and common misalignments between their designed intent and actual reality.

This study explores the lived experience of ILEs through the point of views of educators, school leaders, and school designers, utilizing two phases of research to understand the role both physical and organizational factors have in the alignment between their design and intended use. Phase One completes a content analysis on images and narrative describing 41 ILE schools in Texas, USA that were submitted to the Exhibit of School

Architecture (EoSA), providing a baseline lexicon of anticipated design and use of ILEs. Phase Two includes a case study of three of the schools submitted to the EoSA, exploring educators' and leaders' lived experience and perceptions of how physical and organizational supports enabled a successful transition to their new spaces.

Supported by the Burke-Litwin Model of Organizational Performance and Change (Burke-Litwin, 1992), a socio-material perspective of learning spaces (Mulcahy et al., 2015), and Nudge Theory (Thaler & Sunstein, 2009), this study elevates the need for holistic understanding of how ILEs operate to successfully achieve goals set forth in the design process by school stakeholders. This paper provides comparisons between perspectives regarding the vision of the design team and the subsequent enactment and experiences of school leaders and educators and presents applicable tools to support greater alignment between the design and use of ILEs.

EDRA — A Reflection on its Trajectory and a Look Forward

Lubomir Popov *(Bowling Green State University);* **Ivan Chompalov** *(Edinboro University of Pennsylvania)*

In recent years, the Environmental Design Research Association (EDRA) has had several soul-searching and celebratory occasions. By this, we mean EDRA 47 (EDRA Shift) in 2016 and EDRA 50 that celebrated a great anniversary. EDRA Shift was the first sign that our community is realizing evolution and change that have taken place in the association. Based on our analysis of these major events, we conceptualized a research situation that deserves investigation and additional study.

The goal of this project was to trace EDRA's trajectory in the past fifty years and share interpretations and insights. Our objectives were to conceptualize major periods, thematic circles, shifts, and tendencies. We also attempted to look to the future.

Our methodology was informed by philosophy of science and social studies of science and technology. Thus, we created a research framework that guides our research design. Our research methodology incorporated participant observation, informal interviews, and document analysis, as well as elements of autoethnography. We examined the first 25 years of EDRA mostly through document analysis and informal interviews with the founders. For the study of the second 25 years, we added participant observation, informal interviews, and elements of autoethnography.

Initially, EDRA emerged out of a splinter group from Design Methods Group. This is one of the reasons that it is not named Environment and Behavior Research Association, but Environmental Design Research Association. The founders were indirectly influenced by the progressive movements of the late 1960s and were working for a better and fair world without wars and injustice. The majority of the theoretical developments were produced in the 1970s. The overall intellectual environment was influenced by the emerging discipline of environmental psychology, system's thinking (Man-Environment Systems), and Positivist standards for research designs. Parallel with the initial developments of theories, the community consistently worked on collecting primary data.

After the 2000s, EDRA opened significantly to new thematic areas and paradigmatic orientations. EDRA members became both more scholarly and socially diverse. Postmodern thought and Feminist theory became mainstream. In the spirit of the time, EDRA members gradually moved from the study of environmental interactions to major social issues like gender, (in)justice, equality and equity, diversity and inclusion, health, wellbeing and happiness, resilience and sustainability. The old thematic circles that lead to the EDRA's network system were preserved, but now they were combined with the new concerns. Over time, EDRA managed to keep the tradition of network organization of the conference submissions and events, but at the same time introduced a new track system that brings the new social concerns.

EDRA demonstrates a consistent trajectory strongly influenced by the progressive developments of each decade. The trends of intellectual and social diversity and inclusivity will continue due to trends in the education system, population shifts, and businesses adapting to the new workforce. The trends of sustainability and resilience will persist because of the immediacy of climate change.

Innovate and Validate: Applying Simulation Modeling to Inform Design in Real Time

Alice Gittler *(EwingCole);* ***Maryam Hosseini*** *(EwingCole);* ***Jonathan Cogswell*** *(Northwell Health);* ***Michael M. Hoak*** *(EwingCole)*

The planning of a new facility represents a chance to start over, to redesign the environment of care to enhance clinical quality, integrate state-of-the-art technologies, overcome inefficiencies imposed by layout, and pursue new ways of delivering care. And, while change is required for improvement, the uncertainty around whether a change will result in improvement can often thwart new ideas from adoption. In the early planning of an urban multi-specialty medical office building, several departures from conventional practice were being considered; including maximizing clinical space in patient care villages, shifting offices to non-clinical floors, and centralizing all registration with an integrated digital and in-person strategy. The multidisciplinary team represented strategic planning, facilities construction, architectural planning, ambulatory operations, and design research. The goal of the research was to provide insights into the feasibility of the operational innovations proposed within the constraints of the available space and functional needs of the health system practitioners. A primary objective was to determine the seating and staff requirements for a centralized wellness/registration floor concept under three digital pre-registration adoption levels.

The methodology entailed discovery/data gathering, scenario development, and simulation modeling. Simulation modeling has been established as a valuable approach to test processes in real-time (Alvarado et al., 2018, Kaba & Barnes, 2019). The team mapped key patient flows, visit durations, types and modeled future volumes from current schedules. Based on consultation with operational teams, a baseline and two higher levels of digital pre-registration adoption were modeled. The primary hypothesis was that a higher level of digital pre-registration would be required to accommodate volumes expected in the centralized model. Using the Flexsim simulation environment, multiple experimental replications of future state patient arrivals were simulated. A simulation-optimization feature was used with the objective to minimize check-in stations and self-service kiosks, and quantify seating demand during peak hours while meeting two constraints: wait times less than two minutes and staff utilization less than 85%.

The results of the modeling experiments demonstrated the practical feasibility of adopting a centralized registration strategy under three digital adoption levels. The practical benefit of the approach allowed for maximum square footage to be recovered for patient care spaces on the clinical floors as well as potential for staff resources savings through cross-training and a 37% reduction in FTEs. By measuring average floor census over 15-minute increments and comparing that to maximum census over the same increments, the seating availability as determined by the test fit could accommodate both the peaks and average demand over the day. The impact of digital pre-registration adoption on seating demand was not found to be significant, as a 20% increase over baseline only resulted in an additional demand of four to five people during the peak hours. It did however, offer the opportunity to reduce staffed check-in stations from eight to five. The modeling was conducted during early design process, providing real-time analytics to inform the space planning. The scenario modeling provided proof-of-concept for this innovative strategy while also contributing to consensus-building around pursuing the centralized registration model.

Mapping the Co-Operational Behavior of Healthcare and Healthcare Design Networks and Healthcare Systems in the U.S.

Mina Shokrollahi Ardekani *(Clemson University);* ***Anjali Joseph*** *(Clemson University);* ***David Allison*** *(Clemson University)*

COVID-19 has dramatically altered the pattern of healthcare delivery through the decline of in-person outpatient visits and changed the demands in building design. Healthcare design networks and organizations around the world responded to the challenges posed by COVID-19 by providing resources, guidance, and technical support. It has been a time of mobilizing between those networks, resulting in the activation of contacts, forming new strategies, and developing constructive design approaches. At the same time, there has been a lack of systematic documentation of actions challenging the long-term utilization of knowledge created during the pandemic. To address most of the emergent challenges, we frame a map projecting "Networks' Co-operational Behavior" by outlining their extent of activities in response to changes in time of COVID-19, highlighting the aspects preventing mutual support, and providing potential suggestions to promote efficient cooperation among those networks before the occurrence of crisis. The systematic documentation and dissemination of networks could be extremely valuable to the field to support collaboration and information sharing during a crisis. The primary aim of this paper is to map out healthcare design-related networks and organizations in the U.S and the extent of their activities in response to the COVID-19 pandemic. Two sub-questions are discussed: how various types of networks act to prepare for uncertainties and how the healthcare systems respond to the networks' contributions? The findings will support the development of a coherent understanding of dynamics between the healthcare design networks and the healthcare systems in the U.S and their range of collaboration in a time of crisis.

The methodology expounded in this study includes a systematic web-based search strategy along with a supplemented survey of healthcare organizations and design professionals for data collection to tease out the nature of direct organization to organization interactions. Descriptive analysis will be used to outline a data map, showing the structure of support and cooperation among target networks in the time of COVID-19. For data collection, the first step is to determine a clear and focused term which, for the aim of this study, we used the term "Healthcare Design Networks in the U.S" and "Healthcare Networks in the U.S." We also added some variations in search terms such as "Healthcare architects in the U.S" to track down potential networks for our database. We used a database-appropriate syntax with parentheses, Boolean operators, and field codes for the search process. Finally, we defined a key concept framing several elements to develop a comprehensive and informative inter-organizational map to answer our research questions. "Network's Co-operational Behavior" is the key concept as a leading lane to unfold the complex operational dynamic between active networks in the healthcare sector and the Built Environmental field.

Developing a Framework for Evaluating Movie and Novel -Based Digital Apps for Understanding Urban Landscape

Mina Rezaei *(University of California, Davis);* ***Patsy Eubanks Owens*** *(University of California, Davis)*

The urban landscape is a complex system of various interactions. These dynamics include human-human, human-open space, and urban landscape with its all-physical features. Understanding urban landscape needs exploring all the social, cultural, physical, and environmental aspects of these relationships.

In the twentieth century, with the rejection of the values of the top-down approach of modernism in landscape architecture, new lines of ideas emerged, which relied less on scientific measurements, and more on philosophy, poetics, and sociology in exploring humans and their spaces. In the 1960s, with the rise of postmodernist theories, Edward Soja, one of the most prominent geographical thinkers, made a reassertion to the concept of space by using "spatial turn" in humanities and "social turn" in other fields related to the built environment such as landscape architecture and urban design. The spatial turn in humanities indicates that space is neither a subjective nor objective experience. It maintains that social and cultural dynamics of power relations shape the space. Proponents of spatial turn assert that the traditional map is a form of institutionalization that misses feelings, memories, stories, etc. They believe that lines and points cannot represent the complexities of space. Exploring these different aspects of the urban landscape made landscape and urban researchers more interested in employing materials such as diaries, memories, travelers' notes, novels, etc to explore the complexities of the urban landscape. In recent years, geographic information technologies have also contributed profoundly to the "spatial turn" in humanities. Researchers can include different layers of information on these digital platforms. There has also been a growing interest in the use of films and novels in teaching urban landscape in academia. These courses include many aspects of relations in space, including man-man relations or man-environment relations, etc., which were barely addressed in traditional landscape courses. However, a review of employing geo-web technologies in literary and film geography practices reveals that these practices have mostly remained limited to isolating "geographical" passages from novels or movies. This paper explores new opportunities for designing film and literary geography-based apps using a spatial user-centered design framework. We used textual analysis of literary and film geography course syllabi, and in-depth interviews with the film or story map-based app developers to create this framework. We test our framework (Spatial User-Centered Design (SUCD) framework with young people and landscape educators and found that the framework can bridge the gap between academic literary and film geography and digital practices. This framework can be applied in landscape design learning environments or serve individuals who want to learn about space. The SUCD framework will broaden users' experience to more than interaction, to learn about the "space" that they live in. Our framework empowers users and prepares them for engaging more in making their landscape space.

Sense of Place in the British Columbia Mount Arrowsmith Biosphere Region

Lindsay Joyce McCunn *(Vancouver Island University)*

The most effective civic policies are those that address the attitudes and perceptions of individuals (Nanzer, 2004). This study is part of a broader project examining the impacts of human actions on mountain ecosystems, specifically within the Mount Arrowsmith Biosphere Region (MABR)—a UNESCO-designated reserve in British Columbia, Canada. We examined associations between the psychological constructs sense of place (SOP) (i.e., a combination of place attachment, place identity, and place dependence; Jorgensen & Stedman, 2001) and nature relatedness (NR) (i.e., an appreciation for our interconnectedness with the natural world; Nisbet et al., 2009). We also measured perceived views and walkable access to natural attributes and collected qualitative descriptions of SOP in six different communities inside the MABR. Both SOP and NR have been shown to predict pro-environmental behaviour and correlate positively with the frequency of time spent in nature.

Between August, 2020 and January, 2021, we collected data from MABR community members on their attitudes about the land using a mixed-methods approach. Because this research was undertaken during the COVID-19 pandemic, we sent postcards via Canada Post's unaddressed ad mail service that included a link to an online questionnaire; 296 participants were recruited.

Average scores on scales measuring SOP, NR, and perceived views of, and access to, nature were very similar across communities. Indeed, SOP was quite neutral whereas NR was mildly stronger—as were community members' perceived views of, and access to, nature in their residential area. Overall, statistically significant correlations were revealed between SOP and NR, as well as between SOP and participants' perceived views of, and access to, nature. A statistically significant association was not found between NR and the level of perceived views of, and access to, nature across communities.

Fifteen themes emerged from responses to the open-ended item asking participants to state which physical (e.g., design/architectural) features in the area contributed to their experience of meaning, identity, and attachment. Most responses were classified into a theme to do with the natural environment. The second most common theme contained comments about particular trails and paths and how they are used, followed by a theme related to specific places and parks that were listed by name and distinguished by participants. The remaining themes, such as amenities (i.e., museums, markets, libraries), a sense of safety, a sense of privacy, and urban development, each represented small percentages of the data.

Our findings may help researchers, planners, and developers alike collaborate and understand what the MABR means to those who live there, and which physical features are linked to SOP. Findings may be relevant for municipal decision makers building community in other coastal towns.

References

Jorgensen, B. S., & Stedman, R. C. (2001). Sense of place as an attitude: Lakeshore owners attitudes toward their properties. *Journal of Environmental Psychology, 21*, 233-248.

Nanzer, B. (2004). Measuring sense of place: A scale for Michigan. *Administrative Theory & Praxis, 26*, 362-382.

Nisbet, E. K., et al. (2009). The nature relatedness scale: Linking individuals' connection with nature to environmental concern and behavior. *Environment and Behaviour, 41*, 715-740.

No BS - Boosting Biodiversity with NbS

Jon Calabria *(University of Georgia)*

Nature-based solutions (NbS) are infrastructure and management prescriptions that seeks to move away from grey and toward green infrastructure to meet the challenges associated with climate change, loss of biodiversity and unsightly civil works that fail at providing co-benefits (Cohen-Shacham, 2019). Society may have historically asked engineers to protect for flooding or erosion, but that has occurred at great cost. By lessening the impact of gray infrastructure, landscape architects can work with many other disciplines to create green infrastructure to increase ecological function and aesthetics.

This presentation suggests a structured decision-making process and accompanying graphic suite to encourage stakeholders, designers, contractors and land owners to envision NbS (Bridges et al, 2021) to improve the interaction of the social, biological and physical processes to achieve green infrastructure in coastal settings. By using a systems-based approach, the team envisions how society might meet multiple objectives through discourse and framework approach. The graphic suite could be employed to illustrate transitions from extant or failed works (ex. collapsed seawall) to improved NbS (ex. living shoreline). The co-benefits of NbS include enhancing biodiversity and recreation in more sustainable ways (Gittman, 2016). For example, grey infrastructure is strongest just after construction, yet NbS has an inherent ability to self-heal after adverse events, improving cost benefit analyses.

This process will be implemented on a national scale and seeks to reverse degradation, improve biodiversity and societal cohesion. By embracing biodiversity and engineering, we hope to improve the environment. Improving the landscape performance will benefit society and the environment that sustains us.

References

Bridges, T., Bourne, E., Suedel, B., Moynihan, E., & King, J.. (2021). *Engineering With Nature : An Atlas,* Volume 2. https://doi.org/10.21079/11681/40124

Cohen-Shacham, E., Andrade, A., Dalton, J., Dudley, N., Jones, M., Kumar, C., Maginnis, S., Maynard, S., Nelson, C. R., Renaud, F. G., Welling, R., & Walters, G. (2019). Core principles for successfully implementing and upscaling Nature-based Solutions. *Environmental Science & Policy, 98*, 20-29. https://doi.org/10.1016/j.envsci.2019.04.014

Gittman, R. K., Scyphers, S. B., Smith, C. S., Neylan, I. P., & Grabowski, J. H. (2016). Ecological Consequences of Shoreline Hardening: A Meta-Analysis. *BioScience, 66*(9), 763-773. https://doi.org/10.1093/biosci/biw091

New Public Infrastructures: A Survey of Integrated Art, Design and Engineering

Dwaine Carver *(University of Idaho);* ***Karen Bubb*** *(City of Boise)*

As the discourse and practice of public works infrastructure development in the United States expands to include ecological systems, social justice, and new conceptions of public space, municipalities seeking public works improvements are leveraging arts and cultural programs to execute the next generation of infrastructure projects. Linda Samuels defines next generation infrastructure as "multifunctional; public; visible; socially productive; [...] technologically smart; and developed collaboratively across disciplines and agencies," (Samuels, 2019, p. 17).

Percent-for-art programs and ordinances, designating a percentage of public-funded project budgets to include public art, are significant and effective tools for municipalities to integrate art and design professionals into public infrastructure improvement projects. The integration of architects, landscape architects, urban designers and artists with city engineers and managers into the assembly of interdisciplinary project design teams has arguably become one of the most effective uses of percent-for-art funds within municipal public works and a catalyst for design innovations addressing sustainability, ecosystem health, and social challenges, (Walsh et al., 2017).

This paper presents a 10-year planning document for a municipal public works department, written by the authors, in context to a survey of interdisciplinary public works collaborations across the U.S. The planning document identifies strategic opportunities within future public infrastructure projects in the City of Boise to integrate art and design professionals into design and construction teams. The document addresses each of the public works department programs: air quality, storm and wastewater renewal, material conservation, reuse, recycling and upcycling, and a unique geothermal water system.

Surveying key precedents, the paper identifies public works collaborations across the U.S., assessing interdisciplinary infrastructure projects that critically engage their communities, develop new public space typologies, and expand social, cultural, and educational programming. Through precedent research and interviews, the paper investigates government-funded interdisciplinary models for designers, artists, and engineers, as well as guidelines for community outreach and collaboration.

The paper addresses the following questions: How are municipal percent-for-art policies integrating art and design professionals into public works infrastructure projects in innovative ways that invite boundary crossing into content areas of health, equity, sustainability and environmental resilience? What policies and organizational structures are most conducive to collaborative developments? What evaluative methods are currently used, and what methods can be developed, to most effectively measure project outcomes relative to interdisciplinary collaboration, community health, equity, and resilience?

References

Samuels, Linda C. (2019). A Case for infrastructural opportunism, *Technology|Architecture + Design*, 3:1, pp. 16-22.

Walsh, Elizabeth A; Becker, William J; Judelsohn, Alexandra; Hall, Enjoli. (2017). Civic infrastructure and sustainable regional planning: Insights from the sustainable communities initiative regional planning grantees. *Cityscape: A Journal of Policy Development and Research*, Washington, Vol. 19, No. 3, pp. 63–92.

Exploring Interdisciplinary Design Opportunities in the Development of a Novel Human-Centric Lighting System

Oliver Moreno *(Georgia Institute of Technology);* ***Clayton Feustel*** *(Georgia Institute of Technology);* ***Jennifer DuBose*** *(Georgia Institute of Technology)*

The discovery of ipRGC, the receptor in the eye that provides input to the stimulation of melatonin suppression, has led to a paradigm shift in our understanding of light and its interaction with the human body. In addition to the importance of visual functions of light, evidence shows that light affects nonvisual health outcomes including metabolic function, mood, and cognition (Shin & Hyeon-Jeong, 2019). As people spend an increasing amount of their day indoors with artificial lighting, it is more important than ever that the lighting systems we deploy in homes, offices, and everyday settings fulfill the entire spectrum of human needs. Addressing the diverse facets of this grand challenge requires a holistic, interdisciplinary approach. In this abstract, we explore how a collaboration encompassing molecular researchers, electrical and chemical engineers, and design professionals, facilitated by advanced manufacturing tools, a dedicated lighting lab, and traditional user-centered design process, enabled rapid prototyping of a novel lighting solution.

Lighting engineers rely on metrics that describe the efficiency (luminous power efficacy), quantity (luminous flux), quality (color rendering index), and non-visual effects (circadian stimulus) of light to aid in the development process. While these metrics are useful for describing light, they are, on their own, inadequate for determining the acceptability of the light condition in the appropriate context that the lighting system is intended for; to address that question, human subject research is needed. This type of human experience study is the focus of work conducted by design professionals. Design professionals, however, are limited in the qualities of the light that they can evaluate by the available commercial systems. In this research collaboration, over the course of just one month, we developed, tested, and iterated a new lighting system that fills the green-gap and approaches a more sun-like distribution of light.

We accomplished this rapid-cycle testing of lighting technology by using 3D printer technology to fabricate encapsulations with light-conversion technology that could be applied to off-the-shelf LED bulbs to alter the spectral power distribution for increased melanopic lux. We placed these spectrally modified light bulbs in a controlled lab setting and recruited participants to perform visual tasks. Because the modified bulbs were commercially available and utilized a traditional e26 base, it was simple to compare against state-of-the-art products that were matched in the characteristics we desired to control for (e.g., luminous flux and CCT). Through performance metrics and survey, we evaluated the acceptability of the novel lighting in a quasi-realistic context. The results of user acceptability then provide feedback for the molecular design to improve performance prior to the expensive process of fully implementing a lighting system. Collecting data from intended users of the lights earlier in the light development process will help rapid iteration, leading to the creation of systems that are better able to address the complex lighting needs of users.

References

Shin, C., & Hyeon-Jeong, S. (2019). Awakening effects of blue-enriched morning light exposure on university students' physiological and subjective responses. Scientific Reports (Nature Publisher Group), 9(1). https://doi.org/10.1038/s41598-018-36791-5

TRACK 6: Pedagogies & Methods

This track examines the ways in which teaching promotes design and research excellence, innovation, and/or activism related to health, equity, resiliency and sustainability. What methodologies are being embraced by environmental design faculty in order to innovate and stimulate teaching and research? How are emerging design processes and tools (data, simulation, virtual, etc.) being used in the classroom and/or in research? What new methods, ways of working, or insights can be shared to help advance critical thinking, and the leadership to advocate for change and the practice of environmental design for health? What methods and ways of working can help bring together academics and practitioners?

Diversity in Worship: A Case Study of an Inclusive Faith Center

Sarah Angne Alfaro *(Ball State University);* ***Tony Elliott*** *(Ball State University)*

Religious spaces serve a variety of functions. They connect humans to higher powers and serve as community centers. They support individual needs through reflection and contemplation. They support the larger body with corporate worship and individuals with religious studies. In most settings, a religious space is occupied with one organization aligning with a common set of standards. But, what happens when a facility houses multiple faiths? How is space negotiated? How are symbols portrayed? How are worshipers' needs met? What complications surface with the integration of various religions? Where are best practices when designing these types of spaces? This case study features the United States Air Force Academy Cadet Chapel in Colorado, USA. This iconic space, illustrating an example of classic modern American academic architecture, features a space devoted to a variety of religions. The all-faith center of worship allows cadets of varying beliefs, a place to worship. Within the facility, Protestant, Catholic, Jewish, Muslim and Buddhist chapels are included. Additionally, a room for smaller religious faiths and an area for earth-centered faiths are present. Findings of the case study reveal the strengths, weaknesses, opportunities, and threats that arise in this multi-faith place of worship. Design strategies are presented. Recommendations, focusing on the environment-behavior attributes (privacy, personal space, territoriality, crowding, place attachment, identity, control, environmental stress, environmental press, sensory, stimulation, architectural qualities, and symbolism) are provided for succeeding multi-faith centers to glean.

References

Biddington, T. (2013). Towards a Theological Reading of Multifaith Spaces. *International Journal of Public Theology, 7*(3), 315–328. https://doi-org.proxy.bsu.edu/10.1163/15697320-12341293

Crompton, A. (2013). The architecture of multifaith spaces: God leaves the building. *Journal of Architecture (London, England), 18*(4), 474-496. https://doi.org/10.1080/13602365.2013.821149

Rapoport, A. (1980]. Cross-cultural Aspects of Environmental Design. In I. Altman, A. Rapoport & J. Wohlwill [Eds.], *Environment and Culture*. New York: Plenum.

Photo and Video Elicitation for Remote Architectural Research

Widya Ramadhani *(University of Illinois at Urbana-Champaign);* ***Lynne M. Dearborn*** *(University of Illinois at Urbana-Champaign)*

Physical environmental data are key in architectural research. These data are captured through images and text. 'Image information' helps construct a general understanding of physical space and identify important issues related to design, whereas 'text information' supports design evaluation (Korobkin, 1975). Observation, a common method to collect both types of information in architectural research, requires researchers to be present in the research settings. However, certain conditions may limit researchers' ability to access a research site. One example, the COVID-19 pandemic, has limited human mobility and created barriers to direct human interaction. These limitations impact architectural research, especially data collection incorporating in-person interaction with participants and the settings where they live.

The Food-related activities Engagement and Adaptation Study (FEAST) examines older women's personal and environmental challenges and adaptation strategies when engaging in food related activities (i.e., food preparation, cooking, eating, and cleaning) in their homes. Originally, we planned to visit older adults' homes to observe their food-related activities engagement. Obtaining physical-environment data of participants' homes is critical to identify the environmental press that impacts their adaptive behavior (Nahemow & Lawton, 1973). However, limitations to visiting older adults' homes – a vulnerable group – during the pandemic forced a major adjustment to our research protocol. Hence, we explored alternatives to gather physical-environment data through remote means. Photo and video elicitation strategies were selected to replace direct observation to overcome the challenge of visiting participants' homes in-person. These strategies extended researchers' abilities to develop knowledge of in-home settings by including participants' active involvement in documenting the research setting – their home – through photos and videos. The benefits and drawbacks of employing this method for older adult populations is discussed.

Photo-elicitation has been utilized to afford participants agency by involving them as data collectors while allowing them to impart unspoken stories about places through images (van Hees et al., 2017). While our study also aims to capture participants' experiences and spatial perceptions through photos and videos, our main reason for using this method was to provide knowledge about the research settings. Therefore, we asked participants to take multiple photos and a walkthrough video as if they were giving a tour of the spaces in their homes. Though the photos and videos could not provide precise dimensions of spaces, they were important mediators that allowed researchers to see and explore participants' home environments.

The images of participants' home environments served as the entry point to researchers' comprehension of the space. Then, we conducted interviews through video conferencing technology (i.e., Zoom) that began with an overview of the photos. Participants were asked to verbally explain the images shown on the screen while the researcher sketched and annotated floorplans and furniture layout. While different than originally planned, the utilization of photo and video elicitation has enabled continuation of our study that initially involved direct observation and interaction with a vulnerable group. The restrictions resulting from the pandemic led us to explore technology-supported data collection methods (i.e., camera, smartphone, video-conferencing platform) to successfully conduct architectural research remotely.

Orchestrating the Epiphany: How Integrative, Systems, and Design Thinking Can be Unified to Teach the Interdisciplinary Design Process

Robert Sproull *(Auburn University)*

Environmental designers are uniquely situated to deal with the confluence of modern issues the world faces – especially those related to the collective health of society. The interdisciplinary nature of their work qualifies them to conduct an integrative, multiscale process of problem solving related to the built environment. Seasoned practitioners are well versed in this interdisciplinary process as experience breeds confidence and comfort within it, but to the early design student this can be an enigmatic undertaking. For them the multivalent nature of thought that is incorporated into the process is often convoluted, and at times more suggestive of a siloed approach rather than an interdisciplinary method (Samraj & Swales, 2000).

This paper presents a course clarifying the interdisciplinary design process for students early in their education. It explains three modes of thought that occur when using design as a problem-solving tool: integrative thinking, systems thinking, & design thinking. The course demonstrates how to unify these into an overarching method for solving problems that initially appear unworkable due to their complex nature i.e., 'wicked problems'. These are introduced through lectures and readings, then revisited with a site-specific design research investigation broken down into iterative actions where students utilize each mode of thought for specific steps in the design process. Integrative thinking serves to identifying problems. Systems thinking is used to better understand the relational causes and effects of those problems, and design thinking is utilized for developing solutions to the problems. The project requires students to operate in an interdisciplinary context to create research-based responses to the systemic issues of the built environment they identify.

Along with these intertwined thinking strategies, the course introduces project sites that have been pre-selected to require specific considerations of place related to the collective wellbeing of communities. Students are required to conceive of a project that can serve as a catalyst for future development and improvement. Based on the thought related topics covered in the readings and lectures as well as the nature of the pre-selected project sites, the resulting solutions often reside within the realm of social infrastructure related to health, social inequity, and sustainability. This is because social infrastructure projects are essential for the ongoing development of healthy communities and when these student solutions are considered together, the course begins to support the premise that improving the collective health of society is dependent on the preservation, rehabilitation, or creation of robust social infrastructure. (Klinenberg, 2018).

This paper will present the 1) three modes of thinking explored in the course, 2) the process and logic that the course employs to unify them, and 3) a series of sample social infrastructure projects envisioned by students that demonstrate its value in improving and preserving communities' overall health and well-being.

References

Samraj, & Swales, (2000) Writing in conservation biology: searching for an interdisciplinary rhetoric *Language and Learning Across the Disciplines*, Vol.3, No.3, pp.36–56

Eric Klinenberg, (2018) *Palaces for the People How Social Infrastructure Can Help Fight Inequality, Polarization, and the Decline of Civic Life*, page 22.

Research on the Activation Traditional Villages Based on Social Media Data: Taking Liingshui Village, Beijing As an Example

Chongchong Wang *(Beijing Jiaotong University);* ***Yi Yang*** *(Beijing Jiaotong University);* ***Bo Zhang*** *(Oklahoma State University*

In the past decade, an increasing number of traditional villages in Beijing have been developed into tourist destinations to promote local economic development. The planning, design and redevelopment of these villages are supposed to showcase the local culture and vernacular lifestyle, and enrich tourists experience. Taking advantage of the social media data with its large quantity, wide range of topics, and ever growing amounts, this study adopts Lingshui Village as an example to exemplify the social media based evaluation method. Located at 80 km north of Beijing, the village was developed into a tourist destination in 2012.Boasting a history of more than 600 years, it attracts a large number of tourists for its village landscape, culture and traditional northern quadrangle dwellings and ancestral temple architecture. In this study 1078 tourist reviews on Lingshui Village posted at Dazhongdianping and Tripadvisor platforms from 2012 to 2022 were extracted, along with the posting date, time, photo, and other information. By using Python and Excel, the textual dates was categorized to unveil people's attention to the built environment in five dimensions , including geographical location , folk customs, architecture, landscape features, and business environments. Also, this study also attempts to use social networks to analyze the differences between the protection methods of material and intangible cultural heritage, as well as the role of people in the protection, activation and reuse of traditional villages. From these analysis, we reveal more under standings about 1) tourists' perception of material and intangible cultural heritage, 2) tourists: satisfaction and activities, 3) protection, activation and reuse of traditional villages in western Beijing.

Radically Re-Imagining Landscape Architecture as Liberatory Praxis

Tera Williams *(University of Washington);* ***Lynne Manzo*** *(University of Washington)*

Conflicts in the built environment often seem to emerge from the ether with volatility levels nearing a flashpoint. Waves similarly appear to emerge just before they break. Waves, of water and conflict alike, are not a sudden manifestation. Their origination and progression is called a fetch. The length a fetch travels determines the strength of the wave. Designers are facing conflicts today that result from the "long fetch" of history (Lipsitz, 2007, p. viii).

We use shoaling, as described in the Black Shoals by Tiffany Lethabo King (2019), as a method for carefully observing and investigating landscape architecture's long fetch through history. Landscape architecture defines the spatial orientation and energetic resonance of public community areas in the built environment. In the U.S. design disciplines are a product of the fetch of history and have inherited many of the lingering biases, structures, and frames of thought from that fetch. The fetch of U.S. history originated in genocide and moved through all other forms of subjugation to reach current day.

The end result of this process is a conceptual and procedural set of "tools for seeing the invisible," or tracking the fetch of titular areas of conflict within community design projects, and tools for reconstructing landscape architectural practice towards liberatory praxis (Bowker & Star, 2000). Landscape architecture requires a radical re-imagining to divest from the negative components of design practice it inherited and realign toward liberatory praxis. Liberatory praxis is a practice that seeks freedom from the continuing systemic oppression present in the United States. It moves toward internal, external, and communal freedom from the "depths of suffering," or working to untangle subjugations and begin healing (Syedullah et al., 2016). If this is not intentionally prioritized future design practice risks the outcome of perpetuating the same social harms. Landscape architecture functions as liberatory praxis by uncovering erased histories and amplifying marginalized stories, voices, experiences, and landmarks within a community and democratically leverages that information to advance spatial justice.

References

Bowker, G. C., & Star, S. L. (2000). *Sorting Things Out: Classification and Its Consequences*. MIT Press

King, T. L. (2019). *The Black Shoals: Offshore Formations of Black and Native Studies*. Duke University Press.

Lipsitz, G. (2007). *Footsteps in the Dark: The Hidden Histories of Popular Music*. U of Minnesota Press.

Syedullah, J., Owens, L.R., & Williams, A. K. (2016). *Radical Dharma: Talking Race, Love, and Liberation*. North Atlantic Books.

Exploring Contemporary Rural Community Design through Digitalized Environmental Behavior Research Data: A Case Study of the Elderly- and Dementia-Friendly Community in Zhutian, Pingtung County

Ting-ting Cheng *(National Cheng Kung University);* ***Li-wen Sung*** *(National Cheng Kung University)*

This study explored the effectiveness of data survey research in complementing environmental behavior research to examine rural communities friendly toward older adults and patients with dementia. Rural areas in Taiwan are characterized by close interpersonal relationships among local residents. Previous studies have mostly involved the full participation of researchers in local activities or in-person visits to research sites by researchers. The effectiveness of such research is mainly determined by relationships between researchers, and local residents. However, the ongoing COVID-19 pandemic has prevented researchers from conducting face-to-face interviews with elderly residents, who constitute the major population in rural areas.

In the elderly- and dementia-friendly community targeted in this study, small-scale stations were deployed to provide dementia care services. These stations were located within a walkable distance for older adults and in common gathering places for them. This study collaborated with a smart sensing equipment supplier, who provided proximity cards for 757 residents in the community and installed sensing devices along the community streets. Empirical research, document analysis, and survey methods were used to analyze older adults' daily activities in the community. The environmental behavioral data were visualized and overlayed with various data, including locations where resident frequently assembled and the use frequency of public infrastructures in the community in 2020 prior to the pandemic.

The results verified the importance of environmental behavior digitalization, which is considered a unique research approach in the digital era. This approach extends researchers' scope of observation of the community and increases the likelihood of identifying beneficial resources and select adequate research participants. Digital technology development facilitates spatial research by presenting data in a more three-dimensional perspective. Findings obtained in the case community can be generalized to other communities with similar attributes.

References

World Health Organization. (2017). *Global action plan on the public health response to dementia 2017–2025.*

Hebert, C. A., & Scales, K. (2019). Dementia friendly initiatives: A state of the science review. *Dementia, 18*(5), 1858–1895. https://doi.org/10.1177/1471301217731433

Zeisel, J. (2006). *Inquiry by design. Environment/behavior/neuroscience in architecture, interiors, landscape, and planning.*

The Use of ArcGIS and Story Map in Research-Based Design: A Focus Group Interview Study

Hoa Vo *(Georgia State University);* ***Nedda Ahmed*** *(Georgia State University)*

Research-based design refers to the practice of gathering, analyzing, and applying scientific evidence into the design process (Robinson, 2020). Geographical information analysis technologies such as ArcGIS databases and the web-based interface, Story Map, have long been used in teaching research-based design in architecture, urban planning, and engineering studios (Ma & Ren, 2017). General findings indicate that ArcGIS and Story Map were effective in promoting students' autonomy and exploration. However, ArcGIS and Story Map applications in interior design studios are less prevalent. Journal of Interior Design, for example, has published no articles to date on ArcGIS and Story Map. Hence, this study explores student learning experiences with ArcGIS and Story Map in research-based design in a senior Interior Design studio at a Southeast R1 University.

In sixteen weeks, 18 seniors develop their thesis projects by framing design problems, conducting research in ArcGIS databases, and presenting final design concepts on Story Map. Students attended three workshops on ArcGIS and Story Map tailored to their research needs in the second, fourth, and eighth weeks. Students explored, collected, and visualized data on topics such as racial makeup, median incomes, crime rates, housing instability, homeless population, COVID-19 cases, LEED-certified buildings, building classifications, and city zonings. Each student combined their collected data with a literature review and case studies as evidence to support their proposed solutions to the design problems. One student pointed to the distribution of LGBTQIA+ community centers across the United States to emphasize the lack of local support for the queer community in the metropolitan area around the Southeast R1 University (i.e., none over 196 centers). The student, thus, committed to designing the first LGBTQIA+ community center in the metropolitan area featuring libraries, shared workspaces, gyms, psychiatric and job aid services, all with the goal of combating the high crime and unemployment rates for this marginalized group.

At the end of the studio, students will receive informed consent forms explaining the study purpose and procedure. Those who give consent will enter a pool of volunteers. Five randomly selected volunteers will attend a one-hour focus group interview (Krueger, 2014). The interview will be recorded for transcription purposes. No monetary compensation will be provided. However, water bottles will be provided during the focus group interview. Content analysis will corroborate the transcript in terms of emerging themes on how students perceive ArcGIS and Story Map in their learning experiences of research-based design. Student Story Map submissions (visualizations and written explanations for the ArcGIS data and the proposed design solutions) will be used to illustrate the themes. The presentation will guide the attendees to explore ArcGIS and Story Map and highlight the themes from the focus group interview with Story Map examples. This study is conducted under the IRB approval H22185.

References

Krueger, R. A. (2014). *Focus groups: A practical guide for applied research*. Sage Publications.

Ma, Z., & Ren, Y. (2017). Integrated application of BIM and GIS: an overview. *Procedia Engineering, 196*, 1072–1079.

Robinson, L. B. (2020). *Research-based programming for interior design*. New York : Fairchild Books.

Impacts of Technology on Learning in a Studio-Based Environment: Lessons from COVID-19

Cherif Amor *(Virginia Commonwealth University);* ***Ryad Ghanam*** *(Virginia Commonwealth University, Qatar);* ***Edward Boone*** *(Virginia Commonwealth University, Richmond);* ***Khawla Kittaneh*** *(Virginia Commonwealth University);* ***Kaltham Al-Sulaiti*** *(Virginia Commonwealth University, Qatar);* ***Maryam Al-Sayed*** *(Virginia Commonwealth University, Qatar);* ***Sophie Boone*** *(Virginia Commonwealth University)*

The transition to the virtual mode of operations engendered by the COVID-19 pandemic generated noticeable opportunities for the studio-based courses in the architecture, art and design disciplines, yet this has been accompanied by noticeable pedagogic challenges. The problematic lies in the unplanned implementation of virtual course delivery platforms (Canvas, Google Classroom, and Zoom) and the engagement of students, faculty and other stakeholders in the undesigned collaborative pedagogies and their impact on students' learning.

While a growing body of literature has emerged in the last two decades exploring course delivery platforms and collaboration, nonetheless there is a lack of data relative to gauging the impact of technology and collaboration on students' learning (Apostol, 2020; Dzebic, 2020; Vaux, 2020; Ji Young and Joori Suh, 2019; Amor, 2014; & McCoy, 2012).

This study finds justification in the recommendation of university strategic plans and accreditation councils for the necessity of embracing technology emerging trends and collaborative pedagogies. For instance, the Council for Interior Design Accreditation standard 5 calls for "interior designers to collaborate and participate in interdisciplinary teams" and "recognize the value of Integrated Design Practice (2020 CIDA Professional Standards, p.II-1.). Likewise, CIDA Standard # 9 calls for the "exposure to evolving emerging communication technologies" which could include but are not limited to augmented reality, sensor technology, robotics, interactive products, and online collaboration platforms (CIDA Professional Standards, p. II-26).

The purpose of this line of inquiry is to 1) explore the pros and cons of the emerging communication technologies and collaboration pedagogies, 2) examine the impact of technology on students' learning, 3) appraise the effect of technology on increasing collaboration strategies, and 4) decipher implications for future use of these two concepts.

Based on the exploration of sophomore, junior and senior students, with emphasis on six core studio-based curriculum courses, the research methodology includes qualitative and quantitative approaches. While the qualitative investigation uses grounded theory approach based on open-ended interviews and analysis of design processes and products (conceptual, schematic, and final outcomes), the quantitative approach is based on a psychometric survey utilizing closed-ended questions, rankings and rating to examine statistically students' and faculty's perceptions about the impact of technology and collaboration on learning. Data will be analyzed using two approaches 1) open coding which consists of breaking down, conceptualizing, and reconstructing data in new ways, and 2) Statistical Package for the Social Sciences (SPSS) will be used to analyze numerical data measurement.

The preliminary observations suggest that the virtual collaboration pedagogy paves the way for conducive learning environments that transcends the silo-ed/modular classical pedagogies. Nonetheless, it appears that collaboration leads to challenging and multidimensional issues that are not limited to pedagogy but include behavioral, administrative, and management issues. Relative to the impact of technology on student's learning, the preliminary findings point to rewarding learning opportunities (e.g., improvement of student's engagements and expansion of classroom boundaries) and challenging impediments (e.g., reliability of emerging communication technologies, poor user experience, remote internet speed access and connection, and screen exposure fatigue.

Studio Pedagogy as Advocacy for Social Well-Being

Nisha A. Fernando *(University of Kansas);* ***Vibhavari Jani*** *(Kansas State University)*

Going beyond traditional approaches that involve only aesthetic solutions to design problems, contemporary interior design educators have started adapting diverse pedagogies to immerse students in critical and socio-cultural issues of human well-being. This presentation shares pedagogical examples that have incorporated this direction in two upper-level interior architecture studios at two institutes of higher learning.

At the first institution, undergraduate students analyzed museum interiors as a system of activity settings from an environment-behavior perspective (Rapoport, 1990), (as opposed to patron as a distant, non-engaged observer), where patrons can actively engage in the museum experience. The focus was to provide patrons a deep awareness and understanding on current social and cultural issues and resultant emotional and psychological well-being by generating immersive activities. In addition to the exhibits themselves, the very design of the museum interior - including spatial progression, hierarchy, and rhythmic patterns of display - lets the patron explore, question, wonder, and experience the nature of social issues and human well-being at hand. Based on the museum-as-an-activity-setting theory, each student designed a variety of museum interiors, including a focus on women's body image, queer joy, Latinx experiences within the U.S. and Mexican-US border & immigrant experiences. Each design approach addressed the importance of museum patrons experiencing psychological aspects related to these social issues. The pedagogical approach is to let the particular social issue inform the design of the interior through the tools of space planning principles, experiential variety through lighting, colors, and other multi-sensory explorations.

At the second institution, the author introduced community engagement and service-learning pedagogy to encourage graduate design students in developing empathetic interior environments that provide psychological, neurological, social, and functional support to comfort diverse communities requiring design assistance. These students researched diverse healthcare design and environment-behavior theories to understand how to design for health and well-being. They adapted Roger Ulrich's concept of "supportive design" to design user-centered wellness centers that can provide psychological and social support and comfort (Ulrich, 1997). The students developed design solutions for suicide prevention for veterans, wellness center for women and children experiencing sexual abuse and violence, sex trafficking, homelessness, or body image issues. Involvement of real users from the community provided meaningful opportunities for conversations, and developing empathy for their issues, and understanding of their needs.

Using space planning principles, the students developed meaningful solutions using lighting, colors, materials, textures, sounds, and natural views to provide psychologically and culturally supportive building experiences. The opportunities for exploration of design ideas with the users and community members opened students' minds, and educated the users and the community members about the power of design.

The two studios led students to shift the learning paradigm to purposefully incorporate social and cultural issues of human well-being, acting as social advocates through design. It reinforces the vitality of an interior design pedagogical approach that would reshape the future of the professional field (Turpin, 2010).

Teaching Interdisciplinary Healthcare Design Studio with Real-World Problems

Daejin Kim *(Iowa State University);* ***Cameron Kim*** *(Iowa State University)*

It is well known that interdisciplinary expertise is essential in healthcare design practice (Kansali & Nersessian, 2015). There is a growing demand for an interdisciplinary healthcare design studio to develop a more inclusive and interdisciplinary design approach in design schools worldwide. Especially, the healthcare studio with multiple design disciplines provides a unique opportunity to teach about healthcare settings and improve the strengths of each discipline. Our design programs have leveraged the space between disciplines to teach students the need to cross disciplinary boundaries and learn how to work with, communicate and translate disciplinary knowledge. But, there are challenges and critics of the interdisciplinary design studio. For example, students sometimes are reluctant to truly engage in an interdisciplinary learning environment because they fail to understand the value of interdisciplinary expertise. To bridge the gap between a studio and a practice, real-world experience with interdisciplinary design experts can be essential for the interdisciplinary healthcare design studio. Professional partners have become integral in the delivery of this studio, which encourages and motivates students to learn how to make a design decision together.

Furthermore, the most important involvement is that healthcare designers in all disciplines provide desk critiques, lectures, field trip visits, mid-term and final reviews. Students also learned how designers in practice work with other disciplines and develop their ability to work across disciplines and generate new ideas for a healthcare design project.

The purpose of this presentation is to introduce pedagogical experience in this unique interdisciplinary healthcare design studio and investigate how students' empathy and interdisciplinary competence change through this class. During the spring semester in 2021, students engaged in a micro-hospital design project, and the design firm partner helped to develop a project description and programming. Students engaged in various design assignments such as case studies and evidence-based design research. After gaining approval from the Institutional Review Board, students completed a survey in the first and last week of the Spring semester. The survey was administered using Qualtrics Survey Software and was analyzed using SPSS. The total number of students who participated in the survey was 22, including ten architecture students, eight interior design students, and four landscape architects.

Research findings showed that students' interdisciplinary competence was significantly improved at the end of this studio, but their empathy level was not significantly different between pre and post-test. Students provided positive opinions about their experience with interdisciplinary teamwork and what they learned from this experience. Also, they suggested a couple of pedagogical approaches which help to teach future students. The conference presentation will show pedagogical strategies for teaching interdisciplinary healthcare design with design experts to college-level students and share students' feedback about this experience.

Teaching Climate Action

Rana Abudayyeh *(University of Tennessee, Knoxville)*

Pressing realities of climate change require a prompt and robust response to how we approach a new era of architectural interventions, positioning interior thinking and design modalities at the center of environmentally responsible practice. Accordingly, interiority is a concept of increasing importance to designers, architects, and urbanists today. The future of professional practice and, by extension, pedagogy will have to address generative climate complexities, remediating the irresponsible approaches of the past era while addressing the ever-changing programmatic needs and narratives of contemporary life.

Situated at the intersection of these realities, this presentation will showcase work and pedagogical approaches from two upper-level interior architecture studios intended to engage these complex, multifaceted parameters. The studio set out to reactivate existing segments of the urban fabric through adaptive reuse to assert environmentally conscientious design agendas. Cognizant of the overlap between culture, politics, and climate, the studios required critical stances and remarkable resolutions that speculate upon architecture and urban strategies embodying the qualities of interiority. The work spanning two semesters assumed a manifesto that projected innovative responses to immanent climate issues and stirred up new imaginative design schemas. Working in multiple urban settings, each presenting a set of challenges and opportunities, the studios pinpointed certain buildings that have been abandoned or soon to be retired due to contextual shifts such as migration patterns, sobering economies, diminishing resources, and changing occupancy patterns. Collectively, the projects aimed to formulate an interior-focused agenda for future settings through adaptive reuse, using the reactivated interior spaces as catalysts for placemaking and climate advocacy.

Climate change now touches every aspect of our lives. As the climate continues to shift, how we conceive spatial strategies must become more responsive and resilient to be compatible with these ever-changing climate parameters. To arrive at these design strategies, the studios engaged in studying resilience in nature. Examining models of living organisms and biological processes and cycles that depended on natural parameters such as light, temperature, moisture, sound, etc., was the starting point for the design concepts. The exchanges between the biological systems and environmental stimuli are living, active, and adaptive; they are integral to the subsistence of a robust ecosystem. Organic processes provide a vast repository of knowledge into resilience. Effectively applying these precedents to their design strategies, students developed proposals for adaptive topological systems capable of creating fluid exchanges between interior and exterior spaces while embracing a proactive approach to the emerging ideas that will transform our environments in the near future.

Towards an Evidence-Based Simulation Toolkit for Architectural Design Pedagogy

Michal Gath-Morad *(ETH Zürich, Swiss Federal Institute of Technology);* ***Raphaël Baur*** *(ETH Zürich, Swiss Federal Institute of Technology);* ***Christoph Hölscher*** *(ETH Zürich, Swiss Federal Institute of Technology)*

The presentation addresses the limitations of current architectural design pedagogy to integrate occupancy-related perspectives and analytics in the design studio [1]. To bridge this gap we present the development, dissemination and critical evaluation of an occupancy analytics toolkit grounded in evidence-based design, spatial cognition research and architectural design. The toolkit consists of an agent-analysis tool[2] , a cognitive-walkthrough protocol, a virtual reality platform to conduct behavioral experiments and a collection of evidence-based design literature. Interdisciplinary teams of architecture and STEM students used the toolkit to evaluate and redesign an Emergency Department (ED) in a university hospital, considering occupancy-related aspects such as wayfinding [2], privacy, care-quality [3], productivity and collaboration. Throughout the course students engaged with caregivers at the ED and shared their intermediate analysis and final design proposals. Teaching outcomes are presented and learning outcomes are analyzed. Results highlight the need to incorporate occupancy analytics in architectural design pedagogy and reinforce the potential of the toolkit to inform the design and evaluation of buildings from the perspective of occupants.

References

1. Pilosof, N. P., & Grobman, Y. J. (2021). Evidence-Based Design in Architectural Education: Designing the First Maggie's Centre in Israel. *HERD: Health Environments Research & Design Journal*, 19375867211007945.
2. Gath-Morad, M., Aguilar, L., Dalton, R. C., & Hölscher, C. (2020, May). cogarch: Simulating wayfinding by architecture in multilevel buildings. In *11th Annu. Symp. Simulation for Architecture & Urban Design (SimAUD 2020)* (pp. 27-34). ACM.
3. Pachilova, R., & Sailer, K. (2020). Providing care quality by design: a new measure to assess hospital ward layouts. *The Journal of Architecture, 25*(2), 186-202.

Space Syntax Applications for Window Access and Daylight Design

Sadiqa Al Awadh *(University of Oregon);* ***Linda Nubani*** *(Michigan State University);* ***Ihab Elzeyadi*** *(Dept. of Architecture)*

In office work environments, occupants are often seated in the same workstation for a prolonged period of time. If they do not receive the recommended quantity and quality of light or access to windows, this will be reflected in their decreased wellbeing, satisfaction, and productivity. An isovist, a constructed planar two-dimensional polygon that represents the totality of all visible and potentially visible space from a specific location usually at eye level, can be used to assess spatial compositions and vistas. Space syntax methods have not assessed office interiors from access to windows perspective. This requires designers to pay more attention to isovists and visibility within the indoor building layout to determine if occupants do receive adequate daylight, or whether they do not, despite meeting building performance benchmarks. This paper proposes the use of daylight simulation and isovist analyses methods together as a more holistic approach and method to assess indoor environments from an occupant perspective. An office building was simulated in ALFA for Rhino to run a daylight simulation and the Isovist software was used for the isovist analysis to assess various point perspectives within the building. Several general conclusions were drawn from the analyses that support the use of isovist properties to inform window access and daylight availability. Other more specific recommendations could be applied to the same floorplate types and interior layouts.

The Effect of Virtual Reality Characteristics on Environmental Behavior Research

Luis Mejia *(Oklahoma State University);* ***Tilanka Chandrasekera*** *(Oklahoma State University)*

Virtual Reality (VR) has become an invaluable tool in Environmental Behavioral (EB) research, allowing researchers to manipulate environments that would otherwise be costly to do, and the ability to control certain variables. Nonetheless, it's important to understand how characteristics of VR environments affect human perception, cognitive function, and behavior. In this study three characteristics of VR: Cognitive Load, Virtual Body, Presence, are evaluated.

Cognitive load (CL) is a critical construct that bridges the brain's physical and psychological features. CL is based on cognitive architecture composed of two distinct memories: long-term and short-term memory. The former has unlimited capacity and stores knowledge, whereas working memory can only process a limited amount of information at a given time, and it is mainly task-driven (Paas, Renkl, & Sweller, 2003). Overall, CL is the response to the demand a given task enforces over the working memory. This response is composed of three dimensions: intrinsic, extrinsic, and germane, where the first relates to the task, the second to the environment, and the third to building up schemas. These three types of CL are additive and restricted by the working memory's capacity, but they can be re-allocated while performing the given task.

Presence is a purely psychological construct that bridges the brain's physical and psychological features. Presence is a state of consciousness that refers to the individual's sensation of being there (International Society for Presence Research, 2000). Moreover, this state is a response to the immersive characteristics of the interaction. Traditionally, VR is categorized between non-immersive and immersive experiences (Mizell et al., 2002). In the former, the virtual world is accessed through a computer screen or tablet using gestures or mouse manipulation. At the same time, the latter requires special hardware, such as head-mounted displays (HMD), to generate full-immersive experiences.

In immersive VR, the way individuals are represented within the environment is through the use of avatars. Avatars are humanized depictions of the virtual body (VB). They can be divided into online and offline wherein the former individuals see their VB within the environment. In the latter, they do not but feel they are present (Carruthers, 2008).

This study explored three conditions of VB and assessed their impact on CL and presence. Two conditions used online and offline VBs, both from a first-person point-of-view. A third condition also used an online VB but from a third-person point-of-view. A sample of 72 participants engaged on average for 20 minutes in VR, where they completed a spatial arrangement task. CL was measured through a NASA-TLX questionnaire and a functional near-infrared spectroscopy (fNIR) device attached to the participant's forehead. Presence was measured through a presence questionnaire.

Findings provided statistically significant differences between the three conditions of VB. While some conditions increased individuals' presence, they also increased CL, negatively affecting task performance. Psychophysiological data from the fNIR device evidenced how CL changed over time throughout the VR interaction. Finally, this study contributes empirical evidence for design practice by helping designers select the appropriate VB depending on the VR interaction intents.

Rasterizing the Vector: How Matrix-Based Multilayer Spatial Analysis Support Behavioral Studies

Yeinn G Oh *(Georgia Institute of Technology);* ***Elliot Jeongwon Park*** *(Marble Fairbanks Architects);* ***Tzu-Chieh Kurt Hong*** *(Georgia Institute of Technology)*

Space Syntax researchers have adapted Visibility Graph Analysis to convert the floor plan into a matrix, which is a raster format data, where each cell contains visibility data (Penn & Turner, 2002), and developed a software DepthmapX to perform the analysis (Turner, 2001). While vector format is beneficial when the area of analysis is in large scale, vector geometry becomes difficult to be translated into micro-scale data with multiple layers of information, as it requires geometry data which is not compatible with most of the simulation and analysis. It may not be suitable in interior environments where a more micro-level speculations are needed. Hence, we propose thinking back to a raster mode of representation, dividing the floor plan into a grid, and layering spatial and cognitive information on each cell of the grid.

Expanding the possibility of integrating more layers of information into the matrix, we produced a raster-based spatial analysis tool with IronPython embedded in Rhinoceros. The goal of the tool is to 1) provide a platform of rasterized floor plan where multiple layers of information can be contained in each tile, 2) make it easily accessible for designers with common modeling tools, and 3) reduce the computational burden by routing the analysis in an external software. The tool reads all type of vector floor plans into a rasterized plan and enable to use the grid to analyze the space. As a sample analysis, we demonstrate running the Visibility Graph Analysis with the tool.

Furthermore, we test integrating Agent-Based Simulation that runs on the layers of information on the rasterized floor plan. Agent-Based Simulation supports individual-level behavioral simulation inside the space. The agents act with human-like behaviors being able to read the data embedded on each tile and use them as their spatial knowledge. The agents are limited to the local knowledge that is available to each tile, which may contain spatial and social data. Agents are also able to recognize and interact with other agents, change the social data embedded in the environment, making it possible to test how real-life behaviors emerge. Multilayer information system supports social behavioral simulations by providing local on-site data to the individual level.

By providing a raster-based multilayer information platform in an accessible 3D-modeling software, we make transition between designing and spatial analysis easier. Often, the vector format of drawing produced in modeling software is difficult to be directly analyzed due to its accurateness, but we propose converting the vector drawing into a non-geometrical matrix, and provide it as a platform for designers to use it as a plug-in with Rhinoceros.

References

Penn, A., & Turner, A. (2002). *Space syntax based agent simulation*. Springer-Verlag.

Turner, A. (2001, May). Depthmap: a program to perform visibility graph analysis. In *Proceedings of the 3rd International Symposium on Space Syntax* (Vol. 31, pp. 31-12).

Using Virtual Reality (VR) to Understand Construction, Materials, and Methods in a Landscape Architecture Curriculum

Carla Delcambre *(North Carolina State University);*
Todd Elia-Warnken *(North Carolina State University)*

This paper discusses enhanced learning opportunities for landscape architecture design students using Virtual Reality (VR) as a tool to learn detailing and the construction process. Teaching construction detailing through two-dimensional, analog drawings can be challenging for students who are not familiar with the construction process. Construction documents are static, two-dimensional drawings, whereas VR Sketch offers a dynamic and interactive space where students can experience their three-dimensional models using Oculus Rift. After introducing VR Sketch in a design curriculum, students begin to visualize three-dimensional details in an immersive environment, to determine scale, proportion, and material connections. During the study, qualitative data was collected through surveys and observations. Findings reveal that students' perceptions changed after experiencing their details in VR Sketch. The digital design of virtual reality technology has provided a new aesthetic view for landscape architecture and has injected new vitality into the design and modeling. Li, Cheng & Yuan (2018). This learning tool has the potential to advance knowledge in landscape architecture programs teaching construction, materials, and methods.

Virtual Reality and Spatial Perception: Exploring Sophomore Level Interior Design Students' Sense of Enclosure in VR

Alp Tural *(Virginia Tech)*

As sophomore-level interior design students start working on choreographing spatial experiences, they are expected to demonstrate an ability to "explore and iterate multiple ideas" applying their knowledge on design elements and principles (Council for Interior Design Accreditation, 2020). One of the concepts discussed in the sophomore-level interior design studio related to spatial definition and spatial perception is (sense of) enclosure. Exploring degrees of enclosure, students work on hypothetical space configurations also considering different scales. Since they start designing with hand-built models, transitioning to digital model and developing an understanding of spatial definition and connection can be challenging.

The study proposes the use of virtual reality (VR) environment as a pedagogical tool. It examines the influence of 3D immersion on students' spatial perceptions and subjective impressions related to the sense of enclosure. Within the interior design context, enclosure in VR model is presented in changing degrees by manipulating the permeability of vertical and horizontal planes, their openness and the position of the apertures (Stamps, 2002; Thiel et al. 1986). The students are asked to rank degrees of enclosure and sense of openness in a series of hypothetical space configurations as experienced through a virtual reality headset. The 3D models are created with the software they use in the design studio.

The outcomes of the study will be used to develop immersive pedagogical design interventions that help interior design students with conceptual design, thinking and meaning development. Current study focuses only on sense of enclosure in conceptual design phase. Future iterations will include additional factors such as spaciousness and disclosure, and will also consider changes in the luminosity and surface finish characteristics of the presented spaces.

References

Council for Interior Design Accreditation. (2020). *Professional Standards*. https://www.accredit-id.org/professional-standards

Stamps, A. E. III. (2002). Environmental enclosure in urban settings. *Environment and Behavior, 34*(6), 781-794.

Thiel, P., Harrison, E. D. & Alden, R. S. (1986). The perception of spatial enclosure as a function of the position of architectural surfaces. *Environment and Behavior, 18*(2), 227-245.

WFH: A Perspective of Its Benefits and Drawbacks from the Emerging Interior Designer's Viewpoint

Kelley Robinson *(Florida State University);* ***Amy M. Huber*** *(Florida State University)*

The COVID-19 pandemic disrupted all facets of life, including work. Many market sectors pivoted to work from home (WFH) strategies, which became a new digital reality for approximately 70% of full-time employees (Owl Labs & Global Workplace Analytics [GWA], 2020), causing a shift that impacted both traditional in-person collaboration and focused work (Galanti et al., 2021; Zoonen et al., 2021).

This original research queried emerging professionals in the design industry, where collaborative efforts among project team members are often integral to the nature of project delivery methods. This study sought to understand the perceptions of this cohort, who often receives tacit knowledge by sitting near more experienced colleagues. More specifically, it sought their thoughts on the best and worst aspects of working during this transition since limited literature is available on the emerging designer's perceptions in navigating the pandemic-related WFH experience.

These findings represent inductively coded qualitative data from a mixed-methods survey of emerging designers. Of the 85 responses collected, approximately 62% had returned to the office, with 46% of respondents back in the office full time and 54% engaging in a part-time schedule. Demographic data revealed that nearly 75% graduated in 2016 or later. Market sector results indicated that 35% were employed in workplace design and 19.0% in civic. Additionally, a majority worked in firms with more than 50 designers (46.9%). Twenty-two percent of participants identified as junior designers or architects, while 43.8% indicated they were professional interior designers or architects.

Free responses regarding the best and worst aspects of working in-person, in a hybrid arrangement, or fully remote were coded as benefits or drawbacks for both employers and employees. Some frequently identified best in-person work aspects included collaboration and community connections, while office distractions were notable as some of the worst. Hybrid scenarios seemed favorable among respondents given the benefits of face-to-face teamwork, coupled with desired "heads down" focused time. Both hybrid and fully remote participants mentioned flexibility and reduced commutes positively while noting schedule conflicts negatively. Other findings reveal that difficulties in communication and coordination—a vital part of a design team's workflow—were cited as some of the worst WFH aspects. In addition, blurred boundaries between home and work were also of concern in this scenario.

This presentation shares the full qualitative findings as design teams, particularly emerging professionals, navigate changing directions in design, an area of importance since those with careers in the workplace sector may influence corporate spaces in other disciplines.

References

Galanti, T., Guidetti, G., Mazzei, E., Zappala, S., & Toscano, F. (2021). Work from home during the

COVID-19 outbreak: The impact on employees' remote work productivity, engagement, and stress. *Journal of Occupational and Environmental Medicine, 63*(7), e426–e432.

Owl Labs, & Global Workplace Analytics [GWA]. (2020). *State of remote work 2020*. https://resources.owllabs.com/state-of-remote-work/2020

Zoonen, W. van, Sivunen, A., Blomqvist, K., Olsson, T., Ropponen, A., Henttonen, K., & Vartiainen, M. (2021). Factors influencing adjustment to remote work: Employees' initial responses to the COVID-19 pandemic. *International Journal of Environmental Research and Public Health, 18*(13). https://doi.org/10.3390/ijerph18136966

Architecture Student and Faculty Understanding of Evidence-Based Design and Environmental Psychology in Korea

Jina Lee *(WSP Korea);* ***Mardelle McCuskey Shepley*** *(Cornell University)*

This study examined student and faculty perceptions in architecture schools in Korea regarding the evidence-based design concept, emphasizing design research and environmental psychology principles focusing on the relationship between the human and physical environment. Students and faculty perceptions were measured by their understanding of design research in architectural programs accredited by the Korea Architectural Accrediting Board, human-environment relations principles, and design guidelines. Architecture undergraduates and faculty at seven different universities in Seoul, Korea, participated in the survey (n = 61). Twenty-five individuals participated in the follow-up interviews. Survey data collected was analyzed inferentially to interpret the quantitative results and compare students and faculty responses across various themes. Interviews were transcribed and analyzed using qualitative analysis methods regarding the overarching theme of each question. The results help understand the status quo and limitations of Korean architectural education regarding human-environment relations and provide useful recommendations to incorporate design research.

An Action Study on the Effect of Full Digitalization on Student Learning Effectiveness and Feedback in Basic Architectural Design Courses Under COVID-19—in the Case of the Department of Architecture, National Cheng Kung University

Ting-ting Cheng *(National Cheng Kung University);* ***Li-wen Sung*** *(National Cheng Kung University)*

The purpose of this study was to review the experience of transforming a basic architectural design course from classroom to fully digital teaching and student responses to changes in the learning form under the COVID-19 pandemic in the past year.

Statistics compiled by Crawford et al. (2020), who researched 20 countries and regions affected by COVID-19, indicated that digital learning has become the future trend in education despite several problems to be resolved. In September 2020, Patti Witten from the Department of Architecture of Cornell University maintained that people should reconsider how to provide user with adequate knowledge and resources amidst social and public health crises due to the pandemic.

This study recruited 49 students who took a basic architectural design course in 2020 as research participants. The research methods consisted of a questionnaire survey and structured observation. The present researcher was a teaching assistant of the course, who adopted the role of a participating observer and conducted the research for over 1 year. The research content involved surveying students' computer hardware equipment, extent of digital software use, learning effectiveness, and differences in their thoughts before and after the online design course.

The research results revealed the following:

1. The power relationship between the teacher and learners changed substantially.
2. Students' learning performances varied with their digital equipment, resulting in

differences in their learning effectiveness.

3. Although all students are digital natives, they still demonstrated high interest in making physical models.

References

Brian Whalley, Derek France, Julian Park, Alice Mauchline & Katharine Welsh (2021). Towards flexible personalized learning and the future educational system in the fourth industrial revolution in the wake of COVID-19. *Higher Education Pedagogies, 6*:1, 79-99. DOI: 10.1080/23752696.2021.1883458

Crawford, J., Butler-Henderson, K., Rudolph, J., Malkawi, B., Glowatz, M., Burton, R., Magni, P., & Lam, S. (2020). COVID-19: 20 countries' higher education intraperiod digital pedagogy responses. *Journal of Applied Learning & Teaching, 3*(1), 1–20.

Wettstein, E. (2020). Call to Action. *Journal of Architectural Education, 74*, 182-183. DOI: 10.1080/10464883.2020.1790920

Addressing Neurodivergent Student Needs in Design Education to Create Equity and Remove Barriers

Scott Crisman Sworts *(Oxford Brookes University);* ***Susy Ridout*** *(Oxford Brookes University)*

Under current accessibility law, and good pedagogical practices, achieving comparable outputs from a diverse student population requires rethinking the way courses are delivered. The traditional "equality model" where every student receives the exact same amount of support becomes discriminatory for neurodivergent students and for students from disadvantaged backgrounds. To address this, a fresh, destigmatizing approach to university education is recommended, through the creation of supportive, innovative, and inclusive environments

To attempt to develop solutions to this issue, the authors undertook a pilot program to explore the possibilities of embedding additional academic support within the school in the form of "Academic Mentoring." Academic Mentoring is a form of support absent at most universities, where the typical models of support focus on a "medical model" requiring diagnosis, and/or being centered around wellbeing and mental health support. While both of these have a place in the suite of options for helping students be successful, they fail to address the needs of a wide segment of the student population. This project aimed to fill the gap in support. We will address reasons for students falling through that gap in this paper presentation.

The Academic Mentoring is focused on overcoming barriers to learning in three different areas:

- Information processing, where students need additional input to be able to process their coursework
- Anxiety around coursework, which is often not connected to any "mental health" issue, but instead stems directly from negative self-perception of skills or failure to understand tutor expectations and feedback.
- Differences in expectations and standards for international students, where the students come from cultures with different ways to critique, or different standards for academic output.

Further, as design is an "arts based practice," many standard approaches to student support fail to address the specific needs of these students, as non-arts based tutors often do not understand the working methods required in the coursework. This consequently leads to them guiding the students in ways that are not productive towards success in a design course.

Additionally, the intersectionality of these three dimensions of barriers means that individual support must be highly tailored. While blanket support, such as what is typically offered by centralized student services, can give students options and allow for flexibility in submissions, in a course such as design, where many outputs do not fall within the scope of these mechanisms, they become less effective for students.

20 students were involved in the pilot, and there was an average of a 10-point improvement in the grade, from the initial level to the final marks. Of the 20 students, 13 improved by one grade band. This indicates how addressing structural barriers to

performance can improve performance. It should also be noted that the distribution of grades in this pilot follows the typical grade distribution for the school, indicating that there is no "unfair advantage" from this support. The additional tutorials, therefore, seem to have allowed students to perform at their natural ability level, rather than give them an advantage over students not receiving this support.

Computer Aided Design: Where Design Concepts Go to Die?

Tilanka Chandrasekera *(Oklahoma State University)*; **Zahrasadat Hosseini** *(Oklahoma State University)*

Freehand sketching considered an essential element of designing and ideation (Cross, 2001) and designers use these hand sketches as a means of communicating with design ideas that Goldschmidt (2003) refers to as "backtalk". Research has reiterated that manual sketching provides variations in ideas aiding in developing richer creative processes as compared to "drafting type symbol software" (Goel, 1995) and has advantages in supporting feature perception, alternative solutions, and design problem conception (Bilda and Demirkan, 2003). Computer Aided Design (CAD) tools are often considered inferior to hand sketching (Ibrahim & Rahimian, 2010) and design students are even deterred from using CAD tools in the early stages of their design process given the importance of idea generation and concept formation. Given the highly computer dependent professional designer working in the field, it needs to be questioned as to how the design ideation stage is affected by digital tools? Do designers need to manually sketch anymore? Do designers ideate using digital tools? How do the affordances of these digital tools affect the creative design process?

Chan (1997) stated that Virtual Reality (VR) can be used as a design instrument to increase creativity and as a research tool in design and design education because properties of the interface such as interactivity and representation allow designers to visualize and test design solutions within these virtual environments. It is important to understand how these interfaces affect the design process and thereby the people using them. Especially with new digital interfaces and tools such as VR being used in the design industry, it needs to be questioned as to how these new digital tools such as affect the ideation stage of the design process, and how are concepts affected by these digital tools.

In this project 18 subjects were randomly assigned to three groups and were asked to design a monument for the entrance of a southwestern college town. After the researcher read the brief aloud, each participant was given a maximum of 45 minutes to complete the design task. Before starting on the design project, the participants were fitted with EDA (Electro Dermal Activity), ECG (Electrocardiography) and fNIR (Functional Near Infrared Spectroscopy) sensors. Along with the design brief, participants were also given a site map and photographs of the existing site. Group 1 was provided with tracing paper to ideate the design process. Group 2 used the Sketchup software to develop their design idea. Group 3 was provided with a Virtual Reality sketching tool to develop their design ideas. The participants were instructed to think out loud while they designed. The process was video, and audio recorded. Protocol analysis was used to understand the creativity in the design process. The final products were presented to a panel of designers for them to assess the creativity in the final product. The finding of this study suggests that different digital tools affect creativity in different ways. Especially when the intuitiveness of the tool increases the cognitive load decreases and creativity increases.

Developing Spatial Skills through Immersive Virtual Reality

Luis Mejia *(Oklahoma State University)*; **Tilanka Chandrasekera** *(Oklahoma State University)*

Spatial abilities are a critical component of design discipline and multiple studies have supported their positive influence in creative thinking. Moreover, spatial ability plays an essential role in STEM instruction and development (Uttal & Cohen,

2012), driving special attention to researchers. Relationships have been recognized between spatial ability and anatomy, math, engineering education, and design performance.

From a physiological standpoint, spatial ability relies on motor skills, which can be affected by neural plasticity. Plasticity refers to the changes occurring in short periods of time in the brain, more specifically in gray and white matter associated with those skills. Studies have supported that digital environments influence spatial skills (Wu et al., 2012), but furthermore, virtual reality (VR) can affect neuroplasticity (e.g., Coco-Martin et al., 2020), and positively affect the design process (Lin et al., 2020). Nonetheless, to increase the impact VR can have on the design process, hands-on interaction is required.

The present study used Immersive Virtual Reality (IVR) with three different conditions of the virtual body (VB) to assess how they affected the development of spatial abilities. The VB is the way individuals perceive themselves inside the virtual environment. Traditionally, this perception has been through the use of avatars. Avatars are humanized representations of the body in VR environments. Moreover, the VB is divided into online and offline representations of the body. In the former, the body is somehow present, whereas, in the latter, there is no visual perception of the body, but there is a connection with it. This study selected three conditions of VB. Two of them were online, and one was offline. Participants were required to complete a task through object rotation and wayfinding within an martian-like VR environment. This task was based on the nine-square grid problem commonly used in design studios and required logical thinking to solve the issue at hand.

A total sample of 72 participants was collected and randomly assigned to one of the three conditions. Participants completed a pre-intervention questionnaire which included the first half of a Mental Rotation Test (MRT) to assess spatial skills. The experiment took, in average, 20 minutes per participant. After the intervention, participants completed the second half of the MRT. All three conditions displayed an increase in spatial abilities between pre and post-intervention MRT's. A repeated-measures ANOVA was conducted among the three conditions and revealed statistical significance. Pairwise comparisons between conditions revealed statistically significant differences.

Findings support that even short interventions in VR can help to improve spatial skills in interior design students. Nonetheless, not any VR intervention will work. Interventions must select the appropriate VB and must be carefully thought to include scaffolded actions that help students interpret spatial configurations. Moreover, this study provides a baseline to develop specific VR environments that can be gamified in the academic curricula to help students improve their spatial skills.

Agent-Based Simulation for Studying Social Behaviors in Built Environment: Tested in Office Floor Plan

***Yeinn G Oh** (Georgia Institute of Technology)*

Agent-Based Simulation is a type of simulation involving independent, autonomous agents capable of interacting with each other and the environment surrounding them (Macal & North, 2014). When ABS is adopted in architectural studies, agents correspond to human occupants as 'moving avatars' inside the building with the environment being the built environment such as buildings and urban layouts. Several studies have been done in architecture using ABS in this approach, such as building evacuation study, movements inside urban form. It is generally used to predict human movements in the built environment. However, there are more to be explored in utilizing ABS in the built environment, which are: 1) the human psychology, and the 2) social behavior. These two factors have been explored very little through simulations.

ABS has its roots on object-oriented programming. Once created, agents can have their own attributes, such as mood, stress level, fatigue, personality, and even habits. These attributes are not fixed; they can be constantly updated with a feedback loop, which corresponds to a learning behavior. This nature of ABS makes it a strong tool to study behaviors. Agents can also interact with the environment and each other with their own attributes, just as a real social interaction. They then change their own stress level based on the interaction. Then, collectively, agents make an emergent behavior together, which becomes a social norm. ABS can be used to test how these collective behavior emerge.

We demonstrate an example ABS model created to test spatial preference in office space with social condition. Programmed in AnyLogic, the agents are made to work on their assigned seats, occasionally taking a break traveling to another space. Agents have their own stress level which increases based on their personality type, interacting with other agents and their assigned work amount. When agents reach certain amount of stress level, they travel to take a break. They learn about other spaces when they roam around and change their preference of the break space based on the frequency of exposure to other spaces. If the agent has an introverted personality, their stress level increase when they encounter other people, and try to avoid break spaces that have people inside, and if the agent has an extroverted personality, it has the opposite effect.

The result of the model shows that the emergent behavior shows robust normal distribution. The number of social interactions, spaces they traveled, changes of space preference show stable outcome, which proves that the simulation is stable and able to be utilized in experimentation of behaviors. The advantage of simulations is that the experimentation can be done virtually with very little cost and can be repeated as much as the researcher want. The ABS can be used to test behavioral models and build theories.

References

Macal, C., & North, M. (2014). Introductory tutorial: Agent-based modeling and simulation. *Proceedings of the Winter Simulation Conference 2014*, 6–20. https://doi.org/10.1109/WSC.2014.7019874

An Early-Stage Design Optimization Method for Naturally Ventilated Terminals Based on a Computational Approach

Ammar Nedal Abdeen *(Jordan University of Science and Technology);* ***Bushra Obeidat*** *(Jordan University of Science and Technology)*

As the globe continues to cope with the realities of coronavirus disease, worldwide research groups are rushing to create practical answers that will enable the world to adapt to the new difficulties. Controlling the indoor air quality in the COVID-19 period and beyond is one such difficulty. Since COVID-19 became a worldwide pandemic, the virus's "hyper spread" has continued to astound policymakers, despite public health authorities' efforts to educate the public about the need for social distance, personal cleanliness, and other precautions. The purpose of this study is to construct a computer model to aid in the early stages of design decision-making for naturally ventilated terminal structures. The model is produced in a parametric Rhino Grasshopper environment and validated using computational fluid dynamics (CFD). A suggested airport terminal design was analyzed and optimized as the case study for this research. The numerical findings indicate that the optimal technique would be to combine 100% outdoor air collected through ventilation ducts with air sterilized by vent units. As a result, the risk of infection in the terminal building might be decreased to a minimal level. These results may offer a theoretical foundation and technical application for the prevention and control of COVID-19 epidemics.

Diagnosing the Built Environment and Programming for Transformation

Kendra Kirchmer *(Kansas State University)*

Good health is more than the absence of sickness and injury, it's a complete state of physical, mental, and social well-being. What are typically thought of as determinants of health: genes, cells, biology, and access to healthcare are only a small part of the picture. Instead, a range of factors: education, employment, food, housing, and social cohesion, collectively known as the Social Determinants of Health (SDoH), play a more significant role. (Daniel et al, 2018) Health, good or bad is the result of actions and interactions throughout each day in the places where we live, work, and play. The built environment influences health directly, through its quality, and indirectly, through its influence on a person's behaviors, choices, and opportunities. (Braveman et al, 2011)

Many design programs include curriculum to introduce the ways in which the built environment directly impacts health through environmental factors such as, ventilation, indoor air quality, moisture control, water quality, etc. A growing number of programs also introduce theories such as biophilic design whose tenets promote connections to nature as a pathway to good health/well-being. Instruction on these topics is essential for students to develop an understanding how to create buildings and places that promote health. However, the social determinants, their impact on equitable opportunities for good health and well-being, and the role of the built environment as a social determinant of health are not commonly taught within design curriculum. Understanding how the built environment impacts overall health is critical for the design of healthy places, spaces, and objects. Understanding how the built environment acts as a social determinant is critical for the equitable design of healthy places, spaces, and objects for all.

Addressing social determinants of health through the design of the built environment, is a necessary condition to mitigate health disparities and served as a catalyst for an interdisciplinary graduate studio course with students from Architecture, Interior Architecture, and Landscape Architecture. A series of assignments were created that asked: how might an understanding of the social determinants help students recognize the impact of the built environment on health, specifically for vulnerable populations, and inform the development of transformative project programs that seek to improve equity, health, and well-being for a diverse range of individuals?

Beginning with a brief introduction the role of built environment as a determinant in health outcomes and it's impact/influence on equity and opportunity; the presentation will present practical examples and methods for incorporating the social determinants into a design studio curriculum with special emphasis on a novel approach to inter-/trans- disciplinary project programming. The presentation concludes with discussions of the successes, limitations, and areas of future development for this promising pedagogical approach.

References

Braveman, P. et al. *Exploring the Social Determinants of Health: Neighborhoods and Health*. [Issue Brief]. Princeton, NJ: Robert Wood Johnson Foundation, 2011.

Daniel, H., Bornstein, S., & Kane, C. Addressing Social Determinants to Improve Patient Care and Promote Health Equity: An American College of Physicians Position Paper. *Annals of Internal Medicine, 168* (8), 2018. 577-578. https:// doi:10.7326/M17-2441

Curating a Virtual Museum: The Exploration of Object and Environment Relationships

Michelle Pannone *(Marywood University)*

Visualization and design innovation are interrelated. Visualization techniques, whether they exist in digital or analog methods are the means by which design is communicated to an audience. In the field of architecture, this relationship is consistent from schematic design through construction documents, despite the primary audience changing from client to contractor. In academia, it is imperative to foster the development of software skills through experimentation and discovery that support the creative imagination of the designer. It is of the utmost importance that the creative potential of the student is never limited by their ability to model or visualize a particular form or atmosphere.

This paper will address the pedagogical approach to two sequential Digital Media courses, beginning with the investigation of thematic objects. As students begin learning three-dimensional modeling techniques they are removed from the architectonic elements that make up the built environment. Beginning with objects and forms such as telephones, bicycles, light sources, and cameras enable students to explore the diverse modeling tools and techniques that the software offers. Taking on defined objects with complex, often organic forms, the decision of what to model is not at the discretion of the modeler, but rather dependent on the intricacies of the object's inherent physical form. These objects have complex elements and forms that defy rectilinear confines, forcing them to experiment with a breadth of tools and overcome challenges in rendering their objects. The students are tasked with learning digital software tools through experimentation, investigation, and inquiry within their thematic area. Starting with a series of two-dimensional infographics and later modeling a series of related objects in three dimensions, the progression in complexity scales as the students continue expanding and refining their modeling abilities. The students are invited to conjure up their own "collection" within the topics chosen as a group. While simultaneously learning modeling techniques, each student produces their own unique "collection" that represents the artifacts to inhabit a truly unique and memorable museum of combined digital models. After mastering the modeling of their series of objects, the students model the case study museums with ease. This allows them to focus their efforts on the conceptual design work of implementing their exhibit within the space itself.

The visualizations produced by the students become increasingly advanced as the course progresses, and towards the end of the course students model complex, organic, and unusual objects using a variety of software, tools, and techniques. This establishes a more fundamental ability to model than learning purely from the building perspective, the students not positioned where their modeling technique dictates what they are capable of modeling, but rather the ability to adapt techniques and tools to meet the needs of the design. The results propose that the method by which modeling is taught in many architectural curriculum deserves challenge; learning modeling as its own dedicated craft positions students to visualize what they wish to design, not design what they know how to visualize.

Teaching Community Engagement: Lessons from a Dedicated Course on Participation

David de la Peña *(University of California, Davis)*

Service learning and community-engaged courses are not new to the environmental design fields. Quite appropriately, they often take the form of a design studio with a community partner, in which students learn experientially (Angotti, et al. 2012). Indisputably, students may learn plenty from such engagements; however, these courses are often undertaken through individual instructor initiative, and often without explicit learning objectives around engagement built into the course descriptions or learning outcomes.

More rarely, programs offer specific courses on community participation itself, that is, courses in which the process of co-design is front and center rather than any particular design project. Such courses offer a unique opportunity to delve deeper into the histories and theories of participation, the methods used, and the skills required to undertake inclusive design processes. Because of the focus on process, they are able to draw upon seminal texts (for example, Sanoff, 1999; de la Peña, et al. 2017) and provide opportunities for critique and reflection.

The author's home institution, a public land grant university with programs in environmental design fields, offers both the engaged studio model and a discrete course on participation, and is the subject of this presentation. Over the past two years, this academic program has engaged in efforts around justice, equity, diversity and inclusion (JEDI), to decolonize its curriculum and to advance more equitable and inclusive outcomes in the classroom. This has included student surveys, a review of syllabi, and a complete redrafting of program and course learning outcomes.

The impacts of these efforts were intended to

be distributed across all courses, but it has put a spotlight on the participation courses with its explicit intentions of learning how to engage diverse publics in the design and planning process. This presentation will provide an overview of the program's JEDI process, with a particular focus on its signature participation course. Through an evaluation of course syllabi, student evaluations, and course projects over the past four years, it will describe and critique the course structure, readings, and assignments, and will provide an assessment of how well the course redesign has improved learning outcomes. In the presentation, alignment with overall program learning outcomes will also be discussed - specifically, how the participation course can support more meaningful engaged studio courses. The findings are intended to be useful for any institution considering effective ways of incorporating participatory methods into their curricula.

Authentically Representing Stakeholder Needs: Should We Consider a "Jobs-to-be-Done" Approach Instead of the Conventional "User Persona"?

Kendra Kirchmer *(Kansas State University)*

How do we design equitable, healthy, and inclusive built environments for all people? It's widely understood that to answer this question, designers must first develop an understanding of the behaviors, needs, and wants of the individuals for whom they are designing. Further, it's increasingly understood that to improve equity, inclusion, and health for all people, it's essential to also develop an authentic and unbiased understanding of the barriers to access and opportunities that individuals face, especially for members of vulnerable, historically marginalized populations. Many design tools, such as User Personas, have been developed to aid designers in this pursuit.

The creation of user personas, fictional characters that represent individuals/target users, are an established design tool in fields such as user experience design and industrial design. Benefits ascribed to the inclusion of personas during the design process are that they challenge assumptions about user groups, help focus efforts on the needs and goals of users, and help teams develop empathy toward users. (Aldin & Pruitt, 2010) Unsurprisingly, personas are also being utilized with increasing frequency by practitioners and educators concerned with the design of the built environment. While thoroughly researched and well-developed personas may provide the intended benefits, they also have limitations that are exacerbated in an academic setting. Criticisms of personas include: the time required to create authentic personas that often takes longer than the traditional academic semester; extensive ethnographic research is required in order to generate an authentic representation, too often the information used in their creation is generic and/or unverifiable leading to a lack of credibility; and lastly, biases of the persona creators are often embedded in the personas.(Salminen, et al., 2018) Consequently, personas become caricatures of target users that only serve to reinforce stereotypes and undermine the foundations of an equitable and inclusive design process.

This presentation begins with a discussion of the strengths/weaknesses of user personas in an academic design studio setting and proposes an alternate approach to understanding the needs of users/ stakeholders that seeks to address these critiques through a jobs-to-be-done (JTBD) methodology. One important feature of the JTBD methodology is the way in which it shifts the focus from user characteristics to the circumstances under which a particular action is carried out. A Job in this context is simply "shorthand for what an individual really seeks to accomplish in a given circumstance." (Christensen, et al., 2016) The second half of the presentation will present practical examples of the incorporation of a JTBD approach from a recent design studio and discuss the successes, limitations, and areas of future development for this promising pedagogical approach.

References

Adlin, T., & Pruitt, J., (2010). *The Essential Persona Lifecycle: Your Guide to Building and Using Personas.* Morgan Kaufmann/Elsevier.

Christensen, C., Hall, T., Dillon, K., & Duncan, D., (2016). Know your customers "Jobs to be Done". *Harvard Business Review, 94*(9), 54–62.

Salminen, J., Jansen, B. J., An, J., Kwak, H., & Jung, S.- gyo. (2018). Are Personas Done? Evaluating Their Usefulness in the Age of Digital Analytics. *Persona Studies, 4*(2), 47–65.

Connecting the Dots: Story Circles in Art and Design Studios

Gowri Betrabet Gulwadi *(University of Northern Iowa)*; **Alexandra Dooley** *(University of Northern Iowa)*; **Carolyn Ayers** *(Western Home Communities)*

The need to re-imagine and reshape interpersonal connections is a prominent post-pandemic concern. This paper describes a studio assignment for enhancing intercultural competence of students in an art class (drawing studio) and a design class (residential design studio). The instructors had participated in a service-learning institute and developed a basis for creating service-learning projects to be facilitators of knowledge, to encourage the learners in their classes to learn by doing, be self-reflective, and ensure that new knowledge, concepts and skills are linked meaningfully to learners' personal experiences (Kleinhesselink et al. 2015). It was also critical that the service learning activity was reciprocal and reflective to result in mutually beneficial outcomes for the learners and the community partners, ensuring a balance between what each contributes (gives) and receives (gets).

The 'Meaning of Home' assignment was created in close collaboration with the Director of Volunteer Services at a retirement community - the community partner. The purpose of the assignment was to build connections between the art and design students, between the students and residents of the retirement community, and generate a nuanced understanding of the meaning of home. For implementing this assignment, three sequential steps centered around the philosophy of Story Circles - structured ways for small groups of people to authentically share and listen to their personal stories, and a practical tool to help build intercultural communication and competence (Deardorff, 2019). In this assignment, the learners developed skills for authentic sharing and reflection with each other before they joined a story circle with people who were much older than them and at a different life stage. Six residents from the retirement community volunteered to participate, and were visited in their home twice over three weeks by mixed groups of art and design students. Each time, they were invited into a story circle with previously designed prompts pertaining to the meaning of home. During the first visit, the design students conducted a photo-elicitation interview, and the art students recorded impressions through drawings. All students completed reflections after each visit. When they returned to the studio, the design students conducted a photo-analysis, and the art students created a set of two associated art pieces related to the evolving meanings of home. The residents were invited to a presentation to view and hear about the completed projects.

Overall, the assignment was a useful exercise in having students connect with each other, and with others who are unlike themselves (different life stage). Sharing stories proved to be a way to engage with each other and connect meaningfully, while building a shared understanding of home, thus relating concepts to lived experience. This paper addresses the philosophy behind the assignment, the details and timeline of the process, and the contributions (give) and benefits (get) for the learners and the residents.

References

Deardorff, D. K. (2019). *Manual for Developing Intercultural Competencies: Story Circles.* Routledge.

Kleinhesselink K, Schooley S, Cashman S, Richmond A, Ikeda E, McGinley P, Editors. *Engaged faculty institute curriculum.* Seattle, WA: Community-Campus Partnerships for Health, 2015.

Collective Empowerment: Cultivating a Community Engaged Pedagogy

Michelle Pannone *(Marywood University)*

The terminology "design-build" does not expose the many steps in between those two parts of the process, such as the research, conception, group thinking sessions, and extensive testing period. In the third year since the inception, this community-driven grassroots design-build program has been working to establish a culture of engagement. How must the typical architectural design and build process be challenged in order to achieve a community engaged pedagogy? In particular, what comes before design? And what comes after build? It is beyond the two book ends of the process, but a resilient evolution and adaptive process of transforming a local space together.

To achieve a more just profession, it is imperative to make a cognitive shift from leading with personal values to leading with community values. As Churchman states, "the movement in planning towards more participatory and empowering decision-making processes is a very positive step in the direction of accommodating the needs and preferences of different groups of people" (Churchman, 2002, p. 198). This shift in the approach to design education brings to light the potential of both physical and social manifestations that result from the process of engagement at various scales to achieve social impact. The students partake in a community engaged pedagogy not only practicing, but implementing the ideals of democratic design. The methodology invigorates the process, all the way from the research stage to completion, and highlights the importance of all steps of the process, not just the "design" and "build." Through this examination and integration of participatory design, an understanding of collective action culminating in achieving an installation with the community is established.

The collective narrative prior to design included a desire to instigate "play" addressing reuse through recycled materials. The prevailing interest to investigate the local metalworking trade, in particular obtaining new expertise in welding and utilizing local metal manufacturers, also helped to determine the raw materials that would accompany those that were reused. Engagement is an essential component to empower community members and furthermore the sense of empowerment is a critical element of cultivating ownership. Engagement in the design process was imperative and took both in-person and virtual modalities to reach community members with varying abilities of interaction due to the pandemic.

The final built installation, "Noodles", is a unique take on seating, gathering, and play spaces. The series of three structures consists of a modular grid system that is manipulated to create an infinite amount of interactive moments. Those moments are then enhanced by the canvas noodle (sewn together and stuffed with more than 50,000 cubic feet of recycled materials) that is woven through the rigid metal grid. The contrast between the orthogonal metal structure and the fluid noodle makes for an engaging composition. Each noodle will be freestanding from the structure to allow the community to manipulate the design into what will serve them best in that moment in time.

References

Churchman, Arza. 2002. "Environmental Psychology and Urban Planning: Where Can the Twain Meet." *Handbook of Environmental Psychology*: 191-200.

Effect of Visual Media on Environmental Cognition: A Case Study on the Absence of a Sense of Place

Guan-Ying Chou-Huang *(National Cheng Kung University)*; **Li-wen Sung** *(National Cheng Kung University)*

This study used Tainan City as the research site to explore how viewer's sense of space is affected by the differences in their environmental cognition formed when viewing real photos of Tainan and images from virtual maps. At present, the prevalence of images in everyday life affects the cognition of people. For example, virtual maps have become a primary tool for understanding a new environment. Such maps provide image-based street views to help users become acquainted with an unfamiliar environment. However, because differences exist between their expectation of a location and the actual scenery, virtual map users often become shocked when visiting it in person. This problem mostly occurs when images are used to recreate space. To address this issue, this study was based on a master's thesis to be completed and titled "Surveying and Application of Architecture Photographs."

In this study, 70 undergraduate students in the architecture major who were familiar with Tainan City were recruited as research participants. They were recruited because of their sensitivity toward space, which was fostered during their study in the architecture field. The participants were asked to use two media to capture images of places they have frequented in daily life. The research methods involved a semi-structured questionnaire survey and the use of a tag cloud to describe the participants' reaction toward images created with the different methods detailed below:

1. Google Street View: Images were obtained from cameras mounted on top of vehicles. The latest view of a location is typically different from that of the time when a photo of the location was captured. Consequently, street views displayed in the map often cannot reflect the current conditions of a location.
2. Photos taken on site: The angles of such images are often more diverse. The sense of space experienced by the viewers of an image is mainly determined by the focal length and photography tools adopted by the photographer.

The invention of virtual maps eliminates limitations associated with single view angles. Such maps offer the opportunity for the public to select and view street images to understand an environment. The following research results were obtained:

1. Current learners rely overly on the images presented by Google Street View and search engines. Consequently, they tend to make mistakes in their interpretation.
2. Beginners in professions related to spatial science should not overly rely on Street View when building up relevant knowledge. Working with actual scenes still plays a critical role in their professional development.

References

Scott McQuire. (2008). *The Media City: Media, Architecture and Urban Space.* SAGE Publications Ltd

Andrew Higgott & Timothy Wray. (2014). *Camera Constructs, Photography, Architecture and the Modern City.* In Ben Campkin & Rebecca Ross (Ed.), Negotiating the City Through Google Street View (pp. 147-157).

Integrating a Video-Based Media Practice into Landscape Research

Julia Smachylo *(University of Connecticut)*

While drawing and diagramming ecological dynamics is one way to open up alternative ways of knowing landscape, other audio-visual formats have great potential in their ability to give additional insight into these grounded realities. This presentation will investigate the potential for video-based methods in structuring new ground for research focused on the processes and outcomes of environmental stewardship. This approach draws from scholarship in urban and landscape studies that positions film as a moving map that offers a potential way forward in constructing and defining landscapes (Waldheim, 2012), allowing for a different approach to its manipulation and measurement (Larsen, 2012), and in the inclusion of diverse observational views and everyday narratives (Bruno, 2007).

Set within a broader context of privatized environmental conservation, this research explores that impact of stewardship programs on the socio-ecological relations of forested landscapes through a video-based research approach integrated into fieldwork, analysis and outcomes. The presentation will discuss the use of time-based media as a medium through which to render visible the often unrecognized labor involved in stewardship, alongside an exploration of the resulting material composition of these landscapes. In particular, the presentation will reflect on the outcomes of a recent two-channel video installation as a means through which to navigate the ontology of terms such as 'forest,' and 'stewardship,' serving to complicate conservation narratives to reveal a spectrum of approaches to environmental management.

References

Bruno, G. (2007). Haptic Space: Film and the Geography of Modernity.*Visualizing the City*,13-30.

Larsen, J. (2012). Going to Measures – Cultivating and Appreciating the Contemporary Landscapes. In C. Girot and F. Truniger (Eds.), *Landscript: Landscape Vision Motion* (pp. 63-78). Jovis.

Waldheim, C. (2012). Provisional Notes on Landscape Representation and Digital Media. In C. Girot and F. Truniger (Eds.), *Landscript: Landscape Vision Motion* (pp. 21-35). Jovis.

Evolving Big Data Strategies to Study Neighborhoods and Health: Promises and Pitfalls of Using U.S. Health Insurance Claims Data and Neighborhood Indices

Kim Rollings *(University of Michigan);* ***Andrew Ibrahim*** *(University of Michigan)*

A broad range of stakeholders, including academic researchers, have vested interests in better understanding the neighborhood-health relationship. Policy makers, especially, charged with allocating resources require rigorous evidence of how neighborhood investments affect health. Public health leaders also require guidance to target specific community health needs via built environment investments. As such, there is an unprecedented demand for better data and methods to evaluate neighborhoods and health. One emerging approach is the use of "big data." This presentation will discuss the strengths and limitations of using administrative health insurance claims data ("claims data"), a big data source, with two national neighborhood indices, as well as directions for future research. This analytic approach and both neighborhood indices are used often in health services research.

Claims data collected for billing purposes are frequently used by public health officials and policy makers to understand healthcare utilization patterns, evaluate quality of care, and determine future resource allocation. These data readily identify, for example, how often an individual visits the emergency department, fills certain prescriptions, undergoes certain procedures, or is diagnosed with a new health condition. Because these data are routinely audited for billing purposes, they prove to be quite an accurate reflection of an individual's interaction with the healthcare system. Although a promising and potentially powerful source of information given large sample sizes, claims data availability, detail, and geographic scale (e.g., state, county, or census tract) vary by insurance provider. Additionally, an individual's interaction with a healthcare system may not necessarily reflect true health and wellbeing or associations with neighborhood attributes. Nonetheless, studies analyzing claims data provide insight into healthcare utilization and offer analytical approaches that can build upon decades of traditional and emerging neighborhood-health methods.

Two neighborhood indices often used with claims data to examine the neighborhood-health relation are the Area Deprivation Index (ADI) and Social Vulnerability Index (SVI). Calculated from U.S. Census data, the ADI captures block group-level income, education, employment, and housing quality domains to inform education, health, and government research, planning, and policy development. The SVI captures tract-level socioeconomic, household composition, disability, minority status and language, housing type, and transportation themes to identify communities most in need of support before, during, and after disasters. Both aggregated measures are available nationwide, making them easily accessible for research. These measures will be compared and strengths and limitations of using these and other aggregated indices will be discussed. Although broad neighborhood indices based on aggregated census metrics present one approach to understanding neighborhood influences on health, evidence suggests that use of administrative boundaries as proxies for neighborhoods can result in inaccurate findings, flawed decision-making, and other negative place-based consequences. These particular indices also largely exclude physical neighborhood quality attributes relevant to health. Alternative neighborhood operationalizations may be more appropriate depending on the health and healthcare outcomes of interest. Future research, including that from environment-behavior studies, is needed to identify and test the reliability and validity of using these neighborhood indices as indicators of health within claims datasets.

Evaluating Smartphone LIGHT Meters Efficacy: A Comparison between Industry LIGHT Meters and LIGHT Meter Apps

James Leach *(University of Detroit Mercy)*; **Kristin M Nelson** *(University of Detroit Mercy)*; **Algird Szumlas** *(University of Detroit Mercy)*; **Alan Hoback** *(University of Detroit Mercy)*

Daylighting, the controlled admission of sunlight into a building, can be used to reduce energy waste and to improve physical and mental health. Exposure to adequate daylight provides mental and visual stimulation, regulates our circadian rhythms and encouraging production of serotonin. It is linked to improved occupant satisfaction and performance across a variety of building types, contributing to increases in student learning and test scores, worker productivity, retail sales, and shortened hospital stays. (Hedge, 2018) (Boubekri, 2014) (World Green Building Council, 2013) The ample research documenting the benefits of daylighting has led to its incorporation into widely accepted design guidelines such as the U.S. Green Building Council's LEED Rating Tools and the International WELL Building Institute's WELL Building Standard.

The technical education of architecture and engineering students typically includes exercises in which they evaluate one or more daylit spaces qualitatively and quantitatively. These exercises emphasize an important aspect of daylighting – intensity. In order to be beneficial, daylighting must provide adequate light intensity (measured in lux) by which to see and perform planned tasks, but not so much as to create discomfort or glare. In these exercises, students evaluate light levels in situ with light meters, recording values and comparing them to lighting industry standards. This type of project is foundational to lighting design curricula.

This study was undertaken by a group of faculty and undergraduate research assistants in response to the peculiar conditions of the COVID-19 pandemic and wider questions regarding the suitability of using light meter apps for mobile phones as a substitute to commercial light meters. Within the framework of a large research project on overall campus energy waste reduction, researches were gathered measurements of light levels in campus buildings during different seasons and times of day. At the outset of the study, researchers asked whether they could take the light measurements using a light meter app on their phone instead of checking in and out light meters from the School tool library. The topic of the reliability of phone light meter apps was also raised at a recent building science education conferences. Faculty were interested in limiting the passing of devices during COVID-19, managing equipment costs, and maximizing student participation opportunities in environmental courses. The research team undertook a preliminary study, comparing the performance of commercially available light meter tools to available light meter apps, using a variety of mobile phone devices. The research team identified a group of apps that were both highly rated and highly downloaded for Android and Apple phones. Researchers downloaded the apps onto their phones and took a series of measurements with each phone app, along with a baseline measurement using the light meter. Each app was tested using a control surface in the following conditions: outdoor clear sky, outdoor overcast sky, indoor high light, indoor moderate light, indoor low light. The team compiled the results into tables comparing the performance of each app to the baseline light meter measurements, noting the disparity between different devices in various light levels and settings.

Abstracts: Collaborations

Classroom to Career

Neda Norouzi *(University of Texas, San Antonio);* ***Shonali Bose*** *(McGranahan Architects);* ***Josue (Josh) Mondragon*** *(University of Texas, San Antonio)*

Traditionally, architecture studios are thought based on a hypothetical design problem that students are tasked to solve through creative thinking. Over the years, connecting the classroom experience to architectural practice has become more available through collaboration of different disciplines in academic settings. However, there is still a gap between theoretical research with architecture pedagogy and practice.

The main goal of this session is to present a method of collaboration between a researcher and practitioner showcasing the integration of this collaboration in architectural pedagogy. The presenters will introduce the design process of an intergenerational community center while identifying specific benefits of collaborations between a researcher/educator and practitioners and its impact on architectural education and practice.

Data was collected through three different workshops where the practitioners met with community members to gain a better understanding of their needs for the proposed building. The result of these workshops led to a preliminary design program that was shared with architecture students. After reviewing the workshop results, twelve graduate students read and analyzed literature published on intergenerational programs, interactions, and design as well as architectural design of community centers. The students individually searched for peer reviewed articles published between 2010-2020. By reviewing and analyzing the most relevant scholarly articles, students learned about the impact of intergenerational programs on children, teenagers, older adults, as well as society and how to incorporate these findings into their design projects.

This session will provide a platform to learn from a successful researcher/educator and practitioners collaboration that involved architectural students. The benefits of this collaboration for students was working with an actual client, architects, landscape architects, and interior designers. They learned about the importance of research in architectural practice and different methods of evidence-based-design. Students were encouraged to listen to the client and change their design ideas and solutions based on the clients' needs and wants.

The benefits of this collaboration for the researcher/educator was bridging the classroom to career gap and learn to be the liaison between the students and practitioners. The researcher's focus is generally on data collection, analysis, and publication. A researcher/educator hardly ever gets to witness the incorporation of research in design but this collaboration offers participation opportunities from start to finish.

One of the major benefits for the practitioners is the opportunity to "dream big" as students do while working on studio projects. The architects, consultants, and owners who interacted through student presentations and critiques felt reinvigorated about the design of this building and the impact it will have on the community. Due to the pandemic, Architecture has moved work to online platforms and that opened doors that weren't available before. Generally, the practitioners would have partnered with their hometown universities, but with virtual work they were able to connect across the USA with a graduate students and professor whose expertise is in intergenerational design.

Design for Distancing: Learning from Public Health Crises to Build for Resilience and Equity in Public Space

Jennifer Goold *(Neighborhood Design Center);* ***Carla Hinson*** *(Cross Street Partners)*

The Neighborhood Design Center (NDC) and Morgan State University will share learnings from Baltimore City's Design for Distancing program: a $1.5 million program of the Mayor of Baltimore to support the city's small business districts with infrastructure in the public realm to support safe consumer activity during COVID-19 from summer 2020 to summer 2021. The D4D program consists of a Design Competition, Guidebook, Implementation, and Evaluation. The structure of the panel will mirror the program components to investigate learnings from the program in regard to public health and small business during the pandemic, as well as implications for long term investment in public space to build resilience and racial equity in urban spaces. Jennifer Goold, Executive Director of the Neighborhood Design Center, will share the program overview and outcomes. We'll look at the concepts our design/build teams developed, the process of building the interventions on our streets and sidewalks in 18 neighborhoods, how public health guidance was integrated, and unpack the pitfalls of fast-tracking agency review during an emergency. Carla Hinson, Morgan state University, will describe her program evaluation to determine if Design for Distancing was effective at creating spaces that people actually use; that are inclusive, healthy and equitable; support a return to thriving business; and enable physical distancing. Research methods include site observations supplemented by interviews with community stakeholders. to identify what elements of the Design for Distancing project were successful. The team will deep dive into the challenges of balancing the public need to maintain access to and support small businesses, the demands of working with City resources, and concerns for safety during the evolving public health crisis in environments long beset by racial inequity. We'll conclude with a look at whether the needs and challenges that arise during moments of crisis offer special insight into what we'll need to make our cities more sustainable and equitable in the decades to come.

References:

Design for Distancing. (2020, May 29). *Design for Distancing Ideas Competition Brief.* https://static1.squarespace.com/static/5ec2e7939ccfe46b4d0946b4/t/5ed70662e7e4254b9c1645d7/1591150180802/Design-Competition-Brief-FINAL.pdf

Gehl Institute. (2018, June). Inclusive Healthy Places A Guide to Inclusion & Health in Public Space: Learning Globally to Transform Locally. https://gehlinstitute.org/wp-content/uploads/2018/07/Inclusive-Healthy-Places_Gehl-Institute.pdf

NACTO & Global Designing Cities Initiative (2020, May 21). Streets for Pandemic response and Recovery. https://nacto.org/wp-content/uploads/2020/09/Streets_for_Pandemic_Response_Recovery_Full_20-09-24.pdf

Designing Sustainable and Health-centered Agile Dwelling Units (ADU) for Aging in Place

Widya Ramadhani *(University of Illinois at Urbana- Champaign);* ***Nicole Cevallos*** *(The University of Texas at Arlington);* ***Julia Lindgren*** *(The University of Texas at Arlington)*

By 2030, one in five Americans will be 65 years or older (Vespa et al., 2020). The older adult population has had a continuous upward trend in recent and upcoming decades, exceeding the number of children. Therefore, it is critical for older adults to sustain their health and independence in old age to minimize the demand for care from the younger population. As they age, older adults experience physical and psychosocial changes, from advancing chronic diseases, declining physical and cognitive capacities to loneliness, losses, and retirement. Such complex needs can be supported through an integrated, collaborative, and multidisciplinary effort to maintain their health, independence, and safety in old age.

Home is an essential factor in older adults' health and independence, as it is where they spend most of their time (Spalt et al., 2016). Research shows that older adults want to age in place, meaning that they live in the residence of their choice while maintaining their independence and connection to community (Rogers et al., 2020). A wide spectrum of residential facilities and support networks assist in the successful aging in place, from independent living, assisted living to long-term care. Our project focuses on developing independent living in the form of Agile Dwelling Units (ADUs) — a small, independent residential unit. The coalition between scholars and practitioners from the Center for Advanced Design Research and Evaluation (CADRE), the University of Texas Arlington (UTA), and HKS aims to create innovative and affordable ADUs to facilitate wellness through digital technologies that can support autonomous, secure, and engaged healthy living for our growing, aging population. To develop a proof-of-concept micro-dwelling unit, the research team first mapped the current trends. Through literature reviews, gaps and challenges in designing, building, and deploying ADUs for aging in place have been identified. The next steps will be conducting discovery interviews, roundtable discussions, and town hall meetings with potential users. Then, the findings will inform an architecture studio course to construct a 200-500 sq ft ADU by UTA Students.

The presenters will share their findings from the literature review that were completed in four main fields — architecture, health technology, human factors, and policy. Through this search, various types and sustainable construction methods of ADUs that can be adjusted to the users' needs and affordability were identified, as well as health technologies that could be integrated into these units. Some technologies are attached to home systems, whereas others are detached technologies in accessories and mobile technology. We found potential challenges such as zoning ordinances, health, and digital literacy that may impact the accessibility and adoption of health-centric ADUs. Additionally, designers and developers need to understand older adults' needs and motivation to ensure the affordability, desirability, and attainability of the ADUs for aging in place. The outcome of this coalition is an open-source design framework for aging in place and the ADU model that can be replicated in multiple settings. This initial coalition model is projected to grow and amplify its impact on a more extensive network and community.

Evaluating the Patient and Staff Experience in an Innovative Inpatient Rehabilitation Facility

Kati Peditto *(HDR);* ***Abigail Heithof*** *(HDR Architecture);* ***Sandy Tkacz*** *(HDR);* ***Francesqca Jimenez*** *(HDR Architecture, Inc.)*

Sheltering Arms Institute (SAI) is a high-acuity rehabilitation institute providing recovery care for stroke and general rehabilitation, traumatic brain injury, and spinal cord injury. The planning and design philosophy at SAI revolved around a notion of the building as a therapeutic tool. Through the form of the building, and strengthened through the space program, the building is designed to achieve five client-driven goals. As part of the Practitioner/Research track, we will describe our collaborative evidence-informed design process and the results of our post-occupancy evaluation.

The design of an inpatient rehabilitation facility can impact the recovery process for patients experiencing neurological injury. In a recent review of stroke patients in rehabilitation, although stroke patients recognize that physical activity is important for their recovery, they feel that their physical activity is negatively influenced by their boredom, lack of motivation, and their perceived lack of autonomy while in recovery (Luker et. al., 2015). Lipson-Smith et al. (2019) emphasized the importance of rehabilitation facilities as places of learning both motor and cognitive skills, and the design should maximize efficiency, effectiveness, foster emotional well-being and maximize safety. Providing opportunities in the environment for patients to practice physical, cognitive, and social activity were important for patient outcomes.

As current empirical studies on staff and patient experience are limited, this study makes a substantial contribution to determining best practices and refine current design guidelines for rehabilitation facilities. Our aims were as follows:

Specific Aim 1: Evaluate the role of the facility design on staff experience. The built environment of the inpatient rehabilitation facility is intended to support patients, but also to support staff in their daily work providing care. Mixed methods techniques of a staff survey and focus group interviews shed light on how the design impacts staff, and also how staff perceive the built environment supporting the rehabilitation of patients.

Specific Aim 2: Assess the role of the facility design on patient experience. The intent of the design was to support the physical rehabilitation of patients. Elements of building design positively or negatively influencing patient experience and recovery were identified through qualitative interviews of patients and families to inform design of future inpatient rehabilitation facilities.

We present results including key performance indicators for the SAI facility, as well as occupant outcomes. Through a cross-sectional mixed-methods exploratory study, we evaluated the human influences of strategies incorporated into the facility design of SAI. Results depict the facility strengths and challenges, efficiencies and inefficiencies, and the facility environment's influences on human outcomes such as productivity, satisfaction, engagement, and patient outcomes.

References:

Lipson-Smith, R., Churilov, L., Newton, C., Zeeman, H., & Bernhardt, J. (2019). A framework for designing inpatient stroke rehabilitation facilities: A new approach using interdisciplinary value-focused thinking. *HERD: Health Environments Research & Design Journal, 12*(4), 142-158.

Luker, J., Lynch, E., Bernhardsson, S., Bennett, L., & Bernhardt, J. (2015). Stroke survivors' experiences of physical rehabilitation: A systematic review of qualitative studies. *Archives of Physical Medicine and Rehabilitation, 96*(9), 1698-1708.

Healthy, Equitable, Inclusive Childhoods via Childcare Outdoor Design: A Nature-Based, Policy-Sensitive, Scaling Up Mode

Robin Moore *(North Carolina State University);* ***Nilda Cosco*** *(North Carolina State University);* ***Misty Pearson****, (SC Department of Health and Environmental Control);* ***Cynthia Lara*** *(SC Department of Social Services)*

Goal: To help participants understand how the research-driven, collaborative POD (Preventing Obesity by Design) model/strategy supports equity/inclusion-driven, healthy built-environment intervention in childcare facility outdoor spaces serving children in low resource communities, birth through 5 years of age, and how the model may be adapted to other environments and populations (Cosco, 2007).

Objectives:

1. Review US childcare provision (with exception of Head Start) as highly regulated state-mandated, policy driven/policy sensitive systems applying regulations mostly focused on buildings rather than the entire indoor-outdoor site (Cosco, 2007);
2. Explain the importance of outdoor naturalization as support for both healthy child development and planet-positive care through daily exposure/engagement to/with regional biodiversity (Moore & Cosco, 2014);
3. Describe the POD Model as an environment & behavior construct and comprehensive approach including participatory design assistance, built-environment intervention, pre/post evaluation, professional development, and web-based promotion/communication (Smith et al, 2014);
4. Share the POD Implementation Strategy, including successes and challenges;
5. Describe the POD scaling-up/transfer/adoption by other states, with particular relevance to adoption to South Carolina (Cosco et al, 2014);
6. Engage participants in brainstorming similar models to address built environment nature restoration and sustainability issues in their back home regions.

Methods:

1. Sequence of short slide presentations with Q&A discussion;
2. Collaborative, small, action-orientated, discussion groups (6 max.) informally assigned;
3. Hands-on, group poster, aimed at "selling" a similar model back home.

Outcomes:

1. Participants recognize potential synergies between design research, community engagement with an equity/inclusion lens, goal-directed built-environment change, and cross-sector professional development;
2. Participants understand the critical health links between biodiversity and child development;
3. Participants are inspired to adapt the POD

model/strategy to opportunities related to children and families in under-served communities back home.

References:

Cosco, N. (2007). Developing Evidence-Based Design: Environmental Interventions for Healthy Development of Young Children in the Outdoors. In Ward-Thompson, C. and Travlou, P. (Eds), *Open Space: People Space*. London: Taylor and Francis.

Cosco, N., Moore, R., Smith, W. (2014). Childcare Outdoor Renovation as a Built Environment Health Promotion Strategy: Evaluating the Preventing Obesity by Design Intervention. *AmJ Health Promotion, 28*(3): S27-S32. doi: 10.4278/ajhp.130430-QUAN-208

Moore, R. and Cosco, N. (2014). Growing Up Green: Naturalization as Health Promotion Strategy in Early Childhood Outdoor Learning Environments. Children, *Youth & Environments, 24*(2): 168-191.

Smith W., Moore R., Cosco N., Jennifer Wesoloski J., Danninger T., Ward, D., Trost S., and Ries N. (2014). Increasing Physical Activity in Childcare Outdoor Learning Environments: The Effect of Setting Adjacency Relative to Other Built Environment and Social Factors. *Environment and Behavior, 48*(4): 550-578. doi:10.1177/0013916514551048

Impact of Nursing Unit Design Features on Overall Patient Experience and Perceived Room-level Noise

Hui Cai *(University of Kansas);* ***Francis Fullam*** *(Rush University);* ***Lorissa MacAllister*** *(Enviah)*

Background: Patient experience is of great interest in the healthcare industry. Patients' perception of noise is an important factor of patient experience. Existing research show that common noise sources are human-related (e.g., voices, conversations between staff and visitors, footwear, visitors); care activities, infrastructure-related equipment (e.g., telephones, pagers, carts, alarms), patient-related equipment (e.g., monitors, pumps), and environment (e.g., nurses' station, doors) (Dube et al., 2008; Konkani & Oakley, 2012). Among them, many studies have shown that staff conversations are the main sources of the loudest noise (Park, Kohlrausch, Brujin, Jager, & Simons, 2014). The physical environment plays an important role in affecting patients' perception of noise.

Study Purpose: This study aims to investigate the role of nursing unit environment plays in influencing patient experience. More specifically, it explores the characteristics of nursing unit design, such as the distance between various noise sources and patient rooms on patient's perception of noise as recorded in room-level patient experience scores.

Research Methods: The first part of the study was a retrospective pre-post and cross-sectional study evaluating the impacts of unit design on patient experience at the unit level. The study compared patient experiences based on Press Ganey and HCAHPS surveys in two orthopedic units (existing unit in Atrium Building and new unit in Tower) with differing design features at Rush University Medical Center. The second part of the study was a room-level analysis on the new unit. It evaluated the distance between main typical noise sources (e.g., team station, doors, elevators, ice machines, alarm) and each patient rooms and correlated the spatial relationship with aggregated patient perceptions of noise at the room level.

A chi-square test of independence was performed to compare the relationship between the unit designs (e.g., 9 South and 13 East) and the likelihood of selecting "top-box" in the patient experience in HCAHPS and Press Ganey survey. A one-way between-subjects ANOVA was conducted to compare patients' perception of noise at different patient rooms and evaluate whether the patients' perception of noise vary by its room location. The Pearson correlation coefficient was calculated to evaluate the effect of environmental features (i.e., distance to various noise sources) and patients' perception of noise at the room level.

Results: The Chi-square test of the patient satisfaction surveys show that when moving from the old orthopedic unit to the new unit, patient experience showed statistically significant improvements. More specifically, the decentralized nursing unit in the new 13 East has significantly lowered patients' perceived noise compared to 9

South.

The heat map of patients' perceived noise at the room-level in 13 East suggested that there was a cluster of rooms with an elevated noise level, which seemed to be driven by proximity to noise sources. However, the statistical analysis revealed that room-level analysis on perceived noise did not show a statistical difference between rooms in 13 East. The decentralized nursing unit design seems to be effective in distributing/mitigating the noise from the team stations, reducing the level of perceived noise at the room-level, and improving patients' experience.

Innovative Solutions for Universal Design of Healthcare Facilities

Jonathan White *(IDEA Center, University at Buffalo);* ***Shary Adams*** *(Cannon Design);* ***Erica Mosca*** *(Politecnico di Milano)*

This session highlights a case study in practitioner/researcher collaboration for the development of Universal Design standards in healthcare facilities. Researchers from University at Buffalo's Center for Inclusive Design and Environmental Access (IDEA Center) (in-person) and Politecnico di Milano University (Italy) Department of Architecture, Built environment, and Construction engineering (ABC) (virtual) join a practitioner from Canon Design (in-person) to discuss their ongoing collaboration addressing environmental design issues in healthcare settings. Specifically, this session discusses a project addressing equal access and use of healthcare facilities for people with and without disabilities, and people of diverse social, cultural, and economic backgrounds.

The IDEA Center's isUD (innovative solutions for Universal Design) is an inclusive building certification program based on years of research on the needs of people with disabilities and effectiveness of Universal Design (Steinfeld et al., 2015; Steinfeld et al., 2010). With a desire to expand isUD to healthcare settings, the IDEA Center partnered with a researcher at Politecnico di Milano Design & Health Lab research group, who developed a doctoral dissertation on Universal Design evaluation of healthcare facilities (Mosca, 2021). The research addressed a literature review on existing assessment methods and standards focus groups, best practices , and stakeholders' analysis (Mosca & Capolongo, 2018). The main outcome is the Design for All A.U.D.I.T. (Assessment Universal Design and Inclusion Tool), which measures the quality of Universal Design in healthcare facilities (Mosca et al., 2020).

They connected with a practitioner from Canon Design who designs healthcare facilities based on Canon's Living-centered Design approach, and who is familiar with various challenges and opportunities in healthcare design. The goal of the collaboration is a new isUD program for healthcare facilities and implementation of a new audit tool (i.e. DfA A.U.D.I.T.), which will help improve access, safety, usability, and comfort for all people, especially people with disabilities.

This session presents the research methods and outcomes used in the development and evaluation of the isUD and DfA A.U.D.I.T. Participants will hear examples of specific Universal Design solutions from commercial buildings and offices and how they may be re-imagined for use in healthcare facilities.

References:

Mosca, E. I., & Capolongo, S. (2018). Towards a universal design evaluation for assessing the performance of the built environment. Transforming Our World Through Design, Diversity and Education, 256, 771-779. https://doi.org/10.3233/978-1-61499-923-2-771

Mosca, E. I., Steinfeld, E., & Capolongo S. (2020). Universal design assessment tool to promote well-being and inclusion in healthcare environment. European Journal of Public Health, 30(S-5). https://doi.org/10.1093/eurpub/ckaa165.589

Mosca, E. I. (2021). Evaluating "Design for all" in healthcare environments: A new tool to access physical, sensory-cognitive and social quality: Design for all A.U.D.I.T. (Assessment Usability Design & Inclusion Tool) [Doctoral dissertation]. Italy, Politecnico di Milano: Architecture, Built environment and Construction engineering.

Steinfeld, E., Paquet, V., D'Souza, C., Joseph, C., & Maisel, J. (2010). Anthropometry of Wheeled

Mobility Project: Final Report. Center for Inclusive Design and Environmental Access, University at Buffalo. http://idea.ap.buffalo.edu/wp-content/uploads/sites/110/2020/01/AnthropometryofWheeledMobilityProject_FinalReport.pdf

Steinfeld, E., Weidemann, S., White, J., & Sigal, E. (2015). Effectiveness of design standards in improving residence hall usability and satisfaction. Proceedings from ARCC 2015: architectural research centers consortium 2015 conference. Chicago, IL.

Making Community Engagement More Equitable and Inclusive

Lindsay Fisher *(Perkins Eastman);* ***Rebecca Milne***, *(Perkins Eastman Architects);* ***Brianne Johnson Pham***, *(Perkins Eastman)*

Community engagement has gained traction in recent years as a key component in creating responsive, context-specific design. Understanding users' needs and desires is essential to the delivery of successful projects. However, it is often the case that some voices get excluded from community engagement processes, which can pose risks to the acceptance and meaningful adoption of a project within a given community.

Taking action to support diversity, equity, and inclusion is about more than "doing good"—it improves the standard and quality of living for everyone. Equitable societies are more stable, healthy, and resilient. Diversity, equity, and inclusion needs to be an integral part of our work. No longer a "nice to have", diversity, equity, and inclusion measures are now paramount in the effort to improve the impact our built environments have on individuals and our communities. As shown in "The Business Case for the B Corporation Certifications", companies who invest in some form of corporate social responsibility are starting to see profits increase because of it. As certifications and other metrics gain traction, this profitability will only increase.

As architects, the built environment is our instrument of change, and through it we have a unique opportunity to make a positive impact. We are developing a toolkit to help project teams engage stakeholders and amplify marginalized voices. Community engagement creates the opportunity to build relationships and can bridge disconnected communities. Creating a connection between individuals is key, whether it is through an in-person workshop, a virtual seminar, a hybrid model or beyond. Technology is one tool that can foster connections and improve the engagement process, offering multiple ways to participate. . It also streamlines data collection, efficiently collecting real-time metrics through live polls and other digital tools. An approach that supports diversity, equity and inclusion is fundamental to our philosophy of human-centered design—and it creates a better future for all of us.

Taking Inclusive Restrooms from "If" to "How": Studying Project Implications of Inclusive Restroom Systems in Practice

Michael Ralph *(Gould Evans);* ***Lauren Maass*** *(Gould Evans);* ***Joshua Kehl*** *(Gould Evans);* ***Sam Church*** *(University of Kansas)*

Inclusive restroom facilities are increasingly being recognized as a powerful option for construction and renovation projects that prioritize inclusivity within the built environment. We use "inclusive restrooms", colloquially understood to be gender-inclusive restrooms, and omit "gender" to evoke a paradigm that considers many axes of human identity and reduce the salience of gender in the space conversation. Inclusive restrooms' potential to serve as the primary restroom system for a public, multi-user solution is only recently being recognized in building codes. Recognition of inclusive designs in code and legislation coincides with greater adoption within schools and other public institutions with the goal of enhancing safety and dignity for users. Designers and facilities professionals are moving from questions of "if" they will implement inclusive restroom systems to "how" they can best implement inclusive systems in their projects.

Our research team sought to add to the existing design research on inclusive restrooms by studying the practical considerations and common project constraints of implementing inclusive restrooms as they compare to conventions of design for gendered restrooms. In the summer of 2021, we worked on a client-partnered project to create a process for studying the potential implementation of an inclusive restroom in a project context. We identified 6 lenses of analysis in our work: accessibility, cost, equity & inclusion, maintenance, privacy, and safety. Through an iterative design process, we compared gendered restrooms with inclusive restrooms, including the addition of single-use restrooms to further explicate how inclusive restrooms can be integrated within a public education campus.

Our project combined a wide variety of data sources to create a process for evaluating restroom designs within a project context. We incorporated local quantitative data sources such as community data from the district office of institutional research and incident information from the district police department. We also incorporated broader quantitative findings from national sources like the 2015 U.S. Transgender Survey. In addition, we also created quantitative project data in partnership with a cost estimator for various designs. To contextualize all of the quantitative material, we also conducted 3 qualitative interviews as various stages of the project to create interview data with district facilities professionals, a leading researcher on issues of gender inclusion, and an external design professional with recent experience creating inclusive facilities. We further contextualized the project within a historical framework of evolving restroom legislation, building code, and user stories examining the intersection of race, gender, and dis/ability in public restroom spaces.

Team members focused on design practice will discuss the facility design considerations like code requirements, project constraints, and innovation opportunities. Team members focused on design research will discuss the process of collecting credible data that do not embed marginalizing assumptions about users, the impact of an interdisciplinary collaboration on the quality of the project findings, and the process of connecting research insights to design applications. The session will conclude with a Q&A within the presentation team, in collaboration with participants, to explore the challenges and opportunities in practice/research partnerships to advance equitable design for future projects.

The Application of Discrete Event Simulation and Functional Program Occupancy Evaluation (FPOE) for process and design improvements in an Emergency Department

Zahra Zamani *(BSA Life Structures);* ***Teri Joy*** *(Senior Healthcare Operations Planner);* ***Timothy Spence***, *(BSA LifeStructures)*

Emergency departments are under increasing pressure to provide efficient care while dealing with major challenges, such as overcrowding, delays, length of stay, safety risks, or staffing. Many emergency department visits are non-urgent in nature and can be treated in a different setting. Some new design suggestions include implementation fast-track areas, where lower acuity patients can wait for their pending disposition or results. Studies show that this approach increases patient satisfaction and reduces patients' length of stay.

Another common bottleneck involves the disposition to departure interval. Most likely, emergency departments are the last to get a bed assignment. Suitable demand-capacity matching, and modified admission protocols can be an alternative strategy in reducing ED patients' LOS, and improved boarding times (Amarasingham et al., 2010). This study employed Functional Program Occupancy Evaluation (FPOE), and Discrete Event Simulation (DES) to understand underlying conditions and existing bottlenecks in an existing ED. DES has been often used to improve productivity and system throughput by testing the hypothesis against the primary model to improve system performance in a timely and economical manner (Mielczarek & Uzialko-Mydlikowska, 2012). For emergency departments, simulation models often explore patient flow regarding waiting times or times spent within each treatment (Lane,

Monefeldt& Hisemnan, 2003)

The current process flow involved a "pull-until-full" for exam room boarding. They also implemented bed-side registration after triage was completed. The building has an integrated imaging department that is used for outpatient and ED purposes.

Regardless of the ED's rapid response, it was shown that ESI levels 1, 2, and 3 wait between 2 to 10 hours for inpatient beds. The average bed request, bed assigned, admit, and discharge length of stay was 217, 333, 334, and 131 minutes, respectively. The model showed that on average, patients waited 64 minutes in the ED process. Starting from 10 a.m. exam, CT, and ultrasound rooms showed high utilization rates (81-82%). The simulation model showed that, on average, the CT tech traveled 3 miles per day to escort patients in the imaging room. This implied the need for more efficient proximities between the ED and imaging rooms. Findings showed that between 10 a.m. to 1 p.m., MDs were highly utilized (85%).

DES modeling evaluated the implication of a fast-track room, and "fast-admit" process may enhance the ED efficiency and patient's LOS. Findings showed that the fast admit process reduced the admitted patient's median LOS by 37%. The results pending implication increased the exam room availability by 22% and reduced Admit Median LOS by 30%.

This study suggests the importance of process, staffing, and spatial modifications to achieve improved ED operational improvement. The use of simulation modeling enabled a data-driven approach to evaluate bottlenecks and optimize the system prior to implementing changes in real life. It also contributed to suggesting changes that would save future design costs and improve communication between architects and healthcare clients. Future studies are suggested to explore the impacts of observation units in improving the ED bed assignment process.

University and Practitioner Partnership: Leveraging Strengths to Enhance the Shared Missions of Education and High Performance Design

Heather Burpee *(University of Washington)*

The goals of this session are to

1. Share a successful university architectural research and practitioner partnership model,
2. Communicate a shared research project leveraging the strengths of the academy and the needs of practice, and
3. Share success stories of applying the research tool in practice, increasing awareness and adoption of high-performance design.

Architecture firms value data-driven design, but struggle to incorporate research into practice. Common barriers stem from a culture and profession not traditionally engaged in research – a context in which billable projects constrain staff time and firm structures limit capacity for non-traditional work. In response, an architecturally focused University Research Center, has brought together thirteen partner firms to drive research-informed change in regional practice in the short-term, with a long-term vision to develop uniquely qualified professionals in high performance building design maximize both environmental and human experience goals. The Partnership serves multi-pronged purposes: helping unite practice and academics, sharing in teaching and education, and developing shared research tools and methods.

Partner firms recognize that significant future improvements in buildings will be underpinned in large-part by synergistic qualities of human experience such as occupant perception, organizational mission enhancements, improved health outcomes, and increased productivity. These values of high-performance design are well-accepted, yet how various attributes are supported by research can be difficult for firms to consolidate and communicate. Thereby common understanding, buy-in, and adoption can be challenging for design practitioners to attain.

To address these challenges, this group developed a shared research tool: "The Rosetta

Stone: A Translational Tool for Research-Informed Practice." The idea of this tool ignited out of a collective desire to clearly communicate the synergies of high-performance design, backed by research and evidence. Its aim is to create a high-level translational literature review tool to help disseminate knowledge and information for a range of targeted audiences at varying level of depths of information and to equip firms with consistent, fit-for-purpose messaging and guidance to discuss different value cases of high-performance design.

The initial topics explored, which included design elements such as daylight, thermal comfort, and indoor air quality, were decided via consensus by the researchers and Partners. The researchers conducted a literature review of academic sources for each topic, including relevant academic articles and reports issued by academics or professionals working in the field. Findings were consolidated in various content pieces summarizing empirical evidence for how each design element contributes to different types of value for building occupants, such as productivity, satisfaction, and physical and mental health.

The tool has been tested and utilized in various ways by Partner firms and projects/individuals within those firms. We will share stories from implementation, both expected and unexpected uses of the tool, and the outcomes of those interventions.

This presentation will describe the process of coalescing the university/practitioner Partnership, share the development of the Rosetta Stone tool, outline specific findings for several specific content areas, share stories of implementation of research outcomes, and articulate next steps for the Partnership and the tool.

Wellness as a Heritage Value: The Intersection of Theory, Research, and Historic Preservation Planning Practice

Julie Lawless *(FEMA);* ***Kapila Silva*** *(University of Kansas);* ***Courtney Bonney*** *(Savannah College of Art and Design);* ***Carol Coleman*** *(Waccamaw Regional Council of Governments)*

The cultural significance of historic places provides the rationale for their conservation and preservation. A historic place's cultural significance is in turn determined by the values attributed to that place, which may include values that include tangible and intangible history, social and political activities, spiritual or religious connections, symbolic identity, research, nature, and economic assets. Conservation practice may then focus on the management of these heritage values to prolong the cultural significance of the place for posterity. In conventional historic preservation practice, the definition of heritage values is an academic activity conducted by heritage professionals, leading to the identification of a limited and conventional set of values, which could be called 'experts-defined' heritage values. Studies involving local communities in historic places point towards the ways communities' associate values to their historic places, the difference in 'community-defined' heritage values as opposed to 'experts-defined' heritage values, and why the former is critical in the effective conservation of cultural heritage. One of these community values seems to be the 'wellness value' of historic places, in which communities perceive the significance of historic places in terms of an environmental quality that contribute to their physical, mental, and spiritual wellness. Wellness value of the historic place is likely a collective effect of other heritage values, and thus tends to be an all-encompassing value upon which the focus of values-based heritage management should be positioned. Four aspects are presented to discuss the value-systems approach to heritage conservation and the implementation of values as part of a real-world project:

First, an architectural researcher discusses an ethnographic studies of community heritage values of three World Heritage sites in Sri Lanka and Nepal. Findings from a literature review on community heritage values in historic places in other countries are used to supplement the discussion on the theoretical and methodological implications of the wellness value in heritage conservation.

Second, a design researcher discusses a practice-based assessment tool using heritage values to understand the impacts of historic programs and policies on community wellbeing. Using six heritage values, the tool depicts impact based on social, psychological, and physical influences of community wellbeing to determine specific advantageous/ disadvantageous outcomes. This presentation describes the utility and implementation of the tool in data collection and analysis as part of a planning project.

Third, a professor presents findings from the Preservation Planning class at Savannah College of Art & Design, who undertook semester-long studies of the historic West End in Georgetown, South Carolina and Sweet Auburn in Atlanta, Georgia. This presentation focuses on the students' uses of the heritage map, site study, and lessons learned.

Fourth, a planning professional presents the use of the results of the student study in Georgetown, as the Waccamaw Council of Governments is building a comprehensive planning update using the heritage map and the value system approach to tailor the planning process to the cultural identity and needs of the West End neighborhood.

Abstracts: Workshops

Appropriate Settings: Finding the Right Treatment Environment for People on Continuums of Mental Illness and Criminal Behavior

Erin Persky *(Erin Persky & Associates LLC);* ***Melissa Farling*** *(Gould Evans);* ***Richard Wener*** *(New York University);* ***Jay Farbstein*** *(Jay Farbstein & Associates Inc);* ***Greg Barker*** *(Greg Allen Barker, AIA)*

For reasons related to social conditions, health policy and the criminal justice practices, jails have become the default sites for the institutionalization of many mentally ill patients. Some estimates indicate that incarcerated individuals experience serious mental illness at up to four times the rate of individuals who are not incarcerated (Bureau of Justice Statistics, 2017). Jails have largely been planned and designed to hold people for short periods of time – mostly those who have been arrested and are awaiting hearing, trial or sentencing, or have been adjudicated by the courts to short sentences. The variety, scale and quality of spaces available to this population are usually inappropriate, while programs, staff qualifications and training, and treatment possibilities are consequently limited. Moreover, the selection and training of custody staff typically does not focus on mental health issues and numbers of qualified mental health professionals are often inadequate. Even in the best of situations, where administrators have the best of intentions and attempts are made to provide decent and humane conditions, the settings are usually far from what would be available in an intentionally planned mental health facility. One result can often be that too many of these patients experience time in isolation ("restrictive housing"), which may exacerbate existing mental illness or cause the development of new or additional mental health issues (Kupers, Prison Madness, 1999).

To address this set of problems, it is essential that we take a holistic look at the system and the institutions it has created to serve mental health populations – criminal and civil, inpatient and outpatient – in order to address the policy, legal, budgetary, and facilities-related "gaps" that contribute to the over-representation of mental health populations in detention settings. There is a pressing need to consider the kinds of alternative settings that can provide the best options for treatment for these populations, keeping in mind security concerns where there is risk to self, others and society. And there is an equally pressing need to envision humane and effective secure institutions for those whose crimes and the strictures of the courts dictate that they must be incarcerated.

In this workshop experienced researchers and practitioners will discuss these issues, including the need to address building standards and public policy, as well as existing knowledge and additional design research needs that can support appropriate settings. Melissa Farling will moderate. Rich Wener will discuss the history of these settings, Melissa Farling will discuss current situations in forensic health settings in Arizona. Jay Farbstein, Greg Barker and Erin Persky will present a case study from a major metropolitan justice system where they are dealing with the challenges of providing care in the existing facility and alternative settings.

Architecture for All: Applying Lessons Learned from a Sensory-Sensitive Environment for Children with Autism Spectrum Disorders at Spero Academy across Building Typologies and Users Groups

Herminia Machry *(Georgia Institute of Technology);* ***David Allison*** *(Clemson University);* ***Keith Diaz Moore*** *(University of Utah);* ***Naomi A. Sachs***, *(Cornell University);* ***Neda Norouzi*** *(University of Texas San Antonio);* ***Heather Burpee*** *(University of Washington);* ***Craig Zimring*** *(Georgia Institute of Technology)*

Background: It is challenging and complex to design and create evidence on buildings and environments so that they positively contribute to the health and experiences of individuals. Just as challenging and complex is helping students and young professionals understand the intricacies of environments that promote health, from both conceptual and practical standpoints. Recognizing the high level of specificity, reflection and multidisciplinary collaboration required in creating adequate curricula for education in design practice and research focused on health and healthcare, several universities worldwide have worked to build programs and centers of excellence focused on this topic (Gola, Brambilla, Barach et al., 2020). However, these academic groups are still relatively unique and usually focused on healthcare settings (as opposed to any setting). Additionally, there is a need to bridge existing gaps between theory and practice in this context (Cambra-Rufino, Brambilla, Paniagua-Caparrós, & Capolongo, 2021).

Goals: Recognizing the need to expand and integrate health as a more ubiquitous concept in architectural and design education, this session is aimed at identifying important strategies to improve educational processes and outcomes that successfully and inclusively link health with built and natural environments.

Method: We will bring together six national experts in healthcare design education in the United States, to discuss current challenges and next steps needed to effectively integrate 'health in all design' as part of architecture and design curricula and pedagogy. Experienced professors and directors of architecture and landscape architecture graduate programs, mostly focused on health, in both master's and doctoral levels, will be engaged by a facilitator in a semi-structured discussion to share their most valuable and challenging lessons learned with students, especially in adapting to the recent wave of virtual teaching platforms.

Conclusions: The session will provide a platform to learn from existing healthcare design educators and discuss about the current and future state of education in architecture and health. Results from the discussion will be compiled to summarize important strategies moving forward to improve educational processes and outcomes in the context of education for environments promoting not only health, but also equity and inclusion.

References:

Gola, M., Brambilla, A., Barach, P., Signorelli, C., & Capolongo, S. (2020). Educational Challenges in Healthcare Design: Training Multidisciplinary Professionals for Future Hospitals and Healthcare. *Annali di igiene : medicina preventiva e di comunita, 32*(5), 549–566. https://doi.org/10.7416/ai.2020.2375

Cambra-Rufino, L., Brambilla, A., Paniagua-Caparrós, J. L., & Capolongo, S. (2021). Hospital Architecture in Spain and Italy: Gaps Between Education and Practice. *HERD, 14*(3), 169–181. https://doi.org/10.1177/1937586721991520

Ungendered Restrooms: Weighing the Balance of Equity, Sustainability, and Risk

B. Sanborn *(DLR Group);* ***Penny Cole*** *(DLR Group);* ***Nicole DeNamur*** *(Sustainable Strategies)*

The option to include ungendered restrooms is an increasingly common topic in pre-design and planning conversations; different localities have different guidelines requiring new buildings to have accessible, inclusive restrooms available. Professionals working at the intersection of equity and sustainability foresee a time when ungendered restrooms are a common requirement and design feature intended to contribute to inclusive environments while also reducing embodied carbon. This workshop will introduce participants to current issues around ungendered restrooms through multiple lenses.

Transdisciplinary facilitators from design, research, and legal backgrounds will present case studies illustrating different aspects of ungendered restroom design. Participants will be introduced to topics including space planning, water use, embodied carbon, public health, equity, and privacy in a facilitated dialogue about real and perceived risk. Because this topic is complex and evolving, workshop participants will then engage in activities around risk assessment and management strategies based on their own project experience and expertise, to co-create a playbook of design and communication strategies. This playbook will be shared back to participants to build capacity for productive dialogue about designing ungendered restrooms.

Healthcare is a Right, Not a Privilege: How Design can Integrate DEI Checkpoints to Embrace Individual Needs and the Heart of the Community

Amanda Robinson *(E4H Environments for Health Architecture);* ***Susan Romano*** *(E4H Environments for Health Architecture);* ***Burt Pusch*** *(Accessibility and Safety Consultants);* ***Kimberly Leonard*** *(E4H Environments for Health Architecture);* ***Danielle Rein*** *(Urban Projects Collaborative)*

Driven by a dedication to enhance healing and elevate hope for all patients, this session will explore the unique needs of populations across the country and how design can specifically welcome and embrace not only the needs of the individual but the heart of the community. From patients from various cultures and those with mobility, visual, auditory, cognitive, or mental disabilities, to those facing financial and access challenges, community-based, medical neighborhood-focused care takes a holistic approach to meeting underserved needs. This session will explore the design process, where Diversity, Equity, and Inclusion (DEI) checkpoints can be integrated, how the unique needs of populations can be understood, and how to address the challenges of communities through planning and design. Through the case studies of three organizations, we will review how medical providers are addressing the social determinants of health including physical and behavioral health, food and housing security, accessing community resources, crisis support, transportation, and more.

Three years ago, E4H formalized a DEI initiative called 4wrd – For Women, Resolve, and Diversity, to answer the call to expand diversity in the healthcare design industry to better serve and approach with empathy the broad range of patients our clients serve. The pillars of 4wrd include 1) A more balanced workforce 2) Accountability 3) Education/Programming 4) DEI-based Approach to Design including a DEI Design checklist to collaborate with clients at project kick off. Our commitment to providing our staff with tools to succeed and thrive while maintaining excellence in client service allows an open dialogue and designing with empathy.

This session will explore how a design firm's investment in DEI training for staff, translates to actionable design impacts, brings new voices to the table with emerging leadership, and aligns with DEI client goals through case studies. Leaders from healthcare systems will share how these selected health systems understood the unique needs of their populations, and how they addressed the challenges of their communities through planning and design.

Design for Health and Equity: Insights from the Epidemic Urbanism Initiative Design Competition

Mohammad Gharipour *(Morgan State University);* ***Caitlin DeClercq*** *(Research Design Connections);* ***Louisa Iarocci*** *(University of Washington);* ***Katarina Andjelkovic*** *(Independent Researcher);* ***Irene Hwang*** *(University of Michigan);* ***Bud Shenefelt*** *(University of Nebraska)*

The COVID-19 pandemic has disproportionately affected vulnerable communities across the world including older adults, racial and ethnic minorities, and low-income communities. Like other epidemic illnesses and natural disasters that preceded it, the incidence of COVID-19, death rates due to the disease, and access to medical care were and are patterned along pre-existing social inequities and often aided by inequities in the built environments in which people live and work (Rollston & Galea, 2020; Snowden, 2019).

Recognizing the role that everyday built environments play as both primary places of vulnerability and exposure as well as resources for health promotion and intervention, the Epidemic Urbanism Initiative co-founders organized an international design competition in September 2021 to respond to this urgent need to rethink architecture, urban design, and the built environment toward more critical, just, and equitable solutions in the post-pandemic age. This design competition provoked participants to grapple with questions about how the the cities, schools, homes, and spaces of care and recreation we inhabit might be reimagined in the wake of the recent pandemic and as we anticipate the inevitable next epidemic or pandemic. What might these changes look like? Or, more to the point, what should they look like? How might we re-center health in all design practices and processes? And how might we use this time of rebuilding and rethinking to envision, design, and inhabit built settings that are more just, equitable, and supportive of the needs of diverse populations?

In response to these questions, the design competition, "Designing for Health and Equity: Supporting Vulnerable Communities in the Post-Pandemic Age," welcomed submissions that reimagined existing neglected or underutilized sites in urban environments as one of four categories of design: senior housing, a community clinic, neighborhood school, or public park. This design competition received 52 submissions from 30 countries.

The organizers structured the norms and processes of this design competition to foreground the need for innovative, global, and equitable solutions to promote community and individual health among diverse populations. Submissions for each design category were reviewed by four jurors. Shortlisted projects were announced and discussed by the jury and guest commentators in final review meetings in October 2021 which were open to the public via Zoom and shared publicly via YouTube.

This EDRA workshop, led by the conference organizers and jury chairs, will review and discuss the process of organizing the design competition, reflect on the possibilities for designing for diverse and vulnerable populations with an emphasis on submitted projects, share major feedback given by the jury and the commentators on submissions, and consider lessons learned. The session will end with a collective and collaborative review of this effort and will invite participants to share suggestions and recommendations for future endeavors in regard to designing for underprivileged, global communities.

Sharing VALUES: Interactive View of an Updated Evidence-Based Eco-Charrette Tool

B. Sanborn (DLR Group); Grace Corsi (DLR Group); Lindsey Perez (DLR Group)

Study and practice have shown that sustainability priorities vary by stakeholder group. Design projects must be responsive to real-world constraints: budget, site, new build vs. renovation, and culture - to name a few. During planning and programming of spaces, stakeholder groups are often asked about their goals for sustainability, as well as their vision for using the built environment to further organizational goals or build relationships with the community.

It is tempting for both practitioners and their clients to adhere to familiar sustainability certifications, or to "self-select" out of the conversation too early due to budgetary concerns. Additionally, as societal understanding of sustainability expands, it is increasingly important to center conversations on holistic frameworks for sustainability. Moving the ideation past the conservation of water or energy, or reductions in production of carbon or waste, and into the realm of full climate and community justice is crucial.

This interactive workshop presentation builds on a topic introduced by the team at EDRA50: linking programming to sustainable priorities through the gamification. Participants will hear about the origin of an eco-charrette card tool, then review the iterative development of the tool based on research updates and stakeholder interactions over the past three years. Attendees will learn how eco-charrettes can create an effective conversation about sustainability with key stakeholders, and how to facilitate discussion about the vision and goals of key stakeholders using an enjoyable card game.

Thinking Outside the (Big) Box

B. Sanborn (DLR Group); Grace Corsi (DLR Group); Jose Sanchez (DLR Group)

More than half of all big box department stores that

anchor major mall developments are expected to close by the end of 2021 (Bhattarai, 2016; Howland, 2020; Thomas, 2020). These underutilized spaces are associated with reduced property values, loss of tax revenue, environmental pollution, and a decrease in social capital (Schindler, 2011); such spaces are of little value to communities. At a time when national demand for justice in the wake of a global pandemic has surfaced conversation around development approaches that will address community needs, these empty spaces have the potential to be design solutions.

This paper uses the framework of Social Determinants of Health (SDOH) to propose a path to reorient the relationship with vacant big box spaces. Grounded in research from the CDC and the Kaiser Family Foundation, the SDOH outline the many external factors, such as neighborhood and physical environment, education, community context, and food access, that contribute the health of individuals and communities (Artiga, 2018; WHO, 2017). This framework is widely used to drive processes that holistically address inequities and improve quality of life (Dean et al, 2013). Many of these factors are linked to the built environment, but traditional disciplines (architecture, engineering, and urban planning) have not centered their processes on the SDOH as a guiding framework.

Using the central design challenge "How might we repurpose vacant big-box spaces for positive impacts to community and climate health?" the authors have embraced the SDOH as the guiding framework for a design competition hosted internally to a large integrated architecture, planning, engineering, and interiors firm. Following a series of workshops, teams materialized their discussion around the SDOH into designs that were judged by an external panel for success in addressing environment, equity, community, and diverse uses. The results were synthesized into an interactive, online white paper that will be shared as part of this presentation.

After a short debrief on the white paper, participants will apply the guiding framework from the authors' research to a new case study. They will have the opportunity to critically examine contextual analysis, historical research, and stakeholder engagement strategies framed by the SDOH to provide feedback on the process, identify areas for improvement, develop ideas for future implementation, and brainstorm ways to track impacts of design decisions on improving community health after they are implemented. The outcome of the workshop will be a series of recommendations and next steps for improving and implementing the road map laid out in the white paper.

"Before the Hospital" - Design as Preventative Healthcare: Exploration of USA/UK Regulatory and Multi-Sectoral Practices in Designing Healthier Equitable Communities and Places

Douglas King *(Project Management Advisors Inc.);* ***Michael Chang*** *(Office for Health Improvement and DIsparities);* ***Erika Eitland*** *(Perkins & Will)*

This workshop is a collaboration of USA/UK participants in the 2021 cohort of the ULI - Health Leaders Network and its goal is premised on the proposition that individual and population level health is an asset to invest in, and not just a problem for the health services to fix when it goes wrong. The choices we make, shaped by the environmental, social and economic conditions in which we live, such as housing, green space, food access and active transportation, have the biggest impact on population physical and mental health. Requiring a shifted focus away from treating illnesses within the health system towards preventing problems in the first place through responsive health by planning and design.

Shaping people's well-being through planning is driven by norms and practices which require innovative, multi-disciplinary approaches. The status quo of silo mentalities amongst health commissioners, planners and real estate developers is ineffective, and existing competencies and regulations are not fit for purpose. Drawing from experiences from USA and UA, the workshop illustrates how planners, urban designers and public health teams working at state, county or municipal levels, in partnership with communities and the private sector, are best placed to help design for a healthy and equitable future by leveraging the tools available to them to pursue health objectives.

Complex problems to population health require adapting socio-technical interventions to achieve equitable public health outcomes. Particularly in the context of global to local climate change and sustainability impacts which are coming to the fore of policy makers. So the art and science of public health spatial planning requires professionals with a set of complementary and shared competencies. This means giving priority to efforts to reduce and eliminate health inequalities in national legislation, and promoting wellbeing, and in city plans and policies, when planning, developing and regenerating communities. The unique expertise and backgrounds of the speakers demonstrate their multi faceted approach.

Workshop objectives will be to build a consensus of how the built environment impacts health, how the public and private sectors hold regulatory and financial levers to manage these impacts, illustrate multinational approaches from the UK and USA and co-create healthy places guidelines with workshop participants.

The workshop agenda focused on interactive learning and discussion between the presenters and participants. It begins with strategic context setting 'PechaKucha' presentations from the three speakers for 30 minutes to contextualize and exemplify the issues addressed, approaches taken, impact and outcomes achieved. This will be followed by 60 minutes of interactive small group discussion.

- Erika will begin by framing the challenges and importance of leveraging public health intelligence and data to define community needs through systematically-defined user-based research,
- Doug will illustrate, through case study examples, practical solutions that manifest approaches by the private sector to develop the "swiss army knife"/ toolbox of solutions in a community/ neighborhood-level health settings, and
- Michael will end by setting out the comparative UK's evidence based approach to top-down regulatory promotion of health and reducing disparities through built and natural environment systems.

Building-Level Design Affordances for Healthy, Physical Activity: An Evaluative Framework for Examples from the Field

MaryAnn Sorensen Allacci *(Projects for Environmental Health;* ***Eleni Tracada*** *(University of Derby)*

Design that increases opportunities for physical activity has been of interest for many planners, architects, public health professionals, researchers, etc.. Much of this interest has focused on neighborhood, community, urban, transportation or other exterior-oriented place design access and programming that include design affordances or remove obstacles (RWJ Active Living Research; Evenson, Salas, et al. 2012). Less focus has been on building-level design research, and examples. This Workshop examines existing research and examples of buildings that provide opportunities for youth and/or adults that are either precursors for or directly engage occupants in healthy, physical activity. Topic studies have typically been restricted to design for elder residential environments (Gharaveis, 2020) or specific forms of activity, such as walking (Balsas, 2021).

Goal: This project explores opportunities for expanding building level design for a wider range of population age and physical ability groups in diverse building types. Further, theoretical models of spatial configurations (space syntax) of human movements are considered to understand patterns of walkability. Cognitive patterns of active internal connectivity, often designed by following specific biophilic patterns of free fractal flow, examine how integrated spaces might link harmoniously with immediate surroundings and beyond. Objectives include better understanding of design that provides self-directed recreational, instrumental, hybrid and other affordances for physical activity (Zimring, et al., 2005; Gibson, 1986).

Methods: Collaborators survey building-level examples incorporating design features that encourage healthy, physical activity. A definitional framework for building examples is developed for the selection process, relying on theoretical guidelines from researchers including Zimring and Hillier, et al. to building-level design (1993). Next, the derived selection framework is evaluated using building plan samples to examine robustness of framework guidelines. Building spatial configurations are also analyzed to find preferable permeable pathlines of increased walkability contributing to active and healthy social engagement with co-users. Building examples and images are provided for workshop materials.

Outcomes: A platform for discussion, critique of framework applications, and a shareable compendium of buildings that suggest design solutions for active living.

References:

RWJ Active Living Research (2021). https://activelivingresearch.org/active-living-topics

Evenson, K.R., Sallis, J.F., Handy, S.L., Bell, R., & Brennan, L.K. (2012). Evaluation of physical projects and policies from the Active Living by Design partnerships. *American journal of preventive medicine, 43*(5), S309-S319.

Gharaveis, A. (2020). A systematic framework for understanding environmental design influences on physical activity in the elderly population: A review of literature. *Facilities.*

Balsas, C. J. (2021). The reinvention of indoor walking for sustainable non-motorized active living in winter cities. *Journal of Human Behavior in the Social Environment, 31*(5), 626-641.

Salingaros, N.A. (2012) Fractal Art and Architecture Reduce Physiological Stress. *Journal of Biourbanism, (II)*2, pp. 11-28.

Zimring, C., Joseph, A., Nicoll, G.L., & Tsepas, S. (2005). Influences of building design and site design on physical activity: research and intervention opportunities. *American journal of preventive medicine, 28*(2), 186-193.

Gibson, J.J. (1986). *The Ecological Approach to Visual Perception.* Cornell University Lawrence Erlbaum Associates Press.

Hillier, B., Penn, A., Hanson, J., Grajewski, T., & Xu, J. (1993). Natural movement: or, configuration and attraction in urban pedestrian movement. *Environment and Planning B: planning and design, 20*(1), 29-66.

Interprofessional Collaboration in Health Design: The Importance of Core Concepts and Theoretical Frameworks

Keith Diaz Moore *(University of Utah);* ***Lyn Geboy*** *(Cygnet Innovations Group);* ***Traci Rider*** *(North Carolina State University);* ***Deborah Wingler*** *(HKS);* ***Hui Cai*** *(University of Kansas)*

The transaction between health and the designed environment is complex, dynamic and nuanced with interconnections cross cutting numerous fields of study and domains of knowledge. In order to effectively position the understanding of healthy places, work in the area often relies on a set of clear core concepts and shared theoretical frameworks to help guide collaboration and promote transdisciplinary translation. This workshop will present four newer frameworks developed in the area of healthy places. The first presents a framework developed to facilitate interdisciplinary consideration of health and architectural education (Rider). The second presents a framework that attempts a mapping of the broad landscape of research on healthy places and how that helps make connections to health research. The third presents the Design Diagnostic framework that allows a rapid but triangulated insight into key areas of a facility combining the methods of shadowing, behavior mapping, surveys, interviews, photo-essays, and parametric analysis (Wingler). The last presents a collaborative, practice-based, multiphase POE framework (Cai). As a workshop, the session will leave time for small group discussion of each of the frameworks, their strengths and weaknesses and opportunities for refinement. Audience participants will leave with a greater understanding of these frameworks as well as how they might apply in their own work.

Abstracts: Intensives

Interprofessional Collaboration in Health Design: The Importance of Core Concepts and Theoretical Frameworks

Half-Day Intensive

In Charles and Ray Eames's 1978 documentary, Powers of 10, the duo explores the human experience relative to time and space through a staggering range of scales. In a matter of minutes, the Eames's explore the far edges of the galaxy, 10+23 meters, where life on earth is minimized to insignificant organisms within a universe spanning 10 million light years. Then, reversing course, they zoom deep into the human body, cellular structure, strands of DNA, and molecular compositions, 10-15 meters. From this point of view, humans appear insignificant, simplified to an infinite galaxy of protons, neutrons, and electrons. However, during this trans-dimensional journey the Eames's do not favor or endorse any specific snapshot as being more significant or valuable than the others. Rather, they recognize that each is different, significant, and plays a vital role contributing to a series of inclusive, complex systems and connected infrastructures.

Similarly, designers should take a more inclusive position and attitude towards tackling the challenges of the built environment, then, the probability of attaining a more sustainable and equitable future greatly increases. This workshop will focus on Landscape Laboratories as an effective pedagogical approach for exploring an effective and inclusive range of environmental, experiential, and social issues. We will explore strategies that enable students to be immersed in sustainable research and design through engagement, observation, and application. Additionally, we will discuss the differences and distinctions in our work while making the meaningful connections between our research and the subtle nuances that are perhaps the key to increasing our goals of a more sustainable built environment.

In conclusion, as educators it is critical that we prepare our students with the skills and knowledge to tackle the varied challenges of sustainability, diversity, and equity. And while we aim for discipline fluency, we ought to strive for a broader range of complimentary understanding so that we may make more meaningful connections and innovation. That is, can we challenge students to be better versed in opposing points of view? Will varying scales and lenses enable them to ask better questions and better frame problems and design challenges? The case study pedagogical approaches presented in this workshop will demonstrate innovative research and teaching methodologies that promote innovation, resilience, and sustainability.

Grounded Theory

David Hill *(Auburn University);* ***Emily Knox*** *(Auburn University)*

In a regional landscape otherwise dominated by regimented commercial forestry, large scale agriculture and prototypical suburban form, the Test Plots at Auburn University's Mary Olive Thomas Demonstration Forest provide students and faculty with an immersive space of species diversity, difference, and otherness from which to learn. In the Spring of 2019, five circular test plots of grasses and forbs were surgically inserted into an existing mosaic of forest patches, soil types, shade densities and hydrological intricacies. As small, fast-growing species, these meadow plants have the capacity to more quickly adapt to environmental intricacies and changes in management regimes. Although the test plots are broadly intended to rebuild knowledge about the largely eradicated southeastern meadow landscape typology, they are also intended to fully immerse researchers within the "data" of the meadow, encouraging other unexpected questions to emerge and unplanned discoveries to be unearthed from within. This open-ended process of exploration and curiosity is borrowed from Grounded Theory. First described by Glaser and Strauss in 1967, Grounded Theory seeks to immerse the researcher within the data rather than begin with an overall hypothesis to be proven or disproven. The Test Plots within the Mary Olive Thomas Demonstration Forest offer this space to deeply embed students and faculty within the fast-changing, ever-evolving processes that occur within a meadow. Through coursework and research assistantships, students regularly participate in the day-to-day goings-on in the plots. Hours of extensive fieldwork, labor, and careful observation have led to a wide variety of meaningful discoveries about this ecologically critical and culturally significant landscape type. The Test Plots have served as a space to learn about plants and change through time, to test ideas about representation and landscape advocacy and to gain first-hand experience working directly with the medium of the landscape.

The Landscape Lab: Land Vacancy as Testing Ground

Timothy Baird *(Cornell University)*

Many approaches have been tried in American and European cities to re-purpose, revitalize, and reclaim dormant, vacant land. This presentation will explore variations on an approach that considers the site as a Landscape Lab, a testing ground for experimentation, exploration, research, production, and monitoring of selected landscape components. The presentation will begin with an overview of the Urban Voids International Design Ideas Competition that spurred discussion in Philadelphia about how to revitalize that city's 40,000 vacancies. One of the finalist's proposals, Urban Arboretum, proposed tree production as a means of infusing new life and ecological performance into unused properties. The evolution of this idea, refined through fifteen years of design studios at two universities, has led to the installation of a prototype nursery on a city-owned vacant property in the City of Philadelphia; this facility will provide trees and other plants for riparian remediation, city streets, and public parks and open spaces in Philadelphia. This demonstration project provides not only plants for transplantation in the city but also testing of species, environmental education for the community, and jobs training in the nursery industry for residents. These studios, and the resultant nursery, have created a foundation for the proposed development of a Landscape Lab on land owned by Cornell University.

This form of research by design is envisioned to produce multiple drawings and mapping that represent change over time and can be used to extrapolate the principles needed to produce vibrant urban forests that will contribute to the health and well-being of city residents. This presentation will review the fifteen-year process that led to the development of this timely project that may be helpful to those developing multiple forms of the landscape lab for other sites and contexts.

A Collaborative Cartography

Katherine Jenkins *(Ohio State University)*

Over the last six years, I have developed a practice of walking and mapping that addresses the shortcomings of an increasingly digital design pedagogy. Students walk the landscape together and record their movements via GPS. The traces of all students across numerous site visits are collected and overlaid to produce an evolving site map that reflects every participant's individual relationship with the land as well as the class's collective movements over time. Through this process, we generate our own primary-source site knowledge and produce maps that are free from many of the biases of ready-made digital imagery (i.e., Google Earth and GIS). Critically, the construction of these cartographic studies demands both social interaction and physical engagement with the out-of-doors.

This approach to teaching fosters close reading of the built environment and a heightened

awareness of our position relative to shifting spatial and biotic phenomena. In returning to the same site again and again, my students gain an understanding of dynamic ecological systems and cultivate a meaningful relationship to the local environment.

In this presentation I will share the process of collaborative mapping and its outcomes and the test site at Waterman Agricultural and Natural Resources Laboratory in Columbus, Ohio that I have been growing specifically for these walking exercises.

Connecting the Dots: Experimental Landscapes Micro to Macro

Annie Steele (Clemson University)

The Clemson University Landscape Architecture program has embarked on a collaboration with the university's experimental forest. A Land-grant institution, Clemson's experimental forest is a collection of 18,000 + acers of varying ecological diversity and topography, agricultural practices and land management strategies. Located in the Clemson's South Experimental Forest, the Landscape Lab is a 4-acre plot where students are challenged to critically explore the site using various methods of observation, documentation, and application. A diversity of on-site exercises and activities enable a level of immersion unattainable in the classroom. Experimental methods of teaching critical thought and problem-solving challenge students to dissolve the traditional disciplinary silos and transcend the typical scaled approach of design teaching and promote innovative methods of design teaching. Students are encouraged to observe, analyze and process their experiences and findings from a range of scales varying from the microscopic to regional contexts.

Student work is synthesized and processed through exhibition of artifacts, drawings, photographs and modeling that explore ecological processes and nuanced biodiversity at the lab. By transitioning back and forth between scale, students are able to connect the dots between various micro processes occurring on site and the implications those processes have on the larger ecosystem and regional context.

In the workshop I will share the teaching methods that incorporate a multiscale approach to site discovery, inventory and analysis that lead to an innovative sustainable design approach.

Strategies for Research in Healthcare Settings: Challenges and Opportunities

Half-Day Intensive

This intensive, "Strategies for Research in Healthcare Settings: Challenges and Opportunities" is planned as part of the Pedagogies & Methods track for the EDRA 53 conference. Research in healthcare settings is challenging for a variety of reasons, including hospital bureaucracy, institutional review boards (IRBs), and numerous other gatekeepers. As a result, researchers are often forced to make compromises that undermine the rigor of their methodology, in the process adopting approaches with questionable internal validity. In addition, it is not clear that all practitioners have received sufficient training in research methods to recognize what those threats to internal validity might be (e.g., confounding variables). Thus, studies often move forward that unfortunately, given the effort involved, make only a limited contribution and are not able to rule out alternative explanations for the findings.

The vision for this intensive is to provide information that will enable attendees (as well as presenters) to improve the methodological rigor of their work by discussing the kinds of barriers they have encountered and the solutions they have found to address these challenges. The intensive may also provide the opportunity to draft a mission statement for the field of healthcare design (or at the very least for edra) to identify what steps are needed to improve the quality of research being conducted.

Given that the research question should determine the research strategy, the intensive will focus on the kinds of questions that are suitable to answer with a given strategy (or strategies). A continuum of data collection strategies and research designs will be shared, from experimental lab studies and randomized controlled trials to pre-post (occupancy) designs, qualitative/exploratory studies, and national survey research. Beyond the types of research question(s) that can be addressed by a given approach, presenters will focus on limitations/challenges of sample selection, including participant pools, crowdsourcing platforms such as AmazonMTurk and Prolific, intercept approaches, as well as actual patients. In addition, recent advances using specialized technology such as virtual reality and space syntax will be reviewed. We also hope to highlight the need to work across disciplines and the challenges involved in doing so. We think it is important to address the question: How do transdisciplinary studies emerge?

The order of presentation will move from the laboratory to the field, ending with secondary research Each presenter is allotted 30 minutes and expected to give a 20-minute presentation, with some time for follow-up questions.

The Small Experiment: How Less Is More in Healthcare Environment Research

Ann S. Devlin *(Connecticut College)*

The tension between tightly controlled experimental research and ecological validity is long-standing (e.g., Banaji & Crowder, 1989). Measured on any dimension, field research in healthcare environments is expensive. Before moving into the field, small, tightly controlled experimental research can provide evidence about which healthcare design interventions may be advantageous for healthcare outcomes, setting the stage to test the interventions in situ. Further, many researchers do not have either the connections to or support from healthcare administrators to conduct field research in healthcare settings. This presentation provides information about how to advance the knowledge base of healthcare environments in the absence of connections to a facility and on a small budget.

Drawing on a body of research dealing with inpatient and outpatient settings, the presenter will discuss approaches to conducting research in the lab with the potential for generalizability to healthcare environments. Examples will emphasize the benefits and drawbacks in three major areas: research design, visual stimuli, and participants. In research design, examples will include between subjects, within subjects, mixed design, and mixed methods. Regarding the creation of visual stimuli, approaches demonstrated in published work by the presenter will include taking photographs of real-world settings and using them directly, taking photographs of real world settings and manipulating them (e.g., in Photoshop), taking photographs of staged environments, and acquiring permission to use photographs and/or materials (e.g., posters) owned by others and related copyright issues. Participant issues will explore the use of participant pools, crowdsourcing platforms such as AmazonMTurk and Prolific, and intercept approaches.

In 1996, Rachel Kaplan, a methodological pioneer, published an article in the EDRA Proceedings focusing on what can be learned from small experiments. This session returns to focus on the benefits (and challenges) of doing laboratory work with implications for real word applications in healthcare.

Finding Our Way in the Wayfinding Study: How Laboratory Work Informs a Randomized Controlled Trial

Rebecca Davis *(Grand Valley State University);* ***Margaret Calkins*** *(IDEAS)*

Methods to measure the impact of environmental features on wayfinding are challenging due to many factors, such as changing environmental conditions and lack of reproducibility. The Wayfinding Study team has worked for a number of years to develop sophisticated methods of measuring both the features of the environment and wayfinding ability. Initial studies conducted were aimed at measuring the types of environmental features, such as color, form, size, and placement, that impacted wayfinding ability. These studies were conducted in virtual reality environments in a laboratory. In addition, eye tracking technology was employed to measure visual fixations onto the environmental features, giving evidence for the types of features that are most engaging. Using results from these laboratory data, the Wayfinding Study Team developed an environmental intervention (special signage and art cues) aimed at improving wayfinding ability in persons with cognitive impairment who live in long term care settings. The NIA funded randomized controlled trial is being conducted in 12 real world settings. The team identifies three routes in each community (simple, moderate, and complex) and uses space syntax to measure the objective complexity of each route. A limitation of space syntax is that it does not account for wayfinding signage, lighting, or other environmental features other than connectedness within the building plan. The team has developed a new tool to account for the impact of these features (the TAWC; the Tool for Assessing Wayfinding Complexity). The team uses an innovative technology, DOTT, for measuring wayfinding performance. They also are using real time location tracking to determine if participants in sites receiving the intervention interact more within the community. The evolution of this research is an example of moving from laboratory to real world in the conduct of a RCT to measure the effectiveness of an environmental intervention for wayfinding design.

Development of a Comprehensive Occupancy Evaluation Program for Healthcare Design

Kara N Freihoefer *(HGA Architects and Engineers)*

Traditionally known as post-occupancy evaluation, a holistic occupancy evaluation serves the dual intent of collecting data both pre- and post-occupancy of a particular healthcare design project. The benefit of gathering pre-occupancy data is two-fold; it provides insights on current-state, baseline measures and if gathered during the pre-design phases of a project process, insights can be applied to inform the future-state environment. Then, once constructed and operated in for at least six-months, the same protocol, methods, and tools can be used to gather post-occupancy data. The benefit of having both datasets allows for analyses around the magnitude of change because of the newly designed environment. However, because all design variables changed in construction, attributing findings to one design solution is impossible.

Regardless, there is still immense value in gathering insights and data, pre- and post-occupancy on a project-by-project basis, but with standardization of protocols, methods, and tools a robust and sound comprehensive occupancy evaluation program could provide opportunities for meta-analyses. A comprehensive occupancy evaluation also could encourage translational application of findings and discovery of relationships among key design interventions, all while further advancing the role of design research in practice.

This presentation will build the case for the development of a holistic occupancy evaluation program for healthcare settings, discuss a framework for protocol and tool development that engages design practitioners, review opportunities for standardization among various health facility types and across architecture industries, demonstrate data analyses on a meta-analyses scale, and highlight constructs of a data management system. The presentation will feature strategies, obstacles, frameworks, and limitations in the development of an in-house comprehensive occupancy evaluation program and include discussion on extending a collaborative effort among institutions and firms.

Modelling Asynchronous Experiences: Possibilities and Pitfalls of Space Syntax for Research in Health and Wellness Settings

Saif Haq *(Texas Tech University)*

Human understanding of environments often develops through asynchronous experiences. Individuals are either peripatetic, learning about the 'relations' between environmental units as they move about, or, if stationary, experience the effects of diurnal and seasonal changes. Either way, what they 'see' is always changing. The environmental learning of mobile humans is often called a 'cognitive map', and in turn is related to moving behavior and navigational decision making.

Modelling the effects of continuous changes of location with sufficient rigor for quantitative analyses has been challenging. The theory and methodology of Space Syntax offers precise ways of measuring complex environmental properties that arise from connections of each space to all other spaces contained in the same layout – sometimes directly, sometimes through other intermediate spaces. These analyses indicate a visual 'structure' perhaps comparable to that of a moving human's experience. As such, they can be understood as synchronous models of asynchronous experiences. Increased computational powers now allow finer tuned layout investigations by considering topological, metric, and geometric relationships, defining different kinds of unit spaces, and choosing the radii of analyses. However, since moving humans may or may not travel to or see all spaces in a layout, Syntax analyses might be considered 'idealized' because all spaces in a plan drawing and connections to all other spaces are the base of analysis.

This presentation will couple foundational concepts of Space Syntax with advanced analytical techniques. After a brief review of research that used these variables to investigate human and medical outcomes, it will conclude with a discussion of its drawbacks and opportunities. With respect to the agenda of this conference, the case studies and discussions will focus on healthcare and public health outcomes.

Prescribing Daily Doses of Nature in Virtual Reality for Mental Health: A State-of-Knowledge Overview and Methodological Lessons from a Pilot Study of Safety, Efficacy, and Adherence

Matthew Browning *(Clemson University);* ***Seunguk Shin*** *(University of Illinois);* ***Gabby Drong*** *(University of Illinois);* ***Olivia McAnirlin*** *(Clemson University);* ***Shuai Yuan*** *(Clemson University);* ***David Hoptman*** *(InViro Virtual Reality Environments);* ***Gregory N. Bratman*** *(University of Washington);* ***Wendy Heller*** *(University of Illinois)*

The demand for at-home healthcare systems rose sharply during the COVID-19 pandemic. Mental health also declined from fear, infections and mortality, financial concerns, caregiver demands, and social constraints. This union warranted more research on relatively low-cost, mobile, self-care mental health interventions. Modern virtual reality (VR) technology presents promising delivery mechanisms for these interventions.

VR has existed for decades, but recent advances have allowed head-mounted displays (HMDs) to be accessible and affordable. Users can undertake a variety of clinical interventions, including distraction therapy, mindfulness training, cognitive behavior therapy, guided imagery, and attention/stress reduction from exposure to restorative environments. These virtual, beneficial environments can be created with modest cost and skill using 360-degree cameras. The first half of this talk presents a state-of-knowledge overview on VR devices, the efficacy of VR interventions for different outcomes, approaches to VR content creation, and ongoing research needs for the environmental designer/scholar.

The second half of this talk presents the lessons learned from a pilot study involving a longitudinal VR prescription for mental health. Participants were randomly assigned to VR or a control group. Those assigned to VR were asked to watch 4-min 360-degree blue and green space videos using an Oculus Go HMD daily for 3 to 4 weeks. The study ran over three semesters and collected usable data from approximately 15 students at the University of Illinois at Urbana-Champaign before the pandemic and 20 students at Clemson University in fall 2020. Anhedonic depression, anxious arousal, worry, and risk factors (e.g., low positive affect, high negative affect, and rumination) were measured weekly. We observed some efficacy trends, few technical issues and adverse effects, and good adherence levels (M = 5, range = 2-7 viewings/wk). We conclude this talk with recommendations for additional research lines involving VR, mental health, and at-home healthcare settings.

Hindsight 20/20: Learning from a 2020 National Study of the Outpatient Experience

Nicholas Watkins *(Gensler)*

Pandemic-related, economic, policy, and technological forces have only amplified volatility in a United States healthcare industry where margins are shrinking and patient consumerism spells success or failure. However, investments in innovative outpatient strategies have been paying off by affording greater value to consumers. The outpatient care bellwether, with its flurry of service and facility hybrids, and the innovations emerging from the COVID-19 pandemic create an opportunity for us to take a comprehensive snapshot of the state-of-the industry and understand how social determinants of health, design, and digital design shape outpatient experiences and outcomes. This nationwide survey of 3,578 outpatients represents over 83 diagnoses, 81 health systems, and 16 outpatient settings. The study tested the themes of outpatient engagement, perceived care quality, consumer loyalty, pandemic experience, and virtual visit quality; identified outpatient populations by their demographic characteristics and their experiences with and access to outpatient care; identified design and digital design features that positively impact outpatient experience and outcomes; and explored optimal mixes of outpatient services. Opportunities and unexpected challenges of the pandemic, questionnaire development, sampling, data collection, and analyses will be discussed. Audience members will contextualize the methods and findings to their own experiences and understand ways to position themselves for success when performing similar research.

Increasing Brand Value By Elevating the Human Experience: Qualitative Considerations

***Lorissa MacAllister** (Enviah)*

Increasingly, healthcare providers compete on the strength of their brands for patients, staff, and resources. Since brand value is the product of the aggregate experiences and perceptions of a product's users, it is directly proportionate to the quality of human interactions and encounters with a healthcare provider. To increase the value of its brand, a healthcare provider must satisfy the objective needs and subjective expectations of patients, families, and staff. Focusing on the top line of quality and service results will improve the overall value. With a focus on value, Dr. MacAllister will describe the qualitive data that can be extracted from healthcare organizations (productivity, capacity, efficacy and satisfaction) that directly tie to the outcome of the organizations and how the brand is constructed. She will also share how to apply the data to an operating model focused on designing positive memories and ultimately brand through a deeper application of Dr. Daniel Kahneman's Peak – End rule. Dr. MacAllister's approach assures that there is highest performance in the environment, the most maneuverable elements of the equation to get better results. The limitations of this work focus around the organization's ability to adapt and change to the vision that is established.

Packaging for the Practitioner: The Role of Secondary Research

***Ellen Taylor** (The Center for Health Design)*

We live in an era of information overload or information pollution. Two decades ago, Jakob Nielsen stated that the web was a procrastination apparatus that "can absorb as much time as is required to ensure that you won't get any real work done." Today, access to the Internet can be a blessing and a curse for practitioners who can Google almost anything, and for some, this constitutes a form of research. The reality is that just like all other types of "searchable" information, rigorous research is being published at a rate that no one can realistically follow. As a result, the value of secondary research is increasingly important. This is especially true for practitioners in environmental design where the time and resources to access peer-reviewed research may be more challenging than for their counterparts in academia.

The dissemination of such secondary research can come in a variety of forms, and with a wide range of outputs, the process for creating tools and resources can also vary in rigor. The Center for Health Design has a history of summarizing relevant evidence for design practitioners who focus on the influence of the built environment on a host of outcomes. These tools and resources include peer reviewed publications, Post Occupancy Evaluations, Safety Risk Assessment tools, Interactive Diagrams, Slidecasts, Issue Briefs, etc. As part of this session, participants will learn how packaging for the practitioner involves the creation of its own study design with a choice of research methods (primary and secondary) that need to appropriately address the aims of the deliverable, while at the same time taking into account the age-old triad of scope, schedule, and budget.

Behind the Curtain: The Latest in Practice-Based Research, Year Two

Full-Day Intensive

It is becoming more and more common for design firms, manufacturers, and industry partners to conduct research in practice to understand design's impact and contribute to the knowledge base. Practitioners are using research to improve their products/processes, support client/team decisions, win new work, and for marketing purposes. Many practice-based researchers are adapting traditional, academically rigorous research methods to better suit real-world conditions and applicability to practice. However, without industry standards or relative transparency between companies, many researchers in practice are plotting their own course and defining what research means for their company.

Yet now more than ever, there is interest among design researchers in practice to share what they are doing. In fact, at the EDRA52 conference, a panel of over a dozen design researchers in practice led an intensive session to offer a glimpse "behind the curtain" of how their companies conduct and use design research in practice. Last year's session was well attended and received a lot of positive feedback for both the information shared as well as the forum the event provided for people to discuss these issues.

This year's intensive will be a continuation of that previous discussion, and is accordingly dubbed "Year 2" of what we hope is an annual tradition to explore the latest in practice-based design research. Our session goals are twofold: (1) recognize the varied approaches to research in practice, and (2) consider how we can improve upon and expand our efforts—both as individuals and collectively for the industry. This year's intensive will include over a dozen leading researchers in practice who will guide attendees through three mini-workshops, deep diving into the topics of: pre- and post-occupancy evaluation, partnership models between academia and practice, and translating research into practice.

This session is sponsored by the EDRA Researchers in Professional Practice Knowledge Network.

Pre- and Post-Occupancy Evaluation

Cynthia L Milota *(Ware Malcomb);* ***Danya Hakky*** *(Perkins Eastman Architects);* ***Renae Rich*** *(HGA Architects & Engineers);* ***Nicholas Watkins*** *(Gensler);* ***Rachel Nasland*** *(LPA, Inc.)*

Much has been written on the benefits of Pre- and Post-Occupancy Evaluations (PPOEs), the process of assessing workspaces before and after they have been occupied for some time duration, using rigorous and systematic tools (Preiser, White, & Rabinowitz, 2015). Yet, according to a 2015 US study, PPOEs are conducted in less than 5% of all projects (Hiromoto, 2015). PPOEs are often viewed as time consuming for project teams and the evaluated participants, expensive to conduct, costly for addressing findings, and could potentially expose negative information.

Exploring from the designer, researcher, and client perspectives, this session will assess the value proposition for conducting PPOEs, explore myths, opportunities, challenges, metrics, and models for integrating PPOEs into the project delivery process.

This 90-minute experiential session will be divided into two parts. In the first segment, the group will be divided into teams for a modified "World Café" exercise. (http://www.theworldcafe.com/key-concepts-resources/world-cafe-method/), moving through topic areas including: metrics/measuring, barriers/success, and communication strategies. At the conclusion of this segment, the findings of each topic will be shared with the larger group.

In the second segment, the group will assess and deconstruct a survey instrument/questions with the goal of contributing to a larger dataset, often discussed among researchers but that has yet to be undertaken. At the conclusion of this segment, participants will have a data bank of sample questions appropriate for various methods.

Pre- and Post-Occupancy Evaluations are a powerful source of information about projects: documenting design success, revealing areas for improvement, and building trust with internal stakeholders and clients. Using both quantitative (the what) and qualitative (the why) measures provides robust, actionable results that can be applied efficiently within project timeline and budget constraints.

Partnership Models between Academia and Practice

Sam Coats *(CallisonRTKL);* ***B. Sanborn*** *(DLR Group);* ***Haripriya Sathyanarayanan*** *(University of California, Berkeley)*

The aim of this panel is to speak from multiple perspectives—academic, student, practitioner, and industry outsider—about the opportunities and challenges involved in Academic-Practice partnerships, through case studies that share experiences, successful models, and research practice, to initiate the development of a resource guide/toolkit through the Researchers in Professional Practice Knowledge Network.

Academic-Practice partnerships are long-term, intentional, dynamic, and mutually beneficial collaborations that strive to bridge theory and practice. While there is growing literature on partnerships leading to evidence-based practice, (1) most approaches aim to push research to practice, (2) don't adequately address research agendas informed by practice, (3) lack a feedback loop between academia and practice, and (4) don't always enable ease of adoption and implementation. Additionally, the organizational structure, values, schedule, and funding streams of a university as opposed to an AEC firm do not typically align, forcing collaborators to either come into alignment to create healthy partnerships or achieve temporary consensus without merging values. Other design industries, however, leverage relationships with researchers to a greater extent than the AEC industry, demonstrating that partnerships are possible, while fostering and sustaining fast innovation. The evolving nature of partnerships pose challenges and highlight the pressing need to surface key agreements and perspectives to remove obstacles to create equitable partnerships that align with the goals of all parties in a collaboration.

This session will include a framing presentation on Academic-Practice partnerships, and findings from interviews with stakeholders on the topic using a Pecha-Kucha style narration. Following this, we will conclude with a panel discussion with outside experts sharing their unique and collective perspectives on collaborations, aimed at subsequent development of a resource guide for future projects and partnerships.

The conversation will acknowledge challenges in partnerships and address strategies to improve communication and collect meaningful case stories.

Translating Research into Practice

Rachel Nasland *(LPA inc.);* ***Cameron McKee*** *(Cannon Design);* ***Francesqca Jimenez*** *(HDR Architecture, Inc.);* ***Sally Augustin*** *(Design With Science / Research Design Connections)*

It is widely accepted that evidence-based design and practice can improve design, health, performance, and well-being. But how do architects understand and use research in practice, and what knowledge do they need for research uptake, and to bring value to their clients and practice? There is need for a critical evaluation of research and a deeper understanding of the purpose, methods, intended audience, relevance, credibility, reliability, and limitations of a study to inform design decisions. Design and practice-based research is often project-focused, and research evidence is not always directly transferable to practice due to challenges that may include scientific jargon, presentation, lack of examples (design case studies), limited partnerships between design practitioners and academic-research institutions/universities, and gaps in knowledge transfer between academic-researchers and design practitioners. This makes translation of research findings into accessible formats critical to its application in design practice. Therefore, dissemination, an important stage of a research study, must include the consideration of different formats to effectively communicate research findings in accessible and user-friendly formats.

Lightning talks will address the understanding of research and practice-based research methods, barriers for the application of research in design practice, and how research methods can be plugged into various stages of the design process to address different needs. Following the talks, pairs of researchers and practitioners (and/ or academic and practice-based researchers) will participate in a facilitated conversation on knowledge sharing and research application in their domain. The aim is to address access to and consumption of research, application of findings in design practice, and methods used for communication and presentation. The session will acknowledge challenges in the translation of research into accessible formats for practitioners, capture the perspectives of researchers and practitioners, and address strategies (an action plan) for effective communication and translation of research knowledge in design practice.

Building Authentic Resilience in Diverse Communities

Half-Day Intensive

It is said that the end of every war sows the seeds of the new conflict. Starting in the early sixties the country began, albeit slowly and unevenly, to address the systemic racism embedded in every aspect of how neighborhoods were formed. They tackled important issues such as Redlining, an FHA manual that explicitly required segregation, and "sundown towns." However, these victories over structural racism in the development of communities led to "white flight," punitive property taxation, and ultimately gentrification, resulting in new manifestations of inequality that broke societal bonds. This session will examine ways in which we can reconnect those societal bonds and embed resilience into diverse communities so that it becomes more difficult to obliterate the ties that bind the people together.

We begin this journey examining the issues of "Resilience, Homogeneity, Diversity, and Equity" where we begin to address the issues of the connection between equity and resilience, and the role of these components in the construction of community. This will also bring in the issues of scale, and the importance of understanding these issues across differing gradations of development.

Next, we will explore how urban migration patterns created new forms of homogeneity around "Gentrification and the New Segregation" and discuss ways to bring intersectional diversity back to the urban landscape. In this, we will look at the role of gentrification in displacing established communities, and in marginalizing vulnerable and politically disconnected, communities.

In "Resilient Cities: Manufactured Consensus, Engineered Diversity, and the Ordering of Difference," we will critique how neoliberal systems of governance are manufacturing consensus in the current discourses on climate change and resilience. We will interrogate how the utopian versions and visions of a resilient city and community are de facto exacerbating social, environmental, and economic injustice and we will examine how approaches, foregrounding dissensus and conflict will contribute to the resilience and empowerment of marginalized communities and places.

From there we look at how to create "Community Resilience in Group Form" through examining a matrix of scales and levels of heterogeneity to inform design, focusing in on cohesion in the members of the community and how that builds symbiotic interactions. Once we have established a system to understand how to build group resilience, we will look at indigenous cultures, and their use of community-based design in the creation of "Community Resilience Better Supported by Control of the Built Environment."

From the base of these papers, we will initiate an interactive discussion about how to develop an authentic identity that embeds resilience, equity, and intersectionality into the fabric of the community.

Resilience, Homogeneity, Diversity, Equity

Joseph Juhasz *(University of Colorado)*

There is good evidence that across a great variety of systems, a combination of homogeneous subpopulations coexistent with a great diversity thereof provide greater resilience than alternatives thereto. What is the proper scale for the homogeneous subpopulation is a matter of great import. This is so at the various scales at which we observe and organize. It can be argued that Equity is a function of this sort of Resilience.

One can look at the whole planet, at continents, nations, regions, cities, villages, neighborhoods and building clusters or even individual buildings. Homogeneity and diversity can have their definition and role at each of these scales.

And again, one can examine heterogeneity or homogeneity measured along what dimension or dimensions. There is race, culture, religion, lifestyle, economic arrangements, ideology, gender, age, stage of the life cycle, just to mention a few. At each scale of habitation which is the proper or optimum homogeneity and heterogeneity to achieve maximum attainable resilience?

These are not hypothetical nor philosophical nor abstract issues. They relate directly to our lives and values right here right now in the 21st Century. We, humans, have managed to bring into reality something approaching Hell on Earth--and these issues are directly relevant to how we as individuals, family members, community members, citizens, and humans relate to each other.

Authentic communities are neither completely homogeneous nor completely heterogeneous. They shy away from the notion that there is a universal correct answer or arrangement and have patience and respect both for homogeneity and for heterogeneity. The imperfect but nonetheless resilient equity they achieve lays aside grandiose visions of "development," "progress," and "equality." Homogeneity and heterogeneity both respect the reality that no two things in this universe are equal to one another.

Gentrification and the New Segregation

Scott Crisman Sworts *(Oxford Brookes University)*

One essential aspect of a true sense of community is that it possesses economic diversity. It is critical for people at each end of the economic scale to interact and relate to each other, as this inspires compassion for the struggles of the other groups and makes it far more difficult to stereotype and dismiss them.

In The United States, today's modern suburbs are economically stratified, with each mass-produced subdivision catering to a specific "price-point" where home costs, and consequently incomes, are constrained to a relatively narrow band. Often these bands are also specifically designed to exclude certain demographic groups as well.

However, the older, "Pre-War" neighborhoods do not exhibit this economic homogeny, as on any typical street from this era there will be houses ranging in scale from small bungalows to large, elegant houses. This changes with the birth of the subdivision, bringing waves of change to cities.

In the first wave, coinciding with white flight, many of the larger houses were divided up into small apartments, rented out by remote owners more interested in wealth than community. Around the end of the century, the flight to the suburbs reversed, and these older communities became highly desirable. People bought up these houses, renovating them, and often flipping them for a substantial profit.

After this wave of gentrification was completed, a second wave began, one that was built on bringing the economic homogeny of the subdivisions to the inner city. Any house that was not of a scale to entice the desired wealthy resident was either dramatically enlarged or scraped to be replaced with a "modern" house that met the needs of the new economic elite. This paper will look at ways to reverse this economic segregation and bring intersectional diversity back to American Cities.

Resilient Cities: Manufactured Consensus, Engineered Diversity, and the Ordering of Difference

Joern Langhorst *(University of Colorado, Denver)*

The building of consensus has been a key element of liberal democracies. Decisions on intentional place change and spatial design within this system of governance have been equally consensus oriented. However, the building of consensus, inherent in different approaches to "participation", might be problematic and camouflage hegemonial agendas, serve as a means of control and a way to depoliticize planning and design processes. Space in these contexts is very much the place of and a tool for the ordering of difference(s). The uneven outcomes of such processes for different communities (e.g. environmental, social and economic injustice) call attention to fundamental critiques of consensus-based decision processes:

Dissensus and conflict- based approaches, such as agonistic pluralism, suggest that consensus inevitably produces winners and losers, that the needs and desires of some will always be impossible to meet, and that intentionally heterogeneous conditions and outcomes might be preferable to manufactured homogeneity.

The concept of resilience, enthusiastically embraced by the kind of neoliberal capitalism that makes and remakes cities and urbanity, relies on, institutionalizes and reifies the production of inequality and unevenness that victimizes certain neighborhoods and communities while rewarding economic and political elites, and maintaining the growth machine that relies on the production and reproduction of difference.

Consensus-based discourses on climate change and resilience are investigated and critically interrogated against their utopian claims to environmental, social and economic sustainability and justice. This paper makes a convincing case that "green infrastructure" as well as design and planning to improve climate resilience are merely perpetuating patterns of systemic and systematic injustice. Contemporary forms of "redlining" and "greenlining" under the guise of building more resilient places and communities are co-opting marginalized and disempowered communities in their own victimization, resulting in inauthentic resilience, exacerbating disempowerment and marginalization, and ultimately leading to a loss of community and place identity.

Community Resilience in Group Form

Niccolo Casewit *(Environmental Productions)*

An essential measurement of a community's resilience lies in the capacity to adapt to change through development and expansion, and reuse when faced with both internal and external challenges. This must assert the need for both conformity and individuality at the "proper" scales of intervention and analysis. Resilience is a function of the combination of physical and symbolic forms accompanied by societal interactions, shelters, and privacies. It can be interpreted and signified at different physical and organizational scales as exhibiting heterogeneity, homogeneity and sometimes both.

The levels of Homogeneity (conforming typologies) and Heterogeneity (diversity of forms) one might experience and encounter at different scales of habitation in an attainable community, and shapes environmental/communal from the micro to the macro as a provocation to inform the design of resilient places at different scales.

The resiliency of future communities can be

informed by past success, but also fresh vision for supporting purposeful cohesion between members of the communities we would like to live with and live for. The credo varietas concordia equals unity in diversity

will make the difference in our resilience. In many ways we can see the human habitat as a partly built environment that function best as an ecology of diverse symbiotic interactions, with a variety of forms but also within distinct ecotones, areas, niches, and specific locations adapting in different ways with and separate from each other.

The challenge of community resilience is a challenge of survival in a harsh world. Our resilience will be dependent on the dynamic balancing act between sustainable ecological expansion and the re-development (regeneration) of existing environments. Authentic resilience is not just the mere attempt at survival while trying to "maintain" the same forms of the last 70 years but becomes an impetus to drive change for our survival.

Community Resilience Better Supported By Control of the Built Environment

Lynn Paxson (Iowa State University)

Indigenous peoples have been resilient and struggling as communities while resisting colonization, assimilation, adoption, or adaptation since the contestation with settlers. More recently some communities have been able - through their own economic development or Indigenous philanthropic sources - to achieve greater control over their place-making or place sustaining decision making. Using community-based design Native Nations can create places that not only support community resilience but whose physical places also help support their resilience. Place-making and places that celebrate Indigenous core values and respect the cultures and environments they are part of. Indigenous peoples see themselves as part of places, just one part of places. Although many of our Indigenous peoples were moved off their traditional lands, they made place in the places they were forced into. Also, as land-based practitioners they recognize the spirit and power of places, power that is part of the spaces themselves. They see themselves as just one of the communities or 'peoples' that populate the earth. This means that there is a recognition of all of the peoples of nature – the 4-legged ones, the winged ones, the plants etc. Understanding place and time as circular rather than linear supports many transformative threshold options. This orientation can also support the design of ever-changing cultures while resisting outsider expectations. These topics will be explored using various contemporary Indigenous projects and examples.

The Evolution of the Places of Work in the Communicative Constitution of Work: Workplace Environments & Communication Networks Joint Intensive Session

Half-Day Intensive

As we emerge from COVID, those involved in research, design, and management of the places of work are at a critical moment of change within white-collar work practices. We are assisting a re-shaping of how work is accomplished, where it is done, and how it impacts the well-being of employees, businesses, and the communities they inhabit.

The workplace, for many white-collar workers, is a centralized organization and place to work. While this originated from the need to physically connect workers, machines, and processes for the creation of physical products, communicative practices have always been central to our ability to organize. The introduction and development of information and communication technologies (ICTs) have made it possible for these communicative practices of organizing to occur through digital channels and in mediated spaces. What had been a slow move towards expanding and implementing the use of ICTs for the communicative practice of organizing, the COVID pandemic response pushed to an instant move out of shared place entirely. However, this emergency necessitated ignoring much of what research indicates and practice experiences see about mediated and place-based communicative patterns that enable organizational work.

This session will engage cross-disciplinary theory, research, and practice to examine mediated and emplaced communication patterns in organizations to understand the development of post-COVID places of work.

Understanding How Organizations Are Communicating Constituted through Technology & Place

Sheila Gobes-Ryan *(University of South Florida)*

White collar workers can connect to work without a shared 'place'. However, workers always work in a 'place'. Communication, as the central organizer of white-collar work, is made possible by some combination of information and communication technologies (ICT) and place. While use of ICTs to connect workers not sharing the same organizational space was increasing before COVID, most workers were still 'contained' in organizational spaces. COVID necessitated organizations to use ICTs to connect white collar workers without any being in the same organizational space. And it worked, but not perfectly. Businesses began to identify in what ways the mothballing of their space weakened their essential ways of conducting business. Much of what they identified was about communication.

As organizations return from COVID quarantines, what to do about the places their employees work to support organizational success and employee well-being then becomes the significant question. What is 'place' going to be as ICTs continue to evolve, the use of ICTs in organizational communication will continue to evolve, and how we use 'place' and 'space' continue to evolve? This presentation will be a meta-synthesis of the conceptual frameworks used to understand the communicative processes that constitute organizations. It will identify the workplace research used to examine the significance of places in which we work, as part of the continuum of place and technology that support the constitution of organization though communication.

Understanding How Organizations Are Communicating Constituted through Technology & Place

Ardis Hanson *(University of South Florida)*

White collar workers can connect to work without a shared 'place'. However, workers always work in a 'place'. Communication, as the central organizer of white-collar work, is made possible by some combination of information and communication technologies (ICT) and place. While use of ICTs to connect workers not sharing the same organizational space was increasing before COVID, most workers were still 'contained' in organizational spaces. COVID necessitated organizations to use ICTs to connect white collar workers without any being in the same organizational space. And it worked, but not perfectly. Businesses began to identify in what ways the mothballing of their space weakened their essential ways of conducting business. Much of what they identified was about communication.

As organizations return from COVID quarantines, what to do about the places their employees work to support organizational success and employee well-being then becomes the significant question. What is 'place' going to be as ICTs continue to evolve, the use of ICTs in organizational communication will continue to evolve, and how we use 'place' and 'space' continue to evolve? This presentation will be a meta-synthesis of the conceptual frameworks used to understand the communicative processes that constitute organizations. It will identify the workplace research used to examine the significance of places in which we work, as part of the continuum of place and technology that support the constitution of organization though communication.

The Workplace 22

Sally Augustin *(Design With Science / Research Design Connections)*

A meta-analysis of environmental neuroscience research indicates that there are 22 key design elements and factors that enable user wellbeing and performance to full potential and that need to be considered when workplaces are being developed. These elements and factors are pertinent whether the work area(s) being designed are at centralized commercial sites, at-home, at co-working facilities or elsewhere, and whether particular locations are used exclusively or in a hybrid configuration. This session will present the "Workplace 22" as well as well as key motivations for applying environmental neuroscience and the significant negative consequences for solo focused work and collaborative efforts of failing to do so.

Digital Homes Under Covid-19 and Their Effect on Wellbeing; The Case of Quebec City

Pablo Garcia de Paredes *(Université Laval)*

Covid-19 has led to new work (Barone Gibbs et al., 2021) and mobility habits (Toger et al., 2021) that have transformed how we use our houses and work. Intense telework has changed house use patterns and out-of-home activities, like corporate culture practices, workplace training, and learning. This transition was made possible by many advancements in digital communications. Now, many behaviors are crucially dependent on home and digital skills. This signifies an overlap between house environments, home conceptualizations, and digital technology, fruitful interception for scientific inquiry. Departing from Actor-Network Theory (Latour, 2005), home and objects are players in the network. A house and a digital device are more than objects, symbolically associating commercial, recreational, and familial practices. We developed a conceptual framework studying the interaction between people, house environments, and digital devices, including the traditional skills (Ross, 2004) and symbolic skills (Dion et al., 2014) involved in environmental adaptation and digital technology use. Accordingly, we developed three hypotheses accounting for the networked reality of house and device use: (A) that reported well-being depends on how well a house, a neighborhood, and a given social condition can sustain new skills. And (B) users who effectively developed skills in digital communication and virtual-natural environmental conciliation will make pandemic digital habits permanent and change their housing preferences. We believe -as a complementary hypothesis to A and B -that this re-skilling process was conditioned by their spatial (house and neighborhood), time constraints, activity patterns, family composition, and virtual-natural orientations (Misra & Stokols, 2012) (C). Our data on reported wellbeing comes from the MAVIPAN survey of 3000 households in the 17 regions of Quebec, Canada. We used a mixed-methods approach: first comparing results from a previous environmental wellbeing scale to our digital technology use variables, and secondly applied grounded theory analysis to explain our findings.

Perspectives on Well-Being in a Co-Working Space; Views from inside the Mill

Deborah Bucci *(Fielding Graduate University);* ***Fredrick Steier*** *(Fielding Institute)*

Post-covid coworking spaces, an emerging workplace type, face significant communication opportunities and challenges. Coworking spaces can bring together people interested in collaborative possibilities, perhaps resting on a coffee house metaphor. At the same time, and in direct contrast, these spaces can also function in the same way that an individual cubicle in a more traditional office might. When considering this type of workplace, if we braid issues of wellbeing with communication, important design research questions emerge for coworking spaces. How we think about these workspaces post-covid can benefit from systems perspectives that recognize and value the variety of individual perspectives present in any coworking space. This presentation discusses research on wellbeing, using the CDC Well-Being Concepts and Health-Related Quality of Life Measures, along with input from individual workers about what wellbeing in a workplace means to them.

What can we learn about wellbeing from those who work in coworking spaces? We will share ideas learned from an action-research informed project based in a refurbished textile factory in The Village of West Greenville, South Carolina. The input was collected from Brandon Mill coworking space through member interviews and Zero Day Dialogues, which are dialogic café-like group processes. Insights from both the dialogic processes and interviews will be offered, with a particular focus on what can be learned about communication in coworking spaces in a post-pandemic era, particularly regarding both individual and collective ideas of wellbeing. We will also offer implications for coworking workplace design, as well as workplace design in general.

We propose to offer lessons learned from Brandon Mill to then feed into an interactive session – so both presentation and workshop exploring whole systems design of post-covid coworking spaces.

A Case for Recognizing Employee Needs and Organizational Values in Corporate Workplace

Gretta Peterson *(MillerKnoll)*

As companies across the world continue to consider both their short- and long- term workplace strategies, many will be looking at the actions of other organizations. During the height of the pandemic, MillerKnoll began reimagining their own workplaces and work experiences with a focus on learning, experimenting and evolving – to help determine the new shape of the workplace, it's role in our lives, and how to best support the shift towards hybrid work. This session will present MillerKnoll's own journey in holding place accountable to their people, values, and point of view. Their integrated approach, process and metrics used to understand + evaluate the ongoing needs of their people will be explored in the context of designing workplaces that fulfil a greater purpose.

The Rise of a Local Coworking Model: Community-Driven Approaches to Shape Urban Development Locally

Irene Manzini Ceinar *(The Bartlett School of Architecture, University College London)*

The pandemic caused by the massive spread of the COVID-19 in 2020-2021 has altered the working lifestyle worldwide, with many workplaces in an enforced modification to allow social distancing, marking a massive shift in working culture in the contemporary era. Indeed, when home is not the most efficient workplace and the office cannot host the workers due to social distancing limitations, the "Third place", such as coworking spaces, represents a valuable alternative for remote workers. Focusing on coworking spaces, during history, several waves have transformed their original concept: Initially, it was characterized by independent and affordable workspaces to face the economic recession. An increase in commercialization and neoliberal trends represent the second wave. Following this neo-corporate wave, community-driven, or resilient coworking emerged with the purpose to benefit the local context. Those spaces embrace the evolution of work towards flexibility, enhancing spill-over, and cross-fertilization effects. Many of them pair with charities, local associations, or cooperatives, aiming at supporting the local community, such as Work Heights in Brooklyn, New York, or Outlandish in Finsbury Park, London – a no-profit worker co-op, or.

Although various studies have examined coworking from different angles, there is limited knowledge of the community-driven approaches that CSs can adopt, especially in pandemic times, to support the local community and benefit a sustainable local development.

During COVID-19, several community-driven coworking spaces embraced the evolution of work towards flexibility, enhancing spill-over and cross fertilization effects while contributing as vital spaces of local resilience. This study investigates the role of community-driven coworking spaces during COVID-19, in terms of local socio-economic development in peripheral areas, providing robust frameworks and empirical evidence to support their implementation into urban design strategies in the post-COVID phase.

Places of Work - What Is Happening

Ellen Bruce Keable *(Jacobs)*

In practice there is a need to make the ideas and ideals of research work with the possibilities and challenges of clients of their employees. This presentation will start with a discussion of the post-COVID strategies and design approaches being developed to meet the specific needs of a range of clients. After which it will respond to the ideas presented throughout the session.

Abstracts: Symposia

A Plea for Help: The Crumbling of Mental Health Among Architecture and Landscape Architecture Students

Session Abstract:

News media outlets are sending alarms that there is a national mental health crisis among college students. Surveys show that about 30% of college students suffer from depression, anxiety and/or stress which negatively affects academic performance (ACHA, 2021). While surveys hint that there is a national problem, very little research delves into why mental health issues are increasing among college students and what can be done about it.

According to the Counseling and Psychological Services (CAPS) on one college campus, architecture and landscape architecture students are the most vulnerable to a decline in mental health during the academic semester. Could this be exacerbated by the nature of design studies, the culture of the design studio, expectations, workload demands, time management, or the endless hours working resulting in unhealthy lifestyle choices? Could this be fueled by the pandemic, social inequalities, climate change, and other burdens that are weighing heavy on the minds of our younger generations? The increase in mental health issues among students is a cry for help. Ignoring their cry is simply irresponsible today, a time where there is a heightened awareness of inequalities.

This symposium will tackle these issues and three research questions in particular: (1) What is the overall health and well-being of students in the School of Architecture at one university, (2) What are the most common stressors faced by students and what unhealthy behaviors do students adopt, and (3) What strategies have been found helpful to lower stress and anxiety levels as voiced by students? These questions will be answered from an empirical study at one university using surveys; interviews; screening tools to measure the emotional states of depression, anxiety and stress scales; and ethnographic studies capturing a day in the life of students.

The 90-minutes symposium will be organized in three parts:

- The first part (50 minutes): 1. An introduction to the problem and overall context of the mental health crisis on college campuses – Zinzow (10 minutes). 2 Key findings on undergraduate architecture students - Hambright-Belue (10 minutes), 3. Key findings on undergraduate landscape architecture students - Powers (10 minutes), and 4. Key findings from a mental health assessment, online survey, and interviews for all students – Price (20 minutes)
- The second part (20 minutes): Battisto will lead a Q&A session with the panel to cover strategies and solutions to promote student health and wellness in design programs.
- The third part (20 minutes): An open discussion with the panel and the audience to discuss ways forward and possible research studies across universities to shift the emphasis toward student health and wellness.

This symposium gives architecture and landscape architecture students a voice as to why mental health matters and calls for better advocacy for a culture that promotes student health and wellness. Findings from this empirical study provide a snapshot of design students' mental health and ways to improve their health and wellness.

Mental Health Among U.S. College Students: Risk, Prevalence, and Recommendations for Intervention

Heidi Zinzow *(Clemson University)*

College students suffer from high rates of mental health problems, including mood and anxiety disorders. Prior to the pandemic, one in five college students met the criteria for a psychiatric disorder (Auerbach et al., 2016), and suicide was the second leading cause of death among this population (CDC, 2019). Research has demonstrated an increase in externalizing symptoms and attention problems among college students since the onset of COVID-19, with students utilizing campus wellness programs being less affected (Copeland et al., 2021). Students have encountered numerous stressors, including relocation, financial strain, transitions in academic modalities, and reduced access to services. Researchers highlight the need to (1) identify which students are at highest risk for mental health problems; (2) develop targeted health promotion strategies for these students; and (3) utilize accessible, evidence-based interventions to prevent and ameliorate mental health symptoms among this population (Liu et al., 2020).

In this presentation, we will present data on risk and protective factors, as well as the prevalence of mental health symptoms among [University name] students. For example, in 2020, 38% of [University name] students reported that stress impacted their academic performance, and 21% utilized professional mental health services (NCHA, 2020). These data will be contextualized within the broader landscape of the national mental health crisis at U.S. colleges and universities. Recommendations for campus health promotion and mental health service provision will be discussed.

Challenges of Being a First Year Architecture Student

Sallie Hambright-Belue *(Clemson University)*

Mental health has come to the forefront of recent conversations, but it is not a new challenge. The American Institute of Architecture Students' recent publication notes that this issue has been acknowledged since the 1990's (AIAS, 2020). While some changes have been adopted, issues have not been addressed adequately and students are struggling more than ever with their health and wellness.

A study to investigate the health and wellness of first-year architecture students at one university was completed in the fall of 2021. At the beginning of the semester, 140 students were surveyed to understand their expectations and needs as beginning architecture students. This survey was followed by four others to further examine studio time commitment, counselor drop-in opportunities, the needs and services offered to students, and their effectiveness.

This session will highlight the results and offer possible ways to improve wellness for first-year students. Findings show that students are genuinely excited about this next life chapter. One student said, "I am most excited to focus more intently on architecture and design. I am excited to collaborate with new people and professors." The rigors of college quickly set in, especially in a project-based discipline where time management becomes an essential skill. Access to materials, studio/building environment, and extended studio class times are additional barriers to a healthy learning environment.

Findings from the surveys led to changes in the first-year studio and pointed to strategies that should be considered across the undergraduate program. These include instruction on developing good time management skills, mental health breaks, informal learning spaces, and improved access to project materials. A major takeaway from this study is that Schools of Architecture should seek ways to revisit program offerings and mechanisms for delivery to align with the expectations and needs of their first-year students.

Repositioning Design Education As Precedent for Health, Wellness, and Learning

Matthew Powers *(Clemson University)*

Designers like landscape architects and architects are vital to creating healthy, therapeutic, restorative, and healing environments. Many publications suggest that healthy places are often successful because of design professionals (Latané, 2021; Hamilton, 2013; Guenther, 2013; Marcus & Sachs, 2014; Souter-Brown, 2015; Carr, 2021). In fact, the affordance of safety, health, and welfare are foundational to professional licensure and continuing education. But just as landscape architects and architects have established themselves as experts at designing healthy environments for others, there are growing concerns about the health and wellbeing of their own offices and schools. Now, new investigations into mental health and its relationship to pedagogy, education, and the workplace are emerging. These studies are beginning to show that unhealthy behaviors and stressful working conditions may be emblematic of design practice and education.

This presentation examines how undergraduate landscape architecture and architecture students' concepts of mental health and wellness behaviors change over time. The study uses multiple methods, including pre-and post-instruction concept mapping, focus group interviews with landscape architecture students, and multiple questionnaires distributed to over 140 first year students. Preliminary findings indicate that first year students' understanding of the concept of a "healthy student" differs significantly from more experienced students. Results suggest a complex picture of how stressors like time affect student stress and anxiety differently, often making projects and everyday studio activities even more challenging.

When pedagogies and schools cultivate student health and wellness, they give learners a roadmap for thriving academically. Additionally, design learners experience work (and play) in healthy and supportive environments. Subsequently, they are motivated towards creating similar environments in both practice and their own workplaces. The result is a repositioning of design education as precedent for practitioners interested in designing healthy, safe, and resilient built environments.

Voices from Students in Architecture and Landscape Architecture Programs

Katherine Price *(Clemson University)*

The Clemson University Counseling and Psychological Services (CAPS) has acknowledged that architecture and landscape architecture students suffer from mental health issues at a higher rate than students in other schools within the university. While there is extant research available on the mental health of university and graduate students, there remains a gap in the knowledge of the mental health of students in design-based programs. Architecture and landscape students devote most time to cultivating design skills in a studio-based learning environment. Most times, the focus is on comprehensive, semester-long design projects that accelerate throughout the semester in lieu of quizzes, exams and essays. Because their learning modalities differ from traditional college students, architecture students often display a range of distressful symptoms.

This session reports on students' health and well-being enrolled in the School of Architecture using a mixed-methods research approach. Findings are reported from the synthesis of four types of primary data. First, a mental health screening tool was administered to obtain snapshot of the emotional states of depression, anxiety and stress. Second, an online survey was administered to explore the factors that may evoke stress among students' such as the COVID-19 pandemic, academic workload, and environmental setting. Third, personal interviews were conducted with 50 students throughout year levels to gain a more robust understanding of student wellness. Finally, a student narrative portraying, "A Day in the Life of an Architecture Student" was produced to illustrate the daily challenges that architecture students encounter, both in and out of school. These research strategies were utilized to raise awareness on student health and wellness.

The evidence gained from this research will be used to implement solutions within one School of Architecture to improve student wellness. It may also provide a basis for cross-comparison research conducted with other architecture schools.

Design and Health within Architecture Education: Diverse Teaching Approaches and Career Pathways

Session Abstract:

Within higher education, Design and Health programs and course offerings, as well as teaching approaches, vary widely by institution, discipline, and instructor. Students interested in Design and Health careers must navigate the complex pathways created by these variations. This series of presentations from faculty, researchers, students, and practitioners in Architecture, Design Science, and Medicine at the University of Michigan shares a sampling of teaching approaches and course offerings that prepare students for diverse Design and Health career pathways. The first presentation describes a foundational course that leverages synergies between healthy living and sustainable design to introduce the field of "built environment and health." Course content, learning goals, assignments, and learning outcomes; delivery and assessment methods; and strengths and limitations of this approach will be discussed. Motivations for and challenges to teaching such a course within an Architecture program and to multidisciplinary students related to curricular and accreditation requirements, competing motivations, and community engagement will also be highlighted. The second presentation shares the experiences of two graduate students with varying disciplinary backgrounds and interests in Design and Health. Considering the emerging status of Design and Health within architecture and other academic programs, understanding and incorporating student perspectives and career preparation needs into course and curricular development is essential. Formation of interests in Design and Health, resources and difficulties encountered when searching for relevant academic programs and career pathways, and future career goals will be described, as well as suggestions for prospective students, faculty advisors and mentors, and programs offering Design and Health coursework and programming. The third presentation introduces two complementary approaches to architectural education focused on bridging to practice. Real-world and clinical data relevant to clients and stakeholders are applied and integrated into the design process for students. Both examples illustrate how Design and Health curricula are exploring unconventional approaches to education that sit on the intersection of design and outcome, architecture and medicine, and academy and practice enable students to follow diverse career pathways.

Leveraging Synergies between Healthy Living and Sustainable Design

Kim Rollings *(University of Michigan)*

The intersection between healthy living and sustainable design presents a unique opportunity to introduce interdisciplinary built environment and health knowledge to students from architecture and other disciplines. Drawing from urban planning, public health, environmental psychology, and architecture, an innovative multidisciplinary course taught in an accredited U.S. architecture department will be discussed. The course briefly introduces theories and methodologies before presenting content in three units: healthy people, healthy places, and a healthy planet. Content addresses connections between the built environment at multiple scales (products, spaces, buildings, and cities) and physical health, mental health, and social well-being, as well as environmental, economic, and social sustainability. Issues of social and environmental justice, especially for vulnerable populations, are embedded throughout the course. The advanced introductory class introduces students to systems thinking surrounding built environment, health, and sustainability issues as students work with content and students from multiple disciplines. They are introduced to and attempt to bridge "research-practice gaps" when applying course content to assigned exercises.

Course activities include discussing seminal literature; guest lectures; interactive exercises; observation and evaluation of campus public and indoor spaces; and a community-based semester project that--after in-depth study of a topic selected by each student--requires application of course content to a real-world problem defined by a community partner. The semester-long project engages students with the community and real-world contexts; offers instructors and students flexibility with content to adapt to different interests and program requirements; and provides opportunities for students to work in groups which promotes communication across academic fields. In addition to course activities, learning objectives and outcomes, formative and summative assessments, institutional and department structures such as program and accreditation requirements, and instructor limitations such as class size and demands of community-based teaching will be discussed.

Pursuing Academic and Career Interests in Design and Health: Student Perspectives

Maya Fraser *(University of Michigan);* ***Hannah Myers*** *(University of Michigan)*

Students interested in pursuing the study of and career pathways in Design and Health must navigate complex academic and professional pathways. Complexities result from varying student disciplinary and professional backgrounds, differing career preparation needs, and a lack of standard program and course offerings across institutions and disciplines. Students interested in entering the field must rely on conducting extensive research, networking, and securing mentorship to pursue their academic and career interests. These challenges are particularly pronounced for students from marginalized backgrounds, for whom these strategies and resources are less accessible. This talk will share the experiences of two current graduate students pursuing Design and Health interests at the University of Michigan: one transitioning from architectural practice, and the other transitioning from public health. Topics described by each author will include: academic and professional backgrounds, formation of interests in health and design, resources integral to finding their paths into Design and Health, difficulties encountered when searching for relevant academic programs and career pathways, and future career goals. Suggestions aimed at aiding prospective students, faculty advisors and mentors, and programs offering health and design coursework, programming, and concentrations will also be discussed.

Toward Data-Driven Design for Real World Architecture Practice

Upali Nanda *(HKS);* ***Andrew Ibrahim*** *(University of Michigan)*

In this presentation we will focus on our approach toward the elusive goal of bringing together research and design, and academy and practice. In particular, rigorous healthcare data-analytics to real world design practice will be shared as a key need in setting an educational foundation.

First, insights from three semesters of Health By Design seminar courses will be shared which focus on designing with a specific outcome (e.g., brain health) in mind that can be measured with real world-data relevant to clients and stakeholders. Project exemplars that focus on housing and physical and mental health will be discussed, and the challenges of posing real-world immediately implementable solutions that are addressed in an open forum.

Next, specific attention will be placed on how commonly applied data-driven analytics (extracting data from clinical health records, econometric risk- and reliability- adjustments) in healthcare are applied and integrated into the design process for students. We underscore how we unite these otherwise siloed frameworks by presenting our complimentary work in starting a Health and Design fellowship that provides a grounding in rigorous data analytics to architecture professionals.

Both examples illustrate how Design and Health curricula are exploring unconventional approaches to education that sit on the intersection of design and outcome, architecture and medicine, and academy and practice enable students to follow diverse career pathways.

Design Education for Change: Models, Momentum and Pathways

Session Abstract:

Context and Issue: Dewey (1938) proposes that education is a social process and emphasizes the exploration of issues-based curriculum that deal with local and global concerns. At the core of this model, it is critical to understand the history of bias and structural injustice, as well as the need for humility, empathy, and the development of cultural and intercultural awareness in design education. According to Freire (2018), knowledge emerges through invention and re-invention, a hopeful method of inquiry that human beings pursue in the world, with the world, and with each other. Design education should empower students to understand practices and methods of engagement that help to facilitate trusting relationships between communities, clients, and the design team. These relationships foster the unpacking of true concerns of the community, generating thoughtful and more democratic design solutions. In this open classroom environment, the learners understand themselves as capable facilitators of effecting change for social and ecological justice. The integration of current social challenges into the curriculum has been inadequate in response to contemporary issues. Through collaborative efforts across courses and institutions, this symposia will examine the role of design education as a tool for equity in action.

Perspective and Pedagogy: To generate active participants and leaders in society, we educators should discard the linear step-oriented approach and instead identify expansive and iterative forms of thinking that acknowledge the response to the limiting impact of past constraints. To foster an environment where students can fully understand the systemic issues, we also need to educate beyond our disciplinary scale. This includes an exploration of both the centripetal activities reinforcing the core values of our discipline and centrifugal activities directed towards absorbing additional information that exists at the periphery of the discipline. The collaboration needs to bring the community actively into the classroom while also taking the classroom out into the community to unravel questions around race, inequalities, and power. Through various modalities of inquiry, students learn practices to facilitate community engagement that can result in socially responsible design solutions within the classroom and beyond.

Discussion Questions: An opportunity exists to collaborate, reflect on past practices, and consider limitations on how we can come together to advance the role of design education in the development of global citizens. The panelists will participate in a thoughtful discussion reflecting on the pedagogies that they have tested to foster the development of informed judgments and responsive action for immediate social change. Questions posed to panelists include: How do you engage students in a critical dialog on the issues that impact marginalized communities? What strategies do you implement that prompt students to carry a commitment to equity throughout their future practices? How do you foster innovation and creativity within the well-defined programmatic requirements of community-based projects? What are the challenges or inherent dangers encountered when we teach about design for social change? The panel will conclude by mapping opportunities to transform design pedagogy to include design activism as a foundational practice.

Perspective: Associate Professor + Director

Milagros Zingoni Phielipp *(University of Tennessee)*

"Give a man a fish and you feed them for a day, teach them how to fish and you feed them for life" (Tzu, n.d.). While this quote is related to the general principle of alleviating poverty by facilitating self-sufficiency, it also relates to developing agency in others, empowering them to have an active role in their destiny. Education is all about teaching others to fish. Multiple publics and a pluralistic society necessitate a variety of approaches to improving the lives of others.

Interior design is responsible for the human condition leveraging our place and culture beyond the physical context through an empathic response that addresses others' needs and values. As academics and scholars, we have the opportunity to create new pedagogical approaches that advance the profession and expose students to the power of design to benefit those in the periphery. Service Learning Projects (SLP) are at the front of these pedagogical approaches. Their worth stems from their potential to provide our students with lifelong learning opportunities (Fink 2003, Davies 2006), and foster the development of empathy, informed judgments, and responsive action (Sears, 2004). They empower students to (1) do good to the public, (2) develop empathy, (3) improve others' conditions, and (4) understand the power of interiority.

As one of the panelists, I will discuss eleven SLP studios carried out for the last five years through participatory design collaboration with youth from Title I schools as the first phase of design-build interventions. The learning outcomes of this pedagogy include: (1) the opportunity to address the ongoing aspirations to diversify the design fields, amplifying the voices of historically underrepresented populations; (2) develop technical, and financial competency by building full-scale installations; and (3) it places the disciplines of interiors as a humane right other than aesthetics.

Perspective: Professor

Tasoulla Hadjiyanni *(University of Minnesota)*

As the Twin Cities of Minnesota became the global epicenter for social and racial justice following the murder of George Floyd on May 25, 2020, I found myself frozen. For the past 25 years, I have been focusing my research and teaching to advocate for Culturally Enriched Communities, that is using design to create communities where everyone can thrive. And yet, questions crowded my mind: Do I have the right to tell the stories of Black and indigenous people? What if I make a mistake, further perpetuating stereotypes? And where would I find the mental tenacity to handle the potential public shaming that could follow?

I was ten years old when Turkey invaded Cyprus and my life as a refugee began to unfold. In my mind, shared experiences of displacement, injustice, and marginalization, could override differences such as those due to race, ethnicity, history, language, and religion. The conversations that ensued after the protests helped me see the dent in this premise and recognize that as a White educator and researcher, I would never be able to fully connect to racial experiences of space. I still had a choice, though: Do I continue to engage with politically charged discourses? Or do I leave the work of social justice to those most greatly impacted? This questioning left me exhausted—it's the decisions we perceive as involving the most psychological trade-offs that are really exhausting (Wang, Novemsky, Dhar, & Baumeister, 2010).

In this panel, I will share how embarking on a series of introspections translated into my teaching and commitment to transform students into global citizens. I am now more intentional in exposing students to difficult conversations, connecting with colleagues in decolonizing the curriculum, and embracing pedagogies that take advantage of dialogue as a means of fostering connections (Broockman & Kalla, 2016).

Perspective: Adjunct Professor

Jennifer Meakins *(Kent State University)*

Ahrentzen and Groat (2002) describe the role of "hidden curriculum" in architecture education as it contributes to "educational rituals of power, hierarchy, and competition", specifically as it relates to gender and patriarchal imbalances in the academy. Thirty years later, the hidden curriculum across architecture education-built on enduring systems of favoring maleness, whiteness, and privilege-continues to uphold an inequitable learning environment, through access, content, and methods. Examples include labor culture—emphasizing time rather than critical thinking and quality—and the use of predominantly white and male precedents for case study research methods.

As a part of the symposia, this presentation will discuss the importance of incorporating anti-racist teaching pedagogies into architecture and design education, through the dismantling of the traditional hidden curriculum of the design studio. While content and exposure to diverse views and references is critical, so to is the understanding of racist systems, both within the discipline and outside of it, in order "to engage in self-reflection about what it means to be white and how it 'affects our thinking, our behaviors, our attitudes, and our decisions." (Scheurich, 1993).

Specific examples and experiences will be discussed to establish tangible methods for changing the structure of architectural education to be more inclusive. Examples such as developing in-class collaborative curriculum development challenges the "master-mystery" tradition of professor-student relationships, reaching out and engaging with the stakeholders of a project, community groups, and advocates, and incorporating sources and references beyond the traditional canon, emphasizing the importance of diverse perspectives.

Ultimately, as emphasized in Barriers and Strategies by White Faculty Who Incorporate Anti-

Racist Pedagogy, it is not enough to acknowledge racism and inequity our classrooms, "educators ought to adopt a paradigm of equity and justice." (Phillips, Risdon, Lamsma, Hambric & Jun, 2019). To conclude, the role of design educator as advocate and activist will be discussed.

Perspective: Assistant Professor

Asha Kutty *(University of North Carolina, Greensboro)*

Teaching interior architecture students to understand and fully engage in the various dimensions involving the complexity of African American History requires a pedagogy that imparts a deeper understanding than the traditional studio format of a design professional delivering lectures and critiques. This panel presentation will focus on an interdisciplinary design studio collaboration between faculty and students of both Interior Architecture and African American Diaspora studies . The two departments collaborated to design a memorial space of Guilford County's lynching monument. This studio forms a part of Guilford County's effort to retrieve its lynching monument from the National Museum for Peace and Justice in Montgomery Alabama. In 2018, the Equal Justice Initiative (EJI), a non-profit organization, opened the National Memorial for Peace and Justice to the public. The memorial was conceived with the hope of creating a sober, meaningful site where people could gather and reflect on America's history of racial inequality. Part of the journey through the memorial includes a public square with 800 steel monuments, one for each county in the United States where lynching took place. Each monument bears an engraving of the names of the lynching victims who perished in that particular county. As part of an initiative by the EJI to make counties acknowledge and amend from their racial pasts, counties have been offered an opportunity to reclaim a replica of their monument. In order to fulfill this opportunity, counties need to propose a design idea to explain how they will honor and showcase their monument within a particular location. Through this interdisciplinary intersection, I will present the outcomes of the studio which helped students unravel questions around race, inequalities, and power to reveal how social change can become the center of design thinking and studio culture.

Dynamics of Design Studio: Community Engagement & University-Community Partnership

Session Abstract:

Increasing population and social-cultural diversity in urban areas have often left underrepresented and underserved communities neglected, left out from the city's development plan or threatened with gentrification. The 'Back to the City' movement that began in the early 2000's nationwide, has had the unintended consequence of displacement as a negative aspect of gentrification. Communities that suffered from decades of racism and the resulting disinvestment are now facing mounting pressure to keep up with Gentrifiers who acquire the benefits and convenience of these, once forgotten, neighborhoods.

The Dallas-Fort Worth Metroplex, the 4th largest and fastest growing metropolitan area in the country is facing similar issues. Attracted by a thriving economy, new urban dwellers are growing in numbers and are collectively applying pressure on cities to provide housing options in the region. As in many other cities, policies that shape neighborhoods and cities continue to incentivize developers instead of community building. This, often, leads to profit driven development that perpetuates historical inequities and injustices that lead to segregated communities.

The presenters' university is located in the heart of the Dallas-Fort Worth Metroplex and the College of Architecture, Planning and Public Affairs (CAPPA) offers the only accredited programs in architecture, landscape architecture and planning in North Texas. UT Arlington is one of the largest and most diverse universities in Texas and the university serves many first-generation college students and has been recognized as the No.1 school in Texas for the success of first-generation students. With these conditions, a growing number of design courses at CAPPA include university-community partnership projects with partner communities that are underrepresented and underinvested with minority populations, decreasing population density and housing, lower household incomes, and/or degraded environmental conditions. University-community partnerships can provide a vehicle to empower such communities to overcome historical injustices to improve their own communities.

However, university-community partnerships can be challenging to plan and execute. Most design courses are limited by the academic calendar which, often, impedes meaningful relationship building with partner communities. Additionally, defining the scope and managing expectations is a major challenge when working with students. Finally, once a relationship is stablished with a community partner, continuing that relationship depends almost exclusively on the faculty member leading the collaborative effort.

With these challenges in mind, this session investigates how design pedagogy has evolved to better serve partner communities by considering socioeconomic and environmental issues while incorporating community engagement and participatory design practices in underinvested communities and addressing equitable design & planning in our built environment through various types of design studio curricula. The session will include project presentations from architecture and landscape architecture design studios of various scales that delivered meaningful outcomes for partner communities. The presenters will also share findings that may help others who have similar issues in working with partner communities. There will be a panel discussion at the end of presentations to share experiences and have an in-depth discussion regarding design pedagogy among presenters and the audience.

Design Pedagogy for Equity in Design & Planning and Student Learning

Dennis Antonio Chiessa *(The University of Texas at Arlington);* ***Joowon Im*** *(The University of Texas at Arlington)*

Design schools often work with various communities in need, however it is critical to develop tailored solutions to address their needs as well as curricular responsibilities. Typically, a design studio will enter a partner community and engage with stakeholders. This outreach is an integral part of such design studios because the deliverables should address the community's needs to help them materialize their visions for their community.

Often, partner communities lack adequate infrastructure, local businesses, adequate housing and are at high risk of environmental pollution/disaster. Additionally, they are in constant threat of displacement as a result of gentrification. Therefore it is critical to consider equitable approaches in addressing issues with partner communities. The approaches should include the establishment of policies and practices that effectively address issues of sustainability and resiliency while centering existing community members.

The authors will present three projects conducted in architecture and landscape architecture design studio courses that worked with underinvested and underrepresented communities of color. They include communities primarily with Hispanic and African American populations in the Dallas-Fort Worth Metroplex in Texas. The authors will discuss challenges in conducting community based research within the confines of the design studio and the strategies developed to address these challenges regarding class curricula The presentation of the three case studies will show the different characteristics of partner communities and the effectiveness of the different community engagement processes. The authors will also discuss how design studio courses with university-community partnership projects can be a constructive and effective learning tool for students and faculty.

Amplifying Community Power through Design-Build Academic + Community Partnerships

Julia Lindgren *(The University of Texas at Arlington)*

This work explores the impact of university and

community partnerships through best practices and lessons learned in Joppa, a Freedman's settlement in Dallas, Texas. Models of academic community engagements have historically been unbalanced, structured to elevate the power of the "researcher" while creating an extractive process from communities. Illustrated through case studies, this relationship is inverted centering community interests and amplifing neighborhood power to build local capacity. Three acts of design and making between community residents and academic interests will be shared. The collaborations include a design build project, Joppy Momma's Farm, a letter writing campaign, "Dear Melissa Pierce," and a neighborhood registry, "House Stories."

Community engaged design-build pedagogy exposes students to real life complex problems. By introducing students to the role of "citizen architect," they are encouraged to confront a way of working that expands their traditional architectural education and the role of the architect beyond the confines of a single site patron model to address systemic issues of environmental, economic, social and physical injustices. This approach centers on diversity, equity and inclusion. Students are encouraged to reflect upon their individual experiences to build connections with the place and project partners. For the community, these activities result in organized action and built projects. At what point does the university's goal to educate students, using the community as a lab, become extractive? And, can we as designers prioritize community interest over pedagogy? This is the struggle within community engaged design education.

Sparking rich dialogue about the opportunities and challenges of academic and community partnerships, an engaged design-build model offers real world examples for participants balancing the similiar power dynamics.

How Richard J. Neutra's Survival Through Design Foresaw Health in All Design

Session Abstract:

In 2021, the Neutra Institute for Survival Through Design, led by Raymond Neutra, the last surviving son of Richard J. Neutra, inherited the remaining Neutra archives, properties, and legacy. In 2022, we are beginning new engagements with edra and other design and architecture research organizations to bring that legacy into the 21st century. This will entail renewed attention to RJN's design and theoretical writings, which are even more timely now with our current climate change and societal challenges. Our year's work includes an updating and republication with extensive notes and commentary of Neutra's masterful mid 20th Century Survival Through Design. We will also be working with research organizations to encourage extension of the research themes Neutra started, that emphasize the biological and behavioral bases of design, and the critical role responsive design plays in our evolving world.

In this Symposium, we will have an introduction by Dr. Raymond Neutra to his father's work and themes, followed with a presentation by the leading Neutra historian and scholar, Dr. Barbara Lamprecht, and concluding with remarks of the prominent architectural researcher, Lisa Heschong, who will show how RJN's work became a central assist to her own. The session is moderated by Dr. James A. Wise, an early member of edra who introduced 'person-environment relations' into architectural education in the 1970s, and is now an Institute board member.

How "Survival Through Design" Foresaw "Health in All" Design

Raymond Richard Neutra *(Neutra Institute for Survival Through Design)*

My father, architect Richard Neutra, started writing his essays for Survival Through Design in the late 1930s. This was a human centered, health centered approach to design, almost 40 years before the founding of edra. He already had practical experience in designing everything from a forest cemetery, furniture, a variety of building types of "social concern" and city plans. Each practical experience triggered his speculations on the sociological, psychological and neuroscience implications of his commissions. He researched the extant scientific literature to get clues about what would work to produce well-being and delight and why.

Why might the constantly changing elements of nature have the neurophysiological effect that they do in his architecture? He asked himself how we could recognize the constraints of what is not biologically acceptable even when it had become temporarily fashionable. How do we convince others to resist fashion when it is harmful? These and other themes in the book are still salient in the field of public health: Witness our struggles with cigarette smoking, seatbelts and vaccine acceptance. Here, I point out the many public health themes in his seminal book and his designs, and I will extrapolate from my own experience in environmental epidemiology to address the "is/ought" dilemma when science validated prediction of consequences may be validly ignored as other consequences are assigned greater value in exchanges among stakeholders. The present and future of environmental design, from the personal to the regional scales, always begins with Health, Safety, and Human Well-Being. Here is how Richard Joseph Neutra, my father, saw and practiced that responsibility.

Richard Neutra's Biorealism: Choregraphing the Body's Experience on Behalf of Human Wellbeing

Barbara Lamprecht *(Modern Resources)*

Richard Neutra's philosophy of biorealism reflected his belief in the role of the body and the role of the senses in the physical experience of space. For the Austrian-American, Los Angeles-based Neutra (1892 – 1970), architecture was not about the representation of life but a material setting for life. Biorealism assumed the requisite interconnectedness of the nature of the natural world and human nature, body and mind, but also called for research into strategies that supported human well-being. Neutra's extraordinary repertoire of roots and sources in the emerging sciences and landscape theories of the late nineteenth and twentieth centuries included physiological psychology, Gestalt aesthetics, medicine, evolutionary biology, and landscape theory; it was that immersion into realms other than conventional theories of architecture that distinguished him from his iconic peers of the 20th century. Major figures such as Wilhelm Wundt (1832 – 1920), the first to distinguish psychology from philosophy and the founder of the first laboratory of experimental (physiological) psychology, and horticulturist/landscape architect Gustav Amman (1885 – 1955) embody these roots and sources.

Neutra established principles for designing well-being that he expressed in a series of essays written in the 1940s and compiled as his manifesto, Survival Through Design, published in 1954. He rendered these principles as what might be termed "strategies for trickery" in his architecture, integrating a keen knowledge of perception with the attributes of the natural world. Using the vocabulary of Modernism, Neutra designed what he termed "soul anchorages" that encouraged the body to freely moving in a logical space melding interior and exterior.

My talk will examine Neutra's background and illuminate those "strategies for trickery" in his work.

Richard Neutra Passes the Torch

Lisa Heschong *(Heschong Mahone)*

Richard Neutra and I were apparently soul mates, but I only discovered this more than 40 years after he died. In the 1960s, we were both living in Los Angeles, distressed by the environmental degradation all around us. In 1969, a year before he died, Neutra wrote an impassioned plea to the architectural profession, called "Cross Section of a Credo," to step outside of its normal boundaries and to embrace a much broader sense of responsibility for how humans could and should relate to their environment:

As Neutra was writing this final essay, I had just graduated from high school and was heading off to study architecture at UC Berkeley. This was during the great 1970's wave of enthusiasm for interdisciplinary studies. Eventually I was also able to enroll in some upper-level architecture and planning classes. I ended up pursuing a Master's of Architecture at MIT, admitted as the token 'ecologist.'

Learning about Neutra's deeper motivations had to wait for an evening on the stage in 2011. I was there to speak about Thermal Delight in Architecture, and how such an intangible sensory experience as thermal comfort could inform architectural design. The event was opened with a reading of Richard Neutra's essay. As the actress read Neutra's words, I realized that he was speaking directly to me, especially to the high school student I had once been. He pleaded with his readers to continue forward with further evolution of his understanding of bio-realism. My life changed then.

In this presentation, I will explore prospects for how to carry Neutra's vision forward, in education, research and practice.

Impacts of Daylight and Window Views on Health and Well-being: New Research Findings

Session Abstract:

Light is critical for human functioning, in that it allows us to see things and perform activities. However, light is also critical for regulating the human circadian rhythm and impacts sleep patterns, depression and fatigue. While light can be delivered indoors through electric light sources or as daylight, there is a strong human preference for natural light. Several studies also emphasize the importance of views from a window, especially of green spaces, in improving productivity, well-being and the healing process. Building siting and design, façade design and window design play important roles in determining access to window views and daylight in building interiors.

In this session, we discuss findings from four recent studies that explored the impact of daylight and views experienced through windows in healthcare, work, and home environments. In one study, 651 participants responded to a survey about their previous stay in the hospital, their perception of windows in their room and views from their bed, and their ratings of the hospital, their room and quality of care. This study also explored the use of blinds in controlling daylight and views and the relationship between an occluded view and patient satisfaction. In the second field study, 20 residents in a multifamily apartment participated in a one-month long study of their health. They wore sleep tracking devices, completed surveys and provided saliva samples in the evening prior to bed to look at their melatonin levels, the hormone associated sleep onset. These factors were compared based on their exposure to light under different daylight conditions in their apartment. The third study evaluated the effect of daylight on performance on two study populations of office workers and healthcare providers. In both settings, workers completed cognitive assessments designed to simulate their work functions and responsibilities. Participants were scored on their real-world productivity and well-being when exposed to daylight and when daylight was filtered by blinds. In the fourth study, bacteria, viruses, and fungi were placed in a controlled chamber and exposed to daylight through different facades designs such as clear glass, smart tinted glass and glass occluded blinds. The viability of microbial species was then assessed to test the influence of daylight intensity and spectrum on infectious disease risk. In this symposium, we will share the findings from these individual studies, followed by a panel discussion focused on identifying key design and practice implications of this work for architectural design.

Exploring the Relationship Between View Quantity, Quality, and Ratings of Care in the Hospital

Sahar Mihandoust *(Clemson University)*

There is a need to understand how patient room window and view characteristics may be related to patient's perception of the quality of care received. A quantitative exploratory study was set up to (a) explore the relationship between presence and content of window views, and size of windows in hospital units and ratings of the room, care, and hospital quality and (b) also investigate the impact of presence and content of window views, and size of windows on satisfaction with daylight in the room and patient's perceived stress and healing. Data was collected from 652 participants regarding their previous stay in the hospital, their perception of windows in their room, the use of blinds during their stay, and their perception of their room, hospital and quality of care received. The participants were also presented with images of rooms with and without blinds installed and asked to indicate their satisfaction with these healthcare environments.

Patients who perceived views to nature and green spaces from their rooms perceived higher hospital, care, and room rating in comparison to patients who only perceived urban views. Patients in rooms with views to nature and green spaces also rated the hospital to have higher qualities for stress reduction and healing. Although patients with nature views also found their windows to be large, they indicated the need for more windows. On a scale of one to ten, the mean hospital ratings of their previous hospital stay were significantly higher for rooms with open blinds compared to rooms with closed blinds. In mediation analyses, daylight quality accounted for 74%, 78%, and 60% of the total effects of blinds positioning on room, hospital, and care quality ratings, respectively. Similarly, respondents reported higher room ratings when reacting to the images of hospital rooms without blinds.

Access to Daylight at Home Improves Circadian Alignment, Sleep, and Mental Health in Healthy Adults: A Crossover Study

Mariana Figueiro *(Icahn School of Medicine at Mount Sinai)*

Light can have a profound effect on humans. It is the major synchronizer of our circadian rhythms to our local position on Earth. Without exposure to daylight or architectural light during the daytime, especially in the morning, we lose synchrony between our biological clock and our daily routines. This lack of synchrony can lead to circadian disruption, which has been associated with sleep disturbances, poor performance, diabetes, obesity, cardiovascular disease, and even cancer. Daytime light exposure can also promote alertness, like a cup of coffee, which increases our daytime energy levels.

Twenty participants working from home during the COVID-19 pandemic participated in a 4-week study. After a baseline week, half of the subjects experienced a smart windows intervention and the other half experienced clear windows with blinds drawn halfway (control) condition; we then reversed the intervention/control and collected another 2 weeks of data. Throughout the 4-week study, participants were asked to wear a wrist actigraph (to measure their rest-activity patterns) and personal light metering devices. During 4 assessment periods performed during the last day of each baseline and intervention weeks, participants were asked to collect saliva samples for melatonin assay and complete questionnaires probing their alertness, vitality, and energy over the course of the day.

The results revealed that participants received less circadian-effective light in the clear windows intervention compared to the smart windows condition. In addition, participants exhibited 15-min delay in melatonin onset, 22 min later sleep onset, had greater sleep debt compensation on Friday night, and delayed energy and vitality levels when they were exposed to the control condition compared to the smart windows intervention.

Impact of Daylight on Healthcare Providers

Usha Satish *(SUNY Upstate Medical University)*

Healthcare providers go through extensive training, with doctors spending 10 years or more in training. However, their ability to be effective in their role is a function not only of their knowledge but also their decision-making performance, which is highly dependent on the physical environment they are in. Research has consistently tied environmental conditions, such as lighting, to performance. The healthcare environment also plays a role in provider burnout, which afflicts one-half of physicians and one-third of nurses reporting symptoms.

20 health care providers at State University New York (SUNY) Upstate Medical Center spent 3 hours on 2 days in a room under two daylighting conditions: one with ample daylight and long-distance views and one with the windows obscured by blinds. The health care providers participated on different days, with each condition spaced one week apart to align with the same day of the week and time of day for each test. Both groups answered standard questions on environmental satisfaction and well-being and participated in a simulation based cognitive assessment.

Results showed that when the participants worked with the blinds up, they showed significant improvement in several important outcome measures. Overall participants managed patients more effectively, made fewer errors, demonstrated safer behaviors, and were able to attend to multiple concurrent tasks. They also scored better on adaptability and focus, two common burnout indices in healthcare.

Influence of Daylight on Microbial Viability Under Different Window Conditions

Sepideh Pakpour *(University of British Columbia)*

Built environment, as the main habitat of the modern human, encompasses a complex mixture of viable and dead organisms (known as indoor microbiome), which can not only affect occupants' wellbeing and productivity but also deteriorate different parts of the buildings, leading to undesirable changes in the materials' structural properties. While studies have looked at the importance of temperature and humidity on the indoor microbiome, less attention has been dedicated towards lighting conditions and specifically daylight. We developed an environmentally controlled chamber with smart windows with electrochromic coating. The intensity of the light was controlled using different tint levels and the effect was assessed on the stability of different microbial species plated on different materials within the chamber. The viability of the microbial species on various surface materials when exposed to different light levels was assessed by counting of bacterial colonies of MRSA, E. Coli and Klebsiella and viral plaque forming units of MS2 and influenza. Following the chamber study, the influence of daylight on microbial viability was tested in hematology/oncology patient rooms from admission to 5 days following admission to the hospital to investigate the potential for patients to be exposed to harmful bacteria and evaluate the risk of a hospital acquired infection.

Window VIEW Quality: Why It Matters and What WE Should Do

Sepideh Pakpour *(University of British Columbia)*

Window views that provide visual connections to the outdoors have been shown to have multiple positive effects on occupants (Heschong, 2021). These effects include improved health, well-being (Beute and de Kort, 2014), emotion (Ko et al., 2020), cognitive performance (Boubekri et al., 2020; Jamrozik et al., 2019; Ko et al., 2020), environmental satisfaction (Yildirim et al., 2007), reduced discomfort (Aries et al., 2010) and stress recovery (Ulrich, 1984). A good window view may also increase the economic value of buildings (Baranzini and Schaerer, 2011; Damigos and Anyfantis, 2011; Turan et al., 2021). Even though many benefits from window views have been recognized, there are few design guidelines for assessing window view quality (CEN/TC 169, 2018; IWBI, 2020; USGBC, 2019). We convened an international group of leading experts, which defined window view quality as the quality of the visual connection to the outdoors that satisfies building occupants. View quality is a function of the content (the sum of the visual features seen in the window view), access (the amount of the view an occupant can see from the viewing position) and clarity (how clearly the content appears in the window view when seen by an occupant) of the view. In this session, we will share the consensus position of 55 international experts in the fields of biophilia, environmental quality, design and health on what constitutes a high quality window view.

Investigating the Impact of the Built Environment on Patient and Family Engagement in Healthcare Design and Delivery within the United States

Session Abstract:

Patient and family engagement (PFE) is a model of care that defines how patients and families are integrated in healthcare settings as part of the care system. When a patient goes to a hospital, their experience is not only determined by the medical care provided to them, but also by their interactions with staff, by their waiting experience, by their accommodations, and by organizational policies that often shape the patient and family experience. Previous studies have noted that family presence and involvement in care helps reduce medication errors and contributes to patient comfort, especially in spaces like the intensive care unit (ICU), where patients are critically ill and may not be able to care for themselves (Olding, McMillan, Reeves, et al., 2016). In 2001, the Institute of Medicine identified involvement of family and friends as a key element of high-quality care in healthcare settings. Since then, the dynamic of patient care has shifted to a patient and family-centered approach where individual patient's needs, goals, and values are integral to decision-making in healthcare (Igel & Lerner, 2016). Embodying this approach, patient and family engagement is aimed at supporting patients and families in becoming active participants in their own care while in the hospital, for a more effective and safe transition to home and recovery (Hibbard & Greene, 2013).

Various strategies have been outlined to promote patient and family engagement improvements in organizational culture and activities related to communication and education. The built environment has been identified as a factor that can potentially contribute to these activities and organizational factors in healthcare settings (Bosch & Lorusso, 2019). However, there is a dearth of studies that focus on PFE as an overall outcome of the healthcare-built environment.

The purpose of this symposium is three-fold: first, to clearly define and operationalize patient and family engagement in healthcare so that it can be clearly measured in relation to the built environment research in healthcare settings. Second, to discuss the relationships between built environment features and patient and family engagement outcomes. Third, to discuss methods and approaches to measure patient and family engagement in healthcare design research studies. Another objective is to understand how family presence within healthcare settings influences the patient, family themselves, nurses and the clinicians.

References

Bosch, S. J., & Lorusso, L. N. (2019). Promoting patient and family engagement through healthcare facility design: A systematic literature review. Journal of Environmental Psychology, 62, 74-83.

Hibbard, J. H., & Greene, J. (2013). What the evidence shows about patient activation: better health outcomes and care experiences; fewer data on costs.Health affairs, 32(2), 207-214.

Olding, M., McMillan, S. E., Reeves, S., Schmitt, M. H., Puntillo, K., & Kitto, S. (2016). Patient and family involvement in adult critical and intensive care settings: a scoping review. Health Expectations, 19(6), 1183-1202.

Igel, L. H., & Lerner, B. H. (2016). Moving Past Individual and "Pure" Autonomy: The Rise of Family-Centered Patient Care. AMA Journal of Ethics, 18(1), 56–62. https://doi.org/10.1001/journalofethics.2017.18.1.msoc1-1601

Does the Built Environment of an Adult Intensive Care Unit Support the Families' Needs as Part of the Patient and Family Engagement Model of Care?

Swati Goel *(Clemson University);* ***Anjali Joseph*** *(Clemson University)*

In an adult intensive care unit (ICU), the engagement of patients and families in the care process is a critical part of patient recovery and transition back home after discharge. Patient and family engagement (PFE) models of care are emerging as a significant part of the care philosophy in healthcare settings such as ICUs

(Olding et al., 2016). A trend towards providing a family zone within the patient room has been rising in the past decade because the family often spends long hours and sometimes weeks in an ICU (Rippin et al., 2015). Therefore, in addition to caring for the patient, it is important to understand and cater to family needs as part of the PFE model (Al-Mutair et al., 2013). While studies indicate that the built environment is a crucial component in incorporating the PFE model (Bosch & Lorusso, 2019), there is a need for an evidence-based understanding of the role of the built environment in promoting patient and family engagement within critical care units (Olding et al., 2016).

This investigation utilized the Preferred Reporting Items for Systematic reviews and Meta-Analyses (PRISMA) 2020 framework to explore the role of the design environment in promoting patient and family engagement in an adult ICU. A total of 2,351 articles were screened from three databases, and over 100 articles met the inclusion criteria determined based on the Levels of Evidence for Healthcare Design (Marquardt & Motzek, 2013; Stichler, 2016). The findings were organized according to the five outcomes of the PFE model identified by Olding et al. (2016), including presence, having needs met/being supported, communication, decision making, and contributing to care. Key findings include identifying the built environment features that cater to family needs identified in the literature, along with additional needs for social support and positive distraction, to name a few.

Supporting Family Engagement in the Neonatal ICU: The Role of Single-Family Rooms

Herminia Machry *(Georgia Institute of Technology)*

In the neonatal intensive care unit (NICU), family engagement is an important process that recognizes family members as critical contributors to infant development, encouraging them to become active care partners to staff in preparation for their role after discharge. NICU family engagement contributes to family activation by including family members in actions and interactions such as counseling, training sessions, medical rounds, breastfeeding, and skin-to-skin care. These behaviors can potentially be affected by the built environment, and the design of NICUs has developed to encourage family presence and involvement in these activities by incorporating single-family rooms (SFRs). While NICUs adopting SFRs have shown improved family-related outcomes in comparison to previous design models (i.e. open bay design), there is no evidence showing how SFR types and interior design features can support family engagement behaviors.

The purpose of this study was to better understand how the built environment of SFRs may be influencing behaviors across four key family engagement concepts – family presence, care, information exchanges, and caregiving. In a multiple case-study and qualitative approach, we conducted interviews with family and staff, in-depth field observations, and a physical assessment in two NICUs representing the SFR design model. Interviews and observations collected data on the characteristics of actions/interactions involving family members in each NICU. An observation log recorded the type, location, people involved, and design elements involved in these actions/interactions. Observational sketches, notes, and interview responses compiled descriptions of how built environment characteristics of SFRs were supporting or hindering such actions/interactions. Constant comparative analysis and pattern matching strategies looked for cross-case environment-behavior relationships in the data.

Five overarching themes emerged showing the SFR supporting behaviors across all four family engagement concepts. SFR features such as room layout, furniture design and information displays were identified as relevant factors to family engagement behaviors in both NICUs.

Design Thinking for Healthcare

Lesa Lorusso *(Gresham Smith)*, **Sheila Bosch** *(University of Florida)*

The complex healthcare system incorporates diverse factors including varied stakeholder groups, constantly changing policies, and rising costs, to name a few. While designing healthcare environments has always been challenging, emergent needs from the global pandemic have been a catalyst for design firms to better integrate PFE in healthcare design. The methods with which design research teams collect data regarding PFE are rapidly changing which necessitates an agile, resilient approach. In order to inform the design of healthcare environments in the midst of so much change, innovative problem-solving methods are essential to effectively gather PFE focused data. Never before have healthcare design teams been faced with facilitating kickoff sessions and user meetings fully virtually with a displaced web of clinical stakeholders. Join us for a discussion of the co-design process using Design Thinking, a team-based creative problem-solving method known for successful application to difficult problems. Design Thinking is a creative brainstorming process that is human-centered, empathetic, and focused on the people at the center of a problem to be solved. It is an effective method in understanding the needs and desires of end-users to effectively grasp the core of an issue. By gaining a clear understanding of the core needs and desires of a client, design professionals are better able to create a solution that meets the requirements of the end-user and therefore increases satisfaction with both the process and the end result.

The purpose of this session is to share lessons learned and practical tools for applying design thinking methods both face-to-face and virtually throughout the design process.

- Gain an appreciation for the design thinking process as a tool to gather descriptive information regarding population health management.
- Collaborate and develop springboards for implementing strategies within participant's organizations.
- Understand how to structure a design thinking workshop to explore a research topic.

Positive Mental Health Through City Planning and Design

Session Abstract:

The significance of mental health and happiness has been well established in the past few years. In the wake of the King of Bhutan coining the term 'Gross National Happiness'- and several Happiness indices, consequently, being developed by experts across the world- ensuring positive mental health in the lives of common people, is increasingly becoming an important priority for civic authorities. The symposium focuses on how design may contribute towards the happiness and positive mental health, and presents an exploration into the association of city design with it. It further explores the hypothesis that the way cities and city neighborhoods are designed and maintained, can have a significant impact on the mental well-being of its communities. It is progressively being recognized that there is enormous potential for social and behavioral scientists to add a spatial dimension to it by identifying characteristics and factors of cities and regions that affect positive mental health and well-being measures.

Most significantly, since the past year, which has been a frightening time amidst this worldwide pandemic, anxieties about COVID-19 seem to have taken a psychological toll. The unpredictability surrounding COVID-19 has further led to magnifying and spiraling out into devastating apprehension and terror. As lockdowns and restrictions soothe in various cities, many people find it exceptionally challenging to re-adapt to "normal" life. As these restrictions soothe, mental health experts are noticing a phenomenon as the next emerging mental health crisis - anxiety about life after lockdown. This emerging phenomenon of the post pandemic anxiety imperatively calls for a solution. Will psychotropic medications be the only way out in the times to come? Maybe not.

Undoubtedly, there is a pressing requirement of taking the design parameters for positive mental health into account while designing and planning. It may be advisable to add mental well-being/ happiness/emotional well-being ratings into the assessment of every design. Mental health maps concerning built environment indicators should be generated so that better strategies and a well-being plan could be formulated to enhance the mental health of the citizens. Involving all the relevant fields of expertise such as health care professionals, architects, urban designers, academicians, researchers and practitioners, in the design process, would give a holistic approach to achieve this comprehensive vision. Theories may evolve when these experts collaborate in transdisciplinary research that integrates the knowledge base and theoretical approaches of each discipline. An in depth enquiry into the complex interaction, among physical features, social processes and individual behaviors in relation with the built environment, may be the way forward. The prospective of a theoretically extracted and empirically authenticated system for assessing the urban environment, for mental well-being among its' users, may offer assurance for future research and theory building that can inform policy and design.

This symposium presents four ongoing researches at the research group 'Happiness by Design', Department of Architecture and Planning, Indian Institute of Technology (I.I.T) Roorkee, India, along the same lines, which attempt to address the issue of rising mental health concerns, through city planning and design.

The Association between Urban Environments and Eudaemonic Well-Being

Asesh Sarkar *(Indian Institute of Technology, Roorkee);* **Tina Pujara** *(Indian Institute of Technology, Roorkee)*

Studies have established that there is a substantial link between urbanization and the rise of mental health-related problems among the urban population. Urbanization is at an all-time high worldwide and therefore, understanding how it may be triggering an increase in the mental disease cases, is crucial. Past researches suggest that urban environments may directly impact mental well-being. These researches also categorically state that, depending on the environment characteristics, these impacts may be favorable or harmful. However, less is known about how, the physical and social settings of the urban environment, individually, may impact the city dwellers' mental well-being .The concept of mental well-being encompasses three categories of well-being which are interconnected: the hedonic, psychological, and social well-being. The psychological and social well-being are two aspects of what is termed as the eudaemonic well-being. Few studies seem to have particularly explored the plausible association between the social and physical environments, individually, and the eudaemonic well-being. This study fills the gap by this exploration, through an extensive literature review. A hundred of research articles and review papers were examined to determine the plausible links between the physical environment, the social environment and the eudaemonic well-being. A list of urban environment indicators (via the extensive review of the selected papers) were identified, and categorized under two heads, the physical and the social environment. Furthermore, the plausible assessment (using the generated list of indicators) of the physical and the social environments for eudaemonic well-being was categorized under positive and negative impacts. The identification of these indicators, with a particular focus on the urban scenario's physical and social settings, is the first step towards building a methodology for analyzing the influence of urban environments on eudaemonic well-being. The study may also be a contribution towards the building of healthy cities in the times to come.

Does Neighborhood Design Contribute Towards Positive Mental Health?: A Study of Residents' Perceived Urban Stress

Iqra Rafiq *(Indian Institute of Technology, Roorkee);* **Tina Pujara** *(Indian Institute of Technology, Roorkee)*

Urban spaces potentially seem to impact people's quality of life, particularly their mental well-being. It has been well established that developing countries such as India, China etc. are likely to see a disproportionately large increase in the burden attributable to mental disorders in the coming decades. In fact, a report by World Health Organization states that mental disorders account for nearly 12% of the global burden of disease. The capital city of India, Delhi houses a population of more than 1.8 Crore in different neighborhood typologies. This paper attempts to answer the question 'Does neighborhood design contribute towards positive mental health?' by focusing on the perceived urban stress of residents of a neighborhood in Dwarka, Delhi. The primary objective of the study was to assess the perceived urban environmental stressors using perceived stress scale (PSS) among the people living in the neighborhood through exploratory techniques using structured and semistructured questionnaires. The findings indicated that though the residents primarily described their neighborhood as pleasant, a high level of stress was also perceived. This study highlighted that the major reasons for this stress were-high level of social isolation, commutation issues, noise and polluted air. The findings of the study suggest that a neighborhood design may hold opportunity in addressing the positive mental health of the residents, via promoting, innovating and creating healthy spaces, further making the place livable and providing good quality of life. This paper also demonstrates the significance of the various spaces in a neighborhood that could possibly provide to reduce and achieve positive mental health. It was found from the study that people were willing to relocate for minimal social isolation, less air and noise pollution to any part of Delhi, India. The research contributes insights on mental health and further provides knowledge base for urban planners and designers.

Street Design and Urban Anxiety

Sayna Anand *(Indian Institute of Technology, Roorkee);* ***Tina Pujara*** *(Indian Institute of Technology, Roorkee)*

Cities and mental health are found to be significantly associated with each other. Cities are composed of public spaces such as outdoor neighborhood spaces, open spaces and streets, all having different usages and characters. Streets are essential elements of the city structure, constituting significant space. It has been observed in the recent past that cities may generate various mental health issues such as stress, anxiety, and depression which, as per extensive literature studied, are found to be associated with urban environments. Anxiety seems to be one of the dominant issues that many citizens face every day in the current times. This study explores the link between urban anxiety and streets and analyses street design and its impact on anxiety. The street identified for this study was in Mumbai, India, one of the major hubs for the city's working population. The methods included a field study comprising a survey schedule (closed and open-ended questions) and the state anxiety test (STAI-S) done through interviews with the street users.

The study reports that one-third of the respondents have predominant feelings associated with anxiety on the streets. The major cause of anxiety seems to be the perceived sense of insecurity from vehicular traffic (while walking) and high temperatures (without respite via tree plantation). The responses further suggested that the anxious street environment also impacts the respondents' behavior towards each other. Results prove that larger the width of walking space, the more relaxed the pedestrian population is. The study infers that points of rest are called for on the street, and the segregation of pedestrian and vehicular traffic is an important quality for achieving anxiety-free streets. This study may be a step towards a methodology for assessing streetscape designs for anxiety and may offer assurance for future research and theory building informing policy and design.

The Color Palette of Urban Street Facades and Perceived Emotional Well-Being

Surya Panavelil Sadasivan *(Indian Institute of Technology, Roorkee);* ***Tina Pujara*** *(Indian Institute of Technology, Roorkee)*

The urban environment is becoming ever more recognized as a potential persuasive factor of well-being. However, many cities, and particularly their streets, seem to create urban stressors that impede people's ability to restore their well-being. Previous studies indicate that street facades are known to be one of the visually most dominant components of a street. Prior studies hint at the fact that the appearance and feel of the façades on streets can have a measurable impact on the perceived emotional well-being of the citizens. Emotional well-being is understood as the presence of positive emotions such as joy, affection and the absence of negative emotions such as sadness, anger. Attractive and high-quality façade design can make us feel happy and comfortable, whereas poor design can make us sad. Further, a multicolored façade is well-thought-out as a high-quality façade that can elicit positive responses in users. It has also been well established that color and its physiognomies, promote dynamism and vitality in people. Thus, it may be conjectured that the color specifications of street facades have a significant role to play with regard to perceived emotional wellbeing. This study attempts to interrogate the association of color of urban street facades and the perceived emotional well-being of its users. An extensive literature review was conducted where 77 papers primarily from peer-reviewed journals were identified for the interrogation of color-emotional wellbeing association of street facades. The study infers that the harmony, visual complexity and vibration of colors on street façades generate positive emotions and balanced visual stimulations. The consistent experiences of these two aspects - positive emotions and balanced visual simulations contribute to the emotional well-being of the inhabitants. The findings of this study may inform urban policies with regard to street facade color planning in the times to come.

Reimagining Career Pathways for Emerging Professionals in Research-Informed Practice

Session Abstract:

As the built environment and human behavior continue to be shaped by the aftermath of the COVID-19 pandemic, there is a renewed focus on designing for human health and well-being. Organizations have placed a growing importance on designing for health and academic institutions have introduced programs that focus on the intersection of design and health to meet this demand. Students can now choose to approach architecture, urban design, user experience design and product design through the lens of improving health in a tangible way. With the burgeoning interest in this field, there exists an opportunity for the industry to increase the talent pipeline from the ground-up by investing in emerging professionals who demonstrate a passion for advancing healthcare excellence through transformative design and understand how to apply an evidence-based process to contribute to health, safety, and well-being.

The highly competitive E. Todd Wheeler Health Fellowship at Perkins&Will is one such early career offering that attracts recent graduates and emerging healthcare design leaders. Conceived by the firm's Health Practice Council, the vision of the Fellowship was to prepare the next generation of professionals who understand critical thinking and collaboration as central to healthcare innovation. Fellows work under the direction of the Health Practice Leader, gaining hands-on professional work experience on project teams. The Fellowship is driven by the idea that diversity of ideas, backgrounds, and disciplines are essential to solving the challenges of healthcare access and service delivery. Past fellows have included individuals with backgrounds in architecture, design research, biomedical engineering, and public health.

During the Fellowship year, each fellow works with their local studio to advance healthcare design through creative thought and applied research. This takes the form of a research project on a topic of interest under the guidance of a mentor within the health practice.

The Class of 2022 Fellows Sabah Mohammed, Kinjal Shah and Neha Rampuria are based in Atlanta, Dallas, and Los Angeles studios respectively, and have each conducted research on three unique populations- patients with behavioral health needs, pregnant women, and geriatric patients- with unique needs that shape their individual care. During this symposium, the Fellows will describe their experience conducting research in a large firm; engaging with experts in data collection; participating in an innovation incubator project; conducting user group meetings; balancing research and client projects simultaneously and engaging with their mentors to shape their Fellowship year.

The goals of this session are to increase awareness about Fellowship opportunities, the role of research in practice, and the importance of mentorship. The primary objective of this symposium is to engage with student attendees and recent graduates to showcase early career pathways to research informed practice and engage in a dialogue about building a career in healthcare design.

Target audience: Current students, recent graduates, emerging professionals

Care in the Times of Crisis- Designing for Patients with Behavioral Health Needs in the Emergency Department

Sabah Mohammed *(Perkins & Will)*

Behavioral health needs are increasing at an alarming rate with one in five adults experiencing a mental illness of varying acuity (Hedden et al., 2015). Prior research shows 68% of adults with behavioral health conditions also have chronic medical comorbidities (Alegria et al., 2007).

However, current behavioral health services are plagued by access, payment, and provider gaps. The lack of care continuity results in a failure to engage patients before their needs become severe. As a result, patients with behavioral health needs often present in the Emergency Department (ED) for initial treatment. Given that one out of every eight ED visits are due to a BH issue, inappropriate utilization of the ED is a serious concern (Weiss, Barrett, Heslin, & Stocks, 2016). The unpredictable volume of BH patients prevents timely triage, increases wait times, stretches physicians thin, and requires a higher level of immediate, specialized care that strains many EDs. Consequently, BH patients are often placed in ED spaces that are not designed to treat them, which can be dangerous and demoralizing for both patients and staff.

Some providers have begun to dedicate specialized support models that guarantee immediate access to psychiatric care and connect patients with ongoing support which improves overall ED patient throughput (decreased wait times, length of stay); reduces utilization (admissions, readmissions); and reduces total cost of care for behavioral health patients. This study aims to provide insights on the myriad factors influencing the need for psychiatric crisis services and how design can be leveraged to support human-centered care. The study documents expert interviews with clinicians and behavioral health designers; interventions that serve behavioral health patients and the associated outcomes in the function and flow of ED services; ultimately facilitating the provision of quality acute care for patients in crisis.

Keywords: Behavioral health, emergency department, acute care

Improving Women's Birthing Experience in Hospitals through Qualitative Study

Kinjal Shah *(Perkins & Will)*

During the pregnancy journey, mothers endure a lot of physical and mental changes. These conditions require an environment to reduce their stress levels and pain. Research shows that the built environment plays an important role in the health and well-being of the mother and infant during labor. In the United States, maternal mortality ratio has increased by 58% from 2001 to 2017. However, most hospitals have an obstetrics program that lacks patient-centered care and empathy. To solve the issues of maternal mortality and physical challenges during care, the need for reimagining birthing model is evident.

This research aims to study the needs of birthing women, with a focus on enhancing the delivery of care and developing a new obstetrics program supporting patient-centeredness. A narrative literature review of the clinical needs of labor and delivery care is described to understand the importance of spatial conditions. The study will involve a descriptive evaluation of current facility standards and workflow of the obstetrics program in existing hospitals. The comparison from lessons learned from the current state will be tabulated to identify the gaps in care delivery. An online survey will be extended to mothers and caregivers to assess qualitative feedback. Results from the survey will be used as the basis for design guidelines. The guidelines will serve as the desired design outcomes needed for a better patient experience in birthing models. The findings from the research will be presented in the form of a design matrix that includes key program units, a prototype for women's obstetric flow, and the general layout of the department. The outcomes from this research strives is to serve as planning and design guidelines for a women's department in any healthcare setting.

Keywords: Women's Health, Labor & delivery, empathy

Evolutions in Senior Care: Designing for an Ageing Population

Neha Rampuria *(Perkins & Will)*

Major demographic changes are anticipated in the coming years due to three trends: the total population becoming older than usual with a longer life expectancy rate; a dip in the middle-aged population due to Gen X being smaller in size compared to Baby Boomers and Millennials; and a continuous slowdown of population growth as Millennials choose to have fewer kids.

The aging population is living longer than usual. Research shows that in the next 10-15 years, the population of people 65 and older will outnumber the population 18 or younger. Geriatrics, or adults over the age of 65, are one of the most vulnerable groups of patients the health and social care systems across the world are caring for (K Barnett et al., 2012). Research also shows that 65% of adults in the 65 - 84-year-old range have two or more chronic conditions. How does the future of healthcare look like for this population? With the increase in the use of technology to deliver health care, how will this ageing population receive care while still adapting to new technology?

This research aims to study the current behavioral trends seen in the elderly population post-pandemic in terms of healthcare needs and compare geriatric cases of care pre-pandemic and during the pandemic to anticipate the future trends. The literature review will focus on new innovations in environmental design and technology catering to this ageing population. This study aims to analyze the effects of these evolving trends on healthcare facility planning and design, senior living communities and housing.

Keywords: Senior citizens, virtual healthcare, COVID-19, Geriatrics, care at home

References:

K Barnett et al., "Epidemiology of multimorbidity and implications for health care, research, and medical education", *Lancet*, July 7, 2012.

Abstracts: Digital Media Shorts

Addressing Trauma in Design and Planning: Trauma-Informed Placemaking

Joongsub Kim *(Lawrence Technological University)*

The COVID-19 pandemic and George Floyd's death in 2020 refocused attention on structural disparities and their associated trauma, which still exist today in underserved communities. Advocates of trauma-informed approaches to design and planning argue that considering the history and lived experiences of residents in communities of color is essential to building a just society. On the other hand, others call for asset-based planning or resident participation to promote equitable and sustainable community development. Peter Marris' seminal 1974 book, entitled Loss and Change, dealt with the trauma and grief of urban renewal victims. What role can design and planning through placemaking play to help traumatized people cope with their loss and change? We answer this question through qualitative analysis of outcomes from the case of Detroit, as well as interviews and an interdisciplinary literature review. Using the concepts of kindness from Forester and of hope from Inch and other scholars, this theory-building article explores an integrative framework for addressing trauma in design and planning. In order for the kindness-hope integrative framework to support trauma-informed placemaking, we propose four socials just values for a democratic, equitable, and inclusive development process: relevance, equity, governance, and participation and engagement. By linking theory to practice, we examine the benefits of trauma-informed placemaking and discuss the challenges associated with implementing it, and suggest how to address those challenges.

References

Inch, A., Slade, J., & Crookes, L. (2020). Exploring Planning as a Technology of Hope. Journal of Planning Education and Research, 0739456X20928400.

Forester, J. (2021). Our curious silence about kindness in planning: Challenges of addressing vulnerability and suffering. Planning Theory, 20(1), 63-83.

Marris, P. (1974). Loss and Change (New York Pantheon, 151.

Covid-19 Pandemic and Equity within the Built Environment: Exploring Mobility, Energy, and Health Disparities Using Smart Data

Narjes Abbasabadi *(The University of Texas at Arlington)*; **Mehdi Ashayeri** *(Assistant Professor)*

The COVID-19 pandemic brought to sight unforeseen synergies between spatial, environmental, and human dynamics impacting equity and resilience within the built environments. In this research, we developed a conceptual framework and a spatiotemporal model to explain the human-built environment interactions considering the spatial disparities of access to critical infrastructure, environmental issues (including the energy burden of households and their exposure to pollutants (e.g., PM2.5)), and health crisis (COVID cases) and on the other hand response behaviors and resilience capacities associated with the households' socio- economic characteristics. We developed the spatiotemporal model at the county level in Texas, US., and at daily-basis time intervals using big data obtained from conventional and smart meter platforms, including the U.S. Department of Energy (DOE), Environmental Protection Agency (EPA), Center for Diseases Control and Prevention (CDC), Census Bureau, Google, and OpenStreetMap (OSM) among others. The time horizon for this study is from Feb. 1st, 2020, to May 22nd, 2022. Findings show changes in occupancy patterns in public and private buildings associated with environmental issues (e.g., the households' energy burden and exposure to pollutants), health crises, and socio-economic characteristics. For example, demand for public transportation increased for households with a higher level of energy burden and COVID cases. In contrast, demand substantially decreased for less-energy-burdened households and COVID case, indicating that socio-economic status determined households' daily behaviors on their modality of mobilities during the pandemic. The results also show that the use of parks and green spaces increased substantially during the COVID pandemic while the low-income households' presence in parks and green spaces decreased. Furthermore, presence in residential buildings was lower for low-income households, indicating less possibility for working from home or having service jobs. The findings of this study can aid the allied design, planning, and policymaking fields in the built environment in better understanding human dynamics in relation to the socio-economic characteristics and infrastructural systems, taking into account spatiotemporal dynamics to ensure resilience within the built environment to not only enable the city as a system to resist, cope with or bounce back from disturbances but also empower transformative solutions framed in an equitable manner. We highlight the need for grounding design, planning, and placemaking strongly in human needs, equity, and environmental sustainability, which require developing reflective indicators and metrics and harnessing emerging technologies and innovative solutions to make healthier, sustainable, equitable, and resilient built environments.

Development of Senior Living Design for Cognitive Health of Older Adults

Seokyung Park *(Texas A&M University);* ***Soyi Cheong*** *(Land and Housing Institute)*

South Korea is one of the fastest-aging societies in the world and is predicted to enter a super-aged society in 2025. This means that more than 21% of the total population is aged over 65 years old. An increase in the elderly population inevitably leads to an increase in dementia patients. The onset of dementia deteriorates an individual's quality of life and causes a huge increase in social costs. Therefore, it is important to prepare for senior-friendly environments that contribute to the prevention of dementia.

The purpose of this slide presentation is to introduce Cognitive Health Design (CHD) and its development process. The CHD is a residential design that aims to contribute to preventing or delaying the onset of dementia by helping older adults maintain an independent and healthy life as long as possible. It was developed based on the analysis of extensive literature reviews, case studies, and in-depth interviews. First, through an interview with a dementia specialist, a design strategy was established by reducing the risk factors and strengthening the protective factors for dementia. Environmental and lifestyle factors that can be controlled through physical modification were selected. Second, the characteristics of the elderly related to the selected factors were derived through literature research. Based on interviews with older adults, senior housing managers, and social workers, scenarios were set up for problematic situations and solutions that older adults experience in their daily life. Third, the design requirements to implement the solution were developed based on the analysis of case studies, housing design guidelines for people with dementia, universal design, and cognitive training manuals.

The results of this study are as follows. First, the following four design principles were established:

- Enhancement of cognitive functions,
- Safety in daily life,
- Promotion of physical health, and
- Participation in the community.

Second, a total of 15 design items were developed to provide a convenient life for the elderly and help them maintain their cognitive function. Moreover, design guidelines on how to apply the items to units, communal spaces, outdoor spaces, and a community center were developed. Finally, a pilot project was conducted and an apartment with CHD was constructed.

The CHD is expected to benefit older adults in maintaining their cognitive functions and shape an environment that contributes to preventing dementia. Further studies will be conducted to evaluate the practical impact of the CHD on older adults and to discover design improvements for future constructions.

Looking Down the Line: U.S. Plumbers Survey

Margaret Carneal *(Radford University)*

Saving water and repurposing our existing buildings are sustainable things to do. As we remodel and use more low-flow fixtures, we need to think about the back-end of water consumption, particularly drainlines. When there is less water in our pipes, solids sit in the pipes longer, causing them to degrade. In the United States, the urgency to address drainline concerns is growing because the plumbing infrastructure is due for an overhaul. Remodeling of primary plumbing spaces like kitchens and baths is on the rise using water-conserving fixtures. Homes are becoming larger with fewer people in them, using less water, decreases drainline flows. While plumbing supply systems have been revolutionized with the use of flexible PEX pipes, drainline system innovation has remained relatively stagnate with the continued use of large, rigid pipes with bulky fittings, and codes that have been in place for nearly 100 years. The time has come to rethink drainline design, and who knows what's going on with those pipes? Plumbers.

Plumbers across the United States were surveyed via email about their drainline experiences to better inform drainline redesign (n = 105-139). Qualified, experienced plumbers answered questions about their drainline encounters regarding installation processes, operating problems, and future drainline development goals and ideas. Quantitative questions had follow-up qualitative responses options so participants could give more detail.

In existing structures, relocating a drainline is much more problematic than replacing current pipes because of the spatial requirements for maintaining proper slope for draining. Plumbers discovered improper installation 25% of the time when remodeling and completing service calls. Primary causes for slow drains and stoppages were identified as user behaviors (54%), followed by system failures (36%), and other causes (10%). "Flushable" wipes, (that aren't really "flushable") were quantitatively noted very high as a major issue of stalls/stoppages, followed by grease, and then tree roots, which were specifically mentioned often and across the board for stalls/stoppages relating to user behaviors, system failures, and "other" issues. During times of drought, trees seek out water and break the lines causing unhealthy, foul backups. Plumbers assessed 11 drainline system issues, tree roots were the second-highest ranked issue (66%) following sags in the line (69%). The next issue was incorrect slope (60%), followed by low-flow fixtures with plumbers suspecting this issue 43% of the time. Since the implementation of water conservation fixtures, 66% of plumbers across the U.S. noticed an increase in drainline issues. In California, where low-flow fixtures have been in place the longest, 75% of plumbers believe water conservation has had a detrimental effect on drainline carry. Regarding drainline redesign, plumbers prioritized simplifying drainline installation and fitting connections, increasing flexibility, maintaining durability, and incorporating a lightweight solution.

This survey validates what plumbing engineers have suspected for years about what takes place down the drain based on real-world observations. With the aging pipes in our buildings, the country is due for drainline innovation, especially with the continuing need to conserve water and repurpose our existing buildings.

Manifesto for Birth Environment Design

Davis Harte *(Paradigm Spaces, LLC and Boston Architectural College);* **Doreen Balabanoff** *(Ontario College of Art & Design University);* **Nicoletta Setola** *(Dipartimento di Architettura Università di Firenze);* **Elizabeth Newnham** *(Griffith University)*

Our proposed six-minute video features the authors outlining the manifesto that drives our current research project, and discussing our research agenda and methodological approaches. Our work is focused on addressing the complex problem of challenging and transforming the birth culture we have inherited from the 19th and 20th centuries, and the clinical biomedical spaces and approaches to maternal and infant care that it spawned. To this end, our transdisciplinary project's objectives seek to actively contribute to a much-needed global paradigm shift for birth environment design.

The video will be 'live-action'. Each team member will present their role, and contribute examples of our working sessions, images from multiple stages of our work in progress, and snippets of recordings from our presentations at conferences in 2020/2021. An Insight Development Grant from the Social Sciences and Humanities Research

Council of Canada (SSHRC) is preparing the ground for our end goal – an inclusive web resource (under development) which is intended to be the go-to resource to inform practitioners (architects, designers, midwives, healthcare professionals) about childbirth environment evidence and cutting-edge best practices.

A touchpoint we will refer to is a recent integrative review that compliments and builds on previous work we have delivered. Visualizations of our process will be essential to the piece and will include images of case studies, Miro board insight development work, and our growing Zotero group library resource. The digital media short is an ideal platform to showcase our ongoing international project which is amplifying childbirth environmental design as an important architectural/design problem of our time.

Restore, Connect, and Streamline: Exploring How the Built Environment Can Mitigate Healthcare Worker Burnout

Alice Gittler *(EwingCole);* ***Gabriella Lentini*** *(EwingCole);* ***Kaitlyn Paulsen*** *(Healthcare Design Research Intern)*

Described as a consequence of "severe stress and high ideals in 'helping' professions" (Institute for Quality and Efficiency in Health Care (IQWiG), 2020), levels of burnout have been steeply increasing. From higher rates of mental illness to empathy-fatigue, this is driving many professionals out of the healthcare industry which impacts patient outcomes.

The World Health Organization (WHO) defines burnout as "an occupational syndrome that results from unmanaged or poorly managed chronic workplace stress." WHO defines 3 key dimensions of burnout: "feelings of energy depletion or exhaustion, increased mental distance from one's job (or feelings of negativism or cynicism related to one's job), and reduced personal efficacy (WHO, 2019).. Particularly in oncology, long working hours, continued exposure to fatal illness, limited autonomy over daily roles and responsibilities, and stressful working conditions can all lead to burnout syndrome (Copur, 2019).

Design considerations that have been shown to reduce medical provider stress and improve job satisfaction include a consistent layout, a high degree of visibility, open decentralized workstations, and ample access to natural light and outdoor spaces. (Nejati, 2016; Zborowsky, 2010; Rollins, 2015). There appears to be a considerable gap in the relationships between the features and locations of staff spaces and burnout. Further exploration of all pathways to reduce stress and promote resiliency and healing for healthcare teams is needed.

The objective of our ongoing study is to further uncover the relationships between healthcare facility design and burnout. The first part of the study includes a literature review as well as benchmarking staff spaces within outpatient oncology centers to understand and document five-year trends in the design of these spaces. Specific design attributes measured include access to natural light/views, levels of acoustical and visual privacy, as well as space per person. Part two of the study will include direct observation of team spaces and interviews to develop a grounded theory of staff support spaces in oncology settings.

This session will share the findings of the literature review and benchmarking and engage the participants in several interactive activities proposed to better understand these relationships and to target important areas for improvement in staff space design.

References

Copur M. S. (2019). Burnout in Oncology. Oncology (Williston Park, N.Y.), 33(11), 687522.

InformedHealth.org [Internet]. Cologne, Germany: Institute for Quality and Efficiency in Health Care (IQWiG); 2006-. Depression: What is burnout? [Updated 2020 Jun 18]. Available from: https://www.ncbi.nlm.nih.gov/books/NBK279286/

Nejati, Adeleh, Mardelle Shepley, and Susan Rodiek. "A Review of Design and Policy Interventions to Promote Nurses' Restorative Breaks in Health Care Workplaces." Workplace

Health & Safety 64, no. 2 (February 1, 2016): 70–77. https://doi.org/10.1177/2165079915612097.

Rollins, Judy A. "The 12-Hour Shift." Pediatric Nursing 41, no. 4 (July 1, 2015): 162–64.

World Health Organization. (n.d.). Burn-out an "occupational phenomenon": International Classification of Diseases. Burn-out an "Occupational Phenomenon": International Classification of Diseases. Retrieved December 2, 2021, from https://www.who.int/news/item/28-05-2019-burn-out-an-occupational-phenomenon-international-classification-of-diseases

Zborowsky, Terri, Lou Bunker-Hellmich, Agneta Morelli, and Mike O'Neill. "Centralized vs. Decentralized Nursing Stations: Effects on Nurses' Functional Use of Space and Work Environment." HERD 3, no. 4 (2010): 19–42. https://doi.org/10.1177/193758671000300404.

Abstracts: Posters

Jurors

A Checklist for Designing Convenience Store Considering Health & Well-Being

Sharmin Kader *(Kent State University);* **Shawon Samdani** *(MTS Engineering and Design);* **Musfiques Salahin** *(MTS Engineering and Design)*

A convenience store or neighborhood corner shop is a small retail place which carries a range of everyday items, such as coffee, groceries, snack foods, or alcoholic drinks. In recent years, there is a trend of accommodating a commercial kitchen and serving preparing food, such as, pizza. This study has developed a design checklist of the convenience store based on three research-informed design projects in Texas. All these projects are new construction (during pandemic) and similar in functions, and space requirements (above 6,000 sq ft). To practice evidence-based design considering health and well-being, a systematic literature review was conducted to develop the initial list of design criteria. One of the primary design objectives is to reduce the risk of people being exposed to the virus or improving infection prevention of the overall facility. A face-to-face meeting was conducted (Delphi method) with the stakeholders, designers, and contractors to develop the final list of design considerations. All these considerations were implemented during architectural, engineering, and interior design phases: layout, lighting, ventilations, finish material selections, restroom, kitchen, or serving areas. For example, using kitchens encased in glass cubes, providing sneezing shield in the food serving areas, using light color and easily cleanable floor finish materials in heavy-traffic zone, or using floor-to-ceiling windows (garage-style). This study is in the process of measuring the outcome. The design checklist with three practical examples with be helpful for future planning, design, and research.

Activation and Renewal: Research on the Community Agricultural Garden from the Perspective of Aging

Yang Xinyao *(Dalian University of Technology);* **Yan Xinhang** *(Dalian University of Technology);* **Pai Liu** *(Dalian University of Technology)*

A key issue causing mental health problems among older adults is the lack of social engagement. For senior citizens who live in the urban areas, especially those living in the communities built before 2000s, the only spaces for outdoor activities were the sidewalks with no green features. The narrowed outdoor spaces cause the lack of community engagement, which decrease the quality of life of both senior and younger residents. s In China, older adults tend to grow vegetables in any places as they can. The planting process and the harvest promotes the social engagement and enhance the sense of achievements. This study aims to investigate how the urban agricultural garden benefit community engagement in the old residential areas in northeast China. To identify the residents' perception of agricultural garden, a study was conducted in a selected neighborhood in Dalian, northeast China, where is an old residential area with a large aging population.

Mixed methods were used to collective the data. Before field study, we browsed the articles including the key words of agricultural garden, community engagement, mental health, and older adults to investigate the correlation between agricultural activities and the well-being of the senior citizens. We observed the residents' behaviors during different time periods to collect their usage of outdoor spaces.

Face to face surveys were conducted on site to gather their perceptions of the community environments and their preference of outdoor activities and spaces. Most of the participants were 60—70 years old with some younger residents. The results indicated a dissatisfaction of the existing outdoor environments. The residents had a high preference of community engagement space and agricultural garden. "Growing vegetables and fish" were the most preferred activities.

Based on the results, this study proposed an

alternative plan of an agricultural community garden to enhance community engagement. In terms of design strategy, the site is equipped with several multi-functional spaces, including a slow-moving loop, a fitness area, and a playground. To enhance the communication among different age groups, different functional spaces were connected by a roofed corridor around a Mulberry fishpond, whose circulation system is used to moderate the microclimate of the neighborhood. At the same time, a farmer's market is regularly held in the garden active the community and promote the mental health of older adults who desire to communicate and being held in esteem.

References

Han Yuanban (2005) Role of Garden in Urban Park, *Construction Building Technology* ,1020-1021

Li Mengnian , Lin Wenjie , Yang Xubo (2016) Comparison and Analysis of Urban and Rural Old People Demand for Elderly Care Services, Illustrated by the Case of Changping, Beijing. *Elderly's demand*, 2-5

Clements Willi (1989) *Ministry With the Aging: Designs, Challenges*, Foundations. New York: Imprint Routledge, 286

Dikann Alain (2020) Land art therapy, a return to the essence of the creative process. *Soins. Psychiatrie*, 27-30

Adaptation of New Agricultural Activities Due to COVID-19

Yuling Liu *(University of Tsukuba);* ***Minghui Tang*** *(University of Tsukuba);* ***Naoko Fujita*** *(University of Tsukuba)*

While COVID-19 preventive guidelines recommend to "avoid crowds of three" and adopt a "new lifestyle," the need for farming activities are increasing. A newspaper article reported that the number of new contractors for rental farms are going up. However, some studies have investigated the actual conditions of COVID-19 and its impact on agricultural activities.

This study aims to clarify the actual conditions of farming activities before and after the influence of COVID-19, countermeasures, changes in the consumer's behavior and factors, and to explain the new demands of consumers in the post / during COVID-19 era. It is to clarify various farming activities.

The research methods used were a hearing survey, field survey, and questionnaire survey. In the hearing survey, we acquired basic information from the farms such as the number of plots used and the number of people used in the past five years, including before and after the outbreak of COVID-19. In the field survey, questionnaires were distributed, and the location of each municipal farm was obtained. The questionnaire survey was divided into two categories—for users and managers that investigated the status of farm usage, changes in lifestyle consciousness, and overall changes before and after the occurrence of COVID-19. The results were analyzed using the Statistical Package for the Social Sciences (SPSS) software.

The results showed that the composition of the municipal farms in Ibaraki Prefecture mostly comprised the elderly while several new contractors were young, the frequency of visits by consumers before and after the outbreak of COVID-19, the length of stay, and growth of vegetables. It became clear that the attachment to the product was increasing, and that after the occurrence COVID-19, consumers often visited the site while shopping. In addition, it was revealed that the change in lifestyle consciousness caused by COVID-19 decreased the frequency of eating out and gave importance to avoiding food wastage and eating more vegetables.

Aging Simulation to Build Learning and Empathy Among Interior Design Students

Erica L. Elsey *(Illinois State University);* ***Gabriela Fonseca Pereira*** *(Illinois State University)*

The GERT suit is a series of braces and accessories that, when worn, simulate the experience of the common impairments of aging. It was created by Wolfgang Moll and is meant to help people empathize and give an insight into the needs of the aging population. It simulates changes in eyesight, hearing loss, mobility restrictions, stiffness, and loss of strength (Moll, n.d.; Yumuşak, 2019).

In the Interior Design Program at the college level, students theoretically learn about the aging process and how to address the needs of older adults in different types of designs. However, there is an age gap of at least 40 years between most college students and their target clients. Therefore, this study is aimed at understanding what students experience while wearing the GERT Aging Simulation Suit and if it has made them more understanding of the design needs of the aging process. The research question guiding this study was: how does wearing a GERT Aging Simulation Suit influence students' learning about the aging process and applying design solutions for the aging population?

This study was proposed at the 'Human Factors in Interior Environments' class at Illinois State University in the Fall of 2021. There were 22 students in this class composed of sophomores, juniors, seniors, and two graduate students. Each student put on the GERT suit and completed five tasks: Go up and down a flight of stairs, sit down and get up from a seat, enter and exit a bathroom and bathroom stall, get directions from someone in the hallway, and use a wheelchair to leave and return to the classroom. After completing these tasks, students were given a series of questions to answer based on how they felt physically and mentally during the simulation (Johnson et al., 2018). Content analysis was conducted, and emerging themes were identified based on students' common experiences and feelings.

The results showed that students most frequently experienced changes with hearing loss, eyesight, and problems with their coordination. Words that also appeared in responses frequently were 'Tired' and 'Uncomfortable'. The majority also felt that it was difficult to complete their tasks safely and felt self-conscious walking through the university building. When it comes to the learning experience, students empathized with the aging population and thought that this would have been much more difficult with any cognitive impairments and felt that this simulation would make them more aware of older adults' needs when designing different spaces.

This study shows that students were able to experience some of the bodily changes that come with age and with this, a better empathy for and understanding of the experiences and needs of the aging population. By experiencing a portion of the difficulties that arise with the aging process, it helps students to understand the diverse range of needs that must be taken into consideration during the design process.

Agrihoods and Cooperatives: Community-Based Initiatives for Food and Housing Sovereignty

Nadia Anderson *(University of North Carolina, Charlotte)*

The U.S. Department of Agriculture (USDA) defines food deserts as "low-income census tracts with a substantial number or share of residents with low levels of access to retail outlets selling healthy and affordable foods" (Ver Ploeg, 2011). In addition to lack of healthy food access, these neighborhoods also often suffer from lack of quality affordable housing, business development resources, and access to employment and quality education and are typically communities of color. Describing these neighborhoods as "deserts," however, suggests they are barren, devoid of resources. Nothing could be further from the truth! The West Boulevard Corridor in Charlotte, North Carolina is a low-income, African American food desert but it is also a place with community spirit, sense of history and place, and desire to make visible its cultural heritage. "Food apartheid" more accurately identifies lack of healthy food access as rooted in a racist, corporate food system that "reduces food to an economic commodity" that does not value local practices or traditions (Sevilla, 2021). Food sovereignty is anchored in local knowledge and practices and provides a path for not only improving food access but also providing a scaffold for broader local control of systems such as housing, economic development, and education. This paper describes two projects in the West Boulevard Corridor developed through community-engaged design and other engagement methods as part of a university-community partnership focused on food sovereignty as the anchor for a larger place-driven ecosystem.

While Charlotte is one of the fastest-growing cities in the U.S., it also has one of the lowest social mobility rates and most significant racial wealth gaps (Chetty, 2014). Decades of large-scale, market-driven development has left African American neighborhoods with few resources and at risk of displacement and gentrification. After years of meetings with grocery retailers, all of whom refused to locate a branch in the area because it did not meet their business models, the West Boulevard Corridor Coalition began looking at locally owned and operated food cooperatives as an alternative. The projects in this paper look at what local sovereignty can mean at the scale of a food co-op, a neighborhood activity hub, and locally determined affordable housing. They confront the behemoth of global capitalism from a perspective that values local knowledge over profit margins, flexibility, and adaptiveness over formulaic fixity.

References

Chetty, R., N. Hendren, P. Kline, E. Saez (2014). Where is the land of opportunity? The geography of intergenerational mobility in the United States. *The Quarterly Journal of Economics, 129*(4), 1558-1623.

Sevilla, N. (2021, April 2). *Food Apartheid: Racialized Access to Healthy Affordable Food.* National Resources Defense Council.

Ver Ploeg, M., D. Nulph, R. Williams (2011, December 1). *Mapping Food Deserts in the United States.* USDA: Economic Research Service.

Amman Alternative Futures: The Pulse of Current and Future Jordanian Municipal Growth & Resilience of Place and People

Rula Awwad-Rafferty *(University of Idaho);* ***Daniel Cronan*** *(University of Idaho);* ***Hala Barakat*** *(University of Idaho)*

Throughout the world, sprawl within our large urban areas reflects population growth and societal needs for space. For the last century, as Jordan grew to become for 10,342,556 people in 2021; Amman, Jordan demonstrates an example of this growth trend (1% increase in the last year alone). Since 1950 to 2021, the population has grown exponentially from 90,000 to 2,182,000 citizens. Urban growth has increased by 162 km2 which is approximately 509 times the original urban area (Al Rawashdeh et al., 2006). Along with this growth, issues and impacts arise such as decrease in fertile land, increases in impervious surfaces thus leading to impacts for water quality and urban heat island effect. During the ebbs and flows of demographic shifts and external political pressures, the stories of people and the spaces in which they inhabit and inherit have changed in the face of turmoil of political conflict, stressed resources and the juxtaposition of hospitable cultures rooted back to Bedouin traditions. As this flux and pressure continues, understanding growth through Alternative Futures analysis has the potential to portray a trajectory of change for this rich cultural landscape.

Within this project and presentation, we would like to demonstrate hindcasting methods used to track previous growth over the last century. We will then demonstrate what trajectories of growth might look like under three growth scenarios: A) Business as Usual with Current Growth, B) Higher Density Planned Development with Higher Growth, and C) Low Density Development with Higher Growth. We aim to use permutations of growth trends for the year 2037 per the United Nations Growth Projections operationalizing Artificial Intelligence (AI) models to track this growth geospatially. To disseminate our results, we aim to provide representations and visualizations of these Alternative Futures (Hulse, 2008) through various geospatial tools to demonstrate impacts of this growth under various scenarios. This research intends to provide a proof of concept to contribute to Alternative Futures and scenario-based body of knowledge by addressing current and relevant issues through novel approaches in computational land cover projection tools. This presentation offers an approach to link human behavior and land cover change through hindcasting methods to project a suite of Alternative Futures for the city of Amman.

References

Al Rawashdeh, S., & Saleh, B. (2006). Satellite Monitoring of Urban Spatial Growth in the Amman Area, Jordan. *Journal of Urban Planning and Development, 132*(4), 211–216. https://doi.org/10.1061/(ASCE)0733-9488(2006)132:4(211)

Hulse, D., Branscomb, A., Enright, C., & Bolte, J. (2008). Anticipating floodplain trajectories: a comparison of two alternative futures approaches. *Landscape Ecology, 24*(8), 1067–1090. https://doi.org/10.1007/s10980-008-9255-2

An All-Inclusive Playground

Zahra Ghazanfari *(ADC Engineering)*

Kid-venture 2 is an inclusive playground with objective to include everyone, thoughtfully designed to provide a safe place where children of all abilities can play together and are developmentally appropriate for children with and without disabilities. By addressing the needs of the whole child, Kid-venture 2 offers an abundance of meaningful experiences, and provides opportunities for children to engage the Senses, play in cozy spaces, and to experience the joy and benefits that come from playing together.

Kid-venture 2 is an accessible playground that has gone beyond ADA to ensure that people using wheelchairs can use the playground. Inclusion is ensuring that people feel they belong, are engaged, and connected. Kid-venture 2 provides accessible path from the parking lot to the edge of the play area, path from the edge of the play area to the play equipment, and accessibility of Surface Systems Under and Around Playground Equipment. Additionally, we ensure access to equipment by adding features such as a ramp leading to a piece of equipment.

First priority over everything else is safety, and to protect children at all times. There were also several other vital considerations when Kid-venture 2 designed as an inclusive playground, including: universal design, compliant design, accessible route, elevated play component, elevated accessible route, ground-level play component, use zone, clear floor space, ramp, and transfer station, to name a few. Various play equipment selected according to different needs of disabled kids. Perhaps the most important byproduct of an inclusive playground is that it could lead to better communities.

An Analysis of Accessibility of Privately Owned Indoor Public Space for Publicness: Office Buildings in Seoul

SooMin Yoon *(Hanyang University);* ***YeaEun Park*** *(Hanyang University);* ***Yeonsook Hwang*** *(Hanyang University)*

Overcrowding of office buildings in today's cities has created private spaces excessively within the cities, degrading their publicness. The public open-space that was introduced to promote the publicness in South Korea have problem in responding to weather changes and drastic environmental shifts. In response, Korea introduced privately owned indoor public space (indoor POPS) centered on Seoul. The indoor POPS increases the usability of public space, so accessibility to indoor POPS should be increased. Since the accessibility enables users to reach public spaces and makes indoor POPS to be used for urban publicness, it is critical to urban publicness. This study analyzes the characteristics and planning elements of indoor POPS with respect to accessibility and proposes measures to promote the publicness. This study is concentrated on literature review-the concept of indoor POPS and the element of accessibility with respect to publicness- and field investigation. The regional scope is Jongro, Gangnam, and Yeouido, with a high concentration of offices in Seoul. The spatial scope is office buildings with a total ground area of 100,000 sf or more, and the temporal scope is buildings built in 2011 and later. Based on these, the following five cases are selected: D-Tower, IFC seoul, Parnas, Centropolis, and Pine Avenue. This study analyzes the findings with respect to visual perception, physical access from outside, and movement between indoor facilities. Regarding visual perception, the majority of information signs outside indicates the brand names of retail and lacked of floor-wise information. Since the density of office buildings in Seoul makes the streets complex, it is difficult for pedestrians to access to indoor facilities without information acquisition from the outside. Hence, outside signs should provide systematically composed information. Regarding physical access from outside, to solve the density of population in Seoul, degree of connection between subway stations, bus stops, and crosswalks is high. The distance between main entrances and transportation facilities is within a walk of 1 to 3 minutes. In three cases, since entrances are connected to subways through underground passage, it is easy to access from underground. However, in some cases, the side entrances are located in an alley and difficult to spot. Because the concentration of adjacent buildings makes the width of the sidewalks narrow. Therefore, entrances should be located near wide sidewalks, so that it is easier to access while walking from outside. Regarding movement between indoor facilities; the open structure of indoor POPS and the arrangement of facilities according to the type increase publicness. Office buildings in Korea are high-rise, so the indoor POPS has large vertical spaces. However, when it has separate floors depending on facility types, the circulation is lengthened since a person must move to different floors to use a particular facility. Furthermore, some cases have closed ceilings, making it impossible to gain visual perception of each floor and, thus, diminishing accessibility. To solve these problems, vertical circulation such as open staircases and escalators can be used, so that it can visually and physically connect each floor and improve accessibility.

An Ecological Farm Design Incorporating the Natural Cycle to Create Agricultural Experiences for Disabled Individuals

Ding Ma *(University of Tsukuba);* ***Naoko Fujita*** *(University of Tsukuba)*

This study aims to test whether the incorporation of the natural cycle into the ecological farm design can improve the protection and restoration of agricultural ecosystems. Additionally, agricultural activities are used to rehabilitate and improve the mental health of disabled individuals. Lastly, communication between elderly, able-bodied, and disabled individuals are established through agricultural activities. The incorporated design allows for convenient access for disabled individuals and tested the impact of agricultural experiences on the rehabilitation and mental health of disabled individuals. This design also examines the effect and disadvantages of communication between able-bodied, elderly, and disabled individuals through agricultural activities.

A model for a natural material cycle is developed at the study site in Tsukuba, Japan, based on ecological research and site suitability and included material circulation and water circulation systems. A circular ecological environment, incorporating natural regeneration, will be established using a multi-cropping system, a waste treatment device, methane fermentation and a minimum water-saving device. The development of this system may promote the understanding of farmlands that have small ecological loads.

Furthermore, we want to combine regional professional industries with plantation activities to create a plantation landscape design and to create jobs for local disabled individuals.

With agricultural experience and job creation as the focus, we will study the suitability of agricultural areas for elderly, able-bodied and disabled individuals. We will also investigate how to apply a barrier-free design and a rehabilitation design in the context of agricultural activities. Agricultural activities will be used to assess communication between able-bodied and disabled individuals and to explore interests of people with disabilities during rehabilitation.

This study will provide a farming experience for elderly, able-bodied and disabled individuals by allowing them to grow and nurture plant life with their own hands. The experimental design promotes material circulation and harnesses the natural cycle of small ecosystems in ecological farms. The promotion of a circular ecological environment in ecological landscape construction will increase awareness and knowledge of national ecology and create a more ecologically conscious society.

We believe this study will break down social barriers and enhance mutual understanding by promoting social communication between elderly, able-bodied, and disabled individuals. The results of this study may provide suggestions to create more opportunities for disabled people to engage and integrate with society and improve their physical and mental health.

An Investigation of the Residential Environment on Students' Learning at Home during the Pandemic: A Qualitative Interview Study

***Jing Tian** (University of Minnesota); **Abimbola Asojo** (University of Minnesota)*

The spread of COVID-19 has impacted the entire world. Most people have to stay home to work or study in response to the COVID-19 pandemic. Since 2020, most studies have focused on how to design hybrid workplaces to satisfy the hybrid working model so as to improve the efficiency of working at home. However, there is still a lack of research focusing on how the residential environment affects students' learning when they study long-term at home. The goal of this study is to explore the views of students on what kind of residential environmental factor affects their learning at home during the pandemic era. Three college students are interviewed in this pilot study. Thematic coding (inductive) is applied to analyze all transcribed interview data. Finally, it is found the below five factors affect students' learning at home: 1) blurred boundary; 2) natural elements; 3) room size; 4) social interaction; 5) acoustic environment. The ideal residential environment for students should have a clear boundary between sleeping and work area, enough natural daylight and ventilation, less noise, bigger space, more plants. Through this study, it is hoped that designers would learn more about which environmental factors need to be considered so as to improve students' productivity at home in the post-pandemic era. The researcher hopes to obtain feedback from interdisciplinary EDRA experts about ways to further develop, expand and improve this study.

Analysis of Publicness Evaluation Indicators and Users' Perceptions to Improve Urban Publicness

***GyeongYeon Lee** (Yonsei University); **Ji Eun Oh** (Yonsei University); **Soohyun Lee** (Yonsei University); **Mi-Kyoung Ha** (Yonsei University); **Gidong Byun** (Yonsei University)*

In modern society, quality of life and publicity have a deep relationship. The measure of social development is shifting from GDP to "healthy life" and "sustainability," such as diagnosing the social environment and the quality of life of social members and areas that need to be improved, centering on international organizations. According to several indicators, Korea's international level is at the bottom of the world far below its economic level. Accordingly, Korea recognizes the importance of maintaining the community to solve the healthy lives and social problems of social members, and emphasizes social and environmental well-being beyond individuals.

In particular, the demand for 'strengthening publicness' for the physical environment, which is a basic human living environment, is increasing. In response, active research is being conducted to realize the public values pursued by members of society beyond the traditional public concept in the field of architectural space but is still focused on the function and architectural behavior of physical space rather than a user-centered approach (Lee et al., 2021). For publicness to have a positive effect on our lives, users' empathy and social consensus are needed.

This study aims to realize an urban environment that provides comfortable rest and positive experiences to urban residents by establishing standards for evaluating publicity for various public spaces constituting the urban environment. To prepare specific items, promotional elements were derived based on research conducted in Korea, and a checklist for each element was prepared. As a result, seven publicness factors were derived:

'accessibility', 'connectivity', 'openness', 'amenity', 'convenience', 'sense of place', and 'sustainability'. Based on this, a survey was conducted to analyze the perception of the importance of each element. This is expected to greatly influence the direction of publicness and the design of the urban environment in the future.

It can be used as basic data to identify the strengths and weaknesses of urban public spaces and to prepare solutions and improvement plans for each space to improve the quality of life of urban residents. In addition, by expanding the publicness of public places that are closely related to life, it will be possible to realize a good society to live in, leading to the recovery of local communities, the establishment of local identity, and local attachment.

Analysis of Social Fear Influencing Factors for Creating a Safe Environment: Focus on the Young Women's Group

Ji Eun Oh *(Yonsei University);* ***GyeongYeon Lee*** *(Yonsei University);* ***Soohyun Lee*** *(Yonsei University);* ***Gi-dong Byun*** *(Yonsei University);* ***MiKyoung Ha*** *(Yonsei University)*

When asked if our society is safe and if we feel safe in society, no one will be able to easily say yes. In the 21st century, society is experiencing rapid and multifaceted changes that have never been experienced before, such as rapid change, growth, development of advanced technology in the process of knowledge informatization, confusion in values, diversification of social crimes, and increase in frequency. In particular, our reality is that the prolonged COVID-19 outbreak in Wuhan, China in January 2019 is leading to unpredictable times, with a large population facing illness and death around the world, adding to anxiety over the virus. As a result, 40.7% of all Koreans said they experienced "COVID Blue." COVID-19 refers to depression or anxiety experienced by infection anxiety and heavy social atmosphere after the this incident, with women (50.7%) having a higher experience rate of COVID Blue than men (34.2%) (Korea Health Promotion Institute, 2020). In addition, according to the "2020 Gender Statistics in Korea" published by the Seoul Government, 39.9% of the total population living in Korea had anxiety from society and did not feel psychologically safe. As such, the level of anxiety in the society we live in is steadily increasing regardless of the improvement of the people's quality of life, and direct and indirect experiences of events and accidents affect various members of society and furthermore, within individuals and communities, affects their quality of life and satisfaction.

The purpose of this study is to investigate the factors that give women social fear in the local community from the perspective of disorder and social control, and through this, to suggest factors and planning methods that should be considered first for the creation of a safe environment. To this end, the spatial scope is limited to a specific street in Sinchon-dong, Seodaemun-gu, Seoul, Korea, and the difference in factors that each person feels social anxiety and fear is analyzed to help people understand the 'Disorder' and 'Social control' of the surrounding environment. Let's look at how different perception tendencies appear.

The subjects of this study are adult women who live or frequently visit Seodaemun-gu. Various universities are located in Sinchon-dong, Seodaemun-gu and young people frequently visit it. Fear is likely to show different aspects, so the study subjects were limited to adults 19 years of age or older. In order to find out the factors affecting their social anxiety and fear related to environmental cognition, the study was conducted in the following way. First, the related literature was reviewed and a questionnaire tool was prepared. Second, 30 women who expressed their intention to participate were secured through the announcement of the recruitment of survey respondents, and a survey was conducted with them. Third, analysis was conducted using IBM SPSS.

Characteristics of Urban Areas Related to Natural Surveillance and Children's Sense of Safety: Focusing on Street Lights, Cctvs, and Spatial Configuration

Sojeong Lee *(Korea Advanced Institute of Science and Technology)*; **Wonjun No** *(Korea Advanced Institute of Science and Technology)*; **Giyoung Byun** *(Korea Advanced Institute of Science and Technology)*; **Jae-Jun Park** *(Mapo-gu Office)*; **Lisa Lim** *(Korea Advanced Institute of Science and Technology)*; **Young-chul Kim** *(Korea Advanced Institute of Science and Technology)*

The study asks if the urban facilities related to natural surveillance can explain the children's perception of 'dangerous' places. The degree to which people feel safe got attention from the researchers since it encourages or discourages physical activities (Bennet et al., 2007). The increased natural surveillance is one of the key factors to make a city not only actually safer but also allow people to feel safe. Children, as objects with independent needs from the adults' instructions, show more or less physical activity due to their perception of a particular space (Min & Lee, 2006). The relationship between various environmental variables and children's perception is being interested in researchers, yet the studies often targeted children's certain activities or places. This study is in line with previous studies studying the relationship between urban environment and perception of children but differentiates itself as it focuses on how the urban facilities related to natural surveillances would affect children's perceived safety.

Targeting an elementary school and its surrounding areas, two main methods were used in the study. First, we conducted a survey to figure out the locations and reasons of places where children actually feel dangerous about the streets around the school. Second, we performed statistical analysis with the physical factors of the streets in relation to children's perceptions. Independent variables were the number of street lights, the number of CCTVs, and the average integration value of streets by the space syntax according to the top reasons why children think the place is dangerous. The dependent variable was the number of 'dangerous' places that children think. We counted and calculated the values of each variable using a 30-meter by 30-meter grid as a unit of analysis.

The statistical analysis shows the average integration value a positive correlation with the number of dangerous places that children think. This shows that higher pedestrian volumes may affect children noticing the places dangerous, which is different from the previous studies. We think it may be related to other pedestrian-related reasons. For example, high integration means there would be a lot of people on the streets, not only the good people but also bad people who can put kids in danger. Additionally, the street lights and CCTVs show very low relation to the children's sense of safety. This is an important finding to investigate the difference between adults' and children's perceptions of safety on streets in the future. This study may have some limitations in that the number of variables is small and the variables should be more verified whether it represents the survey results well. The increased variety of variables and their proper selection would be covered in the future study.

References

Bennett, G. G., McNeill, L. H., Wolin, K. Y., Duncan, D. T., Puleo, E., & Emmons, K. M. (2007). Safe to walk? Neighborhood safety and physical activity among public housing residents. *PLoS Medicine, 4*(10), e306.

Min, B., & Lee, J. (2006). Children's neighborhood place as a psychological and behavioral domain. *Journal of Environmental Psychology, 26*(1), 51-71.

Children's Healing Gardens: Two Case Studies in Chile

Daniela Casanello Frisius *(Ecoplan)*

Healing gardens are a relatively recent topic in Chile, and Fundación Inspira is the main nonprofit organization dedicated to recover places in health care facilities transforming them, together with the communities, into Healing Gardens to provide therapeutic benefits. However, the global pandemic changed the way participatory processes were guided until then.

There are few children's healing gardens in Chile. These places are designed not only to be beautiful and to connect with nature, which improves children's health, the sense of wellbeing, reduce their stress; but also, incorporate play therapy. This type of therapy adds the variable of being playful and enjoyable, which invites children to interact with the physical world by stimulating their curiosity1 and inviting them to discover through play.

Two healing gardens are part of this study. Both gardens were managed by Fundación Inspira and designed by Ecoplan, a Landscape Architecture office focused on children and nature. The first case study is located in a health care facility of a nonprofit organization specialized in burned children in Pudahuel, Chile. A healing garden was proposed for the Rehabilitation Center's Guest House in order to help in the healing process of children, to reduce their and their families' stress level, and to create an outdoor learning space for the Rehabilitation Center's school. The place also serves as a relaxation space for staff members and visitors.

The second case study is a healing garden in a School for visual impaired children situated in La Cisterna, Chile. The school become the first school for visually impair children in Latin America in 1947, currently being an educational referent at national and Latin American level.

The design process in both cases was totally different, and this research identifies how the design methodology was adapted in pandemic time. The Rehabilitation Center´s Healing Garden had a complete face-to-face participative design and construction process, which involved different stakeholders such as patients, families, staff, institutions, and volunteers. However, the School´s Healing Garden design process was developed during Covid-19 pandemic, which incorporated an online approach. Both case studies had different methodologies, though interesting results.

Some design considerations and requests during interviews for both gardens were: accessibility, shade, play areas, outdoor learning space, nature, among others. Nevertheless, the Rehabilitation Center Garden required big-group rest areas and familiarity, while the School Garden asked for sensory areas and a vegetable garden. Different Chilean native plants were tested to provide biodiversity in both cases.

In conclusion, the incorporation of online approach had advantages and disadvantages. The advantages are the less time-consuming commutes to the site. However, one-on-one interaction is crucial to gain confidence and affectivity from the interviewee, which is hard to achieve during an online process.

Keywords: Healing garden, therapeutic landscape, children playground, children's participation, children natural environment, outdoor learning.

References

Moore, R. (1999). Healing Gardens for Children. In C. Cooper Marcus and M. Barnes (Eds.), *Healing gardens: Therapeutic Benefits and design Recommendations*. New York: John Wiley & Sons.

Color Healing: Exploring the Transformation of Urban Spaces in Old Districts

Yuxuan Wang; Pai Liu *(Dalian University of Technology)*

Color influences human behaviors while involving in different environments. Outdoor spaces design with appropriate colors have been verified the benefits of improving the well-being of older adults(da Silva, 2012). For older adults, their declined body functions cause a heavy dependence of their living environments(Han et al., 2016). However, in northeast China, the outdoor spaces have very limited considerations to complement the needs of older adults from the perspective of color, which affects the happiness and comfort of the senior citizens in their retirements. The declined mobility and the environments with limited auxiliary design cause anxiety and depression among the older adults living in an central city neighborhood in northeast China. How could color influence the participation of outdoor activities among the older residents in the old neighborhood in northeast China? What are the color preferences for difference activity sites? This research aims to explore the use of color in creating an aging friendly urban space to promote the mental health of older adults through facilitating the participation of outdoor activities. A site, which was an abandoned factory, located in a neighborhood built around 1980s in Dalian, northeast China was selected. This neighborhood now has a large aging population. We interpreted the area through field study and the UAV. There were very limited outdoor spaces in the neighborhood but the sidewalks, where the residents use for outdoor activities. Even the one-meter sidewalk is basically covered by sidewalk trees, garbage, and vehicles. Based on the interviews, the older residents had a safety concern of doing activities on the sidewalks, while their primary outdoor activity is walking. They had a desire of a colorful outdoor space to highlight the old community and support outdoor walking at the same time.

To facilitate the needs of the older adults, this project proposed a corridor with roof to promote outdoor walking. By analyzing the 22 articles regarding the color and environmental use of older adults, six principles have been summarized to inform the design of the corridor. Using a variety of material and different colors, the walking experiences changed at every turning point to create a sense of rhythm. At the same time, the different forms of windows on both sides of the corridor connect the scenery inside and outside the site.

A group of old residents in the neighbor was invited to review the proposed corridor model. The results show that the outdoor corridor with color rhythm improved their willingness of walking outside and decreased their feeling of anxiety and depression.

References

da Silva, F. M. (2012). Color and inclusivity: a visual communication design project with older people. *Work, 41*(Supplement 1), 4746-4753.

Han, J. W., Kim, B. G., Choi, I., & Park, S. (2016). Senescent effects on color perception and emotion. *Architectural research, 18*(3), 83-90.

Combined Use of Natural Lighting, Artificial Lighting, and Curtains in Patient Wards

***Zhe Wang** (Henan University); **Yan Wang** (Henan University)*

Background: Previous research indicates that natural light plays a positive role in patients' psychological and physiological healing. Full utilization of natural lighting generally reduces the demand for artificial lighting. Both natural lighting and artificial lighting are widely applied in patient wards. Adjusting the intensity of lighting, there are window curtains and privacy curtains between beds in the wards. To promote patient care, the combined use of natural lighting, artificial lighting, and the curtains in patient wards should be investigated.

Objective: Aim of this research is to identify the intensity of lighting in patient wards and the most popular behaviors using natural lighting, artificial lighting, and curtains there. The lighting environment in a patient ward is influenced by a variety of environmental and behavioral factors such as natural lighting, artificial lighting, window curtain, and privacy curtain, etc. However, the reality of lighting environments in a ward is rarely researched.

Methods: The site of research is in a tertiary hospital in Central China. On the 8th and 9th floor of an inpatient building there, we measured the intensity of lighting in four south-facing patient wards. These wards had the same room plan and each of them was shared by three patients. Of the wards, two had larger window areas whereas the other two had their windows partly blocked by outdoor wall decorations. On-site measurements of the intensity of combined lighting in selected locations in these wards were collected in the morning, noon, and afternoon in two weekdays in summer 2020. The ways that people used the artificial lighting and curtains were observed and summarized. The differences in lighting intensity in these wards were identified.

Findings: Lighting environment in a patient ward is influenced by both environmental and behavioral factors. In the wards with smaller window areas, artificial lighting was more likely to be applied during the daytime. However, the intensity of lighting in the wards with larger window areas was still significantly higher than that in the wards with smaller window areas. Moreover, the privacy curtains between patient beds were more likely to be used in the wards with smaller window areas.

The combined use of lighting in patient wards is complicated in the context of local cultures. Intensive analysis of the lighting environments in patient wards should be conducted in the context of individual dataset in order to optimize the integrated application of natural lighting and artificial lighting.

Creating a Workable Workspace: Office Design Solutions for Individuals with Autism Spectrum Disorder

Farzane Omidi *(Texas Tech University);* ***Kristi Gaines*** *(Texas Tech University)*

The unemployment rate of adults with autism spectrum disorder (ASD) in comparison with other adults that suffer from other disabilities is high in the United States (Ohl et al., 2017). People need to participate in some activities in order to transition from childhood to adulthood. Some of these identified activities include graduating from high school, financial independence through having a job and income, and leaving their parental home and establishing a family (Anderson et al., 2014). This shows the importance of having a job to provide independence for individuals, but in general, 85% of adults with ASD are unemployed which is roughly two-thirds of this population. One potential reason for this high unemployment rate is that the design of most workplaces does not consider the needs of these individuals. Since those with ASD are sensitive to sensory and visual input, some design characteristics, such as high auditory levels in open-plan offices or harsh lighting conditions, can cause problems (Lorenz et al., 2016). Since there is a broad spectrum of sensitivities, creating appropriate adaptive workspaces that address these individuals' needs is crucial. For example, lighting, access to nature or quiet places, audio conditions, proper materials, and colors, are some of the sensory needs that should be addressed through special physical design. Some common designs such as open-office plans are not appropriate as they may increase tension and prevent individuals with ASD from concentrating on their works. Thus, controlling the light and noise, establishing an environment that makes wayfinding easier, and providing spaces that allow individuals to concentrate or offer natural views can all contribute to creating productive workable places for people with ASD.

This study examines the main issues that people with ASD are facing in indoor environments and identifying the factors that contribute to their negative experience. These issues cause some challenges in workspaces for them, and this study identifies possible design solutions for maintaining a workable workspace for these individuals. These strategies can reduce the sensitivity of people with ASD in workplaces and it can help them to engage with their work, and finally increases their self-confidence and independence. In the presentation, researcher outlines the aspects of this project design and discuss these potential solutions.

References

Anderson, K. A., Shattuck, P. T., Cooper, B. P., Roux, A. M., & Wagner, M. (2014). Prevalence and correlates of postsecondary residential status among young adults with an autism spectrum disorder. *Autism, 18*(5), 562–570. https://doi.org/10.1177/1362361313481860

Lorenz, T., Frischling, C., Cuadros, R., & Heinitz, K. (2016). Autism and overcoming job barriers: Comparing job-related barriers and possible solutions in and outside of autism-specific employment. *PLoS ONE, 11*(1). https://doi.org/10.1371/journal.pone.0147040

Ohl, A., Sheff, M. G., Little, S., Nguyen, J., Paskor, K., & Zanjirian, A. (2017). Predictors of employment status among adults with Autism Spectrum Disorder. *Work, 56*(2), 345–355. https://doi.org/10.3233/WOR-172492

Creating Urban Habitats through Ecological Design of Schoolyard Spaces: Addressing the New Normal of the COVID-19 Era

Naoko Fujita *(University of Tsukuba);* ***Yuki Yokoyama*** *(Kyushu University)*

Habitat, also called biotope, refers to where organisms live. Artificial habitats are being created in cities, often as part of ecologically designed urban spaces, including rooftop gardens, and as part of the environmental protection measures associated with building development. Schoolyard habitats—school nature gardens and ponds—are part of this trend. Previous research has indicated that they are effective in increasing local biodiversity, stimulating children's outdoor activities, and helping to create a sense of community between schools and local residents. The objectives of this study were twofold. The primary objective was to understand how many elementary schools have established schoolyard habitats. The secondary objective was to derive a general solution by examining in detail a good practice schoolyard habitat. The long-term aim was to identify an ecological design for green infrastructure at school sites, that will be adaptable in an era of change brought about by COVID-19, through the creation of urban biological habitats. All 426 elementary schools in a Japanese city with a population of around 100,000 were selected as study sites. First, a questionnaire survey was conducted by return postcard to investigate the number of schools that had backyard habitats. Next, an interview survey was conducted with teachers in charge of successful and sustainable schoolyard habitats as case studies, to understand the conditions necessary for creating such habitats. The tested schools were selected based on the results of the first stage of the study and the characteristics of the school habitats, which had been successfully revitalized and maintained after a period of stagnation. An analysis of the maintenance system of these schools was conducted. For schools without schoolyard habitats, the rationale for not having them was identified. The results of the survey indicated that there are three necessary conditions for sustainable schoolyard habitats: "children must be the main maintainers," "it must be a place for education," and "it must be set up to restore and conserve local biodiversity." Since the COVID-19 outbreak began in early 2020, adaptation measures have been required to prevent the spread of the disease. Avoiding the "Three Cs"—closed spaces, crowded places, and close-contact settings—has been pointed out as an effective way to prevent infection. Schoolyard habitats are natural outdoor spaces set up in elementary schools within the community. They can be a valuable sanctuary where children can come into contact with nature while avoiding the Three Cs. The results of this study showed that creating schoolyard habitats could add more ecologically designed city spaces, perfect for the "new normal" of the COVID-19, and post-COVID eras.

Design for Student Engagement and Improved Health Outcomes at William & Mary's Integrative Wellness Center

Jennifer Amster *(EYP)*

Promoting wellness among college students is more important than ever. The American College Health Association (ACHA) stated in a recent 2014 report that stress, anxiety, and sleep difficulties were the top three factors affecting student performance. Ready to address increasing concerns over students' struggles with these issues, William & Mary needed a new facility that would inspire students to actively seek programs supporting both mind and body.

Asking, "What can design do to improve campus health and wellbeing?" the team partnered with William & Mary to design The McLeod Tyler Wellness Center — a peaceful oasis in the heart of campus, surrounded by a natural wooded area. Taking advantage of a centralized location, the center offers all major health facilities, wellness services, and recreation wellness programming under one roof. Students can meet with a physician, attend Yoga class, exercise in the fitness center, or speak with a counselor – all in one location.

The designers applied certain characteristics to

the design of the facilities to support the paradigm shift towards a holistic environment where students can flourish:

- Massing and site design that integrates with natural surroundings
- Modern exterior design that engages students and draws them into the building
- Calm, comfortable, and welcoming interior that puts students at ease
- Positive distractors such as biophilic elements and expansive natural views
- Layout that effectively meets the many operational needs of healthcare personnel.
- Transparency that promotes availability of multiple opportunities to experience integrative wellness.

In conjunction with a team of researchers at the University of Virginia, the author's firm engaged in a research study to confirm the positive outcomes of changes in the physical environment.

The Pre-Occupancy Survey in Spring 2018 provided a landscape of current health and wellness services on campus to identify gaps that may exist according to student and staff perspectives. The data indicated that students value wellness, but were not clear on the various opportunities available.

In Spring 2019, the Post-Occupancy Survey and focus groups explored utilization of services and staff collaboration after departmental integration in co-located space. Two samples were included in the study: students (n = 4,000), and staff (n = 52). The goals were to capture students' motivation to visit the center, engage with the service offerings, and staff experiences with the integration.

Post integration results revealed that student use increased, and they are reporting positive interactions and engagement. The design and co-location of services are driving utilization of more interventional services. Staff report increased collaborative behaviors and are overwhelmingly satisfied with the facility design and amenities.

In summary, with the knowledge of the role health and wellness plays in the success of students and rise in the need for these services on campus, the investment in accessible and welcoming facilities is well worth it and the payoff can be measured in multiple ways. This poster will include survey design and results, as well as specific design strategies that were implemented to produce a cultural shift toward other wellness dimensions.

Development of an Environmental Lab to Test Cognitive Assistive Technology to Support Instrumental Activities of Daily Living in Dementia Homecare

Emily Roberts *(Oklahoma State University)*

This poster presentation describes National Institute of Health (NIH) funded research into Cognitive Assistive Technology (CAT) for dementia homecare and the subsequent development of a lab for testing the CAT. The research lays the groundwork for innovation in CAT for support of Independent Activities of Daily Living (IADL) in response to increasingly significant homecare issues facing individuals with dementia and their family caregivers. In the United States, 5.5 million individuals have Alzheimer's disease or some form of dementia and by mid-century, the number of people with dementia (PWD) in the United States is projected to grow to 13.8 million (Alzheimer's Association, 2021). About half of the PWD currently live at home, 43% require occasional support, 47% daily support, and 10% continuous support; with most of this support provided by informal family caregivers. Many IADLs such as cooking, house cleaning, doing laundry and getting dressed can require extra help from caregivers for PWD (Henry, et al., 2018) as these tasks require complex cognitive processing and are cognitively demanding (de Olivera Silva et al. 2020; McAlister et al., 2016). The goal of this research is to improve caregiver resilience and sustainability of dementia homecare via a low-cost wearable CAT system that can support the IADL task cueing intervention for care recipients. Our CAT system embraces three kinds of contextual and environmental cueing functionalities, including affordance cueing of objects, navigation cueing for indoor wayfinding and task cueing, which directly address the prevalent IADL challenges facing those living with dementia at home (Matthews, et al, 2015;

Meditskos, et al, 2018). These cueing functionalities will allow the care recipient autonomy in the home environment, as the system will respond to cueing needs in real time based on the location and intended task. This poster describes outcomes from the initial survey research conducted to support the development of an environmental testing lab for the CAT project. Through the subsequent development of a lab-based mock-up of environmental relationships which would be found in a home (i.e. connection between a kitchen and dining room) we have begun to evaluate the CAT programming features and system usability and will describe initial system navigation cueing through the 3D model retrieval. The research questions being addressed in this poster include:

1. What are the major cueing tasks that are essential to individuals with dementia for accomplishing in-home IADLs?
2. Where do these tasks take place and how can the testing lab be developed to align with these needs?
3. How can a testing lab support research/ evaluation of the functionality of the CAT components?

Discovering Contextual Narratives through Play: Game Design in Architectural Education

Michelle Pannone *(Marywood University)*

In architecture and design, a network of cultural, spatial, and human variables and their interrelationships with each other define the existing context that must coexist with design interventions. Game theory presents unique parallels between the built environment and play. By incorporating game design as a methodology to discover a contextual narrative of the existing conditions, design students develop an empathetic understanding of their stakeholders and the complex interplay between various elements of a city across a variety of scales.

Emergency Department Design in Response to Pandemics: A Systematic Literature Review

Marzia Chowdhury *(The University of Kansas);* ***Hui Cai*** *(The University of Kansas)*

The Covid-19 pandemic has presented serious challenges to emergency departments (EDs). EDs play an important role in responding to pandemics, as they made the first substantial strides to recuperate patients and protect them from infectious diseases, as shown in experiences of earlier infectious disease surge events (e.g., SARS-CoV, H1N1, and Ebola, etc.). However, there is limited evidence on how facility design can support EDs' response to pandemics. This chapter aims to provide a systematic literature review (SLR) of EDs' challenges and responses to pandemics, with a primary focus on facility design strategies. The authors followed the "Preferred Reporting Items for Systematic Reviews and Meta-Analysis" (PRISMA) guideline and searched the databases; PubMed, Web of Science, Science Direct, PubMed central database, covering the literature from March 2000 to March 2021. 2489 studies were identified by the initial database keyword search and additional hand search based on literature search. Finally, 20 articles met the inclusion criteria. Key findings include a) negative pressure rooms b) split flow and cohort isolation that can create various zones for patients with different risk and acuity levels are the most addressed approaches for infection control and accommodating surge capacity. Convertibility and flexibility concept (e.g., reconfiguration of spaces, temporary separation within spaces, reversible air pressure, flexible use of treatment and non-treatment spaces within and adjacent to ED) is key to address unique challenges of evolving nature of pandemic outbreaks. This study provides a summary of existing design strategies for EDs to respond to pandemics. Multiple design strategies need to be combined to minimize the disease transmission in EDs during pandemics and providing surge capacity for overflow of patients. Detailed design principles were synthesized based on the SLR and translated to a design prototype that can respond to evolving stages of pandemics. This article can be helpful to front-line staff in clinical settings, hospital administrators, public or government officials, architects, and the like. It also identifies opportunities for further research on EDs design to better respond to pandemics.

Employee Needs in Laboratory Workspaces: Findings from Facility- and System-Wide Evaluations

Abigail Heithoff *(HDR Architecture);* ***Jeri Brittin*** *(HDR Architecture)*

The Bureau of Labor Statistics predicts that job growth among laboratory technologists and technicians will increase by 11 percent between 2018 and 2028, more than double the expected average job growth among all fields. Facility evaluation for these job roles and within this workplace typology have rarely been documented. To inform design of these highly technical settings, design research should explore the current and future space needs for advanced research at different scales and focus not only on the space needs for a single facility, but more broadly on system-wide needs.

This session will report the findings from two cross-sectional survey-based facility evaluations conducted at laboratory workplace settings. Altogether, over 2,000 laboratory-based staff from across the research work spectrum participated in these facility evaluations. Data for the two surveys were collected during late 2020 to early 2021 with the goals of informing the design of future laboratory research facilities and developing laboratory design standards.

Taken together, the results of the evaluation reflected the needs of biomedical laboratory-based researchers and clinical science researchers. In biomedical research, the evaluations found a growing need for specialized wet-lab research space, including specialized cell and tissue culture clean space, medicinal chemistry development space, and associated ancillary areas. The studies found a lower demand for other specialized closed-room laboratory research space among biomedical researchers.

Among clinical science researchers, the research supported the development of spaces to flexibly accommodate translational research work as well as support interaction with patients and study participants. The evaluations also suggest that clinical researchers require access to specific core and clinical facilities, secure spaces for records storage, and tissue and biospecimen banking facilities

Session participants will discover how to address the facility needs of both biomedical and clinical researchers and learn how laboratory workplace facilities can support research-based work that flexibly responds to program needs and work styles, improve collaboration, allow for virtual work and enhance staff retention.

Evaluation on Design of Baby Care Rooms in Shopping Malls from the Gender Perspective -- a Case Study of Tianjin, China

Yilin Song *(Tianjin University);* ***Hanqi Guo*** *(Tianjin University);* ***Suwen Xiong*** *(Tianjin University);* ***Tong Hu*** *(Tianjin University);* ***Weisong Lv*** *(Tianjin University);* ***Boxi Sun*** *(Tianjin University)*

In China, the demand for baby care rooms has increased with the implementation of the three-child birth policy and the improving life quality and requirement, especially in the big cities. For merchants of shopping malls, the high quality of facilities and services may attract more customers; providing better designed mother and baby space has a positive impact on business. However, mother and baby space is not only related to the two population groups, fathers is also an important role in parenting.

From the gender perspective, we visit 18 shopping malls in Tianjin, one of the four municipal cities of China to collect the general information of baby care rooms of them and conduct surveys and interviews of customers of both genders. There are more than 70 percentages (13 out of 18) of shopping malls with baby care rooms: three are as large as more than 20 m^2, 8 are in the middle size between 10 and 20m^2, and two are smaller than 10m^2; what should be paid attention is that only three of them allow male access in. Among the collected 437 valid questionnaires, 262 are female and 175 are male. 89.90% of male respondents express the willing to access to the baby care room while 68.04% of female would like male doing so, and in reality, only 25.36% of male could do so. Another important finding is that 61.59% of male respondents agree that current baby care rooms show a gender preference due to the feeding and nursery requirement, while 92.24% of female respondents express the willing to have the feeding space with higher privacy.

The reasons of evaluation differences between genders may include the followings: first, baby care rooms are designed for the female with emphasize on the genderist design concept of perceiving women as the main body, resulting in the space design being feminine. Secondly, there are differences in the perception of the spatial environment between male and female, which makes the perceptions different from the actual needs. There is complementary and mutual exclusion in the needs of baby- and child-care, as long as the contradiction between openness and mutual assistance versus the privacy in the spatial need. In addition, social stereotype bias is also one of the important factors affecting male involvement.

Based on the results, we propose three models of baby care room design in shopping malls: placing small but flexible baby care room in the old shopping malls with limited area; arranging the middle size baby care room with spatial exclusivity; and optimize the functional and spatial design of large ones.

From Boomers to Zoomers: Designing Spaces for Intergenerational Formal and Informal Interactions

***Esmirna Moya** (The University of Texas at San Antonio); **Neda Norouzi** (The University of Texas at San Antonio); **Eric Polo Rosales** (The University of Texas at San Antonio)*

The importance of wellness in design is often overlooked. Designing environments that prioritize diverse populations, life experiences, cultural influences, and identities is critical. The current global pandemic has made it imperative to focus on the user's movement and experience throughout a space. By applying universal design principles, we can meet the goal of a more equitable building environment. This project is focused on designing a new community center that serves different generations by providing spaces that support intergenerational interactions between older adults and adolescents.

An Architectural firm conducted three workshops with community members. The goal was for the community to voice out their wants and needs. During these sessions, the community members discuss site location, architectural features, and design program. The authors of this study analyzed the findings resulted from the workshops and conducted literature analysis of scholarly articles focused on intergenerational program and design that have been published in the last decade.

The workshops made it possible to identify community members' expectations of this intergenerational center. The findings included spatial requirements for monogenerational and intergenerational learning, childcare, community gardens, and physical activities. The community also requested flexible spaces that can be used for different types and levels of interaction. The literature analysis resulted in spatial design that affords both planned and spontaneous intergenerational interactions and are equally accessible to all users.

These findings led to incorporation of universal design principle in the architecture of this intergenerational community center. The architectural program divided the building into four wings connected through an intergenerational green house. The wings offer opportunities for union connections, community relations, recreational activities, and educational endeavors. Design features such as proper natural and artificial lighting, indoor and outdoor spaces for social and solitary activities, as well as color and furniture choices were based on universal design principles to provide privacy and choice while fostering relationships and encouraging intergenerational community interactions.

From the Outset: Architectural Design of an Intergenerational Community Center

Josue Mondragon *(The University of Texas at San Antonio);* ***Neda Norouzi*** *(The University of Texas at San Antonio)*

Supporting intergenerational relationships is an important way of creating unity in a community. Therefore, it is imperative for architects to design buildings that foster intergenerational interaction. With this in mind, a city in the Pacific Northwest of the United States is developing an intergenerational center to connect adolescent with the older adult members of their community. The city hired an architectural firm who partnered with a university to research the requirements for designing an intergenerational community center. This research culminated with a design proposal for the city's intergenerational center.

Data was collected through community workshops and an extensive literature analysis. The workshops consisted of a series of meetings followed by smaller group discussions where the community's needs were discussed. The workshops were hosted and designed by the city government. The extensive literature review was conducted to uncover more information about intergenerational relationships. The goal was to understand the societal and interpersonal attributes of older adults and adolescents, and to determine how spatial and programmatic interventions serve to foster intergenerational relationships (Cerruti & Shepley, 2016).

The workshops revealed community members perceptions of one another as well as some of their specific needs from this community center. The result of these meetings led to the production of preliminary architectural program desired by the community members. The literature review provided significant guidance in breaking down societal preconceptions placed on older adults and adolescents (Burgman & Mulvaney, 2016). This understanding led to a proposal for the design of this intergenerational community center that celebrates diversity by incorporating universal design principles to respond to people of all ages and abilities.

Culturally the building responds to diversity by providing communal spaces where the community members can show, exchange, and celebrate their rich social and generational tapestry of the city. Diverse ability is supported through a central ramp system that celebrates this diversity and connects to spaces for different levels of interaction. It is also responded to through contrasting elements to provide indicators for people with visual impairments. Integrity of individuals is respected through architecture. The comfort levels of the occupants were designed for through interior spaces that support different types and levels of intergenerational interactions (Norouzi et al., 2019) as well as spaces for private reprieve of different age groups.

Get More from Your Corridors: Balancing Patient Care and Staff Respite in the MICU

Kirsten Miller *(GBBN Architects)*

Studies show that the restorative quality of break areas may significantly improve nurses' satisfaction and stress reduction in these emotionally charged environments (Nejati et al., 2016). But where is that supposed to occur in intense environments such as the MICU and especially during a pandemic?

As Verderber et al. (2021) states, there is an acknowledgement of the therapeutic role of staff amenities, but it is undefined as to what would serve the staff best.

A recent UK Healthcare/GBBN study helped define answers for a new MICU.

When UK Healthcare decided to design a new MICU, it was important to have flexibility for any infectious disease or massive event along with addressing needs for staff satisfaction and quality patient care. The study undertaken by UK Healthcare and GBBN focused on the culture for the staff at UK Healthcare in Kentucky and the needs to provide care on the new MICU. The study's objective was to learn design guidelines that will positively transform daily care in the MICU while dual purposing spaces on the unit to prepare for any type of catastrophic event, but it also revealed ways to address staff respite.

To learn from other systems during the 2020 pandemic, the UK/GBBN research team reviewed five ICUs and five biocontainment units as case studies. Then correlated with a literature review of current trends, research areas of focus include bolstering resistance to pathogens and access control & entry function through the built environment. Additional opportunities developed in building systems, patient areas and process & flow procedures. Primary research methods included a staff preoccupancy survey, interviews, staff shadowing, and observations. Key themes were revealed through these methodologies including the need for staff respite & support, flexibility in the support core and staff visibility access on the unit especially for the multidisciplinary teams.

Ten built environment design guidelines were the outcome of our findings, and they all related to the hospital's goal for flexibility. One of these guidelines focuses on the patient corridor as Carthey (2008) suggests in her article about the value of the corridor for communication, efficiency, and function. Guidelines generated opportunities for staff respite, recharge, taking a break, privacy, and the ability to control sound. Daily use of the MICU guidelines included development of the workspace, visibility across the unit, supply standards and maximizing virtual ICU capabilities. Additional pieces to consider for infectious disease and other massive events include adding a serious communicable disease lab and hot zone to the unit.

References

Carthey, J. (2008). Reinterpreting the Hospital Corridor: "Wasted Space" or Essential for Quality Multidisciplinary Clinical Care? *HERD: Health Environments Research & Design Journal, 2*(1), 17–29. https://doi.org/10.1177/193758670800200103

Nejati, A., Shepley, M., Rodiek, S., Lee, C., & Varni, J. (2016). Restorative design features for hospital staff break areas: A multi-method study. *HERD: Health Environments Research & Design Journal, 9*(2), 16-35.

Verderber, S., Gray, S., Suresh-Kumar, S., Kercz, D., & Parshuram, C. (2021). Intensive Care Unit Built Environments: A Comprehensive Literature Review (2005–2020). *HERD: Health Environments Research & Design Journal, 14*(4), 368–415. https://doi.org/10.1177/19375867211009273

Greening, Gentrification, and Equity: Consequential Questions on the Ethics of Compromise

Mariana Junqueira *(Kansas State University)*

Vast scholarship has looked at urban interventions that change the urban environment by introducing new or improving the existing green spaces in often degraded urban areas (i.e., greening). Green spaces have been found to have restorative qualities that strengthen urban dwellers' health and wellbeing, recreational properties, and aesthetic benefits provided to citizens. However, the academic consensus is that environmental greening is not value-neutral (Checker, 2011; Dale & Newman, 2009). If designed uncritically, green spaces can perpetuate existing inequalities, disproportionally harming underserved communities. Thus, despite being knowingly an environmental indicator of sustainability and resilience, health, and wellbeing, greening interventions have, most notably, become a synonym for valuable urban land, a phenomenon referred to as green gentrification. By recognizing the advances backed by evidence-based design approaches, this paper asks, "How have design strategies been proposed to prevent green gentrification?" An interpretive-historical review uncovers numerous strategies presented as this transdisciplinary scholarship attempts to characterize the tenuous line between greening and gentrification. In other words, innovative design strategies for greening that support the benefits of green spaces while attempting to reduce gentrification as a subproduct have been conceptualized. However, by critically engaging in a content analysis of such strategies, consequential questions of equity arise. Can these proposed strategies be considered compromises? If so, to whom are these strategies imposing tradeoffs, and consequently, are these ethically-acceptable solutions? From an equity and ethics perspective, findings reveal that widely accepted design strategies have focused on constraining the design product (e.g., size or amenities of green space) to the detriment of introducing participatory design processes, such as community placemaking (Moroni, 2013). Such partial strategies (e.g., green enough approach) do not guarantee the prevention of gentrification. However, they guarantee a restrained greening that may not improve an underserved community's health and wellbeing as a more extensive greening would. These concerns present underserved communities with what Checker (2011) characterized as a "pernicious paradox." This study contributes to theory by illuminating the crucial ethics concerns involved in the very practice of environmental design and suggests that the answer is within the design process, which calls for the designers' ethical responsibility to design with meaning.

References

Checker, M. (2011). Wiped out by the "Greenwave": Environmental gentrification and the paradoxical politics of urban sustainability. *City & Society, 23*(2), 210-229.

Dale, A.; & Newman, L. L. (2009). Sustainable development for some: Green urban development and affordability. *Local Environment: The International Journal of Justice and Sustainability, 14*(7), 669-681.

Moroni, S. (2013). Afterword: Ethical problems of contemporary cities. In C. Basta & S. Moroni (Eds.), *Ethics, Design and Planning of the Built Environment* (pp. 197-212). Springer.

Home Modification Project: Design Strategies for Better Adaptability in Minimum Dwellings

Maggie Ma Kingsley *(The Chinese University of Hong Kong)*

Under the laissez-fair housing market in Hong Kong, the insufficient provision of affordable housing results in the appearance of extreme small dwelling units - Subdivided-units (SDUs). SDU is a type of rental micro-apartment divided from a single unit into multiple, self-contained households with a median area of 10sqm. In 2020, there were 100,943 SDUs in the private housing market, with 226,340 inhabitants. The high density and over-crowding living conditions threaten the user's physical and psychological wellbeing. The quality of living in small domestic spaces becomes an immediate issue under the threat of home confinement during COVID-19. The Home modification project investigates the interior spatial quality of these homes to improve adaptability, with an aim to improve the future prospect of the users.

Home Modification Project is a collaborative project between architects and social workers. Providing design and advisory services to more than 300 families living in SDUs, the project focuses on enhancing the home study environment for children of low-income households and providing better living space, thus improving the families' long-term prospects and wellbeing. The design of the internal home environment aims to improve the adaptability of the users, fulfilling some of the design principles of "Flexible housing" by Jeremy Till yet in a smaller scale context. The adaptability of housing generally refers to its capacity to accommodate the future changing needs of the users. In the condition of SDUs where users move home within 2-3 years, the project focuses on users' immediate and transitional needs – facilitating daily routine, family relationships, household safety, and catering for the instability. Intensive designers' input is required to define the "hard space" of the home in the limited area to facilitate better adaptation. The research investigates domesticity and the sense of home and establishes essential criteria for spatial enhancement for daily resilience for the families living in minimum dwellings.

By implementing modular furniture as a spatial tool, the project avoided benefiting the landlords that risk rental increases, allowing the users to be direct beneficiaries of the improvement. Modular furniture addressed tiny homes' organization problems and could be mass-produced to respond to the vast scale of the housing problem. The furniture acts as a spatial tool to redefine order for homes by creating appropriate zonings conducive to learning and daily activities. It helps establish a sense of home in a transitional context by providing flexibility and improved adaptability. Various spatial approaches have been developed through the project to improve the internal environments, including utilization of height, creating zonings, introducing alignments, creating square spaces, grouping free spaces, and defining privacy. The design strategies could act as a guide to the spatial planning of tiny homes with a sustainable outcome.

This research contributes to applied knowledge on spatial design for small dwellings and aims to inspire the developmental policy with human-centered considerations for marginalized living environments for low-income communities. The outcome supports providing a fair and inclusive basic living standard for the general public to work towards a healthier and more sustainable city.

How Do Students Use the Outdoor Space on Campus? A Case Study on a Campus Design and Its Relation to Outdoor Activities

Jaechang Noh *(Korea Advanced Institute of Science and Technology);* ***Sojeong Lee*** *(Korea Advanced Institute of Science and Technology);* ***Lisa Lim*** *(Korea Advanced Institute of Science and Technology)*

The number of college students suffering from psychological problems is a growing issue. For instance, 41.6% of college students are concerning anxiety, and 35.8% of students are experiencing depression (American Psychological Association, 2013). Recent studies have found that physical environments can promote physical activity and the health of users. For instance, attractive public open space encourages various users to enjoy physical activities and social communications, and poor building surroundings are more likely to increase the depression rates of the residents.

A college campus is not only a setting for teaching and learning but also a living space where students live for several years. Students study, eat, play, sleep, and exercise, spending significant hours on campus. Furthermore, recent studies have reported that the physical environments of campus play critical roles in students' physical and mental health. However, the importance of campus design is usually neglected compared to personal treatment (Baum & Fisher, 2014). Therefore, this study aims to identify design strategies and attributes that could encourage physical and social activities of college students on campus, which in turn will improve their health.

Using a higher education college campus in South Korea as a case study, this study investigates design attributes affecting college students' physical and social activities on campus, especially focusing on the outdoor spaces. This study uses a mixed-method approach to demonstrate what characteristics affect students' preference for the spaces.

Users' experiences and opinions regarding campus outdoor environments are investigated by interviews and surveys. College students, including undergraduate and graduate students, were asked how often they use outdoor spaces, why they use those spaces and how much they are satisfied with the outdoor spaces. Simultaneously, the physical attributes of the outdoor environments are analyzed and quantified using various spatial analysis tools, including Space Syntax and GIS. This process is expected to find a correlation between students' perception of the outdoor space and its physical elements. The data will be gathered and visualized in GIS and it will be analyzed using multiple statistical analysis methods. The process aims to find the relationships between students' experiences and characteristics of campus outdoor spaces.

Based on this result, the status quo of outdoor environments for students will be organized and the design strategy for improvement will be suggested. The findings of this study are expected to contribute to improving students' physical and mental health through the design of the college campus.

References

Baum, F., & Fisher, M. (2014). Why behavioural health promotion endures despite its failure to reduce health inequities. *Sociology of*

Health and Illness, 36(2), 213–225. https://doi.org/10.1111/1467-9566.12112
American Psychological Association. (2013). College students' mental health is a growing concern, survey finds. *Monitor on Psychology, 44*(6), 13.

How Does the Community Design Process Impact Their Sense of Community?

Charleston Yi *(North Carolina State University);* ***Kofi Boone*** *(North Carolina State University)*

Human society is impossible to comprehend without acknowledging humanity's interdependence. As human society evolves continually, leadership, practitioners, and scholars who closely serve on social life focus on community values. Environmental design cases based on community participation show how community design could assist the community's daily life (de la Peña et al., 2017). Also, many research in design, sociology, or psychology examined multiple dimensions of community. Theoretical and empirical knowledge let us understand collective experiences in community life. Based on the learning, designers could thoroughly consider the community and their experiences to propose the design solution. However, human society is highly complicated, so the relationship between design efforts and the community's life is hard to state in a complete sentence.

This poster introduces; 1) the conceptual framework, the connection between sense of community (McMillan & Chavis, 1986) and community design, drawn from the literature review; and 2) the community engagement processes conducted by the authors to support the local community.

While acknowledging multidisciplinary efforts for communities, various sources such as scholarly articles, case studies, and organizational reports from social, psychological, or design fields are reviewed. The review sketches possible connections between design impacts and a community's perceptions and senses by design processes and products (Rohe, 1985). Based on the review, community design can have positive outcomes: socially suitable plan, community empowerment over their lives and environment, and potentially, community development by enhanced sense of community among the community members.

However, it is hard to support that existing cases developed the definite link between sense of community and design because designers used multiple meanings of terminology. In addition, most studies described a few key actors' responses and designers' observations. Evidence without community members' perspectives might not determine successful community development as an outcome of community design. Therefore, it would be beneficial to support the existing studies by documenting direct and indirect participants' reflections on community design experience through the prepared research strategies.

The authors will conduct several naturalistic survey methods before, during, and after the community engagement. Interview, questionnaires, and focus groups would help researchers understand participants' design experiences. Then based on observation and interpretation of participants' responses, authors will demonstrate processes and outcomes to develop the connections between sense of community and design. This understanding of community experiences and impacts will strengthen the existing efforts of community designers by empirical evidence. Moreover, a more detailed description of the design impacts on community senses will be included. Besides, future designers will learn to adopt community design values for the successful practice for the ultimate goal of community development rather than simply finding needs from the community.

References

de la Peña, D., Allen, D., Hester, R., Hou, J., Lawson, L., & McNally, M. (Eds.). (2017). *Design as democracy: Techniques for collective creativity.* Island Press.
McMillan, D., & Chavis, D. (1986). Sense of community: A definition and theory. *Journal of Community Psychology, 14*(1), 6-23.

Rohe, W. (1985). Urban planning and mental health. *Prevention in Human Services, 4*(1-2), 79-110.

How Pervasive Virtual Reality (PVR) Can Augment the Perception of Working from Home (WFH) Environments

Zahrasadat Hosseini *(Oklahoma State University);*
Tilanka Chandrasekera *(Oklahoma State University)*

Communication technologies have revolutionized the type and nature of work. Working From Home (WFH) has allowed companies to be more agile and adapt to crises such as the Covid 19 pandemic. WFH is expected to become more popular in the coming years as traditional workways evolve (Klopotek, 2017). Furthermore, the recent launch of affordable Virtual Reality (VR) Head Mounted Display (HMD) devices in the consumer market has drawn attention to this technology, since these HMD's when combined with the advancements in wireless communication technology, mobile technology, and context-aware devices, facilitate the use of mixed-reality environments at home. There has been a lot of research on traditional WFH issues; some of them have highlighted concerns such as equipment deficiencies, social isolation, and insufficient spatial dimensions (Ipsen et al., 2021; Johansson, 2017). The purpose of our study is to demonstrate how Pervasive VR (PVR) which constructs mixed-reality environments using real-world environmental information can augment the perception of WFH environments in comparison with the traditional WFH environment to mitigate these issues. In the first phase of the research, we surveyed interior and architectural designers who were working from home, to collect primary data and to find out what type of equipment, furniture, and settings they have in their home offices. The second phase consisted of creating a home workspace environment, based on the data we gathered in the first phase, then recreating this room in PVR with the same characteristics (a digital twin). 20 participants were randomly assigned to two groups: the physical WFH environment and the PVR environment. The overall impressions of these two rooms were measured on participant responses in relation to five variables consisting of arousal, pleasure, satisfaction, productivity, and cognitive load. ECG (Electrocardiogram) sensors, EDA (Electrodermal activity) sensors and fNIR (Functional near-infrared spectroscopy) devices were used to collect psychophysiological data that corroborated subjective survey data on the above variables during a task assigned to the participants. The results suggest that the PVR environment reduced the Cognitive load on the task, thereby increasing productivity as compared to the physical WFH environment.

Keywords: Covid 19, Working from Home, Pervasive Virtual Reality, Arousal, Pleasure, Satisfaction, Productivity, Cognitive Load

References

Ipsen, C., van Veldhoven, M., Kirchner, K., & Hansen, J. P. (2021). Six key advantages and disadvantages of working from home in Europe during COVID-19. *International Journal of Environmental Research and Public Health, 18*(4), 1826.

Johansson, C. (2017). Today's Home Office-an Answer to the Needs of the Contemporary Home Worker. *Diploma work.*

Klopotek, M. (2017). The Advantages and Disadvantages of Working Remotely from the Perspective of Young Employees. In *Management Challenges in a Network Economy: Proceedings of the MakeLearn and TIIM International Conference 2017* (pp. 535-535). ToKnowPress.

How to Improve Students' Understanding of Health-Related Lighting Design Concepts: Hands-on Learning Activities with a Light Booth

Elif Tural *(Virginia Tech)*

The impact of lighting on task performance and safety are well-documented in the literature. The nonvisual effects of lighting on human health with respect to circadian rhythms and sleep patterns have been increasingly considered by design researchers and professionals. This is also due to the healthy building standards, such as the WELL

Standard (IWBI, 2020), and their respective lighting guidelines. These lighting guidelines address the color and spectral power distributions (SPDs) of light sources in relation to human health and comfort, and, thus, make a holistic understanding of light and color vital to designers. Teaching and learning lighting is difficult as it is technical in nature but requires addressing the qualitative/perceptual aspects of lighting (Gustina, 2011; Brown, 2004). This empirical study tests the effectiveness of using a light booth and hands-on learning activities in improving students' understanding of fundamental lighting design constructs related to color properties of light.

In Spring 2021, third-year interior design students in a CIDA-accredited program (n = 30) took a pre-test after the light and color constructs are introduced using a traditional lecture/reading assignment method. Lighting demonstrations and hands-on learning activities were introduced in the course using the light booth and color cards, and filters. Following the on-hands activities, the students took a post-test. They were also invited to complete an online survey on the perceived impact of the lighting demonstrations on their learning.

The Wilcoxon signed-rank showed that the light booth activities elicited a statistically significant increase in students' test scores (Z = -4.607, p < .001). The pre-demonstration quiz scores (Mdn = 6.25) significantly improved following the intervention (Mdn = 12), with 27 students improving their scores, two ties, and one with a lower post-test score. The Qualtrics survey had 10-point Likert-scale questions on student perceptions on how light booth activities influenced their learning. The students reported that they have a better understanding of lighting and color constructs as a result of the light booth demonstrations/ learning activities (M = 8.57, SD = 1.31), and found those activities helpful (M = 9.13, SD = 1.20). they also suggested ways to integrate the tool throughout the lighting course and in the interior design curriculum, such as design studios and materials courses.

This study demonstrated that the light booth is a useful learning tool for interior design students. Light and color concepts can be rather confusing to novice learners, and the findings supported that this approach is preferable to students and enhances their learning. This visual presentation will provide examples of these learning activities and encourage attendees to discuss and provide feedback on how to teach lighting concepts for supporting human health and wellbeing.

References

Brown, N. C. (2004). Aesthetic Composition and the Language of Light, a Subject of Academic Inquiry. Journal of Interior Design, 30(3), 8-22.

Gustina, C. (2011). Light Fantastic: Teaching Introductory Lighting to Interior Designer Students. Design Principles and Practices: An International Journal, 5(5): 521-532.

International Well Building Institute. (2020) The Well Building Standard, v.2. New York: International Well Building Institute. Retrieved from https://www.wellcertified.com/certification/v2/

I. Mélange: A Primary and Urgent Care Facility By Design

Reem Bagais *(Texas Tech University);* ***Debajyoti Pati*** *(Texas Tech University)*

Background: The purpose of this project is to address the issue of "no show" or missed appointments in healthcare and its relationship with physical design. Studies reveal how "no show" affects not only the population's health, but also hospitals and physician practices. This project will examine the use of garden activities and natural outdoor adventure environment in the context of healthcare and wellbeing with considering regenerative design aspect.

Challenges: i.mélange is a collaborative environment that integrates healthcare services targets not only treating illness with educational programs, services, and vendors, but also aims to prevent illness through healthy living. The project aims to create a regenerative design destination for the community. Studies showed a great value and relationship between vegetable gardening and physical activity, quality-of-life, and physical function. By addressing some challenges in the targeted population, i.mélange is creating a destination "community" that speaks back to the users including children and the site (Lubbock, TX).

Method: . A literature review was conducted by searching different databases and websites related to study constructs using keywords such as no show in health care, natural learning environment, the healthcare environment, collaborative environment, regenerating design. Potential studies considering the health care environment were identified from the review and were considered in the project design.

Goal: Through considering 13 different design settings suggested by the natural learning initiatives, the design incorporates fruit and vegetable gardens, greenhouse, outdoor/indoor transitions, water, earth, and loose play, gathering places, and a multipurpose lawn. The overall aim is to create a site that reflects the purpose of regenerating design and enhancing health and wellbeing and circulate this idea through the design functionality provided. Furthermore, the design aim to create an environment that can support learning through a natural adventure play environment for both children and families.

ICU Design & Nurse Stress: Developing a Nurses' Physical Environmental Stress Scale (NPESS)

Dagmar Rittenbacher *(Gresham Smith)*

Working within the healthcare field is stressful and comes with a high level of responsibility for nurses, especially intensive care unit (ICU) nurses. The ICU is a highly stressful work environment associated with risk factors such as excessive workload, increased expectations and long working hours that can lead to burnout among nurses. There is some evidence that environmental design has the potential to prevent or mitigate work-related stress, however, an adequate assessment tool to identify physical environmental stressors or supports for moderating stress is lacking. This study aimed to develop a nurses' physical environmental stress scale (NPESS) that explores the relationships between the physical environment in the ICU and work-related stress among ICU nurses. It is comprised of seven parts and 81 items. To develop the environmental assessment tool, an exploratory sequential methodology was used that consisted of two distinct phases. The development of the physical environmental assessment tool (NPESS) was based on (a) qualitative content analysis of existing focus group data; and (b) a qualitative content analysis of pertinent literature utilizing environmental assessment tools in a healthcare context. The refinement of the physical environmental assessment tool (NPESS) consisted of interviews with ICU nurses and subsequent tool modification based on their feedback.

Increasing STEM Motivation in Middle School Students through Spatial Design

Tilanka Chandrasekera *(Oklahoma State University);* ***Piper Bott*** *(Oklahoma State University);* ***Allison Howard*** *(Oklahoma State University);* ***Katelyn Allen*** *(Oklahoma State University);* ***Nicole Colston*** *(Oklahoma State University);* ***Cynthia Orona*** *(Oklahoma State University);* ***Tutaleni Asino*** *(Oklahoma State University);* ***Oluwafikayo Adewumi*** *(Oklahoma State University);* ***Clement Audu*** *(Oklahoma State University);* ***Angelina Dayton*** *(Oklahoma State University);* ***Norma Neely*** *(Citizen, Potawatomi Nation)*

Spatial design involves thinking and visualizing space and is used as a general umbrella term commonly associated with the domains of architecture, landscape architecture, landscape design, and interior design. Spatial thinking is a crucial skill for student success in many STEM degrees (Newcombe, 2010) and is defined as a combination of three elements: concepts of space, tools of representation, and processes of reasoning (Downs & DeSouza, 2006). Even though not traditionally considered as STEM fields, domains such as architecture and interior design often work in collaboration with other traditional STEM fields such as engineering disciplines. Furthermore, spatial skills are utilized in a variety of STEM disciplines that could range from a biologist focusing on the double helix of a DNA structure to an engineer designing and manufacturing 3D structures. Research suggests that spatial skills can be enhanced through spatial design education (Stringer, 1971; Sarı, 2010). These methods of improving spatial intelligence offer guidance for expanding spatial design curricula using VR/AR technologies to develop critical spatial abilities for a wide range of STEM careers.

To be part of the future STEM workforce, it will be important for students to have the skills and expertise to use these types of technologies. Introducing students at an early age to these technologies will prepare them for the future workplace. Current research indicates that traditional classroom learning alone is not sufficient to teach students about science or the opportunities for STEM careers (Dierking 2010). Afterschool programs have had success in helping those from underrepresented communities (Afterschool Alliance, 2011). For this project, we use the Generative models of culturally relevant teaching framework (Eglash et al., 2020) to focus on developing narratives that inform students of cultural idioms and translations into creative architectural forms using the immersive nature of Virtual Reality (VR) and Augmented Reality (AR) technology.

The use and exposure to technology in education can be a means of motivating students. When used in education, technologies such as VR have facilitated knowledge acquisition (Mikropoulos, 2001). Some studies indicate that technologies such as VR and AR offer motivation to students to improve information encoding, retention, and later performance (Huang et al., 2010; Stone, 2001). Furthermore, Hsu et al., (2017) states that using technologies such as AR increases the motivation of students to pursue STEM-based majors and careers. These studies suggest that innovative teaching using technology will enhance scientific research, upgrade the technological capabilities of industrial sectors, align with United Nations Sustainable Development goals focusing on building resilient infrastructure, promote inclusive and sustainable industrialization, and foster innovation.

This presentation documents a federally funded project to provide afterschool STEM education through VR, AR, and 3D printing using environmental design projects through the spatial design-focused curriculum for Native American middle school students. The curriculum consisted of 7 modules and was developed around Native American creation stories related to that tribe. Our research questions focus on how culturally situated, spatially focused STEM curriculums improve motivation and spatial abilities in students through the use of immersive technology.

Investigating Lighting Quality in Senior Residential Environments

Alexis Mihalyfi *(Lawrence Technological University);*
Emilija Vilkaite *(Lawrence Technological University)*

It is estimated by the National Center for Assisted Living that there are more than 800,000 Americans residing in assisted living facilities, and around one million seniors living in some form of senior living community. A majority of these residents are age 85 and older and do not require 24-7 nursing care. When performing visual tasks, senior citizens may have difficulty seeing if the lighting in their surroundings is not adequate. Studies have shown that lighting strategies such as reducing glare, minimizing reflectance, providing even illumination levels, and increasing the illumination of task lighting can be beneficial for the aging eye.

This study aimed to investigate senior's required lighting levels for conducting daily tasks such as reading or working with a computer, and probability of glare in two bedroom environments in a senior living facility located in Detroit, Michigan. The windows in the bedrooms had different orientations (east versus southeast) and had minor differences in size and furniture layout. The study incorporated literature reviews and existing guidelines pertaining to lighting in senior living facilities (e.g., IESNA Lighting Handbook and LEED v4.1) and digital simulations (ClimateStudio) to examine natural lighting conditions in the rooms.

Digital simulations (spatial daylight autonomy, daylight factor analysis, glare probability, and illuminance) established baseline lighting conditions for the work plane of interest, which was a desk located adjacent to the window in each room. Lighting recommendations from the

IESNA Lighting Handbook and LEED v4.1 helped to determine whether or not the bedrooms being studied had adequate light levels over the workplane of interest. Simulation results concluded that the baseline illumination levels during the day in both senior bedrooms were not adequate for the visual tasks that would be performed by the users. The recommended illuminance level for seniors 65 and older performing visual tasks (reading and writing) at a desk was 800 lux. The digital simulations demonstrated that the East bedroom only received around 330 lux over the workplane of interest, which is not enough light for seniors to perform visual tasks. The Southeast bedroom received around 5400 lux over the workplane of interest, which increases the glare probability over the desk area. In both bedrooms, glare probability over the desks ranged from disturbing to intolerable throughout most of the year. The study was followed up with a digital simulation study (solar study) of natural lighting conditions with exterior horizontal overhang shading devices. The outcome of the shading devices used demonstrated that the devices used were not adequate to control natural lighting to decrease the effects senior residents experienced.

This study contributed to determining similarities and differences in natural lighting quality for daily tasks of senior citizens in windowed rooms with different orientations. The findings also provided appropriate lighting recommendations for the windowed bedroom suites of senior living facilities which could help to inform the design of future senior living facilities.

Non-Linear Workflow in Trauma Rooms and Its Impacts on Physical Environment Design

Hossein Mirzajani *(Kent State University);* ***Hamid Estejab*** *(Kent State University);* ***Sara Bayramzadeh*** *(Kent State University)*

Background: Trauma rooms are among the most complex environments in healthcare facilities dealing with critical patient conditions under an extreme time constrain. Advanced trauma life support (ATLS) is an educational program that provides systematic training to perform the necessary measures and assessments of trauma patients for the first (golden) hour in level-1 trauma centers. The priorities of emergency trauma care, according to the ATLS principles, have different levels of interdependencies that could be supported or hindered by the physical environment.

Objective: This study aims to investigate interdependencies in different stages of trauma care and highlight the most critical aspects of the physical environment to address the patient and staff needs and challenges in the delivery of care.

Methods: A qualitative approach was adopted by conducting focus group sessions with clinicians. Twenty sessions of semi-structured focus groups were conducted with a total number of 64 trauma level 1 team members to better understand different roles and responsibilities during a trauma scenario. The questions included discussions about the flow of care, their individual roles, and challenges they experience.

Results: According to the participants' feedback, a trauma scenario can be divided into six major stages, including patient's pre-arrival, primary survey, procedures (interventions), secondary survey, imaging, and patient discharge. The focus group findings revealed multiple interdependencies in trauma workflow that require the trauma team to have back and forth steps during a trauma treatment case. Easy access to the imaging unit, blood bank, elevator, and OR plays a critical role in facilitating trauma workflow. Participants indicated that appropriate access to medical supplies, power outlets, medical gas, suction hoses, and adequate space is essential to support the interdependent tasks during a trauma case.

Conclusion: Considering the limited studies about trauma room, this study serves as a foundation to identify the relationship between the physical environment and different stages of trauma procedures and their interdependencies. A non-linear workflow in a trauma room significantly impacts trauma room design in macro and micro levels of physical characteristics of the environment. Given the critical role of proximity to the support areas, location and adjacencies of the trauma room should be considered at the early phases of the design process. Additionally, physical characteristics of trauma rooms such as interior circulation, accessibility to resources, and zoning are critical supporting the trauma workflow.

Omaha Lead Pollution: Proactive and Restorative Strategies for Environmental Justice in Landscape Architecture

Jacob Essink *(University of Nebraska, Lincoln);* ***Salvador Lindquist*** *(University of Nebraska, Lincoln)*

Marginalized communities around the world are disproportionately impacted by unjust infrastructures and environmental conditions. Unjust conditions result from irresponsible planning policies and actions that fail to consider what detrimental effects might come to some communities. Through engagement in proactive and restorative approaches, landscape architects can improve these conditions through their practice by understanding their role to consider the relationships between people and the environment and recognize potential risks. Utilizing the methods of risk assessment presented in the book At Risk: Natural Hazards, People's Vulnerability, and Disasters (Blaikie et al., 1994) can better help us not only minimize the hazards but also recognize and expose the vulnerability that certain populations face. This research studies the effect of lead pollution in Omaha, NE through a comparative study of similar superfund sites in the United States and proposes an alternative framework that moves beyond simply restorative methods of remediation by providing proactive solutions to improving these conditions of significantly impacted urban areas. By doing so, this project closely investigates the relationships between superfund sites, impacted communities, and affected infrastructures.

This research has been developed in three different phases. The first phase involves the analysis of superfund sites around the United States that feature significant lead pollution. In this analysis, a framework for understanding the factors that contribute to injustices examines the impact of historic redlining, the breakdown of demographics, and proximity to residential land use. Geographic Information Systems (GIS) are used to analyze the spatial relationship between these conditions. The second phase of the research aggregates resources, approaches, and institutions that currently exist to assess potentials for remediation, building off of Hyejung Chang's conceptions of justice — distributive, procedural, and restorative (Chang, 2018). These resources were broken down into projects, policies, and foundations and collated by their relationship to each justice typology as well as to each other. The third phase of this research investigates the Omaha Lead superfund site. Using the same analysis conducted in the first phase, we examine the factors that contributed to widespread lead pollution. It exposes the vulnerability that certain populations are facing in Omaha, and examines the lead pollution levels of particular locations within the superfund site to dissect the hazard that these populations face.

This research suggests the importance of both policy and design in the prevention and remediation of environmental injustice and aggregates the available perspectives and resources necessary to equip landscape architects and policymakers with the frameworks to design for a more just and inclusive urbanity.

References

Blaikie, P. M., Cannon, T., Davis, I., & Wisner, B. (1994). *At Risk: Natural Hazards, People's Vulnerability, and Disasters.* Routledge.

Chang, H. "Environmental Justice as Justification for Landscape Architectural Design." *Landscape Journal 37*, no. 2 (2018): 1–17. https://doi.org/10.3368/lj.37.2.1.

Wu, X. (2015). *Reclaiming a Brownfield Site by the Combination of Landscape Design and Remediation Strategies* (Newtown Neighborhood, Gainesville, Ga) (thesis).

Open and Accessible? Testing the Design of an Innovation Center Serving a Higher Education Campus

***Ashley Elizabeth Tannebaum** (The Boston Architectural College)*

Innovation centers represent the best of current designs to reduce siloes, increase openness, and encourage accessible space for a diverse range of students on higher education campuses. Their designs boast features ranging from increased transparency and flexibility to informal social spaces in an attempt to welcome and foster collaboration among occupants from a range of disciplines. This mixed methods study employed semi-structured interviews with 45 building occupants and 5 design team members to understand whether a case study innovation center achieved its goals of increased openness and accessibility for students on a higher education campus. Occupants of the space generally reported that the design of the space did support their innovation activities, particularly through the use of informal social space. However, they reported that some features of the built environment contradicted the concept of "openness" and made access difficult for certain groups within the population. Several respondents noted that building features such as security desks, key card access, difficult to locate and open doors, and remote locations of critical spaces discouraged use of the space and made them feel less welcomed. This study concludes with a series of questions for future design teams to create more open and accessible spaces on higher education campuses.

References

Becher, T., & Trowler, P. (2001). *Academic tribes and territories*. McGraw-Hill Education (UK).

Somol, R., & Whiting, S. (2002). Notes around the Doppler Effect and other Moods of Modernism. *Perspecta, 33*, 72-77.

Personalized Age-Friendly Home Modifications: A Web-Based Application

***Sung-Jin Lee** (North Carolina A&T State University); **Hyun Joo Kwon; Jiyoung Oh** (Pusan National University)*

Although many seniors wish to remain in their current home as long as possible, most houses lack age-friendly housing design features (Luciano, 2020). Many researchers have emphasized the importance of home modification with accessible design for successful aging in place (Sixsmith, 2014; Smith, 2012). As the number of seniors is growing globally, many developed countries focus on aging in place, not only for the quality of life of older adults but also for national finance reasons (WHO, 2007). Age-friendly home modification is one aging-in-place solution, and several guidelines exist for this purpose (AARP, 2015; NYC Health, 2018; U.S. Consumer Product Safety Commission, 2015). However, in most cases, seniors do not need or are unable to apply all age-friendly housing design features in their homes. A simple and convenient evaluation system to assess an older adult's physical condition and their housing situation would allow effective and efficient home modification. The purpose of this study is to develop a web-based personalized age-friendly home modification suggestion application based on the older adult's physical status and housing condition. The web-based application consists of four parts: questions about socio-demographic and housing characteristics, a health condition checklist, a housing condition checklist, and age-friendly housing design items. The health condition checklist, which was developed by three medical experts, includes items about the senior's musculoskeletal system, balance evaluation, and senility evaluation. It includes questions about the Five Times Sit to Stand Test (FTSST) (Buatois et al., 2008), the Timed Up and Go Test (TUG) (Bennie et al., 2003), the fatigue, resistance, ambulation, illness, and loss of weight (FRAIL) scale (Chong, 2017; Wei, 2018), and the Functional Reach Test (Bennie et al., 2003; de Waroquier-Leroy, 2014). Three housing experts participated in compiling a housing condition checklist. This checklist included questions about whether the house had age-friendly housing design features in its entrance, living room, kitchen, master bedroom, master bathroom, and laundry room. A total of 81 age-friendly housing design items were included in the final version. The suggestions for each age-friendly housing design feature include two possible options based on different budgets and/or construction methods. This personalized application is intended to simplify the process of home modification for older adults. It would be useful for both older adults and service providers. It is necessary to evaluate the application's effectiveness in the future.

Play Spaces: Alternative Strategies for the Revitalisation of Informal Settlements

Francesco Rossini *(The Chinese University of Hong Kong);* ***Sruthi Atmakur-Javdekar*** *(City University of New York)*

This research explores how the incremental implementation of play spaces could become a strategic bottom-up tool for testing alternative strategies for the revitalization of informal settlements and for creating more child-friendly urban environments.

Contaminated areas and dumping sites often inadvertently become playgrounds for the children living in BaSEco compound, one of the largest informal communities in the Manila Port Area. According to Article 31 of the United Nations Convention on the Rights of the Child, play is a fundamental right of children's holistic growth and, in BaSECo, there is an urgent need to formulate a strategy for implementing inclusive open spaces where they can play freely and safely. Children make up almost 45% of the residents of this congested urban area, and it is essential to take actions to support their social and recreational needs. The pilot tests realised by the PI in the district demonstrated that play facilities could have a crucial role in the revitalization of informal settlements, thus becoming a strategic tool for promoting a more child-focused planning approach. Although the problematic condition of informal settlements has been well documented, few studies have examined how to combine the formulation of an inclusive and sustainable upgrading strategy with the delivery of a more child-friendly urban environment.

Making cities and human settlements safer as well as more inclusive, resilient and sustainable and additionally, where the wellbeing for all is promoted, is at the core of goals 3 and 11 of the UN-Habitat. By using the BaSECo compound as a case study, this research seeks to: a) develop a participatory strategy to engage the children and local community in the planning process; b) implement a play space prototype to be tested in a selected residual area of the district; c) examine the impact of this project on the space and on residents' behavior; and finally, d) formulate a long-term strategy for transforming dumps and residual urban spaces into safe and inclusive play areas for children and the community as a whole.

The findings of this research will contribute to a better understanding of urban informality by exploring the interface between formal and informal spheres. The results of this study will also serve as a bridge between local authorities and the community by contributing to the implementation of strategic policies and programs for informal communities, thereby establishing an alternative framework for significant spatial and programmatic changes.

Preserving the Future Food Environment with Traditional Technologies through Cultural Landscapes: An International Comparison between Yamagata Prefecture and Sichuan Province, China

Suxueer Sun *(University of Tsukuba);* ***Naoko Fujita*** *(University of Tsukuba)*

This study focuses on the sustainable production of food and hygiene, as well as the impact and change of food production and inheritance on the regional environment. We propose a landscape evaluation and conservation method that is conducive to the sustainable development of the region. We use Yamagata Prefecture's "Seisai pickles" and "Omi pickles" as well as China's "Guangyuan pickles" from Sichuan Province as examples. This study also enhances the self-healing of the region through the exploration of values in the framework of cultural landscape. Through a literature survey, we found that the vegetables used in both the Sichuan Province and Yamagata Prefecture pickles are the same species. Yamagata Prefecture's "Yamagata Seisai" was introduced from Chongqing City, Sichuan Province in the 1990's, and after development and improvement, the pickles forms are now different for both regions.

We used ArcGIS and analyzed the topography, soil, land use, and hydrology of the two areas, representing changes in time and space. In addition, we identified their landscape components and clarified the characteristics of cultural landscapes. We found that the formation of the landscape in the two regions has both similarities and differences. We visualize the wisdom and sustainable systems that have emerged through the establishment of production, processing, people's work styles, and living landscapes in the two regions as a "green landscape." We present a method to comprehensively evaluate and consider the tangible and intangible elements that have supported pickles making throughout the region in one value system by clarifying the related landscape components.

A comparative analysis had conducted on the following four points: 1) comparison of the craft, geographical, and cultural differences in the production of pickles between the two regions; 2) comparison of the differences in the concept and positioning of cultural landscapes between the two regions; 3) comparison of laws, regulations, and standards regarding cultural landscapes in both regions; and 4) comparison of the differences in the changes in cultural landscape, conservation, management, succession and development between the two regions.

PUZZLE Desk and Chair in Response of COVID 19 to Create Portable Furniture to Study Outdoor and Promote Mental Health

Hafsa Akter *(University of California, Davis);* ***Alejandra Ruiz*** *(University of California, Davis);* ***Justin Marsh*** *(University of California, Davis);* ***Brett Snyder*** *(University of California, Davis)*

As the COVID 19 pandemic hits, outdoor learning appears as a solution to ensure the continuation of curriculums in different levels of education. In many universities and colleges, like UC Davis, there's a need for an immediate response in order to upgrade or pair existing infrastructure with current health and well-being guidelines.

The objective of our group was to propose a fast, sustainable, and low-cost solution that would allow the minimum conditions necessary to have a study experience to be transferred to the open-air environment, either as part of a whole class or individually.

Research on case studies of outdoor learning education from the past 100 years suggested the persistence of basic horizontal surfaces to seat and/or lean as the minimum requirement, which was attained, in the more urgent cases, with at-hand resources in the educational setting.

Through rapid prototyping technologies, we sketched scale mockups that tested expected qualities of the final product like weight, stability, portability, ease of storage, ease of assembly/disassembly, production times, and smart material use. The iterations aimed at finding the best relationship between nominal material sizes, final furniture size, and the environmentally-friendliness of the design.

The current version of Puzzle is a simple, lightweight piece of portable wooden furniture that can be assembled without tools or nails, or glue. A flat, portfolio-like structure, easy to store and be carried, holds smaller wood pieces that can be joined intuitively following color codes on their borders. The set can be used both indoors and outdoors and is intended for personal use.

Sustainability issues in the piece are addressed

by reducing waste generation to less than 5% and laser cuts to its minimum. Replicability is also taken into consideration as the original file is openly shared with the community so new users can generate their own versions.

Besides the portable and environmentally-friendly design, the interaction that the object proposes to the user in the form of a small puzzle-solving activity can bring a fun moment in the middle of the study routines and pressures and the fulfillment of accomplishment, thus promoting mental health and well-being.

Puzzle requires further research to make it more accessible to disabled and alternative bodies as a work in progress. A more profound materials and manufacturing technologies exploration would also be helpful in order to make the project more replicable in contexts with different levels of access to resources like makerspaces and prototyping labs, as right now it relies heavily on fast prototyping technologies and computer-aided design and manufacturing.

Research on Disaster Prevention and Mitigation, Utilizing Ecosystems As Flood Adaptation for Urban Climate Change in Asia

Minghui Tang *(University of Tsukuba)*; **Naoko Fujita** *(University of Tsukuba)*

Research on disaster prevention and mitigation, utilizing ecosystems as flood adaptation for urban climate change in Asia

In Asia, natural disasters such as floods, landslides, and storm surges are increasing due to climate change, while urbanization is being promoted along with development. Therefore, more sustainable adaptation measures to natural disaster risks are required. There are many densely populated areas in Asian countries, and there is often great damage each time a disaster occurs. Particularly, if disasters occur consecutively, the damage will be even greater, significantly impacting human life and the economy.

This study aims to clarify the traditional knowledge about disaster prevention, mitigation and natural resources management, and how to use natural resources for disaster prevention in landscape ecology, both socially and economically, from geospatial science data. Further, this study aims to elucidate the ideal method of flood disaster prevention and mitigation in major Asian cities through an analysis of the legal system.

The stages of urbanization in Tokyo, Shanghai, and Jakarta were discriminated from the aspects of population and land use, and the stages with the same rate of increase or decrease were extracted. In the wide-area analysis, the landscape pattern of each urbanization stage of an individual research target area was read from Fragstats, using land use data (public satellite data), and changes in landscape pattern were analyzed. Fragstats is a landscape pattern analysis program for land-cover and vegetation maps. Next, for regional analysis, soil storage capacity and coastal vulnerability were evaluated in terms of ecosystem services, using InVEST. This is an ArcGIS program developed to provide a comprehensive assessment of ecosystem services and their compensation. It can evaluate changes in habitat quality, coastline ecosystem risk, sediment conservation capacity, etc. In addition, land cover data of important points in each region was taken using UAVs, converted to GIS data using image analysis tools, and introduced into InVEST. After conducting wide area and regional analyses, the spatial characteristics theory of landscape ecology, the theory of ecosystem services, and the theory of rainwater management were applied to examine the spatial, related, and regional characteristics of each research target area.

Our notable findings are as follows: In 1986, Tokyo exhibited a peaceful period of urban development. In urban development, the area of construction land is the largest, and the area of rice fields and forests is small. However, the area of water and coastal land is still large. In Tokyo, the landscape element ratio is the largest for forestland, and smallest for construction land. There was little difference in the proportion of landscape elements between rice fields and agricultural land. Comparing Tokyo in 1986 and 2006, the proportion of landscape elements in forestland tended to decrease from 10.5387 to 9.5204. On the other hand, the proportion of landscape elements on construction sites tended to increase from 0.721 to 0.2627. In addition to the results from Tokyo, we have results from Shanghai and Jakarta and report a comparison of the three countries.

Research on the Design Effect of Rural Theme Park Evidence from Big Data——Take Kentucky Horse Park As an Example

Pang Shaojie *(Beijing Jiaotong University);* ***Yi Yang*** *(Beijing Jiaotong University);* ***Bo Zhang*** *(Oklahoma State University)*

The rural theme park is a rural tourism destination that integrates leisure, entertainment and service reception based on a specific theme, in the form of modern science and technology and multi-level spatial activities. In recent years, the research of rural theme park has also attracted the attention of scholars. At present, the research on rural theme parks mainly adopts content analysis method, importance-performance analysis method (IPA and ASEB grid analysis method to analyze the image perception of theme parks, the quality of tourist experience, tourist satisfaction analysis and post-use evaluation. However, there is a lack of in-depth research on the design of rural theme parks from the perspective of tourist experience. Taking advantage of the social media data, of large data types, large data volume, fast speed and high authenticity, this study takes Kentucky Horse Park as an example to exemplify the social media-based evaluation method. Horse Park is located in Kentucky, mid-eastern United States. As a rural theme park, horse culture is used as a link to develop a series of commercial arts, equestrian competitions, education and other industries, forming a rural theme park tourism destination, with nearly 500,000 tourists each year.

Therefore, using python technology, we can quickly obtain 3297 reviews and about 100,000 words of data on the TripAdvisor website from May 2003 to September 2020, along with the comment time, satisfaction level, and other information. Using Gooseeker and Excel, the textual data was categorized to five elements related to architectural design, such as architectural style, space construction, landscape design, accessibility design and business environment, aiding our understanding of tourist motivation, activities, attentions, perceptions in rural tourist destinations. We then use gephi to conduct the data visualization. From these analysis, we reveal more understandings about:1)the balance point between rural theme park design technique and natural environment, in order to create attractive characteristic space;2)tourists in the comments mentioned in the wooden structure barn building and outdoor theme landscape design can mobilize their enthusiasm;3)Tourists' Positive Evaluation of accessibility facilities in the Park;4)tourists' focus on the Horse and Horse Culture as the carrier of related theme activities;5)research on the specific methods of rural theme park design. This study creates a rural theme park tourist experience research system, providing theoretical guidance for the construction and development of rural tourism in the United States.

Through this study, we can learn:

1. Research on planning and design of rural theme park based on big data, from data mining, cleaning, classification to visual analysis;
2. Exploring the focus of tourists on rural theme parks and the focus of designers in design and planning;
3. Starting from the elements of architectural style, space construction and landscape design, this paper explores the correlation mechanism between the design strategy of American rural theme park construction and the surrounding environment;
4. Learning about tourists ' attention to non-theme elements in theme parks and their impact on tourists' enthusiasm.

Research on the Development Guidelines for after-School Day Services: Through Behavioral Observation and Needs Assessment

Kurumi Takezawa *(Utsunomiya University);* ***Eiji Satoh*** *(Utsunomiya University)*

Background: For the well-being of healthy living for all people, it is an important topic to consider how to design spaces to provide diverse and comprehensive services suitable for each individual to those who need various kinds of support.

Currently in Japan, the environment surrounding children with disabilities is changing as the number of children with disabilities increases and the multiple and severe disabilities become more apparent.

Past in Japan, the Child Welfare Law was revised in 2012. In recent years, there has been a marked increase in the number of after-school day care centers for children with disabilities between the ages of 6 and 18. After-school day service is a service that provides necessary support for school-going children with disabilities.

The number of after-school day service facilities has quadrupled in the five years since 2012. On the other hand, the increase in the number of low-quality establishments that maintain only minimal facilities in order to profit from subsidies, etc., has become a problem.

In 2015, the After-School Day Service Guideline was published. However, it is difficult to guarantee the quality of services uniformly with the guideline alone.

Therefore, the purpose of this study was to understand the actual activities of children with disabilities in after-school day service facilities and to obtain knowledge for designing spaces that are friendly to children with disabilities.

Research Method: In this paper, we conducted interviews with six distinctive facilities among those that were able to cooperate with our survey through a questionnaire survey of after-school day service facilities in provincial city in 2018, to understand the current status and needs of the facilities from the perspective of the employers. Then, behavioral observations of staff and children were conducted to understand how the rooms are used and the problems that arise. Finally, a questionnaire survey of parents was conducted at 15 facilities to understand the needs and problems of the parents in the facilities

Results: In the actual operation, about 10 children spend time in a room of 100 square meters. In the behavioral observation survey, the room was not completely divided between dynamic and static activities, but the activities were separated by setting up desks, mats, and other interior furnishings. In addition, children of various ages, disabilities, and degrees of disability spent time in the same space, and some children had difficulty coping with the space due to the mixture of static and dynamic activities.

Conclusion and Discussion: From the actual situation where children of different ages and with different types and degrees of disabilities spend time in the same space, it is considered necessary to develop flexible spaces that can be divided according to the content of treatment and education. In addition, the type of facility should be selected according to the type of operation (stand-alone or attached), the content of treatment and education, and the characteristics of the children accepted. The current guidelines do not provide detailed guidelines, and it is necessary to examine the details.

Research on the Outdoor Spaces in Senior-Living Facilities in Zhengzhou

Zhe Wang *(Henan University);* ***Yahong Zhu*** *(Henan University)*

Background: Associated with fast urbanization and high levels of population density in China, the outdoor spaces in senior-living facilities in Chinese cities are limited. In design practice, the consideration regarding senior-living residents' needs for outdoor spaces and the ways they use the outdoor spaces is limited. To promote health and quality of life in senior-living facilities, research is needed to investigate the needs and residents' usage of the current spaces there.

Methods: Taking four senior-living facilities in Zhengzhou as examples, we collect data on the needs and current usage of existing outdoor spaces through field observation and questionnaire survey. Based on weekday observations, the diagrams of residents' activities in outdoor spaces will be developed and the most popular types of outdoor activity will be identified. Focusing on the needs for outdoor spaces and environmental satisfaction, questionnaire data will be collected from the current residents in the facilities. Space syntax will be applied to analyze the visibility and accessibility of the specific locations where residents aggregate in the outdoors. ANOVA tests will be conducted to identify the differences in environmental needs between facilities.

Findings: We expect to see that residents' outdoor activities in these facilities are both similar to and different from each other. Residents at different care levels have different needs for outdoor spaces. Independent-living residents are active in the outdoors and may need support to travel outside the facility, whereas assisted-living residents are more likely to stay and engage in activities in the outdoors and nursing-care residents may spend more time indoors and watching. The most popular types of their outdoor activity include siting, walking, chatting, exercising, and playing chess. It is expected to see some patterns of their outdoor activities and the most popular time slots would be mid-mornings and late-afternoons. Regarding the needs, shaded sitting areas are needed for summer months and windy days. The pedestrian-vehicle separation is required to reduce traffic conflicts and ensure the safety of residents. Multi-purpose areas should be provided to improve the flexibility of space use for their outdoor activities. Levels of space enclosure should be improved to meet the needs for privacy. The quality of landscaping should be promoted to ensure environmental attractiveness in the outdoors. Outdoor furniture and associates including street lamps and signage systems may need more management and maintenance. More design and practice are needed regarding the needs of visually impaired residents, such as braille, blind paths, and voice prompting devices.

Discussion: The needs of older adults for outdoor spaces in senior-living facilities vary. The design of outdoor spaces should start from the actual needs of the residents, and comprehensively consider design factors addressing multi-level needs, which include overall planning layout, road system, activity areas, landscaping, outdoor furniture and associates to promote healthy living and aging in the facilities.

Residential Happiness Elements That Affect the Daily Happiness of Koreans

Byungsook Choi *(Chonbuk National University);* ***Jung-a Park*** *(Wonkwang University);* ***Jin Lee*** *(Jeonbuk National University)*

This study aims to analyze the factors and elements that can improve residents' happiness in their houses. The 'residential happiness' was measured using the tool consisting of 61 measurement elements of 7 conceptual factors suggested by Choi (2021). The 'daily happiness' was measured in 14 items of five concepts: Positive emotion, Engagement, Relationship, Meaning, and Achievement, according to the flourishing concepts of positive psychology. The data of 'residential happiness' and 'daily happiness' were collected from 2,160 people through an online survey on April 2021, and the data were analyzed using SPSS 26.0. The reliability of the measurement tool is the reliability of 'residential happiness' (Cronbach's = .970) and the reliability of 'daily happiness' (Cronbach's = .964), so the tool's reliability has been proven.

As a result of the analysis, the factors of housing happiness that affect 'daily happiness' are comfort (β = .188) and personality (β = .207), economic feasibility (β = .106), convenience (β =.092), safety (β = -.043) appeared. In addition, each element of housing happiness by personality factor is style or personality expression (β = .104), direct participation in the design, architecture, interior, and renovation process (β = .088), and decorating the family history with family photos or objects containing memories (β = .089). Each element of comfort factor is an emotionally stable feeling (β = .181), plants such as flowers, flowers, and trees (β = .068), and indoor noise control (ß = .073), it was identified as the sense of openness of the indoor high ceiling (ß = -.047). The element of each convenience factor is the installation of electrical outlets where necessary (ß = .054) and internet environment (ß = .049) was found to be the safety factor, the risk of slipping and falling on the porch and toilet floors (ß = -.046), and the economic factor showed an appropriate level of housing cost (rental deposit, rent, management fee, heating and cooling cost, electricity fee, etc.). In other words, to promote daily happiness through the house, above all, it is judged that residents achieved what they wanted by engaging themselves in the relationship with the environment of housing and giving meaning by expressing their style and personality.

Safe Residential Environment for Single Female Household: Using Eye-Tracking Method

Soohyun Lee *(Yonsei University);* ***GyeongYeon Lee*** *(Yonsei University);* ***Ji Eun Oh*** *(Yonsei University);* ***Gi-dong Byun*** *(Yonsei University);* ***MiKyoung Ha*** *(Yonsei University)*

Safety is one of the main factors that determine the quality of life. The Better Life Index(BLI) developed by the OECD selected individual safety as a major indicator of quality of life, and Korea also cited safety as a major indicator of "people's quality of life indicator." In other words, a society where individuals feel safe means a healthy society with a high quality of life. According to a survey released by the National Statistical Office in 2018, only 16.6% of women said that Korean society is generally safe. The biggest reason for lowering women's sense of safety is the occurrence of crimes, and 57% of respondents said they felt fear of crime(FOC).

This study focused on women, especially single-person households. Single female households are classified as the group with the highest fear in daily life. They are paying additional personal efforts and costs to alleviate fear, such as paying higher housing costs to secure a safe residential environment. As such, fear goes beyond the inconvenience of daily life and has a great negative effect on their overall psychological well-being. Since single female households are expected to increase day by day due to changes in the family paradigm in modern society, it is necessary to recognize the sense of safety they feel as a major problem and establish practical measures to guarantee it.

In order to improve safety and psychological well-being, an appropriate environment must be created to alleviate their fears. Until now, studies related to fear have been conducted focusing on CPTED, which puts a high emphasis on crime "prevention." However, the actual crime-prone area and the fear-prone area are often inconsistent, and fear tends to appear across a wider range of areas. In other words, in order to create an environment that guarantees a sense of safety for single female households, awareness of major environmental factors related to fear should be prioritized in addition to the CPTED.

The purpose of this study is to identify spatial factors that cause fear in a residential environment and to present improvement measures to create a safe residential environment. Therefore, this study limited the scope of the study to multiplex housing in low-rise residential area which is representative residential type of single female households, analyzed the relationship between each physical environmental factor and fear through eye-tracking method based on case photos of entrances. As a result of the study, it was concluded that in order to improve the sense of safety, plans to improve the territoriality of entrance, filoti, and windows should be considered first. Based on the results, this study intends to present improvement measures for creating a safe residential environment.

This study is differentiated in that it identifies the user's intuitive perception of the residential environment by using an eye tracking with visual data along with the survey. The results of this study can be used as useful data for improving the safety of residential environment, and finally improve single female household's psychological well-being and quality of life.

Senior Friendly Street Environments in Historic Districts —Taking Shunbei District in Daokou As an Example

Zhe Wang *(Henan University);* ***Guoxiang Li*** *(Henan Uiversity)*

Aim: Aim of this research is to identify the current situation of street environments in historic districts and the needs of older adults for friendly street environments.

Methods: In Shunbei district in Daokou ancient town in China, field observation focusing on the popular locations where older adults gathered on streets were conducted. Focusing on older adults on the streets, personal information, self-reported street behaviors and needs for friendly street environments were collected through interview. Environmental data focusing on the frontier buildings, street signs, and public toilets along the streets were observed and collected by using the Cat's Eye applet. Geographic coordinates of older adults' street activities were identified and imported into the Geographic Information Systems. ArcGIS (version 10.2) was applied to analyze the possible influence of environments on behavior. Both quantitative and qualitative methods were used to analyze the data.

Findings: Outdoor areas for gathering were very limited and the locations were unevenly distributed in Shunbei district. Older adults' street activities had a peak period in the mid mornings. Public facilities such as streetlights, safety cameras, and fitness facilities were in need of updates and better management and maintenance. More aging-friendly and barrier-free furniture should be located along the streets. More and higher-quality landscaping were asked to promote street vistas and the attractiveness of street environments.

Discussion: This research investigated older adults' street activities in a historic district and their needs for better street environments. Based on data analysis, suggestions were proposed to promote senior-friendly street environments. First, the historic characteristics of Daokou should be maintained along the streets to protect local cultures. Appropriate places should be selected and refined for older adults' daily gathering. Street furniture and auxiliary facilities should be more senior-friendly. Suggestions on the entrance and exit of a building, outdoor sitting, signage systems, drainage systems, and public transportation were put forward. Three-dimensional landscaping should be considered to improve the quality of street environments.

Signage Systems in Senior-Living Facilities – a Study in China

Zhe Wang *(Henan University);* ***Enguang Li***

Introduction: Influenced by age-related functional declines, older adults are more likely to be challenged in way-finding than young adults. In senior-living facilities providing both medical care and daily-living services, spaces may be complicated to the residents. Appropriate signage systems can help to facilitate their living in the facilities. However, relevant research is very limited.

Aim: To investigate to the current situation of signage systems in senior-living facilities providing both medical care and daily-living services and identify the direction for future development.

Methods: On-site observation and questionnaire surveys were conducted to collect data on the current situations of signage systems in five senior-living facilities in China. These facilities provided both medical care and daily-living services and were in Kaifeng, Zhengzhou, Qingdao, and Shanghai. Objective data on the locations, functions, sizes, colors, and design details of varied signs applied in these facilities were recorded during on-site observation. Levels of satisfaction and suggestions regarding these signs were collected through questionnaire surveys of the residents.

Results: Based on both quantitative and qualitative analysis, three factors were summarized to represent the current situation of signs applied in senior-living facilities. 1) The locations should be more systematic. 2) The patterns of design should be more senior friendly and warmer. 3) The contents should be more consistent. The residents reported that the signage systems had incomplete functions, inconsistent forms, unscientific locations, and low-levels of recognition.

Discussion: Updates are needed to promote the signage systems in senior-living facilities. It is suggested to locate the signs in the key points of space inside and outside the buildings, including space junctions. Lighting in the spaces with a sign should be sufficient to help older adults identify and read the sign. More signs focusing on traffic safety are needed. Elements used in the signs could be standardized. Sharp corners and reflecting materials should be avoided. Finding of this research could be used in both design practice and facility management to promote the quality of signage systems for senior living.

Spatializing Fractals: Fractal Complexity of Interior Spaces

Joori Suh *(University of Cincinnati);* ***Steen Petersen*** *(Wright State University)*

Building on the contemporary theories on healing environment, such as Attention Restoration Theory and Biophilic Hypothesis, this study investigates what particular principles of the natural environment constitute humans' well-being focusing on the remarkable characteristics of fractals. A fractal is a complex organic or geometric figure in which the same patterns are repeated at multiple different scales. The uniqueness of the properties of fractals is known to have effects on human's psychological well-being (Joye, 2007) and especially mid-range fractal dimension (D value of 1.3-1.5) has shown to have stress dampening effects (Taylor, 2021). Despite their artistic values as well as their psychological benefits, detailed fractals have not been actively explored as a spatial design driver in the interior design profession. In this research we explore the role of spatial fractals to answer the following question: When fractal principles are spatialized three-dimensionally in a real world environment, what aspects increase or decrease the fractal complexity?

This research investigates the interplay between spatial components and fractal complexity using simulated prototype models of interior enclosure structures. Various fractals including geometric, organic, and abstract patterns were applied to enclosures of 12'x12'x12' spaces. A total of 360 three-dimensional spatial prototype models were created based on the application types of spatial depth (shallow, medium, and deep), and additional controlled models with various non-fractal slatted enclosures were also created to verify the preliminary findings. The fractal dimension was calculated using a box counting method, implemented in the Python programming language. For each model global fractal dimension (an overall fractal complexity) as well as local fractal complexity (fractal complexity of individual 132 sub-images within each model scene) were calculated. After analyzing the fractal dimensions and the fractal distributions of each scene, the results of this research showed the following: (a) the clarity of fractal principles with a higher degree of scale variations within the sub-image is closely related to the fractal complexity; (b) multiple layering of the same fractal screen: If layering of a fractal screen makes the clarity of fractals diffused, the fractal dimension decreases; however, if layering of a fractal screen adds more scale variations due to perspectival effects, fractal dimension increases; (c) non-fractal slatted walls produce a fractal dimension with perspectival effect; (d) space can be highly complex without increasing fractal complexity; (e) fractal complexity of a space can be reduced with furniture arrangement; (f) visual texture of interior materials can increase fractal complexity.

The research is meaningful in that it transcends the theoretical parameters of the study of fractals and suggests proactive applications of fractals in practical and spatial realms. It is our hope that the study of spatial fractals inspires designers, students, and manufacturers to consider spatial fractals as powerful design drivers in designing fractal inspired spaces in order to ultimately enhance people's psychological wellbeing.

References

Joye, Y. (2007). Fractal architecture could be good for you. *Nexus Network Journal, 9*(2), 311-320.

Taylor, R. P. (2021). The potential of biophilic fractal designs to promote health and performance: A review of experiments and applications.

Sustainability, 13(2), 823.

Stitching the Community to the Nutritious Ground in the Urban City Landscape through Help Yourself!

Riya Premani *(University of Massachusetts, Amherst);*
Carey Clouse *(University of Massachusetts, Amherst)*

Stitching the community to the nutritious ground in the urban city landscape through Help Yourself! After the Covid-19 pandemic, cracks in American food security became clear. Long ago, communities, cities and regions were relatively self-sufficient; now much of the food consumed in Western Massachusetts is outsourced. The pandemic provided an opportunity to rethink this relationship between food production and consumption. One response to food insecurity is found in foraging, particularly through fruit orchards managed by an organization called Help Yourself! In Northampton, MA. These fruit trees are planted in accessible open greenways or corridors in order to provide free food to the community. These are generally planted according to their type, such as bushes and grapevines along rail trails, with smaller trees planted in green spaces in the downtown. Urban landscaping of this type requires supportive urban planning, municipal allowances, and access to a commons via US property law (Clouse,2022; Hahn,1982). This practice not only addresses the needs of the hour, but also instils value into the landscape for future generations. It is possible to conceive of a future for food access that provides for all living beings, regardless of their capacity to pay. Why can't there be an abundance of fruits and vegetables for the community to pick it up from the trees directly? Why can't we build a nutritious surrounding for ourselves and give it back to the land that we live on? Help Yourself! provides this framework, enabling a more equitable future for food security. The organization's main goal was to create a nutritious public landscape which provides free food to the community. The process included reimagining empty spaces around Northampton, MA and the rail trails that connect it with the nearby cities. Their goal is to transform the unused and ignored green spaces into forest gardens, which they call-fruit tree "Islands" that also help to revive and build urban soil. This work ignites and encourages the curiosity about perennial agriculture and food access. It is supported by volunteers that is connected through design, harvest and implementation. The volunteers are also a part of different educational organization and plan food access and land use workshops to educate and strengthen the bond between the future community and the land. The public orchards stretch through Western Massachusetts, helping to increase biodiversity and also provide pollinator habitat. In different ways, it is a promising way of giving back to the city and community as well as involving edible forests into the urban city landscapes, while also contextualizing the spaces around downtown.

Table Design and Its Effectiveness for the Visually Impaired

Momoka Hirai *(Tohoku University)*

According to the International Classification of Functioning in Life by the World Health Organization, the functioning of the life of people with disabilities is determined by the interaction between health status and background factors, and the physical environment influences the functioning of life. Previous studies on the environment of the visually impaired have revealed the factors they refer to while wayfinding in public spaces and such factors have been considered in architectural designs and rehabilitation. These studies also addressed the behavior in a given environment. In the house of visually impaired persons, they construct a user-friendly environment by themselves.

Here, we clarify how the visually impaired construct their home environment and gain helpful knowledge for product and space designs. This survey is also useful for the visually impaired to live safely and comfortably in small houses in Japan.

This study was conducted in three steps. First, the characteristics of the environment were clarified through surveys and interviews at the houses of 8 visually impaired persons. Next, a table that takes advantage of these characteristics was designed (the Obon Table was released in 2020 and has won the Wood Design Award and the Social Product Award in Japan. Obon is the Japanese word for tray). Finally, the effect of the table design was tested by comparing the coffee brewing behavior of 4 visually impaired people using the Obon Table and an ordinary table.

The result is as follows:

1. Visually impaired people could devise their ways of arranging furniture and storing items, creating an easy-to-understand environment. For example, they place furniture in a way that prioritizes walking traffic lines. Moreover, frequently used items are stored in places that are easy to reach by arm. They have also devised ways of arranging books and folding clothes so that they can easily keep track of the grouping of things at their fingertips.
2. Considering the arrangement of objects on the table in the houses of visually impaired people, we found that they arrange objects along the edge of the tabletop, making it easier to touch and explore along the edge. Additionally, eating on a tray makes it easier to grasp the area where dishes are placed.
3. To facilitate exploration on a top board of the table by contact, the top board was designed with crater-like indentations. It can fix the placement of objects and make them easier for cognition and grasp.
4. In a coffee brewing experiment, the subject places objects along the edge of the crater, and the crater serves as a cushion before they encounter objects, such as kettle and cup. Furthermore, even if they spill, the area to be wiped up is straightforward.

As described above, visually impaired people create an easy-to-understand environment according to their physical characteristics. The results also suggest that this method can also be applied to designs.

Teaching Community Resilience in Detroit's Good Stock Neighborhoods

Ceara O'Leary *(Detroit Collaborative Design Center)*

Healthy neighborhoods and community resilience have distinct implications in Detroit's more vacant neighborhoods, where land is both a liability and an asset. From 2019 to today, the author and her university-based community design center have been working with community-based organization Eastside Community Network on a series of projects that unpack questions of resilience on Detroit's eastside Good Stock neighborhoods – self-named for the quality housing, people and other assets the area boasts. The area also boasts ample vacant land and buildings, which residents are seeking to repurpose for community use, contributing to a more beautiful and healthy neighborhood. The design center worked with resident leaders to develop a green stormwater infrastructure initiative in the area which re-envisions vacant land as an opportunity to leverage Detroit's stormwater policy and invite outside investment that would reduce investor drainage bills by building green infrastructure that would beautify and stabilize the neighborhood, offering a myriad of benefits from flood reduction to identity building. Subsequently, resident leaders invited the design center to continue planning with the neighborhoods in the development of a land use framework that proposed new uses for vacant land, opportunities for neighborhood businesses, and concentrated of resources to benefit the distributed community. In the midst of this work, the author also introduced architecture students to the Good Stock community via a Public Interest Design studio. Students were charged with the design of a "community resiliency hub" in the Good Stock area, repurposing an existing building with programming and design defined and informed by Good Stock resident leaders. The studio invited students to engage with Good Stock residents (over Zoom in the midst of the pandemic) to learn what a resilient community means to neighbors and integrate community conversations into program and design development. Programs and site varied by student. This presentation will unpack this collective body of work with and in the Good Stock neighborhoods with a focus on how architecture studio students engage with community members, integrating experiential learning with their own design production, and the pedagogical implications at the intersection of community design and design studio.

Teaching Thermal Comfort in Interior Design

Alp Tural *(Virginia Tech)*

Standard 14 of the Council of Interior Design Accreditation (CIDA), addresses student learning expectations related to environmental systems and comfort (2020). Typically, the fundamentals and strategies of thermal design and their impact on interior design solutions are introduced in Building Systems courses in the interior design curricula. Unlike light and color (standard 12) or building code-related learning goals (standard 16), which are also discussed in system courses, the learning expectations for thermal environment and comfort conditions do not necessitate demonstrated student work for attaining the expectation, and students of interior design are seldom required to demonstrate such knowledge on their interior design studio projects (unless specifically listed as part of the project prompt). While student understanding can be demonstrated via in-class exercises, assignments and projects, hands-on learning opportunities merging empirical thermal data and subjective thermal sensations are vital to ensure that the information on thermal environment is not addressed only in studio-supportive courses.

To enhance the teaching modules and better help students develop their own meanings in the Building Systems course—in line with constructivist teaching methods, pedagogical interventions were proposed during the Fall 2021 term (for thermal comfort, building codes and structures modules). This presentation will focus on the employed strategies for teaching the thermal comfort module and report findings of the thermal comfort data collected not only to reinforce students' understanding of thermal design concepts but also to expose them to interior design research and qualitative and quantitative data collection methods.

Following the in-class thermal comfort, passive and active heating and cooling strategy discussions, sophomore level students filled out a point-in-time thermal comfort survey that was prepared in line with the American Society for Heating, Refrigerating and Air Conditioning Engineers (ASHRAE) standard 55 (2013 edition). Same survey was also made available to the junior design studio students since they share the same space with the sophomores. The survey inquired students' thermal comfort sensation in the design studio space and included questions that helped the researcher calculate predicted mean vote (PMV) data. To determine PMV and discuss comfort-related variables in relation to the psychrometric chart and comfort zone, seven temperature and two relative humidity loggers were installed in the design studio space prior to the survey, and air velocity was measured at desk height. The collected empirical data were analyzed in relation to students' seating map, their subjective thermal comfort sensation responses and HVAC supply grill positions.

Initial findings showed a better agreement of the PMV with sophomore student responses when compared with junior studio students who did not have had chance to use the studio space due to the pandemic. Those findings were shared with the students in the class to further emphasize the importance of thermal design and non-quantifiable factors such as user expectations and familiarity. Correlation analyses between multiple variables such as seating location and PMV, and clothing value and thermal sensation are ongoing and will be shared with the students during the spring 2022 term.

The Positive Effects of Biophilic Design: The Relationship between Indoor Plants, Positive Emotions, and Prosocial Behaviour

Bing-Tao Lee *(University of Cambridge);* ***Koen Steemers*** *(University of Cambridge)*

Built environments exert a significant impact on human emotions and behaviors, with nature being an important element (Baker & Steemers, 2019). Including natural elements in built environments is known to have a significant impact on human emotion and cognition; however, their positive influence on prosocial behavior has received comparatively little attention. It is hypothesized that exposure to plants increases positive emotions, and so enhances prosocial behaviour (Zhang, Piff, Iyer, Koleva, & Keltner, 2014). As people spend much time indoors, an indoor-plant-office scenario has been chosen.

An experiment was carried out in three rooms. The first room was used for prior mood measurement. The other two rooms were used for post-mood measurement and a prosocial behaviour task, for the experimental group and control group respectively. Plants of a variety of types and colors were available for the experimental room to assess: mixed design with scenarios (i.e., either with or without plants); between-participants factor and phase (i.e., before and after exposure to plants); within-participants factor. Participants' mood before and after exposure to the plants was recorded, and lastly, their prosocial behaviour was measured. The methods have been widely used in previous studies. The experiment was conducted from 11am to 5pm on March 15th, 18th and 19th 2019. The daylight and weather conditions remained the same on those days. The participants were international post-graduate students and they were randomly assigned to conditions.

The results demonstrated that the emotion metrics worked well and showed that exposure to plants changed the participants' emotions, which is in line with the literature; happiness, pleasure and relaxation seem to be strong indicators. However, there was no clear pattern concerning prosocial behaviour because the sample size was too small. There were also potential confounding factors, which could be reduced by applying propensity score matching with a bigger sample. Regarding limitations, the experimental rooms were not identical in the pilot study. Ideally, they should be two adjacent identical rooms. The contribution is to specifically define emotion and prosocial behaviour in this context and quantify them properly in a way that is coherent with multi disciplines and existing knowledge. This research attempts to combine psychology and architecture to not only advance research on biophilic design but also potentially provide guidance for its characteristics for built-environment experts and architectural designers. As urban density continues to grow it is believed that biophilic design will be of ever-increasing importance in promoting mental health and general well-being.

References

Baker, N., & Steemers, K. (2019). Healthy homes: designing with light and air for sustainability and wellbeing. Routledge.

Zhang, J. W., Piff, P. K., Iyer, R., Koleva, S., & Keltner, D. (2014). An occasion for unselfing: Beautiful nature leads to "prosociality. Journal of Environmental Psychology, 37, 61–72. https://doi.org/10.1016/j.jenvp.2013.11.008

Toilet Design: Hidden Corner in the Campus

Yilin Song *(Tianjin University);* ***Junxuan Li*** *(Tianjin University);* ***Shuyan Zhang*** *(Tianjin University);* ***Zhejia Li*** *(Tianjin University);* ***Rongxuan Mu*** *(Tianjin University)*

The toilet is an essential facility for meeting the most basic human needs. Insufficient amount, inconvenient location and circulation, and poor design with regard to privacy, hygiene, and safety may have widespread negative effects on physical, emotional, and mental health, especially for the young adults who are still in the development on physiology and psychology.

Most of the university and/or college students in China live in the shared-room dormitory in campus without private toilets; they spend the whole day in campus, of which relatively high percentage in teaching buildings. Therefore, the toilet in teaching buildings is an important factor among infrastructures of the campus; a reasonable humanized design and optimization based on necessary analysis should be carried out according to its characteristics.

Starting from the human-centered perspective of environmental psychology, the research team take some toilets in teaching buildings in the campus of Tianjin University, Tianjin, China, as an example, combine the corresponding design principles and research methods and proposes optimization and improvement plans based on actual analysis. The research explores student users' feelings when using the selected toilets and their evaluations towards the physical environment through field observation and questionnaire survey. It also combines physical sand table, three-dimensional digital modeling and other technical means to conduct in-depth research on the spatial design and conduct simulation deductions based on digital models. The information of physical conditions of toilets such as the dimensions and area, light and thermal environment, and layout are recorded. The questionnaire goes deep into the toilet usage time and frequency, psychological feelings and experience, evaluation comparisons, etc. In total, 268 valid questionnaires and sand table simulation data of 26 volunteers are collected. The results suggest: 1. insufficient publicity and lack of privacy of the selected toilets; 2. unfriendly facility environment for the cleaning staff.

Furthermore, advantages and disadvantages of campus toilets in human-centered design, such as comfort and privacy, are discussed. Combining research findings from environmental behavior, psychology, ergonomics and other related disciplines, design recommendations and optimized projects of campus toilets are provided to give a practical reference.

This research aims to provide valuable theoretical and practical suggestions for the research and construction of public toilets and other health-related facilities in colleges and universities in the future.

Transportation Evaluation and Optimization of School Areas

Yilin Song *(Tianjin University);* ***Hanzhang Liu*** *(Tianjin University);* ***Xinlei Sheng*** *(Tianjin University);* ***Zhiqing Gao*** *(Tianjin University);* ***Ni Xia*** *(Tianjin University)*

In China, despite the policy of nearby enrollment of school, many parents still choose to pick up and drop off their children at the entrance of kindergartens, primary and secondary schools. In particular, the increasing proportion of private cars causes traffic congestion and safety problems. We choose the site at the Hubin Road intersection, where entrances of a primary school, a kindergarten and a university all converge at in Tianjin, China.

In order to discern the safety risks caused by traffic congestion in this region, the author learned about the geographical situation, management policy and traffic status of the schools entrance by means of network data, literature review, on-site observation and inquiry. We used the method of literature analysis, access to the basic information of the campus, and master the number of students, entrances and exits, etc. Consult the relevant literature on the safety of school hours around the campus, and summarize the evaluation indicators such as campus surrounding environment, pick-up behavior, obstacles and so on.

Using the questionnaire survey method, 115 questionnaires about the safety of campus after school time were distributed to students from Tianjin University, and the questionnaires were distributed to the parents of the primary school and the kindergarten respectively to understand the parents' views on campus after school safety and improvement measures, and 65 valid questionnaires were recovered. According to the improvement strategy of the paper, the feedback questionnaire on the improvement measures of campus after school time safety was supplemented to parents, and a total of 60 valid questionnaires were collected. Through questionnaire survey and on-site observation and inquiry, we learned about the views of teachers and students in the nearby university on traffic problems and opinions and demands of children's parents.

On this basis, we developed a range of proposed solutions to the potential problems such as increasing the school entrance and exit, divided into different groups to dismiss the class setting up drop-off point and so on. Then we made a second questionnaire by comparing the optimization strategy with the current situation and distributed it to parents to test the effectiveness and practicability of the improved methods.

Typologies of Therapy Cluster in Radiotherapy Departments Developed from Comparative Floorplan-Analysis

Carolina Kolodziej (Technische Universität Dresden)

Cancer treatment is an individualized therapy with the possibility of surgery, chemotherapy and/or radiotherapy. Radiotherapy is an essential part in cancer treatment and is the forefront of effective treatment therapies offered to cancer patients. (Abshire & Lang, 2018) The implementation of evidence-based design in health care facilities can positively influence workflow, travel paths, well-being, and quality of stay. (Mahmood, 2021) Transferred to radiotherapy, an optimized architecture and built environment of radiotherapy departments is a prerequisite for treatment. With the current lack of planning requirements of radiotherapy departments, the configuration of room clusters and typologies was approached.

The complexity of radiotherapy departments with different cluster-formations and various users is a challenging endeavor. For evidence-based typologies on cluster and room constellations various methods were conducted. As a first step a list of rooms was drafted and clusters were categorized to structure the complexity of radiotherapy departments. Six cluster formations were conducted: Outpatient, Imaging, Planning, Therapy, Personnel and Service, with each dedicated room.

The heart of the department, where all user groups come together and the patient receives the radiation treatment is the therapy cluster. The therapy cluster consists of the following rooms: a) therapy room, where cancer patients receive their radiation treatment; b) control room, where staff controls the radiation-device and monitors the patient in the therapy room; c)changing cubicle for patients and d)anteroom connecting all rooms including the waiting area. This study establishes typologies and spatial criteria of room organization in the therapy cluster by analyzing floorplans of radiotherapy departments in German hospitals.

"By comparing a wide range of building layouts for similar organizations one may achieve a good understanding of the ways in which goals and values can be expressed in spatial solutions. It offers the opportunity to develop a spatiofunctional typology of design solutions" (van der Voordt et al., 1997). For developing typologies and planning requirements a comparative floorplan analysis of 80 therapy clusters with linear particle accelerators in different German radiotherapy departments was conducted. The therapy clusters were analyzed by room formations to identify their relation, distance and arrangement towards each other. The analysis was inspecting differences and similarities in patterns of spatial relationship of the rooms.

The comparative analysis of floorplans shows a spectrum of built environment and room arrangements, which lead to typologies and planning requirements. Typologies and spatial characteristics of the therapy cluster were derived and visualized. Further research will be conducted by combining these typologies with workflow, individual travel paths, environment behavior and requirements of all user groups and expert knowledge. With this multilayered study, design recommendations for planning radiotherapy departments can be identified.

References

Abshire, D., & Lang, M. K. (2018). The Evolution of Radiation Therapy in Treating Cancer. *Seminars in Oncology Nursing, 34*(2), 151–157. https://doi.org/https://doi.org/10.1016/j.soncn.2018.03.006

Mahmood, F. J. (2021). The role of evidence-based design in informing health-care architects. *Journal of Facilities Management, 19*(2), 249–262. https://doi.org/10.1108/JFM-09-2020-0062

van der Voordt, T. J. M., Vrielink, D., & van Wegen, H. B. R. (1997). Comparative floorplan-analysis in programming and architectural design. *Design Studies, 18*(1), 67–88. https://doi.org/https://doi.org/10.1016/S0142-694X(96)00016-6

Utilization of Sustainable Placemaking: Fostering Spatial Conditions Based on Various User Behaviors in Urban Spaces

Zile Tian *(University of Tsukuba);* ***Naoko Fujita*** *(University of Tsukuba)*

Depopulation and urban decline are rapidly increasing due to a super-aged society. Financial and personnel restrictions are becoming problematic for the Japanese government. Urban spaces have also been affected by certain circumstances and issues such as aging facilities and spatial desolation, especially in the small cities of Japan. Therefore, strategic, and effective methods of utilization and management of urban spaces are required. However, for the purpose of revitalizing urban spaces by addressing its relationship with the people, it is important to make the users active entities by ensuring their cooperation and to understand their needs to revive and renew urban spaces by taking the help of previous research and projects. Thus, to reconsider the arrangement of an urban space, utilizing a method called "Placemaking" is required to stimulate the user-led setting making it more spontaneous and creative, to support diverse user behaviors and to flexibly meet their needs in urban spaces.

This research focused on Tsukuba Center Square and Tsukuba Central Park, two urban spaces in the central area of Tsukuba, a small city in Japan, and conducted field surveys and utilization analysis using a questionnaire to clarify the actual situation and problems on spatial conditions, utilization, and management of research sites. According to the results, this research probed sustainable methods of utilization and introduced an interaction called "hardware-software-orgware" which is especially important in the process of exploring the method of "Placemaking," improving spatial conditions, better management, simulations, and flexible utilization in the Tsukuba Center Square and Tsukuba Central Park. Furthermore, this research visualized user behaviors and sustainable methods of utilization through "Placemaking" by extracting design requirements and the specific method of "Placemaking" that fostered better spatial conditions and management for user behaviors in research sites.

Research results emphasized the importance of placemaking when solving problems found during analysis and clarified the specific methods of placemaking in the design proposal for urban spaces. The design proposal indicated the "hardware-software-orgware" interaction as the design methodology. The concept of "Multitasking" and "Movable Unit" was raised to simulate more diverse user behaviors and regenerate urban spaces. Moreover, placemaking was considered to make real communication and coexistence in the urban spaces.

Virtual Simulation of Trauma Rooms: Lessons Learned from an Augmented Reality Simulation Tool Development

Hamid Estejab *(Kent State University);* ***Sara Bayramzadeh*** *(Kent State University)*

Background: Simulations in healthcare settings facilitate effective communication between designers and end-users and are one of the cost-efficient ways to evaluate designs before construction. With emerging technologies such as augmented reality (AR), designers are able to employ more sophisticated approaches to simulation and complement the conventional physical mock-up simulations.

Objective: This study aims to develop and utilize an AR application for Hololens 2 to complement a full-scale, physical mock-up for simulation and evaluation of a trauma room design prototype.

Methods: This study is developed based on direct observation of the trauma room mock-up simulations. Clinicians, representing trauma room roles, participated in three different trauma scenarios. Given the low-fidelity construction of the mock-up, participants were unable to simulate some of the ley tasks. Examples include lack of ceiling-mounted objects such as medical boom, inability to move objects, and inability to accurately evaluate interactions with the physical environment. The AR application was refined based on two pilot testing sessions to address limitations. The two software used for developing the application were Unity3d and Autodesk 3DsMax for 3d modeling.

Results: To address the physical mock-up limitations, three main features were implemented in the application for further investigation. First, implementing eye-tracking feature with 3d heat map texture to study where the clinicians look during simulations to help designers avoid crowded and distracting designs. Second, developing and adding detailed 3d models of medical booms and other pivotal objects for the simulation that were not feasible to be built into the physical mock-up given the low-fidelity construction. Finally, the application features a replay system of objects' interactions with storing objects' information and video recording.

Future: The AR technology is new in its application in design fields. As such, designers are challenged in realizing the potential and ways to employ this technology in design evaluations. The AR technology can be extremely time- and cost-efficient when the design team intends to lower the costs for the physical mock-up construction.

Who Will Take Refuge in the Open Space of the University Campus? - Evacuation Sites for Diverse Populations

Yoshihiro Osawa *(Tokyo Denki University);* ***Chiaki Konishi*** *(Tokyo Denki University);* ***Yuka Honda*** *(Tokyo Denki University);* ***Hiroshi Tsuchida*** *(Tokyo Denki University)*

In areas such as Chiyoda Ward, Tokyo, where the difference between daytime and nighttime populations is large, strict evacuation plans are needed for employees and visitors other than residents. According to the disaster prevention plan of Chiyoda Ward, most transportation such as railways will be suspended in the event of a seismic intensity of 5 upper. Therefore, when a large-scale earthquake occurs, it is estimated that about 500,000 people will be stranded from the daytime population of about 850,000 announced by the ward. In Japan, it is basic to use an open space such as a park or a square as a temporary evacuation place at the time of a disaster. In Chiyoda Ward, large parks and plazas are designated as evacuation sites, but because of the large daytime population, it is necessary to consider designating other vacant areas as evacuation sites. Therefore, we focused on the campus of a university with a large site. The purpose of this study is to investigate the possibility of the open space of the university campus in Chiyoda Ward as an evacuation place.

Chiyoda Ward has a large number of employees and visitors, and there are few residents, so the difference between the daytime population and the nighttime population is large. According to the census in 27, the daytime population was 853,068 and the nighttime population was 58,406, a difference of 794,662. A comparison of the total floor space of buildings in Chiyoda Ward shows that there are many commercial and public facilities. As a result, many people are thought to flow during the daytime.

Looking at the agreement between the university and the ward, we can see that they are proceeding with the following.

1. Development of Student Volunteers.
2. Provision of temporary facilities to local residents and disaster victims such as stranded people.
3. Provision of stockpiled supplies to disaster victims housed in university facilities.

Comparing the building-to-land ratio of university campuses with that of surrounding urban areas, we found that Sophia University, Hosei University and Senshu University have lower building-to-land ratios than surrounding urban areas, while Otsuma Women's University, Meiji University and Kyoritsu Women's University have higher building-to-land ratios than surrounding urban areas. The open spaces of Sophia University, Hosei University, and Senshu University are larger than those of surrounding urban areas, and there is a possibility that they can be used as evacuation sites in the event of a disaster. In addition, Otsuma Women's University, Meiji University and Kyoritsu Women's University may use it in the building.

References

Architectural Institute of Japan : Creating a Campus Like a Town, While Using The Town Like a Campus -Campus Design for Regeneration of University-, *Architectural Institute of Japan*, pp.78-83, 2020.2 (in Japanese)

Moe Wakabayashi, Hiroshi Tsuchida, Chiaki Konishi and Hiroki Saito. : Study on Space and Elements that Symbolize University Campuses, *Summaries of Technical Papers of Annual Meeting, Architectural Institute of Japan, Urban Planning*, pp.255-258, 2020.9 (in Japanese)

Shigo Yanagihori, Hiroshi Tsuchida: Study on space construction and openspace in campus, *EDRA47 Raleigh, Display Poster Presentations*, 2016.5

Appendix A: Posters

Adaptation of New Agricultural Activities Due to COVID-19

Yuling Liu, Minghui Tang & Naoko Fujita, University of Tsukuba

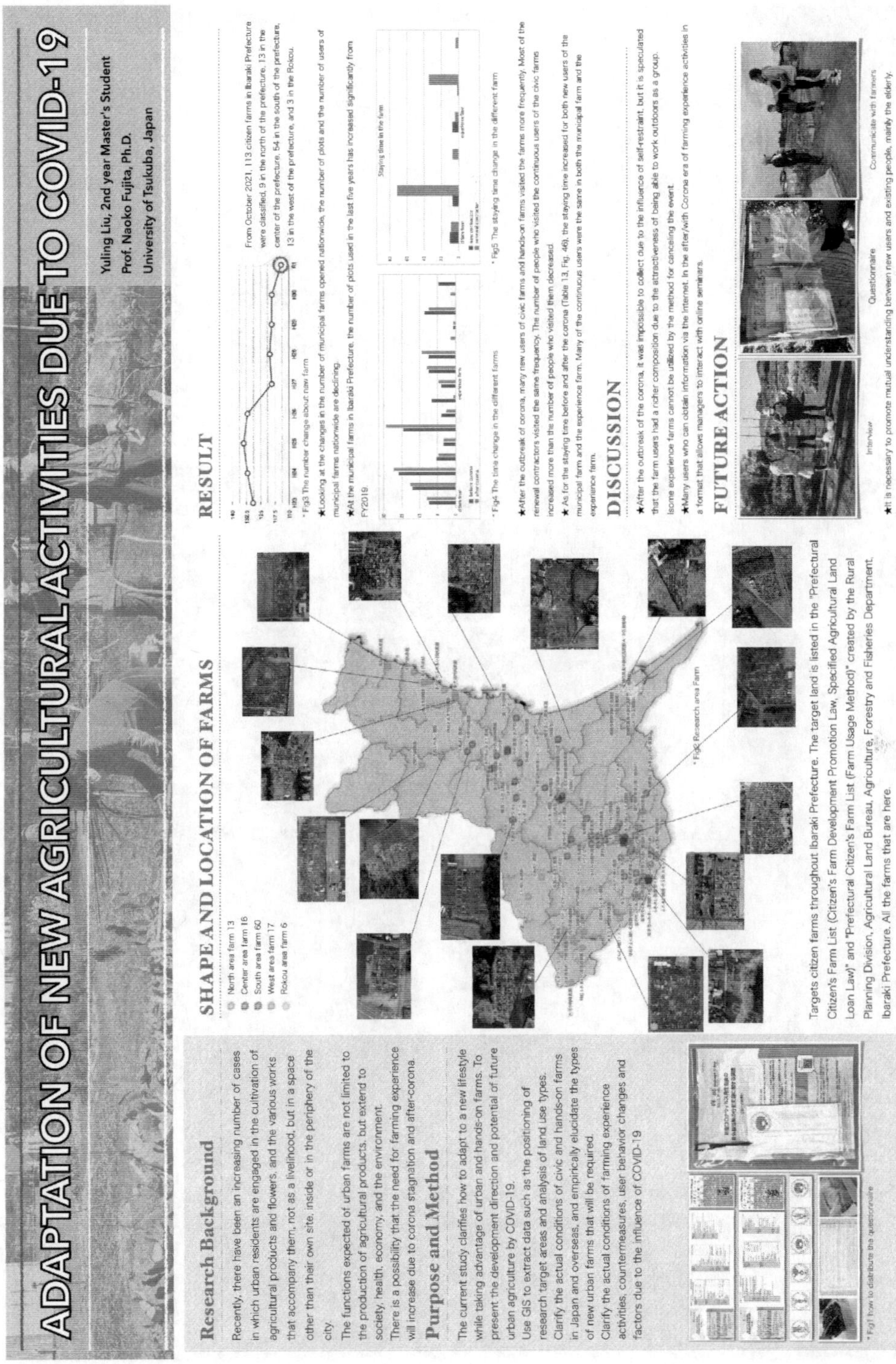

Aging Simulation to Build Learning and Empathy Among Interior Design Students

Erica L. Elsey & Gabriela Fonseca Pereira, Illinois State University

GERT Simulation to Strengthen the Knowledge and Empathy of Interior Design Students

Erica Elsey (she/her/hers)
Interior Design Student, Illinois State University

Dr. Gabriela Fonseca Pereira (she/her/hers)
Assistant Professor, Interior Design, Illinois State University

BACKGROUND

The GERT suit is a series of components that simulate the aging experience, aiming to help people empathize and gain insight into the needs of the aging population. It simulates changes in eyesight, hearing loss, mobility restrictions, stiffness, and loss of strength (Moll, n.d.; Yumuşak, 2019).

PURPOSE

In the Interior Design Program, students theoretically learn about the aging process and how to address the needs of older adults. However, there is an age gap of at least 40 years between most college students and their target clients.

This study is aimed at understanding what students experience while wearing the GERT suit and if it has made them more understanding of the design needs of the aging process.

RESEARCH QUESTION

How does wearing a GERT suit influence students' learning about the aging process and applying design solutions for the aging population?

METHODS

22 students wore the GERT suit and completed five tasks (Figures 1 and 2):

1) Go up and down a flight of stairs (Figure 3)
2) Sit down and get up from a seat (Figure 4)
3) Enter and exit a bathroom and stall (Figure 5)
4) Get directions from someone in the hallway
5) Use a wheelchair to leave and return to the classroom (Figure 6)

After finishing, students were given questions to answer based on how they felt physically and mentally during the simulation (Johnson et al., 2018).

By doing content analysis, emerging themes were identified based on students' common experiences and feelings.

Figure 1. GERT front view

Figure 2. GERT side view

Figure 3. Students going up a flight of stairs

Figure 4. Student performing a sit to stand position

Figure 5. Student using a bathroom stall

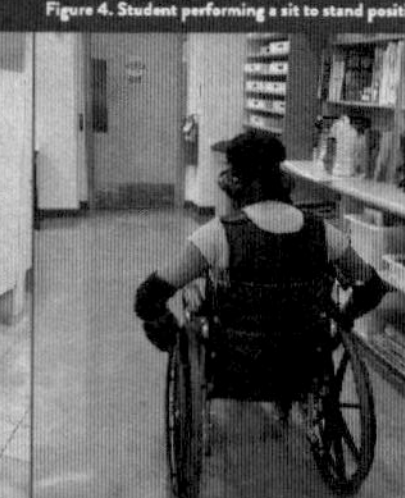
Figure 6. Student using a wheelchair

RESULTS

Students frequently experienced changes with hearing loss, eyesight, and coordination. Words that appeared frequently in responses were 'Tired' and 'Uncomfortable'.

The majority also felt that it was difficult to complete their tasks safely and felt self-conscious walking through the building.

Students empathized with the aging population and reflected that this activity would have been more difficult with any cognitive impairments.

Additonally, they felt that this simulation would make them more aware of older adults' needs when designing different spaces in the future.

CONCLUSION

From this activity, students were able to experience some of the changes that come with age and gained a better understanding of the experiences and needs of the aging population.

By experiencing some of the difficulties that arise with the aging process, students understand the diverse range of needs that must be considered during the design process which can help guide future decisions.

REFERENCES

Johnson, C. E., Jilla, A. M., & Danhauer, J. L. (2018). Didactic content and experiential aging simulation for developing patient-centered strategies and empathy for older adults. *Seminars in Hearing* 39(01), 74–08. doi: 10.1055/s-0037-1613707

Moll, W. (n.d.). Produkt + Projekt. Retrieved October 26, 2021 from https://www.produktundprojekt.de/

Yumuşak, I. (2019, May). Influence of simulated physical ageing on heuristic evaluation in airport enviroments [Doctoral dissertation, Bilkent University]. http://repository.bilkent.edu.tr/handle/11693/51459

Amman Alternative Futures: The Pulse of Current and Future Jordanian Municipal Growth & Resilience of Place and People

Rula Awwad-Rafferty, Daniel Cronan, & Hala Barakat, University of Idaho

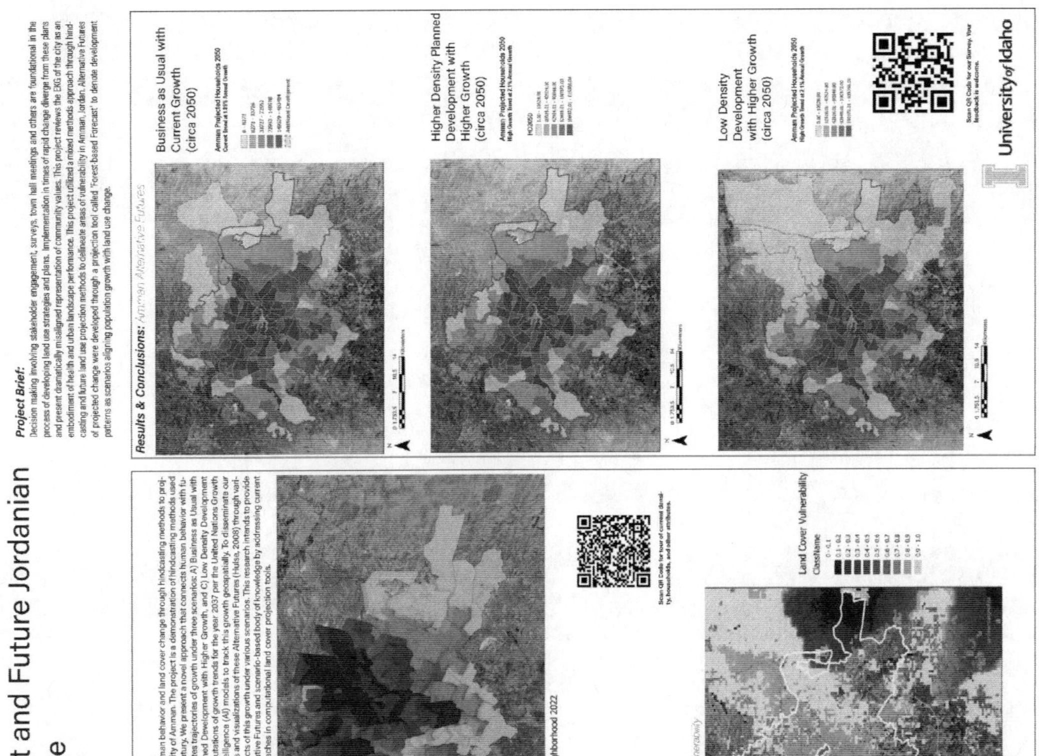

An Analysis of Accessibility of Privately Owned Indoor Public Space for Publicness: Office Buildings in Seoul

SooMin Yoon, YeaEun Park, & Yeonsook Hwang, Hanyang University

Ⅰ. Introduction

Overcrowding of office buildings in today's cities has created private spaces excessively within the cities, degrading their publicness. In response, Korea introduced privately owned indoor public space (Indoor POPS) centered on Seoul. The Indoor POPS increases the usability of public space, so accessibility to Indoor POPS should be increased. The accessibility enables users to reach public spaces and this role is achieved by following factors: how buildings are open visually and physically, how buildings are connected with entrances or transportation facilities, and how buildings assign interior circulation and living facilities. These factors decide the publicness of buildings and make Indoor POPS to be used for more people. That is why the accessibility is critical to acquiring the urban publicness. This study analyzes the characteristics and planning elements of Indoor POPS with respect to accessibility and proposes measures to promote the publicness.

Ⅱ. Method of Research

This study is concentrated on literature review-the concept of indoor POPS and the element of accessibility with respect to publicness- and field investigation. The regional scope is Jongro, Gangnam, and Yeouido, with a high concentration of offices in Seoul. The spatial scope is office buildings with a total floor area of 100,000㎡ or more, and the temporal scope is buildings built since 2011. Based on these, the following five cases are selected: D-Tower, Centropolis, IFC seoul, Pine Avenue and Parnas.

Ⅲ. Literature Review & Checklist

The accessibility refers to the ease of access without physical and visual obstacles to a particular environment, the nature of the environment that supports it, or the connection with other spaces. Through this accessibility, it is possible for the user to reach the public space and enjoy the public functions that buildings perform. Therefore, for the high publicness of urban space, it is important to increase the accessibility of "the privately owned indoor public space". The following checklist is about analysis of the accessibility: visual accessibility, external accessibility, and internal accessibility.

Accessibility	Features	
Visual Accessibility	V1	Installation of information sign and information on each floor and facility
	V2	Not blocked by obstacles or fence
External Accessibility	E1	Number and location(front, side, rear) of entrance
	E2	Types of transportation facilities (subway station, bus station, ground and underground passage, crosswalk etc.) and distance
Internal Accessibility	I1	Types and layout of vertical circulation(stairs, escalator, elevator etc.)
	I2	Division of circulation and floor according to the purpose of use of internal facilities

Ⅳ. Case Analysis

A : D-Tower

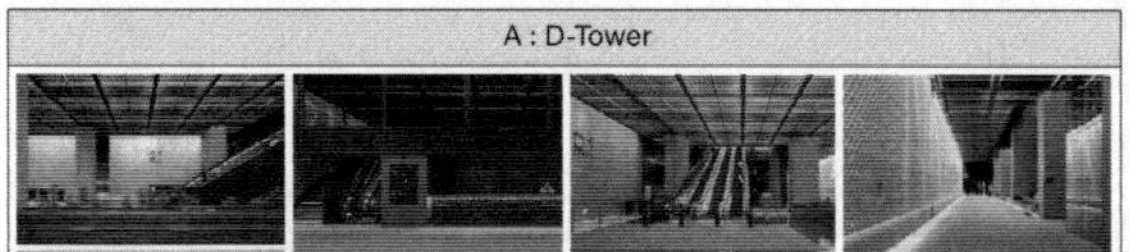

Site	17, Jong-ro 3-gil, Jongno-gu, Seoul, Korea
Total Floor Area	105,450m²

Visual Accessibility In this case, the visual accessibility is higher because of the information signs and open transparent facade. The facility information signs are installed outside and inside the building, and the signs involved amenities information per floor. Moreover, Easy access as the entrance is open without fences or obstacles, but also, whole facade is transparent, so it is easy to perceive the inside of the building.
External Accessibility There is one entrance at the front and two at the side. Each entrance is adjacent to the sidewalk so that it makes a natural connection between the buildings and pedestrian. The transportation facilities are located a minute's walk away, as the closest bus stop is 198 m from the D-Tower, and the closest subway station is 205 m away. However, there is no direct connection to the underground passage.
Internal Accessibility A large vertical void characterizes it, as the 1st-5th floors are open without a ceiling. Accordingly, a straight line was formed with the escalator in the center of the 1st-5th floors. From the first basement floor, facilities are classified by floor depending on the purpose of the space, such as the lobby, food and beverage space, and exhibition space.

B : Centropolis

Site	17, Jong-ro 3-gil, Jongno-gu, Seoul, Korea
Total Floor Area	141,475m²

Visual Accessibility This case has high-level accessibility physically through eight guide signs for the facilities and floor which are installed at each entrance. Also, it has high visual accessibility as there are no fences or obstacles in the entrance or inside. So, people can perceive the inside on the sidewalk and people who are inside the building can observe the outside at the same time.
External Accessibility Some entrances are conveniently connected to the outside by an escalator. There are six entrances: two at the front, tow at the side, and two at the rear. The shortest distance from the nearest subway station is about 70 m, and the bus stop is 5 m. There is no underground passage, and it has outside escalators which connect the inside and outside, ground access is easier than other cases.
Internal Accessibility The basement and the first floor are connected by escalators and central stairs. The first basement floor is used as an exhibition hall, restaurants occupy the second basement floor, and the first floor is used as a rest area, lobby, and passage. Therefore, routes and floors are divided depending on the facility's purpose.

C : IFC Tower

Site	Gukjegeumyung-ro, Yeongdeungpo-gu, Seoul, Korea
Total Floor Area	505,236m²

Visual Accessibility This case provides all amenities and facilities by installing the information signs at the side and the interior of the building. Also, no fences or barriers obstruct access to the facilities, and floor-to-ceiling windows increase visual accessibility.
External Accessibility The IFC Tower has the highest entry accessibility. There are nine entrances: three at the front, three at the side, two at the IFC Mall, and one underground passage, enhancing access to a large building area. Also, this building has the most pleasant underground passage. The shortest distance from the nearest subway station is about 411 m, a 7 minute walk and a 2 minute walk to the bus stop. It is connected to Yeouido Station Exit 3 and an underground passage to complement the long walking distance.
Internal Accessibility The floor height is elevated, and in the case of the IFC Mall, it is in the form of a galleria with four continuous floors, connected by open stairs and escalators in a vertical line. The basement is connected to the shopping center, and the first floor is a restaurant, convenience store, and café. Facilities such as business facilities and conventions are operated on the 2nd floor, and above, and facilities are separated by floor.

D : Pine Avenue

Site	100, Eulji-ro, Jung-gu, Seoul, Korea
Total Floor Area	129,999m²

Visual Accessibility In this case, the information signs are installed outside the basement entrance and on the lobby wall. And this signs has systematical structure, so it is useful to get sufficient information about indoor facilities by floor. Moreover, no fences or barriers obstruct access, and floor-to-ceiling windows increase visual accessibility.
External Accessibility This case has an appropriate number of entrances: three at the front, two at the side, one at the rear, and one in the basement. In addition, it has the highest connection between transportation facilities. It is connected to Exit 12 of Euljiro 3-ga Station, a bus stop, an underground passage, and a crosswalk within a 1-minute walk.
Internal Accessibility There is a central, wide-open space, and the passage runs along the wall. Accordingly, facilities are distributed on each floor and connected by elevators and emergency stairs. As the facilities are arranged along the wall passage, the route is long, and the facilities are not separated by floor.

E : PARNAS

Site	Teheran-ro, Gangnam-gu, Seoul, Korea
Total Floor Area	219,385m²

Visual Accessibility The Parnas has the lowest visual accessibility on account of insufficient information signs. The information signs are installed next to elevators. However, this case lacks signs compared to the total floor scale. On the other hand, it has large scale void and has no obstacles or pillars that block our view so that it is easy to visually access to indoor space.
External Accessibility There are sufficient six entrances: two at the front, two at the side, one at the rear, and one in the basement. Four entrances are adjacent to the sidewalk, and accessibility is high when walking. The shortest distance to the nearest subway station is about 40 m, and the bus stop is 63 m. You can access it within a minute on foot, and it is accessible via an underground passage connected to the subway station.
Internal Accessibility It is mainly accessed by a closed elevator instead of open moving facility. The basement is a shopping space centered on the first floor, and the ground is divided into business facilities. The Parnas has a central elevator and grid type passage structure, facilities are arranged along the wall, and the routes are separated.

Ⅴ. Conclusion

This study analyzes the findings with respect to visual perception, phisical access from outside, and movement between indoor facilities. Regarding visual perception, the majority of information signs outside indicates the brand names of retail and lacked of floor-wise information. Since the density of office buildings in Seoul makes the streets complex, it is difficult for pedestrians to access to indoor facilities without information acquisition from the outside. Hence, outside signs should provide systematically composed information. Regarding physical access from outside, to solve the density of population in Seoul, degree of connection between subway stations, bus stops, and crosswalks is high. The distance between main entrances and transportation facilities is within a walk of 1 to 3 minutes. In three cases, since entrances are connected to subways through underground passage, it is easy to access from underground. However, in some cases, the side entrances are located in an alley and difficult to spot. Because the concentration of adjacent buildings makes the width of the sidewalks narrow. Therefore, entrances should be located near wide sidewalks, so that it is easier to access while walking from outside. Regarding movement between indoor facilities; the open structure of indoor POPS and the arrangement of facilities according to the type increase publicness. Office buildings in Korea are high-rise, so the indoor POPS has large vertical spaces. However, when it has seperate floors depending on facility types, the circulation is lengthened since a person must move to different floors to use a particular facility. Furthermore, some cases have closed ceilings, making it impossible to gain visual perception of each floor and, thus, diminishing accessibility. To solve these problems, vertical circulation such as open staircases and escalators can be used, so that it can visually and physically connect each floor and improve accessibility.

An Ecological Farm Design Incorporating the Natural Cycle to Create Agricultural Experiences for Disabled Individuals

Ding Ma & Naoko Fujita, University of Tsukuba

Analysis of Publicness Evaluation Indicators and Users' Perceptions to Improve Urban Publicness

GyeongYeon Lee, Ji Eun Oh, Soohyun Lee, MiKyoung Ha, & Gidong Byun, Yonsei University

Analysis of Publicness Evaluation Indicators and Users' Perceptions to Improve Urban Publicness

GyeongYeon Lee, JiEun OH, Soohyun Lee, MiKyoung Ha and Gidong Byun
Dept. Interior Architecture & Built Environment, Yonsei University, Seoul, Korea

Introduction

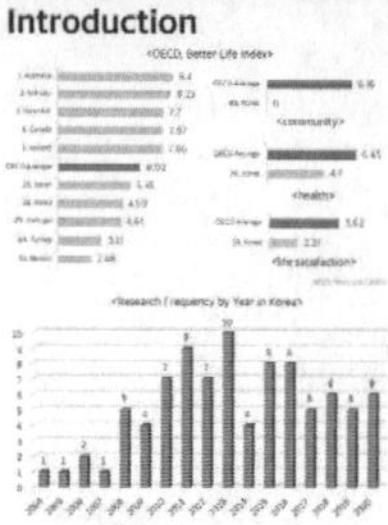

In modern society, **quality of life and publicness have a deep relationship.** Measures of social development are shifting from GDP to **"healthy life"** and **"sustainability,"** with various international organizations diagnosing the quality of life of social environment and social members and areas of improvement. According to various indicators, Korea's international level is the lowest in the world, far below its economic level. Accordingly, **in Korea, social and environmental well-being is emphasized beyond individuals,** recognizing the importance of maintaining a community to solve healthy lives and social problems of social members.

Accordingly, in Korea, 'strengthening social responsibility' is being emphasized to improve the quality of life of the people and solve social problems. In particular, **the demand for "strengthening publicness" for the physical environment,** which is the basic living environment of humans, is increasing. In response, active research is being conducted to realize the public value pursued by members of society beyond the traditional public concept in the field of architecture space, but it is still focusing on the function and building behavior of physical space rather than a user-centered approach (Lee et al., 2021). **For publicness to positively affect our lives, users' empathy and social consensus are needed.**

The purpose of this study is **to grasp users' perceptions of public spaces** in order to realize social functions (communication, etc.) and emotional functions (stress relief, etc.) of public spaces, which account for a large part of the urban living environment.

Purpose

The purpose of this study is to **establish a standard for evaluating the publicness** of each space in the range of the most basic public spaces constituting the city to realize an urban environment that provides **comfortable rest and positive experiences for urban residents.**

Method

■Literature Analysis

• The dictionary meaning of publicness is related to the entire members of society, and refers to common sense standards or standards that ordinary people think are right without harming the interests of most people.

• The concept of publicity in architecture and urban space is stipulated in *the Framework Act on Building.*

• Specifically, it refers to **the Living Spatial Publicness of Architecture** for a safe and healthy daily living space, **the Social Publicness of Architecture** for the fidelity of social assets, and **the Cultural Publicness of Architecture** for respecting culture and locality.

** Framework Act on Building was enacted on December 21, 2007, to improve the health and welfare of the people through the promotion of architectural culture.*

■Survey

Purpose		
To find out the general characteristics of survey participants, the behavior of using public spaces, and the importance of factors and elements of public spaces.	Subject	Ordinary people over 19 years old, Korea
	Period	February 16th ~ 21st, 2022
	Questionnaire	The importance of the publicness factors and elements.

Research Process

Step 1 — *Selection of advanced indicators*
- **The selection of papers through keywords**
  : "publicness," "public architecture," and "public space."
- **Review the title and abstract**
- **Content analysis**
  : Environmental indicators (Classification/Evaluation factors/Detailed factors)

Step 2 — *Integration and Removal of item*
- **Removing ought-to-be items** (72 items → 54 items)
  : Exclusion of terms whose concept is unclear or broad.
- **Integrating similar items** (integrated into 15 items)
- **Extract key factors** (7 factors in total)
  : Selection of factors with a frequency of 10 or more. Including sustainability in terms of timeliness. Exclusion of aesthetics, which is a subjective evaluation criterion.

Step 3 — *Classification & Scope of Pubilness factors*

Publicness factors can be largely divided into spatial and program perspectives. After spatial-centered factor extraction, the range of each factor was set in terms of urban and architectural (external/internal).

Step 4 — *Checklist by Pubilness factors*
- ACC: Public Transportation(4)/Parking(3)/Walkway(3) / Pedestrian-centered(3) / Diversification(3)
- CONN: Visual(3) / Functional(3) /Spatial(3)
- OPN: Interior(3) / Exterior(3) / Transparency(4)
- AME: Facilities(3) / Natural(4) / Indoor Environment(4)
- CONV: Diversification(4)/Operating(3)/User-centered(4)
- SOP: Local Identity(3) / Visual Symbolism(3)
- SUS: Space Utilization(3) / Eco-friendly(4)

Step 5 — *User perception survey & analysis*
- **User perception survey**
  : A survey of the public's perception of publicness evaluation indicators.
- **Statistical analysis**
  : Determining the importance of each factor and the priority of indicators.

Research Tool

Accerssibility (ACC)
- Accessibility from Public Transportation
  1. Location and distance of the subway station
  2. The number of subway stations
  3. Location and distance of the bus stop
  4. The number of bus stops
- Accessibility from Parking Facilities
  5. Securing parking facilities on the site
  6. Location and distance of the public parking lot
  7. The number of parking in a public parking lot
- Accessibility from the Walkway
  8. The number of walkways accessible
  9. The separation of Vehicle lanes and Sidewalks
  10. Width of accessible walkways
- Pedestrian-centered Accessibility
  11. Securing personal mobility facilities
  12. Facilities for Weak Pedestrians
  13. Pedestrian Guidance facilities
- Diversification of access routes
  14. Various connection paths
  15. The number of entrances
  16. Location of entrance

Connectivity (CONN)
- Visual Connectivity
  1. Similarity of form to surrounding facilities
  2. Finishing materials similar to the surrounding facilities
  3. Integrated Design of Street Public Facilities
- Functional Connectivity
  4. Adjacent between similar facilities
  5. Connection of Interior Space by Type
  6. Provide convenient space for residents
- Spatial Connectivity
  7. Link with residents' activities
  8. Connection of movements with surrounding public spaces
  9. Internal circulation system

Openness (OPN)
- Interior Space Openness
  1. Vertical Openness of Interior Space (atrium, top open ect.)
  2. High ceilings by floor
  3. Vertical Design
- Exterior Space Openness
  4. Securing Visibility from the Sidewalk to the Entrance
  5. Securing open space on the lower floor
  6. Adjacent arrangements between outer open spaces
- Visual Transparency
  7. Blockage Ratio of Indoor Space
  8. Blockage Ratio of outdoor Space
  9. Use transparent exterior materials
  10. Use interior materials with high reflectivity

Amenity (AME)
- Comfort through Facilities
  1. Various open space plans
  2. Installation of environmental sculptures
  3. Various amenity plans
- Comfort through Natural Elements
  4. Rich landscapes
  5. Indoor and outdoor water space
  6. Indoor Daylight
  7. Use eco-friendly materials
- The Comfort of the Indoor Environment
  8. Smooth ventilation
  9. Proper temperature and humidity
  10. Adequate indoor illumination
  11. Adequate noise

Convenience (CONV)
- Diversification of facilities
  1. Various Rest facilities
  2. Various Sanitation facilities
  3. Various Information facilities (information desk, media board ets.)
  4. Various Support facilities
- Reinforcement of user-centeredness
  5. Reservation & Visit System
  6. Spatial Planning Considering the Socially Disadvantaged Groups(SDG)
  7. Program Plan Considering the SDG
  8. Support for Community Activities
- Convenience of the operating system
  9. Facilities sharing with surrounding areas
  10. Disclosure of information related to facility operation
  11. Establishing a user management system

Sense of Place (SOP)
- Local Identity
  1. Composition programs suited to regional characteristics
  2. Resource Conservation and Management of the region
  3. Consider regional identity and theme
- Visual Symbolism
  4. Exterior Design Considering Urban Context
  5. A sculpture that symbolizes the region
  6. Forming a SOP Through Design

Sustainability (SUS)
- Space Utilization
  1. Utilization of idle space
  2. Configuring Expandable Space
  3. Organize efficient space utilization programs
- Eco-friendly
  4. Harmony between nature and artificiality
  5. Planning Considering Energy Efficiency
  6. Use of alternative energy

• ACC: Accessing the ENV(environment) without physical or visual obstacles.
• CONN: Two or more spaces with similar functions and uses have physical and visual associations.
• OPN: Eexpand the area of activity through omission of part of the ENV or visual transparency.
• AME: Satisfy human physical and mental needs in a positive direction by the ENV.
• CONV: Enable users to efficiently achieve a given goal through physical CONV within a given ENV.
• SOP: Distinguished from other places in consideration of the specificity of the region and place, historical and socio-cultural contexts.

Result

Looking at the importance of the seven publicness factors, 'SUS(3.98)', 'CONV(3.95)', 'ACC(3.93)', 'AME(3.76)', 'CONN(3.72)', 'SOP(3.69)', and 'OPN(3.44)' appeared in order.. Next, looking at the importance of the detailed factors of publicity, **'Accessibility from Parking Facilities(4.12)' was the highest,** followed by **'Eco-friendly(4.02),' 'Pedestrian-centered Accessibility(3.99),' 'comfort of indoor environment(3.99)' and 'diversification of facilities(3.99).'** The top five items were found to have an accessibility factor(2 items), convenience factor(1 item), comfort factor(1 item), and sustainability factor(1 item). Finally, the importance of each detailed element was examined. **The top 10 were 'AME-8(4.21)', 'SUS-5(4.16)', 'ACC-12(4.15)', 'AME-9(4.15)', 'CONV-2(4.15)', 'ACC-7(4.14)', 'ACC-5(4.13)', 'CONV-6(4.10)', 'ACC-6(4.09)', 'SUS-3(4.05)'.** It belongs to ' ACC(4 items),' 'AME(1 item)', 'CONV(1 item),' and 'SUS(1 item).' Through this, it can be seen that ACC components are relatively important. **In order to improve the publicness of public spaces, 'ACC,' 'SUS,' 'AME,' and 'CONV' should be strengthened, and among them, 'Accessibility' and 'Sustainability' need to be considered first.**

Conclusion

This study derived the criteria for evaluating the publicity of public spaces and investigated the perceptions of users, to improve the publicness of public spaces.

Users recognize that all seven factors have an important influence on improving publicness, and among them, **'Accessibility' and 'Sustainability' are important.** To improve the publicnsess of urban public spaces, **both vehicle and pedestrian access should be strengthened, and efforts should be made to harmonize with nature,** such as the use of alternative energy and eco-friendly materials.

If these measures are applied first, **the physical and emotional needs of urban residents staying in public spaces will be positively satisfied,** social values will be realized through community recovery, and the quality of life will be improved naturally and a healthy society.

■ Figure

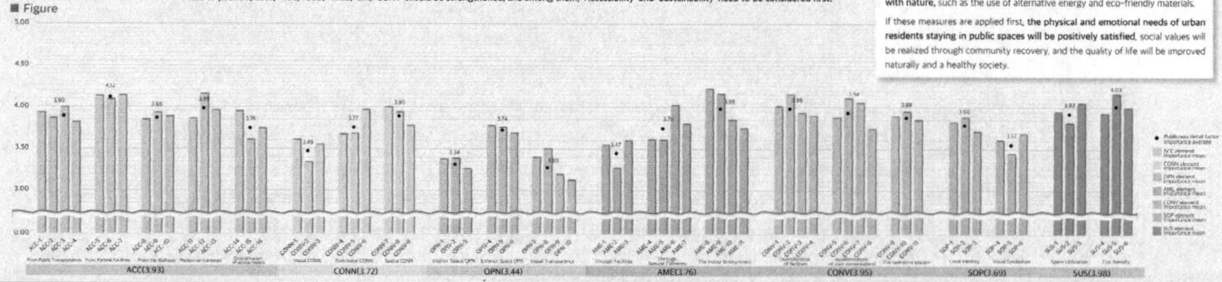

This research was supported by BK21 FOUR and the 2020 Korean Ministry of Education and the National Research Foundation of Korea(NRF) support project for up-and-coming researchers in the humanities and social fields (NRF-2020S1A5A8042212)

Analysis of Social Fear Influencing Factors for Creating a Safe Environment: Focus on the Young Women's Group

Ji Eun Oh, GyeongYeon Lee, Soohyun Lee, Gidong Byun, & MiKyoung Ha, Yonsei University

Analysis of vulnerability and cognitive tendency according to social fear for the psychological safety of the community

Jieun Oh, Gyeongyeon Lee, Soohyun Lee, Gidong Byun, Mikyoung, Ha
Dept. Interior Architecture & Built Environment, Yonsei University, Seoul, Korea

INTRODUCTION

When asked if our society is safe and if we feel safe in society, no one will be able to easily say yes. In the 21st century, society is experiencing rapid and multifaceted changes that have never been experienced before, such as rapid change, growth, development of advanced technology in the process of knowledge informatization, confusion in values, diversification of social crimes, and increase in frequency. In particular, our reality is that the prolonged COVID-19 outbreak in Wuhan, China in January 2019 is leading to unpredictable times, with a large population facing illness and death around the world, adding to anxiety over the virus. As a result, 40.7% of all Koreans said they experienced "COVID Blue." COVID-19 refers to depression or anxiety experienced by infection anxiety and heavy social atmosphere after the COVID-19 incident, with women (50.7%) having ahigher experience rate of COVID Blue than men (34.2%) (Korea Health Promotion Agency, 2020). In addition, according to the "2020 Gender Statistics in Korea" published by the Seoul Metropolitan Government, 39.9% of the total population living in Korea had anxiety from society and did not feel psychologically safe. It was found that 33.8% for men and 45.7% for women correspond to this. As such, the degree of anxiety in the society we live in is steadily increasing regardless of improving the quality of life of the people, and direct and indirect experiences of events and accidents across the world and society affect various members of society.

PURPOSE

The purpose of this study is to propose a strategy to efficiently reduce social fear in the community. To this end, we will limit the spatial scope to a specific distance in Sinchon-dong, Seodaemun-gu, Seoul, and analyze the differences in factors that each person feels social anxiety and fear to find out how people tend to perceive 'disorder' and 'social control' of the surrounding environment.

Research Subject

Adult women in their 20s and 30s who live in Seodaemun-gu or visit frequently (With a focus on the young women's group).

Women are a gender group with a higher social fear on average than men, and the fear of adolescents and adults is likely to show different patterns, so the subjects of the study were limited to adults aged 19 or older. A total of 40 women participated in this study, including 25 in their 20s and 15 in their 30s. These are composed mainly of women who currently live in Sinchon-dong, Seoul or frequently visit Sinchon.

Research Methods

1. The relevant literature was reviewed and Questionnnaire tool was prepared.
2. Through the recruitment announcement of survey respondents, 40 women who expressed their intention to participate were secured, and a survey was conducted on them.
3. The analysis was conducted using IBM SPSS.

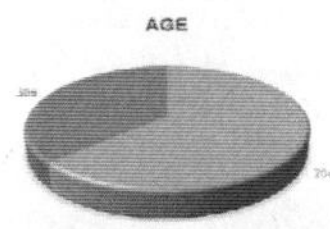

SURVEY

A total of 40 questionnaires were used to investigate women's general perceptions of disorder and social control. Disorder was composed of Management, Dirty, Obscure, and Illuminance centering on physical disorder (P.D.), and social control items were composed of Movilization, Help, and Degree of risk.

Questionnaire survey items

Model	Item	Question
Disorder model	Management	It was poorly managed
	Dirty	It was dirty
	Obscure	There were a lot of backwater
	Illuminance	It was dark
Social Control model	Mobilization	If people report a crime, the police are likely to be called in immediately
	Help	It looks like people will help if someone is being bullied/assaulted
	Degree of risk	What do you think is the risk of feeling afraid if you walk alone on this sidewalk?

Daytime evaluation of pedestrian paths

Nighttime evaluation of pedestrian paths

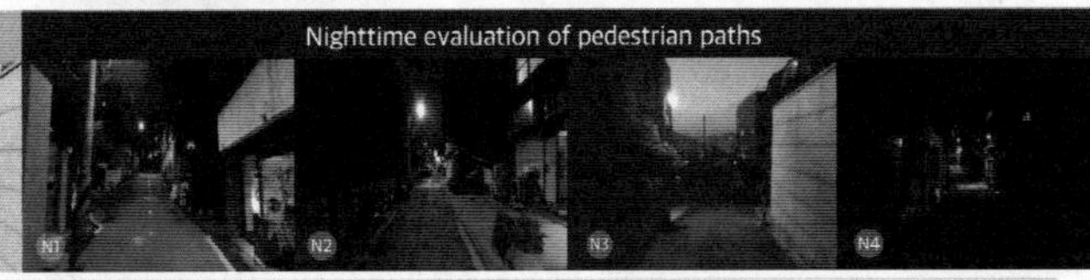

Disorder and Social control Factors

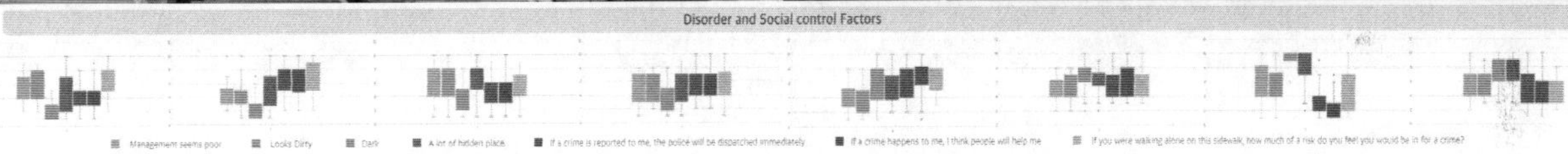

In the video you wached, Which of the following items makes you feel that the walkway is safety?

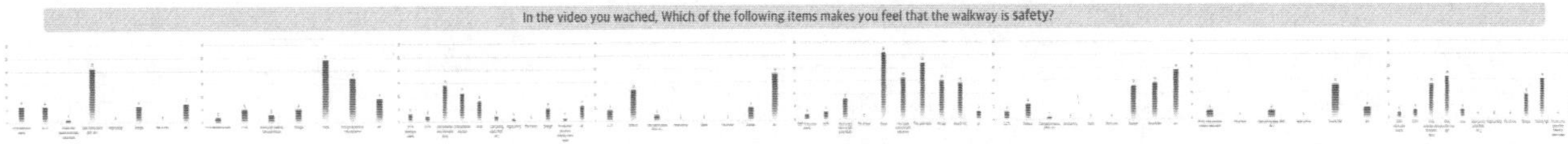

Which of the following items makes you feel afraid of walking paths in the video you wached?

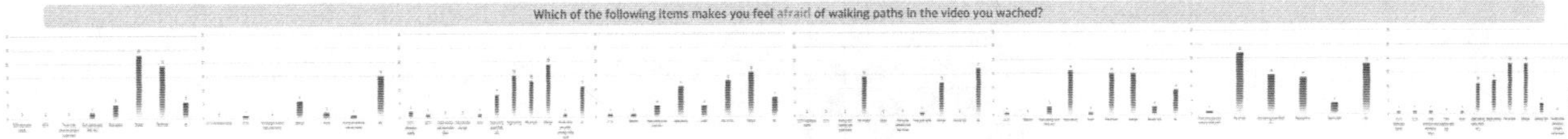

RESULT

Disorder and Social control Factors

	Management seems fool	Looks Dirty	Dark	Hidden place	If a crime is reported to me, the police will be dispatched immediately	If a crime happens to me, I think people will help me	If you were walking alone on this sidewalk, how much of a risk do you feel you would be in for a crime?
D1	5.6	5.9	1.9	4.8	4.1	4.2	6.7
D2	4.1	4	2.3	4.7	6.5	6.3	6.8
D3	6.2	6.1	3.7	6.3	4.4	4.6	5.6
D4	5	5.1	3.3	4.8	5.5	5.7	5.9
N1	3.9	4	5.3	5.2	6.4	7	6.7
N2	4.9	5.5	6.6	6.1	5.7	6.3	5.7
N3	6.4	5.7	3.6	8.1	3.3	3.5	4.3
N4	5.8	5.6	7	4.9	5	4.3	4.6

N3 N3 District 3 had the most negative evaluation of street conditions both during the day and at night. Therefore, the women felt the greatest fear when passing through the third street.

N1 N3 In Day 1 and Night 3, people rated that they would be able to get the most help from the police, citizens, or someone in case of difficulties. But paradoxically, people felt the greatest risk of committing a crime on these two streets.

Which of the items makes you feel afraid of walking path?

D1	Stranger, pile of trash	N1	Etc, pile of trash
D2	Etc, Stranger	N2	[illegible], Stranger, pile of trash
D3	Stranger > pile of trash	N3	Stranger > pile of trash
D4	Stranger > pile of trash	N4	Stranger > pile of trash

Which of the items makes you feel that the walkway is safety?

D1	Stranger, pile of trash	N1	Etc, pile of trash
D2	Etc, Stranger	N2	[illegible], Stranger, pile of trash
D3	Stranger > pile of trash	N3	Stranger > pile of trash
D4	Stranger > pile of trash	N4	Stranger > pile of trash

※ Top 2 items listed

RESULT

The purpose of this study was to confirm the adult women's perception of 'general fear of crime'. The survey was conducted by setting the Seodaemun-gu area as a spatial range, and the results of the analysis are as follows.

1. On Street 3, the women felt fear day and night.
The biggest factor in feeling fear here whas the high level of **Stranger and Pile of trash**
2. Paradoxically, it was rated as most likely to be helped by someone on the third street where they felt the most fear.
The reason was that there was a **signboard for the children's sanctuary**, and the **colorful houses** acted as a factor to feel safe.
3. Fear of **strangers** and passersby is the biggest fear factor for women, and they feel fear even on unorganized streets such as **pile of trash**. In particular, the fear of **darkness**, such as dark alleyways or dark spaces.
4. Factors that women felt safe were **open shops**, **lighted houses**, **security lights**, and **passing women**.
This makes women feel safe on bright streets and tend to feel safe from people of the same gender, even strangers.

Consequently, for a lively street, the street must be bright and the street must be well-groomed. In addition, it should be possible to recognize that the street is being managed by installing a signboard for the protected area.

[This work was supported by BK21 FOUR and the National Research Foundation of Korea(NRF) grant funded by the Korean Government (2020R1I1A1A01070900)]

Characteristics of Urban Areas Related to Natural Surveillance and Children's Sense of Safety: Focusing on Street Lights, Cctvs, and Spatial Configuration

Sojeong Lee, Wonjun No, Giyoung Byun, Lisa Lim, & Youngchul Kim, (KAIST); *Jae-Jun Park,* Mapo-gu Office

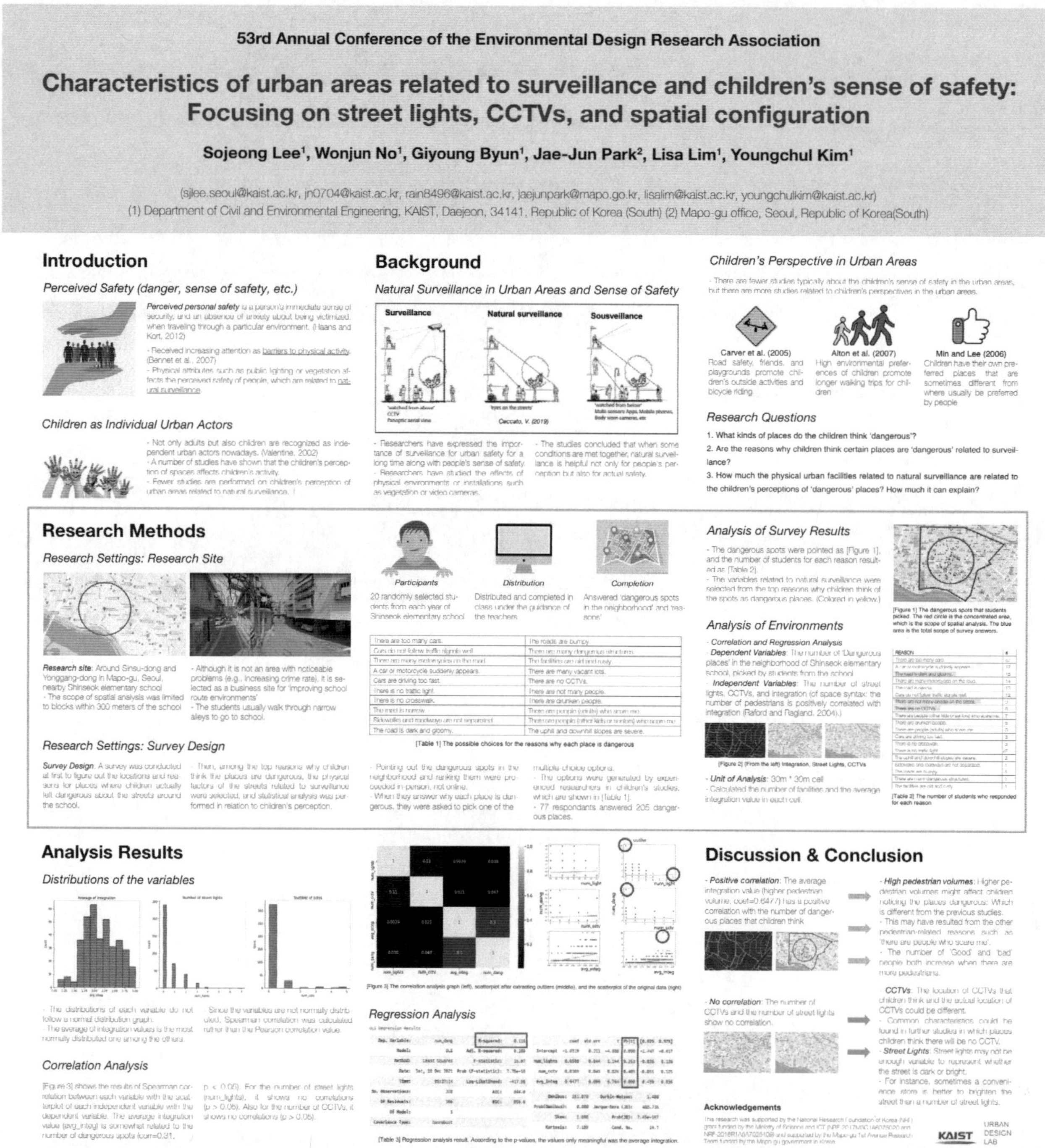

Combined Use of Natural Lighting, Artificial Lighting, and Curtains in Patient Wards

Zhe Wang & Yan Wang, Henan University

edra53 HOSTED BY CLEMSON HEALTH IN ALL DESIGN JUNE 01-04, 2022 GREENVILLE, SC

Combined Use of Natural Lighting, Artificial Lighting, and Curtains in Patient Wards

WANG Yan M. Design & WANG Zhe, Ph.D.Henan University

Background

Previous research indicates that natural light plays a positive role in patients' psychological and physiological healing. Full utilization of natural lighting generally reduces the demand for artificial lighting. Both natural lighting and artificial lighting are widely applied in patient wards. Adjusting the intensity of lighting, there are window curtains and privacy curtains between beds in the wards. To promote patient care, the combined use of natural lighting, artificial lighting, and the curtains in patient wards should be investigated.

Objective

Aim of this research is to identify the intensity of lighting in patient wards and the most popular behaviors using natural lighting, artificial lighting, and curtains there. The lighting environment in a patient ward is influenced by a variety of environmental and behavioral factors such as natural lighting artificial lighting, window curtain, and privacy curtain, etc.However, the reality of lighting environments in a ward is rarely researched.

Methods

The site of research is in a tertiary hospital in Central China. On the 8th and 9th floor of an inpatient building there, we measured the intensity of lighting in four south-facing patient wards. These wards had the same room plan and each of them was shared by three patients. Of the wards, two had larger window areas whereas the other two had their windows partly blocked by outdoor wali decorations. On-site measurements of the intensity of combined lighting in selected locations in these wards were collected in the morning, noon, and afternoon in two weekdays in summer 2020. The ways that people used the artificial lighting and curtains were observed and summarized. The differences in lighting intensity in these wards were identified.

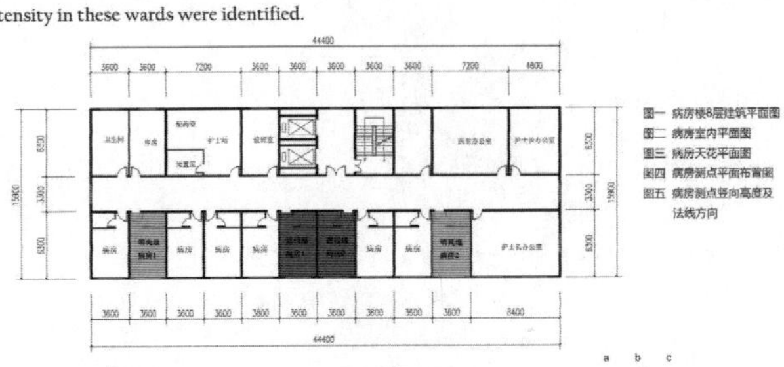

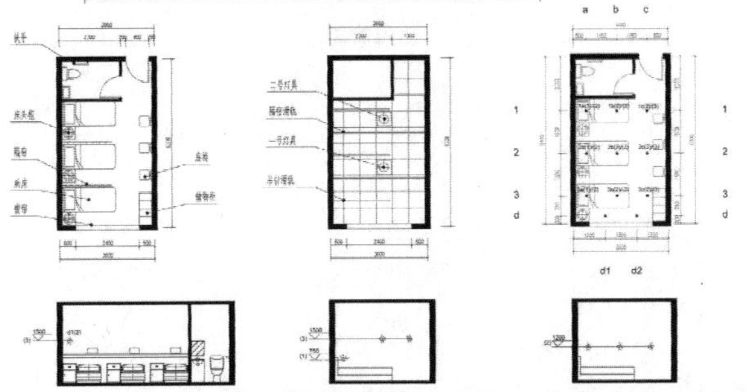

Finding

Lighting environment in a patient ward is influenced by both environmental and behavioral factors. In the wards with smaller window areas, artificial lighting was more likely to be applied during the daytime. However, the intensity of lighting in the wards with larger window areas was still significantly higher than that in the wards with smaller window areas. Moreover, the privacy curtains between patient beds were more likely to be used in the wards with smaller window areas.The combined use of lighting in patient wards is complicated in the context of local cultures. Intensive analysis of the lighting environments in patient wards should be conducted in the context of individual dataset in order to optimize the integrated application of natural lighting and artificial lighting.

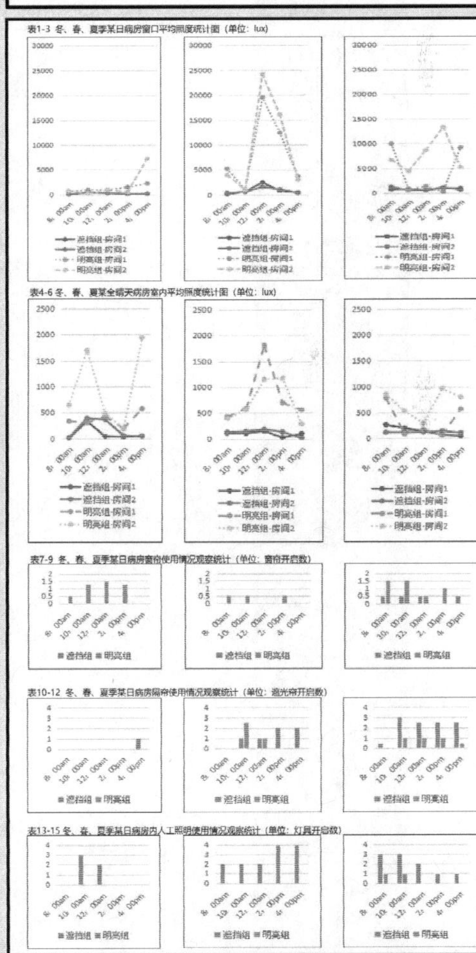

WANG Yan & WANG Zhe (2022). Combined Use of Natural Lighting, Artificial Lighting, and Curtains in Patient Wards. Presented at the Environmental Design Research Association's 52th annual conference: Greenville, SC. 2022 June 01-04.

Creating a Workable Workspace: Office Design Solutions for Individuals with Autism Spectrum Disorder

***Farzane Omidi & Kristi Gaines,** Texas Tech University*

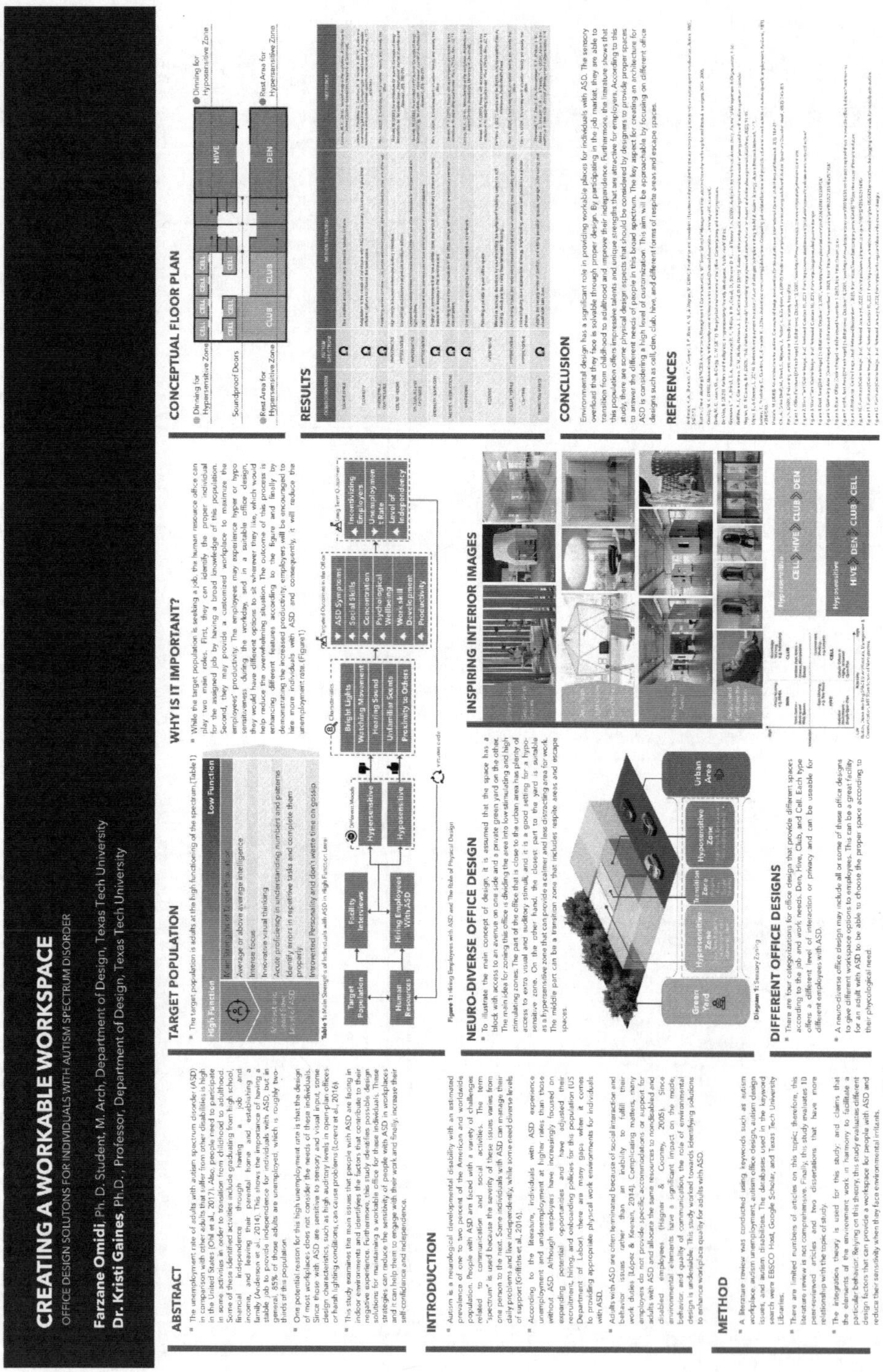

Creating Urban Habitats through Ecological Design of Schoolyard Spaces: Addressing the New Normal of the COVID-19 Era

***Naoko Fujita**, University of Tsukuba; **Yuki Yokoyama** Kyushu University*

Design for Student Engagement and Improved Health Outcomes at William & Mary's Integrative Wellness Center

Jennifer Amster, EYP

Development of an Environmental Lab to Test Cognitive Assistive Technology to Support Instrumental Activities of Daily Living in Dementia Homecare

Emily Roberts, *Oklahoma State University*

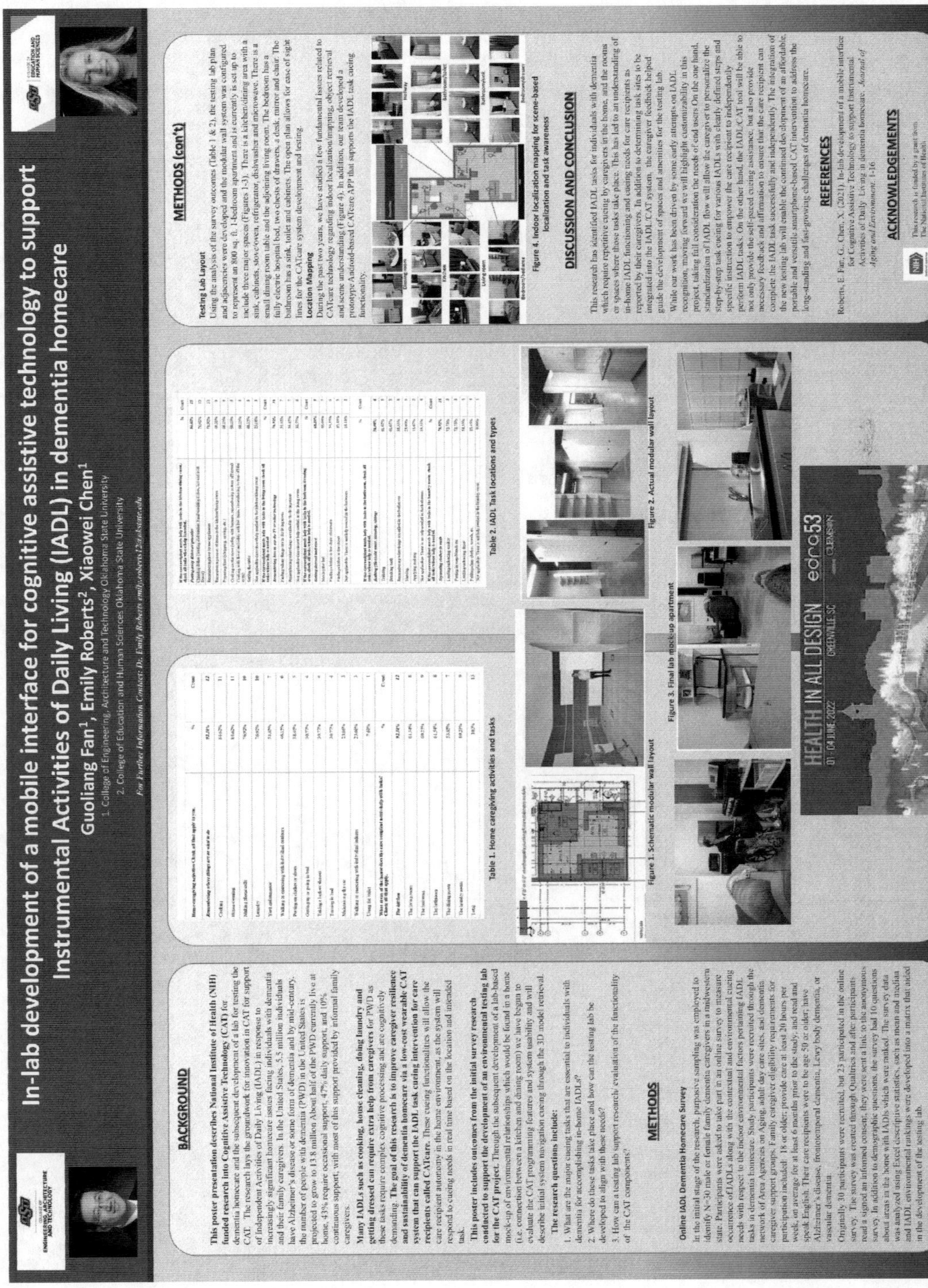

Emergency Department Design in Response to Pandemics: A Systematic Literature Review

Marzia Chowdhury & Hui Cai, The University of Kansas

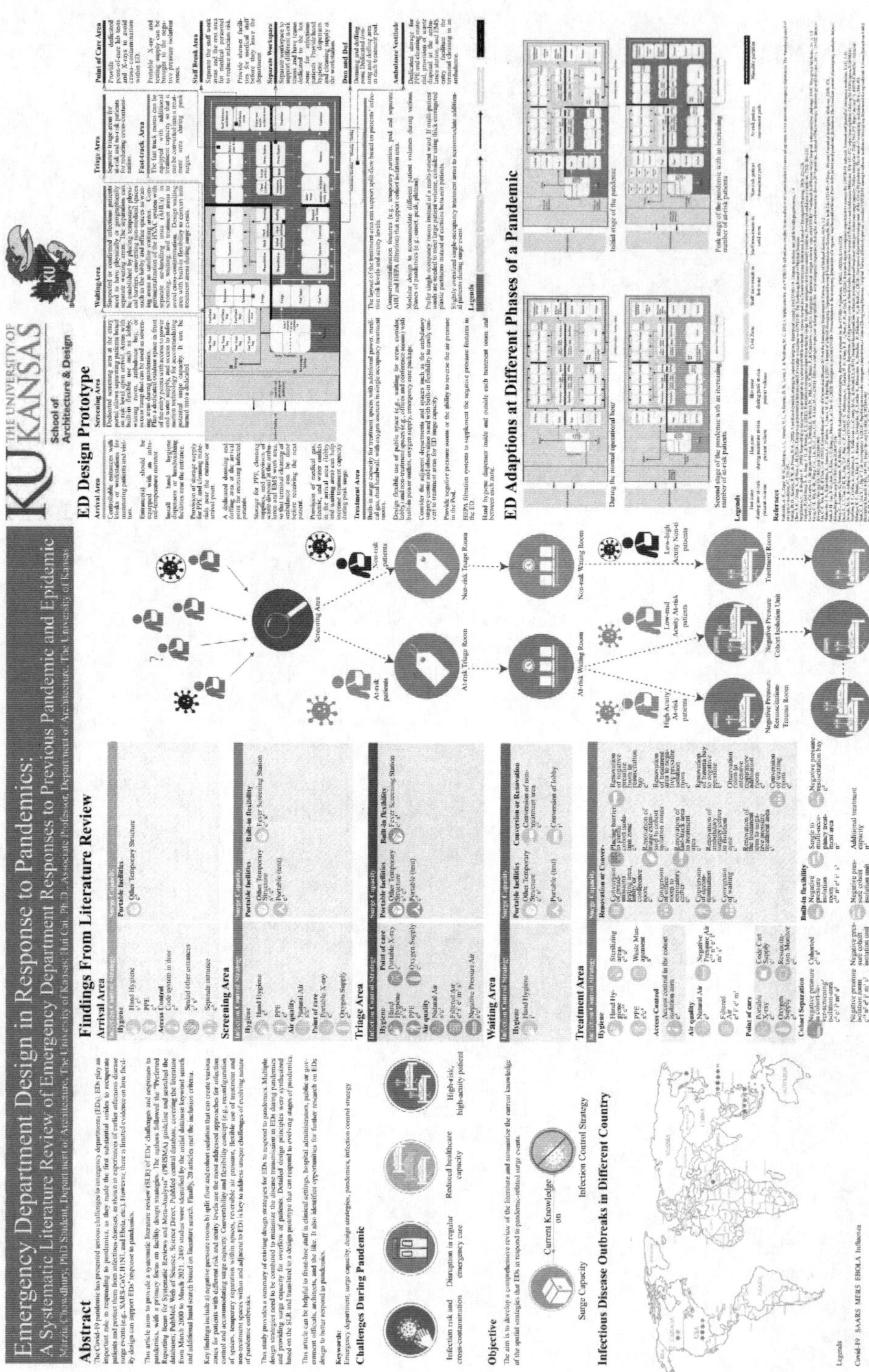

Employee Needs in Laboratory Workspaces: Findings from Facility- and System-Wide Evaluations

Abigail Heithoff & Jeri Brittin, *HDR Architecture*

Employee Space Needs in Laboratory Environments: Findings from System-Wide Facility Evaluations

Abby Heithoff, MS, Senior Research Coordinator, HDR
Jon Crane, FAIA, EDAC, LEED AP, Director of Translational Health Sciences, HDR
Jeri Brittin, PhD, Research Director, HDR

ABSTRACT

The Bureau of Labor Statistics predicts laboratory roles will grow at more than twice the expected average job growth rate by 2028. To inform design of workspaces for these technical roles, HDR conducted system-wide facility evaluations during late 2020 and early 2021. These evaluations included over 2,100 respondents in research and development roles. Academic-affiliated and non-affiliated organizations were included.

The results were disaggregated across biomedical, laboratory-based, clinical science, and translational researchers and reflect the distinctions across groups. Key findings follow:

Clinical Science Research

- Growing demand for centrally located, core research spaces. These cores should be outfitted with inviting areas for participants to wait, private interview rooms, and research spaces equipped for psychometric testing, electrophysiology, physical exams, and video capture.
- Sustained need for core computing facilities, analysis cores and tissue and biospecimen banking.

Biomedical Laboratory Research

- A growing need for specialized wet laboratory research space in biomedical laboratories, including tissue culture, particularly clean cell culture rooms.
- Continued smaller demand for viral vector culture space, necessitating BSL-2 or BSL2+ controls.
- A growing demand for infectious disease culture requiring BSL-2 through BSL-3 controls.
- Lower demand for chemical and radioisotope use requiring fume hoods and specialized closed room space, including microscopy, histology, procedures space and electrophysiology.

Translational Research

- A growing need for unique or novel research spaces, supported by relatively higher rates of use of specialized spaces including gait labs, imaging facilities, and engineering and fabrication areas.
- More highly variable work space use patterns compared with other groups.
- Critical key adjacencies support effective translational research work. Key adjacencies were identified between wet lab support space areas, clinical research spaces, vivarium and core laboratory facilities.

Implications for Design

- To maximize laboratory workspace, consider placing lower-utilization equipment in shared common labs.
- Shared dry workspace plans must include accommodation for private phone calls and video conferencing.

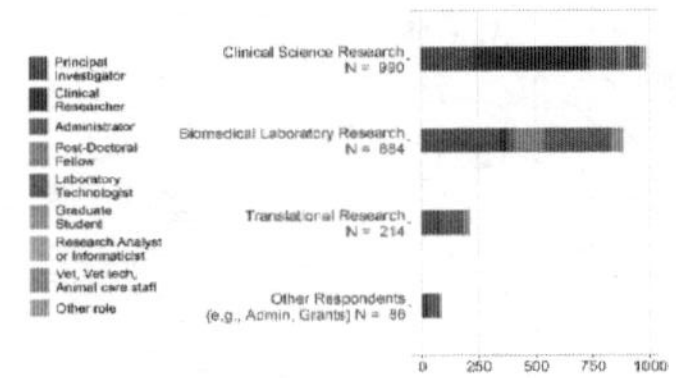

Distribution of Respondent Roles

Respondents came from a variety of job roles, and represented the spectrum of experience and responsibilities. The plurality of respondents reported working in clinical science.

Geographic Distribution of Response

A total of 2,177 respondents represented scientific R&D facilities in 38 states. Above, point size is proportional to the number of respondents per state.

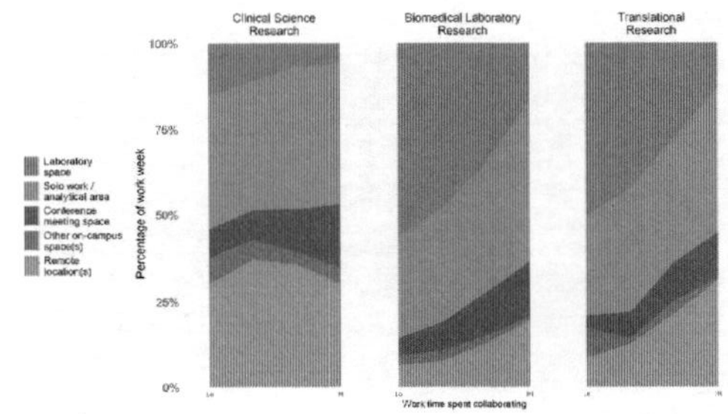

Collaboration & Space Use

At left, weekly space use is plotted for those who spend the least to most amount of time in collaborative activities. The most collaborative respondents reported less time working in the lab and a greater proportion of time in solo workspaces, conference and meeting rooms.

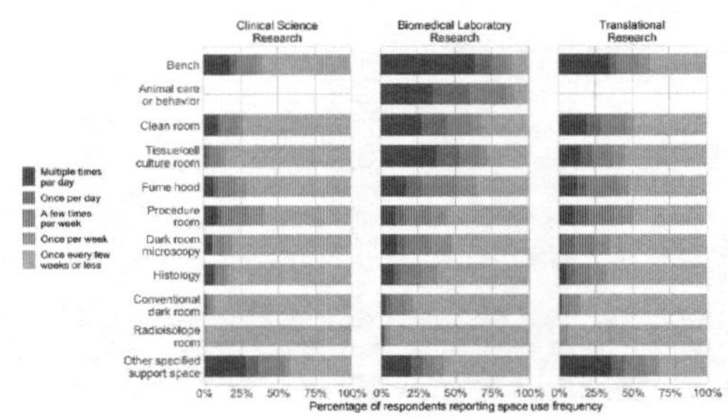

Support Space Use

Daily individual bench space use was high, as was reported use of clean rooms and cell and tissue culture areas.

Clinical and translational researchers were the groups most likely to indicate daily use of another space. Common spaces included assessment rooms and computing cores.

Evaluation on Design of Baby Care Rooms in Shopping Malls from the Gender Perspective -- a Case Study of Tianjin, China

Yilin Song, Hanqi Guo, Suwen Xiong, Tong Hu, Weisong Lv & Boxi Sun, *Tianjin University*

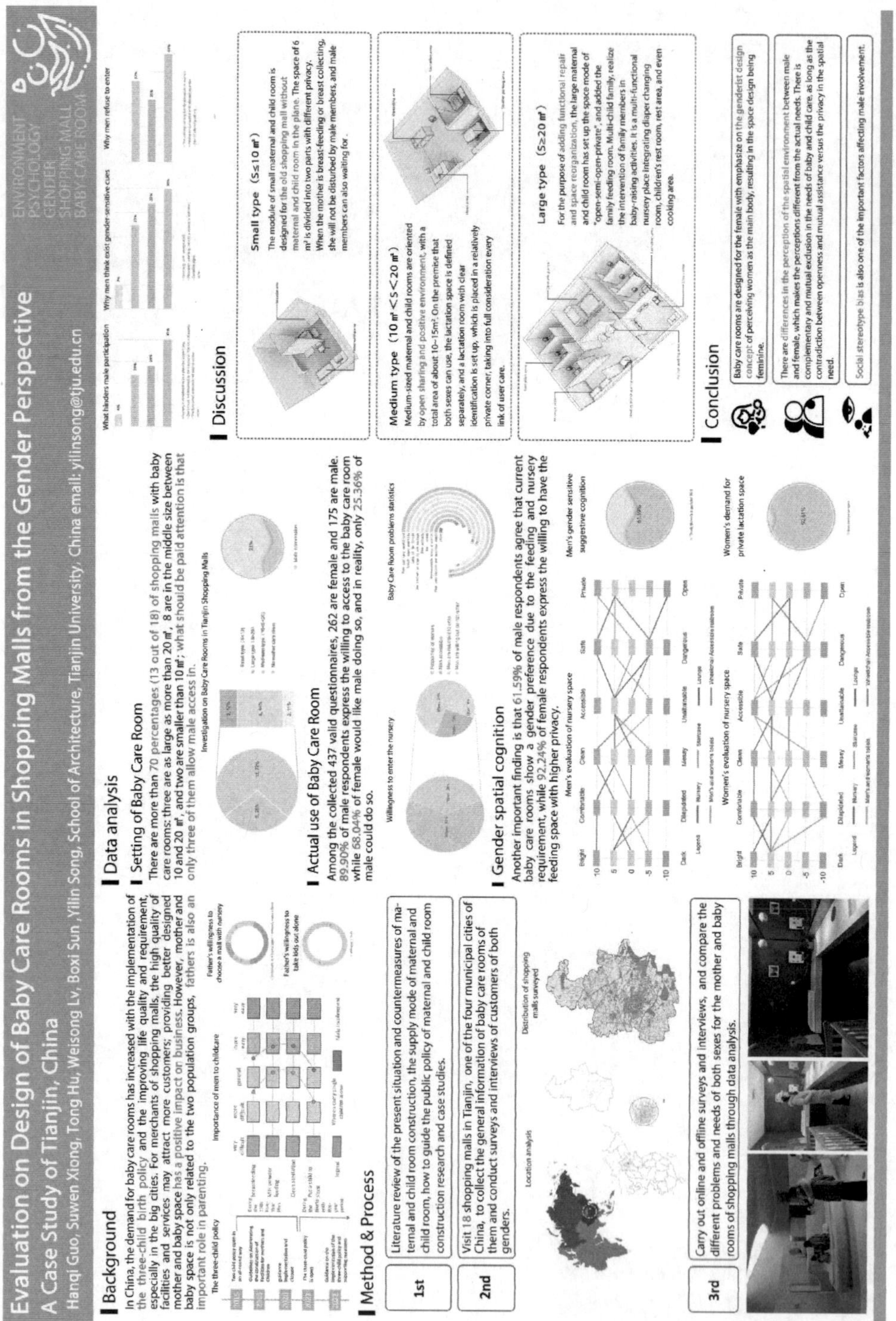

From Boomers to Zoomers: Designing Spaces for Intergenerational Formal and Informal Interactions

Esmirna Moya, Neda Norouzi & Eric Polo Rosales, The University of Texas at San Antonio

From the Outset: Architectural Design of an Intergenerational Community Center

Josue Mondragon & Neda Norouzi, *The University of Texas at San Antonio*

Get More from Your Corridors: Balancing Patient Care and Staff Respite in the MICU

Kirsten Miller, GBBN Architects

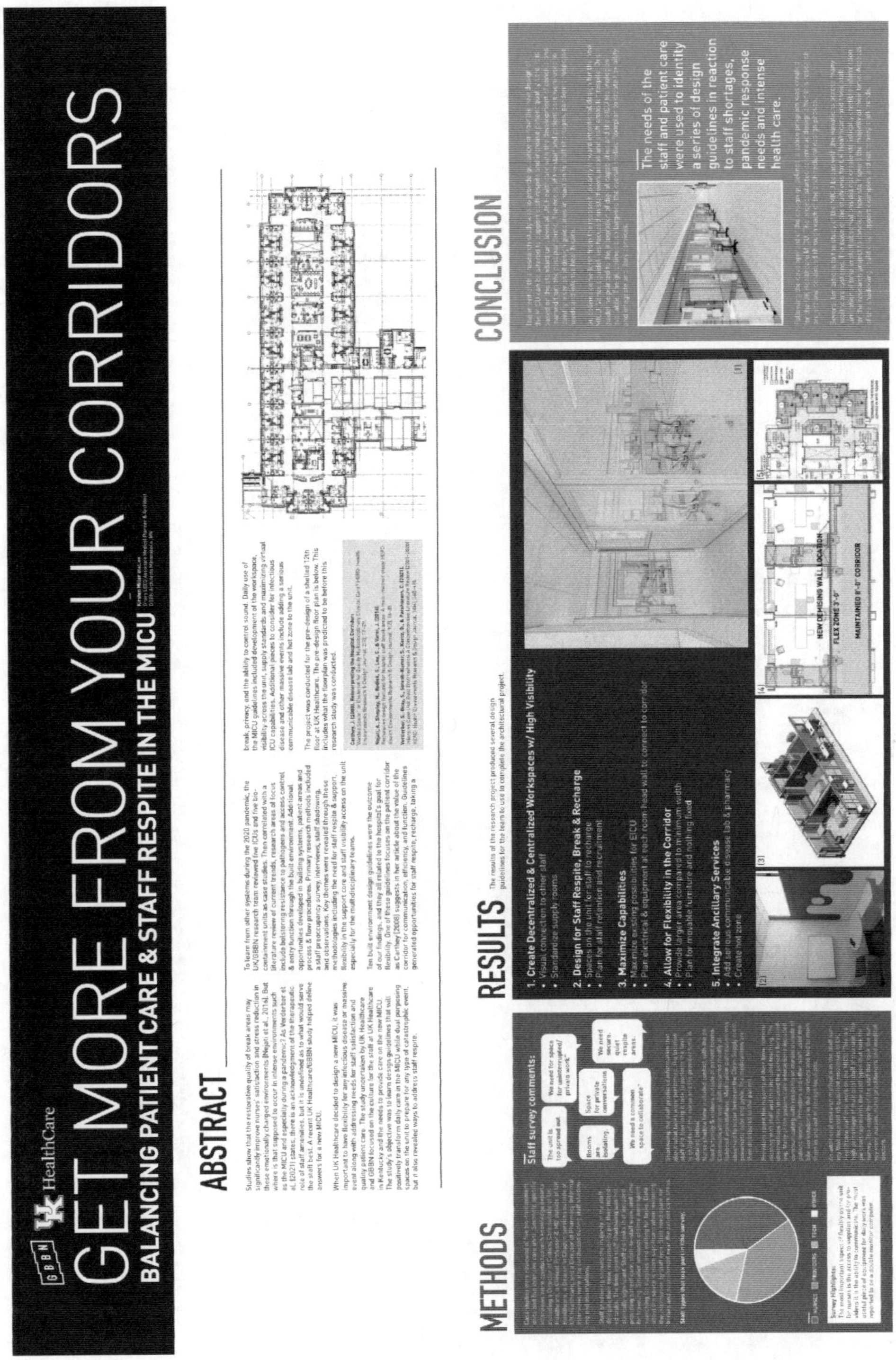

Greening, Gentrification, and Equity: Consequential Questions on the Ethics of Compromise

Mariana Junqueira, Kansas State University

Greening, Gentrification, and Equity:
Consequential Questions on the Ethics of Compromise

Mariana Junqueira, Ph.D.

mjunqueira@ksu.edu

Assistant Professor, Department of Interior Architecture & Industrial Design at the College of Architecture, Planning and Design

KANSAS STATE UNIVERSITY

Greening

- Urban interventions that introduce new or improve existing green spaces in often degraded urban areas.
- Known restorative qualities that strengthen urban dwellers' health and wellbeing, recreational properties, and provide aesthetic benefits.

Gentrification

- Greening is not value-neutral [1][2].
- Green spaces can perpetuate inequalities and disproportionally harm underserved communities.
- Greening has become a synonym for valuable urban land, i.e., green gentrification.

Equity

- Numerous design strategies attempted to characterize the tenuous line between greening and gentrification.
- They seek the benefits of green spaces while mitigating gentrification as a subproduct have been conceptualized.

"Green Enough"

Can these proposed strategies be considered compromises?

To whom are these strategies imposing tradeoffs? Are these ethically-acceptable solutions?

Content analysis revealed that widely accepted design strategies **have focused on constraining the design product** (size or amenities of green space) to the detriment of introducing participatory design processes, such as community placemaking [3]. Such partial strategies **do not guarantee the prevention of gentrification.** However, **they guarantee a restrained green space** that may not improve an underserved community's health and wellbeing as a more extensive greening would.

These solutions present underserved communities with a "pernicious paradox" [1].

References

[1] Checker, M. (2011). Wiped out by the "Greenwave": Environmental gentrification and the paradoxical politics of urban sustainability. *City & Society*, 23(2), 210-229.

[2] Dale, A.; & Newman, L. L. (2009). Sustainable development for some: Green urban development and affordability. *Local Environment: The International Journal of Justice and Sustainability*, 14(7), 669-681.

[3] Moroni, S. (2013). Afterword: Ethical problems of contemporary cities. In C. Basta & S. Moroni (Eds.), *Ethics, Design and Planning of the Built Environment* (pp. 197-212). Springer.

Home Modification Project: Design Strategies for Better Adaptability in Minimum Dwellings

***Maggie Ma Kingsley**, The Chinese University of Hong Kong*

Home Modification Project: Design Strategies for Better Adaptability in Minimum Dwellings

Maggie Ma Kingsley
School of Architecture, Faculty of Social Science, The Chinese University of Hong Kong, Hong Kong

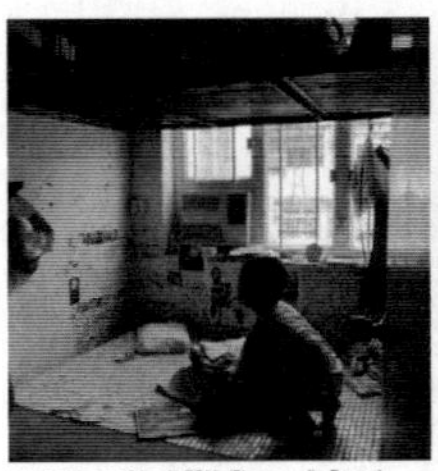

Inadequate condition in SDUs (Photo credit: Domat)

Sub-divided Units (Photo credit: Society for Community Organization)

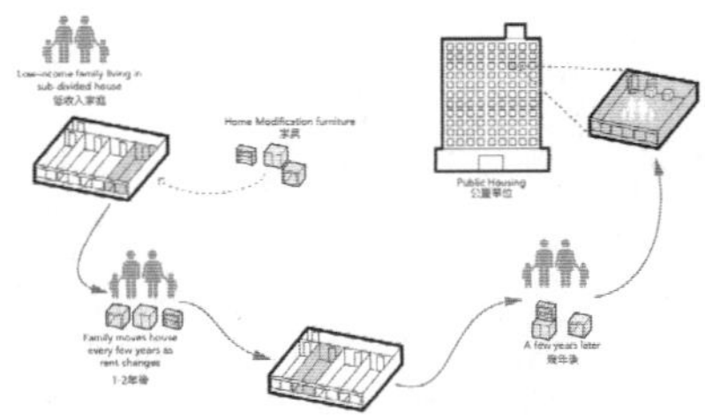

Modular furniture acts as spatial tools for families and withstand the moves before housing security is reached.

Background

Under the laissez-fair housing market in Hong Kong, the insufficient provision of affordable housing results in the appearance of extreme small dwelling units - Subdivided-units(SDUs). SDU is a type of rental micro-apartment divided from a single unit from an aged building into multiple, self-contained households of a median area of 10sqm. In 2020, there were 100,943 SDUs in the private housing market, with 226,340 inhabitants. The high density and over-crowding living conditions threaten the user's physical and psychological wellbeing. The quality of living in small domestic spaces becomes an immediate issue under the threat of home confinement during COVID-19. The Home modification project investigates the quality of spatial configuration inside these homes to improve adaptability with an aim to improve the future prospect of the users.

Method and strategies

Home Modification Project is a collaborative project between architects and social workers. Providing design and advisory services to more than 300 families living in SDUs, the project focuses on enhancing the home study environment for children of low-income households and providing better living space, thus improving the families' long-term prospects and wellbeing. The design of the internal home environment aims to improve the adaptability of the users, fulfilling some of the design principles of "Flexible housing" by Jeremy Till yet in a smaller scale context. The adaptability of housing generally refers to its capacity to accommodate the future changing needs of the users. In the condition of SDUs where users move home on average within 2-3 years, the project focuses on users' immediate and transitional needs – facilitating daily routine, family relationships, household safety, and catering for the instability. Intensive designers' input is required to define the "hard space" of the home in the limited area in order to facilitate better adaptation. The research investigates domesticity and spatial sense of home and establishes essential criteria for spatial enhancement for daily resilience for families living in minimum dwellings.

Long-term Sustainability

By implementing modular furniture as a spatial tool, the project avoided benefiting the landlords that risk rental increases, allowing the low-income families to be direct beneficiaries of the improvement. Modular furniture addressed tiny homes' organisation problems and could be mass-produced to respond to the vast scale of the SDUs housing problem. The furniture acts as a spatial tool to redefine order for homes by creating appropriate zonings conducive to learning and daily activities. It helps establish a sense of home in a transitional context by providing flexibility and improved adaptability. Various spatial approaches have been developed through the project to improve the internal environments, including utilisation of height, creating zonings, introducing alignments, creating square spaces, grouping free spaces, and defining privacy. The design strategies could act as a guide to the spatial planning of tiny homes, with an aim to improve the future prospect of users.

This research contributes to applied knowledge on spatial design for small dwellings and aims to inspire the developmental policy with human-centred considerations for marginalised living environments for low-income communities. The outcome supports providing a fair and inclusive basic living standard for the general public to work towards a healthier and more sustainable city.

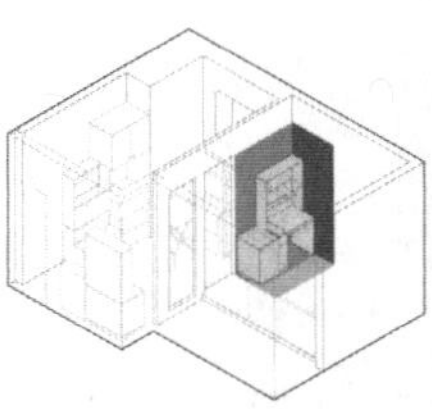

1 Create Quiet Corner

Using furniture to screen sights and sounds allow different family members to have their own spaces for louder activities and quieter activities simultaneously.

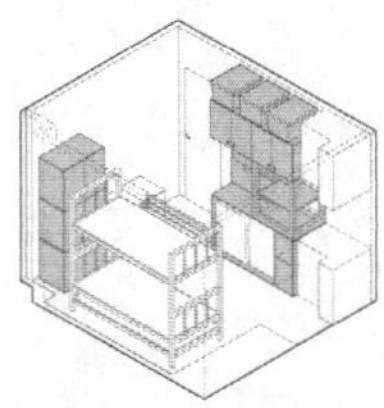

3 Utilize High Ceiling Space

Expanding storage area to upper space by stackable furniture to free up more area at ground level to allow for daily activities.

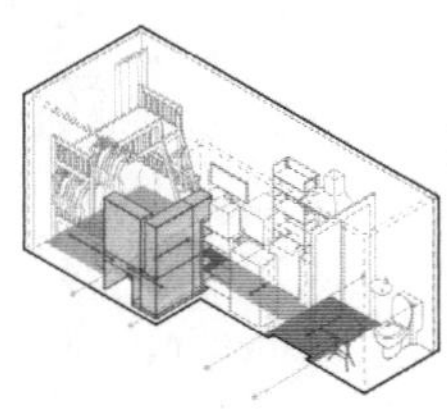

5 Divide Long Space

Dividing long-shaped units by change in orientation of space to allow multiple activities to occurs simultaneously and avoid grouping free spaces to one long corridor, providing different view angle by changing body orientation for different activities.

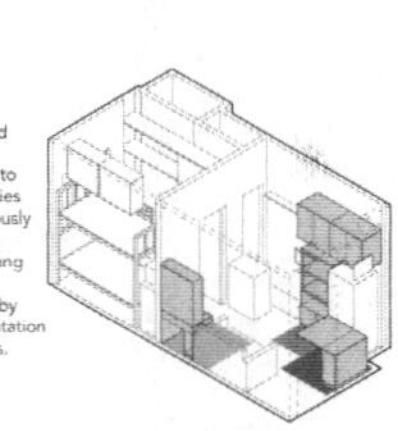

6 Create Zoning

Using furniture to define zones with different purpose, e.g. cooking, study, gathering, sleeping areas to reduce crossing of circulation across different activities.

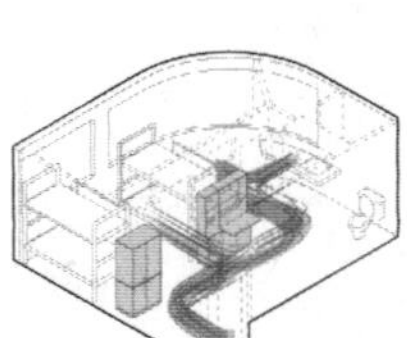

2 Free up Common Spaces

Organise negative spaces to clear furniture off circulation space to allow free and safe movement in daily activities.

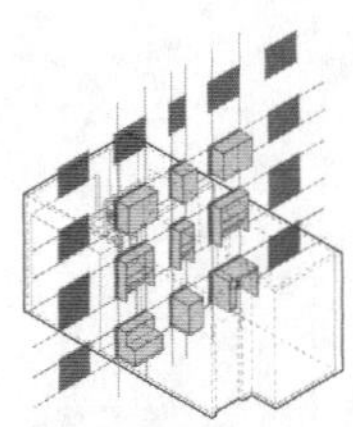

4 Utilize modularity

Furniture modules are designed to be easily handled with standard modular size, which could be rearrangement with different combination for new space, cater for transitional condition.

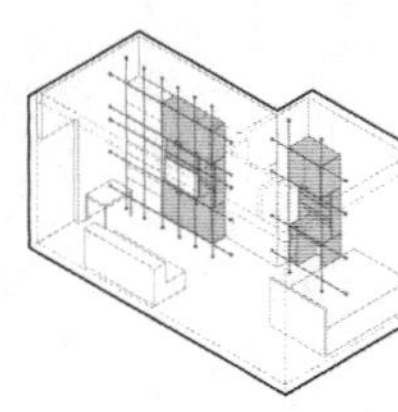

7 Introduce Alignments

Creates visual organisation through alignments enable the users to live and practice in an organised space with hierarchy and clear classification, and provides a harmonious and calm environment.

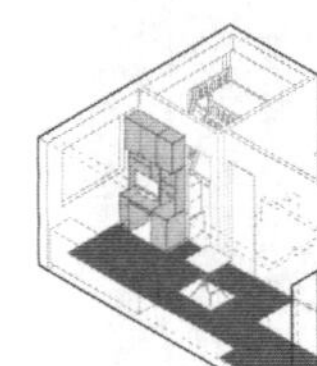

8 Create negative space

Designing empty space provides clarity to free areas, and ensures rooms for flexible activities and contemplation.

Aligned environment after modification

Furniture defines home space in multiple zones

Furniture defines home space in multiple zones

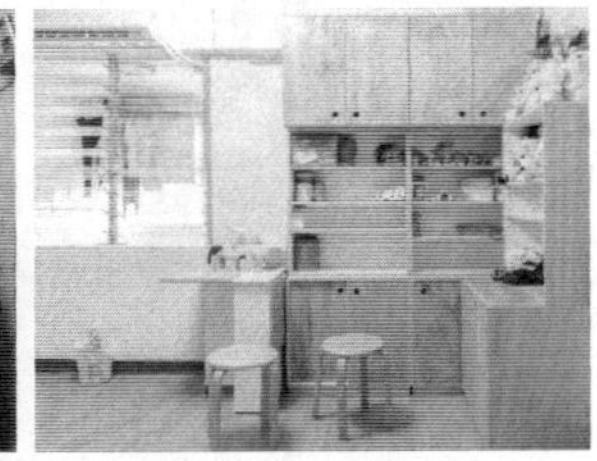

Furniture moved to public housing as a family move.

How Do Students Use the Outdoor Space on Campus? A Case Study on a Campus Design and Its Relation to Outdoor Activities

Jaechang Noh, Sojeong Lee & Lisa Lim, Korea Advanced Institute of Science and Technology

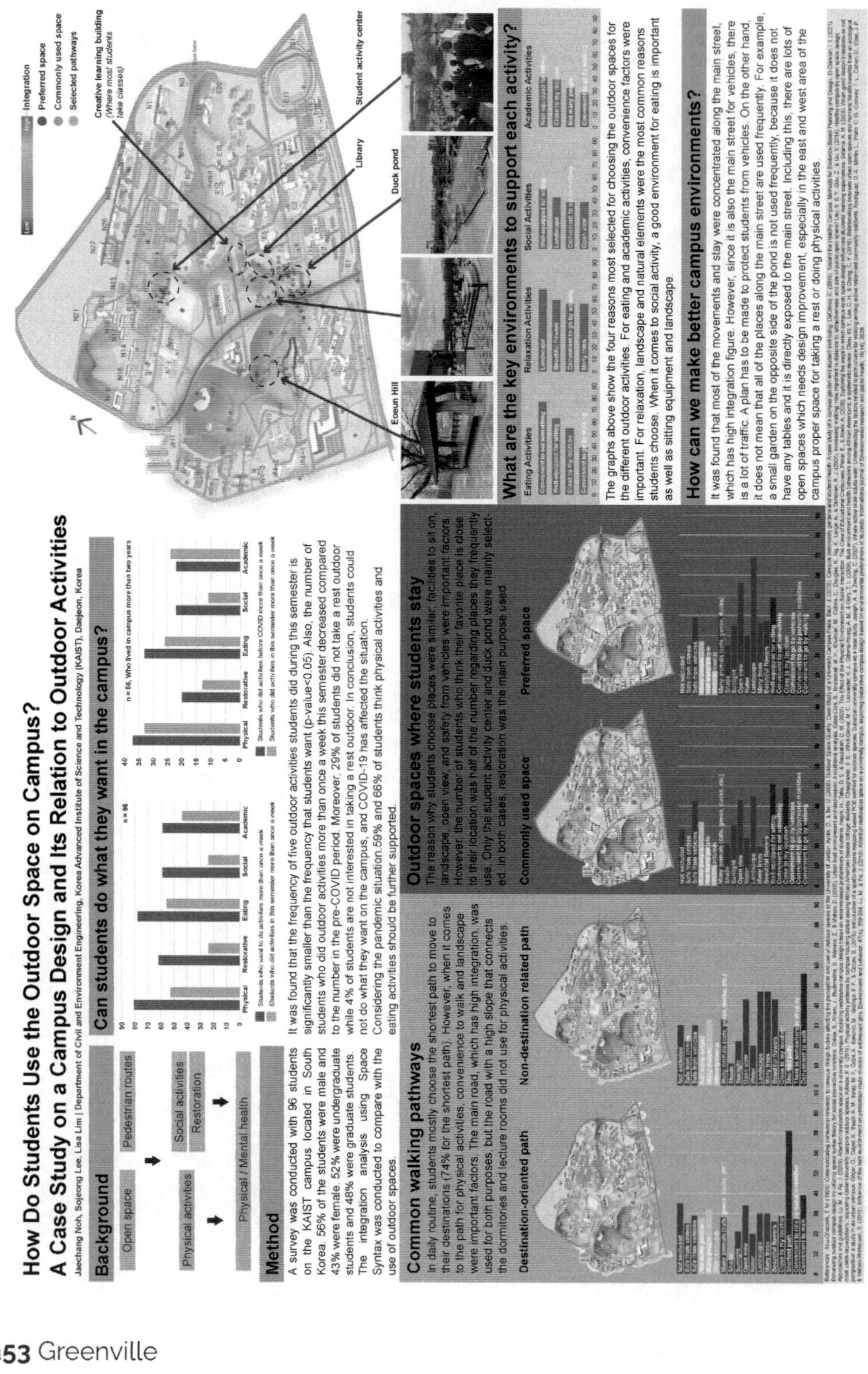

How Does the Community Design Process Impact Their Sense of Community?

Charleston Yi & Kofi Boone, *North Carolina State University*

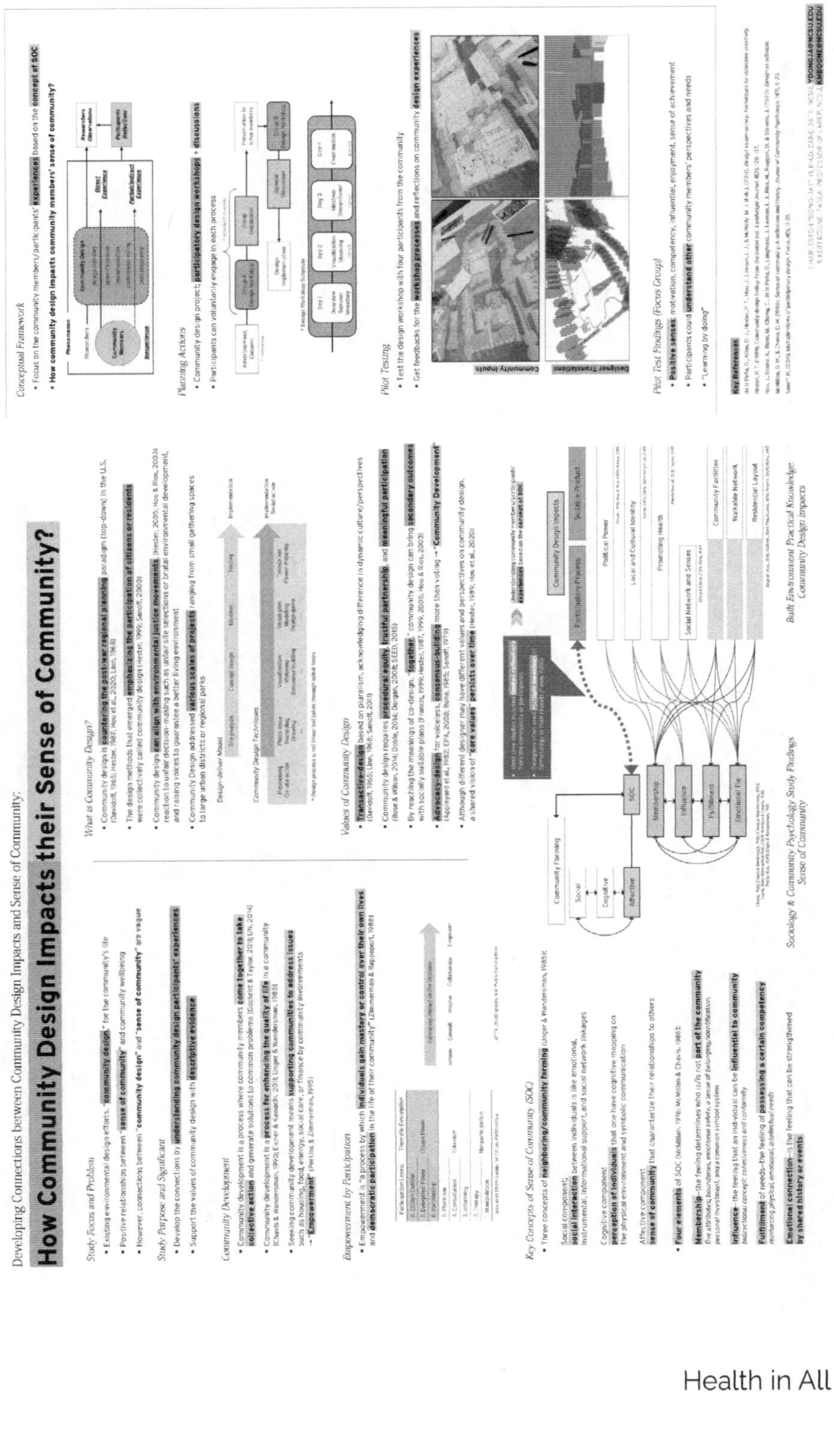

How Pervasive Virtual Reality (PVR) Can Augment the Perception of Working from Home (WFH) Environments

Zahrasadat Hosseini & Tilanka Chandrasekera, *Oklahoma State University*

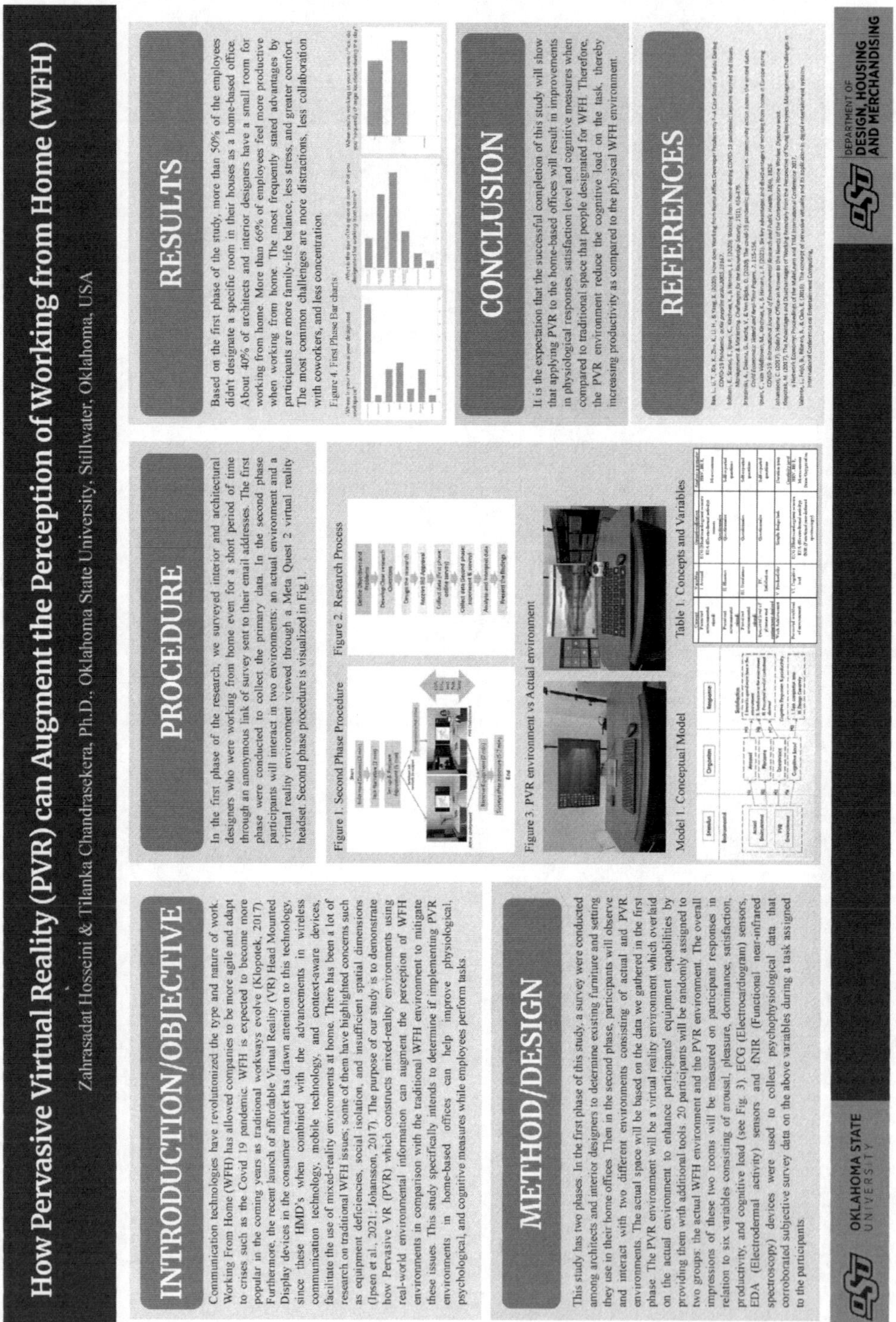

ICU Design & Nurse Stress: Developing a Nurses' Physical Environmental Stress Scale (NPESS)

Dagmar Rittenbacher, *Gresham Smith*

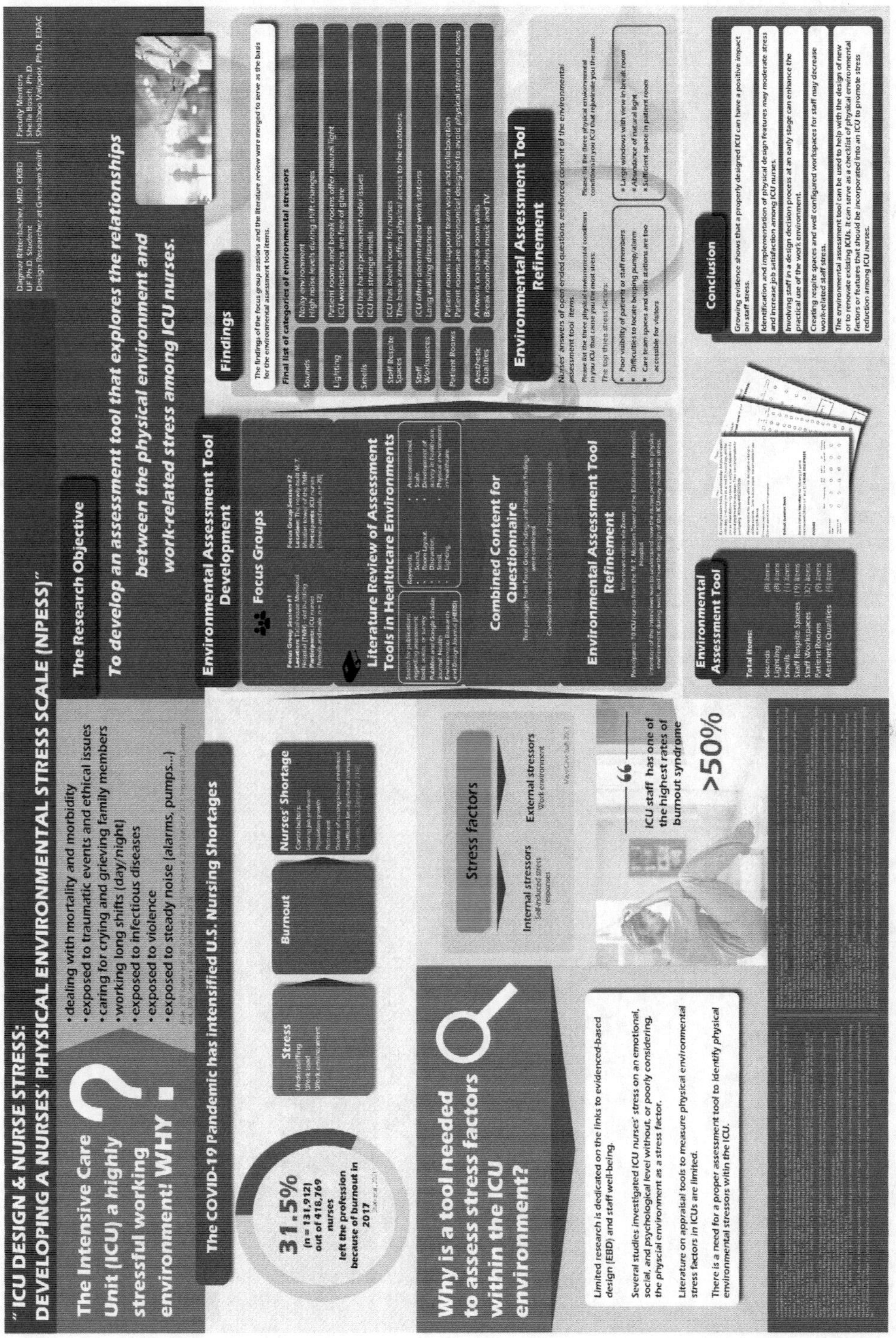

Increasing STEM Motivation in Middle School Students through Spatial Design

Tilanka Chandrasekera, Piper Bott, Allison Howard, Katelyn Allen, Nicole Colston, Cynthia Orona, Tutaleni Asino, Oluwafikayo Adewumi, Clement Audu & Angelina Dayton, Oklahoma State University; ***Norma Neely*** Citizen, Potawatomi Nation

Investigating Lighting Quality in Senior Residential Environments

Alexis Mihalyfi & Emilija Vilkaite, Lawrence Technological University

Investigating Lighting Quality in Senior Residential Environments

Alexis Mihalyfi, Emilija Vilkaite, College of Architecture and Design, Lawrence Technological University

Introduction:

The objective of this study was to investigate senior's required lighting levels for conducting daily tasks such as reading, writing, or working at a computer. In addition probability glare was investigated in two bedroom environments at a senior living facility located in Detroit, Michigan. Each bedroom was located at a different orientation, East and Southeast.

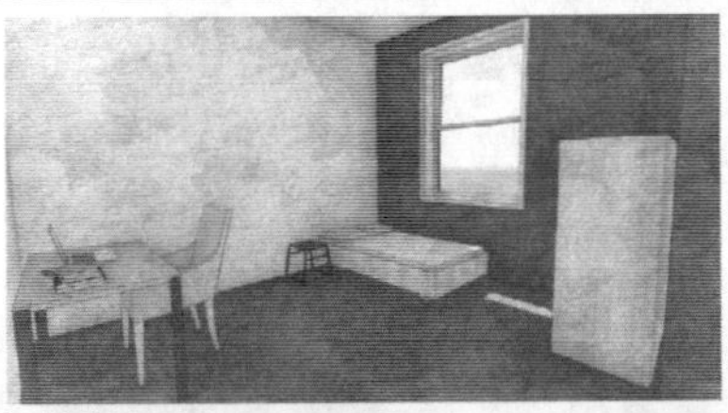

East Bedroom

Southeast Bedroom

Methods:

Research Questions

- What are the similarities and differences in average daylight autonomy and daylight factor in bedrooms with different orientations?
- What is the illuminance level in the rooms at bed and desk level?
- How do the illuminance levels at the bed and desk level in rooms support daily tasks such as reading and writing for seniors?
- How can artificial lighting be designed to support these tasks at night?
- What is the average glare probability at the bed and desk levels in the room?
- Considering the existing lighting guidelines and recommendations, which room provides better lighting conditions for seniors to conduct reading and writing tasks?

Variables

- Illuminance levels at work plane level related to reading and writing
- Glare probability at work plane level related to reading and writing
- Daylight Autonomy
- Daylight Factor

Simulation

- Revit
- Autodesk Insight
- ClimateStudio
- Lumion

Results:

East Senior Bedroom

- Does meet the minimum required daylight factor on the workplane of interest.
- Spatial daylight autonomy is achieved throughout the year.
- Glare levels on the workplane of interest are often disturbing and intolerable during the course of the year.
- Without luminaires, the workplane of interest does not provide enough illumination for visual task during the day.

Southeast Senior Bedroom

- Does meet the minimum required daylight factor on the workplane of interest.
- Spatial daylight autonomy is achieved throughout the year.
- Glare levels on the workplane of interest are often disturbing and intolerable during the course of the year.
- Without luminaires, the workplane of interest provides copious amounts of lighting with a large probability of glare.

Guidelines and Recommendations (LEED v4.1 vs. IESNA Lighting Handbook)	LEED v4.1	IESNA Lighting Handbook
DAYLIGHT FACTOR	[illegible]	[illegible]
DAYLIGHT AUTONOMY	Spatial daylight autonomy is achieved for at least 55% of regularly occupied spaces.	Spatial daylight autonomy is achieved for at least 50% of regularly occupied spaces. Users are progressively more satisfied as the area increases above 75% to an upper feasible limit of 95%.
GLARE	[illegible]	N/A
TASK ILLUMINATION	Minimum illuminance level is 300 lux. Maximum illuminance level is 3000 lux	[illegible] General (dressing) - 100 lux. Reading and Writing (desk) - 800 lux
COLOR	[illegible]	[illegible]
LIGHTING CONTROL	Lighting Control Should provide dimmable or multilevel lighting for 90% of the occupied spaces.	Controls should be easily located at the entry point of a space. Luminaires should be controlled separately or collectively to achieve desired effect. Wall box switches and dimmers, programmable dimmers, home automation systems.
SURFACE REFLECTIVITY	[illegible]	[illegible]

Daylight Factor

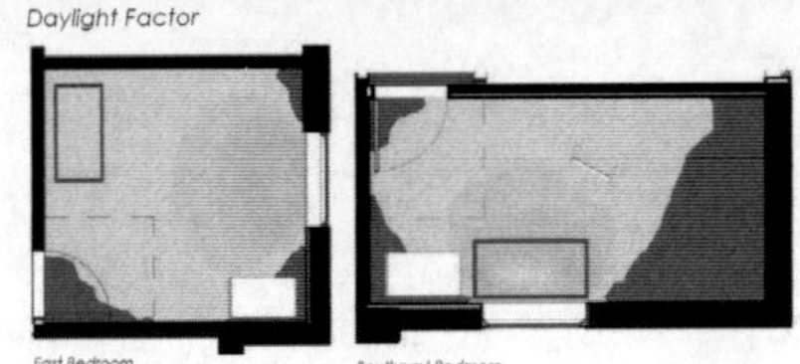

East Bedroom September 21st at 10 a.m. — Southeast Bedroom September 21st at 10 a.m.

Glare Probability

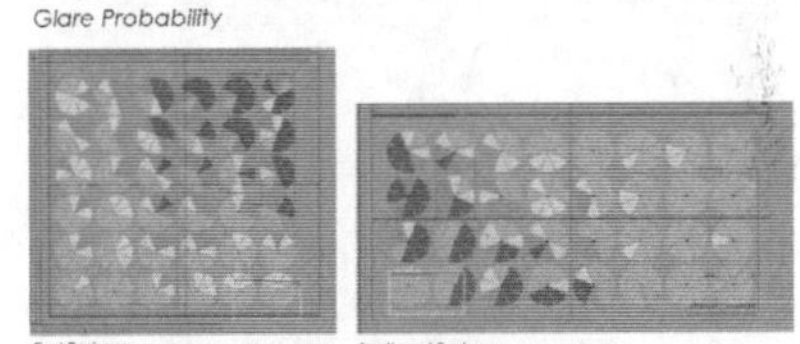

East Bedroom September 21st at 9:30 a.m. — Southeast Bedroom September 21st at 9:30 a.m.

Daylight Autonomy

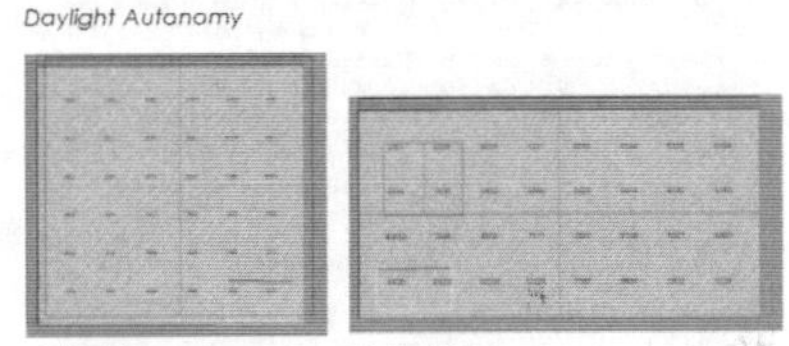

East Bedroom September 21st at 9:30 a.m. — Southeast Bedroom September 21st at 9:30 a.m.

Luminaire Illuminance

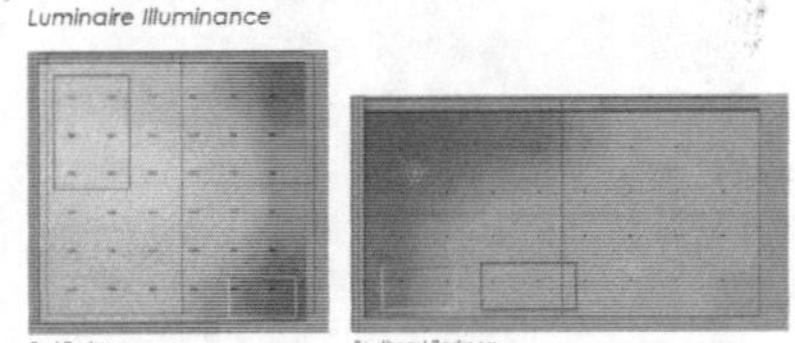

East Bedroom — Southeast Bedroom

Conclusion:

Future Design Implications Include

- Changing the room orientation
- Changing the furniture layout
- Adding internal or external shading systems to reduce glare on the workplace.

Practical Implications:

- Findings can inform the design of future senior bedroom environments.
- Findings provide appropriate lighting recommendations for windowed bedroom suites.

Non-Linear Workflow in Trauma Rooms and Its Impacts on Physical Environment Design

Hossein Mirzajani, Hamid Estejab & Sara Bayramzadeh, *Kent State University*

Non-linear workflow in trauma rooms and its impacts on physical environment design

Toward a model of safety and care for Trauma Room Design

Environmental Design Research Association
Greenville,SC | 01-04 June, 2022

Hossein Mirzajani, MHD., M.Arch.
Graduate Research Assistant
Kent State University

Hamid Estejab, MHD.
Graduate Research Assistant
Kent State University

Sara Bayramzadeh, PH.D., M.Arch.
Coordinator and Elliot Professor
Kent State University, Healthcare Design Program

Background

Trauma rooms are among the most complex environments in healthcare facilities dealing with critical patient conditions under an extreme time constrain. Advanced trauma life support (ATLS) is an educational program that provides systematic training to perform the necessary measures and assessments of trauma patients for the first (golden) hour in level-1 trauma centers. The priorities of emergency trauma care, according to the ATLS principles, have different levels of interdependencies that could be supported or hindered by the physical environment.

Objective

This study aims to investigate interdependencies in different stages of trauma care and highlight the most critical aspects of the physical environment to address the patient and staff needs and challenges in the delivery of care.

Methodology

Journey Maps

A Journey Map table was created and developed to depict the differences among the roles of the trauma team members during a trauma case. The data represented in this table are based on the conversations with trauma team members from various facilities in the United States. Below is a table showing a brief description of one of the primary roles:

Trauma Surgeon | Assumes care of the patient through operative and non-operative management.
Resident | Access and monitor airway, manage airways, stabilize neck, perform Neuro exam, HEENT portion of the exam, FAST exam
Respiratory Therapist | check Airways, adjuncts suctioning, pulse oximetry, end tidal, CO2, Ambu. **Physician** | Assumes responsibility of the patient until arrival of the trauma surgeon, as well as supervises the EM Resident
Charge nurse | Manages overall supervision & delegation of nursing care, documents vital signs, assists with the primary & secondary survey and all care rendered to the patient
APP (Advanced Practice Provider) | Assists with secondary surveys and procedures

Focus Groups

A qualitative approach was adopted by conducting focus group sessions with trauma team members including physicians, surgeons, pharmacists, technicians, residents, and nurses. Participants were recruited from six hospital systems with a Level I trauma center. Each focus group had diverse participants with background in different roles within the trauma team. The discussions among different roles created a rich discussion to understand their competing needs. The online focus groups were one hour long and were held through Microsoft Teams platform. Twenty sessions of semi-structured focus groups were conducted with a total number of 64 trauma level 1 team members. The focus group questions were semi-structured and included discussions about the flow of care, their individual roles, and challenges they experience.

20 Sessions | **64** Participants | **15** Roles

Result

According to the participants' feedback, a trauma scenario can be divided into six major stages, including patient's pre-arrival, primary survey, procedures (interventions), secondary survey, imaging, and patient discharge. The focus group findings revealed multiple interdependencies in trauma workflow that require the trauma team to have back and forth steps during a trauma treatment case. Easy access to the imaging unit, blood bank, elevator, and OR plays a critical role in facilitating trauma workflow. Participants indicated that appropriate - - blood bank, elevator, and OR plays a critical role in facilitating trauma workflow. Participants indicated that appropriate access to medical supplies, power outlets, medical gas, suction hoses, and adequate space is essential to support the interdependent tasks during a trauma case.

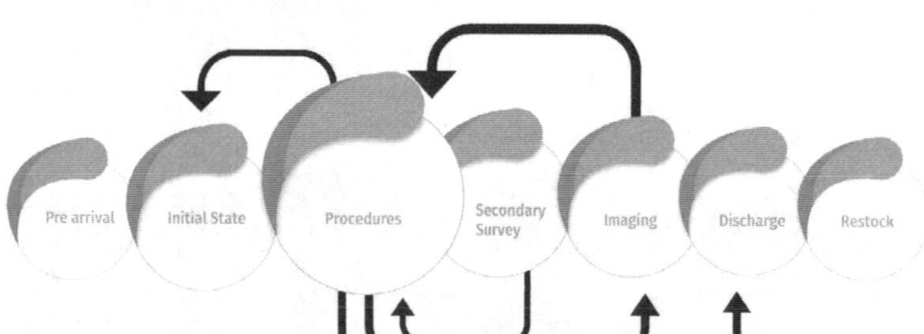

Figure 1. Phases of trauma care

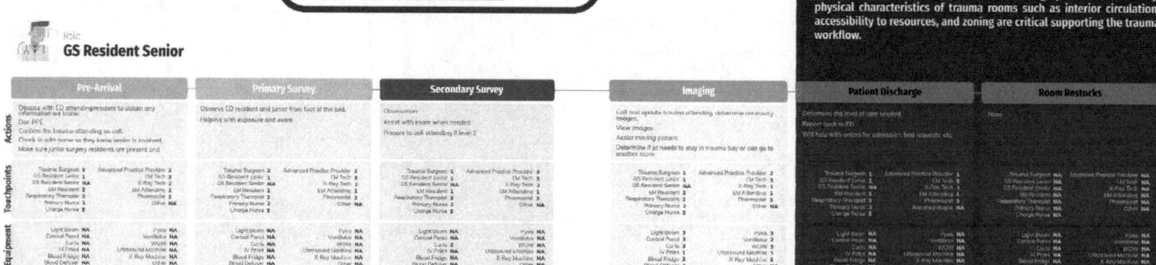

Figure 2. Journey Maps

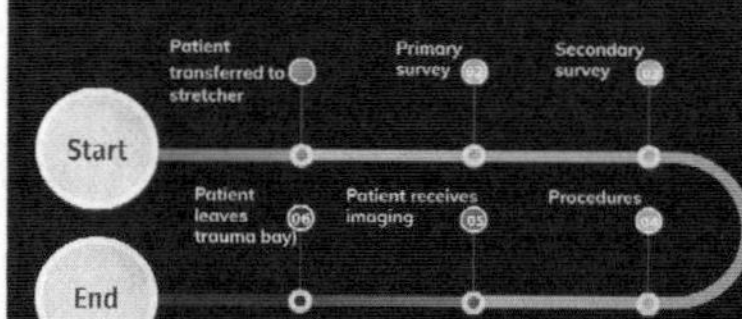

Figure 3. Flow of patient care

Conclusion

Considering the limited studies about trauma room, this study serves as a foundation to identify the relationship between the physical environment and different stages of trauma procedures and their interdependencies. A non-linear workflow in a trauma room significantly impacts trauma room design in macro and micro levels of physical characteristics of the environment. Given the critical role of proximity to the support areas, location and adjacencies of the trauma room should be considered at the early phases of the design process. Additionally, physical characteristics of trauma rooms such as interior circulation, accessibility to resources, and zoning are critical supporting the trauma workflow.

Refrences:
-Brasel, K.J. (2013), "Advanced trauma life support (ATLSVR): the ninth edition", The Journal of Trauma and Acute Care Surgery,
- Bayramzadeh, S., & Aghaei, P. (2021). Technology integration in complex healthcare environments: A systematic literature review. Applied Ergonomics, 92, 103351. https://doi.org/https://doi.org/10.1016/j.apergo.2020.103351

KENT STATE UNIVERSITY | College of Architecture and Environmental Design
Healthcare Design Program

Funding Acknowledgment
This project was supported by the Agency for Healthcare Research and Quality [grant number R18HS027261]. The content is solely the responsibility of the authors and does not necessarily represent the official views of the Agency for Healthcare Research and Quality.

Personalized Age-Friendly Home Modifications: A Web-Based Application

Sung-Jin Lee, *North Carolina A&T State University,* ***Hyun Joo Kwon, Jiyoung Oh***, *Pusan National University*

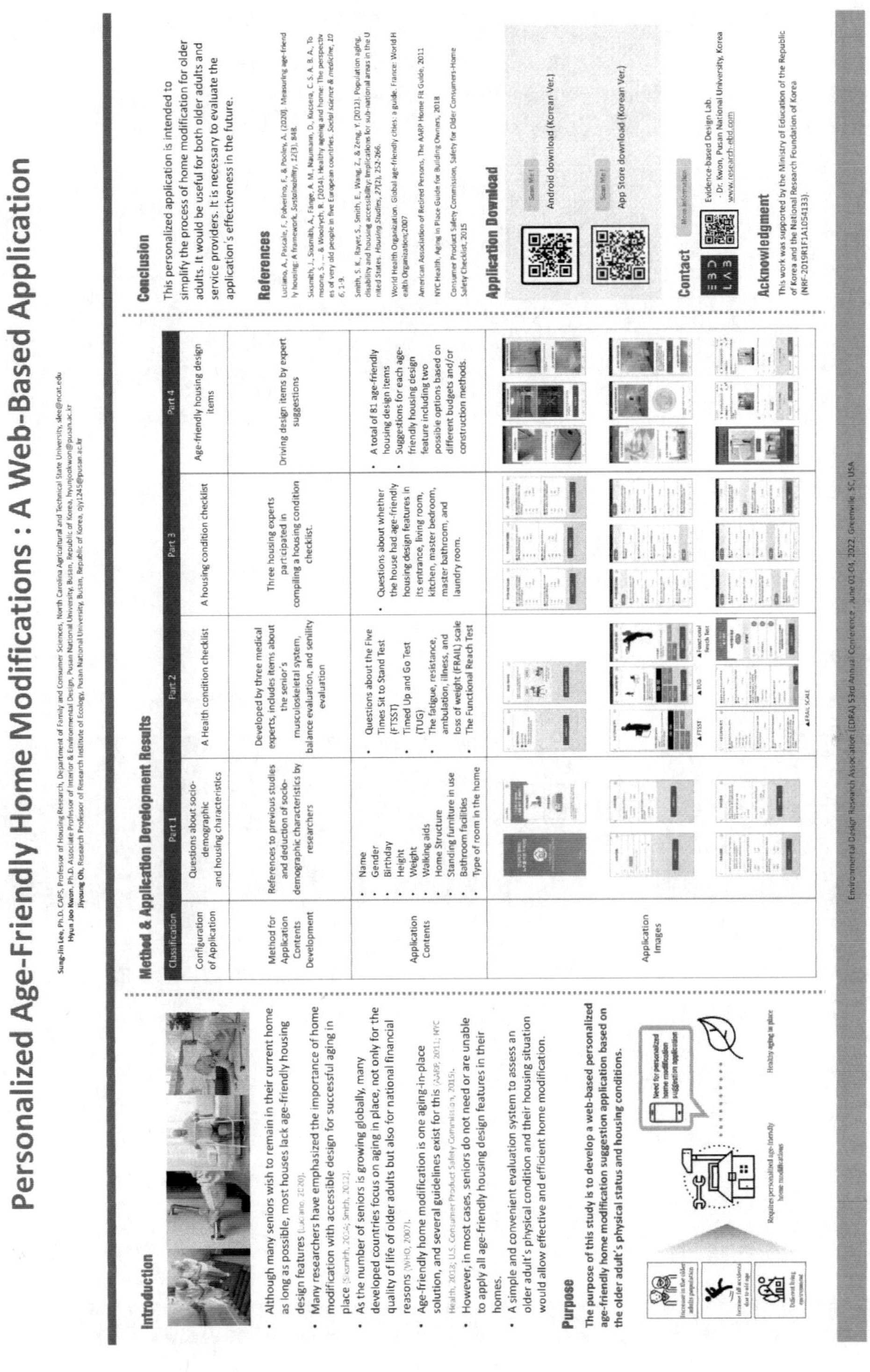

Personalized Age-Friendly Home Modifications : A Web-Based Application

Sung-Jin Lee, Ph.D. CAPS, Professor of Housing Research, Department of Family and Consumer Sciences, North Carolina Agricultural and Technical State University, slee@ncat.edu
Hyun Joo Kwon, Ph.D. Associate Professor of Interior & Environmental Design, Pusan National University, Busan, Republic of Korea, hyunjookwon@pusan.ac.kr
Jiyoung Oh, Research Professor of Research Institute of Ecology, Pusan National University, Busan, Republic of Korea, ojy1245@pusan.ac.kr

Introduction

- Although many seniors wish to remain in their current home as long as possible, most houses lack age-friendly housing design features (Luciano, 2020).
- Many researchers have emphasized the importance of home modification with accessible design for successful aging in place (Sixsmith, 2014; Smith, 2012).
- As the number of seniors is growing globally, many developed countries focus on aging in place, not only for the quality of life of older adults but also for national financial reasons (WHO, 2007).
- Age-friendly home modification is one aging-in-place solution, and several guidelines exist for this (AARP, 2011; NYC Health, 2018; U.S. Consumer Product Safety Commission, 2015).
- However, in most cases, seniors do not need or are unable to apply all age-friendly housing design features in their homes.
- A simple and convenient evaluation system to assess an older adult's physical condition and their housing situation would allow effective and efficient home modification.

Purpose

The purpose of this study is to develop a web-based personalized age-friendly home modification suggestion application based on the older adult's physical status and housing conditions.

Method & Application Development Results

Classification	Part 1	Part 2	Part 3	Part 4
Configuration of Application	Questions about socio-demographic and housing characteristics	A Health condition checklist	A housing condition checklist	Age-friendly housing design items
Method for Application Contents Development	References to previous studies and deduction of socio-demographic characteristics by researchers	Developed by three medical experts, includes items about the senior's musculoskeletal system, balance evaluation, and senility evaluation	Three housing experts participated in compiling a housing condition checklist.	Driving design items by expert suggestions
Application Contents	• Name • Gender • Birthday • Height • Weight • Walking aids • Home Structure • Standing furniture in use • Bathroom facilities • Type of room in the home	• Questions about the Five Times Sit to Stand Test (FTSST) • Timed Up and Go Test (TUG) • The fatigue, resistance, ambulation, illness, and loss of weight (FRAIL) scale • The Functional Reach Test	• Questions about whether the house had age-friendly housing design features in its entrance, living room, kitchen, master bedroom, master bathroom, and laundry room.	• A total of 81 age-friendly housing design items • Suggestions for each age-friendly housing design feature including two possible options based on different budgets and/or construction methods.
Application Images		▲FTSST ▲TUG ▲Functional Reach Test ▲FRAIL SCALE		

Conclusion

This personalized application is intended to simplify the process of home modification for older adults. It would be useful for both older adults and service providers. It is necessary to evaluate the application's effectiveness in the future.

References

Luciano, A., Pascale, F., Polverino, F., & Pooley, A. (2020). Measuring age-friend ly housing: A framework. *Sustainability, 12*(3), 848.

Sixsmith, J., Sixsmith, A., Fänge, A. M., Naumann, D., Kucsera, C. S. A. B. A., To msone, S., ... & Woolrych, R. (2014). Healthy ageing and home: The perspectiv es of very old people in five European countries. *Social science & medicine, 10 6*, 1-9.

Smith, S. K., Rayer, S., Smith, E., Wang, Z., & Zeng, Y. (2012). Population aging, disability and housing accessibility: Implications for sub-national areas in the U nited States. *Housing Studies, 27*(2), 252-266.

World Health Organization. Global age-friendly cities: a guide. France: World H ealth Organization;2007

American Association of Retired Persons, The AARP Home Fit Guide, 2011

NYC Health, Aging in Place Guide for Building Owners, 2018

Consumer Product Safety Commission, Safety for Older Consumers-Home Safety Checklist, 2015

Application Download

Scan Me! Android download (Korean Ver.)

Scan Me! App Store download (Korean Ver.)

Contact

More information

Evidence-based Design Lab.
- Dr. Kwon, Pusan National University, Korea
www.research-ebd.com

Acknowledgment

This work was supported by the Ministry of Education of the Republic of Korea and the National Research Foundation of Korea (NRF-2019R1F1A1054133).

Environmental Design Research Association (EDRA) 53rd Annual Conference, June 01-04, 2022, Greenville, SC, USA

Play Spaces: Alternative Strategies for the Revitalisation of Informal Settlements

***Francesco Rossini**, The Chinese University of Hong Kong); **Sruthi Atmakur-Javdekar**, City University of New York*

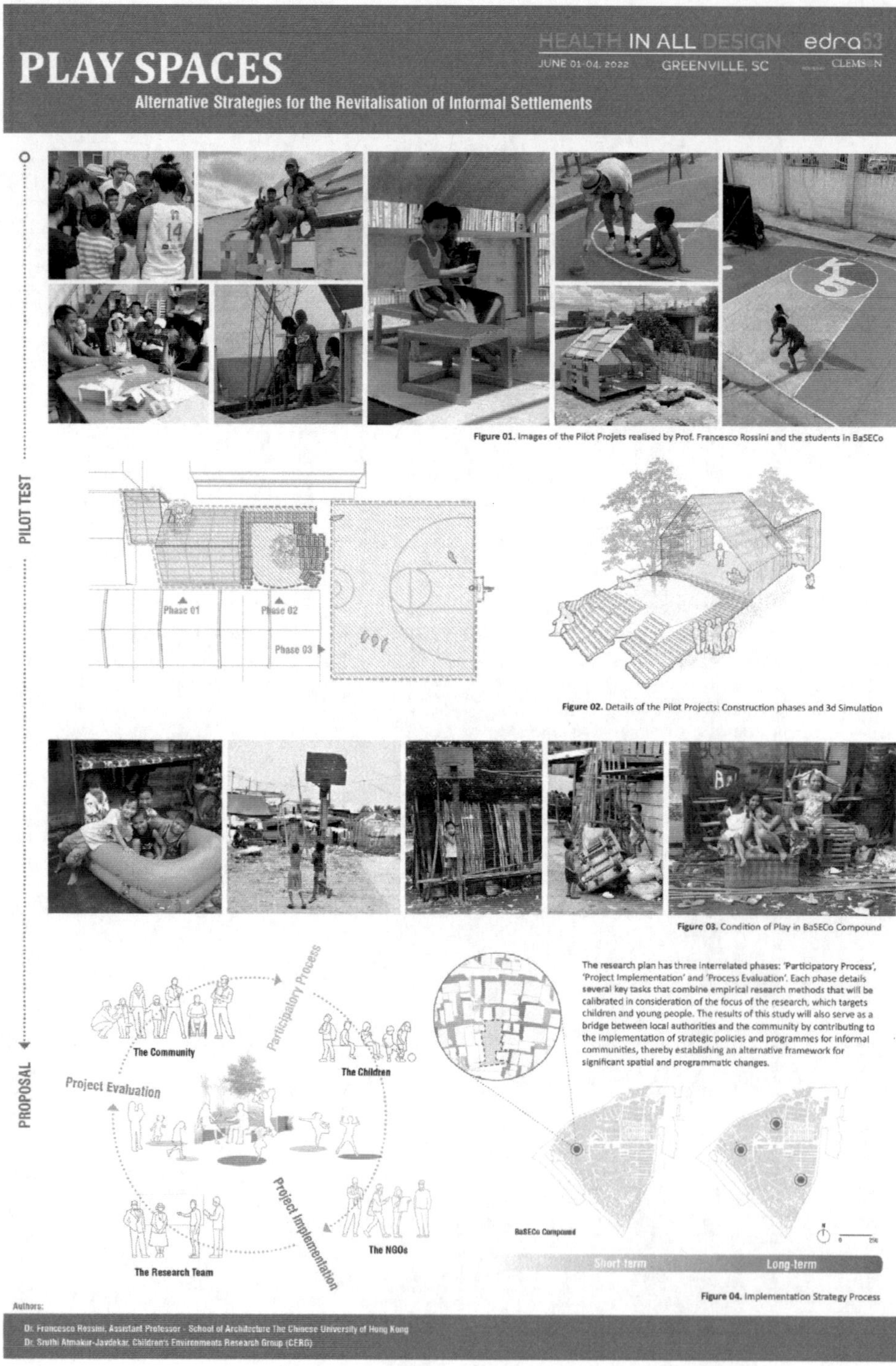

Preserving the Future Food Environment with Traditional Technologies through Cultural Landscapes: An International Comparison between Yamagata Prefecture and Sichuan Province, China

Suxueer Sun & Naoko Fujita, *University of Tsukuba*

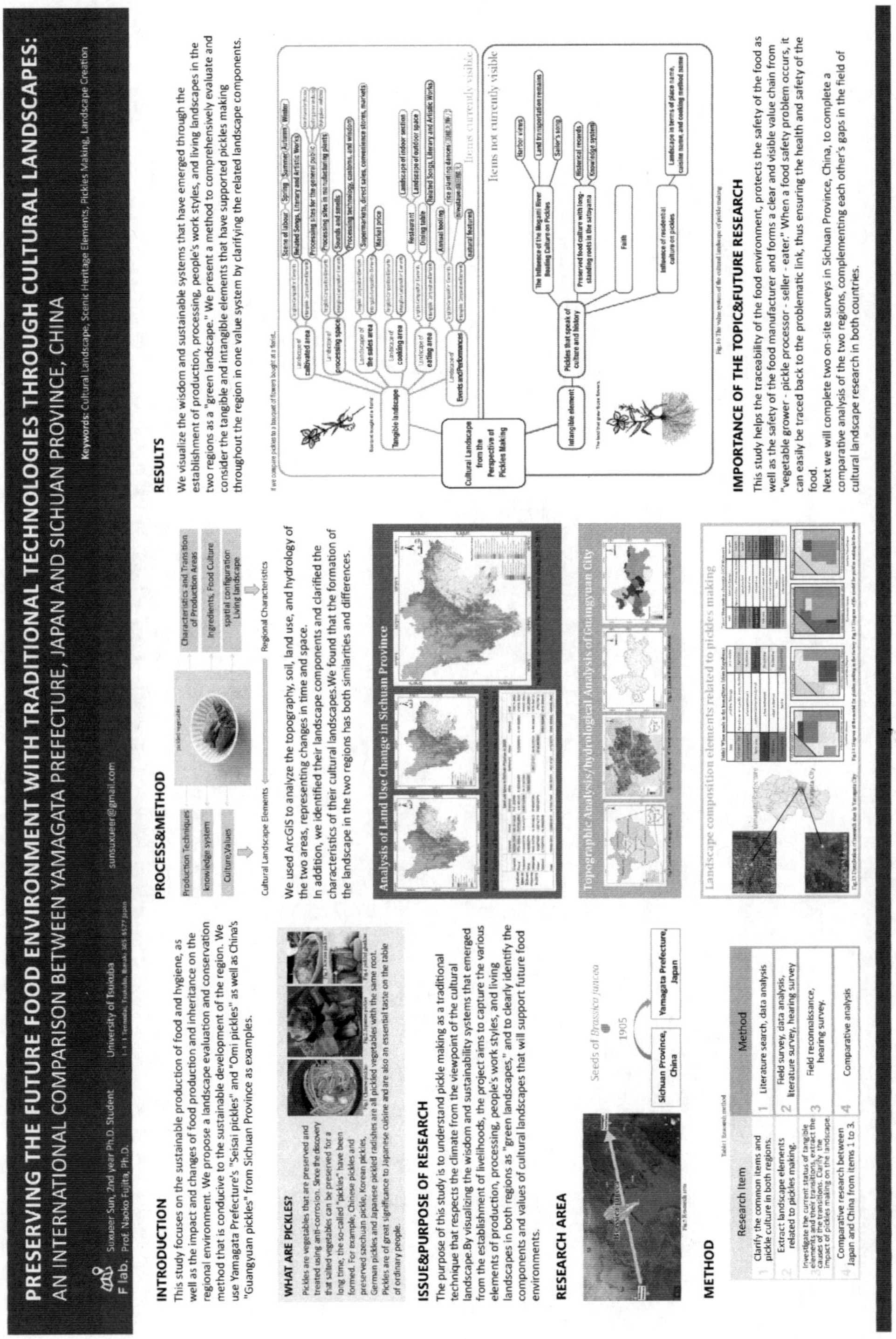

PUZZLE Desk and Chair in Response of COVID 19 to Create Portable Furniture to Study Outdoor and Promote Mental Health

Hafsa Akter, Alejandra Ruiz, Justin Marsh & Brett Snyder, University of California, Davis

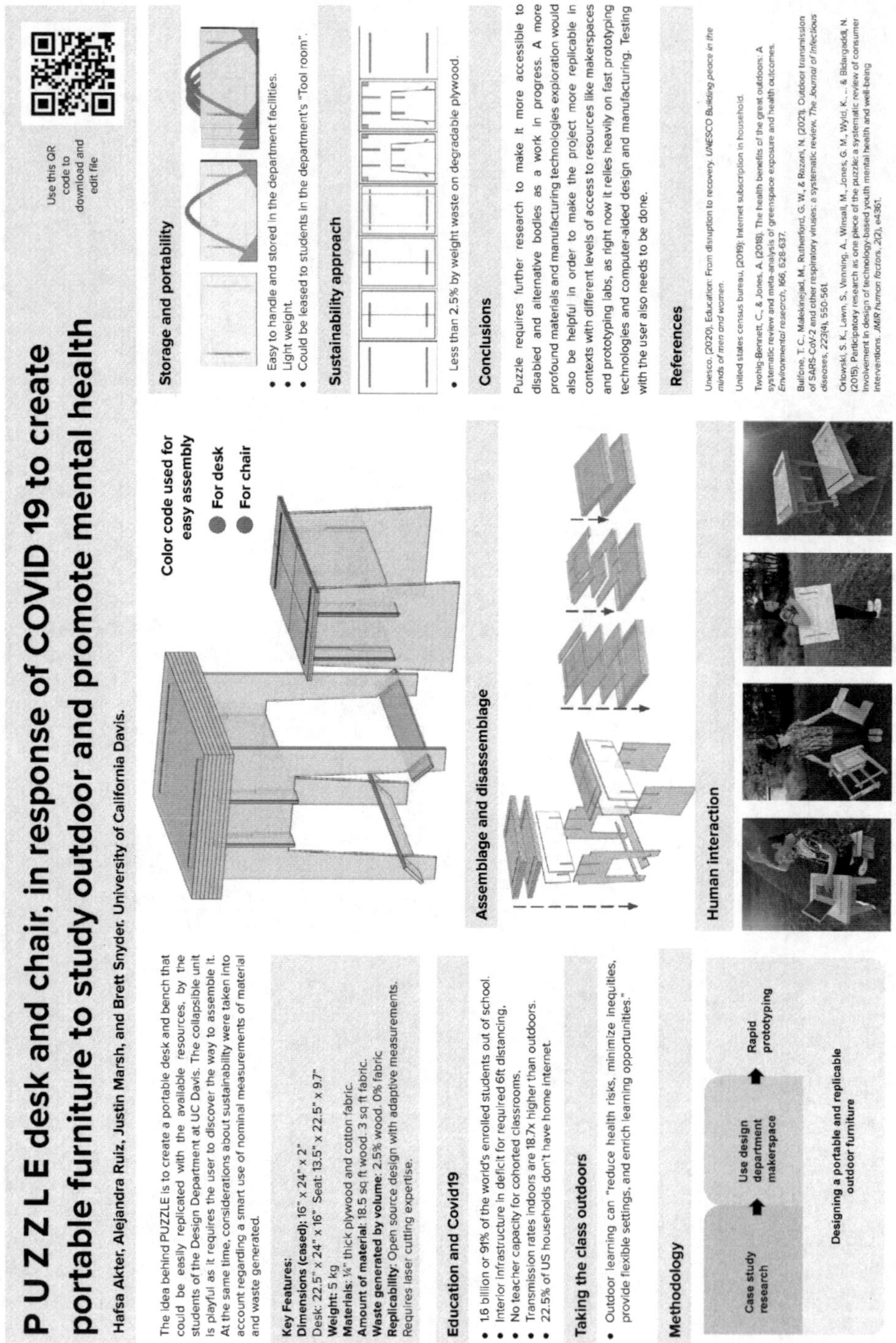

Research on Disaster Prevention and Mitigation, Utilizing Ecosystems As Flood Adaptation for Urban Climate Change in Asia

Minghui Tang & Naoko Fujita, University of Tsukuba

RResearch on Disaster Prevention and Mitigation, Utilizing Ecosystems As Flood Adaptation for Urban Climate Change in Asia

Minghui Tang, 3rd year Ph.D. Student
Prof. Naoko Fujita, Ph.D.
University of Tsukuba, Japan

RESEARCH BACKGROUND

◆Recently, large natural disasters have occurred frequently due to extreme meteorological phenomena affected by climate change.
◆Large cities in Asian countries are experiencing major land changes along with their development.
◆More efficient and flexible measures must be considered for disaster prevention in large cities.
◆Research on disaster prevention and mitigation using ecosystems has been promoted in each country, but the current situation is that research on disaster prevention methods from the aspect of landscape design has been delayed in response to disasters conducted in large cities in Asia.

PURPOSE OF RESEARCH

◆The purpose of this research is to clarify the traditional knowledge about disaster prevention and mitigation and management of natural resources and how to use natural resources that can be used for disaster prevention in landscape ecology from the data of geospatial science, socially and economically. The purpose is to elucidate the ideal method of flood disaster prevention and mitigation in major cities in Asia through analysis of the legal system.
◆The main result of this poster is to clarify the weaknesses of land allocation for disaster mitigation and disaster prevention by using the ecosystem seen from the landscape pattern of an entire metropolitan area

RESEARCH AREA

◆The location of research area overview
◆The study area had selected as an Asian metropolitan area . At this stage, the study area had been selected with in parks and green spaces in consideration of disaster prevention, targeting Jakarta, Indonesia in Southeast Asia and Shanghai, China; Tokyo, Japan in East Asia.
◆In this poster, we focus on Tokyo.

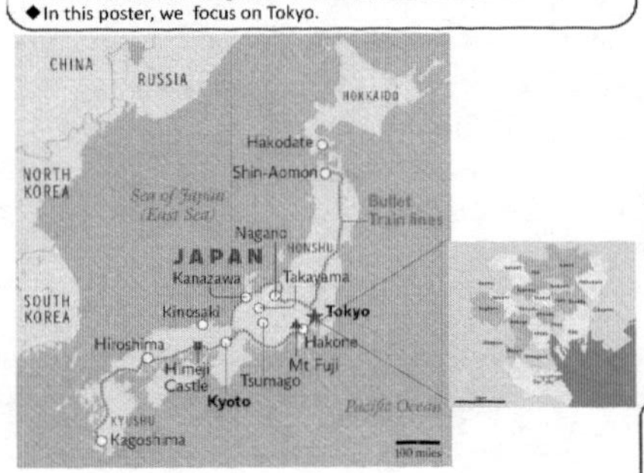

Fig1 Research area in Japan

RESEARCH METHOD

◆This research method steps the urban development status based on data sources such as population distribution and GDP and cuts out the land use data of urban development at each stage by overlapping the land use data during that stage with the data of the administrative area.
◆After preparing the land use data at the urban stage, convert it to TIF format for Fragstats analysis, classify the types of land use data, and set each type analysis index. Combine the obtained analysis result table with GIS data and visualize it

RESULT

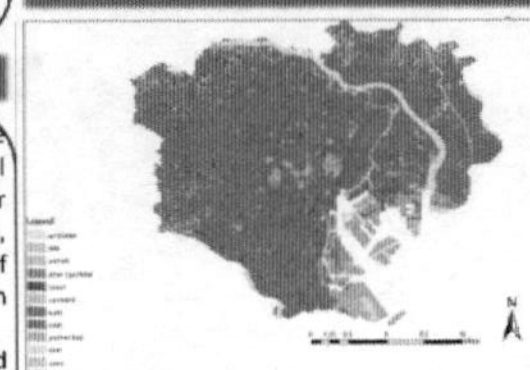

Fig2 Land-use in Tokyo in 1986

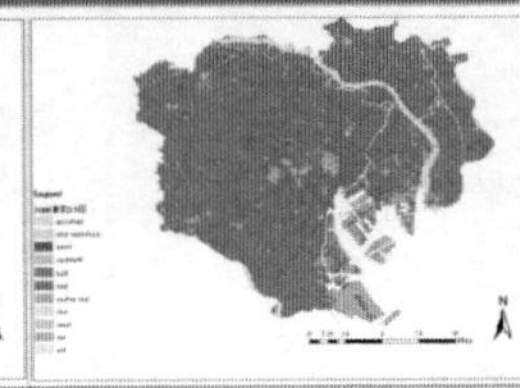

Fig3 Land-use in Tokyo in 2006

★It was found that Tokyo was in the period of urban redevelopment in 2006, and the area of construction land was the largest in urban development, and compared to 1986, some coastal land became such sites as airports.

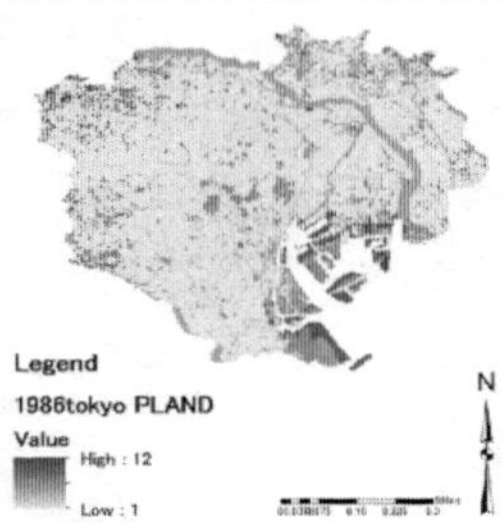

Fig4 PLAND in Tokyo in 1986

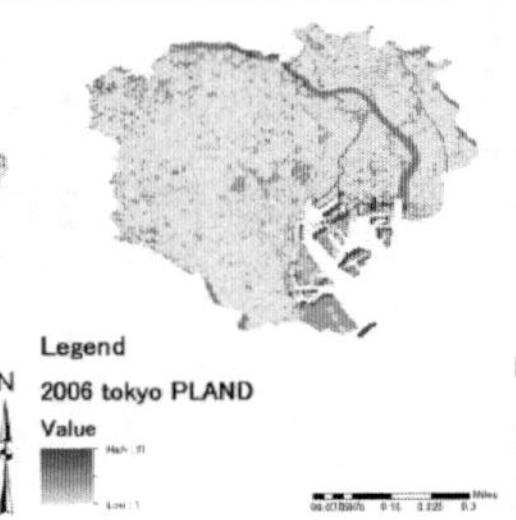

Fig5 PLAND in Tokyo in 2006

Note: TA-Total Area PLAND: Percentage of landscape LPI: Largest Patch Index TE: Total Edge ED: Edge Density

★In Tokyo, the landscape element ratio is the largest for forest land, and the landscape element ratio is the smallest for construction land. There is little difference in the proportion of landscape elements between rice fields and their agricultural land.

Table 1 Landscape pattern result in Tokyo in 1986

TYPE	PLAND	LPI	TE	ED	AREA_CV
forest	10.5387	0.8672	2.451	569827.7265	357.7808
river	1.7065	0.093	0.397	92297.6774	153.7567
agriculture	5.3612	0.2441	1.271	295492.0605	232.011
Rice field	5.954	2.2272	0.992	230627.9497	548.5395
coast	0.4231	0.1093	0.176	40917.862	201.1169
build	0.0721	0.007	0.038	8834.5384	44.9303
sea	0.172	0.0116	0.072	16739.1254	62.8342
wasteland	0.73	0.0418	0.287	66724.0137	106.2444
road	0.0442	0.007	0.028	6509.6599	44.3482
orichard	2.8085	0.6138	0.59	137167.833	206.3738
another land	0.007	0.007	0.004	929.9514	0

Table 2 Landscape pattern result in Tokyo in 2006

TYPE	PLAND	LPI	TE	ED	AREA_CV
forest	9.5204	1.5739	1.87	434752.3	357.7808
agriculture	5.9122	0.3999	1.281	297816.9	153.7567
river	0.9718	0.0535	0.199	46265.08	232.011
another agriculture	5.1171	2.025	0.918	213423.8	548.5395
sea	0.0116	0.0046	0.005	1162.439	201.1169
build	0.2627	0.1279	0.142	33013.28	44.9303
coast	0.0302	0.0093	0.017	3952.294	62.8342
wasteland	0.4743	0.0186	0.198	46032.59	106.2444
another land	2.1273	0.272	0.509	118336.3	44.3482
road	0.0093	0.007	0.007	1627.415	206.3738

★Compared to Tokyo in 1986 and 2006, the proportion of landscape elements in forest land from 10.5387 to 9.5204 , tends to decrease. Alternatively, the proportion of landscape elements on construction sites from 0.0.721 to 0.2627 tends to increase compared with Tokyo in 1986 and 2006.

DISCUSSION

★According to LIU et al. (2021), the occurrence of geological hazards has a significant positive correlation between landscape CONTAG (infestation) and SHDI (diversity).
★landscape CONTAG (infestation) increased but SHDI (diversity) decreased compared to re-urbanization and suburbanization.
★It can be inferred that the maintenance and management of biodiversity will be burdened if the landscape elements become single.
★From the perspective of Eco-DRR, ensuring the diversity of landscapes will be advantageous for disaster mitigation and disaster prevention in cities.
★To make up for the limitations of this study, we would like to analyze regional ecosystem services in future studies and propose a verification of the results obtained in this study.
★For that purpose, in addition to the land use data handled in this study, it is necessary to clarify the soil storage capacity of ecosystem services.

Research on the Design Effect of Rural Theme Park Evidence from Big Data——Take Kentucky Horse Park As an Example

Pang Shaojie* & *Yi Yang*, *Beijing Jiaotong University); Bo Zhang, Oklahoma State University

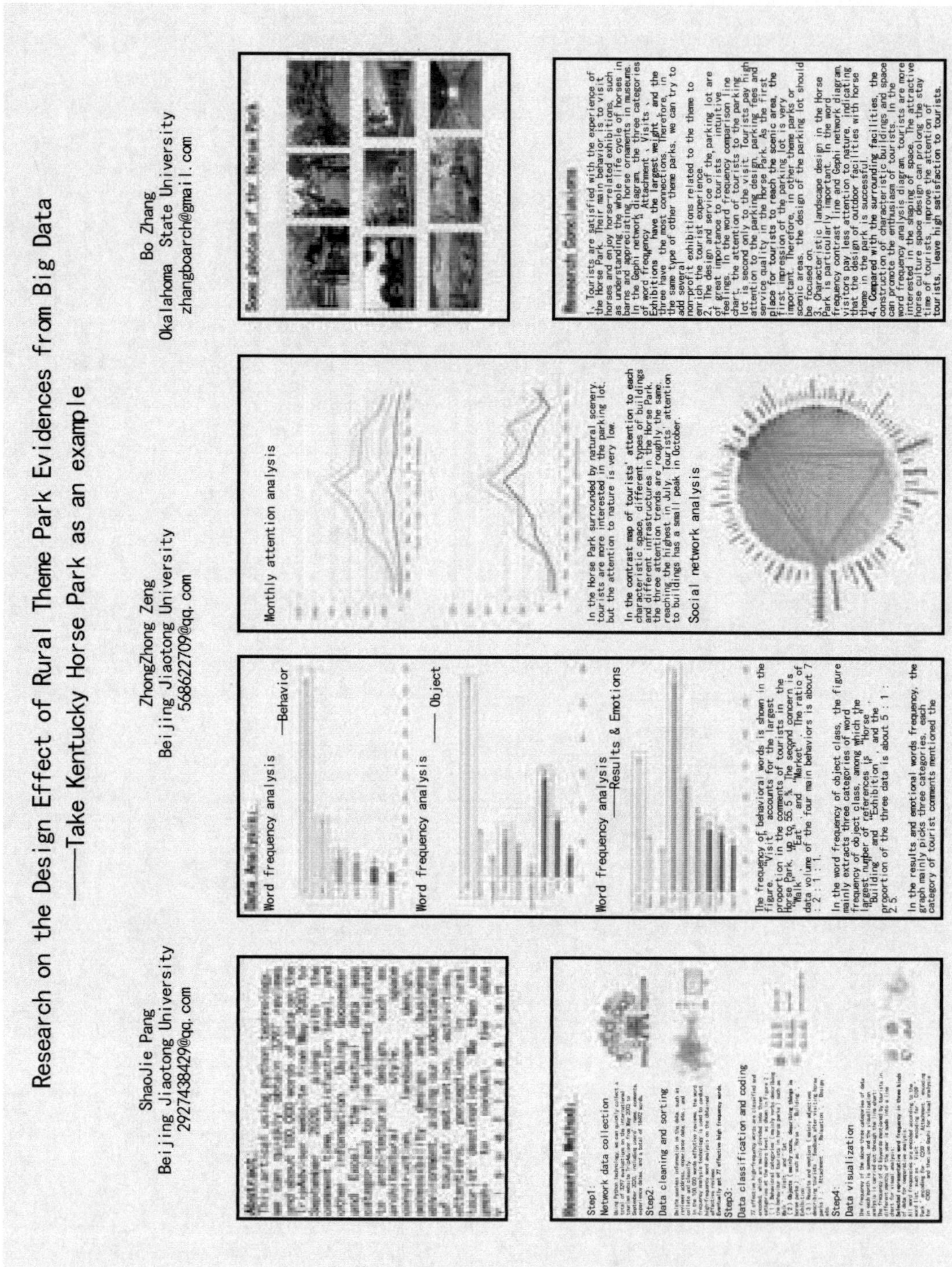

Research on the Development Guidelines for after-School Day Services: Through Behavioral Observation and Needs Assessment

Kurumi Takezawa & Eiji Satoh, *Utsunomiya University*

Research on the Development Guidelines for After-School Day Services : Through Behavioral Observation and Needs Assessment

Kurumi TAKEZAWA, Graduate School of Regional Development and Creativity, Utsunomiya University, Japan, kurumi.takezawa.uu@gmail.com
Eiji Satoh, Utsunomiya University, Japan

1. Background and Objective

Currently in Japan, the environment surrounding children with disabilities is changing as the number of children with disabilities increases and the multiple and severe disabilities become more apparent.

In Japan, the Child Welfare Law was revised in 2012. In recent years, here has been a marked increase in the number of after-school day care centers which taget age from 6 to 18 for children with disabilities. After-school day service is a service that provides necessary support for school-going children with disabilities(Fig.1). The number of after-school day service facilities has quadrupled in the five years since 2012(Fig.3).

On the other hand, the increase in the number of low-quality establishments that maintain only minimal facilities in order to profit from subsidies, etc., has become a problem. This is partly due to the ease of entry for after-school day service facilities.

In 2015, the After-School Day Service Guideline was published. However, it is difficult to guarantee the quality of services uniformly with the guideline alone. Therefore, the purpose of this study was to understand the actual activities of children with disabilities in after-school day service facilities and to obtain knowledge for designing spaces that are friendly to children with disabilities.

2. Research Method

In this research, we conducted interviews with six distinctive facilities among those that were able to cooperate with our survey through a questionnaire survey of after-school day service facilities in Tochigi Prefecture in 2018, to understand the current status and needs of the facilities from the perspective of the employers(Fig.2). Then, behavioral observations of staff and children were conducted to understand how the rooms are used and the problems that arise. Finally, a questionnaire survey of parents was conducted at 15 facilities to understand the needs and problems of the parents in the facilities.

3. Results

3.1. Results of Questionnare Survey and Interviews

3.1.1. Buildings Figure 4 shows that the ratio of possession and rental buildings is about half. Private companies that have recently started providing services tend to use rental buildings. On the other hand, social welfare corporations that have been providing services for a long time tend to use possession buildings. In addition, 46% of the businesses using rental buildings use them without renovations.

3.1.2. Difficult to use Table 2 shows that there is a wide range of opinions about toilets and water supplies. It is pointed out that it is difficult to support wheelchair users if the toilet entrance is narrow. It is also pointed out that the number of water supply wants a little more. There is also an opinion that in the case of an old building there are many steps and not barrier-free. The following two types are noted as characteristic of this type.

(1) Attached type There is an opinion that it is difficult to use the room properly. Therefore, there are ADS that use drawing cards and posters to make it possible for children to understand the purpose of the room visually. There is also an opinion that it is not possible to utilize the vacant room well. The use of the room is a problem because the area is large.

(2) Rental - Single type There is an opinion that the shelves and switchboards installed are dangerous. It is a problem that there is a place that is not barrier-free because this type's building is not designed as a building to support disabled children.

3.2.Behavioral observations The results of the behavior observation survey at Facility A are shown in Figures 5 and 6. Facility A accepts children regardless of disability type. It did not completely separate rooms for dynamic and static activities, but rather separated activities by setting up desks, mats, and other interior furnishings. In addition, children of various ages and disability types and degrees were spending time in the same space, but some children had difficulty coping with the space due to the mixture of static and dynamic activities. Especially in Training Room C, static activities such as reading books and calligraphy were mixed with dynamic activities such as playing with a balance ball.

Figure 6 shows the characteristic children's activities. Characteristic activities were observed in Child A with hyper sensitivity and Child B with severely retarded disabilities. Child A rarely moved from training room A and was quiet. Child B was always with the staff, changing clothes, having snacks, etc. Children A and B moved less than the mentally

4. Conclusion and Discussion

From the actual situation where children of different ages and with different types and degrees of disabilities spend time in the same space, it is considered necessary to develop flexible spaces that can be divided according to the content of treatment and education. In addition, the type of facility should be selected according to the type of operation (stand-alone or attached), the content of treatment and education, and the characteristics of the children accepted. The current guidelines do not provide detailed guidelines, and it is necessary to examine the details.

After School Day Service(ADS):
It was founded by the revision (2012) of the Child Welfare. It is support that can receive the training necessary for improving living capacity and promoting exchange with society for disabled children between 6 and 18 years old.

Installation Standard:
Provide a teaching and training room, and equipment and equipment necessary for providing support. In addition, the teaching and training room should be equipped with the necessary equipment for training.

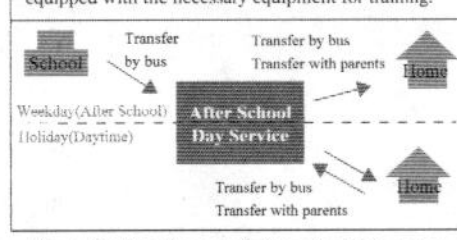

Fig. 1 Outline diagram of after school day service

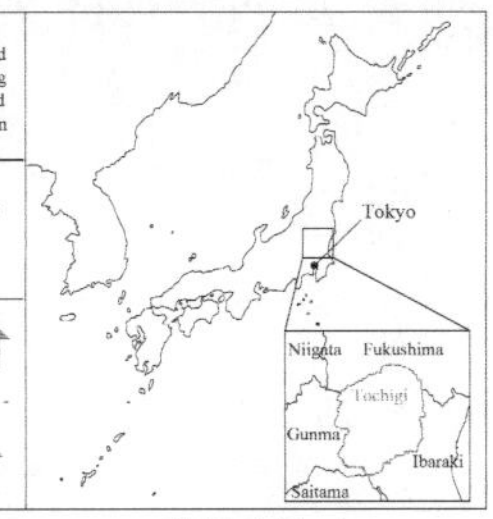

Fig. 2 Analysis terget

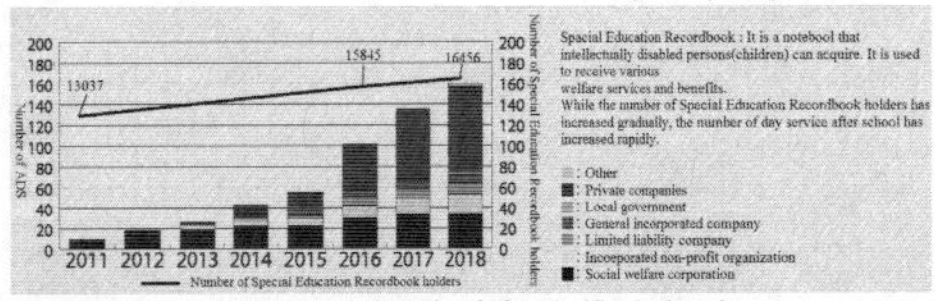

Fig. 3 Changes in the number of After School Day Service and the number of special education recordbook holders

Table. 1 Questionnaire outline

Item List of Questionnaire Survey ※Implementation : 2018.12 Recovery rate : 44/166(26.5%)
①Operation situation of day service after school
Installation subject, Operating body, Main target of business, Year of service start, Transfer, Used building, Staff number, Contents of nursing care, Event, Daily flow
②Use child
Capacity, Contract number, Age, Frequency, Degree of disability, Trouble, Thoughts about the environment in which the user will live in the office
③Floor plan
Request for attachment of floor plan, Presence of office, consultation room, Difficult to use, The place where the usage is devise

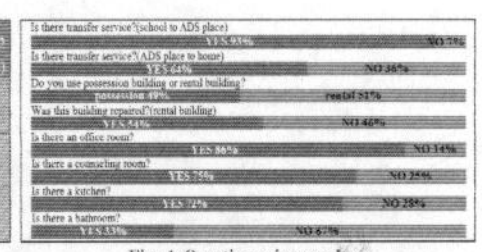

Fig. 4 Questionnaire results

Table. 2 A place that is difficult to use and a place that is devised

		Possession		Rental		
				Single type(19)		
Operation form		Single type(3)	Attached type(17)	A room in the building(11)	One building(8)	Attached type(5)
		service only after school day service	service after school day service and other services in the same building	Rent a room in a building and service only after school day service	Rent an one building service only after school day service	service after school day service and other services in the same building
Difficult to use	toilet, water services	The entrance is narrow. There are few	Want the number of water supply a little more	There is no sink or water supply	Toilet, water supply is not child size, want the number of water supply a little more	
	Barrierfree	There are many steps because of old building		Step before the toilet, switchboard are dangerous	There is no slope at the entrance	There are many steps because of old building
	Other	There is no door to the learning room, so children can not concentrate	· Can not utilize an empty room · Because we offer various services on one floor, it is difficult to set up activities · There are too many doors and children can not concentrate · Too much light from the room	· A child wants to climb on the provided shelf · There is a problem with sound insulation because air conditioning is shared · Entrance space is narrow · There are too many doors and children can not concentrate		When parents come to pick up, children gather at the entrance
To devise		· Children who can not concentrate learn in private rooms such as the counseling room · The furniture is arranged according to the number and features of the children	· In order not to support in the same space as children who use other services, we divide the rooms · The room where children can not enter is locked	Partitioning materials storage space, office space	· Attached the key to a high position that children can not reach · Divide rooms according to children's characteristics and scenes	· Divide the room visually, by puting poster between after school day service and other service rooms

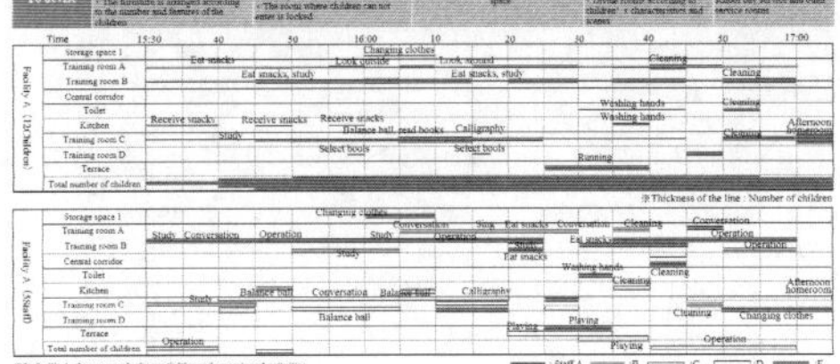

Fig. 5 Activities at facility A

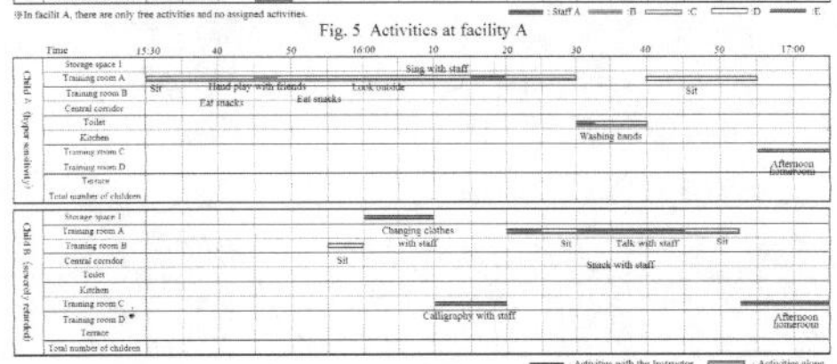

Fig. 6 Characteristic children' s activities

This reserch was funded by the Interdisciplinary Research Grant from School of Regional Design, Utsunomiya University.

EDRA53(Environmental Design Research Association),Greenville,SC,Jun1-4,2022 #12332

Research on the Outdoor Spaces in Senior-Living Facilities in Zhengzhou

Zhe Wang & Yahong Zhu, *Henan University*

Residential Happiness Elements That Affect the Daily Happiness of Koreans

Byungsook Choi, *Chonbuk National University;* ***Jung-a Park***, *Wonkwang University;* ***Jin Lee*** *Jeonbuk National University*

Residential Happiness Elements that Affect the Daily Happiness of Koreans

Byungsook Choi, Jin Lee
Jeonbuk National University, S.Korea

edra Environmental Design Research Association

JEONBUK NATIONAL UNIVERSITY

Introduction

- The interest and importance of 'happiness' is increasing worldwide. Happiness, which has recently been discussed, is not an increase in subjective life satisfaction, but an increase in 'flourish' due to an increase in positive emotion and engagement, relationship, meaning, and accomplishment(Seligman, 2011).
- Among the various happiness factors for enhancing human happiness, 'residential' is very important. Home is the most essential place for humans and the place where humans spend the most time in daily life. In addition, the importance of homes is increasing as we have recently suffered from COVID-19. In general, housing studies have been studied using the POE theory focused on residents' satisfaction to improve the quality of life of residents in a residential environment or to provide a better residential environment for them. This E-B theory presupposes that the residential environment affects the behavior of residents, and recently, the relationship between the residential environment and the resident's mental health with happiness has studied. Above all, this relationship will be revealed, which is easier to make a happy residential environment with the development of a residential happiness index (Choi, 2021), a tool that can evaluate the happiness felt by residents in a residential environment.

OBJECTIVES

this study focused on the residents' happiness felt through the residential environment, and the contents of residential happiness that leads to the daily happiness of residents were analyzed to improve the overall happiness of residents.

Residential Happiness		Daily Happiness (PERMA)
• Safety • Security • Comfort • Convenience • Sustainability • Economic Feasibility • Personality	→	• Positive Emotion • Engagement • Relationship • Meaning • Accomplishment

Methods

Measurement tools

- To measure residential happiness, a residential happiness measurement tool consisted of 7 conceptual factors and 61 measurement elements proposed by Choi (2021) was used. This used a 5-point Likert scale that responds with 1 to 5 points depending on the degree to which residents feel happy in the residential environment.
- Residents' daily happiness was viewed as an increase in PERMA, factors that promote well-being, based on Seligman's well-being theory(2011). To measure daily happiness, Positive emotion, Engagement, Relationship, Meaning and Accomplishment, Butler & Kern (2016)'s PERMA-Profiler 14 items scale was used. The respondents used an 11-point Likert scale that gives scores from 0 to 10 for the happiness they feel around their daily lives.

Data Collection

- The subjects were 2,160 people who were allocated in consideration of gender(male, female), age(20-30's, 40-50's, 50' and above), residential area(Seoul, metropolitan city, and other cities in local area), and housing type(detached house, condominium apartment, multi-family housing, and studio) and data were collected through an online survey from June 18 to June 24, 2021.
- Reliability: Residential Happiness measurement Tool (Cronbach's α=.970) / Daily happiness measurement tool (Cronbach'α=.964)

Data Analysis

Analysis Contents	
1) General characteristics of respondents	Frequency analysis
2) Level of residential happiness and daily happiness	Descriptive analysis
3) Effects of the residential happiness factors and elements on daily happiness	Multiple regression analysis

General Characteristics of Respondents(N=2,160)

Characteristics		f	%	Characteristics		f	%
Gender	Male	1080	50	Residential area	Seoul	720	33.3
	Female	1080	50		Metropolitan	720	33.3
Age	20-30 years	728	33.7		Others	720	33.3
	40-50 years	724	33.5	Housing type	Condominium Apartment	550	25.5
	50 and above	708	32.8		Detached house	546	25.3
Income	Below 4,000,000won	1686	78.1		Multi-family housing	540	25.0
	4,000,000-6,000,000 won	310	14.4		Others	524	24.3
	6,000,000won and above	164	7.6	Ownership	Owner	1032	47.8
Family size	Single-person household	616	28.5		Rental	1093	50.6
	Multi-person households	1544	71.5		Others	35	1.6

Analysis Results

Level of residential happiness and daily happiness

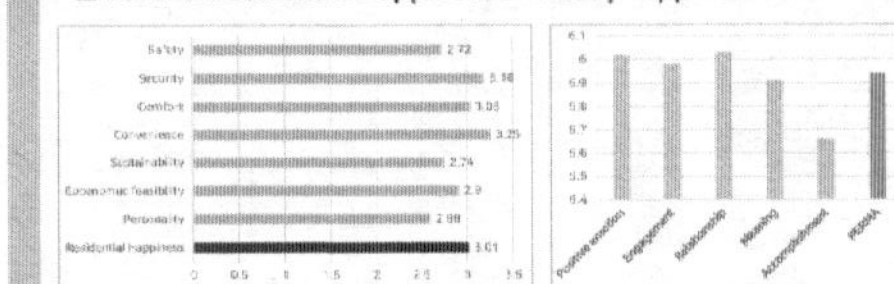

Effects of the residential happiness factors on daily happiness

Variables	B	SE	β	t	Adj. R^2	F
(Const.)	2.184	.268		8.145***	.293	180.103***
Comfort	.520	.099	.188	5.264***		
Personality	.436	.062	.207	7.020***		
Economic feasibility	.223	.060	.106	3.720***		
Convenience	.235	.090	.092	2.615**		
Safety	-.133	.060	-.043	-2.226*		

*p<.05, **p<.01, ***p<.001

Effects of the residential happiness elements on daily happiness

Variables	B	SE	β	t	Adj. R^2	F
(Const.)	1.921	.209		9.195***	.309	88.781***
Expressing one's style or personality	.195	.054	.104	3.640***		
feeling of emotional stability	.367	.051	.181	7.133***		
Decorating with family photos or objects with memories	.163	.049	.089	3.308**		
Appropriate level of housing costs	.167	.044	.086	3.795***		
Indoor noise control	.130	.041	.073	3.177**		
Internet environment	.095	.046	.049	2.075*		
Participation in design, architecture, interior design and renovation	.151	.046	.088	3.325**		
plants such as flowers, and trees	.112	.038	.068	2.968**		
Risk of slipping and falling on the floor of the entrance and toilet	-.086	.035	-.046	-2.462*		
Electrical outlets installed where necessary	.121	.053	.056	2.273*		
Sense of openness of the indoor high ceiling	-.088	.044	-.047	-1.995*		

*p<.05, **p<.01, ***p<.001

Conclusion

- As results of the analysis, it was found that in order to enhance daily happiness through housing, above all else, it is necessary to express one's personality in a residential environment, to feel of emotional stability like a relaxing comfortably, and to be convenience without worrying economically. In particular, it was found that there was an effect of enhancing daily happiness when expressing one's style or decorating with family photos or objects with memories. In relation to the comfort factor, it was found that the residential environment in which the interior was quiet without noise, not too open, and a sense of stability enhances daily happiness. In addition, it was found that the convenience of using the Internet, properly equipped electronical outlets where necessary, the use of non-slip tiles in the bathroom and entrance, and the residential environment with flowers and trees enhances daily happiness.
- Among these residential happiness factors, the expression of personality and comfort of residents have the greatest influence on daily happiness. It can be seen that the house is formed in the relationship with the resident, and the residential environment is the existence that reveals the inner side of the resident as it is. In the end, it can be understood that residents are happy only when the meaning of dwelling has a psychological and philosophical meaning, not just a physical shelter, but also an environment that contains the residents themselves. Therefore, it can be seen that Korean housing designers should induce residents to reveal themselves beyond simply providing only physical space for housing planning and supply.

This work was supported by a grant from the National Research Foundation of Korea (NRF) funded By the Korean Government (MEST) (No. 2018R1AB6005965)

Safe Residential Environment for Single Female Household: Using Eye-Tracking Method

Soohyun Lee, GyeongYeon Lee, Ji Eun Oh, Gidong Byun & MiKyoung Ha, Yonsei University

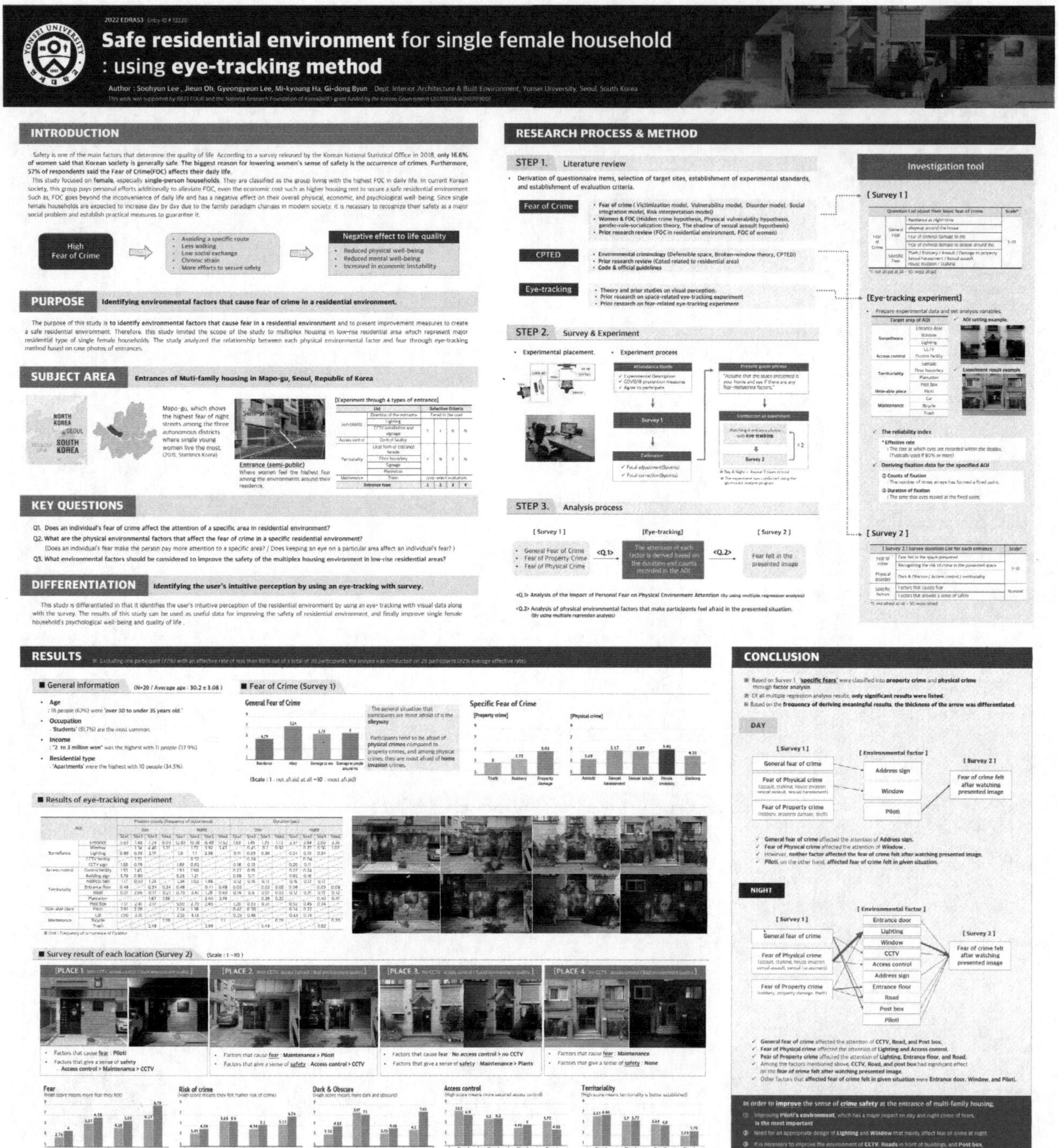

Senior Friendly Street Environments in Historic Districts —Taking Shunbei District in Daokou As an Example

***Zhe Wang & Guoxiang Li**, Henan Uiversity*

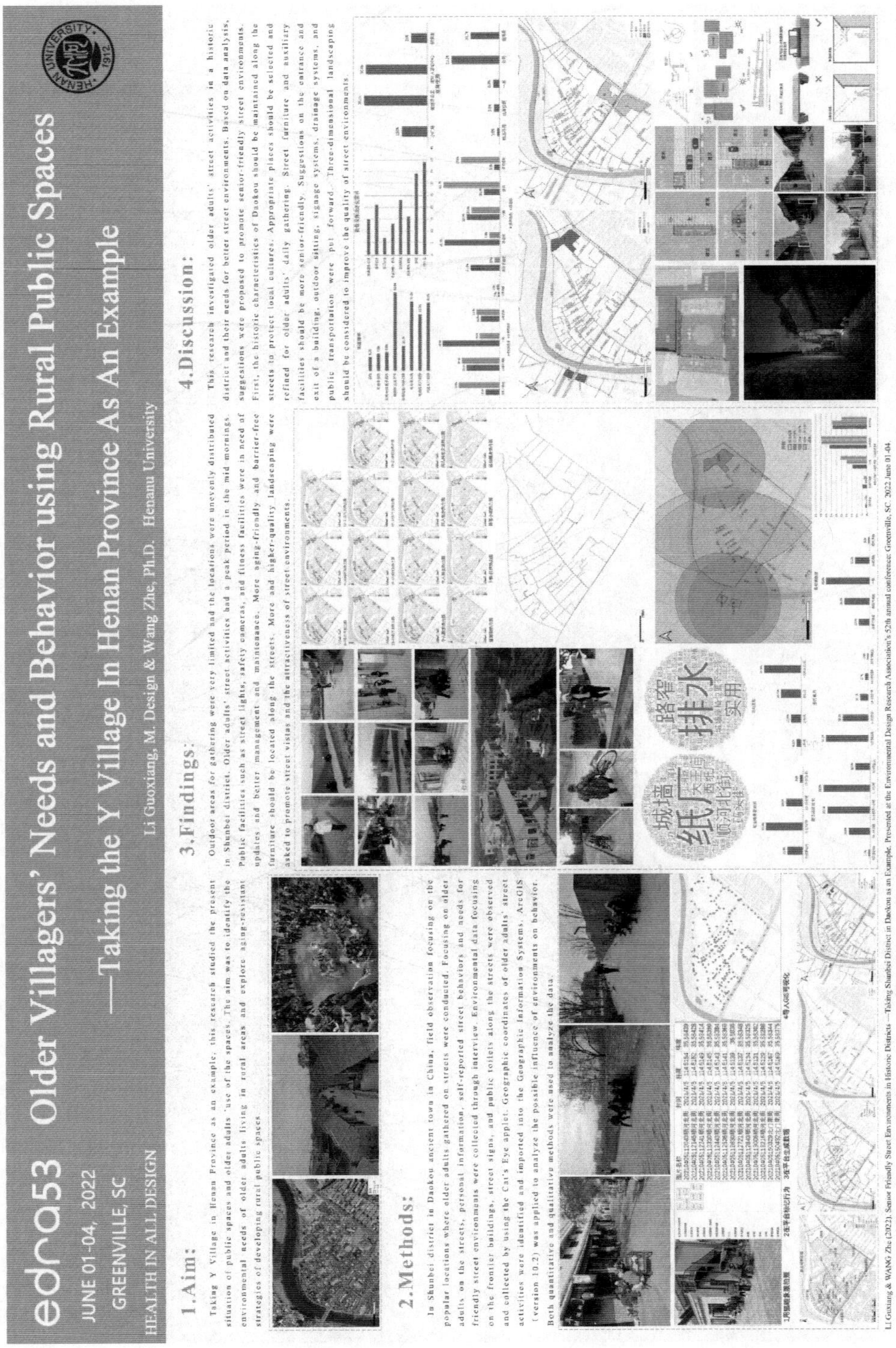

Signage Systems in Senior-Living Facilities – a Study in China

***Zhe Wang**, Henan University; **Enguang Li**, M. Design*

Spatializing Fractals: Fractal Complexity of Interior Spaces

***Joori Suh**, University of Cincinnati); **Steen Petersen**, Wright State University*

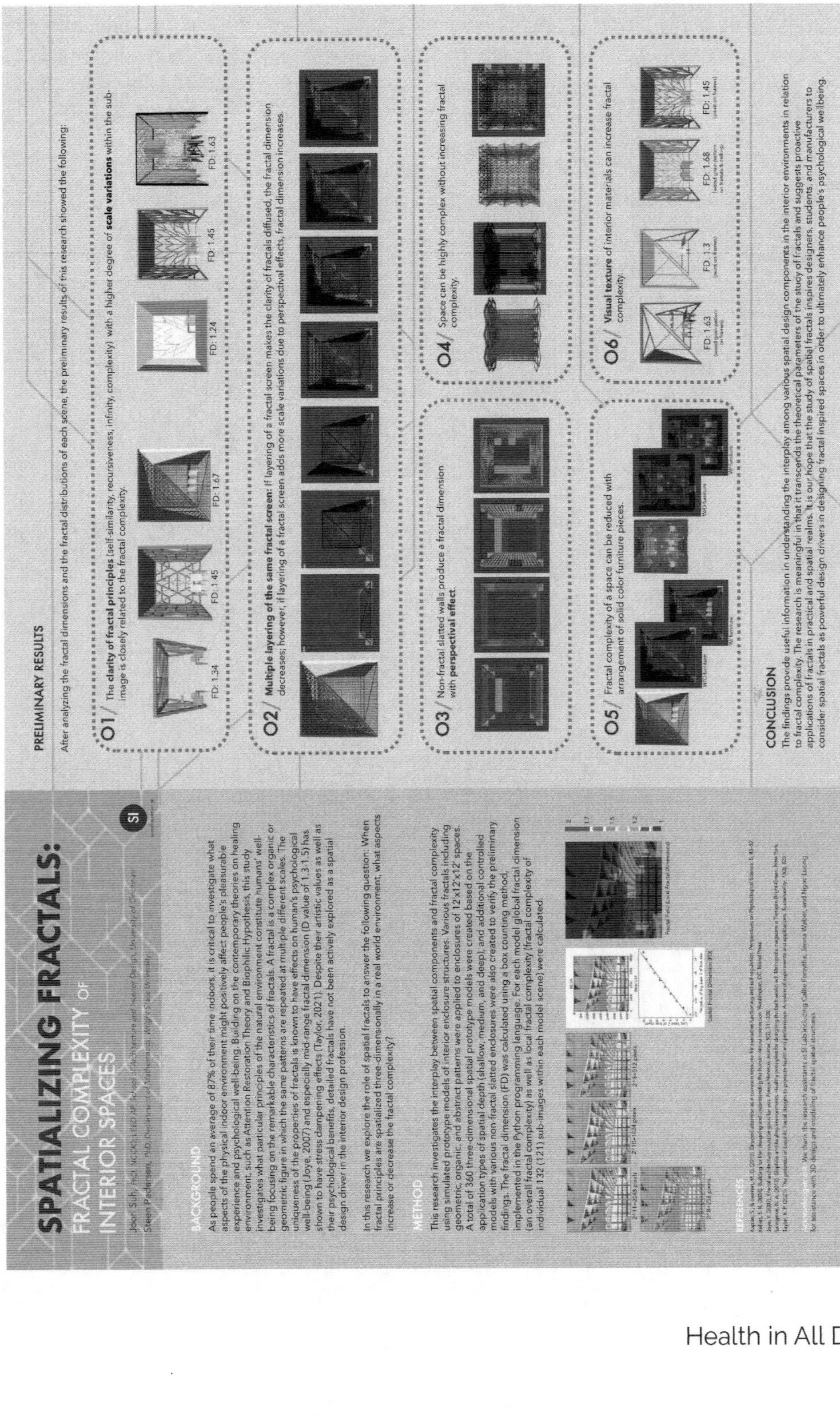

Stitching the Community to the Nutritious Ground in the Urban City Landscape through Help Yourself!

***Riya Premani & Carey Clouse**, University of Massachusetts, Amherst*

Table Design and Its Effectiveness for the Visually Impaired

***Momoka Hirai**, Tohoku University*

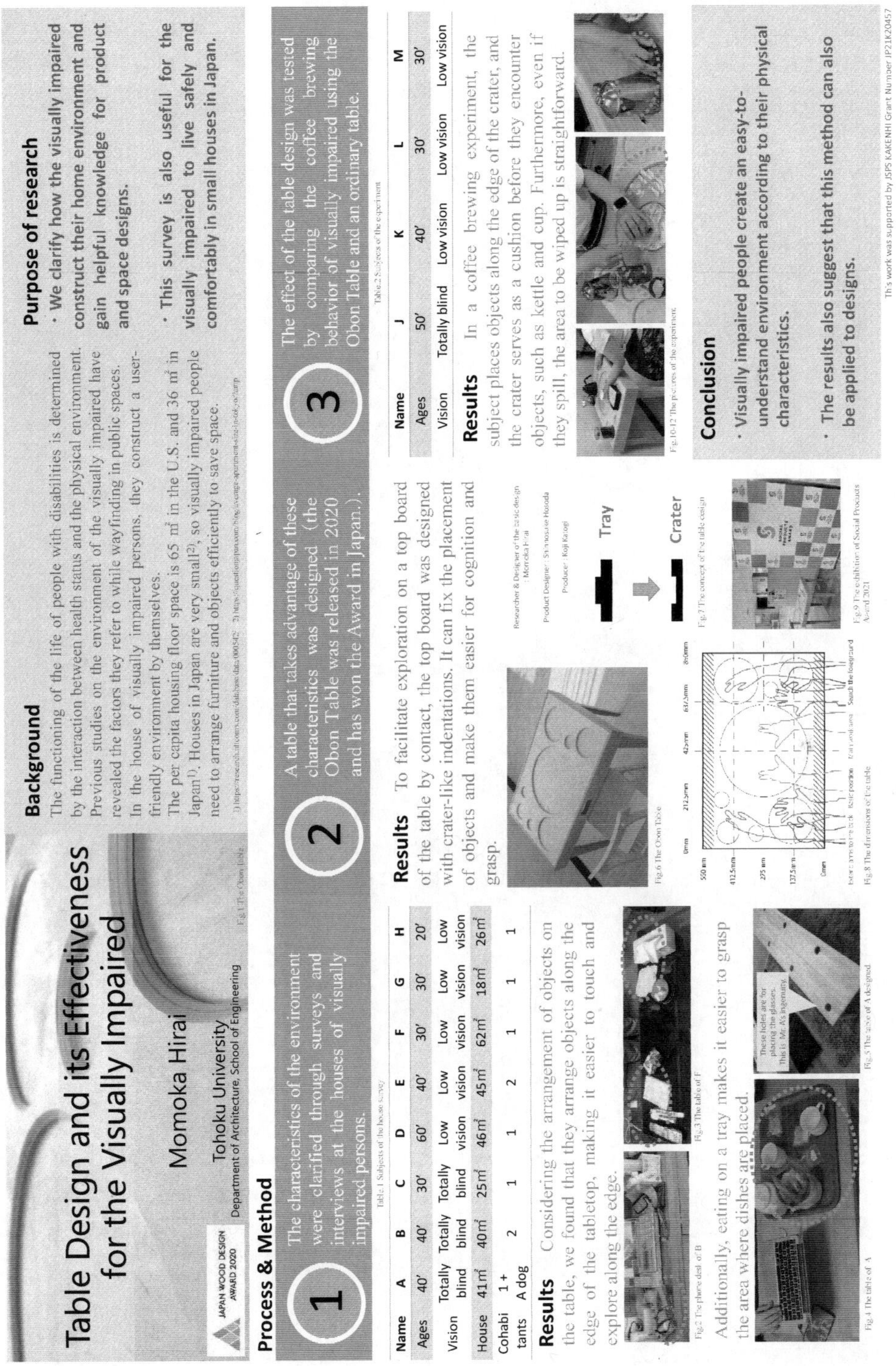

Teaching Community Resilience in Detroit's Good Stock Neighborhoods

***Ceara O'Leary**, Detroit Collaborative Design Center*

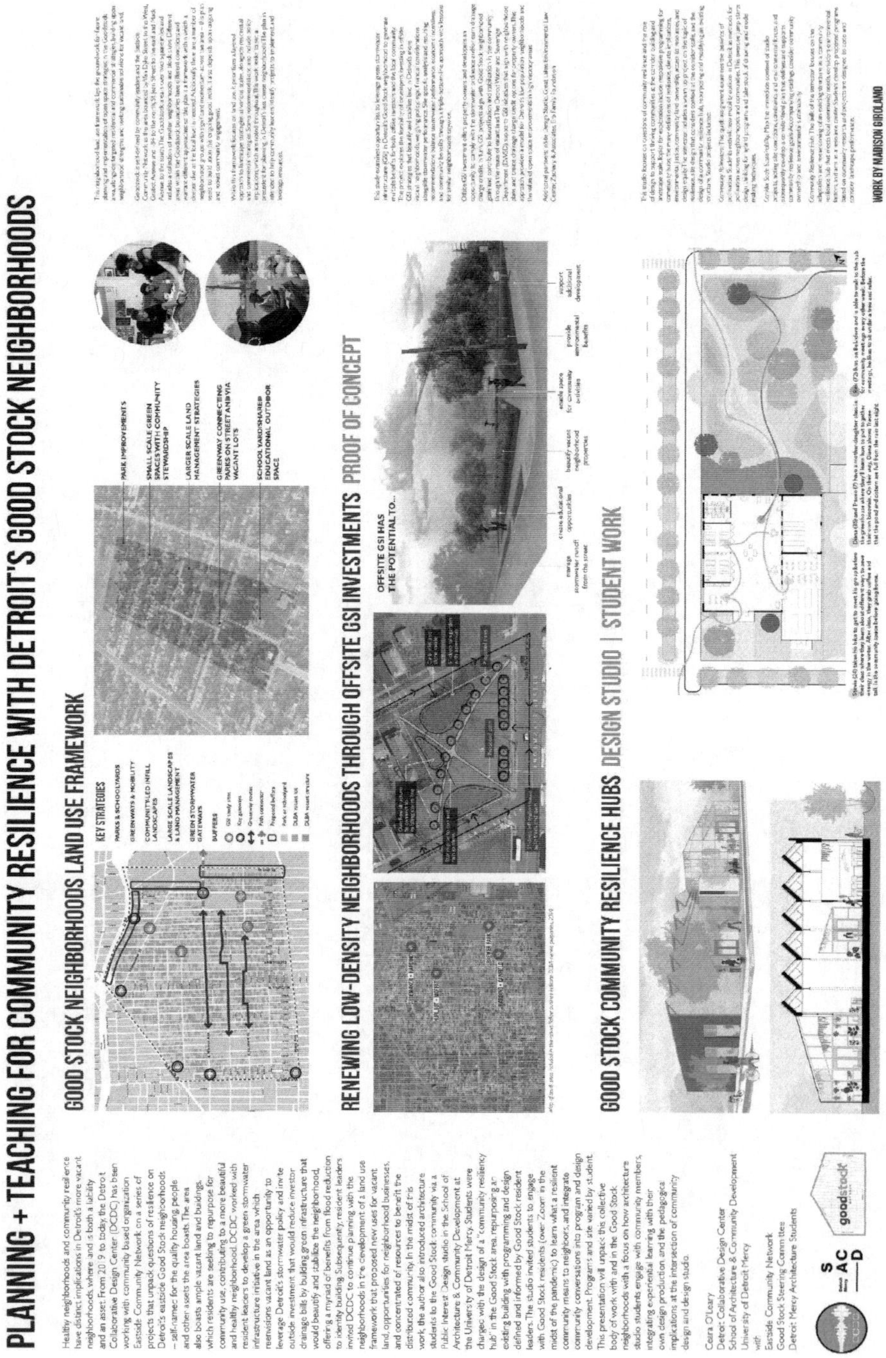

The Positive Effects of Biophilic Design: The Relationship between Indoor Plants, Positive Emotions, and Prosocial Behavior

***Bing-Tao Lee & Koen Steemers**, University of Cambridge*

The Positive Effects of Biophilic Design: The Relationship Between Indoor Plants, Positive Emotions, and Prosocial Behaviour

UNIVERSITY OF CAMBRIDGE

Bing-Tao Lee (3rd year PhD candidate); btl30@cam.ac.uk
Supervisor: Professor Koen Steemers
Department of Architecture, University of Cambridge

Introduction:

Built environments exert a significant impact on human emotions and behaviours, with nature being an important element (Baker & Steemers, 2019). Including natural elements in built environments is known to have a significant impact on human emotion and cognition; however, their positive influence on prosocial behaviour has received comparatively little attention. It is hypothesised that exposure to plants increases positive emotions, and so enhances prosocial behaviour (Zhang, Piff, Iyer, Koleva, & Keltner, 2014). As people spend much time indoors, an indoor-plant-office scenario has been chosen.

Methodology:

An experiment was carried out in three rooms. The first room was used for prior mood measurement. The other two rooms were used for post-mood measurement and a prosocial behaviour task, for the experimental group and control group respectively. Plants of a variety of types and colours were available for the experimental room to assess: mixed design with scenarios (i.e., either with or without plants); between-participants factor and phase (i.e., before and after exposure to plants); within-participants factor. Participants' mood before and after exposure to the plants was recorded, and lastly, their prosocial behaviour was measured. The methods have been widely used in previous studies. The experiment was conducted from 11am to 5pm on March 15th, 18th and 19th 2019. The daylight and weather conditions remained the same on those days. The participants were international post-graduate students and they were randomly assigned to conditions.

The figure below presents an overview of the entire experiment.

Group 1 <No plants>	Group 2 <plants>
1.Prior-emotion test (Time 1) 2.Bring them to a room without plants 3.Post-emotion test (Time 2) 4.Prosocial behaviour test	1.Prior-emotion test (Time 1) 2.Bring them to a room with plants 3.Post-emotion test (Time 2) 4.Prosocial behaviour test

First room:

Second room:

Control group vs Experimental group

Results and Discussion :

The results demonstrated that the emotion metrics worked well and showed that exposure to plants changed the participants' emotions, which is in line with the literature; happiness, pleasure, and relaxation seem to be strong indicators. However, there was no clear pattern concerning prosocial behaviour because the sample size was too small. There were also potential confounding factors, which could be reduced by applying propensity score matching with a bigger sample. Regarding limitations, the experimental rooms were not identical in the pilot study. Ideally, they should be two adjacent identical rooms.

Conclusion & Contribution:

The contribution is to specifically define emotion and prosocial behaviour in this context and quantify them properly in a way that is coherent with multi disciplines and existing knowledge. This research attempts to combine psychology and architecture to not only advance research on biophilic design but also potentially provide guidance for its characteristics for built-environment experts and architectural designers. As urban density continues to grow it is believed that biophilic design will be of ever-increasing importance in promoting mental health and general well-being.

Reference list:

Baker, N., & Steemers, K. (2019). Healthy homes: designing with light and air for sustainability and wellbeing. Routledge.

Zhang, J. W., Piff, P. K., Iyer, R., Koleva, S., & Keltner, D. (2014). An occasion for unselfing: Beautiful nature leads to prosociality. Journal of Environmental Psychology, 37, 61–72. https://doi.org/10.1016/j.jenvp.2013.11.008

Toilet Design: Hidden Corner in the Campus

Yilin Song, Junxuan Li, Shuyan Zhang, Zhejia Li & Rongxuan Mu, Tianjin University

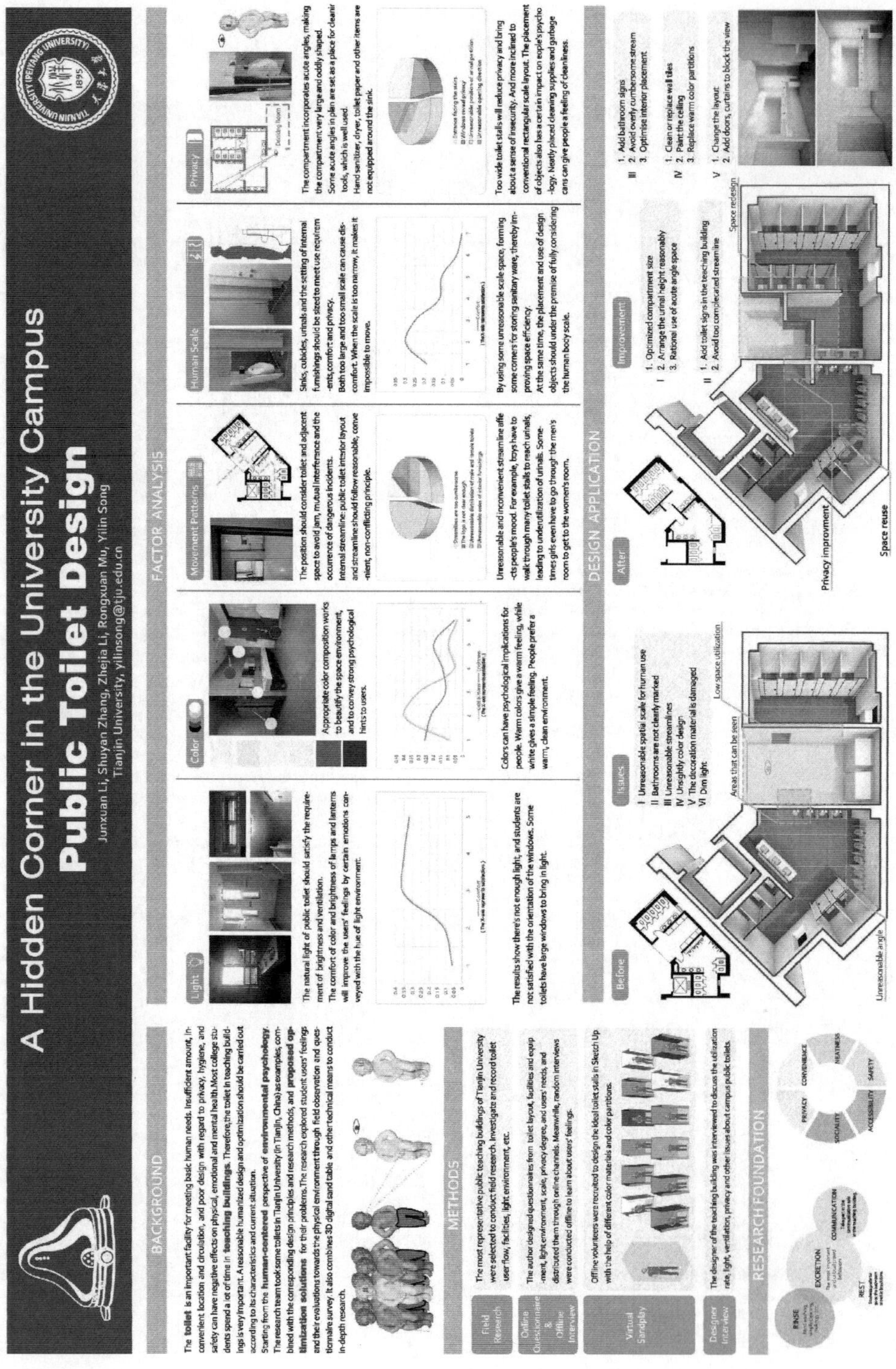

Transportation Evaluation and Optimization of School Areas

Yilin Song, Hanzhang Liu, Xinlei Sheng, Zhiqing Gao & Ni Xia, Tianjin University

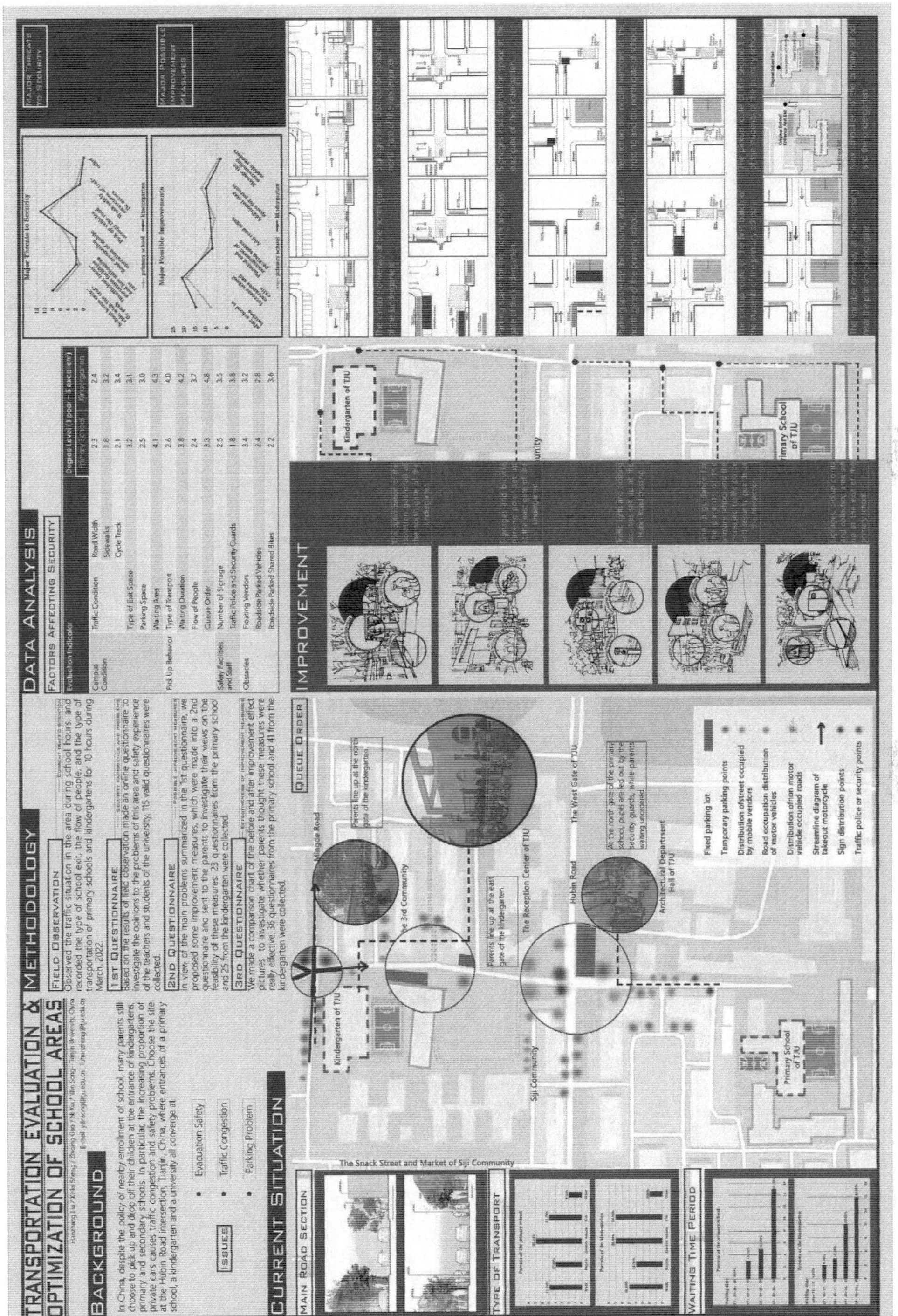

Typologies of Therapy Cluster in Radiotherapy Departments Developed from Comparative Floorplan-Analysis

***Carolina Kolodziej**, Technische Universität Dresden*

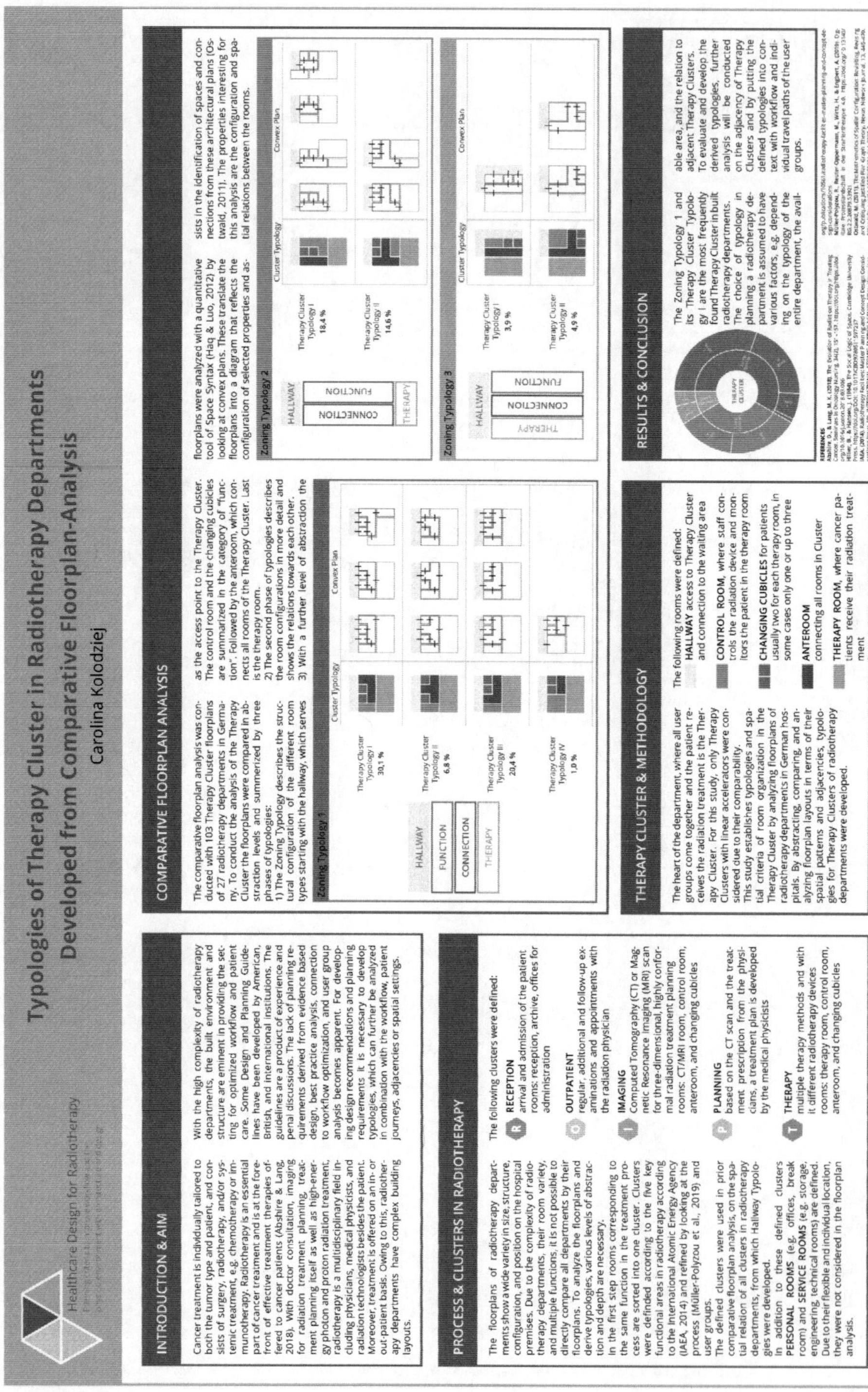

Utilization of Sustainable Placemaking: Fostering Spatial Conditions Based on Various User Behaviors in Urban Spaces

Zile Tian & Naoko Fujita, University of Tsukuba

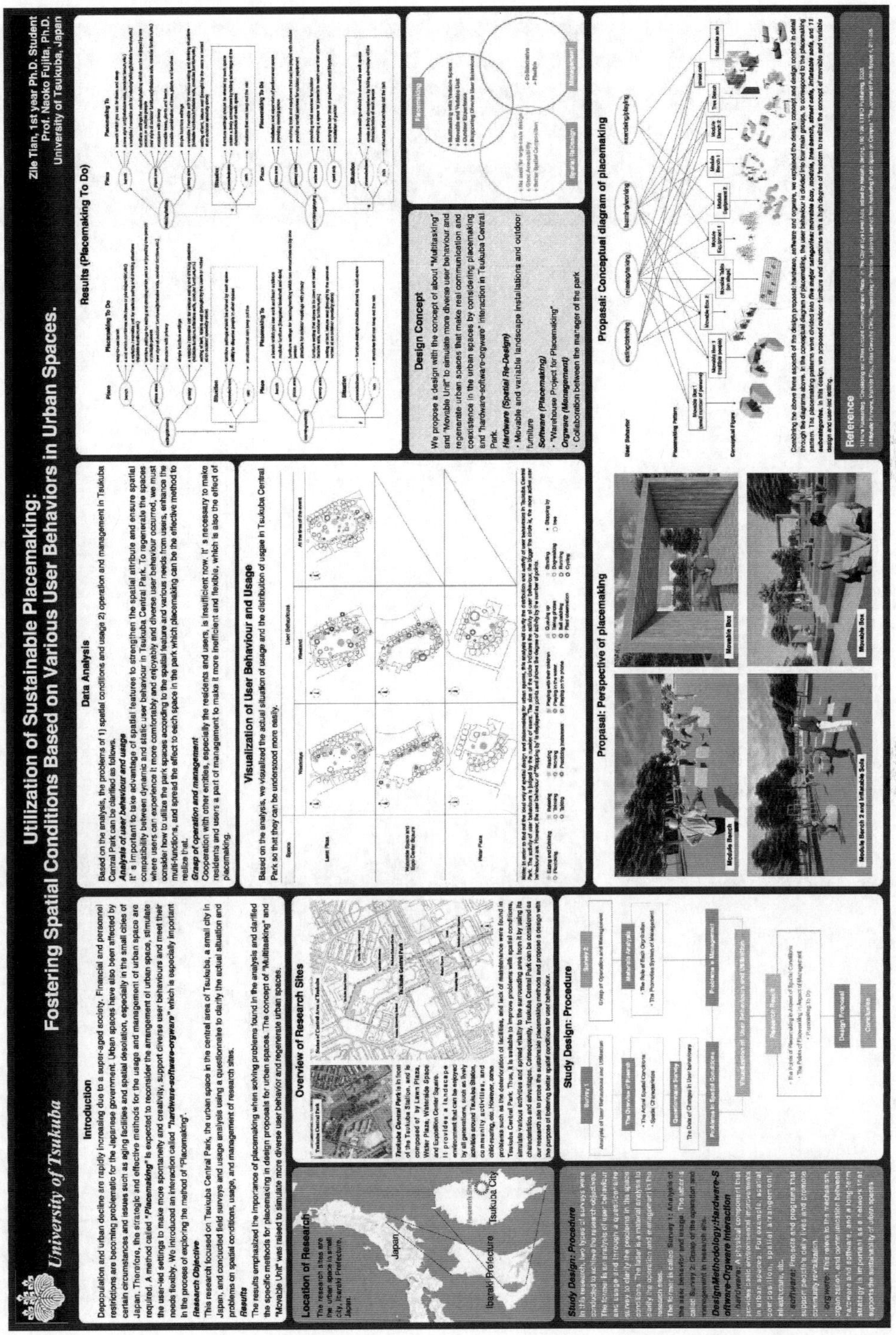

Virtual Simulation of Trauma Rooms: Lessons Learned from an Augmented Reality Simulation Tool Development

***Hamid Estejab & Sara Bayramzadeh**, Kent State University*

Toward a model of safety and care for Trauma Room Design

VIRTUAL SIMULATION OF TRAUMA ROOMS:
LESSONS LEARNED FROM AN AUGMENTED REALITY SIMULATION TOOL DEVELOPMENT

Environmental Design Research Association 53
Greenville, SC | 01-04 June, 2022

Hamid Estejab, B.Arch
Graduate Research Assistant
Kent State University

Hossein Mirzajani, M.Arch, MHD
Graduate Research Assistant
Kent State University

Sara Bayramzadeh, Ph.D., M.Arch.
Coordinator and Elliot Professor
Kent State University

BACKGROUND

Simulations in healthcare settings facilitate effective communication between designers and end-users and are one of the cost-efficient ways to evaluate designs before construction. With emerging technologies such as augmented reality (AR), a technology that let users view virtual objects in their field of view along with the physical space, designers are able to employ more sophisticated approaches to simulation and complement the conventional physical mock-up simulations.
Following is a brief research background and milestones that have been met prior to the implementation of AR simulation.

Literature Review | Case Studies | Focus Group | Design Thinking Sessions | Mock-up Simulation

METHODS AND OBJECTIVES

This study aims to develop and utilize an AR application for Hololens 2 to complement a full-scale, physical mock-up for simulation and evaluation of a trauma room design prototype.
This study is developed based on direct observation of the trauma room mock-up simulations. Clinicians, representing trauma room roles, participated in three different trauma scenarios. Given the low-fidelity construction of the mock-up, participants were unable to simulate some of the key tasks. Examples include lack of ceiling-mounted objects such as medical boom, inability to move objects, and inability to accurately evaluate interactions with the physical environment. The AR application was refined based on two pilot testing sessions to address limitations. The two software used for developing the application were Unity3d and Autodesk 3DsMax for 3d modeling.

Floor Plan Layout:

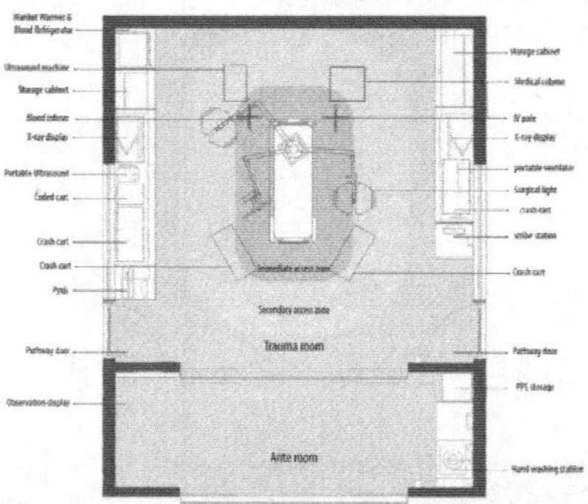

AR APPLICATION

Followings are some of the features that have been added to the AR application after the pilot studies.

Detailed 3D Models:
Detailed 3d models of the medical booms and other pivotal objects for the simulation were developed and added to the application. These objects were not feasible to be built into the physical mock-up given the low-fidelity construction.

Eye Tracking
Using the "record" button, the eye gaze of the user can be recorded. Based on the focus, the time, and the sequence of users' eye gaze, a 3d heatmap texture would be generated. All the interactions such as moving, rotating, scaling with objects as well as user's head positioning will be stored in an Excel file or unity3d with timestamps for further investigation and analysis.

Interactions
Users can have interactions with the components of the room. Interactions consists of moving, rotating, changing scale, changing the opacity and hiding and unhiding the components. Interactions are available with hand gestures or voice commands.

Collaboration
This app gives the users the ability to collaborate in an AR environment and see the result in real-time. For example, in AR, when a trauma surgeon changes the position of the carts, the nurse can see the changes in real-time with their AR goggles on.

User Interface
The User Interface (UI) of the app is in front of the face of the users which allows users to control their intended interactions. It can be opened or closed with a voice command and it follows the user when they want to move.

Replay and recording system:
the application features a replay system of objects' interactions with storing objects' information and video recording.

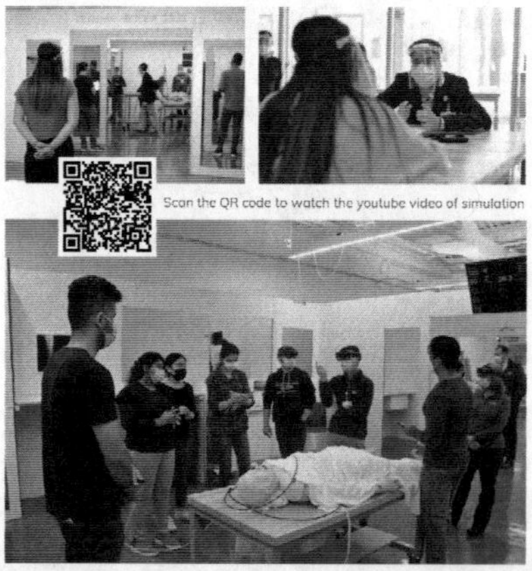

Scan the QR code to watch the youtube video of simulation

AR LIMITATIONS:

HoloLens:
Researchers should bear in mind that the rendering quality of the HoloLens is limited. So design elements of the application such as 3D models and textures should be optimized. Also, the field of view of the headset is narrow and users can only see a portion of the screen. HoloLens can get heated, and its battery can be drained easily which prevents continuous work. This happens especially when the screen recording or screen mirroring is used for a while.

Software Workflow:
Most of the 3d modeling tasks in Architecture are done in Revit, Rhino, or Sketchup; however, these 3D modeling programs are not recommended in the workflow of the AR development considering the optimization of the 3D models. The reason lies behind the fact that these programs mostly use the NURBS modeling system or their mesh modeling features are limited, on the other hand, game engines that are used for AR prefer mesh modeling. Since the conversion between these two systems is challenging in terms of mesh polygonization, importing objects to software like 3Ds Max, Maya or Blender is beneficial.

User Experience:
Although the user interface of the application was relatively simple, training sessions were held for clinicians to help them become familiar with the application. Despite these, some clinicians found it difficult to use. Having one of the researchers in the virtual environment as a moderator and mirroring the screen on a monitor can be helpful for troubleshooting and supporting users.

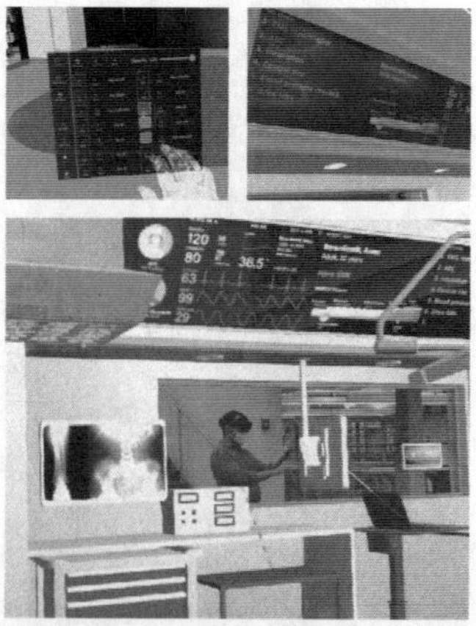

This project was supported by the Agency for Healthcare Research and Quality [grant number R18HS027261]. The content is solely the responsibility of the authors and does not necessarily represent the official views of the Agency for Healthcare Research and Quality.

KENT STATE UNIVERSITY | College of Architecture and Environmental Design
Healthcare Design Program

Who Will Take Refuge in the Open Space of the University Campus? - Evacuation Sites for Diverse Populations

Yoshihiro Osawa, Chiaki Konishi, Yuka Honda & Hiroshi Tsuchida, Tokyo Denki University

Research on University Campus Focusing on Space Contributing to Regional Disaster Prevention.

-Evacuation sites for diverse populations-

Yoshihiro Osawa, Chiaki Konishi, Yuka Honda, Hiroshi Tsuchida
Tokyo Denki University,Japan

1.Background,Purpose

·Background

In areas such as Chiyoda Ward, Tokyo, where the difference between daytime and nighttime populations is large, strict evacuation plans are needed for employees and visitors other than residents. According to the disaster prevention plan of Chiyoda Ward, most transportation such as railways will be suspended in the event of a seismic intensity of 5 upper.

Chiyoda Ward has a daytime population of 850,000.

If a major earthquake occurs, it is assumed that 500,000 people will be stranded.

·Purpose

In Japan, it is basic to use an open space such as a park or a square as a temporary evacuation place at the time of a disaster.

In Chiyoda Ward, large parks and plazas are designated as evacuation sites, but because of the large daytime population, it is necessary to consider designating other vacant areas as evacuation sites.

Therefore, we focused on the campus of a university with a large site and an open space with good quality maintenance.

The purpose of this study is to investigate the possibility of the open space of the university campus in Chiyoda Ward as an evacuation place.

Location of Chiyoda Ward in Tokyo

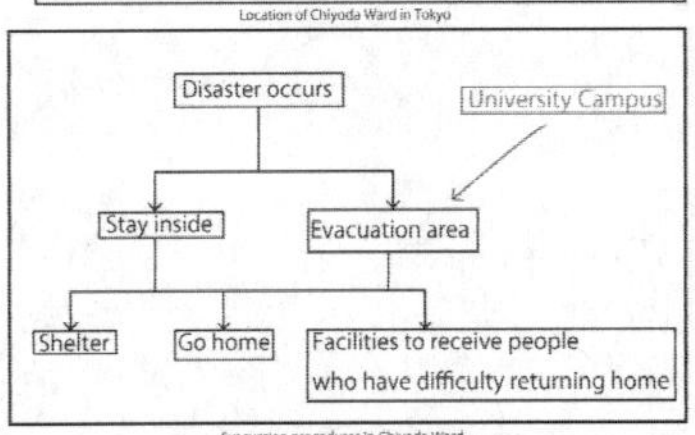

Evacuation procedures in Chiyoda Ward

2.Research method

- organize daytime population data for Chiyoda Ward.
- study the use of buildings throughout Chiyoda Ward.
- look into the agreement between the Chiyoda Ward campus and the ward.
- study the use and population of buildings around university campuses.
- compare the building coverage ratio of the university campus with that of the surrounding area.

3.Population and Building Status of Chiyoda Ward

· Daytime population of Chiyoda Ward

Chiyoda Ward has a large number of employees and visitors, and there are few residents, so the difference between the daytime population and the nighttime population is large.

The daytime population is 853,068.
The nighttime population is 58,406.
So the difference is 794,662.

Therefore, open spaces and facilities that ensure the safety of about 800,000 people are needed in the event of a disaster.

· difference between daytime and nighttime populations

Nighttime population is the number of residents.

The daytime population is those who gather there in the daytime.

Daytime population(Unit: Number of people)				
Total	Employed person	School commuter	Those who do not work or attend school	Other
853,068	755,559	69,443	11,159	16,907

Table of daytime population

Employed person(Unit: Number of people)			
Total	Resident worker	Inflow commuter	Outflow commuter
755,559	24,692	740,387	9,520

Table of employed person

School commuter(Unit: Number of people)			
Total	Resident student	Inflow student	Outflow student
69,443	5,654	65,405	1,616

Table of school commuter

·Building area in Chiyoda Ward

A comparison of the total floor space of buildings in Chiyoda Ward shows that there are many commercial and public facilities.

As a result, many people are thought to flow during the daytime.

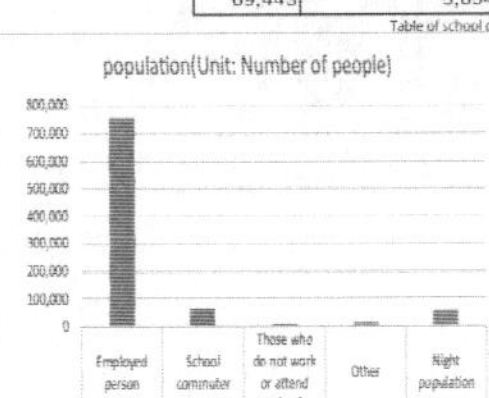

	Employed person	School commuter	Those who do not work or attend school	Other	Night population
population	755,559	69,443	11,159	16,907	58,406

Comparison of daytime and nighttime populations

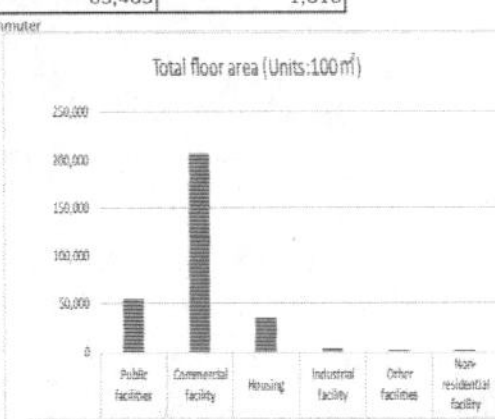

	Public facilities	Commercial facility	Housing	Industrial facility	Other facilities	Non-residential facility
Total floor area	56,112	206,540	34,747	3,885	115	48

Total floor area by building use

4. Agreement between the ward and the university, and population and building conditions around the campus

• Agreement between the university and Chiyoda Ward

Looking at the agreement between the university and the ward, we can see that they are proceeding with the following.

(i) Development of Student Volunteers
(ii) Provision of temporary facilities to local residents and disaster victims such as those who have difficulty in returning home
(iii) Provision of stockpiled goods to disaster victims housed in university facilities

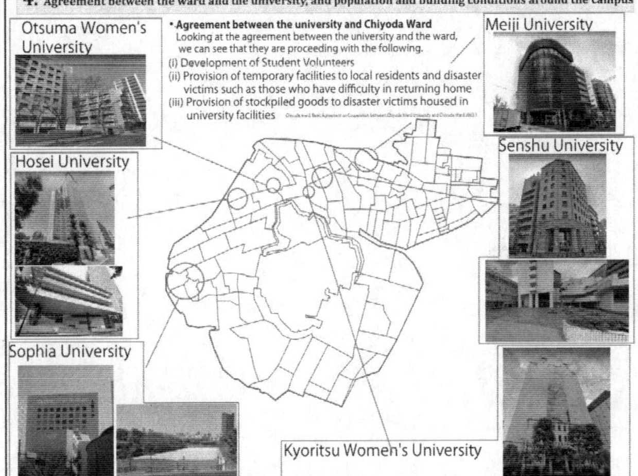

Unit: 100㎡	Name of the town street	Public facilities	Commercial facility	Housing	Industrial facility	Other facilities	Non-residential facility
Sophia University	Kinicho	1,251	8,761	514	0	1	0
Hosei University	Fujimi 2-chome	2,261	1,024	4,064	0	1	0
Otsuma Women's University	Sanbancho	1,391	2,240	2,041	14	11	0
Meiji University	Kanda-Surugadai 1-chome	3,322	431	39	0	0	0
Senshu University	Kanda Jimbocho 3-chome	468	1,427	175	4	0	0
Kyoritsu Women's University	Hitotsubashi 2-chome	1,191	1,352	237	9	0	0
	Kanda Jimbocho 2-chome	167	1,850	321	7	0	0
	Kanda Jimbocho 3-chome	468	1,427	175	4	0	0

Total floor space for each building use in a town with a university campus

Unit: Number of people	Name of the town street	Number of people
Sophia University	Kinicho	16,004
Hosei University	Fujimi 2-chome	5,514
Otsuma Women's University	Sanbancho	5,895
Meiji University	Kanda-Surugadai 1-chome	1,357
Senshu University	Kanda Jimbocho 3-chome	4,211
Kyoritsu Women's University	Hitotsubashi 2-chome	3,815
	Kanda Jimbucho 2-chome	7,682
	Kanda Jimbucho 3-chome	4,211

The daytime population of a town on a college campus

5.Comparison of building-to-land ratio between university campuses and surrounding urban areas

·Campus with possible use of open space

Sophia University

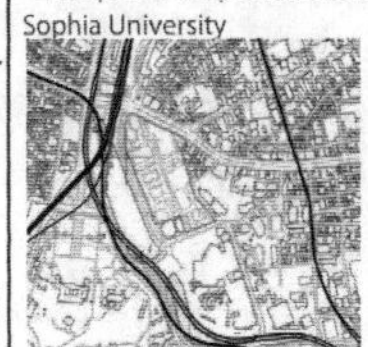

	Building-to-land ratio
Sophia University	35%
Category 1 residential area	60%
Category 2 residential districts	60%
Commercial area	80%

Hosei University

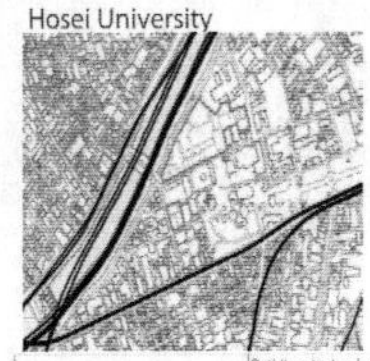

	Building-to-land ratio
Hosei University	58%
Category 1 residential area	60%
Category 1 residential area	80%
Category 2 residential districts	60%
Category 2 residential districts	80%
Commercial area	80%

Senshu University

	Building-to-land ratio
Senshu University	58%
Category 1 residential area	60%
Category 2 residential districts	60%
Nearby commercial area	80%
Commercial area	80%

·Campus for possible use in the building

Otsuma Women's University

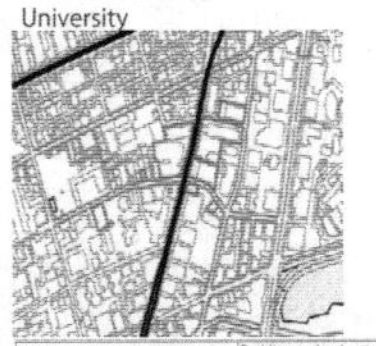

	Building-to-land ratio
Otsuma Women's University	67%
Category 1 residential area	60%
Category 2 residential districts	60%
Commercial area	80%

Meiji University

	Building-to-land ratio
Meiji University	62%
Category 1 residential area	60%
Nearby commercial area	80%
Commercial area	80%

Kyoritsu Women's University

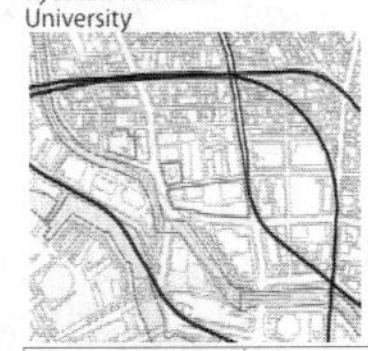

	Building-to-land ratio
Kyoritsu Women's University	63%
Category 1 residential area	60%
Category 2 residential districts	60%
Commercial area	80%

•In the event of a disaster, the above-mentioned university campuses may use open spaces, and the following campuses may use buildings.

Appendix B: Graduate Student Mentoring Workshop Abstracts

GROUP A: Health Equity, Resilience & Sustainability

Mentors:

Lesa Lorusso, Ph.D.
Rich Wener, Ph.D.
Elisa Worden, B.S.

Benjamin Okenwa, *Cardiff University*

okenwacb@cardiff.ac.uk

The public health field is faced with much concern about low levels of physical activity (PA) and increasing obesity (Center for Disease Control, 2021) which are associated with numerous health conditions such as cardiovascular diseases (Khan et al., 2020; Rothenbacher et al.), diabetes (Laaksonen et al., 2005), mental health (Landwers and Arent, 2007; Steingberg et al., 1997) and some types of cancers (Bray et al., 2018; National Cancer Institute, 2020) generally leading to lower life expectancy in most developed worlds (Warburton et al., 2006). This outcome has emerged global environmental and policy interventions aimed to drive population-wide change towards improving PA; (Sallis, Bauman and Pratt 1998). While social-ecological models have been used collectively or individually to explore the correlation between designed environment and public indulgence in PA; (Grzywacz and Fuqua, 2000). More studies conclude that the built environment has a significant impact on PA; (Troped et al., 2010; Wang et al., 2021).

According to speculated changes in the urban landscape stemming from the United Nations report in 2018, "55% of the world's population currently lives in urban areas, a proportion expected to increase to 68% by 2050"; (UN report, 2018). Previous studies make corroborative evidence on a persistent lack of physical activity in the cities or urban areas despite the presence of urban open spaces, which may result from multiple issues related to the physical, social and individual factors. Significant associations have been found between PA and exercise equipment in the home, neighborhood aesthetics, convenient facilities, proximity of destinations, and the overall urban environment (Ball et al., 2001). Recent research has advanced our understanding of PA and built environment factors, yet much of the evidence regarding the influence of the environment on physical activity remains mixed, especially in urban environments. Previous studies have explored how spaces can be designed to encourage or discourage PA, most correlations found can only be attributed to specific contexts where the study was conducted, therefore lacking generalizability. The problem remains understanding the specific physical environment factors of a place and how to decide a suitable location for an urban open space that promotes PA for its users.

My doctoral research focuses on understanding the physical environmental factors that significantlyimpact PA in urban open spaces and how these factors can be considered when making design and site selection decisions for urban open spaces. With the development of digital age technologies and the significant increase in the relevance of urban design studies, new technologies and algorithm languages have penetrated urban design from numerous perspectives. The nature and role of computation design tools have a significant role in planning and designing open spaces within urban environments that facilitate various types of PA. Computation has been critical in enhancing the design process by encoding design decisions using a computer language. My research aims to explore the possibilities of using machine learning as a computational tool that can assess the urban environment based on existing data and make decisions on the suitability of a site for improved PA.

Devi Soman, *Clemson University*

dsoman@g.clemson.edu

Culture is "a complex and global variable that represents the beliefs, language, rules, values, and knowledge held in common by members of a society" (Rice & O'Donohue, 2002). Frequent interaction, collaboration, and sharing of space between various cultures result from globalization (Tirino et al., 2017). Most of the research and advancements in healthcare facilities originate in the western world. Thus, architects often design these facilities with a particular culture in mind, often their own. As a result, our healthcare facilities are yet to follow the world in being inclusive and embracing various cultures. The increasing awareness and move towards patient-centeredness and patient satisfaction have helped identify this gap. The acknowledgment of diverse healthcare-user groups is forcing a change in this pattern. As a result, healthcare facilities now aspire to be more inclusive by providing patient experiences that are sensitive to their respective cultures. The use of terms such as 'culturally sensitive' and 'culturally competent' to describe care is rising.

"Cultural sensitivity is employing one's knowledge, consideration, understanding, respect, and tailoring after realizing awareness of self and others and encountering a diverse group or individual" (Foronda, 2008). It emphasizes the perceptions and feelings of patients regarding the responsiveness between the healthcare experience and their cultural values and beliefs (Tucker et al., 2015). However, cultural competence refers to the understanding of and respect for culturally different patient groups resulting in the tailoring of healthcare to accommodate the cultural differences in health-related values and beliefs (Tucker et al., 2015). Studies indicate that cultural sensitivity in the healthcare experience positively influences the patients' adherence to treatment and, therefore, the outcome (Tucker et al., 2015).

Cultural sensitivity and its challenges are gaining prominence in public health, medicine, and nursing.However, it is ineffective when viewed through the isolated perspectives of the organization and its staff. Cultural sensitivity is most effective when it encompasses the whole healthcare experience and a continuum of such experiences. The physical setting plays a vital role in the healthcare experience. These settings provide the opportunity of reflecting organizational values and create inclusive and culturally safe environments that are sensitive to the needs of the diverse patient population. Culturally sensitive environments have no universal design solutions as these will vary depending on the cultural factors of the various user groups. In design, cultural sensitivity and inclusivity is the perspective that changes designers' approach. It is the practice that leads to the participation of diverse user groups in the design and the process that makes designers more receptive and sensitive to the needs of these users.

Cultural sensitivity has great potential in healthcare design as it helps designers create inclusive spaces, reducing disparity. Being in the initial stages of my research, I am exploring this subject further with a scoping literature review to understand health disparity, and culturally sensitive and inclusive health environments.

Fullah Hazazi, *University of Minnesota*
hazaz002@umn.edu

The mission of The Sanctuary is to enlighten and support students and faculty in search of spiritual renewal through connection to nature, meditation, contemplation and self-reflection. The retreat is non-religious and is open to people of all backgrounds and beliefs. The unlikely pairing of spiritual and environmental organizations acknowledges the strong need humans have to be more connected to their natural environment and the rhythms of the natural world. By pausing the always-on aspects of our modern lives, slowing down, observing the world around us, immersing ourselves in meditative endeavors and embedding ourselves in nature we can realize spiritual renewal, live more peaceful healthful lives and be better caretakers of our world. Through the experiential and contemplative aspects of this retreat and connection to our natural ecology users will experience a sense of restoration, renewal and mindfulness. The value of nature in our lives will be advanced through indoor/outdoor experiences within the retreat, optimization of natural daylight, contact with natural materials, and enhancement of the senses.

Gisou Salkhi, *Texas Tech University*
gisou.salkhi@ttu.edu

Walking as a healthy mode of transportation plays a crucial role in the livability/sustainability of college cities. Many studies from different disciplines have documented Walking's importance to urban sustainability, including urban planning, health, safety, security, and environmental viewpoints. Primarily because of pandemic-related health concerns in indoor environments, a holistic assessment of the urban outdoor environment is needed to understand whether it is socio-spatially appropriate for physical activities. Improved walkability can promote public health and make the urban environment more pleasant, safer, and less polluted.

This study explores how built environments' features in micro-scale has an impact on pedestrian tendency to walk. This paper aims to assess the walkability of the university neighborhood in the college city of Lubbock. This study explores how built environments' features (e.g., greenery, shading, infrastructure, safety) in microscale impact pedestrian tendency to walk. In order to do that, the selected main routes in the university neighborhood will be evaluated as a case study.

First, the physical characteristics of the neighborhood walking routes will be evaluated using Google Street View and on-site audit. Secondly, questionnaire was used to collect the sampled individuals' environmental perceptions of walkability. The majority of students who responded to the survey (60%) said they are satisfied with the sidewalk quality, while a majority of female graduate students (37%) and male graduate students (25%) said they are not. This means that 62 %of all students whose primary mode of transportation is walking are dissatisfied with the sidewalk quality.

Furthermore, the results revealed that the primary suggestions of students who walk to campus are sidewalk quality, greenery, and lighting. Finally, we will examine the relationship between participants' perceptions with routes' physical characteristics. Based on the results, this paper will suggest the design and planning guideline framework according to Complete Street policies to help policymakers and urban planners to increase the public tendency towards walking by assessing and improving built environments infrastructure and attributes.

Holly Nelson, *Rutgers University*
hgrace@sebs.rutgers.edu

Drawing on past environmental design research, various theories and research methods could be used to train landscape architects about the social construction of space. First would be building upon earlier environment and behavior research to evaluate social needs and values, including adopting aspects of design ethnography. Ethnographic qualitative research set within a design context could inspire and illuminate inclusive design (Cranz, 2016; Ganji & Rishbeth, 2020; Marcus & Francie, 1998; Rishbeth & Rogaly, 2018; Simões Aelbrecht 2016, 2019). We also need to investigate notions of inclusion and accessibility from new perspectives in terms of spatial justice (Soja, 2009) --to think about what we mean when we 'design for all.' Nuanced ethnographic 'readings' of social interactions in public places could be extremely useful educational tools to teach design students about how people interact with one another in outdoor places. If we can step beyond the technical answers, we can address real lives—the meaning, the magic, the unexpected, and the possible.

A Landscape Architecture Class to Teach a Critical Social Perspective

Design education has stressed form-making (Blikstein, 2014; Ching, 2014), or the articulation of space (i.e., what is space). However, in addition to needing to know about form, space and order, students also need to know the why of space (its history), and the theories behind landscape formation (why spaces evolve the way they do through social practices and social histories) (Mitchell & Breitbach, 2011). The landscape is physical (the geographic landscape), and it is also socially constructed (the cultural landscape); yet landscape is also about power (the political landscape).

The proposed course, The Social and Cultural Aspects of Design, is devoted to teaching designers to consider people as part of design. Short-term outcomes would be a critical understanding of power and landscape at the societal level. At the site scale, they will communicate a solid understanding of the socio-spatial qualities of a particular place. Long-term, it is hoped that students will apply these sociocritical understandings to solve real-world problems through design. To read the landscape at the societal scale, ethnographic documentaries concerning public housing, gentrification, homelessness, and surveillance demonstrate that landscapes are shaped by power (i.e., how the redlining of Black neighborhoods has created segregated landscapes). Students then apply a socio-critical perspective to the site scale to scrutinize how people interact with the space and with one another. At the site scale, students investigate the qualities of a place that support or undermine social practices. Using different mapping techniques, students visit repeatedly to explore site accessibility broadly—in terms of gender, age, ability, race/ethnicity, legibility/wayfinding, predictability, and safety.

Concepts such as proxemics (interpersonal spatial behavior), kinesics (body language), gaze, territoriality, prospect-refuge theory, environmental preference theory, need for privacy (non-intrusion) and other aspects of comfort and control will be considered. Attention will also be paid to temporal and climatic aspects (time of day, seasonality, sun/shade, temperature, breeze, etc.) and emotions generated from the visits - since accessibility can be felt as well as seen or experienced.

Jiaying Dong, *Clemson University*
jiayind@g.clemson.edu

Mounting evidence has confirmed the positive effects of green space on health outcomes. Green space has long been recognized as an essential natural resource that has the power to restore ailing health, promote public health and preserve planetary health. However, green space is not equally distributed across the United States, with potential variations across social context. Studies show that disadvantaged people (those with low incomes or racial minorities) tend to have less access to green space. In addition, this disparity could also apply to the elderly population, who have been proven to be more vulnerable to health problems and hence might benefit more from green space. However, there is still no clear explanation on the protective effects of green space on the older adults. Thus, this research aims to conduct a nationwide assessment to investigate the correlations between green space and mortality rate of the elderly group within US urban areas, with races and income being mediators.

This exploratory correlational study takes a quantitative approach. Secondary datasets will be utilized to obtain socioeconomic status (SES) data, access to green space, all-cause mortality and cause-specific mortality rates. Multilevel regression models will be conducted to examine the relationships among those three research constructs.

This research is expected to display complex correlations among SES, access to public green space and mortality rates. Statistical evidence and the Palma ratio indicate how green space inequality and health disparity might vary across population groups in different regions and states. Collectively, these results can provide new insights into the policy-making process pertaining to green space planning and design, and bring about more discussions and reflections on strategies to achieve better health outcomes.

Sophia Philip, *Carnegie Mellon University*
sphilip@andrew.cmu.edu

Throughout the spring 2022 semester, we will be conducting focus groups, interviewing subsets of the Carnegie Mellon student population to inform wellness space development. We have multiple goals in our research; how are students doing since the return to in person learning, how do students understand their own well-being and how they might support themselves and others, their knowledge and expectations of school provided well-being services, and how a new well-being focused programmatic space, currently referenced as a Well-being Lab, can be structured to best support student well-being exploration, skill-building, practice, and iteration.

CMU supports an ecological model that recognizes population-level and individual-level determinants of health and intervention. In honor of CMU's commitment to data-driven human-led DEI work, we plan to use this ecological model as a guide to conduct our qualitative research. We are collaborating with CMU's Institutional Research and Analysis and Educational Assessment to craft our questions to promote inclusion and utilize ethnographic interview methodologies to identify emergent themes. Our goal is to interview 50 students through virtual interviews and surveys. We are working with Student Affairs and other student engagement departments, such as school deans and student groups, to identify possible interview candidates. Groups will be stratified based on demographic identifiers and interests, such as graduate students and international students.

In preparation for focus groups, we are also conducting stakeholder interviews with champions and providers of care to CMU students, such as the Director of Counseling and Psychological Services, the Dean of Diversity, Inclusion, Climate and Equity, and the Associate Vice President of Community Health and Wellbeing. These stakeholder interviews will allow us to understand the history and current landscape of wellness care offered to students. The findings from these interviews also inform what types of questions we can ask focus groups and ensure that our questions and research goals align with the programming visions for student wellness across the sectors of higher education that also provide that support as well.

Prior to starting interviews, Wellness Initiatives recognized a need to do an environmental scan of campus, alongside our qualitative research, as well as benchmarking assessments and inventory of current wellness resources at CMU and across higher education. Through collaborative efforts, we are identifying current projects that support holistic health, such as an inventory listing of neurodivergent resources and support and the creation of a restorative space map. We are also researching benchmarks of wellness programming and wellness spaces at other universities. From the stakeholder interviews, environmental scan and focus groups, I will present a report for student affairs leadership with recommendations on how they might structure wellness programming in the new center and support the execution of their decision. We have been able to secure initial funding through grants to develop marketing materials as well as incentives for student participants.

GROUP B: Designing for Diverse Populations

Mentors:

Sharmin Kader, Ph.D.
Dagmar Rittenbacher, MID, CKBD
B.D. Wortham-Galvin, Ph.D.

Alicia Valencia, *Cornell University*
aiv9@cornell.edu

The risk of medication nonadherence, including misuse, abuse, and diversion (MAD), is of great concern for community-dwelling older adults with mild to moderate cognitive impairment. Older adults are at risk due to high comorbidity and other factors, and even a modest increase in cognitive impairment significantly exacerbates the potential for nonadherence (Thiruchselvam et al., 2012). Medication nonadherence is both varied and complex, and previous research has described the ability to manage medication as a delicate balance between patient factors, healthcare professional factors, and medication regimen-related factors (Elliott et al., 2015).

Several studies address the prevalence of nonadherence, associated risk factors, and conditions that lead to adherence behaviors (Kaasalainen et al., 2011; Smith et al., 2017). Research reveals that adherence rates vary widely from 2% to 70% because of measurement methods ranging from selfreported measures to electronic monitoring through pill counts or pharmacy data (Hudani & Rojas-Fernandez, 2016). Others identify solutions to counter nonadherence and the respective barriers towards implementation (Campbell et al., 2016). Gathered insight shows that a combination of strategies is more effective than any single intervention and identifies the need for multifaceted and individualized approaches.

Despite evaluation of intervention strategies and medication adherence devices, there is no standardized approach to sustaining success (El-Saifi et al., 2018; Steinkamp et al., 2019). Several strategies have been used to support adherence (e.g., compliance packaging, medication dispensers, reminder messages, visual or audio clues, simplifying regimens, training toolkits), yet little research underpinning these strategies exists, and few have sought to turn these approaches into routine practice. Lack of comprehensive solutions leaves providers unable to coordinate with each other and meet the complex needs of their patients. A standardized needs assessment tool for healthcare professionals is necessary to build effective long-term solutions.

The purpose of this project is to develop and implement a needs assessment survey tool for healthcare professionals across New York State to examine the critical criteria surrounding medication nonadherence among community-dwelling older adults with cognitive impairment. The aims of this survey include (1) documenting the current state and magnitude of medication nonadherence, (2) understanding risk factors, and (3) exploring both solutions that have helped and barriers towards implementing and adapting solutions to this population.

Study participants include caregivers at Certified Home Health Agencies (CHHAs) or Licensed Home Care Services Agencies (LHCSAs) across New York State working with community-dwelling older adults with cognitive impairment. The Ascertaining Barriers for Compliance Questionnaire (Clyne et al., 2016) was adapted through a synthesis of previous literature, expert review, and pilot testing with Visiting Nurse Services of Ithaca and Tompkins County. A survey pilot testing is underway, and data collection will begin by Summer 2022. The outcomes of this survey will inform current research initiatives and ultimately allow older adults to live safely at home for as long as possible. Findings will address statewide challenges to adherence and inform future directions for healthcare professionals and policymakers.

Anne Cramer, *Cornell University*
ajc44@cornell.edu

I plan to take an evidence-based design approach to proving that the introduction of a medication management system can not only be effective in reducing cases of misuse, abuse, and diversion among community dwelling older people with cognitive decline, but also be a cost-effective way to prevent unnecessary emergency department or doctor visits among this population.

I plan to investigate the following:

- Current state of medication safety among older people with cognitive decline
- Evidence of the prevalence of medication problems (misuse, abuse, and diversion)
- Evidence that medication mis-management results in the population being forced to enter into assisted living facilities
- Significance of healthcare utilization such as ED visits, complications, morbidity and death
- Cost of unmanaged medication to society at the national level not only in terms of the financial perspective, but also the effect on quality of life
- Current coverage by Payers and how likely they might be to reimburse for such a system
- Risk factors of cognitive impairment, comorbidities, and polypharmacy
- Decision-making stakeholders and their potentially competing priorities
- Policies that affect this issue (particularly the linkage to the opioid crisis)

Some members of this population take many pills per day. Keeping these organized and ensuring the right medication is taken at the right time is critical to keep them on target for their desired health outcomes, as well as a crucial component of ensuring that they can stay in their own homes for as long as possible. Should an individual wish to remain at home as they age, I will investigate multi-modal systems that incorporate education, technology, and in-home support from caregivers and providers.

The main question I seek to answer is how insurers and policy makers can be convinced that the introduction of and reimbursement for a medication management system is the right economic decision so as to avoid risk of negative health outcomes and reduce costs. I will look at the opportunity for building a seamless and supportive financial and policy model for medication management that aligns patient, provider, community, and insurer goals. Ultimately, this system will become a critical part of the population's daily life, allowing them to remain in their homes and maintain their desired quality of life.

Manju Aishwarya Adikesavan, *The City University of New York*

madikesavan@gradcenter.cuny.edu

Mobile information and communication technologies such as wireless and mobile internet services and portable devices such as smartphones, laptops, and tablets are transforming universities by enabling the flexibility to learn, teach, and research (LTR) from anywhere and at any time. This shift from the campus as the locus of LTR activities, exemplified by hybrid (a combination of on- and off-campus) and remote (fully off-campus) arrangements, was intensified by the widespread adoption of remote work due to the social distancing practices implemented to contain the COVID-19 pandemic in 2020.

Universities are no longer spatially limited to their campuses but distributed across an ecosystem of diverse on- and off-campus settings falling under five categories: (1) dedicated LTR spaces - classrooms, labs, studio, faculty and research staff offices, etc. (2) co-working spaces within the campus serve members who may not know each other, e.g., maker space, library, and student or faculty commons, and off-campus coworking locations (e.g. Regus, WeWork, etc.), (3) third places – cafeteria, the fitness center, squares, parks, etc., (4) home office – on- and off-campus homes of students, faculty members and researchers, and (5) spaces of movement – campus hallways and external walkways, on and off-campus bus, train, and associated stations. This ecosystem marks the diversification of LTR settings.

In a distributed university, faculty and staff members do not visit the campus every day. Intensification of workspace usage manifests as nonterritorial practices (e.g., hotdesking) where workspaces are claimed or booked on a session-by-session or daily basis and cleared of all work and personal possessions at the end of every work session. Since nonterritorial workspaces are not tied to a single user, they can be used whenever vacant thereby increasing the average number of users per workstation (Kim et al., 2016), reducing the organizational spatial footprint, and lowering facility management costs.

This two-part dissertation examines the design, planning, and policymaking implications of two processes driving the spatial transformation of universities: (1) the intensification of workspace usage and (2) the diversification of LTR settings. Part 1 (completed) focuses on hotdesking which is likely to become the norm in a hybrid campus where employees divide their time between on- and off-campus locations. Part 1 employs participant observation and interviews to examine the themes and coping behaviors associated with hotdesking and identify on- and off-campus workspace policies needed to foster productivity, connection, and well-being of hotdesking faculty members, researchers, and staff members. Part 2 (ongoing) focuses on post-pandemic distributed LTR modes such as "hybrid", "hy-flex", "bi-chronous", etc. which are predicated on a diversified ecosystem of settings. Part 2 uses content analysis of public recordings of virtual meetings, panel discussions, and conferences on post-pandemic campus space planning and policy-making and interviews with campus planners to examine how distributed LTR are reshaping the function and purpose of campus spaces according to the discipline (humanities, social sciences, engineering, natural sciences, etc.) and setting (seminar, lab, studio, lecture rooms, etc.).

Seyedmohammad Ahmadshahi, *Clemson University*

sahmads@g.clemson.edu

The COVID-19 pandemic has caused a significant global impact by spreading through major cities across the world. As of September 2021, nearly 220 million cases and 4.5 million casualties have been reported worldwide. The United States with 42 million cases and over 700,000 deaths have been one of the epicenters of the outbreak. In major cities across the US, the pandemic has put a significant strain on hospitals with a considerable portion of the patients requiring critical care. The pandemic has forced a major impact on Emergency Departments (ED) across the world, changing the ED patient population and disrupting the usual functioning as the front line of response. These changes and challenges have required immediate adaptations in operational workflow and the built environment of the EDs (Uppal et al. 2020).

During the peak of the pandemic, the patient flow in major city hospitals (i.e. New York) far exceeded the capacity of the EDs and created backlogs of infectious patients in waiting areas (Uppal et al. 2020). The sheer volume of the patients has necessitated changes in staff deployment, workflow, and supply management, resulting in adaptations in the ED to support the operational adaptations. Overall, there has been a significant variation between the EDs' responses and adaptations during the pandemic, and due to the unique structure of each ED it is impossible to provide a blanket strategy to address these issues (Gopinathan et al. 2020). However, there are potential similarities in ED functioning and built environment features that have potentially supported or hindered ED operations during the pandemic.

In this study, we are trying to explore the role of the ED built environment in supporting the changes and adaptation necessitated by the COVID-19 pandemic. In this context, we aim to answer the following questions:

- How have different EDs responded to the changes required in response to the COVID-19 pandemic?
- What types of strategies were employed to cope with changes required in response to COVID-19 (Operational, resource management, built environment, etc.)?
- What are the built environment adaptations that may be required by hospital based EDs in response to future pandemics?

These research questions are addressed through an in-depth literature review. A range of external factors impacted the response required by ED including the location of the ED, disease prevalence rates, and disaster preparedness. The types of built environment adaptations that were documented in published studies are also included. In this presentation, the key findings of this literature review and an evaluation framework, based on this literature review, for evaluation ED readiness for pandemic is shared.

Stacy Scott, *Clemson University*
shs5@g.clemson.edu

This dissertation aims to serve as an exploratory investigation into the role that cultural capital and sense of belonging play in identity and persistence in architecture as a degree and career interest for Black Students. The extent to which socialization in architecture studio education sustains the racial inequity present in the field's demographics. The nucleus of design education in any architecture program is the design studio (Sopher, Fisher Gewirtzman & Kalay, 2019; Mohareb & Maassarani, 2018; Corazzo, 2019). The lessons learned in architecture education combine artistic creativity and technical application, requiring that the curriculum include an intricate mix of theory and applied science. Integrating these two components through the curriculum and allowing students to combine those tenets themselves is exemplified most fully through studio (Heath, 2010; Salama, 2008; Sangafi, et al. 2020).

This research will place emphasis specifically on studio instruction and the experience of Black students within this context, using both Field Theory and Bourdieu's Social Reproduction Theory as analytical lenses. Black students achieve varying levels of sense of belonging in their architecture education depending on the environment. This research investigates how these differences can be observed in four settings: the high capital PWI, the mid capital PWI, and the High Capital and Mid Capital HBCU. Depending on the fluctuating levels of capital that a Black student caries with them depending on their environment, an architecture program will either foster or hamper them in their capacity to adjust to the cultural climate of architecture.

The socialization component of many other professional higher education programs (such as medicine, nursing, and law) has been well documented. Like architecture, these programs transform students from outsiders to insiders through rigorous training and the inculturation of norms that are osmosed through the implicit curriculum (Hafferty, 2015). However, within architecture, many of the models infused within the curriculum may repeatedly reinforce the prevailing white-washed culture of architecture, further entrenching the existing questions of persistence and attrition. Despite the observable phenotype of architecture and the abundance of literature that points to a critical need for architecture to enter a new era concerning diversity, the profession has continued to move slowly. While outliers have surged from the Civil Rights act of 1964 to the present day, the two percent makeup Black Architects have reached in the total of licensed architectural professionals represents a multi-year stasis.

Belonging is an intricate part of education success and avoiding attrition (Strayhorn, 2012). Given that the retention rate of Black students in Higher Education is already low, and the number of Black students who complete a professional architecture program is even lower, the attrition of nonwhite/non-Caucasian may begin while they are in architecture school. Yet, little research has been done on this issue (Chamberlin, 2012).) Though the problem may impact other demographics, the current study focuses specifically on Black students and how their sense of belonging in studio culture influences cultural reproduction.

Widya Ramadhani, *University of Illinois Urbana-Champaign*
wramadh2@illinois.edu

Older adults are more likely to experience age-related diseases and capacity decline, impacting their health and wellbeing if not supported appropriately. Hence, adequate support is critical to maintaining older adults' independence in their place of residence, known as aging in place (Rogers et al., 2020). The majority of older adults prefer to age in place in their own home (Binette & Vasold, 2018; Stones &; Gullifer, 2016). They spend the majority (≥70%) of their time at home, where they conduct various everyday activities (Spalt et al., 2016). Activities related to food, such as cooking, are central to older adults' health. However, declining physical and cognitive capacities may lead to restricted mobility, increasing the risk for food insecurities (Wolfe et al., 1996). Such risk is more prevalent among older women because food-related activities have generally been considered the responsibility of women, who are more likely to live alone or act as primary caregivers (Sidenvall et al., 2001). Therefore, the spaces for older women to conduct food-related activities should match their changing needs (Maguire et al., 2014). My dissertation project examine a range of food-related activities – food preparation, cooking, eating, and cleaning – that take place in the home environment. I aim to understand (1) what is the sociocultural context that influences the food-related activities for older Indonesian women? (2) what are the challenges that older women encounter when conducting food-related activities? (3) how do older women's personal capacity and built environmental conditions influence their strategies to maintain their independence in conducting food-related activities?

Participants are 24 community-dwelling Indonesian older women (60+) who live independently; not needing assistance to carry out basic daily activities. There are two groups of participants, older Indonesian women who have lived in Indonesia their whole life and those who migrated to the United States. Their experiences will be compared to explore how the change of sociocultural context may influence one's challenges and adaptation strategies when aging in place. There are two data collection strategies: photo and video elicitation, followed by an interview. Through the photo and video elicitation, participants take photos and videos of the space where they conduct food-related activities. In the interview session, participants are asked to elaborate their food-related activity routine, their personal capacity, and built environmental challenges that impact their independence, and adaptation strategies, while showing the photos and videos of their food-related activity spaces. Photo and video elicitation provide spatial information, whereas interviews provide experiential information, which is essential to construct knowledge on activity engagement and its manifestation in the built environment.

In this study, I employ Grounded Theory methodology. I am now analyzing data using constant comparative methods (Glaser, 2005). I compare the rich textual and graphical data about participants' food-related activities across the two global contexts. By examining older women's challenges and their personal and built environmental adaptive behavior in food-related activities, this study's findings will inform home design strategies for aging in place that meet older women's personal and contextual needs to stay healthy and independent.

Xiaoyu Chen (Alice), *University of Florida*
alicechen00501@gmail.com

Research questions:

- What are the main critical sustainability factors associated with high contact surfaces in an ambulatory healthcare facility?
- What is the Cost of Quality (CoQ) associated with integrating sustainable high contact surfaces in an ambulatory healthcare facility?

The sustainability of the high touch contact surfaces is an essential factor in healthcare. The time required to maintain or replace these surfaces depends on many factors, such as the type of material, installation method, and useful life of the material.

The selection of high-contact surfaces for healthcare facilities requires consideration of multiple factors, including safety, visible wear, durability, maintenance, and cost. Budget constraints usually limit the choice of materials. Material key performance is also affected by useful lifespan, which is affected by space use and care delivery type. The need for more tenable sustainability measures integrated into healthcare building due to climate change (Loh et al., 2020; Press et al., 2016; Younger et al., 2008). The need for resilient infection prevention in healthcare design (Chaudhury et al., 2005; Platt, 2020). The need for materials that are robust and adaptive to use and maintenance requirements (Jelle, 2011; Luttropp &; Lagerstedt, 2006).

Proposed Mixed Methods Methodologies:

- Comprehensive Literature Review and Scientometric Analysis
- Quality Functional Deployment (QFD) guided interviews
- Cost of Quality (CoQ) analysis

Sections to fulfill goals:

- Mining sustainability strategies: Sustainable Healthcare High Contact Surfaces: A Comprehensive Review of Performance Efficacy, Cost Effectiveness, and Workplace Safety.

Method: Comprehensive literature review (VOS viewer and Microsoft Excel)

- Evaluating facility managers perceptions for finish applications: High Contact Surfaces Selection in the
- Design of Healthcare Facilities: Interviews with Facility Managers.
- Quality function guided interviews (ZOOM, Microsoft Word, and Excel)
- Examining sustainable strategies: A Cost of Quality (CoQ) Analysis of High Contact Surfaces

Method: Cost of quality analysis computation (RS Means and Python).

This proposed study intends to evaluate the CoQ of high contact surfaces in a "typical" ambulatory care setting. The aim of this analysis is to produce a method that allows decision-makers to understand the long-term CoQ based on Technical Performance Measures (TPM) related to infection prevention safety, durability, visible wear, and sustainability. Additionally, it aims to connect Design Dependent Parameters (DDP) associated with achieving these TPM.

GROUP C: Designing for Health & Well-Being

Mentors:

David Allison, FAIA, FACHA
Sue Weidemann, Ph.D.
Emily Roberts, Ph.D., M.A., M.Arch

Carolina Kolodziej, *Technische Universität Dresden*
carolina.kolodziej@tu-dresden.de

Cancer treatment is an individualized therapy with the possibility of surgery, chemotherapy and/or radiotherapy. Radiotherapy is an essential part in cancer treatment and is the forefront of effective treatment therapies offered to cancer patients. (Abshire & Lang, 2018) The implementation of evidence-based design in health care facilities can positively influence workflow, travel paths, wellbeing, and quality of stay. (Mahmood, 2021) Transferred to radiotherapy, an optimized architecture and built environment of radiotherapy departments is a prerequisite for treatment. With my PhD project, I want to fill the current lack of planning requirements for radiotherapy departments by analyzing and developing the configuration of room clusters and typologies to optimize the built environment for all user groups. Six user groups were identified: Medical Staff, MTRA, Medical Physicists, patient, administration and service personnel.

For evidence-based typologies on cluster and room constellations various methods for analyzing settings, workflow and pathways are being conducted. From a list of rooms, six clusters were categorized to structure the complexity of radiotherapy departments: Outpatient, Imaging, Planning, Therapy, Personnel and Service, with each dedicated rooms.

For developing typologies, a comparative floorplan-analysis from 25 radiotherapy departments in Germany was conducted. The rooms of the analyzed floorplans were categorized by cluster-formations to identify their relation, distance and arrangement towards each other. The analysis was inspecting differences and similarities in patterns of spatial relationship.

To include the users, the methods Behavior Mapping and Shadowing for daily routines, workflow and process analysis were conducted. The method Shadowing was executed with different personnel user groups. Behavior Mapping was conducted at the entrance with the reception, the therapy cluster and in the hallway with waiting area mapping all user groups. With these methods, individual travel paths, wayfinding challenges, workflow settings and distances can be analyzed. Furthermore, path-crossings of same or different user-groups can be acknowledged. In addition, a short survey was conducted on personnel, to gather additional requirements and architectural barriers in daily routines.

Combining the results of the floorplan analysis with findings of shadowing, mapping, survey and

findings, planning requirements and typologies for radiotherapy departments can be developed. In the final phase results are to be discussed with a panel of experts. The refined planning requirements will be guidelines and tools for future architectural planning of radiotherapy departments. Stage of research process: The floorplan analysis was conducted and first typology sequences of cluster formations were derived. So far nine clinics have been visited, in four of them analysis of behavior mapping and shadowing were conducted. Next steps will be to analyze more clinics, evaluate completed analysis and combine all findings in developing planning requirements.

Specific questions to be addressed: How best to include patients, who are in a vulnerable state, in the research? Especially in times of Covid-19, where direct contact is not possible?

Hannah Myers, *University of Michigan*

hewmyers@umich.edu

The connections between the built environment and human behavior and experience should be integral to the practice of architecture and urban planning. As an architect and urban designer, I remain surprised that throughout my collective 15 years of undergraduate, graduate, and continuing professional education, systematic analysis of the effects of the built environment on human behavior was never the subject of instruction. To address this omission, I have redirected my career from practicing single family residential architecture to the advanced study of relationships between human behavior and the built environment at the intersection of housing design and public health. Informed by a strong background in residential architecture, I am most interested in how the design of residential space - especially that serving marginalized communities - can cultivate positive health effects, support social infrastructure, and promote well-being.

My research endeavors to identify and explore relationships between aspects of the built environment and human health. I plan to employ a mixed methods explanatory study design, starting with quantitative data analysis, then leveraging qualitative methods to enrich understanding. First, by using quantitative research methods founded in statistics to mine existing data sets including census data and health insurance claims, combined with geospatial information gathered from Google street view and GIS, it becomes possible to link health outcomes in relation to quantifiable variables of the built environment (e.g., land use mix, population density, presence of nature, neighborhood walkability, public transit availability, materiality, scale, architectural expression, use of ornament, etc.). Following up the quantitative study, qualitative methods including interviews and focus groups with members of the target population will help to provide context and aid in interpretation of findings.

The cornerstone of my research is the idea that our physical environment should be designed in such a way that it serves the emotional and physical health of all those who inhabit it. Through my research, I hope to identify beneficial residential design elements to create a generalizable set of design guidelines - prioritizing health outcomes - against which the quality of a proposed design or existing environment can be empirically evaluated, making housing design for public health an objective and more equitable goal. In addition to research, I hope to teach future architects, planners, and engineers strategies to program for human health and wellness in every project, using empirical data as a design tool.

Julia Jaffe, *Cornell University*
jgj57@cornell.edu

My research involves proposing a new approach to the development and utilization of youth-led environmental assessments to inform the planning and design of youth-enabling environments. Engaging youth through participatory action research to both develop and conduct environmental assessments can have positive implications for youth empowerment and well-being while also altering research and planning practices to effectively integrate youth voice. My aim is to work to close the gap in our understanding of how to create everyday environments for youth that speak to their needs and interests and provide opportunities for them to flourish. The proposed approach integrates elements from affordance theory, the Capability Approach, and positive youth development within a youth participatory action research framework to create a process that encourages capability formation, fosters positive youth development, and improves our understanding of what constitutes a youth enabling environment. At present, this work is in a conceptual stage. However, we have begun to develop an affordance taxonomy that links aspects of the physical environment with the desires and needs of youth in order to engender healthy individual, social, cultural, and emotional development in youth. We are in the process of translating those relationships into survey-type questions for the Growing Up In Cities project and prompts for more qualitative work that will further inform what it means to define, design, and evaluate a youth-enabling environment.

The data generation will include youth-led environmental audits of parks or other green spaces in Tompkins County as well as training youth in behavior mapping so they can better understand how environments are utilized (or not). These will be followed by workshops in which we will reflect on the process of conducting assessments and discuss the value, importance, and representativeness of what has been identified in the literature and of items on audits meant for youth-oriented spaces. We will provide an array of qualitative, arts-based methodologies so that youth can participate at whatever level and through whichever mediums they prefer to develop an assessment that they feel reflects their needs and desires and that speaks to what they feel constitutes a youth-enabling environment. The first round of data generation is planned for April 2022-August 2022.

My overall goal with this research is to investigate whether the process of being involved in decisions and environments that affect their lives will support youth in capability formation and positive development. I am also hoping that this research will show that not only are youth fully capable of conducting research, but also of understanding their relationships with their environments to the level of being able to articulate what they need and want in their environments and how to actualize those elements through design.

Kulsum Fatima, *University of Calgary*
kulsum.fatima@ucalgary.ca

My research intends to take water sustainability application on UCalgary campus one step ahead, by transitioning from LEED-certified water-efficient operations to Living Building Challenge (LBC) compliant net-zero operations. The research aims to create a water-independent scenario by proposing water selfsufficiency at sites capacitated with generating, managing, and treating its water resources. This will support, advocate and re-innovate the concept of sustainability, with an attempt to transition linear water systems into closed-loop water systems. For this purpose, the study will be inclusive of reviewing, questioning, assessing, and redefining existing water systems and to learn from the success and failures of existing systems to bridge the gap between actual (practice) and predicted (theory) performance.

The research objectives are two fold:

- To propose a conceptual performance

assessment framework, targeting the existing on-campus water sustainability applications based on LEED guidelines, using linear water systems. For this purpose, the research will be identifying performance gaps between the predicted and actual performance of LEED green buildings, and explore possibilities to enhance the performance of the existing water systems design. This framework will evaluate the possibilities for transitioning linear water systems to closedloop water systems compliant with LBC.
- To propose a water literacy framework to address on-campus water sustainability features, which are critical to our understanding as we move through the campus. This idea underlines the concept of University campuses acting as learning and living labs demonstrating best practices and contributing to inspire and empower user understanding towards water sustainability.

Considering that university campuses have always been the starting points for progress, impacting a wider audience and capable of involving broader participants for change towards water sustainability. This research aspires to demonstrate an all-inclusive perspective to water sustainability, enabling the campus site, to lead its communities and peers with its exceptional, take over water sustainability. In doing so, it will underline the objectives of enhancement in sustainability performance, place-based learning, and enhanced user experience through increased perception and participation towards implemented water sustainability efforts. All of which constitutes towards the United Nations vision of successful sustainable development, and aligns with SDG goal 6, and relates to 11, 12, and 13.

Marzia Akhter Chowdhury, *The University of Kansas*

chowdhury_marzia@ku.edu

During the pandemic, several measures were adopted, such as diverting at-risk and non-risk patients in different zones within the emergency department (ED), cohorting suspected or infected patients in a different zone, and so forth. Literature suggests that the spatial strategies impact the throughput time, such as Length of Stay (LOS) and Door to Provider (D2P) time.

The impact of spatial strategies on COVID-19 and non-COVID-19 patients' during the pandemic is unclear. Therefore, this study will also investigate any differences in the LOS and D2P between the two patient groups: COVID-19 and non-COVID-19 at different stages of the pandemic.

The researchers collected the de-identified patient-level data (from March-2020 to March-2021). The ED visit trends, cohort patient groups' (COVID-19 and non-COVID-19 low, mid, and high-acuity patients), LOS, and D2P during COVID-19 were evaluated from an academic tertiary hospital ED in Kansas. A one-way ANOVA analysis to understand the differences in LOS and D2P across different spatial strategies and cohort patient groups at different stages.

ED visit trends patterns revealed five different stages: outbreak, rebound, plateau, peak and post-peak stage. All cohort patient groups received faster care during the first and third wave strikes than in the previous month. Patient groups in the outbreak stage (when cohort isolation, isolation, and forward treatment strategy was adopted) experienced the lowest LOS and D2P than other stages. Patient groups in other stages (when cohort isolation strategy was not adopted) experienced mixed outcomes. The non-COVID-19 patient always experienced higher LOS and D2P across the study period.

Across the five different stages, the non-COVID-19 mid-acuity patients experienced higher LOS (67.015 minutes) than COVID-19 mid-acuity during an outbreak (286.11 107.313, 43.317 higher minutes during rebound (403.90 213.11), 32.029 higher minutes during peak stage (384.83175.430). The post-hoc test shows that the mid-acuity non-COVID-19 experienced significantly highest difference in LOS (32.260 minutes) than COVID-19 patients.

On the other hand, non-COVID-19 mid-acuity patients during outbreak stage, non-COVID-19 low-acuity patients during plateau and post-peak stage experienced higher D2P time than COVID-19 patients. The non-COVID-19 mid-acuity patients experienced higher D2P time (19.931 minutes) than COVID-19 midacuity patients during outbreak stage. Moreover, the mean difference of D2P between the low-acuity non-COVID-19 patients and low-acuity COVID-19 patient groups reaches significance during plateau 32.26 minutes and 30.75 minutes during peak stage.

The non-COVID-19 patients always encountered the highest LOS and D2P across the different stages of the ED visits. More attention should be paid to how ED operational and spatial strategies can manage non-risk patients during a pandemic to improve care delivery.

Mina Shokrollahi Ardekani, *Clemson University*

mshokro@clemson.edu

Over the last decade, the number of individuals with Autism Spectrum Disorder (ASD) increased drastically. In 2020, the CDC reported approximately 1 in 44 children in the U.S. had been diagnosed with ASD. As the number of individuals diagnosed continues to grow, healthcare facilities are seeing an increase in these individuals seeking care. Through this process, families with children on the spectrum experience difficulties taking their children to doctor visits or hospitals. There are numerous sensory stimuli in a healthcare setting that is overwhelming for this population. The communication and behavioral issues that characterize ASD can also create many obstacles in healthcare delivery. ASD patients are often very dependent on consistency to remain emotionally regulated. The possible need to stray from their day-to-day routine and visit an unfamiliar site with different colors, sounds, textures, and odors can cause anxiety and frustration. These new sensory experiences and the introduction of new caregivers into their lives can all promote anxiety reactions, making the treatment experience more taxing for the patient, their families, and healthcare professionals. Treating a patient with ASD can be difficult, and a few guidelines have been published to aid the care of children and adults with ASD. Hence, the aim of my study could be to investigate the features of the healthcare environment that could contribute to the clinical visits experienced by individuals on the spectrum. To have an idea of which healthcare setting I might explore, I looked into some statistics. The Bureau of Autism Services conducted a needs assessment of individuals with ASD and their families in 2011; respondents reported increased contact with the healthcare system, most prominently through emergency medical services, the emergency department (ED), and acute inpatient hospitalization. Respondents, particularly caregivers for adults with ASD, frequently reported dissatisfaction surrounding interactions with the healthcare system. Over half of this group cited increased acute care resource utilization that was undesired, unwanted outcomes, and poor discharge planning. In general, caregivers reported difficulty finding providers who understood and could address the needs of individuals, particularly adults, with ASD.

Udday Datta, *West Virginia University*

usd0001@mix.wvu.edu

Accumulating studies have identified a positive relationship between the amount of greenspaces in people's living environments and the perceived health status of urban dwellers in multiple studies (Jiang et al., 2020; De Vries et al., 2003; Zhang et al., 2018). However, the relationships between various greenspace metrics and the health of residents in rural communities are inconclusive (Alt, 2008; Jennings & Gaither, 2015). The rural population, which makes up nearly 20% of the U.S. population, has been influenced by the spatial disparities in the distribution of public greenspaces and inequitable access to health care (National Rural Health Association, n.d.; Wen et al., 2013). We intend to explore the relationship between greenspace accessibility and people's physical health in rural Appalachia regions.

The study intends to investigate the relationship between the obesity rate among adults living in small area census geographies and indicators of the neighborhood greenspace environment in 420 counties across 13 states in the rural Appalachian region. Obesity is a multi-factorial disorder related to many other significant diseases such as diabetes, hypertension, cardiovascular diseases, osteoarthritis, and certain cancers (Bray, 2004; Hu, 2008). Behavioral Risk Factor Surveillance System (BRFSS) is a large-scale survey conducted by state health departments to assess health-related risk factors. County-level data from the BRFSS with a particular focus on disadvantaged areas of the country will be analyzed to create maps of obesity prevalence in Appalachia.

The green accessibility index (GAI) will be used to assess the accessibility of various types of greenspaces at the county level (Fan et al., 2017; Comber et al., 2008; Higgs et al., 2012). The index will indicate the overall green cover area, the size of accessible open spaces, tree density around residential addresses, and pedestrian accessibility within 300 m of any greenspace. Using the ModelBuilder workflow in ArcPro, we will rank existing greenspaces according to their accessibility index. ModelBuilder is a visual programming language represented in diagrammatic formats (Chaaban et al., 2012). The diagrams chain together sequences of processes for building a geoprocessing workflow. The National Land Cover Database (2016) will be used to identify accessible greenspaces in the rural Appalachian counties. By modeling the spatial characteristics of existing greenspace provision within a Geographic Information System (GIS) based framework, we will use the landscape metrics to quantify the connectivity and accessibility of existing greenspaces in the rural Appalachian region. The number and location of the accessible greenspaces in each county will be further analyzed concerning the obesity prevalence among adults within residential areas. Initial findings show a higher level of rurality is associated with lower access to outdoor exercise opportunities and a lower number of public parks. Higher rurality is also associated with a greater prevalence of physical inactivity and poorer walkability in rural counties. This resulted in higher obesity rates among adults living in these rural communities. The study findings revealed prevailing spatial disparities and inequitable access to quality greenspaces among rural populations within the framework of social determinants of health (U.S. Department of Health and Human Services, n.d.).

ACKNOWLEDGMENTS

ACKNOWLEDGMENTS

The EDRA53 committee extends its sincere thanks to all our wonderful reviewers, mentors, and volunteers for their assistance with the planning, preparation, and execution of this year's conference!

Reviewers

Fatma Abass
Manju Adikesavan
Peter Aeschbacher
Parsa Aghaei
Ahmed Agiel
Saeed Ahmadi Oloonabadi
Sahar Ahmadpour
Mohammad Ahmadshahi
Aysegul Akturk
Ahmad Alansari
Bader AlBader
Arash Alborzi
Andrew Alden
Majd Al-Homoud
Elke Altenburger
Cherif Amor
Sarah Angne Alfaro
Azizi Arrington-Bey
Passanan Assavarak
Sally Augustin
Bakhtiar Bahrami
Shilpa Bakshi Chandawarkar
Frédéric Bally
Maryam Banaei
Jennifer Barker
Paula Barros
Dina Battisto
Md Rashed Bhuyan
Amy Beth
Noah Billig
Alper Bodur
Caryn Brause
Celina Britto Correa
Matthew Browning
Peter Butler
Kyoungmee Kate Byun
Alicia Campos
Yingsawad Chaiyakul
Si Chen
Leena Cho
SeonMi Choi
Manasi Chokshi
Renee Christensen
Arza Churchman
Carlos Cobreros
Laura Cole
Silvia Collado Salas
Gabrielle Conrad-Amlicke
Carmela Cucuzzella
Sida Dai
Ann Devlin
Keith Diaz Moore
Jiaying Dong
Bryce DuBois
Sabeen Durrani
Mahnaz Ensafi
Kimia Erfani
Onur Erman
Sara Eslamzadeh
Rabia Faizan
Alshimaa Farag
Lian Fathi
Beth Ferguson
Nisha Fernando
Gabriela Fonseca Pereira
Eirini Gallou
Michal Gath-Morad
Arsalan Gharaveis
Swati Goel
Sherif Goubran
Monica Gripko
Gowri Gulwadi
Jaeyoung Ha
Sara Hadavi
Erin Hamilton
Iman Hamza
Davis Harte
Seyedehnastaran Hashemi
Ana Hidalgo
Martin Holland
Lisa Iulo
Saman Jamshidi
Aditya Jayadas
Anjali Joseph
Rutali Joshi
Mariana Junqueira
Sharmin Kader
Sujata Karve
Karen Keddy
Sara Kennedy
Maja Kevdzija
Poonam Khan
Mahdi Khansefid
Farzaneh Khayat
Sara Khorshidifard
Daejin Kim
Seo Young Kim
Douglas King
Maren King
Kendra Kirchmer
Satoshi Kose
Vaisali Krishnakumar
Jeffrey Kruth
Azadeh Lak
Julie Lawless
Jae Hwa Lee
Jisun Lee
Sung-Jin Lee
Maryam Lesan
Xiaowei Li
Marcela Lopez
Xiaojie Lu
Yanhua Lu
Qing Luo
Monty Lynn
Lorissa MacAllister
Herminia Machry
Piers MacNaughton
Stephen Mainzer
Debarti Mimi Majumdar Narayan
Shatha Malhis
Odeta Manahasa
Sepideh Masoudinejad
Zorana Matic

Anastasia Maurina
Lindsay McCunn
Tricia Meehan
Luis Mejia
Katherine Melcher
Shalini Misra
Soheyla Mohammadi Gorji
Hassnaa Mohammed
Traci Montgomery
Jessica Morris
Mozammel Mridha
Anindita Mukherjee
D. Michael Murtha
Kavita Murugkar
Hebatalla Nazmy
Winifred Elysse Newman
Neda Norouzi
Bushra Obeidat
Crispino Ochieng
Ceara O'Leary
Eva Leticia Ortiz
Elvan Elif Özdemir
Mary Padua
Michelle Pannone
Douglas Pardue
Jin Gyu Park
Lubomir Popov
Yoga Pria
Robin Puttock
Xiaobo Quan
Mehrnoosh Rahimian
Nabeela Nushaira Rahman
Urmila Rajadhyaksha
Michael Ralph
Widya Ramadhani
Natália Ransolin
Raha Rastegar
Mohammad Habib Reza
Maryam Rezaei Ghaleh
Kim Rollings
Sohail Sadroleslami
Hossein Saedi
Haripriya Sathyanarayanan
Brian Schermer
Stacy Scott
Mina Shokrollahi Ardekani
Linda Slowik
Jennifer Smith
Saeideh Sobhaninia
Devi Soman
David Spooner
Petya Stefanoff
Mina Sufineyestani
Qingqing Sun
Li-wen Sung
Scott Sworts
Ellen Taylor
Karen Tinker-Walker
Elizabeth Tofte
Eleni Tracada
Paweł Trębacz
Elif Tural
Intisar Ameen Tyne
Uchita Vaid
Shabboo Valipoor
Aanchal Vidyasagar
Caterina Villani
Richa Vuppuluri
Huaqing Wang
Jun Wang
Yujia Wang
Zhe Wang
Judith Wasserman
Sue Weidemann
Richard Wener
Deborah Wingler
Jane Winslow
May Woo
Alanna Wright
Ching-fen Yang
Aia Zaina
Yaoyi Zhou
Parisa Ziaesaeidi
Milagros Zingoni Phielipp

Mentors

David Allison
Sharmin Kader
Lesa Lorusso
Dagmar Rittenbacher
Emily Roberts
Sue Weidemann
Richard Wener
Elisa Worden
B.D. Wortham-Galvin

Volunteers

Mohammad Ahmadshahi
Jiaying Dong
Swati Goel
Monica Gripko
Sara Kennedy
Isabel Korn
Kassandra Landvay
Xiaowei Li
David Mackey
Mina Shokrollahi Ardekani
Devi Soman
Hadley Taylor-Downard
Rebeccah Trefethen
Taylor Wahler

AUTHOR INDEX

HEALTH IN ALL DESIGN

Promoting health, equity, sustainability and resilience through environmental design

www.edra.org

PO Box 43023
Washington, D.C. 20010, USA
headquarters@edra.org
+1 (507) 339-4620